P9-DWI-960

MENTAL RETARDATION:

A FAMILY STUDY

ELIZABETH W. REED, Ph.D.
and
SHELDON C. REED, Ph.D.
Dight Institute for Human Genetics
of the University of Minnesota

A Project of the Minnesota Human Genetics League

W. B. SAUNDERS COMPANY
PHILADELPHIA AND LONDON, 1965

Mental Retardation: A Family Study

 Made in the United States of America. Press of W. B. Saunders Company. Library of Congress catalog card number 65-10291.

PREFACE and ACKNOWLEDGMENTS

This book contains information about each of some 80,000 persons. The information for any one person was often extensive and may have been contributed by physicians, psychologists, teachers and especially by relatives. We do not know how many thousands of persons provided information for this study, and it is impossible to acknowledge their individual assistance. It is unfortunate that even all the members of the Dight Institute staff who have contributed to the project cannot be recognized. We apologize for our errors of omission, to those unmentioned, and for our errors of commission in being unable to express adequately our indebtedness to those who are mentioned.

Recognition of the contributions of some persons is given elsewhere in the book. It is not necessary to eulogize those now deceased, but the two men who were almost entirely responsible for the initiation of this project in the early 1900's deserve more attention than it is possible to provide.

Dr. Charles B. Davenport had one of the most brilliant minds of the early day geneticists. It should be recalled that Mendel's laws were rediscovered in 1900. Many famous biologists failed to comprehend the significance of the laws of heredity for years after, and even today their significance has not penetrated to all branches of learning. Dr. Davenport understood at once the importance of mendelism and espoused it with all the tremendous vigor he possessed. His main failing was his overenthusiasm for his cause—the importance of the gene to mankind. The vilification which he received is still the usual reward for crusaders.

Dr. Davenport was the director of the Eugenics Records Office located at Cold Spring Harbor, New York. The first E. R. O. bulletin on human genetics was published in 1911. During the next 25 years about 90 persons received training as field workers at the Eugenics Records Office. They were college graduates with majors in sociology, biology or other appropriate areas. They were well trained in the techniques of family history taking, interviewing and pedigree construction. These field workers were then assigned to state institutions where they carried out family studies on samples of the patients.

Miss Sadie Deavitt and Miss Marie Curial were assigned to the State School and Colony at Faribault, Minnesota. The superintendent of this institution was the late A. C. Rogers, M.D., the other man most responsible for initiating the long-term project that is the subject of this book. It should be recalled that up to 1910, little distinction had been made between the mentally ill and the mentally retarded. The concept of H. H. Goddard and C. B. Davenport that mental retardation resulted from the homozygous condition of mendelian recessive genes was an oversimplification that had almost breathtaking appeal for superintendents of state institutions who had scientific curiosity. To men like Dr. Rogers, this was the first light shed upon a completely baffling and discouraging area of the medical sciences. The legislature promptly appropriated $25,000 for a family study of feeblemindedness as a result of the enthusiasm and persuasiveness of Dr. Rogers. This was a large appropriation for a single research project in a pioneer state at that time. Dr. Rogers was the superintendent of the institution at Faribault from 1885 to 1917. It was his intention to study the families of all the patients but his untimely death brought an end to that phase of the project. Our present day follow-up of those families could not have been successful without the careful planning by Dr. Rogers in 1910.

The psychological tests were carried out almost as soon as the test instruments were developed. They were carried out by Dr. Maud A. Merrill, Miss Mildred Thomson, Dr. Frederick Kuhlmann, and others.

The study was reopened in 1949 and continued to the present. Financial support has been provided during all of this latter period by the Minnesota Human Genetics League. This project has been the major commitment of the League and has involved the expenditure of the major share of its funds for 15 years. The League has also invested a significant proportion of its resources in the manufacture of this book in order to reduce the selling price. A small grant was provided by the Division of Public Institutions of the State of Minnesota, under contract number E-1126. Generous support was provided by the Rockefeller Foundation and from grant number M-1431 of the National Institute of Mental Health. There were generous donations to the Minnesota Human Genetics League for this project by the Cowles Foundation, the Hamm Foundation and several individual members. Physical facilities for the work have been provided by the Dight Institute for Human Genetics of the University of Minnesota. We wish to thank Mrs. Hertha Jorgensen, financial officer of the Graduate School, for her cheerful assistance throughout the project.

We are indebted to a small army of school superintendents, teachers, and school psychologists throughout the United States and Canada for IQ values and school records.

It is a pleasure to point out that our work has been dependent upon the cooperation and generous assistance of Miss Mildred Thomson, while head of the Bureau for the Mentally Deficient and Epileptic, State of Minnesota, and her staff; and of her staff, we wish to thank Mrs. Naomi Kammen in particular. Other state and city officials to whom we are especially indebted are E. J. Engberg, M.D., superintendent of the State School and Hospital at Faribault and Miss Caroline Perkins, the chief social worker at Faribault. Miss Mary Mercer, psychologist of the Owatonna State School, has given helpful criticism. Misses Mary Connelly and Irene Peterson of the Central Index and Mary Cassady of Vital Statistics have provided important data regarding several hundred persons. Dr. John Pearson, Mrs. H. H. Brasie and Miss Barbara Neid have been particularly sympathetic to our problems involving psychological testing. Mr. A. I. Heggerston of the Minneapolis school system and Miss Valborg Birkeness of the St. Paul school system were always friendly and cooperative.

Professor Dwight E. Minnich provided the continuity of moral support and encouragement throughout the work which carried us to the completion of the project.

Jan A. Böök, M.D., of the State Institute for Human Genetics, Uppsala, Sweden, and John Schut, M.D., gave physical and neurological examinations to all of our probands alive during 1951, thus implementing our confidence in the diagnoses previously available. Ray Anderson, M.D., was also of great help in the medical aspects of the work.

Mrs. Allan Feller and Drs. Wendell Swenson, J. Daniel Palm, N. C. Myrianthopoulos and V. Elving Anderson were particularly efficient in the exhausting field work problems.

Miss Jane McCarthy of the University of Minnesota Press was most helpful in showing us how the pedigree charts could be produced. Some of the college students who drew the charts were James Erickson, Larry Roberts, Robert Selmo and William Rice.

Secretaries who carried much of the burden of the work were Mrs. Peter Briggs, Mrs. Albert Goodman and Mrs. Earl Storts.

Finally, our deepest gratitude goes to Mrs. Ira Phillips and to Dr. James V. Higgins. Neither one wrote any of this book but both contributed much of the hard work that went into the gathering, organization and analysis of the data.

We wish also to thank Mr. John Dusseau and the staff of the W. B. Saunders Company for their excellent cooperation in the production of the text.

E. W. Reed
S. C. Reed

CONTENTS

CHAPTER ONE

INTRODUCTION

Many people think of mental retardation as a kind of mysterious blight that could be eliminated if we had a more liberal government, more special classes, earlier testing for phenylketonuria or some other kind of social action to be initiated by some organization. People do not ordinarily think of mental retardation as being ultimately dependent upon the physiological activity of individual cells located in the brain. In every case of mental retardation there must be some subnormal behavior of some of the cells of the brain, regardless of the cause of the retardation. One may espouse the most esoteric scheme imaginable of the way in which mental retardation is produced by social deprivation but with this scheme, or any other, the behavior of the person depends primarily upon the reaction of the appropriate brain cells. We do not know how the brain cells function but the discoveries of the last decade leave no doubt that the deoxyribonucleic acid (DNA) in their nuclei has the primary role in controlling their activities. The DNA is the material basis of the gene.

The reader may think that we are biased toward a genetic interpretation of the etiology of mental retardation. We are geneticists and have, therefore, an obligation to present the data of our study in genetic terminology. However, we are fully aware that the environmental component of mental retardation is by far the most important variable in some cases, and we are anxious to account for all of these. Our general obligations as scientists outrank our specific ones as geneticists. It is our hope that this family study of mental retardation has achieved a judicious demonstration of the environmental and genetic components of it which is meaningful to social agencies throughout the United States and other countries. We have made every effort to be as objective as our training will permit.

This book is not a text on mental retardation, but is a monograph concerned with the frequencies of mental retardation in various categories of relatives of our original probands. We were not primarily concerned with the social inadequacies of either the retarded or their intellectually normal relatives. We were interested more in the person's ability to solve the types of problems presented by group or individual IQ tests. It may seem that this is a rather trivial part of the whole person's competence, but it is the part that determines school performance to an extremely important degree. It is true that there are cases in which children with very high IQ's fail in school, but they are exceptions to the general rule that school performance depends to a large degree upon intelligence that can be measured by tests.

Our society faces a rapid increase in automation and it is absurd to maintain that this does not pose a threat for the retarded. Automation must result in structural unemployment that will affect the retarded most seriously. Mechanical ditch diggers and machines, which perform all sorts of routine tasks that previously provided employment for the retarded, are multiplying our social problems, because it is the retarded who are incapable of obtaining the more advanced education now essential for employment on both the rural and urban scenes. Åkesson (1961) pointed out that in rural Sweden only 25 per cent of the retarded supported themselves.

The transmission of mental retardation from one generation to the next should, therefore, receive much more critical attention than it has in the past. It seems fair to state that this problem has been largely ignored on the assumption that if our social agencies functioned better, and everyone's environment were improved sufficiently, then mental retardation would cease to be a major problem. Unfortunately, mental retardation will never disappear, but it can be reduced by manipulating the genetic and environmental factors involved.

One reason why opinion about the transmission of mental retardation has been so indefinite is that there are so few satisfactory studies of the subject. It is astonishing that the family study presented in this book is the first one that is both rigorously longitudinal in generations of people and sufficiently objective to include intelligence quotients. It is quite permissible to question the objectivity of the individual IQ values, but to omit them completely from any study involving intelligence is simple scientific negligence. In our study there was usually more than one IQ value available for the person, which means that the subject may have been evaluated independently by several experienced psychologists.

Another fundamental omission of many earlier studies is that of data about the spouses of the retardates. One could hardly expect very accurate predictions about the intelligence of children when the information is always missing for one of the parents.

It is not surprising, considering the above, that our review of the literature can be relatively short without omitting any highly significant family studies concerning the transmission of mental retardation from generation to generation.

Our definition of mental retardation is a simple one. The only persons to be classified as mentally retarded in our study are those who scored below 70 on standard intelligence tests, or those so classified by careful subjective judgment. However, this definition might be objected to on the grounds that it does not include the social performance of the subject. Social performance can be hopelessly inept in persons with high intelligence. Consequently, we do not wish to include such persons with the mentally retarded.

These criteria of our definition do not by themselves have any implications for the genetic endowment of the person; they merely indicate his ability to answer the test questions in comparison with a large population of other persons of the same chronological age. Even though our definition of mental retardation is rather narrow, it agrees with other types of evaluation of mental status, such as the reaction of the general public to a person.

REVIEW OF SOME OF THE LITERATURE

The early family studies are primarily of historical interest because they were short of data and burdened with opinion, and not always well supported with common sense. There were also a number of armchair papers that distracted attention from reality. An interesting example of these flights from reality is the paper by Punnett (1917). He calculated that if none of the retarded reproduced it would take more than 8000 years to reduce the frequency of retardation from 3 per 1000 to 1 per 100,000. This figure is of negative value—in part, because it is based upon several untenable assumptions, perhaps the worst of which is that no assortative mating occurs. It should have been obvious even in 1917 that this assumption was absurd and that any figures based upon it must be erroneous. Fisher (1924) pointed out some of the fallacies of Punnett's article and showed that if none of the retarded reproduced there would be a highly significant drop in the frequency of mental retardation in the next generation, the exact opposite of Punnett's concept. Fisher realized that assortative mating is unusually high for intellectual traits and predicted that at least 25 per cent of the retarded would be found to have one or both parents retarded. Our study confirms his predictions.

The first family study of mental retardation which we wish to mention is that of Goddard (1914). His book includes parents and offspring of selected families. It is inadequate in all respects as a present day study, but was an important and valuable contribution at the time.

A little known study is contained in the Third Annual Report of the Eugenics Society of Vermont, published by the University of Vermont, Burlington (1929). The sample of selected families was probably biased toward an excess of retardation, though an attempt was made to cover all persons in this state of approximately 300,000 persons. The 82 unions of a retarded parent with a normal parent produced 337 children, of whom 26.4 per cent were retarded. From the 22 unions in which both parents were retarded, there were 93 children, of whom 44.1 per cent were retarded.

There were many surveys made in the United States and Europe during the 1920's and 1930's, but these were primarily attempts to establish the frequency of the retarded in specific localities. The definitions of mental retardation were subjective and difficult to compare from study to study. The types of unions were not described. The family aspects were often dismissed with a statement such as "mental deficiency is to a great extent a family problem."

Brugger (1930) carried out studies of close relatives of retarded patients. In this study it was found that 19.5 per cent of the siblings and 24.0 per cent of the parents were retarded. These values are probably low for a number of reasons, one of which was that 40 per cent of the siblings and 40 per cent of the parents had died at the time of the study. Retrospective studies of this kind, because of the lapse of time and memory, always fail to discover some percentage of the abnormal and shorter-lived persons. There were no values for the children of the patients. Brugger found that mental retardation is, indeed, a "family problem." He found that if both of the probands' parents were normal, there were 17.8 per cent retarded siblings; if one parent was retarded there were 41.3 per cent retarded siblings; if both parents were retarded, 93.2 per cent of the siblings were retarded. This last percentage is higher than the usual figure for retardation among the children when both parents are retarded, but this was probably caused by the very few families of this kind included in the sample.

The most interesting of the early studies, to us, is the Report of the Department Committee on Sterilization, of which L. G. Brock (1934) was chairman. The committee called in reports from England and Wales concerning the children produced by the retarded. It is interesting that of the 3733 retarded persons who had produced children there were 3247 women and only 486 men. Two thirds of the retarded women who had produced children were unmarried. Any group which has such a high illegitimacy rate must be very poorly supervised by society.

It is most important to note that there was a ratio of 6.7 to 1.0 of retarded women to retarded men who produced children. This fact is of tremendous social significance because it means that retarded males produce only a relatively small part of the mental retardation of the next generation; on the other hand, retarded women make a greater contribution to the retarded population of the next generation. The Brock report may have missed some retarded males who produced illegitimate children but this group could not have been very large.

The 3733 defectives produced 8841 children, of whom 2001 (22.5 per cent) had died at the time of the study. There is no way of knowing what proportion of these dead children would have been retarded had they survived, but undoubtedly it would have been high. The study also excluded from consideration all children under the age of 7.

The Brock Committee included 1802 children between the ages of 7 and 13, of whom 305, or 16.9 per cent, were classified as mentally defective and 423, or 23.5 per cent, as retarded. Thus a total of 728, or 40.4 per cent, were intellectually handicapped.

There were 1848 children who were over 13, and among them were 599 defectives, or 32.4 per cent, and 240 retarded, or 13 per cent. A total of 839, or 45.4 per cent, of the elder children of the retarded were mentally handicapped. The higher proportion of defectives as compared with retarded in the over-13 group suggests that many of the children in the 7 to 13 group who were classified as retarded would later be found to be defective; their IQ's would have dropped.

The committee stated that "When it is remembered that 22.5 per cent of the children had already died and that these percentages apply to the survivors, the figures indicate that here we have a social problem calling urgently for some practical preventative measure." The reviewers might add that the social problem is still calling as urgently, 30 years later, as it was then in Great Britain and the United States.

The committee realized that if the retarded had children the results would be disastrous, but it also realized that only in rare cases are the retarded *unusually* fertile. It stated that "The supposed abnormal fertility is, in our view, largely mythical and results from the accident that from time to time distressing exceptions to the general rule find their way into the courts and are noticed in the press. It would be easy, though it would serve no useful purpose, to cite cases of excessive fertility; but we are convinced that these cases are exceptional and prove nothing except the terrible results of leaving at large a type of defective wholly unfitted for community life."

The Brock Committee made a number of recommendations, including one calling for the legalization of voluntary sterilization for the retarded. It also recommended that attention be given the Colchester study on mental retardation then being pursued by Professor Penrose. This work of Penrose (1938) is the best known of the family studies on mental retardation. It proceeds from the retarded child (the proband) and studies his parents, grandparents and other close relatives, while the Brock report studied the offspring of retarded parents. The two pieces of research examine two different questions and the answers, naturally, are quite different. The Brock report discovered that about half the children of the retarded die young or are intellectually handicapped. This has painful implications for the future, and is unpleasant reading for those concerned. Consequently, the Brock report has been swept under the rug by many who are responsible for opinion formation.

The Penrose project did not differ greatly from earlier family studies except that it included 1280 probands, an adequate sample size, and in Appendix 3, one can relate the proband to each of his close relatives. Not all of Penrose's probands were mentally retarded, according to our definition, since 179 of them had been so certified chiefly because of problems of social adjustment and had IQ values of 70 or above. Apparently, Penrose utilized the mental ratio (IQ) in classifying his probands, but no IQ value is included in his publication. If these values had been included it would have facilitated a comparison of his results with those which we will present. There are, of course, many other opportunities for direct comparisons. For instance, if we subtract the 179 probands whom we would not have included as retarded there would be 1101 probands in the Penrose sample, of whom 622, or 56.5 per cent, were males and 479, or 43.5 per cent, were females. Our probands were 47.7 per cent males and 52.3 per cent females. There is thus a difference in the sex ratio between the two studies.

A few important differences between the studies are discussed below:

1. Only 7.6 per cent of the parents of the probands in the Penrose study were retarded. In our study, 193, or 33.4 per cent (see Table 20), of the 578 parents of the probands were retarded. The difference between the two samples is striking and difficult to explain. We can only guess that institutionalization in Minnesota was a very different process from what it was in England.

2. Only 67 women and two men of the 1280 probands in the Penrose sample produced any offspring. Only 59 of the 124 children lived long enough for their mentality to be determined; 42 were normal and 17 retarded, or 29 per cent retardation. In our sample there were 40 women and two men among the 289 probands who produced 99 children of whom 80 survived, and of these only 16.3 per cent were retarded. The viability of the Minnesota children of the retarded probands was much better and the percentage of retardation lower than in the Penrose sample. We can think of no satisfying explanation for this difference.

3. The 1280 probands of the Penrose sample had 6629 siblings, or 5.2 siblings each. Our 289 probands had 1239 siblings, or 4.3 each. Only 9.5 per cent of the Penrose siblings were retarded compared with 26.3 per cent retarded siblings in our study.

4. There is no reason why Penrose should have had more difficulty in ascertaining the grandparents than did our early workers. However, Penrose's field workers discovered only 32 mentally defective grandparents among the 5114 grandparents reported. This is only 0.6 per cent retardation, a figure well below that which must have existed in the general population. Our grandparental sample of 1151 persons included 68 retarded, or 5.9 per cent; this is almost ten times the rate in the Penrose study (see Table 21). Our sample may have a selective bias which would explain part of the difference; however, it is also clear that the ascertainment of the Penrose grandparental generation was unsatisfactory because it is not reasonable that this group would have less than 1 per cent of retardation on any theory.

To summarize our analysis of the Penrose

study: The only group of relatives in which Penrose found a higher percentage of retardation than we did was in the children of the probands. He states that "The majority of these children were given standardized mental tests." Apparently, ascertainment of the mental status of all the other groups of relatives in his study was subjective and thus likely to contain gross underestimates of the percentage of retardation present, a situation that is obvious in the grandparental generation but more difficult to detect in the other generations. It is our opinion, derived from considerable experience, that the field workers in the Penrose project classified a significant proportion of persons as dull or normal who would have been found to have IQ scores of less than 70. This criticism does not hold for his population of children of the retarded probands who were given standard tests and who were retarded in 29 per cent of the cases. For this well ascertained generation (the children of the retarded probands), we have seen that the Vermont survey found 26.4 per cent of the children were retarded, the Brock report averaged 25 per cent retarded and our study probands had only 16.3 per cent retarded children.

Halperin (1945), Gamble (1952) and Böök (1953) all made survey-type studies of mental retardation with frequencies of mental retardation fluctuating considerably for the various degrees of relationship to the probands and from study to study. Evaluation of the relatives was still subjective and without the benefits which standardized tests might bestow in classifying the higher grade retardates. Böök included only those propositi who were so retarded that they were unable to attend school.

The Swedish study by Åkesson (1961) showed that of 90 children of retarded probands, 39.8 per cent were retarded. He makes the statement that "More than 53 per cent of the sibs of the high-grade defective probands were mentally retarded or defective." He explains that his figure is higher than that of Böök (1953) because Böök had fewer high-grade defective probands in his sample. Once again it is impossible to compare the data in the different studies because the cut-off point for mental retardation is not known. In Åkesson's study we find that the average morbid risk for the parents of all probands is:

Low-grade mental defective	1.2 ± 1.2 per cent
High-grade mental defective	28.0 ± 5.0 per cent
Subnormal	28.0 ± 5.0 per cent

According to Åkesson, the subnormal group contains those who on a common intelligence test fall between —1 to —2 standard deviation units. Presumably, this group would correspond to an IQ range of 70 to 85 and would not be regarded by us as retarded. Thus the painful sentence with which Åkesson ends his study, "Over 50 per cent of both the parents and the sibs were found to be mentally retarded," is not as frightening as it would appear because it includes a majority of the dull rather than the retarded in the usual sense.

However, if we exclude his "subnormal" category, there are still 18 per cent of the siblings and 29 per cent of the parents of his probands who have either low-grade or high-grade mental deficiency, in Åkesson's terminology. Only probands with mental retardation of unknown origin were studied but ascertainment of the relatives seems to have been of higher quality than in any of the previous studies.

We have omitted many of the papers concerned in some way with family studies of mental retardation. All of the studies, including those cited, have inadequacies of which the worst seems to be the failure of the recent ones to utilize IQ values, which could be obtained from the schools without difficulty. One may have a dim view of the value of the intelligence quotient, but it is more objective than the testimony of relatives which depends upon many emotional factors. Subjective classification of the lower grades of retardation is adequate for family studies, but in the IQ range from 60 to 90 the investigator needs assistance of every kind, including one or more test values.

There are inadequacies in the material to follow even though we have devoted the last 15 years of our research efforts to this project with the hope that a more complete picture of the origin of mental retardation would emerge. Our work shows that the intelligence of the population is not dropping rapidly and that it might be increasing slowly. It also shows that a reduction in reproduction of the higher grade retardates would decrease the transmission of retardation from one generation to the next. The statistical basis for these conclusions is substantial and the reader should be able to accept our findings without feeling that they are threatening to the retarded. The general problem of mental retardation is so serious from all points of view that every humane effort must be devoted to finding ways in which mental retardation can be prevented, and all of them must be utilized, or at least seriously considered, in planning for the future.

CHAPTER TWO

ORGANIZATION OF THE PROJECT

PURPOSE AND SCOPE OF THE INVESTIGATION

Longitudinal family studies in human genetics can yield interesting and valuable information about inherited traits in man. However, extensive research projects covering several generations have not been found in the literature on retardation because reliable data can be collected by one individual for only two or three generations at best. The Dight Institute and the Minnesota Human Genetics League were very fortunate, therefore, in coming into possession of carefully compiled old records (dating from 1911) on the families of 549 persons who were in the institution for the mentally retarded at Faribault, Minnesota, during the years 1911 to 1918. Two well trained workers from the Eugenics Record Office of the Carnegie Institution at Cold Spring Harbor, New York, had collected all the information they could about these 549 retardates, their relatives and in-laws. This old study was reopened in 1949 with the purpose of making a follow-up of all the descendants of the original patients' grandparents in order to ascertain the present social, economic and intellectual status of these families. In this way reliable data could be obtained for six or seven generations of families of the retarded. The information resulting from such a longitudinal study should increase understanding of the problems of mental retardation in our society.

The original investigation was carried on during the years 1911 to 1918 at the State School and Hospital at Faribault, Minnesota, under the direction of the superintendent, Dr. A. C. Rogers, by Miss Sadie Deavitt (deceased) and Miss Marie Curial (now Mrs. Guy Menafee of Rochester, Minnesota). These two workers were college graduates trained in social work and family studies. Their salaries were paid by the Eugenics Records Office and their travel and research expenses were subsidized by $25,000 appropriated by the Minnesota State Legislature. Miss Deavitt and Miss Curial worked in the state for seven years with the original intention of studying the families of all institutionalized patients. However, the study came to an end because of the death of the director, Dr. Rogers, and the subsequent lack of money and loss of workers. The original data were never published. Duplicate copies of the records were kept; one set was sent to the Eugenics Records Office and the other set was stored in St. Paul. A preliminary follow-up of a few of the families was published in the Eugenics Quarterly (S. C. Reed et al., 1954). Other papers devoted to the families in this project are those of Böök et al. (1953), Elizabeth W. Reed and Vivian P. Phillips (1959), Higgins et al. (1962) and S. C. Reed et al. (1962).

The two original workers collected all the material available in the institution records on the patients. In addition, they visited the patients' homes and interviewed as many relatives as possible always including the patients' grandparents and sometimes great-grandparents, in an attempt to assess the mental, social and economic status of the family. They also interviewed teachers, physicians, employers and neighbors. They always reported the circumstances of the retardate's birth and early life, getting medical statements whenever possible; they described the home in terms of economic level and treatment of the children; they were careful to include information about all the normal relatives and to report on all spouses. Informants were questioned about family members who were deceased or who lived far away. The sources of information and the relationships of the informants to the patients were always listed. Pedigree charts accompanied all the family records.

The adventures of these two workers in collecting the information would make interesting reading. They frequently drove alone in hired "rigs" drawn by often balky horses over country roads in all kinds of weather. They sometimes interviewed persons infected with syphilis or tuberculosis, mentally ill persons or ordinary inebriates. All these conditions were reported in a detached manner that gave no hint of the excitement or actual risk in some of their investigations.

In retrospect the work of the early investigators appears to have been accurately and carefully done. Most of their predictions have been fulfilled. Very seldom were they mistaken in their assessment of individuals. A few mistakes were made by the investigators concerning untested young persons they knew as apparent retardates but who were actually underachieving juvenile delinquent types who later became successful in life. The most extreme example of these rare cases was a boy for whom they expected a very poor future and who became a U. S. Congressman! One advantage to the follow-up is that such mistakes can be rectified with the collection of more recent data. The material Miss Deavitt and Miss Curial collected gave information on three and sometimes four generations which included the patient's grandparents, parents, aunts and uncles, siblings, first cousins and occasionally children or nieces and nephews, including, of course, records on the spouses as well. Since many of the patients were young in 1911, many members of the older generations were still alive and could be interviewed. Binet testing was introduced into Minnesota very early, and by 1911 intelligence tests were administered routinely to applicants for admission to the Institution and sometimes to their parents and siblings also.

Minnesota was very fortunate in having outstanding psychologists in that early period, of whom Dr. Kuhlmann was perhaps the best known. He was the psychologist at the institution for the retarded at Faribault from 1910 to 1921. During this time he edited the Journal of Psycho-Asthenics, developed his own psychological tests and set up the Bureau for Psychological Services. As a result of his work, Minnesota had an early and reliable system of psychological testing which is still in effect today.

When the study was reopened in 1949, criteria were set up with which to select those of the 549 families to be followed up. After this had been done, the investigation of each family would include as many of the descendants of the patient's grandparents as could be found. The old data would be used for the records for the older generations and similar information about the more recent generations would be added. The more recent generations would include those who were small children or who were not yet born when the original study was ended in 1918. These people comprise three more generations at least. The widespread use of intelligence testing in recent years allows a better evaluation of the mental status of many persons in the more recent generations, and IQ scores were collected whenever possible, not only for those in the line of descent but also for spouses. It was hoped that not only would the test data collected for retarded individuals be of value but also that some idea might be obtained about the reproductive rates of the retardates as compared with those of their normal relatives. Also the trends in family size over a period of five or six generations are interesting and the types of matings, whether assortative or nonassortative, are important in the family patterns.

There are over 80,000 persons included in the families of our study. This is one of the largest genetic investigations so far completed. It is a large enough sample of the population of the upper midwest to indicate the trends of any changes in measured intelligence of this region and possibly for a more extensive area of the country. It would be unwise to utilize our findings out of context or to consider them relevant to Asian, African or other different cultures.

THE COLLECTION OF THE DATA

The records of the 549 families studied during the period 1911 to 1918 were reread with the object of selecting families for the follow-up. The patients in the original study were "unselected" in the sense that originally the families of all the approximately 1500 patients were to have been investigated. The ones who were included in the sample of 549 happened to be the ones easiest to study from the viewpoint of proximity and availability. At that time the population of the institution was drawn from all parts of Minnesota. In order to accomplish as much as possible with the time and money available, the original investigators chose the most accessible family groups with which to begin their work. When one considers the modes of travel available in 1911, the most practical approach (and the one used) was to select families in near-by towns or within reach of the railroads. The workers did not select patients for a certain type of retardation or because they had institutionalized relatives, so their sample of 549 was a fairly accurate cross section of the total population of the institution at that time, with respect to the factors of interest in our study.

For the follow-up, certain criteria were devised to reduce extraneous variations in the sample. The first criterion was that all probands must have IQ scores of 69 or below. This condition eliminated 33 patients in the original study, including one with an IQ of 112 who was clearly psychotic. The second criterion was that all the probands had to have been in the institution at some time during the period 1911 to 1918 while the workers were doing the research there. This restriction eliminated 38 patients and their families who had been included in the 549 for various irrelevant reasons. The third criterion was that the probands selected must have had no history of epilepsy prior to institutionalization, even of a single convulsion in childhood. It was impossible to tell whether the epilepsy in many of the patients was a contributing factor to the retardation or only concomitant with it. This condition eliminated 182 more patients. This screening left 296 probands. Two of the probands developed convulsive attacks long after their institutionalization and both were diagnosed as nonepileptic attacks by neurologists so they were kept in the sample. In seven of the 296 families the probands were related to other probands in such a way that the families could be combined without loss of information, so this was done, leaving a total of 289 probands.

Once the 289 probands had been selected, the routine collection of data was begun. The research was greatly facilitated by the use of the Central Index in St. Paul. This index is a listing of all persons who have had any contact with any county or state agencies since the year 1924. Permission was obtained for the use of this file and also for use of the files in many state and county offices. In nearly every case school principals gave permission for the use of IQ scores, and the records of the state psychological testing bureau were available to us. This study could never have been carried out without the cooperation of supervisors in many departments and the patient and kindly help of numerous persons in many offices. No person was harmed in any way because of our access to such information. Had individual permission to release IQ values been required, it would not have been possible to complete the project.

The present status of all probands was determined at the reopening of the project. Institution records were consulted for medical and institutional history. There were often long welfare records on probands who had been discharged from the institution and information from these records was valuable, especially the data about relatives. A few probands were never found, but they were retained in the study data.

Names and addresses of relatives of the proband could be found in old records or in directories, and once a contact was made other relatives could be found. Sometimes family members were still living at the addresses given in the original records. All these persons were sent a covering letter explaining that their relatives had cooperated in a population study sponsored by the State of Minnesota in 1911 and that the study was now being brought up to date. Blanks were enclosed asking for the names, dates of birth, occupation, amount of schooling and address of last school attended for the addressee and his spouse, his parents, his children and their spouses, if any, and occasionally for his siblings and their spouses also if they could not be reached directly. Correspondents were assured that the information was for research purposes only. The data about the addressee's parents helped identify him as a family member and the addresses of the last schools attended gave IQ sources. Thank you letters were sent promptly to all who replied.

Nearly half the persons answered the first letter by filling in and returning the blanks. A follow-up letter brought replies from half the remainder. A second follow-up letter was sent special delivery. Again half the remainder replied. The special delivery letter was useful in another way. Often it was impossible to know whether or not the regular letters reached the addressees because the return to the sender depended upon the initiative of the postman or on the knowledge of the present resident at the old address. Special delivery letters required directory service and were either readdressed or returned to the sender with a stamp indicating the reason, such as, "moved," "left no address," "deceased," or rarely, "refused." Telephoning was used if necessary information was still lacking. It is a much more time consuming procedure than one might expect. Many persons are not at home during the day. Some dislike giving information over the telephone, especially on party lines.

It was surprising how many persons answered promptly and completely. A few were hesitant until the project was explained more fully in a second letter. A few thought the project was some sort of money making scheme until a footnote was added to the follow-up letter explaining that the research was supported by a grant. Even the ones who were telephoned because they had not replied to three letters were for the most part quite apologetic, citing lack of time, loss of blanks or just forgetfulness. At the end of each year, a few replies to letters sent four, five or six years ago came in, an indication of the benefits of year-end house cleaning. Most people were helpful and cooperative. A very few correspondents refused to answer anything. One woman returned the blanks with the message, "You have more money than sense already." Poor cooperation and refusals nearly always came from sibships in which there had been numerous divorces, especially if religious differences entered the picture, or in which there had been mental illness. Usually information about uncooperative members could be obtained from other relatives.

There were two chief reasons why some persons could not be located. One was the loss of contact with relatives which occurred when part of the family remained in the home country or when some members moved to distant states. Adopted children were almost impossible to find, but there were not many of them. The second reason some family histories could not be completed was that the family name was so common in the population that the proper person could not be identified.

The collection of data by mail from relatives proved to be easier than expected. Cross checks of data reported by more than one relative showed the information to be quite reliable. This was also true for school information when checked against school records. There was very little up-grading of school achievement or occupational classification by the correspondents. Usually the correspondents reported institutionalized relatives or illegitimate births. Generally these were already known to the investigators from welfare files, and served as a check both on the reliability of reports from relatives and the efficiency of the system of record searching. We soon learned to spot unreliable replies which warranted further search of public agency files, especially those of the state testing bureau for retardates, delinquents, school "problems" and unmarried mothers.

As information about the families gradually accumulated, new pedigree charts were drawn. These charts incorporated the information from the old records and the old charts with the new data for the more recent generations. From these work scrolls the artist redesigned the layout into stadia that would fit on book sized pages. The pedigree charts for large families had to be drawn in several parts. A written summary of information about each person on the pedigree charts was prepared, again utilizing the old information and adding the new. Finally, a short summary of each family was written to accompany the corresponding pedigree chart for publication.

THE PEDIGREE CHARTS

Not long after the data on the families began to accumulate it became obvious that each family was different from every other one. Pooled data on all the individuals might not only be meaningless but actually misleading. A family in which the proband is the only retardate in an otherwise normal kindred is quite different from one in which retardation and social problems recur generation after generation. Therefore it was decided that separate pedigree charts for each family would be included in this report.

The reader may be as surprised as we were to discover how little retardation appeared in some families. It was thought that while it might appear a waste of space to include a nine-part pedigree chart of a large family of some 2400 people of whom less than 1 per cent were retarded, the fact that there are such families is interesting in itself. Obviously, retardation and some of its concomitant social consequences are not distributed at random throughout the population. There were 37 families of the 289 in which the only known retardate was the proband.

A uniform manner of drawing the pedigree charts was adopted. Each individual on the chart has his own number, irrespective of the generation he is in, so that the numbering begins with (1) for the proband's paternal grandfather (or for the grandfather's first wife if he was married more than once) and continues consecutively throughout the entire kindred. If a person appears twice (usually as the result of a consanguineous marriage) he has the same number both times. A person appearing twice has the number from the generation in which he first appears. In a few cases valuable new information came in after numbering was completed. Persons added after the numbering was completed have letters after the number. Sibships are drawn with the individuals in birth order, starting on the left with the oldest, but this was possible only when all dates of birth were known. Miscarriages, abortions, stillbirths and children who died before the age of 2 years are represented by small circles. No connections are made across sibship lines or across generation lines except to indicate incest. If relationships of spouses in two sibships or in two generations needed to be indicated, asterisks were used and the relationships are described in a separate legend at the bottom of the chart. Illegitimacy is indicated by dotted lines and consanguinity, in any degree, by a double marriage line. Arrows indicate persons institutionalized for mental retardation or persons born in the institution, such as children of probands. Persons known in the old history but unknown now as to whether or not they reproduced have U's under their symbols. The continuous dotted line separates information collected in 1911 to 1918 from that of the follow-up.

The primary object of the pedigree charts is to show the number of retardates and their relationships to the proband. For the older generations, the evaluation of the original workers was used unless subsequent investigation showed that they had been mistaken. This rarely happened. For the more recent generations symbols for individuals with IQ's of 69 or below are always filled in. If a person had an IQ of 70 or 71 but had been committed as retarded his symbol is also filled in, because in the judgment of professional people he was considered to function as if retarded. All others with IQ scores of 70 or above were classified as not retarded (although, of course, this group includes the borderlines and the dull normals) and given an open symbol.

Some arbitrary cut off point had to be used to indicate retardation on the pedigree charts. We chose to err on the conservative side in selecting an IQ of 69 as the top for retardation. We are well aware of the fact that the IQ is not a strictly quantitative measurement and that many factors enter into the picture of retardation. Minnesota has no standard cut-off point that could be used. An IQ as high as 75 is considered indicative of retardation by some workers; sometimes an IQ of 72 has been the dividing line.

For persons with no IQ scores, the following criteria were set up.

1. Open symbols were used for:

a. Those who completed school through the eighth grade at the proper age with good grades, or who passed the eighth grade examinations for admission to high school, or who took any extra school work (technical courses included) beyond the eighth grade level. "Social promotions" were not given until recently. IQ scores are available for most such cases and prevent us from being misled into thinking that graduation from the grade school was obtained as a result of ability.

b. Persons in semiskilled and skilled occupations listed as such in the Dictionary of Occupational Titles, published by the U. S.

Department of Labor; or for those who own and operate their own businesses.

c. Persons interviewed who were obviously well informed and alert regardless of their school history. Good correspondents were not so classified unless it was certain they had written the letters themselves.

d. Persons who had been allowed to adopt children. Minnesota has very strict requirements for adoptive parents.

2. Filled in symbols were used for individuals who had records of many grade failures in school, who left school at the sixth or seventh grade levels at ages 15 or 16 years, or whom the teachers regarded as retarded. While an occasional underachiever might be erroneously classified here, the cases in which such classification were made, and IQ scores found later, showed that this judgment was correct with only one exception.

3. Slashes indicate intelligence unknown. Most of these persons probably had IQ's above 70. Their school records were incomplete or their occupations undefined so they could not be reliably classified. Is a person who completed the seventh grade at age 14 years and who is a farmer retarded or not? Is this farmer the owner of a large, well run farm or a farm laborer? What about the housewife who completed the eighth grade at age 16 years, school standing unknown? We are well aware of the possibility of bias had the persons without IQ scores been evaluated according to the type of families they appeared in. In order to avoid this, each person was evaluated individually and apart from any reference to the mental status of his relatives.

The IQ scores shown on the charts are standardized as follows: If several IQ scores were available the one taken nearest age 14 years was used, unless a later one gave a higher score. Low ceilings on some tests penalize the gifted after age 14 years so higher scores were used if they were found. Often the early scores are high for retardates who do not fall much behind their classmates until the early years of grade school. Conversely, low scores resulting from environmental handicaps are often raised after the deprived child has been in school for several years, but there were very few cases of dramatic rises in IQ values in our study. If there was a choice of IQ scores between group tests or individual tests at about the same age level, the individual test score was chosen as being the more reliable. It was surprising how little variation there was among the test scores of most children over a period of years. A drop of about five points over the school period from age 6 to 14 years was common. Larger variations occurred in three types of situations—when the student was a high-grade retardate, the IQ score might drop by 20 or 30 points during this period. There were more of these cases than of their opposite—substantial increases in scores. When the student appeared retarded and came from a very poor environment, the score might rise in a similar manner. And finally, when a mentally disturbed person was tested several times, the scores varied greatly in either direction with no trend. The IQ scores correlated well with occupation and amount of schooling, with a few exceptions, such as a milkman who completed only the eighth grade but who had an IQ of 141.

After the final pedigree charts were drawn by the artist, the drawings were checked against the written summary person by person. Complete accuracy was very difficult to obtain. Undoubtedly there still are some undetected errors in the charts, but we hope they are not serious ones which would affect the total pictures of the families. A total of 83,529 persons appears on the pedigree charts. However, 1312 of these are duplicates because some families are interrelated, thus 1312 names appear in our records twice. The 1312 duplicates have been subtracted from the tables and calculations at all appropriate places.

The summaries that accompany the pedigree charts are highly condensed versions of the material collected on each family. Their chief content is information about all the retardates in the kindreds. However, an effort is made in each case to give a picture of the family regarding its overall mental and social status. In order to do this, reports of delinquency, mental illness, alcoholism or other seemingly pertinent factors are included. Since the reader has no way of reviewing the great mass of data which has been collected, the summaries have been used to give as much information as is possible in a limited space.

CLASSIFICATION OF THE PROBANDS

It seemed desirable for further study of the family constellations to arrange them according to some scheme based upon the roles of heredity and environment in the etiology of the retardation observed in the probands. One can never make a sharp distinction between genetic and environmental factors in their influence upon the degree of intelligence, as both are involved in the development of every individual. However, in some cases it is possible to demonstrate that an environmental factor had a clear-cut effect upon development greater than the genetic factors or *vice versa.* In one case, a 14-month-old infant had pneumonia and meningitis that resulted in subsequent mental retardation. The responsible infectious agent was considered to be the primary environmental factor in the retardation while the genetic factors permitting susceptibility of the proband to the bacteria were of secondary importance. Conversely, the microcephaly in the three individuals of family KMD 133 was, in all probability, the result of the homozygous state of a mendelian recessive.

Unfortunately, the classification of many of the probands is impossible according to the dichotomy of genetic or environmental etiology. There is no known way of determining what factors, genetic or environmental, are involved in the retardation of a large proportion of the mentally retarded children. Our classification is only a rough estimate of what seem to us to be the relative influences of heredity and environment for each proband. Others would, no doubt, disagree as to the disposition of some of the cases. We have no objection to this. We have changed them ourselves during the difficult process of trying to evolve a set of criteria that would allow self-confidence in our classifications. We never achieved a completely satisfactory classification, nor did we expect to. However, the criteria used are describable and are listed in the following section.

Classification Criteria

It should be emphasized that the four categories have only the semblance of being complete. Furthermore, although in some cases a trait such as microcephaly is due primarily to a mendelian recessive in the homozygous condition, there might possibly be other cases of microcephaly without a genetic basis. Environmentally induced anomalies which are indistinguishable from their genetic models are called *phenocopies.* Some phenocopies are probably included in our "genetic" and "probably genetic" categories. An unknown percentage of error must be accepted in attempting any kind of taxonomy of the mentally retarded in terms of etiology.

Genetic Factors of Primary Importance. The evidence indicating the operation of genetic factors to be of primary importance is of the following types:

a. Well-defined anomalies and syndromes known from the literature to behave according to mendelian rules of heredity or to be dependent upon specific chromosomal aberrations, such as is the case with Down's syndrome (mongolism). It might be mentioned that while Down's syndrome is not ordinarily hereditary, because both parents are normal, it is in all cases definitely genetic because the presence of the small extra chromosome upsets the normal gene balance and results in the anomaly. Some examples of other genetic anomalies and syndromes affecting probands of our study are phenylketonuria, microcephaly, hydrocephaly, cretinism, Laurence-Moon-Biedl syndrome and Pelizaeus-Merzbacher disease.

b. Presence of consanguinity in the parents of the proband. It is well known that children with traits that depend upon rare recessives for their expression are often the products of incestuous matings. Consequently, we classify all probands whose parents were consanguineous as genetic types. It would be possible for the child to be retarded without the parents' consanguinity being relevant, but usually the consanguinity of the parents is good evidence that the anomaly of the child depends upon heredity of the recessive type. Consanguinity is a powerful genetic tool.

c. The presence of one or more siblings or half siblings of the proband with apparently identical types of low-grade mental retardation (IQ below 50) in whom no environmental factors are known to be involved. The rationale here is that two or more low-grade patients of similar type are more likely to result from similar genotypes than from two similar environmental calamities.

There are 84 probands in the primarily genetic category.

Genetic Factors Probably of Primary Importance. Our attempts to categorize the primary factor responsible for the appearance of mental retardation in a particular proband rest upon a probability basis. The proband is classified as to what seems to be the most likely explanation for the retardation and the explanation will be incorrect in an unknown percentage of the cases.

a. We have accepted three or more generations of mental retardation without a break as probable evidence of primary importance of genetic factors. To be sure, it might be possible to transmit traumatic environmental factors through three generations, but it seems more likely that the primary factor is the assortative mating of persons at the lower end of the curve of normal intelligence. The reason for this view is that even in sibships in which both parents are retarded there can be normal or even intellectually superior children, although the latter are quite infrequent. Genetic segregation in these sibships seems to explain the extreme variation in the intelligence range much better than assumed trivial differences in an apparently uniformly impoverished environment.

b. Parent and one or more children with IQ below 50.

There are 55 probands in the probably genetic category.

Environmental Factors Probably of Primary Importance. This category includes medically authenticated reports of diseases of the mother or of the proband in the perinatal period or in early infancy which might have resulted in retardation. These include diagnosed cases of meningitis, poliomyelitis and encephalitis, together with records of severe infections of scarlet fever, measles, whooping cough or pneumonia in which the child was reported to have been ill for some time and to have regressed mentally after recovery.

The effects of syphilitic infections are difficult to assess. Usually syphilitic infections were found in families with external environmental problems as well, such as alcoholism, promiscuity and child abuse. The factors of bad environment, infection and deprivation may well have had a combined effect sufficient to lower the proband's IQ to that of high-grade retardate level. Families are included here in which the proband had a frank congenital syphilitic infection and in which there was a history of syphilitic parents and stillbirths, miscarriages or subsequent neurosyphilis among the offspring.

Also included as environmentally caused retardation are probands with medical histories of instrument delivery with obvious birth injuries, and those who had very severe falls followed by mental regression.

All probands have been placed in this third category where there was any suspicion that environmental factors were of primary importance in the etiology of the retardation. It is likely that in some of these cases the environmental factors were merely coincidental and not at all responsible for the retardation. It is well known that people usually search for some accidental event as the basis for any serious misfortune. In our study of Huntington's chorea, in which the heredity is a clear-cut mendelian dominant, the patients usually relate the onset of their disease to some event such as a divorce or a minor accident. On investigation, it always becomes clear that their symptoms were present well in advance of the selected environmental trauma. However, in spite of our recognition that the stated infections or cultural deprivation were probably unrelated to the retardation in some cases, all probands were placed in the environmental category where there was any suggestion in the records that unusual environmental conditions were present.

There are 27 probands in the primarily environmental category.

Unknown as to Whether Genetic or Environmental Factors Were of Primary Importance. This large group of the retarded is the most frustrating, because there is no hint as to the causal factors involved in the retardation. This is the residual category that includes probands about whom the information was too incomplete to permit even tentative conclusions regarding the etiology of the retardation. Several kinds of histories fall into this group. Some histories are included because very little recent information could be collected about the proband and his relatives. Quite a few histories are included because the proband was the only known retardate in his kindred. Several families appear in which both the proband's parents and all his siblings were retarded. These persons were all high-grade retardates in very poor environments who did not produce a third generation which could be assessed for mental status. Sometimes the old medical histories of the probands included associated factors, such as mental illness, or other diseases in childhood. Even today many undifferentiated cases of mental retardation give no clues as to their etiology following most careful examination and study.

The large size of this group of retarded children is a challenge to further research in this field, which, as in the case of phenylketonuria, should permit the isolation of new clinical types from the mass of mysterious cases of retardation of unknown origin.

There are 123 probands in the category of unknown causes.

THE PROCESSING OF THE DATA

The completion of the field work yielded a large mass of statistical data, concerning 82,217 individuals. How was this great amount of material to be handled so as to yield as much information as possible? We decided to approach the problem from two aspects. First, we were interested in the proportions of retarded individuals found among the relatives of the probands. Second, we wanted to know what the reproductive rates of the retardates were when compared with those of the normal individuals in these thousands of family units. The amount of material we had collected was large enough to furnish statistically significant samples in all four descriptive categories.

In order to discover the proportions of retardates among the proband's relatives, the individuals were separated into groups including those within the first degree of relationship to the probands (their parents, siblings and children), those within the second degree of relationship (their grandparents, aunts and uncles, half siblings, nieces and nephews and grandchildren), and those within the third degree of relationship (their half aunts and uncles, half nieces and nephews, great-nieces and nephews and first cousins). The males were counted separately from the females. Each person within each degree of relationship was classified as retarded, normal or unknown, following the criteria described earlier, or as having died before age 2 years, a group which included abortions, miscarriages, stillbirths or infant deaths. The numbers of individuals in each of these three degrees of relationship appear in the tables. Percentages of the retarded and of deaths before age 2 years were calculated, and these figures appear in the text. Parents and grandparents were excluded from the calculations of percentages of lives lost before age 2 years, because, by definition, they had to survive to adulthood. Prenatal and infant deaths were excluded from the calculations for percentages of retardates since they were totally unknown as to mental status; many could have been potential retardates.

As the data were collected it became apparent that the death loss before age 2 years constituted the group for which we had the least information, both as to actual numbers and as to possible mental status. It may be that quite a few retardates are members of this group. On the other hand, those listed as unknown as to mental status can be considered to be mostly persons with normal intelligence, although we did not have enough information to so classify them. Retardates are more likely to be identified, especially among the probands' immediate adult relatives. Many of the unknowns are children who have not yet been tested but who probably would have been identified had they been low- or middle-grade retardates. As the sections on reproductive rates will show, many more normal persons than retardates are to be expected, especially among the more distant relatives of the probands. Hence we think no great bias is imposed by adding the unknowns to the normals and treating them as such. However, those individuals who appear as diamonds on the pedigree charts are not included as of unknown mental status, since they are even unknown as to sex. They can, however, be included in the section on reproductive rates, because they were persons of over 2 years of age.

In order to study reproductive rates, the data were handled in another way. Several questions can be asked here. How much do the retarded reproduce? What mates do they have? What are their children like? Then, does having a retardate in a sibship affect the reproductive rate of normal siblings? Do the probands' siblings have as many children as their first cousins do? Did the probands' aunts and uncles have as many children as the probands' parents had? Are the completed families of the probands' first cousins different in size from those of the probands' aunts and uncles? In answering such questions completed families must be used. These were determined by using a cut-off date of age 45 years for the mother and 50 years for the father. In these families the persons unknown as to sex are counted in order to get the reproductive rate of their parents. Also, all retardates are included, irrespective of their degree of relationship to the proband, and the population is studied as a whole. In some of our very large families quite a few persons are rather remotely related to the proband himself.

The sections on correlations of IQ's of spouse with spouse, or parent with child, are self explanatory. Standard procedures were used and are described in the appropriate chapter.

THE 289 PROBANDS

The 289 probands were a heterogeneous group whose selection has been described. Our first consideration of them was the ascertainment of their present status. In 1961, 50 years after the study was begun, 202 were deceased, 40 were living outside the institution and 36 were still institutionalized. The record for length of institutionalization was held by the female proband in KMD 475 who was admitted as a patient in 1894 and was still living in the institution in 1961. There were 11 probands whose status was unknown to us, either because the families had moved to other areas, including one proband who returned to his native Poland, or because they had such frequently occurring family names that they could not be traced. By 1961 our 289 probands had spent a total of 7090 years in institutions, an average of almost 25 years each. Longevity in institutions has increased greatly since 1911. Therefore we can assume that the *average* residence for those now being institutionalized will exceed 25 years.

The IQ range among the probands was from 1 for a microcephalic proband to our ceiling of 69. The distribution was as follows: In the IQ range 0 to 24 there were 78 probands, 42 males and 36 females. In the range 25 to 49 there were 121 probands, 58 males and 63 females. In the range 50 to 69 there were 90 probands, 38 males and 52 females. The sex ratio changed as the IQ level rose so that there were more females institutionalized in the higher groups than males. This is partly because some of our female probands were institutionalized after the births of illegitimate children.

The types of retardation found among the probands were as follows: The undifferentiated form in which the probands showed no distinguishing features other than a low IQ appeared in the largest number, 221 individuals. There were 39 persons who had identifiable specific disorders including 11 with Down's syndrome (mongolism), six with hydrocephaly and or spina bifida, five cretins (one with ichthyosis), three with microcephaly, two phenylketonurics, three deaf mutes, two retardates with associated polydactyly, one with anophthalmia, one with microphthalmia, one with Laurence-Moon-Biedl syndrome, one with Pelizaeus-Merzbacher syndrome, one with Buhl's disease, one with sex-linked progressive muscular dystrophy and one with ichthyosis.

In addition to these two large categories, there were 29 probands with the following miscellaneous anomalies: six probands developed subsequent psychoses, two had retardation with spastic diplegia, four were blind, one had a "convulsive disorder, non-epileptic," one had cerebral palsy, one was severely crippled, one developed Parkinson's disease, one was very obese, one was acromegalic and one was retarded, hemiplegic and also a deaf mute. The final ten of the 29 miscellaneous probands presented even more obscure pictures. One was a low-grade retardate with a probable central nervous system disorder, one was low grade with multiple abnormalities, one had a very large head but had not been diagnosed as hydrocephalic, one became retarded after a severe fall as an adult and six regressed from fairly high grade to very low grade after institutionalization. In these last six it was impossible to determine whether they had developed a mental illness in addition to their retardation or whether they were the victims of some unknown degenerative disease.

Seven probands were members of twin pairs, four like sex and three unlike sex. One was an identical microcephalic pair, four twins of the probands died in infancy, one proband had a normal twin of the opposite sex and one had a retarded mentally ill twin of the same sex. This last case (KMD 313) is interesting because of the musical ability associated with the retardation in the proband and in his retarded twin brother.

The reproduction of the probands is of great interest. Their marriage and reproductive rates must be lower than those of other retarded persons remaining in the community because of their institutionalization. However, it should be realized that the higher grade retardates may be in and out of the institution several times, and thus have an opportunity for reproduction and sometimes they marry.

Forty-two probands, 40 women and two men, had 99 children, of whom 37 were illegitimate. Sixteen of the 42 probands had 62 legitimate children by 22 spouses. More than half of these 22 spouses (13) were known to have had normal intelligence. The legal marriages of the probands are of considerable interest both genetically and sociologically. How could some of these women with their poor social backgrounds and histories of institutionalization contract marriages with individuals of considerably higher IQ level than themselves? For one thing, it seems likely that the institutionalization led to an improvement in their marital prospects in that these women received considerable training in personal grooming and simple household skills while in the institution. Among the 13 normal spouses there were 12 men and one woman. As far as we know none of the marriages was forced because of pregnancy. The one wife with normal intelligence divorced her retarded husband. He then married a woman with IQ 77 who came from a very poor social background. This second marriage was childless. The 12 normal husbands were as follows: two were foreign born and apparently in a poorer social class than their intelligence and behavior warranted because of their immigrant status. Two of the husbands had good IQ's but were in trouble with the law. One of these was an exconvict, the other was cruel and abusive to his wife and deserted her when he had to leave the state to avoid arrest on white slavery charges. Three normal apparently well adjusted men divorced their retarded wives. One husband was 11 years older than his wife. Four husbands had normal intelligence and no apparent social or psychological problems and remained married to the probands. Of the 13 fertile marriages to normal spouses, four ended in divorce and one in desertion. The occupations of ten of the husbands are known. There was one tavern owner, one restaurant operator, a stone mason, a cabinet maker, a building foreman, a stationary fireman, a plumber, a laborer and two painters. Among the four marriages of probands to retardates one was a forced marriage and one was to a man 34 years older than the proband.

Twenty-nine female probands had 37 illegitimate children. (Three of these 29 probands had both legitimate and illegitimate children.) While we cannot be sure that no male probands fathered illegitimate children, we are reasonably certain that very few, if any, did because the social histories of the probands are so complete. In general the probands came from small towns and rural communities where such affairs are more likely to be common knowledge which would have been imparted to the early workers who were expert interviewers. Miss Curial even uncovered a case of brother-sister incest where the brother and sister had posed for several years as a married couple with three children. Furthermore, in every category except the environmental, male probands were institutionalized at an earlier age than the females.

The percentage of retardation among the illegitimate children was 30.0, while among the legitimate children only 11.3 per cent were retarded,—this figure also includes persons of *unknown* intelligence. This finding is contrary to a common belief that the illegitimate children of retardates are more likely to have normal intelligence than the legitimate ones. Some of the reasons for the difference shown above become apparent when we look at the fathers of the 37 illegitimate children of the probands. Seven of these unions were known to have been incestuous; three were with fathers (two normal, one retarded), two were with retarded brothers, one with a half uncle of unknown intelligence and one with either the retarded father or a retarded brother. An eighth union was suspected to have been with an uncle but this was not established. The seven children resulting from the incestuous matings included four who died in infancy, an institutionalized retardate who may also be schizophrenic, an apparently normal girl who died at age 3 years and a girl with IQ 79 who survived. (See KMD's 67, 90, 151, 163, 252, 428 and 496 for more details.) Only four of the illegal fathers were known to have had normal intelligence, seven were retarded and 24 were unknown. Some of these unknowns may also have been relatives but the facts could not be established from our records.

Table 1. *The Intelligence of the Children of the Probands*

	Range of IQ Scores							IQ Scores not Known			
	0-24	25-49	50-69	70-89	90-110	111-125	126+	Retardate	Normal	Unknown	Died before age 2 Years
Legitimate children	0	0	4	9	17	2	0	2	13	6	9
Illegitimate children	2	0	3	5	4	0	0	3	5	5	10
Total	2	0	7	14	21	2	0	5	18	11	19

The data for all the children of the probands are given in Table 1.

Ten of the 289 probands were sterilized and four of the ten married after the sterilization. Two of these four had had illegitimate children before sterilization.

Finally, the 99 children produced by the 289 probands included 19 children who died before age 2 years. This leaves only 80 offspring, or about 0.28 children per proband. The 80 survivors were produced by 42 of the probands, or 1.9 children per reproducing proband. It is clear that institutionalization prevents such a group from remotely approaching replacement of itself. This point will be considered in detail later.

SUMMARY

A follow-up study based on records compiled 50 years ago yielded data on the mental status, economic, educational and social achievements of 82,217 persons. These persons were the descendants of the grandparents of 289 probands who were resident in the Faribault, Minnesota, State School and Colony for the Retarded sometime during the years 1911 to 1918. The population also includes the spouses who married into the kinships. The family pedigrees extended over as much as seven generations.

Our primary aim was to determine as accurately as possible the mental status of all persons in the study. This was done by collecting school records, IQ scores, data on occupations, and so forth. A family history summary and pedigree chart for each of the 289 probands are included in the Appendix.

The 289 probands were divided into four categories depending upon the extent to which genetic and environmental factors were thought to be of importance in the retardation. The 84 probands placed in the primarily genetic category included those with diagnosed genetic anomalies and those who were the children of consanguineous marriages. The 55 probands in the category of probably genetic origin included those of an undifferentiated type of retardation who were in a three-generation line of retardates and those in which parent and child had a similar low-grade type of retardation. There were 27 probands whose medical records indicated perinatal trauma or early illness severe enough to have accounted for their retardation; these were classified as of environmental origin. Finally, there were 123 probands with no defined anomalies, no evidence of early trauma and no familial history of mental defect. They were put in the category of unknown origin of their retardation.

The life histories and the destinies of the 289 probands were carefully studied. In 1961, 202 were deceased, 40 lived outside the institution and 36 were still institutionalized. The fate of 11 probands could not be determined. Our 289 probands had spent a total of 7090 years in institutions, an average of almost 25 years for each one. Longevity in institutions has been increased greatly since 1911. Therefore, we can assume that the *average* residence for those now being institutionalized will exceed 25 years by a significant amount.

Forty of the women and two of the men reproduced. They produced 99 children of whom 62 were legitimate and 37 illegitimate. Nineteen of the children died in infancy. The legitimate children were retarded in 11.3 per cent of the cases while the illegitimate children showed 30.0 per cent retardation. Half the legal spouses of the probands were known to be of normal intelligence. At least seven of the illegitimate unions were incestuous.

CHAPTER THREE

THE RELATIVES OF THE PROBANDS

THE PRIMARILY GENETIC CATEGORY

The primarily genetic category included 84 probands who were so classified because they had either well defined genetic anomalies, or had one or more siblings with IQ's below 50 or were the offspring of consanguineous unions. There were equal numbers of male and female probands in this category. Ten of the 84 probands were the only retarded members of their kinships.

The largest group of 32 probands was that of the diagnosed syndromes with non-consanguineous parents. There were ten with Down's syndrome (mongolism). Five probands had diagnoses of hydrocephalus or spina bifida. Four probands were cretins, two probands were microcephalic, two had phenylketonuria and two were retarded deaf mutes. There were single cases of retardation with polydactyly, anophthalmia, microphthalmia, a central nervous system disorder, sex-linked progressive muscular dystrophy, Laurence-Moon-Biedle syndrome and Pelizaeus-Merzbacher disease.

The second largest group contained 29 probands with an undifferentiated type of low- or middle-grade retardation and who had one or more siblings with IQ's below 50. Their parents were not related.

The last group of 23 persons was composed of probands whose parents were related in some degree. Six of the probands had diagnosable types of retardation, namely, Down's syndrome, cretinism, microcephaly, polydactyly, Buhl's disease and ichthyosis. The case of Down's syndrome, and perhaps some of the other five anomalies, is not related to the consanguinity of the parents. However, these cases are included in the consanguinity grouping in order to state the total number of cases with consanguineous parentage. Thus 23 probands (8 per cent) out of the total of 289 had consanguineous parents. This is a much higher percentage than the 0.5 per cent of consanguinity found in the general public.

The excess of probands with consanguineous parents is a strong indication of the importance of genetic factors in the etiology of the mental retardation in this group.

The types of relationships of the parents of the 23 probands were as follows: two brother by sister, one father by daughter, one great-uncle by great-niece, one half first cousin, nine first cousin, two first cousin once removed, four second cousin, one second cousin once removed and two known to have been related but of unknown degree.

Only seven of the 84 probands (all from the undifferentiated and consanguineous groups) had any children—a total of 16 plus one retardate who died before 2 years of age. Of these eight were illegitimate. The nine legitimate children and two of the eight illegitimate children had normal intelligence. Neither of the two normal illegitimates reproduced. One was a delinquent girl reared by an aunt and who was unmarried at 40 years of age. The other illegitimate normal child suffered an attack of encephalitis at age 11 years, became an invalid, was hospitalized for mental illness and died at age 20 years. Both of these persons were children of the proband in KMD 3. The six remaining illegitimate

Table 2. *The Relatives of the Probands of the First Degree of Relationship Primarily Genetic Category* (Excluding 105 Deaths under 2 Years of Age)

Class of Probands	Fathers Ret.	Fathers Nor.	Fathers Unk.	Mothers Ret.	Mothers Nor.	Mothers Unk.	Brothers Ret.	Brothers Nor.	Brothers Unk.	Sisters Ret.	Sisters Nor.	Sisters Unk.	Children Ret.	Children Nor.	Children Unk.	Totals	Percentage Retarded
Diagnosed syndromes (32 probands)	8	21	3	7	15	10	14	45	15	6	41	13	0	0	0	198	17.7
Undifferentiated (29 probands)	10	16	3	17	11	1	38	25	5	29	41	6	0	0	2	204	46.0
Consanguineous (23 probands)	8	11	4	9	10	4	19	29	8	30	30	8	2	12	0	184	37.0
Totals	26	48	10	33	36	15	71	99	28	65	112	27	2	12	2	586	
		(84)			(84)			(198)			(204)			(16)			
Percentage retarded		30.9			39.3			35.8			31.8			12.5			33.6

children are classified as follows: one was a low-grade retardate who died in infancy. One is an institutionalized retardate. One is a borderline male whose present status is unknown and who is the only one of the eight illegitimate children of probands who might have reproduced. One illegitimate child died of marasmus in infancy. The other two children died young and were unknown as to intelligence.

All 11 children with definitely normal intelligence (IQ's of 80 or above) belonged to two high-grade retardate probands (KMD 3 and 378). Both these women married normal men, by whom they had their normal legitimate children. In addition, one of these women had two normal illegitimate children by unknown men. The other six illegitimate children were produced by the following unions: two were the products of brother by sister incest, both parents retarded. Of their two offspring, one died in infancy of marasmus and one died as a young child (both were of unknown intelligence). The third incestuous relationship, that of normal grandfather by his retarded granddaughter, produced an institutionalized retardate. The father of one unknown child was an institutionalized retardate, the other two fathers were unknown. With the possible exception of one illegitimate child, only the normal legitimates married and had children, so at least seven of the eight illegitimates did not reproduce themselves. For more detailed information see the Appendix for descriptions for KMD's 3, 67, 90, 151, 163, 274 and 378.

There were 691 persons in the first degree of relationship to the 84 probands, including the 17 children born to seven of the probands (see Table 2). The 168 parents of the probands included 59 retardates (35.1 per cent). There were 506 siblings of whom 104 (20.5 per cent) did not survive to age 2 years. There were 198 brothers and 204 sisters who survived the age of 2 years. The retardates in the group of siblings numbered 136 (33.8 per cent). In the consanguineous subgroup of 23 probands there were 124 surviving siblings with 49 retarded (39.5 per cent), or somewhat more than for the whole group.

It is of interest that in the consanguineous group there were 15 children produced by the 23 probands of whom two were retarded, 12 were normal, and one died before the age of 2 years. Excluding the last child gives 14.3 per cent retarded children from our consanguineous probands compared with the 39.5 per cent retarded siblings of the probands. The siblings are subject to the same genetic risks caused by consanguinity as the probands, but the children of the probands are free of any of the genetic consequences of the consanguinity that produced the proband. We would expect a much lower percentage of retardation on purely genetic reasoning and this was observed. The excess of affected sisters of the consanguineous probands (30 sisters) compared with only 19 retarded brothers was unexpected; it is not statistically significant and therefore may be a purely random fluctuation.

When the 29 families in the undifferentiated group (with the proband and one or more siblings below IQ 50) are studied separately, the percentage of retarded siblings of the probands rises to 46.5 per cent, a proportion greater than that for the consanguineous subgroup. Since the criterion for inclusion in this group requires a retarded sibling, a bias is introduced which may be removed by subtracting the 29 required siblings from the total of 67 retardates. We now have 115 siblings of the proband remaining, including 38 retardates, or 33.0 per cent retardation as compared with the 39.5 per cent retardation in the siblings of the consanguineous group.

The largest subgroup of probands was the 32 diagnosed individuals. None of the 32 had any children nor would they have had any if they had remained in their home communities. A child with Down's syndrome, microcephaly, phenylketonuria, anophthalmia, and so on, is so severely affected by his anomaly that reproduction is extremely rare. The abnormal genes present in the child are eliminated at his death but are replaced in the general population by new mutation.

The family with sex-linked muscular dystrophy and retardation (KMD 402) is of interest as there were four retarded brothers, three normal brothers and one sister of unknown mental capacity. The affected more distant relatives of the proband with Pelizaeus-Merzbacher disease (KMD 215) which behaves like a sex-linked trait, are also of interest, because they demonstrate the form of the pedigrees containing genetically lethal sex-linked traits.

The relatively low value of 17.7 per cent retarded parents and siblings of the 32 diagnosed probands agrees with expectation when it is realized that none of the parents or siblings of the ten cases of Down's syndrome (mongolism) would be expected to display the trait. Nor would we expect the parents of most of the other affected children, such as the phenylketonurics, to be affected.

The second degree of relationship included 1907 individuals of whom 19 were grandchildren of two probands. All these grandchildren were legitimate and were the offspring of the nine normal legitimate children of two probands. These nine children married ten spouses, of whom four were known to have had normal intelligence and six had unknown intelligence but were probably normal (none was a known retardate). Among the ten marriages there have been two divorces and one desertion. The desertion and one divorce involved the same person (No. 204 in KMD 378), and the other divorced person was her brother. There was one known retardate among the grandchildren, ten normals and eight unknown or too young to test.

These 1907 persons (see Table 3) included 154 individuals who died before the age of 2 years. Since the grandparents could not have died before reproducing, they are subtracted leaving 9.8 per cent of the relatives who died before age 2 years. There were 152 retardates among the 1753 surviving relatives (8.7 per cent).

It is striking that the percentages of retardation for the second degree relatives dropped so greatly from those shown for the first degree relatives. For instance, it was noted before that 33.8 per cent of the siblings were retarded and it can be seen from Table 3 that 17.2 per cent of the half siblings were retarded. This is a 50 per cent drop, exactly

Table 3. *The Relatives of the Probands of the Second Degree of Relationship Primarily Genetic Category*
(Excluding 154 Deaths under 2 Years of Age)

Class of Probands	Grandparents			Uncles and Aunts			Half Siblings			Nephews and Nieces			Grandchildren			Totals	Percentage Retarded
	Ret.	Nor.	Unk.	Ret.	Nor.	Unk.	Ret.	Nor.	Unk.	Ret.	Nor.	Unk.	Ret.	Nor.	Unk.		
Diagnosed syndromes (32 probands)	5	36	87	27	108	128	3	17	21	9	160	43	0	0	0	644	6.3
Undifferentiated (29 probands)	11	21	84	29	126	135	2	6	0	17	106	33	0	0	0	570	10.3
Consanguineous * (23 probands)	4	21	62	22	84	93	10	15	13	12	150	34	1	10	8	539	9.1
Totals	20	78	233	78	318	356	15	38	34	38	416	110	1	10	8	1753	-
		(331)			(752)			(87)			(564)			(19)			
Percentage retarded		6.0			10.4			17.2			6.7			5.3			8.7

* One grandfather (KMD 67) is also the proband's father and is included both here and in Table 2. Also, this proband's mother's siblings are the proband's half sisters and are counted as such. In addition, two brother-sister unions having only one set of grandparents each, bring about a deficiency of five grandparents in the consanguineous group.

what would be expected on a genetic basis because half siblings have one half of their genes in common with the full sibling group. However, the same genetic relationship also holds for the grandparents, nephews, nieces and other relatives shown in Table 3, yet these groups show from 6 to 8 per cent retardation, which is significantly below the expectation for their common heredity on a polygenic hypothesis. There were 87 half-siblings produced in 16 families with 15 retardates. Seven of the 15 retardates appeared in one family (KMD 378). Thus this one family was responsible for the elevated percentage of retardation for the whole group of half siblings.

It is not possible to give a complete explanation for the significant excessive decrease in retardation from first to second degree relatives that is seen in comparing Tables 2 and 3. However, this whole group of assumed primarily genetic probands would depend upon single events such as sex-linked inheritance and trisomy of the 21st chromosome for its appearance. Therefore, the polygenic hypothesis is not relevant to this group of probands as a whole, but it may be the type of heredity of importance for many of the retarded parents observed, for the following reason.

There is very probably a strong bias for mental retardation to be found among the parents of our probands. This would be the result of the greater necessity for institutionalizing the retarded child if one or both parents were also retarded. The retarded child would be more likely to remain at home if the parents were of normal intelligence than if they were retarded. The retardation among the parents of our probands of the primarily genetic category will therefore have different causes from those responsible for the retardation in our probands of this category, and this would hold for the other categories of probands as well.

One interesting observation concerning the probands with consanguineous parents is that mental retardation was at least partly responsible for the union of the blood relatives. For example, the union of the father and daughter would probably not have occurred if the daughter had been of normal intelligence.

The third degree of relationship to the 84 probands included 3063 individuals of whom 253 (8.3 per cent) died before age 2 years (see Table 4). There were 2810 survivors, of whom 103 (3.7 per cent) were retarded. A comparison can be made of the different types of relatives of the third degree although numbers are small for the probands' parents' generation. There were 68 half aunts and half uncles of whom ten (14.7 per cent) were retarded. Here again, there was a very uneven distribution of retardates. Eight of the ten retardates were in one family (KMD 163 in the consanguineous subgroup).

In contrast to the group above we have the children of the probands' half siblings, 199 half nephews and nieces, of whom 18 (9.0 per cent) were retarded. Here again, a bias was introduced by small numbers. Two families (KMD 378 in the consanguineous subgroup and KMD 490 with Down's syndrome) contributed 14 of the 18 retardates.

The two largest groups in the third degree of relationship, and therefore probably those with the most reliable data, are the first

Table 4. *The Relatives of the Probands of the Third Degree of Relationship Primarily Genetic Category*
(Excluding 253 Deaths under 2 Years of Age)

Class of Probands	Half Uncles and Aunts Ret.	Nor.	Unk.	Half Nephews and Nieces Ret.	Nor.	Unk.	Great-Nephews and Nieces Ret.	Nor.	Unk.	First Cousins Ret.	Nor.	Unk.	Totals	Percentage Retarded
Diagnosed syndromes (32 probands)	0	7	25	6	66	15	9	191	62	12	364	267	1024	2.6
Undifferentiated (29 probands)	1	5	1	2	4	0	4	107	69	28	350	276	847	4.1
Consanguineous (23 probands)	9	14	6	10	64	32	8	231	58	14	232	261	939	4.4
Totals	10	26	32	18	134	47	21	529	189	54	946	804	2810	-
		(68)			(199)			(739)			(1804)			
Percentage retarded		14.7			9.1			2.8			3.0		-	3.7

Table 5. *The Percentage of Retardation in Relatives of the Primarily Genetic Probands by Generation Level and by Degree of Relationship* (Deaths before 2 Years of Age Omitted)

Degree of Relationship	Grandparents	Parents' Generation	Probands' own Generation	Children's Generation	Grand-children's Generation	Average Percentage
First degree (from Table 2)	-	35.1	33.9	12.5	-	33.6 (197 of 586)
Second degree (from Table 3)	6.0	10.4	17.2	6.7	5.3	9.2 (152 of 1753)
Third degree (from Table 4)	-	14.7	3.0	9.1	2.8	3.7 (103 of 2810)
Average percentage	6.0 (20 of 331)	14.9 (147 of 988)	8.9 (205 of 2293)	7.4 (58 of 779)	2.9 (22 of 758)	8.8 (452 of 5149)

cousins and the great-nephews and nieces. There were 1804 first cousins, of whom 54 (3.0 per cent) were retarded. Great-nephews and nieces numbered 739, of whom 21 (2.8 per cent) were retarded. Here two different generations showed almost no difference in the amount of retardation present.

A summary of the data for the relatives of the probands is given in Table 5. It shows that there is a smaller proportion of retardation in the most distant relationships from the proband. This would be expected on any genetic theory of etiology and also, to some extent, for environmental etiologies. The distinctions between the two will be considered in greater detail after our other categories have been presented.

THE PROBABLY GENETIC CATEGORY

There were 55 probands in the probably genetic group. All these families included at least three generations of retardates in direct line, except KMD's 24, 73, 240, 428 and 448. These five probands were classified in this group because a parent and one or more children had IQ values below 50.

Sixteen of the 55 probands produced children; 15 of these parents were women. There were 38 children, of whom 12 were illegitimate and 26 legitimate; four in each of these groups were retarded. This is a total of eight retarded of 29 children, or 27.6 per cent, after the nine children who died in infancy have been excluded. When the 12 illegitimate children of the probands are considered, it is found that only two of the 12 are known normals; of the ten remaining, one was unknown, four were retarded and five died in infancy. Three of these 12 illegitimate children were the products of incestuous unions.

The picture is much different when the legitimate offspring of the probands are considered. Thirteen of the 26 legitimate children had IQ's from 80 to 120, and five more had borderline IQ's, making a total of 18 children with IQ's of 70 or above. Four children had IQ's below 70 and four died in infancy. Two of the retarded, two of the borderlines and the four infant deaths all belonged to the only male proband in this group to reproduce (KMD 129). His wife was also retarded and the whole family, including the two borderline children, was institutionalized.

The illegitimate children showed 57.1 per cent retardation while the legitimate children included only 18.2 per cent retardates, after exclusion of the infant deaths in both cases.

The subsequent history of the probands' children is interesting. The present status of the five illegitimate survivors is as follows: one is married to a spouse of unknown intelligence and has no children as yet; the other normal could not be traced and is unknown to us. Of the three retardates, two died in the institution and one is still institutionalized. The other four surviving retardates were legitimate children, two were institutionalized and sterilized, and later left the institution and married; one is single and lives at home; one married a man of unknown intelligence and had five children of whom two are retarded (KMD 478). The 19 normal and borderline legitimate children had the following histories: two of the five borderlines were institutional-

Table 6. *The Relatives of the Probands of the First Degree of Relationship Probably Genetic Category*
(Excluding 81 Deaths under 2 Years of Age)

	Fathers			Mothers			Brothers			Sisters			Children			
	Ret.	Nor.	Unk.	Ret.	Nor.	Unk.	Ret.	Nor.	Unk.	Ret.	Nor.	Unk.	Ret.	Nor.	Unk.	Totals
	32	14	9	44	6	5	47	41	22	43	38	13	8	20	1	343
Totals	55			55			110			94			29			343
Percentage retarded	58.2			80.0			42.7			45.7			27.6			50.7

ized and sterilized and later both married (KMD 129); the other three borderlines are all married and have children (KMD 380); the 14 with IQ's of 80 to 120 include five unmarried persons and nine married, all shown in KMD's 91, 126, 380, 432 and 468. The married children of the probands have a total of 28 children so far, none known to be retarded, although one has an IQ of 71 and some are too young to be tested.

There were 424 persons ever born in the first degree of relationship to the probands (Table 6). There were 110 parents, of whom 76 were retarded (69.1 per cent). A very high percentage of retardation is to be expected in this group, of course, since one criterion of selection was three generations of retardates in the direct line of descent. In the 314 siblings and children there were 81 who died before age 2 years, an infant death rate of about 26 per cent. The 233 remaining individuals included 90 retarded siblings and eight retarded children (42.1 per cent). If the proband's children are eliminated in the calculations we have 204 surviving siblings, 90 of whom were retarded, or 44.1 per cent. Among the children of the probands there were 27.6 per cent retarded. The smaller amount of retardation among the children of probands probably indicates that the probands' spouses were of higher intelligence than their parents. Only the high-grade probands, usually with normal spouses, had children who survived. The percentage of retardation among the probands' children is still about ten times that for the population as a whole.

In 25 families both parents of the probands were known retardates. Five of these families had only one surviving child, the proband. The remaining 20 of the families produced 90 children, exclusive of the proband, who survived the age of 2 years. Fifty-five (61.1 per cent) of these children were retarded. If we take the 17 families in which one parent is a known retardate and the other a known normal, there are 16 with children other than the proband. These 16 families had 63 children of whom 17 (27.0 per cent) were retarded, exclusive of the probands. The family size was almost identical in both groups (4.8 and 4.7 children including the probands) regardless of whether both parents were retarded or only one was retarded.

Finally, there were two families in which the retarded parent married a person of unknown intelligence and had no children except the proband, and seven such unions which produced 25 children, of whom 13 were retarded (52.0 per cent), exclusive of the probands.

The second degree of relationship included 1362 persons, of whom 138 (10.1 per cent) died in infancy (Table 7). There were 206 retardates in the 1224 survivors (16.8 per

Table 7. *The Relatives of the Probands of the Second Degree of Relationship Probably Genetic Category*
(Excluding 138 Deaths under 2 Years of Age)

	Grand-parents			Uncles and Aunts			Half Siblings			Nephews and Nieces			Grand-children			
	Ret.	Nor.	Unk.	Ret.	Nor.	Unk.	Ret.	Nor.	Unk.	Ret.	Nor.	Unk.	Ret.	Nor.	Unk.	Totals
	46	34	140	93	107	233	16	35	20	48	266	154	3	18	11	1224
Totals	220			433			71			468			32			1224
Percentage retarded	20.9			21.5			22.5			10.3			9.4			16.8

Table 8. *The Relatives of the Probands of the Third Degree of Relationship Probably Genetic Category*
(Excluding 204 Deaths under 2 Years of Age)

	Half Uncles and Aunts			Half Nephews and Nieces			Great-Nephews and Nieces			First Cousins			Great-Grandchildren			Totals
	Ret.	Nor.	Unk.	Ret.	Nor.	Unk.	Ret.	Nor.	Unk.	Ret.	Nor.	Unk.	Ret.	Nor.	Unk.	
	12	27	51	6	87	35	25	535	263	73	513	565	2	6	4	2204
Totals	90			128			823			1151			12			2204
Percentage retarded	13.3			4.7			3.0			6.3			16.6			5.3

cent). When these data are separated by generations we have 433 aunts and uncles, of whom 93 (21.2 per cent) were retarded, 71 half siblings, of whom 16 (21.5 per cent) were retarded, 468 nephews and nieces, of whom 48 (10.3 per cent) were retarded and 32 grandchildren, of whom three (9.4 per cent) were retarded. Again we have a drop in the proportion of retardates in the more recent generations, as well as the drop correlated with the greater distance of relationship.

The third degree of relationship included 2408 persons, of whom 204 (8.4 per cent) died in infancy (Table 8). The survivors numbered 2204, of whom 118 (5.3 per cent) were retarded, a proportion still above that expected for the population as a whole. By generations there were 90 half aunts and uncles with 12 (13.3 per cent) retarded, 1151 first cousins with 73 (6.3 per cent) retarded, 128 half nephews and nieces with six (4.7 per cent) retarded and 823 great-nephews and nieces with 25 (3.0 per cent) retarded. One proband (KMD 378) had 14 great-grandchildren, two of whom are known to be retarded and two who died in infancy.

Table 9 presents a summary of the percentages of retardation in the three closest degrees of relationship to the probands and also according to generation level. The grandparents of the probands were usually born in the first half of the nineteenth century and the probands' grandchildren in the first half of the twentieth. Thus we cover a time span of about 150 years for which evaluations of intelligence, subjective or objective, have been made by competent observers.

THE PRIMARILY ENVIRONMENTAL CATEGORY

The environmental category includes those probands whose retardation appeared to be primarily the result of environmental factors, such as birth injury or serious disease in infancy. The 27 probands in this grouping were so classified after consideration of two sources of information. The first source

Table 9. *The Percentage of Retardation in Relatives of the Probably Genetic Probands by Generation Level and by Degree of Relationship*
(Deaths before 2 Years of Age Omitted)

Degree of Relationship	Grandparents	Parents' Generation	Probands' own Generation	Children's Generation	Grand-children's Generation	Average Percentage Retarded
First degree (from Table 6)	-	69.1	44.1	27.6	-	50.7 (174 of 343)
Second degree (from Table 7)	20.9	21.5	22.5	10.3	9.4	16.8 (206 of 1224)
Third degree (from Table 8)	-	13.3	6.3	4.7	3.0	5.3 (116 of 2192)
Average percentage retarded	20.9 (46 of 220)	28.6 (181 of 633)	12.6 (179 of 1426)	9.9 (62 of 625)	3.3 (28 of 855)	13.2 (496 of 3759)

was the medical history of the proband himself; the second was the family pattern which emerged after the history was completed.

There is no intrinsic reason why a retarded woman cannot have a birth injured child or one who had meningitis in infancy. The question of whether the child's retardation was then the result of the environmental agent or whether he would have been retarded anyway is one that cannot be answered finally with our present information. However, in cases in which no third generation retardates appeared more weight can be given to the hypothesis that the environmental influence was the primary factor. This seemed to be valid especially for the syphilitics included, for in no case did the proband's own children or his nephews and nieces show any retardation. The probands in the syphilitic group actually had two types of deleterious environment: perinatal infection by a pathogenic organism known to produce severe neurological damage and an extremely bad home environment of neglect, parental alcoholism and promiscuity.

The 27 probands were further subdivided into four groups (Table 10). The first group included ten probands with histories of serious infections in the perinatal period or in early childhood, exclusive of syphilis. Of these, four had spinal meningitis, two had scarlet fever at age 2 years and regressed in their behavior afterward (could no longer talk, for example), one had diphtheria and one pneumonia (both of which infections occurred at about age 2 years and were followed by physical and mental regression), one had a diagnosis of postinfectional trauma and in one case both the mother and infant had severe measles at the time of birth. It must be kept in mind that in the period around 1900, cases of scarlet fever, measles, pneumonia and diphtheria were much more severe since neither effective treatment nor methods of alleviating the severe symptoms existed. The children who did survive had had prolonged illnesses with high temperatures. In our cases, the physical and mental regressions that they showed after recovery seemed to be irreversible.

Ten more probands were grouped together because they had histories of birth injuries, prematurity or accidents. One proband was born two months prematurely after a difficult labor, three had severe head injuries with residual disfigurement, three were born with spinal injuries, one was beaten at age 2 years until he could not walk, one had a severe fall at age 2 years after which he regressed and one regressed after a severe fall at age 20 years (KMD 196).

Six probands were congenital syphilitics with family histories of frank infections, sibling stillbirths and residual signs, such as Hutchinson's teeth and neurological disorders. One more proband was classified in the environmental category because she was severely beaten about the head and subjected to prolonged abuse and deprivation in her home. None of these 27 families falls into the prob-

Table 10. *The Relatives of the Probands of the First Degree of Relationship Environmental Category*
(Excluding 30 Deaths under 2 Years of Age)

Class of Probands	Fathers Ret.	Fathers Nor.	Fathers Unk.	Mothers Ret.	Mothers Nor.	Mothers Unk.	Brothers Ret.	Brothers Nor.	Brothers Unk.	Sisters Ret.	Sisters Nor.	Sisters Unk.	Children Ret.	Children Nor.	Children Unk.	Totals	Percentage Retarded
Infections exclusive of syphilis (10 probands)	2	7	1	0	6	4	2	21	3	0	8	6	0	0	0	60	6.7
Syphilis (6 probands)	2	2	2	3	2	1	8	8	1	3	1	1	0	3	0	37	43.3
Prematurity and birth injury accident (10 probands)	2	6	2	3	6	1	3	12	3	1	18	5	0	0	0	62	14.5
Abuse and deprivation (1 proband)	1	0	0	1	0	0	4	0	1	1	0	0	0	1	0	9	77.8
Totals	7	15	5	7	14	6	17	41	8	5	27	12	0	4	0	168	-
		(27)			(27)			(66)			(44)			(4)			
Percentage retarded		26.0			26.0			25.8			12.5			0.0		-	21.4

ably genetic classification of three uninterrupted generations of retardates. More details can be obtained by reference to the family summaries that accompany the pedigree charts (see Appendix). In several cases the proband had combinations of perinatal difficulties, such as birth injuries, plus early infectious disease. Only the apparent primary cause is given in the above summary.

There were 198 persons in the first degree of relationship to the 27 probands including the five children born to two probands. Only two probands had children. One was a syphilitic man with IQ 62 (KMD 25) who had four legitimate children by a normal wife. One of these children died in infancy, the other three all had normal intelligence and married normal spouses. Their children are too young to be tested as yet. The second proband (KMD 284), a woman with IQ 53 and classified as retarded because of abuse and deprivation, had a normal illegitimate son by a normal man. This son was killed in an accident before he reproduced.

Of the 198 persons in the first degree of relationship, 30 were miscarriages, stillbirths or infant deaths. Since the proband's parents obviously survived infancy, the group of 54 parents was excluded from the total number ever born to give a figure of 144 persons in the first degree of relationship who were either siblings or children of the probands. Thirty of these persons (20.8 per cent) died in infancy. In the six syphilitic families, 19 (43.2 per cent) of the 44 siblings and children of the probands died in infancy.

Excluding infant deaths there were 168 persons ever born in the first degree of relationship. Of these 36 (21.4 per cent) were retarded. Again, the proportion was higher among the syphilitics, 16 retarded among 34, or nearly half.

One might expect that there would be no more retardation among the close relatives of the retarded in the environmental category than among persons in the general population. How, then, can one account for the high percentage of retardation among the relatives in this group who are in the first degree of relationship? Aside from possible errors in classification, we believe it probably reflects chiefly a bias in institutionalization. The damaged child born to retarded parents may be more likely to be institutionalized than a similarly injured child born into a normal family in which he can be well taken care of. In addition, there is a good possibility that in retarded families children are more likely to contract severe infections and to suffer more from them because of lack of care.

Within the second degree of relationship (Table 11), the bias due to the inclusion of the six syphilitic families begins to disappear. There were 679 persons ever born in this group. Exclusive of 108 grandparents, there were 571 persons born of whom 77 (13.5 per cent, including one grandchild) died in infancy. Among the families with syphilis, 32

Table 11. *The Relatives of the Probands of the Second Degree of Relationship Environmental Category*
(Excluding 77 Deaths under 2 Years of Age)

Class of Probands	Grandparents			Uncles and Aunts			Half Siblings			Nephews and Nieces			Grandchildren			Totals	Percentage Retarded
	Ret.	Nor.	Unk.	Ret.	Nor.	Unk.	Ret.	Nor.	Unk.	Ret.	Nor.	Unk.	Ret.	Nor.	Unk.		
Infections exclusive of syphilis (10 probands)	0	19	21	2	68	55	0	1	1	0	104	9	0	0	0	280	0.7
Syphilis (6 probands)	1	6	17	3	11	15	0	1	0	0	35	5	0	0	2	96	4.2
Prematurity and birth injury accident (10 probands)	0	12	28	4	47	41	0	8	1	1	58	5	0	0	0	205	2.2
Abuse and deprivation (1 proband)	0	3	1	1	6	5	0	0	0	0	5	0	0	0	0	21	4.8
Totals	1	40	67	10	132	116	0	10	2	1	202	19	0	0	2	602	-
		(108)			(258)			(12)			(222)			(2)			
Percentage retarded		0.9			3.9			0.0			0.4			0.0		-	2.0

Table 12. *The Relatives of the Probands of the Third Degree of Relationship Environmental Category*
(Excluding 137 Deaths under 2 Years of Age)

Class of Probands	Half Uncles and Aunts Ret.	Nor.	Unk.	Half Nephews and Nieces Ret.	Nor.	Unk.	Great-Nephews and Nieces Ret.	Nor.	Unk.	First Cousins Ret.	Nor.	Unk.	Totals	Percentage Retarded
Infections exclusive of syphilis (10 probands)	0	1	5	0	3	0	0	182	25	7	212	102	537	1.3
Syphilis (6 probands)	1	0	4	0	0	0	1	28	27	0	36	18	115	1.3
Prematurity and birth injury accident (10 probands)	0	2	14	0	19	4	0	70	16	0	130	103	358	0.0
Abuse and deprivation (1 proband)	0	0	0	0	0	0	0	2	0	3	43	3	51	0.0
Totals	1	3 (27)	23	0	22 (26)	4	1	282 (351)	68	10	421 (657)	226	1061	-
Percentage retarded		3.7			0.0			0.3			1.5		-	1.1

per cent of the children died in infancy and quite a few aunts and uncles were known syphilitics.

There were 12 retardates (2 per cent) among the 602 persons who survived infancy, a dramatic drop from the 21.4 per cent among the relatives of the first degree. In the syphilitic families, the drop was even greater, from 43.3 per cent retarded among relatives of the first degree to 4.1 per cent among those of the second degree. There was a difference in generations in this environmental group. There were 258 aunts and uncles, of whom 10 (3.9 per cent) were retarded while among 222 nieces and nephews there was only one retardate. The other retarded person was a grandparent.

One proband (KMD 25) had three grandchildren, one of whom died in infancy and two of unknown intelligence. They were too young to test.

The third degree of relationship includes 1198 persons ever born, of whom 137 (11.5 per cent) died in infancy. There were 1061 persons who survived infancy of whom 12 (1.1 per cent) were known retardates. This percentage was nearly the same in the syphilitics taken separately, one retardate in 115 individuals or about 1 per cent (Table 12).

Table 13 includes the summary of the percentages of retardation in the three closest degrees of relationship to the probands and also according to relationship in time, as evidenced by the generation to which each person belonged.

Table 13. *The Percentage of Retardation in Relatives of the Environmental Category Probands by Generation Level and by Degree of Relationship*
(Deaths before 2 Years of Age Omitted)

Degree of Relationship	Grandparents	Parents' Generation	Probands' own Generation	Children's Generation	Grand-children's Generation	Average Percentage Retarded
First degree (from Table 10)	-	26.0	20.0	0.0	-	21.4 (36 of 168)
Second degree (from Table 11)	0.9	3.9	0.0	0.4	0.0	2.0 (12 of 602)
Third degree (from Table 12)	-	3.7	1.5	0.0	0.3	1.1 (12 of 1061)
Average percentage	0.9 (1 of 108)	7.4 (25 of 339)	4.1 (32 of 779)	0.4 (1 of 252)	0.3 (1 of 353)	3.3 (60 of 1831)

Table 14. *The Relatives of the Probands of the First Degree of Relationship Unknown Category*
(Excluding 164 Deaths under 2 Years of Age)

	Fathers			Mothers			Brothers			Sisters			Children			
	Ret.	Nor.	Unk.	Ret.	Nor.	Unk.	Ret.	Nor.	Unk.	Ret.	Nor.	Unk.	Ret.	Nor.	Unk.	Totals
	20	75	28	24	67	32	44	160	53	34	159	73	3	20	8	800
Totals	123			123			257			266			31			800
Percentage retarded	16.5			19.5			17.1			12.8			9.7			15.6

THE CATEGORY OF UNKNOWN CAUSES

It is not surprising that 123 (42.6 per cent) of the 289 probands had no detectable causes for their retardation. This was true for many who were given careful medical examinations at institutionalization and again many years later by Dr. Jan Böök and Dr. John Schut. Some cases are classified as unknown because not enough information could be collected about the more recent generations to be of help in a possible diagnosis. The proband's immediate family in eight histories is completely unknown at present. In 21 families there were no siblings or none who reproduced. There were 20 families in which the proband was the only known retardate.

Seventeen of the probands of this category (13.8 per cent) reproduced. They had 39 children, 63 grandchildren and 71 great-grandchildren, a total of 173 descendants. There were 164 descendants who survived the age of 2 years and there were four retardates (2.4 per cent) among them. Twelve of the 17 probands had 16 illegitimate children. Four of these children died in infancy, two were retarded, eight were normal and two of unknown intelligence. The fathers of the 16 illegitimate children were all of unknown intelligence except one, the proband's normal father, who was the father of her child. This child had an IQ of 79 (KMD 519). There were no other incestuous unions in this group.

Five probands had 23 legitimate children, 11 of whom belong to one proband (KMD 70). Four of the 23 children died in infancy, one of the survivors was retarded, 12 were normal and six of unknown intelligence. The five fathers of the 23 legitimate children included one retarded male, three of normal intelligence and one unknown. The only retarded child in this group was the offspring of the retarded male who also had two normal children by the proband.

Table 14 provides the usual data for the first degree relatives of the probands. There were 246 parents, of whom 44 (18.2 per cent) were retarded. The probands' siblings included 257 brothers, 266 sisters and 156 additional siblings who died in infancy, a death rate of 23 per cent. The 523 surviving siblings included 78 retardates (14.9 per cent).

The second degree of relationship consisted of 2715 persons including the 63 grandchildren of the probands. The infant deaths were 10.1 per cent, excluding the 492 grandparents who could not have died in infancy. The data are presented in Table 15. The usual drop in mental retardation is seen from 15.6 per cent among the first degree relatives to 2.6 per cent in the second degree relatives. Among the third degree relatives the value drops even lower, to 2.1 per cent. This last percentage may be lower than the correct value because of the disproportionately larger number of young untested children of this degree of re-

Table 15. *The Relatives of the Probands of the Second Degree of Relationship Unknown Category*
(Excluding 224 Deaths before 2 Years of Age)

	Grand-parents			Uncles and Aunts			Half Siblings			Nephews and Nieces			Grand-children			
	Ret.	Nor.	Unk.	Ret.	Nor.	Unk.	Ret.	Nor.	Unk.	Ret.	Nor.	Unk.	Ret.	Nor.	Unk.	Totals
	1	121	370	41	401	585	7	26	23	14	688	152	1	49	12	2491
Totals	492			1027			56			854			62			2491
Percentage retarded	0.2			4.0			12.5			1.6			1.6			2.6

Table 16. *The Relatives of the Probands of the Third Degree of Relationship Unknown Category*
(Excluding 309 Deaths before 2 Years of Age)

	Half Uncles and Aunts Ret.	Nor.	Unk.	Half Nephews and Nieces Ret.	Nor.	Unk.	Great-Nephews and Nieces Ret.	Nor.	Unk.	First Cousins Ret.	Nor.	Unk.	Great-Grand-children Ret.	Nor.	Unk.	Totals
	2	33	66	4	68	40	13	984	320	67	1222	1217	0	34	37	4107
Totals	101			112			1317			2506			71			4107
Percentage retarded	2.0			3.6			1.0			2.7			0.0			2.1

Table 17. *The Percentage of Retardation in Relatives of the Unknown Category Probands by Generation Level and by Degree of Relationship*
(Deaths before 2 Years of Age Omitted)

Degree of Relationship	Grandparents	Parents' Generation	Probands' own Generation	Children's Generation	Grand-children's Generation	Average Percentage Retarded
First degree (from Table 14)	-	18.2	14.9	9.7	-	15.6 (125 of 800)
Second degree (from Table 15)	0.2	4.0	12.5	1.6	1.6	2.6 (64 of 2491)
Third degree (from Table 16)	-	2.0	2.7	3.6	1.0	2.1 (86 of 4036)
Average percentage retarded	0.2 (1 of 492)	6.3 (87 of 1374)	4.9 (152 of 3085)	2.1 (21 of 997)	1.0 (14 of 1379)	3.7 (275 of 7327)

lationship to the probands. The data for the third degree relatives are presented in Table 16.

The summary for this section is Table 17. A comparison of it with Table 9, p. 25, the summary for the probably genetic category, for example, shows sharp differences in retardation among the relatives of the probably genetic and the unknown categories. Thus our classification has meaning and the following section is devoted to a brief consideration of the significance of the differences among the diagnostic categories.

RESULTS FROM ALL CATEGORIES

Several interesting conclusions can be drawn from the data presented in the previous sections concerned with the relatives of our retarded probands. There is a sharp drop in the percentages of retarded relatives with the more distant degrees of relationship. One could expect a drop of 50 per cent in retardation with each decrease of one degree of relationship on purely genetic grounds, if the retardation were due to a dominant gene. What we are saying is that only half of the genes of all kinds present in the retarded proband are transmitted to a particular child. The child then transmits only half the genes that it obtained from the proband to the grandchild. The grandchild therefore obtains one quarter of his genes from the proband and is a second degree relative of the proband. Thus, if a single dominant gene with inevitable expression were responsible for the mental retardation we would expect 50 per cent of the first degree relatives to be retarded, 25 per cent of the second degree relatives, and 12.5 per cent of the third degree relatives. No one would expect that mental retardation depends upon a single dominant gene, except in an occasional rare family. If the heredity were that of a sex-linked recessive, such as was responsible for the probands with sex-linked progressive muscular dystrophy (KMD 402) and Pelizaeus-Merzbacher disease (KMD 215), we would expect 25 per cent of the siblings to be likewise affected but with much lower percentages in other relatives. If a single mendelian recessive gene were responsible for the retardation, we would expect 25 per cent of the siblings to be affected but few of the other relatives would be retarded because of this specific gene, particularly if the gene is of low frequency in the population.

A final genetic situation is probably the most important one. It is very likely that many of our probands represent multiple gene complexes at the left end of the normal curve of intelligence. They may produce children by other retarded persons who have a similar polygenic etiology. Such unions should result in high percentages of retarded children. Assortative mating would be frequent among these retardates and high rates of retardation might be expected to be present among their relatives. Unfortunately, because there usually will be more than two or three pairs of genes involved in the retardation found in this group, it would be difficult to calculate any reliable expected percentages of retardation for our various degrees of relationship.

A summation of the percentages of retardation found in the first three degrees of relationship for the four arbitrary categories is presented in Table 18. The probands are not included in this table, of course. The 289 probands had 18,066 "blood" relatives through the third degree of relationship, an average of 63 relatives per proband. This does not include the several thousand spouses who married into the family. It can be seen that of the 18,066 relatives there were 1283 (7.1 per cent) who were retarded. The retarded were *not* distributed in a random fashion throughout the different categories or the degrees of relationship, but instead were concentrated in specific types of relatives.

The average percentages of retardation for all categories show about one fourth as much retardation in the second degree relatives (7.1 per cent) as in the first degree relatives (28.0 per cent) and one ninth as much (3.1 per cent) in the third degree as in the first degree relatives. Probably the value of 3.1 per cent for the third degree relatives is a little too low, as the largest proportion of children still too young to test for intelligence is in the third degree of relationship. The decrease in retardation from first degree to second degree to third degree relatives is consistent in all four categories and is obviously statistically significant. It is impossible to tell from the general averages how much of the decrease is genetic and how much environmental. However, in the category obtained because an environmental insult could be identified, we see the sharpest drop of all four categories from the frequency in the first degree relatives to the second degree. In these cases, where the proband had a fall or an infection, we would expect little evidence of any genetic differences to appear. It is interesting that, except for the first degree relatives, the percentages of retardation of 2.0 and 1.1 are lower than those expected in the general population. It is clear evidence that the events which lead to the retardation of the proband were not transmitted to relatives beyond the first degree of relationship, to any appreciable degree. In other words, the environmental factors which we were able to identify were not transmitted beyond the immediate family circle—the first degree relatives.

One large bias should be pointed out here. The reader has probably noticed in the

Table 18. *The Percentages of Retardation in the Relatives of the Probands According to Degree of Relationship and Category of Classification*

Category	First Degree	Second Degree	Third Degree	Average Percentage Retarded
Primarily genetic	33.6	9.2	3.7	8.8 (452 of 5149)
Probably genetic	50.7	16.8	5.3	13.2 (496 of 3759)
Environmental	21.4	2.0	1.1	3.3 (60 of 1831)
Unknown	15.6	2.6	2.1	3.7 (275 of 7327)
All categories				
Percentages	28.0	7.1	3.1	7.1
Totals	(532 of 1897)	(434 of 6070)	(317 of 10,099)	(1283 of 18,066)

tables in the preceding sections that among the first degree relatives of the probands the parents and siblings always showed much higher frequencies of retardation than the children for all categories. This doesn't make sense at first glance; one would expect, at least on some environmental concepts, that the children of the retarded probands would have the highest percentage of retardation of any of the first degree relatives because the proband, as a parent, is always retarded. Why are our results so obviously at variance with this concept? It is easy to discover the source of the bias when one considers the following. If a retarded child has normal parents and siblings, there is probably less than one chance in ten that the child will be institutionalized and thus have an opportunity to be a retarded proband in a study like ours. On the other hand, if one retarded child after another is born into a family, in which one or both parents are retarded, it is almost certain that some one or other of these retarded children will be institutionalized and thus become available as a proband for a study. Indeed, if the family situation is too impossible, the whole family may be institutionalized. Therefore, we would expect that an institutionalized child should have a higher percentage of retarded parents and siblings than a retarded child not in an institution. This bias is probably very important and should account for much of the difference between the high percentages of retardation in the parents and siblings of the probands compared with the children of the probands. The children of the probands would often be born *after*, or at the time of, institutionalization and are, therefore, not a part of the "institutionalization bias."

A second bias, previously mentioned, raises the percentage of retarded in both the Primarily Genetic and the Probably Genetic categories. Some of the families placed in the Primarily Genetic category were classified in that way because there was at least one sibling in addition to the proband who had an IQ value of less than 50. Therefore the rate of retardation is high because of the method of classification employed. All of the probands in the Probably Genetic category had to have at least one retarded first degree relative in order to be placed in this category. This bias not only affects those two categories specifically, but it is also a part of the "institutionalization bias" in that a child is more likely to be institutionalized if he has retarded first degree relatives than if the rest of the family is normal.

The data for the 18,066 relatives can be arranged in rough chronological order and are shown in Table 19. The grandparents were born in the early 1800's and are the generation earliest on the time scale. The next chronological group is that of the parents, the uncles and aunts and half uncles and half aunts of the probands. The probands' own generation includes the siblings, half siblings and first cousins. The probands' children's generation includes them as well as the nephews and nieces, and the half nephews and half nieces. The most recent generation includes the grandchildren and the great-nephews and nieces. These five generations cover a time span of about 150 years.

If one looked at the averages for all categories (Table 19), one might think that the percentage of retardation had dropped steadily with the passage of time, presumably due

Table 19. *The Percentages of Retardation in the Relatives of the Probands According to Generation Level and Category of Classification*

Category	Grandparents	Parents' Generation	Probands' Generation	Children's Generation	Grand-children's Generation	Average Percentage Retarded
Primarily genetic	6.0	14.9	8.9	7.4	2.9	8.8 (452 of 5149)
Probably genetic	20.9	28.6	12.6	9.9	3.3	13.2 (496 of 3759)
Environmental	0.9	7.4	4.1	0.4	0.3	3.3 (60 of 1831)
Unknown	0.2	6.3	4.9	2.1	1.0	3.7 (275 of 7327)
All categories						
Percentages	5.9	13.2	7.5	5.4	2.1	7.1
Totals	(68 of 1151)	(440 of 3334)	(568 of 7583)	(142 of 2653)	(65 of 3345)	(1283 of 18,066)

to improved environments, such as health and schooling. However, this is not a very reasonable explanation of the data. The concept collapses when we note that the 5.9 per cent retardation of the probands' grandparents is similar to the 5.4 per cent retardation in the probands' children's time, three generations later. The value of 2.1 per cent for the grandchildren's generation is probably too low because here the proportion of children too young for intelligence testing is the largest. Furthermore, the institutionalization bias should account for much of the retardation in the parents' and probands' generations. Finally, the children's and grandchildren's generations include the most distant relatives such as half nephews and half nieces and grandnephews and nieces. These third degree relatives would not be expected to have appreciably different percentages of retardation from the 3 per cent often assumed to be the value for the whole population, that is, the general public.

It is clear from the above discussion that when we take our institutionalization bias into account, as well as the "diluting effect" of more distant genetic relationship, there will be little chance of demonstrating any decrease in mental retardation over the 150 year period that was caused by improved health or educational facilities. Minnesota has been a state for only a little over 100 years so this period of time covers the whole span of development from log cabin to skyscraper. Indeed, it is possible that the percentage of retardation in the state has *increased* hand-in-hand with the improvement of educational facilities because it is more difficult for the child with minimal basic intelligence to compete in our progressively more complicated society.

It should have occurred to the reader that the classification of our probands into four categories was not merely a matter of putting the families with many affected members into the primarily and probably genetic groups, and those with few affected members into the environmental and unknown categories. To be sure, the first degree relatives were a part of the classification of the primarily and probably genetic groups and thus biased the percentages upwards. However, the second and third degree relatives were not involved in the classification at all. Yet there is a highly significant statistical difference between the percentages of retardation in the second and third degree relatives of the primarily and probably genetic categories as compared with those of the environmental and unknown groups. This means that in the primarily and probably genetic categories something is being transmitted to relatives which causes mental retardation. In a few families, such as those with sex-linked traits and with consanguinity, we can be certain that genes are the important transmitted factors. There ought to be important environmental factors which are producing the retardation in some of the families which we have placed in the two genetic categories by mistake, and which are transmitted to the relatives. These environmental factors were too subtle for us to detect in our study, if they existed. The parents of our probands had no suspicions as to what could have been the environmental causes of the retardation, if there were such.

In the cases in which there were allegations of environmental causes which seemed to be valid, we found only 2.0 per cent of the second degree relatives and 1.1 per cent of the third degree relatives to be retarded (Table 18). Thus there is little, if any, transmission of retardation outside the first degree of relationship in those cases in which the environmental factors could be identified.

What kinds of transmissible subtle environmental factors could there be which would cause three successive generations of mental retardation in direct line (the criterion for 50 of our probands placed in the Probably Genetic category)? It is clear from the syphilitic families (Tables 11, 12 and 13) that there was no transmission to generations more recent than that of the probands of either the syphilis or its retardation. It is possible that there could be reinfections of viruses for influenza or other ubiquitous diseases, although we are not aware of any cases in the literature in which mental retardation has been shown to be caused by an infection of any kind for three successive generations.

Our next thought concerned schooling. The severely retarded were recognized long before reaching school age. Schooling in Minnesota was unavailable for some children in the pioneer days but it is now mandatory for all, including the retarded. It has been pointed out that the frequency of retardation in the grandparents' generation (5.9 per cent) was but little higher than that in the probands' children's generation (5.4 per cent).

Table 20. *The Relatives of the Probands of the First Degree of Relationship* (Excluding 380 Deaths under 2 Years of Age)

Category of Probands	Fathers Ret.	Fathers Nor.	Fathers Unk.	Mothers Ret.	Mothers Nor.	Mothers Unk.	Brothers Ret.	Brothers Nor.	Brothers Unk.	Sisters Ret.	Sisters Nor.	Sisters Unk.	Children Ret.	Children Nor.	Children Unk.	Totals	Percentage Retarded
Primarily genetic	26	48	10	33	36	15	71	99	28	65	112	27	2	12	2	586	33.6
Probably genetic	32	14	9	44	6	5	47	41	22	43	38	13	8	20	1	343	50.7
Environmental	7	15	5	7	14	6	17	41	8	5	27	12	0	4	0	168	21.4
Unknown causes	20	75	28	24	67	32	44	160	53	34	159	73	3	20	8	800	15.6
Totals	85	152	52	108	123	58	179	341	111	147	336	125	13	56	11	1897	-
Percentage retarded		29.4			37.4			28.4			24.2			16.3		-	28.0

Thus, formal education seems to have little relevance to our problem.

A more likely factor is that of very early social deprivation. It is well known that an unfortunately large percentage of babies isolated in institutions turn out to be mentally retarded. It is usually assumed, quite unscientifically, that the retardation results from the failure of the staff to fondle the babies adequately. Advocates of this hypothesis seldom point out that other babies in the same institutions develop normal intelligence, nor do they consider the *parentage* of the babies who find themselves isolated in such an abnormal situation. The work of the Harlows (1962) on social deprivation in monkeys showed psychotic behavior of monkeys raised on terrycloth mothers in isolation, though their physical health was above normal and their intelligence does not seem to have been impaired. It is interesting that the psychological damage resulting from deprivation was apparently not the result of the absence of a live mother, but rather due to lack of social activities carried out with a peer group. The young monkeys must have at least one playmate, though not a live parent, for normal psychological development or something resembling a normal psyche.

We do not make the absurd claim that social deprivation is good for one. The question remains as to how much of an effect it has on the development of intelligence. Is the damage great or small?

In our study occasional children with high intelligence have been reared by severely retarded mothers. It is clear that even when both parents are retarded some of their children have satisfactory intelligence. If both parents are retarded the *percentage* of retarded children increases sharply over the percentage when only one parent is retarded. If this increase in percentage of retarded offspring is due to greater deprivation because both parents are retarded, we could also expect an accompanying lower IQ in our probands where both parents were retarded compared with only one. This was not the case. The average IQ for the 19 probands, whose mothers were retarded and whose

Table 21. *The Relatives of the Probands of the Second Degree of Relationship* (Excluding 593 Deaths under 2 Years of Age)

Category of Probands	Grandparents Ret.	Grandparents Nor.	Grandparents Unk.	Uncles and Aunts Ret.	Uncles and Aunts Nor.	Uncles and Aunts Unk.	Half Siblings Ret.	Half Siblings Nor.	Half Siblings Unk.	Nephews and Nieces Ret.	Nephews and Nieces Nor.	Nephews and Nieces Unk.	Grandchildren Ret.	Grandchildren Nor.	Grandchildren Unk.	Totals	Percentage Retarded
Primarily genetic	20	78	233	78	318	356	15	38	34	38	416	110	1	10	8	1753	8.7
Probably genetic	46	34	140	93	107	233	16	35	20	48	266	154	3	18	11	1224	16.8
Environmental	1	40	67	10	132	116	0	10	2	1	202	19	0	0	2	602	2.0
Unknown causes	1	121	370	41	401	585	7	26	23	14	688	152	1	49	12	2491	2.6
Totals	68	273	810	222	958	1290	38	109	79	101	1572	435	5	77	33	6070	-
Percentage retarded		5.9			9.0			16.8			4.8			4.4			7.1

Table 22. *The Relatives of the Probands of the Third Degree of Relationship* (Excluding 903 Deaths under 2 Years of Age)

Category of Probands	Half Uncles and Aunts Ret.	Nor.	Unk.	Half Nephews and Nieces Ret.	Nor.	Unk.	Great-Nephews and Nieces Ret.	Nor.	Unk.	First Cousins Ret.	Nor.	Unk.	Great-Grand-children Ret.	Nor.	Unk.	Totals	Percentage Retarded
Primarily genetic	10	26	32	18	134	47	21	529	189	54	946	804	0	0	0	2810	3.7
Probably genetic	12	27	51	6	87	35	25	535	263	73	513	565	2	6	4	2204	5.3
Environmental	1	3	23	0	22	4	1	282	68	10	421	226	0	0	0	1061	1.1
Unknown causes	2	33	66	4	68	40	13	984	320	67	1222	1217	0	34	37	4107	2.1
Totals	25	89	172	28	311	126	60	2330	840	204	3102	2812	2	40	41	10,182	-
Percentage retarded		8.8			6.0			1.8			3.3			2.4		-	3.1

fathers were normal or of unknown intelligence, was 44.6 points. If both parents were retarded, the average IQ for the 25 probands was 52.4, not the predicted drop expected for the probands with both parents retarded instead of just the mother. These values are only for the 44 probands from retarded mothers of the probably genetic category. This category is of great interest because, by definition, there were three consecutive generations of mental retardation which means that social deprivation would be greatest in this category. In 25 of the 44 cases, the father was retarded as well as the mother which is a very high percentage (57 per cent) of assortative mating. There were seven cases among the probably genetic probands whose mothers were normal or of unknown intelligence and the father was retarded. The average IQ of 46.0 for these seven probands was similar to that found for the probands with retarded mothers.

Table 23. *Summary of the Percentages of Mental Retardation in the Relatives of the Probands According to the Category of Retardation of the Proband*

Relationship to Proband and Generation Level	Category of Retardation of the Proband: Primarily Genetic	Probably Genetic	Environ-mental	Unknown	Total
First Degree Relatives					
II. Parents	35.1	69.1	26.0	18.2	33.4
III. Sibs†	33.8	44.1	20.0	14.9	26.3
IV. Children	12.5	27.6	-*	9.7	16.3
Second Degree Relatives					
I. Grandparents	6.0	20.9	0.9	0.2	5.9
II. Uncles-aunts	10.4	21.5	3.9	4.0	9.0
III. Half-sibs†	17.2	22.5	-	12.5	16.8
IV. Nephews-nieces	6.7	10.3	0.4	1.6	4.8
V. Grandchildren	5.3	9.4	-	1.6	4.4
Third Degree Relatives					
II. Half uncles-aunts	14.7	13.3	3.7	2.0	8.8
III. First cousins†	3.0	6.3	1.5	2.7	3.3
IV. Half nephews-nieces	9.1	4.7	0.0	3.6	6.0
V. Great-nephews-nieces	2.8	3.0	0.3	1.0	1.8
VI. Great-grandchildren	-	-	-	0.0	2.4

* Dashes in the body of the table indicate that there were less than 20 persons in that item.

† Proband's generation.

Thus we find no evidence for effects of social deprivation on IQ of the proband depending on whether one parent or both was retarded. The wide fluctuations of intelligence in the children reared in the very poor environments of the probably genetic category seem to be more readily explainable by a hypothesis of polygenic segregation than by any other hypothesis which comes to mind. Nonetheless, we cannot ignore the axiom that all traits of importance are the result of both heredity and environment. The data given above do not rule out any effects of social deprivation nor do they provide evidence for them, as we had thought they might.

The tables just presented, in which the frequency of mental retardation for all first degree relatives compared with second and third degree relatives, seem to be the most significant way to display the data. However, in a family study it seems to be reasonable, primarily for the sake of completeness, to give the data for each type of relative. Therefore, we include Tables 20, 21 and 22. The persons with unknown mental status are included as if all were normal, though this could hardly have been the case; thus, our values would be higher if the status of the unknowns could be determined. The children who died before the age of 2 years are omitted from the calculations of the retardation frequencies.

We complete this chapter with a summary of the percentages of mental retardation in the relatives of the probands, according to the category of retardation of the proband. The data are presented in Table 23 and show clearly the gradual, though somewhat erratic, decrease in retardation as the relationship to the proband becomes more distant.

SUMMARY

1. Twenty-eight per cent of the first degree relatives of our 289 probands were mentally retarded. There were 7.1 per cent retarded persons among the second degree relatives and 3.1 per cent of the third degree relatives were retarded. There was an average of 7.1 per cent retarded relatives for the first three degrees of relationship to the probands. These must be underestimates because all persons of unknown intelligence were counted as normal, which could hardly have been the case. Furthermore, there are a large number of children in the third degree of relationship who are counted as normal though they are still too young for testing.

2. In the category obtained because an environmental insult to the proband could be identified, we see the sharpest drop in retardation from the 21.4 per cent in the first degree relatives to 2.0 per cent and 1.1 per cent in the second and third degree relatives. These last two figures are lower than expectation for the general public. These relatives of the second and third degree are relatively free of both the genetic and environmental factors which result in mental retardation.

3. The probably genetic category shows the highest frequencies of mental retardation in all degrees of relationship. This is due in part to the definition of the group: that of three consecutive generations of mental retardation. These values of 50.7 per cent retardation for all first degree relatives, and 16.8 per cent and 5.3 per cent for the second and third degree relatives indicate large genetic and environmental influences on the people involved. Attempts to identify specific variables of any kind were unsuccessful. However, these "loaded" families have two characteristics of interest: they show assortative mating to a very high degree and the retarded are predominantly of the 50 to 69 IQ level. It is clear from the structure of the normal curve of intelligence that the majority of the higher grade retardates must result from the interaction of the many genetic and environmental factors which operate at the left end of the normal curve of intelligence. The result of each gene and each environmental factor is assumed to be so small that individual identification is impossible. This situation is the same as that for the polygenic traits of height or size in man and the laboratory animals.

CHAPTER FOUR

FAMILY DYNAMICS OF NORMAL AND RETARDED PERSONS

THE UNSELECTED RETARDATES IN THE POPULATION

Marital Status, Spouses and Reproductive Rates

There are 83,529 persons shown on the pedigree charts. However, 1312 of these individuals are duplicates who appear in more than one kinship. The different individuals, therefore, number 82,217 ever born. There were 2841 (3.5 per cent) losses of life before age 2 years including all known miscarriages, abortions, stillbirths and infant deaths. The 79,376 survivors include 2156 retardates (1218 males and 938 females), or 2.7 per cent. This percentage of retardation does not differ greatly from that expected in any large random sample of a population; the biased selection of 289 retardates (the probands) is not enough to raise the proportion of retarded persons very much. However, an inspection of the pedigree charts reveals that some families have a much higher proportion of retardation among their members than others. Thirty kinships had no retarded members other than the probands themselves.

The proportion of retardates within kinships ranged from one retardate among 468 persons (KMD 283), or 0.2 per cent, to 33 retardates among 352 persons (KMD 489), or 9.0 per cent. These are from kindreds with very few unknown persons in them.

The population of 2156 retardates falls into three groups. One group includes the retardates selected at the time of the original study. Here we find the 289 probands, their retarded parents and retarded grandparents. There were 549 retarded persons in this group, 261 males and 288 females. The second group includes retardates not in the line of descent (90 males and 67 females) who married into the probands' kindreds. These persons will be described in a separate section. The third group of retardates, related in some degree to the probands, numbers 1450 and constitutes the *unselected* group within the total population of descendants from the probands' grandparents (see Table 24).

Table 24. *Summary of the 2156 Retardates in the Total Population*

Relationship to Probands	Male	Female	Total
Grandparents	37	30	67
Parents	85	108	193
Probands	139	150	289
Others in line of descent	867	583	1450
Spouses who married in	90	67	157
Total	1218	938	2156

The unselected group of retardates includes 867 males and only 583 females, a sex difference that is statistically highly significant when tested by chi square. This sex difference is difficult to account for on the basis of poor ascertainment. Furthermore, this excess of males is consistent in each of our four major categories.

A study of the detailed data we have about this group should yield considerable information about marriage and reproductive rates among the retardates. How many of these persons ever reproduced? Did retarded fathers have more or fewer offspring than retarded mothers? What is the mental status of children resulting from the unions of two retardates? Do retardates replace themselves in the population? Our unselected population of 1450 retardates is large enough to furnish information on all these points. There are only 61 persons among the 1450 whose marital and reproductive status is unknown to us, and only 115 who were institutionalized during their reproductive years.

We find that 630 retardates (401 males, 229 females) never reproduced; this is 43.4 per cent of our total population of retardates (Table 25). This number includes 313 persons who died unmarried and childless, 115 who are presently in institutions, and 69 who are single but too old or too retarded to reproduce. Only 33 persons were sterilized among the 1450 retardates, four men and 29 women. Then there is the group of retardates who were married but were still childless after having passed the age of reproduction (55 men and 45 women).

The group of 507 retardates (out of the 1450) who reproduced at least once includes 247 males and 260 females. These 507 retardates had 2165 children of whom 214 (9.9 per cent) died before age 2 years, and 280 (14.3 per cent) of the survivors were retarded. The family size per reproducing retardate was 4.3, including those who died before 2 years of age. The 247 male retardates had 1126 children, family size 4.6 and 12.2 per cent of the survivors to 2 years of age were retarded. The 260 females had 1039 children, family size 4.0 and 16.7 per cent of the survivors were retarded. The apparent increase in the proportion of retarded children born to retarded mothers is significant at the 5 per cent level, when tested by chi square ($\chi^2 = 5.37$, $p = < 0.05 > 0.01$). When infant deaths are excluded, the effective family size for male retardates is 4.2, and that for female retardates is 3.5 children.

There are 252 retardates (178 males, 74 females) who may yet reproduce. Five are married but childless as yet; the others are quite young with many only of school age. The excess of male retardates is especially large, although this is the group which should have been most free from errors of ascertainment since they are the ones for whom we have a large proportion of psychological tests. It appears that there is a basic sex difference with more retarded males than females in the population. This could result from cultural differences as well as from genetic sex-linkage or sex limitation.

What was the mental status of the spouses of the retardates? Legal and illegal spouses

Table 25. *Reproductive Status of the 1450 Unselected Retardates in the Line of Descent*

Reproductive Status	Male	Female	Total	Per Cent
Never reproduced				
Died single	206	107	313	
Institutionalized 1961	69	46	115	
Single, old, low-grade or sterilized	71	31	102	
Married but old and childless	55	45	100	
Total	401	229	630	43.4
Reproduced at least once				
Had only children who died before age 2 years	7	12	19	
Completed families 1961	188	207	395	
Incomplete families 1961	52	41	93	
Total	247	260	507	35.0
May yet reproduce	178	74	252	17.4
Unknown	41	20	61	4.2
Total	867	583	1450	
Per cent	59.8	40.2		100.0

Table 26. *Mental Status of the Spouses of the 612 Married Retardates* (311 Men, 301 Women)

	Male	Female	Total
All Spouses			
Retarded	36	35	71
Normal	112	104	216
Unknown	218	253	471
Total	366	392	758
Per cent retarded	9.8	8.9	9.4

are classified together, so this group includes parents of illegitimate children. The 612 "married" retardates had 758 known spouses. Among these 758 there were 71 retardates (9.4 per cent). Since only 2 to 3 per cent of the general public is retarded, and not all of these are possible mates, the 9.4 per cent indicates a considerable degree of assortative mating among retardates (Table 26). Oddly enough, when retarded persons "married in" to these kindreds (90 males, 67 females) they acquired a much greater proportion of retarded spouses, 71 retarded among 157 (45.2 per cent), than did the retarded members of our study who "married out." It is difficult to understand why the retardates who married in had 45 per cent retarded spouses while the retardates who married out had only 9.4 per cent retarded spouses.

The proportion of retarded children born to the retardates who "married in" to normal or unknown spouses was 73 in 238 children surviving age 2 years (30.7 per cent). This amount of retardation is considerably larger than that found from unions of retardates in the line of descent with normal or unknown spouses (11.2 per cent). It is difficult to determine whether this large difference in proportion of retarded children is due to the small size of the sample of retardates who married in, or whether it shows a real difference in the mental status of the two groups of retardates. It is difficult to see why there should be any real differences between the two groups.

The Children from Different Kinds of Retardate Unions

How do the children of two retarded parents differ from those of one retarded parent with a normal spouse? There were 536 fertile unions of the 507 retardates (Table 27). Fifty-four of these were retardate with retardate. These 54 unions produced 254 children (family size 4.7) of whom 39 died before age 2 years (15.4 per cent), while 85 of the 215 survivors were retarded (39.5 per cent). The 182 unions of retardates with normals produced 793 children (family size 4.3) of whom 66 died in infancy (8.3 per cent, or about half the proportion of infant deaths when both parents are retarded) and 93 were retarded (12 per cent, about one third the proportion found when both parents were retarded). In the case of retardates reproducing with mates of unknown intelligence, the 1118 children of 300 such unions had 9.8 per cent infant deaths and 10.1 per cent retardates. This last group is very similar to the one which includes unions of retardates with normals. The results help to justify our logical assumption that nearly all persons of unknown intelligence are really normals and not undetected retardates, though there must be a few of the latter type.

Table 27. *Mental Status of All the Surviving Children of Retardate Unions*

Type of Union	Mental Status			Total	Per Cent Retarded
	Retarded	Normal	Unknown		
Retardate × retardate (54)	85	83	47	215	39.5
Male retardate × normal (95)	41	261	128	430	9.5
Female retardate × normal (87)	51	175	70	296	17.5
Male retardate × unknown (133)	39	267	189	495	7.7
Female retardate × unknown (167)	64	287	164	515	12.4
Total (536)	280	1073	598	1951	14.3

Table 28. *IQ Range of Tested Children of Retardate Unions*

Type of Union	IQ Range						Total	Average IQ	Per Cent Retarded
	0-49	50-69	70-89	90-110	111-130	131+			
Retardate × retardate	6	29	36	17	1	0	89	74	39.4
Male retardate × normal	0	12	41	75	24	1	153	95	7.8
Female retardate × normal	6	15	32	43	10	1	107	87	19.6
Male retardate × unknown	3	16	68	80	20	1	188	90	10.1
Female retardate × unknown	10	29	64	79	22	2	206	87	19.0
Total	25	101	241	294	77	5	743	86	17.0

We have one or more IQ scores for each of 743 of the 1951 surviving children with one or both parents retarded. The 743 children have been separated into five groups as shown in Table 28. The effect of this sampling procedure has been to raise the percentage of retardation slightly when we compare it with the entire collection of children shown in Table 27. There were 35 out of 89 children (39.4 per cent) with IQ's below 70 when both parents were retarded. When one parent was known to have a normal IQ and the other was retarded, we find that, among the 260 tested children, there were 33 retardates (12.7 per cent). If one parent was of unknown intelligence, then among the 394 tested children there were 58 retardates (14.7 per cent).

Can we expect many children with IQ's above the normal range in unions in which one or both parents are retarded? Among the 89 children born to two retarded parents (Table 28) only one had an IQ in the range 111 to 130 (1 per cent). If one parent is retarded, the other normal, we found 34 of their 260 children in the IQ range 111 to 130 (13 per cent) and two with IQ's above 126 (0.7 per cent). If one parent was retarded, the other unknown, we found 42 of their 394 children in the IQ range 111 to 130 (11 per cent) and three with IQ's above 131 (0.8 per cent). The proportion of children with IQ scores above 110 expected in a large random population depends somewhat upon the particular intelligence test used, but if the "normal" or "average" range is considered to be IQ 90 to 110, then about 25 per cent would be expected to have IQ's above that range. None of these three groups supplies this "quota."

Gifted and superior children are no more randomly distributed throughout the population than are retarded children; both are clustered around the IQ values of their parents, as a rule. However, the fact that children with high IQ's can appear among children of the retardates indicates that there is indeed a genetic basis for their high scores because some of them come from extremely impoverished environments.

Let us consider further the data in Table 28. The 89 tested children of two retarded parents included 39.4 per cent with IQ's of 69 or below and 40 per cent with IQ's in the range 70 to 89. There were only 17 children (19.0 per cent) with IQ's in the normal range of 90 to 110, and one child who had an IQ of 115. While there was some regression to the mean among the children of retarded parents, 80 per cent of them had IQ scores below the normal range of 90 to 110. While almost 40 per cent of the children of two retardates are retarded, the grandchildren show only about 5 per cent retardation.

When the tested children from the retardate with normal unions were classified, it was found that among the 260 children there were 33 retardates (12.7 per cent) and 73 in the IQ range 70 to 89 (28.1 per cent) or more than one third are below normal. There were 118 children in the normal range (45.4 per cent). Thirty-four had IQ's in the 111 to 130 range (13.1 per cent) and there were two gifted children with IQ's above 131.

A fairly similar group, the 394 tested children of retardate with unknown unions included 58 retardates (14.7 per cent), 132 dull and borderline (33.4 per cent), 159 in the normal IQ range of 90 to 110 (40.4 per cent) and 45 with IQ's above 110 (including three

Table 29. *IQ Range of Tested Children of Retardate Unions in which Both Parents Had Been Tested*

Type of Union	IQ Range						Total	Average IQ of Children	Per Cent Retarded
	0-49	50-69	70-89	90-110	111-130	131+			
Both parents IQ 69 or below; average IQ 60 (12)	5	23	12	6	0	0	46	67	60.9
Father IQ 69 or below, average IQ 62; mother IQ 70 or above, average IQ 92 (26)	3	3	20	43	12	1	82	94	7.3
Mother IQ 69 or below, average IQ 63; father IQ 70 or above, average IQ 98 (15)	0	9	18	20	2	0	49	86	18.4
Total (53)	8	35	50	69	14	1	177	82	24.3

with IQ's above 131), or 11.4 per cent. For any retardate, irrespective of type of mate, the overall expectation of having a retarded child is 17.1 per cent, while the expectation of having a child with IQ 131 or above is 0.7 per cent.

The reader may have noticed in Table 28 that female retardates married to men of normal and of unknown intelligence had an appreciably higher percentage of retarded children than did retarded males married to women of normal and of unknown intelligence. The combination of the two groups of normal and unknown spouses for each sex gave 60 retarded children in a total of 313 children, or 19.4 per cent retarded for the retarded mothers, while the retarded fathers had 31 retarded children in 341, or 9.1 per cent retardation. This difference is statistically highly significant ($\chi^2 = 13.01$, $p = < 0.01$). This difference could be seized upon as evidence for a maternal effect upon intelligence either through adverse uterine conditions or that social deprivation is greater when the mother is retarded instead of the father. However, it is also possible that the difference resulted from some statistical artifact which has evaded our scrutiny. We have no explanation for the difference which does not seem to be supported by any of our other data.

Table 29 summarizes the data for *tested children* of *tested parents* where the unions are classified in the same way. There were 12 unions in which both parents had tested IQ scores below 69. The average IQ of the parents was 60, that of the children 67. This shows a slight regression toward the mean. Twenty-eight of the 46 children (60.9 per cent) were retarded. This increase above the 40 per cent retardation found in the larger samples described before probably reflects the greater likelihood of the identification and complete testing of the most seriously retarded families. In this group only six of the 46 children had IQ's in the 90 to 110 range (13.0 per cent). When one parent tested in the range IQ 69 and below, while the other tested above 69 (41 unions), the 131 tested children included 15 retardates (11.4 per cent retarded). The average IQ of the parents was 79, that of the children 90. There is considerably more regression toward the mean in this group.

The Children of the Highly Intelligent Compared with Those of the Retarded

It is interesting to contrast the data in Table 29 with those in Table 30 in which similar figures were collected for marriages in which one or both parents had IQ scores of 131 or above. There was one union in which the parents had IQ's of 157 and 151; their three tested children had IQ's of 132, 134 and 149, respectively. There was one union in which one parent had an IQ of 135, the other was retarded, IQ 67. Their five tested children had IQ's of 112, 115, 113, 97 and 131 (average IQ of parents 101, average IQ of children 114). In all 34 unions in which one parent had an IQ of 131 or above there were 77 children, none of whom was retarded, only four were borderline, 21 were in the range 90 to 110 (27.3 per cent) and the remaining 52 all had IQ's above 110, including 12 in the superior or gifted range (15.6 per cent).

Table 30. *IQ Range of Tested Children of Unions in which One or Both Parents Had IQ's of 131 or Above*

Type of Union	IQ Range							Average IQ of Children	Per Cent IQ 131 or Above
	0-49	50-69	70-89	90-110	111-130	131+	Total		
Both parents IQ 131 or above, average IQ 154 (1)	0	0	0	0	0	3	3	138	100.0
Father IQ 131 or above, average IQ 136; mother under IQ 131, average IQ 106 (16)	0	0	0	15	18	8	41	116	19.5
Mother IQ 131 or above, average IQ 137; father under IQ 131, average IQ 99 (18)	0	0	4	6	22	4	36	115	11.1
Total (35)	0	0	4	21	40	15	80	123	18.7

In comparing two groups of tested parents, one in which one parent is a retardate (41 unions) with one in which one parent tests IQ 131 or above (34 unions), we find that while the retardate can expect 11.4 per cent of his children to be retarded and only 0.8 per cent to be gifted, the parent with IQ 131 or above has a very small chance of having a retarded child (none was retarded in our sample, but there is nothing to prevent a deleterious recessive from coming out in some marriages), but he can expect about 15 per cent of his children to be of superior or gifted intelligence. The family size for the gifted group of 2.3 is probably enough to replace the gifted person in the population. Our tested highly intelligent parents were, on the whole, younger than our tested retarded parents who were often given special tests because of social and family problems; the families of the gifted in the sample may not all be completed yet. It is also possible that not all the gifted in our population were identified, since the group intelligence tests have low "ceilings" and high testing children seldom receive the individual testing that low testing children do. Our superior parents contribute much more than their share of the gifted in the next generation.

The "Garden Variety" of Retardates

One group of retardates is of special interest. This is the 50 families who exhibit a definite "familial" type of retardation with several generations of high-grade retardates. These families are in the Probably Genetic category together with five other families in which there was a close resemblance between a parent and child of low- or middle-grade retardation of a nonspecific type.

When these two groups are compared we find that of the 2253 individuals in the five family group, 93 died before age 2 years (4.1 per cent) and only 32 (1.5 per cent) were retarded. The 50 "familial" families had 18,730 members, of whom 671 died in infancy (3.0 per cent) and 741 (4.1 per cent) were retarded.

What reproductive patterns do the retardates in the "familial" type kindred show? There were 495 retardates (287 males, 208 females) exclusive of 20 unknowns and the group of 168 retardates that included the 50 probands, their retarded parents and retarded grandparents. Of 495 known retardates, 198 (40 per cent) never reproduced. The 216 who are known to have reproduced had 972 children, a family size of 4.5 children ever born. This figure is not significantly different from the family size found for the entire population of *reproducing* retardates. There were 8.7 per cent deaths before age 2 years and 13.7 per cent of the surviving children were retarded. This pattern of reproduction of retardates in "familial" kindreds is similar to that of retardates in other categories, and probably represents the type characteristic of the high-grade retardate within any category. The women did not show the commonly held picture of extremely high fertility. The 107 reproducing females had 431 children, family size 4.0 children ever born, and 64 retarded, or 16.5 per cent.

The grandchildren of the retardates in

this Probably Genetic category were also studied. From the union of retardate with retardate there were 247 surviving grandchildren, with ten of them retarded (4.0 per cent). When the original union was of a retardate with a normal or unknown spouse there were 1306 surviving (to 2 years of age) grandchildren of whom 48 (3.6 per cent) were retarded. Thus the 495 retardates in the "familial" kindreds of the Probably Genetic category had 1553 grandchildren, of whom only 58 were retarded. We find an 11.7 per cent of replacement of the retarded grandparents with retarded grandchildren. Because only one set of grandparents is known (the other set being unrecorded "in-laws"), the actual number of retarded grandparents must be somewhat larger than the 495 known from one side of each family only, and thus the actual replacement of the retarded would be something less than the 11.7 per cent.

The study of children from unions in which both parents were retarded showed that the family size (4.7) was greater than necessary for the replacement of the parents in the population. The question then arises whether this excess of replacement is also characteristic of matched unions in which both parents are of normal intelligence. It might be more useful to make the comparison of the number of grandchildren of the two types of unions in order to determine also whether the families of the retardates tend to "die out" in the second generation.

We searched through all the 289 kinships to find families which matched as to age and social class of the parents. All of their children had to be over 40 years of age so that the grandchildren would all have been born, and the families completed. We found 13 families of each type which seemed to be properly matched. The 13 unions of retardates with retardates produced 66 children and 155 grandchildren, while the 13 normal unions produced 62 children and 161 grandchildren. The sample is small but presumably representative of the most fertile of the retarded. It is clear that even the most fertile retardates do not have any appreciable advantage in reproduction over couples of normal intelligence of the same social class. When the large group of retarded who do not reproduce at all are included, it is clear that the retarded as a whole do not replace themselves in the population.

It is interesting to see if there is a difference in the per cent of retardation between the legitimate and the illegitimate children of retarded persons. There were 2165 children ever born to our retardates exclusive of the probands and their retarded parents and grandparents. The known illegitimate births numbered 78. Twelve of these were infant deaths and 17 of the remaining 66 (25.7 per cent) were retarded. The corresponding figure for legitimate births was 11.1 per cent retarded.

The illegitimate birth rate is lower than one might expect. This result is probably dependent upon our definition of illegitimacy. Quite a few of the legitimate births may have been to common law marriages or were illegitimate conceptions, legalized by subsequent marriages. The illegitimate children known to us were so classified either because no sort of permanent union was entered into by the parents, or because these children were the products of incestuous matings. It may be that persons with IQ's in the normal range have more illegitimate children than the retardates. The lower proportions of retardates found among legitimate children of retardates as compared with the illegitimate children are in agreement with those found for children of the probands whose marital histories are much better known. It was shown (p. 18) that 30 per cent of the illegitimate children of the probands were retarded, while 11.3 per cent of the legitimate children were retarded.

Reproduction of Normal Siblings

The question has been raised whether or not the presence of a retardate in a sibship resulted in a decrease in the size of families produced by his normal siblings. In order to assemble data for a study of this problem, the following criteria were set up.

A comparison was made between the reproduction of normal persons from sibships including a retardate and that of normal first cousins from sibships without a retardate. Each normal sibling was matched with a normal first cousin of the same sex and approximately the same age (birthdates within ten years of each other). In all cases the person with the birthdate closest to that of the like-sex sibling was selected. Often two normal siblings were matched with cousins from different sibships. All individuals used were required to have known normal intelligence, to have survived to age 15 years, to have been born before 1917 (in order to make sure their reproductive lives had ended) and they could not be siblings either of the proband or of the proband's parents. The persons selected were of either sex and either married or single.

The final sample yielded data on 208 siblings and their 208 matched first cousins. Consideration of the large population from which this sample of 416 persons was drawn might lead one to believe many more should have been found. Our strict criteria not only reduced the sample size greatly but also reduced variation within it. In addition, some retardates had no normal siblings, and in some families there were no first-cousin sibships without at least one retardate.

The 208 siblings of retardates included 102 males who had 232 children and 106 females who had 266 children. The matched first cousin males had 242 children and the females had 252 children. Thus the 208 siblings of retardates had 498 children, or 2.4 children per person, while their matched first cousins had 494 children, or 2.4 children per person. Thus no significant difference in reproduction was found between that of normal persons from sibships including a retardate and their normal first cousins from sibships without retardates. There were more married female siblings than male siblings in both groups. Only five females of the 106 were unmarried as contrasted with 14 of the 102 males. A similar but smaller difference held for the matching cousins, 15 of the males were unmarried while only 11 of the females were single.

Changes in IQ Scores on Subsequent Tests

There were 741 persons who had more than one intelligence test. Most of the second and third tests had been administered routinely to normal school children. Several questions arise here: was the score on the first test similar to that on the last? Are the test scores of retardates, normals or superior persons more variable? Are some first test scores misleading as to the mental status of the child tested? An examination of the data from this large sample was directed toward searching for answers to these questions.

In this analysis the first IQ score was compared with the last. There were 166 persons among the 741 who were tested more than twice. Among this latter group, 81 persons tested low the first time and 85 tested high the first time. The difference in favor of a lower score with later tests is in agreement with the data from the larger sample of 741 persons whose score on first test was compared with that of the last one (which was the second test in 575 of the 741 cases). When the first IQ score was compared with the last one there were 310 persons whose first scores were lower, 401 whose first scores were higher and 30 whose first scores were exactly the same as their last scores (Table 31). The difference between the number whose IQ score decreased by more than 5 points (241) and the number whose IQ score increased by more than 5 points (205) is not significant ($\chi^2 = 2.9$).

Since it is not expected that IQ scores for the same person will be exactly the same on successive tests, the number of those persons with IQ scores which stayed the same, whose scores decreased 1 to 5 points on a later test and those whose scores increased 1 to 5 points were added together in a group considered as not showing any significant change in IQ score on successive tests. These persons numbered 295, or 39.8 per cent of the total sample. This uniformity was especially interesting because the subjects had been tested at different ages and often with different tests.

A careful look at Table 31 shows that many more persons showed a decrease in their IQ score of 1 to 5 points than showed an increase of 1 to 5 points. However, this is a trivial change and can be ignored. We find that there are no significant differences between increases and decreases for the larger changes in IQ values.

Then the data were separated into IQ score changes for persons within the IQ ranges of retarded (IQ 60-69), dull and borderline (IQ 70-89), normal (IQ 90-110), above average (IQ 111-125) and superior and gifted (IQ above 125). For the first two groups, a few more IQ's rose upon the second testing than fell, but in neither of the groups was the difference significant when tested by chi square. For the other three groups the excess of decreasing IQ's rose at each level until in the range of IQ 126 and above, only

Table 31. *Changes in IQ Scores between the First and Last Tests*

	IQ Score on First Test						
Last score	0-69	70-89	90-110	111-125	126 up	Total	Per Cent
Increased							
1-5 points	7	22	53	22	1	105	33.8
6-10 "	8	15	54	13	2	92	29.7
11-15 "	6	13	27	10	0	56	18.1
16-20 "	1	8	17	8	0	34	10.9
21 or more	3	5	9	4	2	23	7.4
Total	25	63	160	57	5	310	
Per cent increased	52.1	49.6	43.1	35.2	15.1		41.8
Decreased							
1-5 points	7	20	91	38	4	160	39.9
6-10 "	7	19	48	32	12	118	29.4
11-15 "	4	7	35	12	5	63	15.7
16-20 "	1	4	16	13	3	37	9.2
21 or more	1	5	8	5	4	23	5.7
Total	20	55	198	100	28	401	
Per cent decreased	41.7	43.3	53.4	61.7	84.9		54.1
Remained the same	3	9	13	5	0	30	4.1
Per cent	6.2	7.1	3.5	3.1	0.0		
Total	48	127	371	162	33	741	100.0
Per cent in each IQ range	6.5	17.1	50.1	21.9	4.4		100.0

five persons achieved an increased score with a second test while 28 received a lower score. We think that these drops in IQ scores for the higher levels can be attributed, at least in part, to the limiting ceilings of some of the group tests. A child could test at the top of the IQ scale at a younger age, and thereby achieve a very high score, but when tested at an older age could not achieve a high enough score to reflect accurately his mental status. Special individual tests have been devised for gifted students to provide high enough "ceilings" for them. The superior and gifted in this study seldom had individual tests, whereas most of the retardates did have at least one individual test. There will be some regression toward the mean in addition to the foregoing considerations.

How many children are classified incorrectly on the basis of a single IQ score? All IQ changes for the 741 persons were scrutinized for those in which a person might have been moved from one classification to another by a retest.

In the group of 48 persons who ranked as retarded on the first test, 15 moved to a higher category on the basis of a second test. Eleven of the 15 moved up to the 70 to 89 classification while the remaining four moved into the normal 90 to 110 range. However, one of the last four who was considered retarded, had the first test at the age of 2 years which is too young for fine distinctions among IQ values to be made. The next point concerns the 16 persons who moved into the retarded group on second or later tests from higher classifications. Three of the 16 dropped from the 70 to 89 IQ range at the age of 3 years to the 60 to 69 range by age 14. A fourth person dropped from 71 at 3 years of age to IQ 59 at age 20. The remaining 12 moved from the 70 to 89 range to lower scores but were tested at more appropriate ages. Persons who moved up in IQ scores were matched by others who moved down into the retarded group. The moral to be found in these data is the old one that IQ values obtained for *pre-school* children are too liable to change to be of much value. However, when this pitfall is avoided, we find that in the great mass of school-age children there is little change in IQ values of an important nature on successive tests. This is particularly true if individual tests with sufficient ceiling to accommodate the gifted are administered.

It should be emphasized that no one will ever devise an intelligence test for which test and retest scores for an individual will always be the same. It would be as foolish to expect this as to expect a baseball player to hit a home run every time he comes to the plate. Human behavior will always be variable. Nonetheless, we can learn a great deal by combining the IQ value with other observations in estimating the intellectual capacity of the individual. In this study there could be a great deal of inaccuracy in individual IQ values, but this would tend to cancel out so the averages we have obtained should be valid.

Mental Status of the Parents of the Unselected Retardates

The 1450 unselected retardates were all those in our population of over 82,000 persons, except the retarded probands, their retarded parents, their retarded grandparents and the retarded who married into the kinships. The retarded children of the probands and the retarded siblings of the probands were included in the unselected sample of retardates on the premise that the proband was not selected because of possible retarded children that might appear later, nor would we expect the institutionalization of the proband to be dependent upon his retarded siblings to any large extent. While our unselected sample is not absolutely "random," it is well known that the selection of a truly random sample is seldom possible. Let us remember the difficulties of random sampling but we need not be overwhelmed by them; they are not of major importance for our study.

There were about 80,000 persons, excluding parents and grandparents, who formed the population from which our 1450 unselected retardates were drawn—a ratio of 1450 retardates to about 78,550 other persons. Many of the 78,550 are children or adults with unknown intelligence, so that the total number of normal persons must be less than 78,550 because some of the "unknowns" must have been retarded. Thus, in roughest terms, there was about one retarded to 50 normal persons in our sample, excluding the probands, their parents and grandparents. This ratio is approximately 2 per cent of retardation, a little lower than the usual estimates of other workers. If there were a purely random association between retardates, we would not expect a retardate to have a retarded parent very often. We will show that the unselected retardates had one or both parents retarded in almost 50 per cent of the cases—an obviously gross deviation from random expectation. It means that mental retardation is transmitted from one generation to the next much of the time. It does not give us any evidence, of course, as to what proportion of the transmission is primarily genetic or primarily environmental, in the arbitrary sense in which such a distinction has to be made.

We have shown that two retarded spouses can expect that nearly 40 per cent of their children will be retarded. One retarded parent with a normal spouse can expect about 13 per cent of his children to be retarded. Does this production of retarded children by one or both retarded parents contribute a *significant* proportion of the retardates to be found in the next generation, or does it make little relative difference whether or not re-

Table 32. *1450 Unselected Retardates Separated by Degree of Retardation and Mental Status of Parents*

Degree of Retardation	Mental Status of Parents: Both Parents Retarded	Per Cent	One Parent Retarded	Per Cent	Neither Parent Retarded	Per Cent	Total	Percentage with One or Both Parents Retarded
IQ below 25	10	8.3	31	25.9	79	65.8	120	34.2
IQ 25-49 to third grade in school	26	17.1	28	18.4	98	64.5	152	35.5
IQ 50-69 – employed or through third grade in school	197	20.0	320	32.3	471	47.7	988	52.3
Retarded but IQ value unknown	26	13.7	62	32.6	102	53.7	190	46.3
Total	259	17.9	441	30.4	750	51.7	1450	48.3

tarded persons reproduce? We can answer this question with reasonable accuracy by classifying the parents of our 1450 unselected retardates as to whether, one, both or neither of the parents was retarded.

The 1450 unselected retardates were first subdivided as to their degree of retardation and according to the mental status of their parents. The results are shown in Table 32. It should be remembered that all 1450 persons were retarded, though the separation of them into distinct categories of retardation was not always possible. One important finding to be derived from this table is that the higher grade retardates have one or both parents retarded more frequently (52.3 per cent) than do the lower and middle grade retardates (an average of 35.0 per cent). The most striking finding, however, appears in the last row of the table. The reader may well be shocked to see that 700 of the 1450 unselected retardates (48.3 per cent) were produced in families in which one or both parents was retarded. This is an unpleasant fact, and one which the reader may not like to accept. The idea that 48.3 per cent of the retarded in our society have one or both of their parents retarded is generally unpalatable. The general attitude has been that the great majority of the retarded are produced by normal persons. It has been assumed frequently that the retarded of this generation make only an inconsequential contribution to the population of retardates in the next generation. This assumption is fallacious. The concept that the retarded do *not* contribute any important percentage of the retarded in the next generation has been eagerly accepted because it relieves society of any responsibility for attempting to limit the reproduction of the retarded. The idea of limiting anyone's reproduction is naturally repugnant but this neither decreases the magnitude of the problem, nor does it justify ignoring the relevant data. It should be emphasized that it is the transmission of the retardation from one generation to the next that is of primary importance, and it is only of secondary importance whether the transmission of the retardation is mainly environmental or genetic. The methods employed to prevent this transmission may be different depending upon the environmental or genetic factors involved. However, the responsibility of society to decrease the transmission of mental retardation remains.

We next looked at our 289 probands to discover what proportion of their parents was retarded. The results were almost identical with those for the unselected retardates. There were 144 of the probands (49.8 per cent) who had one or both parents retarded.

There is a good possibility that the probands of our study were different in some way from unselected retarded persons as a group. One method for testing this supposition is to determine the percentage of our 1450 retardates with one or both parents retarded, according to the degree of relationship of the unselected retardate to the proband. The unselected retardates who are first degree relatives of the probands must be either their children or their siblings as all other first degree relatives were excluded. The children of the probands all had a retarded parent (the proband) and would give 100 per cent with one or both parents retarded. The siblings of the probands would have both parents normal in some cases. The combined percentage for the two groups of first degree relatives shows that 73.5 per cent of these retarded persons had one or both parents retarded (Table 33). There are several vari-

Table 33. *1450 Unselected Retardates Classified by Degree of Relationship to Probands and Mental Status of Parents*

Degree of Relationship to Probands	Mental Status of Parents: Both Parents Retarded	Per Cent	One Parent Retarded	Per Cent	Neither Parent Retarded	Per Cent	Total	Percentage with One or Both Parents Retarded
First degree	130	38.4	119	35.1	90	26.5	339	73.5
Second degree	56	15.3	126	34.4	184	50.3	366	49.7
Third degree	50	15.6	112	34.9	159	49.5	321	50.5
More than third degree	23	5.4	84	19.8	317	74.8	424	25.2
Total	259	17.9	441	30.4	750	51.7	1450	48.3

eties of second degree and third degree relatives and the results from the two groups are hardly distinguishable as 49.7 and 50.5 per cent had one or both parents retarded (Table 33). Table 33 also shows that only 25.2 per cent of the retardates who were more distantly related to the probands than the third degree had one or both parents retarded.

It is not clear why only 25.2 per cent of this group had one or both parents retarded when the third degree retardates had one or both parents retarded in 50.5 per cent of the cases. This discrepancy is too large to be ignored but we have no explanation for it. Let us assume that this value of 25.2 per cent of our 424 retardates with one or both parents retarded is too low and that the value of 50.5 per cent of our 321 retardates of the third degree of relationship with one or both parents retarded is too high (Table 33). If these two assumptions are reasonable, we can combine these two groups of the most distant relatives of our probands with the result that 269 retardates of 745 had one or both parents retarded. This is 36.1 per cent of our retardates (who were truly unselected because they were such distant relatives of the probands) with one or both parents retarded. *This means that the 1 to 2 per cent of our population composed of fertile retardates produced 36.1 per cent of the retardates of the next generation, while the other 98 to 99 per cent of the population produced only 63.9 per cent of the retarded persons of the next generation.*

Dr. Elving Anderson suggested that we take a subsample of the distant relatives which would be more sharply defined than the sample just studied. We took only first cousins of our probands and their children, excluding all first cousins whose reproductive histories were unknown. The first cousins and their children are sufficiently distant relatives to be free of institutional bias and should be an excellent "control" population.

There were 200 retarded first cousins; 90 were married and produced offspring; there were 83 who never married and 27 who married but had no children. Thus 55 per cent of the retarded transmitted no genes to the next generation. The total of 200 retarded first cousins represented 4.5 per cent of the 4437 first cousins of our sample; this is somewhat higher than the 3 per cent retardation usually assumed for the general public. However, the ascertainment of the 4.5 per cent retardation is probably more reliable than any other value reported up to the present.

The 4437 first cousins produced 9149 surviving children, plus 441 children who died in infancy. This is only 2.06 surviving children per cousin and suggests that some of the families were not completed at the conclusion of the study. There were only 154 retarded children (1.7 per cent) among the 9149 offspring of the first cousins. A significant proportion of the children of the first cousins were still too young to be detected as retardates so the figure of 1.7 per cent retardation is too low and is not reliable. Nonetheless, of the 154 children who had been detected as retarded, 51 (33.1 per cent) had one or both parents retarded. This is in excellent agreement with 36.1 per cent of retardates with one or both parents retarded found for the larger sample of third degree or more distant relatives shown previously.

Let us summarize the most important data obtained from the cousins of our probands. There were 2876 unions of normal cousins with normal spouses which produced 8781 children of whom 103 (1.2 per cent) were retarded. The 92 unions of a retarded parent and normal spouse resulted in 359 children of whom 46 (12.8 per cent) were retarded. There were only six unions of two retarded persons which produced nine children of whom five (55.7 per cent) were retarded. Thus 98 of the 2974 unions with children, or 3.3 per cent, displayed retardation in one or both spouses. There were 518 unions of the first cousins that resulted in no children and 27 (5.2 per cent) of the 518 cousins were retarded. There were 945 unmarried cousins of whom 83 (8.8 per cent) were retarded. One inescapable conclusion is that the transmission of mental retardation from parent to child is by far the most important *single* factor in the persistence of this social misfortune.

Some readers might object to our exclusion from the calculations just given the probands and all their first and second degree relatives. These exclusions were a part of the Minnesota mental retardation problem and their need for institutionalization, along with other retardates, was the only reason for maintaining an institution for the retarded. However, by using only the distant relatives in obtaining our value of 36.1 per cent, we have been extremely conservative and have presented the most optimistic picture possible in regard to the transmission of mental retardation.

Table 34. *1150 Unselected Retardates Classified by the Number of Retardates per Sibship and Mental Status of Parents*

Number of Retardates per Sibship	Mental Status of Parents: Both Parents Retarded	Per Cent	One Parent Retarded	Per Cent	Neither Parent Retarded	Per Cent	Total Number of Sibships	Total Number of Retardates
One	13	2.8	97	20.9	354	76.3	464	464
Two	13	10.0	34	25.9	84	64.1	131	262
Three	7	13.2	26	49.1	20	37.7	53	159
Four	5	19.3	9	34.5	12	46.2	26	104
Five	6	40.0	5	33.3	4	26.7	15	75
Six	2	25.0	2	25.0	4	50.0	8	48
Seven	0	00.0	1	33.3	2	66.7	3	21
Eight	1	100.0	0	00.0	0	00.0	1	8
Nine	1	100.0	0	00.0	0	00.0	1	9
Totals	48	6.8	174	24.8	480	68.4	702	1150

It is enlightening to ascertain the number of our unselected retardates to be found in each sibship. This time we have excluded the probands, their parents, siblings and children; that is, the first degree relatives. There were 1150 unselected retardates left after these exclusions, distributed among 702 sibships. The majority of the sibships had only one retardate in each, though there was one family with nine retarded siblings. Both parents of these nine retarded children were retarded. It is interesting that in each of two families there were seven retarded siblings with both parents normal (Table 34). It can be seen that 31.6 per cent of these *sibships* with one or more retarded children in them had one or both parents retarded. The persons in this table are only distant relatives of the original 289 probands.

Our final comparison is that of the number of retardates, according to the mental status of their parents, for the sibships of our 289 probands. These data are in Table 35 and show that 49.8 per cent of the *sibships* of our probands had one or both parents retarded. There is therefore a difference of 18.2 per cent between the proportion of the probands' sibships with one or both parents retarded (49.8 per cent) and the proportion of the more distantly related retardates whose sibships showed only 31.6 per cent with one or both parents retarded. This difference is substantial and is probably dependent, in part, upon the "institutional bias" mentioned previously. It means that our probands and other institutionalized persons are likely to come from families with more than an average number of retarded persons.

Table 35. *Sibships of the 289 Probands Classified by Number of Retardates in Sibship and Mental Status of Parents*

Number of Retardates per Sibship (Including Proband)	Mental Status of Parents: Both Parents Retarded	Per Cent	One Parent Retarded	Per Cent	Neither Parent Retarded	Per Cent	Total
One	7	5.0	33	23.6	100	71.4	140
Two	10	17.2	25	43.1	23	39.7	58
Three	9	27.4	12	36.3	12	36.3	33
Four	14	33.3	21	50.0	7	16.7	42
Five	5	55.6	2	22.2	2	22.2	9
Six	3	75.0	0	00.0	1	25.0	4
Seven	2	100.0	0	00.0	0	00.0	2
Eight	1	100.0	0	00.0	0	00.0	1
Total	51	17.6	93	32.2	145	50.2	289

Table 36. *The Number of Children Produced by the Different Relatives of Our Probands* (For Unions with at Least One Child Ever Born)

Category of Proband	Grandparents	Parents	Aunts and Uncles	Siblings
Primarily genetic	6.54 ± 0.26	6.51 ± 0.40	4.53 ± 0.16	3.25 ± 0.18
Probably genetic	5.04 ± 0.32	4.84 ± 0.38	4.54 ± 0.03	4.15 ± 0.26
Environmental	6.11 ± 0.47	5.31 ± 0.64	4.89 ± 0.21	3.69 ± 0.38
Unknown	5.59 ± 0.21	6.09 ± 0.28	4.64 ± 0.12	3.43 ± 0.17
Totals	5.77 ± 0.15	5.84 ± 0.19	4.61 ± 0.08	3.54 ± 0.11

REPRODUCTION OF THE RELATIVES OF THE RETARDED

Family Sizes in a Frontier State

The reproduction of all the retardates in the study has already been considered. We have also given the percentages of retardation found among the children of the first, second and third degree relatives of our retarded probands. We were interested in the number of children ever born to the close relatives of our probands. Are these families large or small? The answer will be of eugenic interest, because the part of the general public having an interest in this subject seems to think that these will be jumbo-sized families.

The grandparents of our probands reproduced for the most part during the period 1825 to 1875. This was the period when Minnesota obtained statehood. The last large Indian massacre in Minnesota was at New Ulm in 1862. Thus the grandparents' generation was composed of pioneer stock with a positive attitude toward reproduction. The parents and their siblings, the aunts and uncles of our probands, would have been reproducing from about 1850 through 1900 and the siblings of the probands would have reproduced between the years 1875 to 1925. There will be some chronological overlapping of the different generations but this will do no violence to the expected finding that the number of children born to the probands' siblings will be smaller than the number born to the grandparents.

Table 36 shows the average number of children ever born, with standard errors, for the relatives given. The reader may be surprised that the average number of children produced by the parents of the probands was slightly higher than the number produced by the grandparents. The high average number of children produced by the probands' parents probably represents the "institutional bias" mentioned before, that is, the retarded child who is a member of a large family with retarded parents is more likely to become a part of our sample of probands than a retarded child from a small family with normal parents.

We do not know the average number of children ever born to parents having at least one child for either of the 50 year periods from 1825 to 1925 in Minnesota. Common sense would indicate that it was as high or higher than the numbers found for the grandparents, aunts and uncles and siblings of our probands. Furthermore, many of the children produced by the above unions in our families were mentally retarded. We have seen earlier that about 40 per cent of the retarded have no children. In addition, many of the children born under pioneer conditions in the 1800's failed to survive long enough to reproduce. Thus the reproduction of the relatives of our probands seems to have been rather modest.

Let us make a few calculations to find the *absolute minimum* number of persons expected in our study if each person were to replace himself and with no population growth at all. We start with the four grandparents of our proband. They must produce four children to replace themselves. Two of the four children marry to become the parents of the proband and the other two marry "out," which gives a necessary minimum of six persons in this parental generation. There will be 12 persons in the proband's generation and 24 in the proband's children's generation and 48 in the proband's grandchildren's generation. For these five generations we expect a total of 94 persons to appear on the pedigree chart for a single kinship. As there were 289 kinships in the study we would expect to find an absolute minimum of 27,166 persons on our pedigree charts. Actually we had seven generations in some kinships, and individuals in the line of descent often married more than once, bringing in outsiders who would have to be replaced by additional reproduction. Furthermore, not all persons ever born could be expected to reproduce. We estimate that there should be about 40,000 persons shown on our pedigree charts, if the grandparents were to just replace themselves with the minimum number of descendants at the end of the fifth generation.

It is interesting that 86 of our 289 kinships had less than the 94 persons necessary for replacement. Thus 29.8 per cent of the kinships, as a rough estimate, did not succeed in replacing themselves. The total of 82,217 different persons who appear on the pedigree charts thus represents a possible doubling of the population of the grandparents and their descendants over five generations. This is certainly a modest increase in population growth for a frontier state and no claim could be made that these kinships, *in toto,* were swamping their contemporaries in rate of reproduction. In fact, the failure of 40 per cent of the retarded persons to reproduce at all indicates that our 289 kindreds may have lagged behind comparable families in reproduction over the five generations. It is obvious that the 82,217 individuals represent less than the actual number of persons in the 289 kindreds because some individuals disappeared and their possible descendants are unknown to us. However, those lost would not increase our total much over 100,000 persons at the most.

Our 289 family groups are interesting because they are so different. They should be of interest to investigators in the social sciences who are concerned with family structure, the high frequencies of divorces in particular sibships and the correlation of them with neuroticism or other mental health problems. In addition, they should be of interest for these same investigators in studying other psychological and sociological aberrations which cannot be studied thoroughly without some knowledge of the whole family constellation.

Risk Figures for Genetic Counseling

The Dight Institute for Human Genetics has pioneered in bringing genetic counseling to those who want it. Minnesota was the first state to install a unit of human genetics in its state Board of Health. The reader should consult the text by Reed (1963) devoted to counseling in medical genetics for an idea of what is involved in this work, with the chapters on mental retardation and on Down's syndrome being of the most immediate interest.

There are many requests for counseling concerned with mental retardation. They are all different and no formula fits any appreciable number of cases. Counseling for Down's syndrome, Pelizaeus-Merzbacher disease and other named varieties of retardation is usually quite specific and is based on the mendelian rules or the results of a chromosome study. But we are not helpless when confronted with mental retardation of the undifferentiated type, though in these cases the counseling has to be in more general terms. The present study provides extensive data which are helpful for counseling in different degrees of relationship in which only generalized estimates can be provided. These are the so-called empiric risk figures. They should never be thought of as giving the *precise* chance that the next pregnancy of a couple would result in a retarded child, but rather they should be considered as a very rough estimate of a range of probabilities which should include the value appropriate for them.

In this section of the study in order to reduce possible bias we have excluded the sibships of our original probands and also all sibships without at least one member whose intelligence had been definitely determined.

The first value we wish to determine is the percentage of retarded children produced by the normal siblings of a retarded person. These normal siblings of a retarded person could marry either a retarded person or one in the unknown-normal class, thus we can derive two different risk figures.

a. There were 16 normal siblings of a retarded person who married a retarded person. They produced 71 children of whom 63 survived infancy and 15 of them (23.8 per cent) were retarded. This value is higher than the earlier finding for the unions of a retardate with a normal or unknown in which 11.4 per cent of the children were retarded. We would expect a higher risk, on a polygenic hypothesis, for these unions in which the normal person had both a retarded sibling and a retarded spouse, when compared with the risk of 11.4 per cent of retardation for unions of a retarded person and a normal, usually without a retarded sibling. The reader may wonder why there were only 16 families in this group. It is because of the rather low probability of finding a marriage of a normal person with a retarded sibling to another retarded person. This is not only a statistically small group, but it also would be discriminated against by assortative mating, as normals do not as often marry retardates as one would expect for random mating.

b. There were 351 sibships in which the normal sibling of a retarded person married a normal or unknown person. There were 753 normal siblings (in the 351 families) who produced 3210 children, of whom 2996 survived infancy, and of the latter there were 73 retarded (2.5 per cent).

It is of interest to separate the data into two groups depending upon whether the normal person had only one retarded sibling or more than one. There were 1958 surviving children, of whom 36 (1.8 per cent) were retarded in the category of only one retarded sibling of the normal parent. If the normal parent had two or more retarded siblings there were 37 (3.6 per cent) retarded children among the 1038 who survived to 2 years of age. Thus, if a normal person has two or more retarded siblings his expectation of having a retarded child is doubled (3.6 per cent) compared with his expectation of 1.8 per cent if there was only one retarded sibling.

It is also worthwhile to see if there are any large differences in the percentages of retardation among the children of normal persons with one or more retarded siblings when the persons are sorted according to the category of the pedigree to which they belong. The results are as follows:

Primarily genetic,
17 retarded in 1087 survivors (1.6%)
Probably genetic,
34 retarded in 997 survivors (3.4%)
Environmental,
7 retarded in 248 survivors (2.8%)
Unknown,
15 retarded in 664 survivors (2.2%)

Totals 73 2996 2.5%

The highest value is for the probably genetic category and this gives support to our hypothesis that the probably genetic probands are often the result of combinations of many genes for lower intelligence at the left end of the normal curve of intelligence. Such genes could be expected to be most frequent in the normal members of the kindreds of the probably genetic group and thus provide a large percentage of retarded children.

What kinds of retardation are present in the children produced by the normal siblings of retarded persons? Table 37 lists the diagnoses for the 73 retarded children found among the 2996 surviving children already considered. It can be seen that 61 of the 73 retarded children (83.5 per cent) were of the undifferentiated type.

Our second group of interest is the large mass of persons of normal intelligence who have only normal siblings and normal spouses. These marriages would be the usual ones in the population and for them there is no par-

Table 37. *The Kinds of Retarded Children Born to Normal Siblings of Retardates*

Diagnosis	Degree of Retardation			
	IQ 0-49	IQ 50-69	Degree Unknown	Total
Undifferentiated	9	51	1	61
Schilder's disease	1	1		2
Down's syndrome	1	1		2
Pelizaeus-Merzbacher	1	1		2
Cretinism		1		1
Myxedemic	1			1
Deaf and retarded		1		1
Seizures		1		1
Unknown diagnosis			2	2
Total	13	57	3	73

Table 38. *The Kinds of Retarded Children Born to Normal Siblings from All-Normal Sibships*

Diagnosis	Degree of Retardation			
	IQ 0-49	IQ 50-69	Degree Unknown	Total
Undifferentiated	7	23		30
Cerebral palsy	1	2		3
Down's syndrome	2			2
Phenylketonuria	2			2
Microcephaly	1		1	2
Undifferentiated with psychosis		2		2
Hydrocephaly			1	1
Cerebral-spastic hemiplegia	1			1
Seizures	1			1
Blindness		1		1
Post encephalitis		1		1
Prenatal anoxia	1			1
"Possible birth injury"		1		1
Unknown			2	2
Total	16	30	4	50

ticular expectation of having a retarded child. We had 1837 such sibships which included 3391 normal persons with normal spouses and with at least one child with known mental status. The probands' families were excluded, of course, as were all consanguineous unions. The 3391 normal persons had 9476 children who survived infancy and there were 50 retardates (0.53 per cent) among them.

The kinds of mental retardation found in these normal sibship families are shown in Table 38. The majority, 60 per cent, are again of the undifferentiated type, though it is a smaller majority than that in which there was a retarded sibling. This is again what might be expected if the undifferentiated retarded are usually dependent upon combinations of numerous genes which result in lower intelligence.

We can examine these data a bit further. If genetic factors were of little or no importance we would not expect it would make any difference whether there was a retarded sibling of the normal parents or not. Furthermore, if the normal parents have already had one retarded child, one would not expect that their having a retarded sib would have any effect on the percentage of retardation in the remainder of their offspring, if genetics is of no importance. However, we do find a difference. The 73 retarded children of the 2996 already mentioned were produced by 55 of the 753 normal persons having a retarded sibling but married to a normal or unknown spouse. Each of the 55 persons had a retarded child and there were 18 retarded and 230 normal and unknown children in addition, or 7.3 per cent retardation, excluding the 55 retarded children we started with. In the other group of normal siblings with normal or unknown spouses and with no retarded siblings of the normals, there were 50 retarded children produced by 44 of the 3391 normal persons. When the 44 retarded are deleted from the children we have six retarded and 157 normal or unknown children left, or 3.7 per cent retarded, in the 44 families. The difference between 7.3 per cent additional retarded children with a retarded uncle or aunt and 3.7 per cent additional retarded children without a retarded uncle or aunt is impressive even though these are small samples, and the difference is not highly statistically significant, the probability being between 0.05 and 0.01.

The reader has already seen that there were 753 normal persons who had a retarded sibling and that 55 of the 753 (7.3 per cent) produced one or more retarded children. The 3391 persons who had no retarded sibling included only 44 (1.3 per cent) who produced one or more retarded children. It is once again clear that the existence of a retarded sibling increases considerably the likelihood that a normal couple will have a retarded child. The

Table 39. *Data for the Distinctly Different IQ Curves Shown by the Children of Normal Parents* with *Retarded Siblings and of Normal Parents* without *Retarded Siblings*

Midpoints of IQ Ranges	Children of Normal Persons with Retarded Siblings		Children of Normal Persons without Retarded Siblings	
	Number	Percentage	Number	Percentage
24.5	9	0.9	14	0.2
59.5	22	2.1	19	0.3
79.5	159	15.2	352	5.9
100.0	545	52.0	2917	48.8
118.0	259	24.7	2122	35.4
135.0	53	5.1	564	9.4
	1047	100.0	5988	100.0
Average IQ	101.6 ± 0.52		108.2 ± 0.19	

degree to which this fact is of importance in counseling will depend upon the type of retardation involved. It would be of practical concern for normal parents with a retarded sibling of the undifferentiated type. If the retarded sibling were clearly the result of some environmental infection or accident, we would not consider the retarded sibling to be so much of a threat.

It is not surprising to a geneticist that those normal persons who had one or more retarded siblings had a five-fold greater risk (7.3 per cent) of producing a retarded child than those normals who had no retarded sibling (1.3 per cent). We were somewhat surprised to find that the fact of a retarded sibling of a normal person lowered the average IQ (101.6 ± 0.52) of the whole population of children from these unions compared with the population of children from the normal persons without retarded siblings (IQ = 108.2 ± 0.19). The difference in average IQ between the two groups is 6.6 ± 0.56 which is statistically highly significant (Table 39). There is no doubt that the whole IQ curve for the children of the normal parents with retarded siblings is shifted downward to the left compared with the curve for the children of normal parents with normal siblings (see Figure). Furthermore, the shift is present at each of the midpoints of the IQ ranges. This consistency, together with the large number of children involved, 1047 from the parents who had a retarded sibling and 5988 from the parents who did not, gives considerable reliability to this finding.

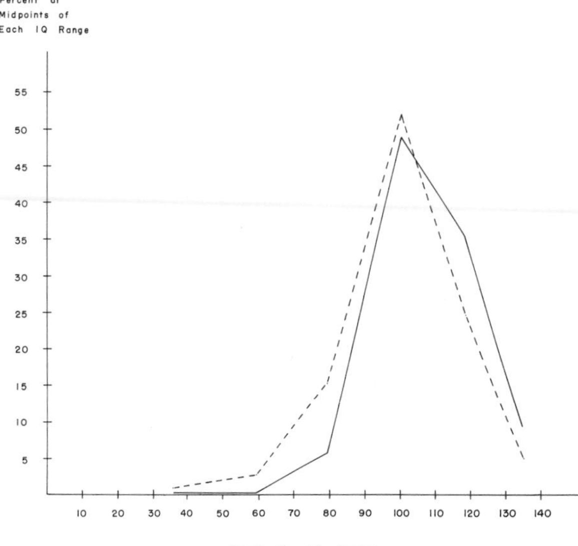

The IQ curve for the children of normal parents with one or more retarded siblings is shown by the dotted line (1047 children). The curve for children of normal parents without a retarded sibling is shown by the solid line (5988 children).

What is the significance of our finding of an average difference of 6.6 IQ points in favor of the children who had no known retarded aunt or uncle compared with those who had one or more such retarded relatives? One group of normal parents transmits something different to their children from what is transmitted by the other group of normal parents. But what is it that is transmitted which could shift the whole IQ curve downward? It is *not* plausible to assume that some virus or other environmental accident is passed from the retarded uncles or aunts through the normal parents to the whole population of nieces and nephews. It seems more likely that social deprivation and stimulus deficiency could be communicated through the normal parents to their offspring. But, perhaps of most importance, we know that because of the meiotic divisions in men and women the nieces and nephews must have 25 per cent of the same genes possessed by their aunts and uncles. This is not only one of the most basic biological facts of life but we also know that, barring mutations, 25 per cent of genes common to the aunts and nieces, for instance, are precisely identical. These genes in common have not been contaminated or changed in any way during their passage through the two generations involved. It is therefore reasonable to assume that there are more genes for lower intelligence in the families in which there was a retarded aunt or uncle than in those with only normal aunts or uncles. Polygenes for lower intelligence would be expected to affect children at all levels of intelligence and to shift the whole group of children to the left of the normal curve of intelligence.

We wished to study this phenomenon in greater detail, that is, to include the IQ values of both of the parents in the two groups. When the requirement of an IQ value for both parents of the child is added, our sample size must drop rather sharply. The smaller samples have larger standard errors, but as can be seen below, the results are consistent throughout. It is remarkable that assortative mating is clearly evident as the spouses of the normal parents with one or more retarded siblings had a lower average IQ (99.9 ± 1.90) than the spouses of the normal parents without retarded siblings (104.6 ± 0.48).

Let us summarize the findings for these two populations:

a. The family grouping in which the normal parent had one or more retarded siblings.

	Mean IQ S. E.	*Number*
Parents with retarded siblings	98.0 ± 1.98	54
Spouses of these parents	99.9 ± 1.90	54
Children of these parents	104.6 ± 1.69	119

b. The family grouping in which the normal parent had no retarded sibling.

	Mean IQ S. E.	*Number*
Parents with no retarded sibling	103.8 ± 0.50	674
Spouses of these parents	104.6 ± 0.48	674
Children of these parents	108.3 ± 0.36	1306

The retarded aunts or uncles of the children in the first group are not personally responsible for the lower intelligence of the parents, spouses and children that is so striking. However, they are part of a genetic-socioeconomic cosmos that pervades not only the first and second degree blood relatives but also includes the unrelated spouses who married into the families. It is interesting that the IQ values for these spouses were obtained when they were children, many years before they married the parent with one or more retarded siblings. It is not possible for us to make an evaluation of what portion of this cosmos is genetic and what portion is socioeconomic. Most people would assume that it would be easier to remedy the socioeconomic deficiencies than the genetic ones, but there is no proof that this is the case. It is possible that natural selection as it works today may be more effective in raising the average IQ of the population than our present improvements in medication, education and

Table 40. *Empiric Risk Figures for Normal Persons Who Have Not Had Any Children*

Type of Union	Chance that the First Child will be Retarded (as a Percentage)	
1. a. Normal (with retarded sibling) × retardate	23.8	
b. Normal (with retarded sibling) × normal		
(1) First parent had only one retarded sibling	1.8	combined average = 2.5
(2) First parent had two or more retarded siblings	3.6	
2. Normal (with all siblings normal) × normal	0.53	

social well-being. This is an exciting and challenging question but the factors involved are so complex that no one should expect to obtain very definite answers for some years to come.

The counseling data for normal persons contemplating reproduction who have so far produced only normal children have now been presented and are summarized in Table 40. It is clear that the risks in marrying a retarded person are grave because there is a large chance of having one or more retarded children. On the other hand, if normal persons marry normal persons, and all have only normal brothers and sisters, the chance that the first child will be retarded is 0.53 per cent, a low risk in the biologically hazardous world we inhabit.

Reed (1961) has presented the details of the methods for calculating empiric risk figures. These vary depending upon the type of marriage involved and whether the couple has already had a retarded child or not. We have considered the figures obtained for various types of unions before the advent of any children, and now will deal with the situation in which the couple has already produced at least one retarded child and wishes to learn what the likelihood of a repetition of the retardation may be at each subsequent pregnancy. It has been stated that if the parents are consanguineous or the affected child has a recognized clinical type of retardation, the counseling can be fairly precise as far as risk is concerned. If the child has some undifferentiated retardation, we are forced to fall back upon empiric risk figures which provide a useful rough estimate of the magnitude of the risk.

There are several methods for determining empiric risk figures. If all the children of parents who have produced one or more retarded children are included, the risk figures will be too low. This is because some families who have produced several normal children before the retarded child will stop reproducing at this point. These families will contribute only normal children to the sample because their retarded child will be excluded from the risk calculation in all methods. Another method is to include all children born subsequent to the first retarded child. This will give a risk figure which is statistically too high, but it is the worst situation which the family could expect to face, and they wish to

Table 41. *Empiric Risk Figures for Normal or Retarded Persons Who Have Had at Least One Retarded Child*

Type of Union	Per Cent Retarded after the First Retarded Child
1. Retardate × retardate	32 out of 76 (42.1%)
2. Retardate × normal or unknown	63 out of 317 (19.9%)
3. Normal × normal	
a. One normal parent had one or more retarded siblings	18 out of 139 (12.9%)
b. All siblings of one normal parent known to be normal	6 out of 104 (5.7%)

know the worst! It is surprising to them that the risk is not nearly as high as they had expected. There are also other methods which give values between those of the two methods mentioned. We will use the second method now, namely, the percentage of retarded children born subsequent to the first retarded child in the family.

The counseling data for couples who have had at least one retarded child are given in Table 41. It should be remembered that our original 289 probands, their grandparents, parents and siblings have been excluded from these figures in order to reduce the bias of selection, and that no consanguineous unions are included. Despite these exclusions we still find very high risk figures. The risk of 42.1 per cent of having another retarded child, if both parents are retarded and have had a retarded child, is too high to be taken when we consider the best interests of the children, the parents and society. The retarded parents may not appreciate their dangerous situation. It is here that the welfare department must take the initiative and make certain that no further children will result. This will usually involve institutionalization or sterilization, whichever is more appropriate in the individual situation.

Counseling in human genetics involves more than a citation of the appropriate risk figure. The counselor must listen willingly to the recitation of the problems encountered by the parents of the retarded child. This not only contributes to the relief of the parents but also the counselor sometimes obtains unexpected information in this way. The counselor also should help by referring the parents to persons and agencies where proper assistance of many different kinds may be obtained. If the counselor discovers that he has a reputation in the community as being sympathetic, he will know that he has succeeded in his job.

ASSORTATIVE AND NONASSORTATIVE MATING BEHAVIOR

Correlation of IQ Values in Spouses

Our population of nearly 83,000 persons included 1866 unions for which the IQ scores of both spouses were known. We think that IQ scores for spouses can be compared reliably because these persons have been tested at similar ages with standard group tests. Individuals with low scores or with school difficulties and personality problems were usually tested again with individual tests. The IQ score is the most uniform single measure of the mental capacities of individuals, and therefore should serve as one kind of test of assortative unions. Years of schooling is a similar measure, but this item is of less value (especially since the law now requires school attendance through eight grades or until age 16 years), and also is much more dependent upon the social and economic status of the family. In general, successful completion of eight years of schooling requires an IQ score above 69, but in our sample of 3071 married adults (1496 males and 1575 females) for whom we had both IQ scores and years of schooling, there were 12 male retardates and eight female retardates with eight or more years of schooling. Eleven of these completed the eighth grade, seven had some high school work and two of the female retardates actually graduated from high school. These individuals are the recent students in the compulsory school system who have received "social promotions." The older individuals at this intelligence level in our population would have left elementary school after repeating several grades and failing to pass the eighth grade examinations for high school entrance. So for our older generations, successful school achievement is generally reliable as a measure for identifying normal intelligence and was so used in our classifications, while the IQ scores were used for the younger persons in the study (those born from about 1912 to 1955) for determining both retardation and normal intelligence.

The IQ scores of the persons involved in the 1866 unions are arranged in Table 42 in order of degree of difference between IQ scores of spouses. The IQ scores ranged from those in an incestuous union of a brother (IQ 10) with a sister (IQ 41) to three unions in which both spouses had IQ scores in the 150 to 159 range. Differences between IQ scores of spouses ranged from 0 to 71 points. The correlation of IQ scores for spouses when calculated from data for one point intervals was + 0.326. When the same data were recalculated for ten point intervals the correlation rose to + 0.464. Since any one person's score can vary by 5 points on successive intelligence tests, the scores of two persons may

Table 42. *The Distribution of IQ Differences between Spouses in 1866 Marriages*

IQ Difference in Points between Spouses	Number of Marriages
0- 5	498
6-10	384
11-15	348
16-20	247
21-25	145
26-30	110
31-35	50
36-40	46
41-45	15
46-50	8
51-55	6
56-60	3
61-65	3
66-70	2
71-75	1
Total	1866

vary as much as 10 points, without a real difference between them. When IQ differences are grouped by tens these probably random variations can be reduced and the correlation of + 0.464 then obtained seems to us to be a fairly accurate figure.

It will be seen from Table 42 that there is a break where IQ differences between spouses become 31 points or more; beyond this point there are 134 unions, or about 7 per cent of the sample. In 21 of the 134 unions (16 per cent) one spouse was retarded. A second demarcation point for highly nonassortative unions was chosen in which IQ scores for mates differed by 51 points or more. There were 15 unions in this class, including eight (53 per cent) in which one spouse was retarded.

This arbitrary cut-off at 31 IQ points difference between spouses was selected as indicating a nonassortative type of union. There were 1732 unions appearing before this point on the scale of differences and 134 appearing after it. Two unions in the latter group were omitted from the calculations because one was that of a proband and the other was an aberrant incestuous union of a brother (IQ 10) and a sister (IQ 41). The remaining 132 unions are considered below.

It surprised us to discover that 90 of the "high IQ" spouses were women; only 42, or fewer than half, were men. In other words, the women were the spouses who "married down" most of the time. This pronounced sex difference ($\chi^2 = 17.4$ p = < 0.001) prompted a detailed analysis of the 132 nonassortative matings to see if any difference could be detected between the 90 women who "married down" and the 42 women who "married up."

The mean IQ for the 90 women who married down was 122.2, that for their spouses was 81.3. The mean IQ of the 42 girls who married up was 81.2, that for their spouses was 122.6. There was no significant difference between the two groups of women other than in average IQ score. Their educational status was the same, 11.8 years of schooling for those marrying down versus 11.4 years of schooling for those marrying up. Did early pregnancy force the high IQ girls into early and unsuitable marriages? No, the mean age at birth of first child for the high females was 22.3 years, for the low females, 22.0 years. Did the high female spouses marry men like their fathers? Apparently not any more than the low IQ girls did. The occupations of most of the males in this group ranged around the semiskilled and skilled categories so that meaningful comparisons could not be made.

There were only six college graduates in this group of 264 spouses, five males (all of whom had low IQ spouses) and one female. This one woman who graduated from college had an IQ of 121, while of the 35 other married women with IQ's of 121 or higher (including one with IQ 153), one completed the ninth grade (IQ 130), one the tenth, two the eleventh, 17 graduated from high school, eight continued some work beyond high school and the educational careers of six are unknown. Similarly the male spouse with the highest IQ (151) only graduated from high school.

When we look at the 15 highly nonassortative unions (IQ difference of 51 points or more between spouses), we again find a 2 to 1 ratio of females to males; ten females were the high IQ spouses to only five males as high IQ spouses. Now some reasons for these highly nonassortative unions begin to become apparent. The most exceptional of these unions was the one with an IQ difference of 71 points between a gifted girl (IQ 139) and a retarded man (IQ 68). After their marriage the wife was hospitalized for mental illness while the husband was institutionalized for retardation. Perhaps it could be argued that this childless marriage was really assortative, since both partners had mental disabilities. The second highest discrepancy was 70 points, a girl with an IQ of 150 who was a high school graduate and who married a man with an IQ of 80 and a ninth grade education. This girl was fifth in a sibship of ten. The next highest IQ discrepancy also involved a gifted girl (IQ 135) who married a retarded welder with a fourth grade education. She, too, was the product of a large family. She was the youngest of 12. Marriage number four, IQ difference 64 points, was like number one, the high spouse (male IQ 128) psychotic, the low spouse, retarded, delinquent, institutionalized and sterilized. Two marriages (IQ differences 62 and 51, respectively) involved one sibship, the high spouse in one was the brother of the low spouse (female) in the other.

The remaining nine marriages with a range of IQ difference between spouses of 51 to 61 points included five for which no explanation could be found from the information we have. In the last four marriages there were two in which the high spouses were girls from large sibships, one from an eight child family who married a deaf retardate, and one (IQ 146) who was the youngest of six; one case was an illegitimate girl with IQ 147; and finally one male with IQ 144 was a truck driver who had only high school training. Of these 15 unions in which there was a difference of 51 IQ points or more, three were childless, one was unknown as to reproduction and of the 11 fertile ones, in only two was the mother under 20 when her first child was born; in both these instances the mother was 19.

Apparently the great leveler in many of the 132 nonassortative unions (for the nonpsychotics) was the poor education of the high IQ spouses. It is probable that if these persons had had training commensurate with their IQ scores they might have obtained spouses more nearly like themselves in mental status. Early pregnancy did not seem to be an important factor. In the 119 fertile marriages, only 19 mothers were in their teens and nine of these were 19 years old when their first child was born. Six were 18, two were 17 and two were 15. In the latter two cases, one female spouse had IQ 104, male 72, in the other the female had IQ 115, the male IQ 81. One of these two very early marriages ended in desertion and divorce. On the whole, persons marry individuals like themselves in mental status. When the partners are very unlike in mental capacity there is some contributing factor, such as mental instability, inadequate education, family pressures (as in large sibships) and probably many other factors which have eluded us.

It is clear that poor socioeconomic status prevented the appropriate education and marriages of a number of individuals of unusually high intelligence. Presumably these persons were much less productive than they would have been if they had had better educations. Societies for the gifted are trying to identify and develop the abilities of these neglected brilliant children but have accomplished relatively little so far. It is hoped that the general public will come to realize the tremendous loss we are suffering because of the failure to utilize the exceptional abilities of so many of the high IQ children in the population.

It occurred to us that there might be twice as many women with high IQ's as men, which would explain why so many girls "married down" in terms of intelligence ratings. We found that there were more boys at the lower IQ ranges and more girls at the higher IQ ranges. The mean IQ for the 1866 males was 100.7 $\pm$ 0.36 and for the 1866 females it was 103.5 $\pm$ 0.33. The difference between the means is 2.8 $\pm$ 0.48. The difference is statistically highly significant. It will be recalled that there are also many more retarded males than females and that many more retarded males fail to marry than retarded females. If these retarded persons who fail to marry were included, the difference in intelligence would be even more in favor of the females. Presumably much of this difference is environmental in that girls apply themselves more diligently to school work; but it is also probable that some of the difference results from the girl's presumed advantage in having two X chromosomes instead of only one as is true of boys. We don't know how this advantage results, but it is clear that femininity is not only conducive to longer life, but also to higher intelligence as it is measured by the IQ tests.

Table 43 provides the IQ data for our 1866 unions where the IQ values for both partners were known. While the consistent superiority of women over men is obvious, there is no appreciable excess of *gifted* girls over boys that would account for the "marrying down." We cannot think of any explanation for this statistically significant marrying down process that is presumably of sociological origin. It should be pointed out that the "marrying down" is not restricted to high IQ girls, but only to girls for whom there are

Table 43. *The IQ Ranges for the 1866 Unions in which the IQ Values for Both Partners Were Known*

	IQ Ranges												
	41-60	61-70	71-80	81-90	91-100	101-110	111-120	121-130	131-140	141-150	151-160	Total	Average
Men	17	57	108	230	442	548	321	114	21	7	1	1866	100.7 ± 0.36
Women	16	24	66	168	453	573	410	129	18	7	2	1866	103.5 ± 0.33

large IQ differences between themselves and their spouses. Does it mean that women are more desirous of marrying than are men and that they are willing to reach lower down on the IQ scale, if necessary, to secure a mate? We do not know the answer to this question of female attitudes.

This area is of sufficient interest to warrant more exploration. Let us look at the marriages of all males and females in our study with IQ values of 131 and above. This is different from our previous consideration of the unions in which the marriages were most nonassortative, and the IQ differences between the spouses were at least 31 points. We are now considering the top IQ persons in our population as individuals and looking at the IQ's of their spouses and children. There were 29 men and 30 women with IQ's of 131 and above and for whom we had an IQ value for the spouse. People with IQ's of 131 and above were omitted if there was no IQ for the spouse.

The range of IQ values for the wives of the high IQ men was from 78 to 151 with an average of 107.8. The 29 high IQ men themselves had an average IQ of 137.4. The range of IQ values for the husbands of the high IQ women was from 67 to 134 with an average of 103.7. The high IQ women themselves had an average IQ of 137.8. We see that both men and women at the top end of the IQ curve marry down by an average of about 30 IQ points while the average IQ of the husbands of the gifted wives was only 4.1 IQ points below that of the wives of the gifted men. Thus the gifted women marry a little further down the IQ scale than do gifted men but the difference is not great at this extreme end of the intelligence curve, and it is because the mean IQ of available men was lower.

The average IQ of the couples when the male had the IQ of 131 or above was 122.7 and that of the 43 children for whom we had IQ's was 117.7. When the female had the IQ of 131 or above the average for the couple was 119.4 and for their 45 children for whom we had IQ's, the average IQ was 116.0. We find that Galton's regression toward the mean was only 5 IQ points for the first type of union and 3.4 points for the other. Much more interesting is the fact that the average IQ of the children from the gifted mothers was 116.0 and for the children from the gifted fathers it was 117.7. The two groups of children from the reciprocal unions should be genetically the same and they have about the same IQ values as we have just seen. We might expect that there would be a cultural difference in favor of the children from the high IQ mothers (average 137.8) and that the children from the lower IQ mothers (average 107.8) would have the lower average IQ; but this was *not* the case. The children from gifted parents do not become more or less intelligent in accord with the IQ of the mother but averaged between the high and low parents as would be expected for a polygenic character with only random effects due to environmental differences. These environmental effects would be similar to those observed when an individual is retested with the same IQ test.

There were no retardates among either group of children.

The relationship of IQ, years of schooling and sex is shown in Table 44. In our population of 1866 unions there were 1496 males and 1575 females for whom we had both IQ scores and records of the number of years of school completed. The average IQ of the women was higher at all educational levels. The social dominance of the male led him to obtain more advanced education than the female obtained, but it also resulted in greater numbers of "drop-outs" of males at the lower educational levels. Thus 109 males went no further than eighth grade compared with only 67 females who stopped school at that point.

It is of interest to look at the educational achievements of the persons with IQ's above 125. There were 44 men and 58 women in this group. (This difference is not significant

Table 44. *The Relationship between the Amount of Schooling and the Intelligence of our 1496 Males and 1575 Females*

	Males			Females		
		IQ			IQ	
Amount of Schooling	No.	Range	Mean	No.	Range	Mean
College graduate or more	136	83-157	114.7	40	88-139	117.7
Some college	110	75-148	109.2	159	86-151	111.1
High school graduate	844	70-150	102.4	1032	62-153	104.9
Some high school	297	63-128	95.4	287	59-130	96.9
Completed eighth grade	84	59-135	88.5	42	71-119	92.2
Less than eight years	25	60-110	77.4	15	71-100	80.4
Totals	1496	59-157	101.4	1575	59-151	103.9

by a chi-square test.) Sixteen of the 44 men completed college (36 per cent) and 14 of the 58 women completed college (24 per cent). There were seven individuals with IQ's above 146. Only one of these completed college; he had an IQ of 157. Of the other six, three had some college and three completed only high school, including one girl with an IQ of 151. On the other hand, two retardates graduated from high school. The range of IQ for each educational level is very great. Only among the college group was there no retardate, while an IQ of 135 was found in an eighth grade graduate who did not go on to high school. Once again, we see an appalling educational underachievement of many individuals with high IQ's, which is probably due to their lack of motivation because of unsatisfactory socio-environmental conditions.

Sibling and Twin Differences

The wide differences in IQ values between some spouses in nonassortative unions can also be found among the children of some couples. The parents may have both a retarded child and a genius among their children. We have also noted that the males varied more in their IQ values and education than did the females, there being a large excess of retarded males.

We were interested in finding out what the variability in IQ points would be for siblings and twins according to their sex. We expected that the point difference between brothers would be greater than between sisters, and it was. This difference was not apparent for the twin pairs but there were too few of these to give reliable answers. There were, however, 20,840 pairings of siblings with IQ values available, so these results have considerable stability. It is obvious that the averages for twin and sibling pairs will be rather unsatisfactory statistics because the presence of retarded and bright children in the same family will give a few very large discontinuous differences and the curve of the differences between siblings will not be a normal one. Therefore, we have included the values of the medians for our comparisons as well as the averages. The medians are the values which separate the two halves of the distribution of differences; the median is the middle difference with half of them larger than it is, and half smaller.

Table 45 presents the results. There

Table 45. *Mean and Median Differences in IQ Values for Pairs of Full Siblings and for Twins According to Sex*

	Sibling Pairs (Excluding Twins)			Twin Pairs		
	No. of	IQ Differences		No. of	IQ Differences	
Sex of Pairs	Pairs	Mean	Median	Pairs	Mean	Median
Girl – Girl	5040	11.59 ± 0.14	8.72	62	9.53 ± 1.59	5.00
Girl – Boy	10,409	12.67 ± 0.11	9.45	60	10.70 ± 1.26	8.00
Boy – Boy	5391	12.76 ± 0.15	9.64	57	9.28 ± 1.45	5.17
Totals	20,840			179		

should be about the same number of pairs of siblings of opposite sex (10,409) as there are of girl-girl and boy-boy pairs added together (10,431). We see that this agreement is excellent. There were 119 pairs of like-sex twins to 60 pairs of unlike-sex twins. We would expect, roughly, two pairs of like-sex twins to every pair of unlike-sex twins. This exact agreement was a pleasant surprise, as almost all twin researchers suffer the agony of nonrandom samples. We must point out that with our twins no attempt was made to determine the zygosity of any of the pairs. About half of our like-sex twins should be dizygotic and all the unlike-sex pairs must be dizygotic. We can still obtain some information from our data in spite of this limitation.

The variation in intelligence of the twin pairs of all kinds is decidedly less than the variation between full siblings of all kinds. The median difference between the girl-girl pairs of twins of 5.00 IQ points is about the same as is found when a single person is retested. The like-sex twins gave embarrassingly small differences in view of the fact that many of them must be no more alike genetically than the like-sex siblings.

We can make a meaningful comparison of the opposite-sex twins and opposite-sex siblings because the opposite-sex twins would have no greater genetic similarity than our opposite-sex siblings. It is clear that it doesn't make much difference within the family whether the opposite-sex children are born at the same time (twins) or spread over a reproductive generation (siblings). The difference between the two medians of 8.00 and 9.45 was only 1.45 IQ points. Thus the environmental factors related to variations in intelligence are not usually concentrated at particular points in time, as would be expected, say, for virus attacks, but exert their influence throughout the reproductive years of the parents and on each successive child without much preference.

The Consanguineous Unions in the Population

Data on the intelligence and infant death rate of the children of consanguineous unions in the population were classified according to the degree of relationship of the spouses. All unions of probands, their parents or grandparents were excluded from this group, in order to eliminate selection bias. There were 83 consanguineous unions found. Six of these were childless, so only the remaining 77 are included in Table 46. These persons had 400 children with a large family size of 5.2 children ever born.

No doubt there were more unions of relatives than we could verify in the follow-up, because the only ones we could attempt to confirm were those between spouses who had the same last names or two names both frequently occurring in the kindred. When a relationship was suspected, these persons were sent a blank asking for the names of the parents of the spouse marrying in. These names could be checked against those of known relatives. Also, these persons were asked if they

Table 46. *Mental Status of the Children Born to the Consanguineous Unions*

Degree of Consanguinity	No. of Unions	Children Ret.	Nor.	Unk.	Died before Age 2 Years	Total Children	Percentage of Retarded Survivors
First degree							
father-daughter	4	2	2	0	1	5	
brother-sister	1	1	0	0	0	1	
Total	5	3	2	0	1	6	60.0
Second degree							
uncle-niece	2	4	7	0	3	14	
half brother-half sister	1	0	0	1	0	1	
Total	3	4	7	1	3	15	33.3
Third degree							
first cousin-first cousin	44	22	111	72	31	236	10.7
More distant than third degree	25	6	87	27	23	143	5.0
Grand total	77	35	207	100	58	400	10.2

had been related to their spouses "before they were married," and some candid replies were received.

There were five unions between relatives of the first degree of relationship, four father-daughter and one brother-sister. The brother-sister union involved two retarded siblings who produced a retarded child. In the four father-daughter unions, one involved two retardates, two involved one retardate and in the fourth, both spouses were borderline with IQ scores of 74 and 75, respectively. Six children were produced, one of whom died in infancy and three of whom were retarded.

There were three unions of relatives of the second degree, two uncle-niece and one of half siblings. One uncle had normal intelligence, niece IQ 70, the other uncle-niece union was that of spouses of unknown intelligence. Neither of the half sibling spouses was retarded. Fifteen children were born, of whom one fifth died in infancy and one third of the survivors were retarded.

The largest number of consanguineous unions were those between relatives of the third degree, first cousins. There were 44 unions of first cousins with 236 children born. Among these children 13.1 per cent failed to survive to age 2 years and 10.7 per cent of the survivors were retarded.

There were 25 unions of relatives of more than the third degree of relationship. These included eight unions of second cousins, ten unions of first cousins once removed, five unions of half first cousins, (the children of half siblings), one union of half first cousins once removed, and one of an unknown degree of relationship. These individuals had 85 children with a 16.1 per cent infant death rate and a 5 per cent rate of retardation.

Among all the 400 children born to consanguineous unions of varying degree of relationship, there was a 14.5 per cent loss of life before age 2 years and 10.2 per cent retardation among the survivors. The degree of consanguinity does not seem to affect the infant death rate in the way in which it affects the proportion of retarded children born. The proportion of retarded children decreases dramatically from 60.0 per cent for relatives of the first degree to 5.0 per cent for relatives beyond the third degree of relationship. The infant death rate remained fairly constant throughout. There seemed to be a deficiency of high IQ children among the 85 tested children as there were 32 with IQ scores below 90 but only 11 with IQ scores above 110. The mean IQ was 92.2 for the 85 tested children.

It should be mentioned again that the data in Table 45 were unselected in that they were chanced upon in the collection of all descendants of the grandparents of our 289 probands. Any consanguineous unions of the grandparents themselves, the parents or the probands were excluded.

Fathers and daughters do not ordinarily produce children, or even have sexual intercourse, if both are of normal intelligence. However, if one or both is retarded, the chances of reproduction will be increased. Thus, mental retardation increases the likelihood of the taboo unions of first and second degree relatives. Mental retardation of itself produces consanguineous unions. Furthermore, when one or both members of the first degree union are mentally retarded, we would expect a very high proportion of the children to be retarded because the daughter or sister will possess half of the same genes for mental retardation as the father or brother. Unions of nonrelatives will often bring together different genes for retardation and, if these genes are recessives, the offspring can be normal carriers of the different retardation genes without harm to themselves. Hence, we can expect that the unions of nonrelated retardates would usually produce at least a majority of normal offspring, but when the unions are of genetically related retardates we can be certain of high risks of retardation in the offspring, such as those shown in Table 46.

It is generally known that a disproportionately large number of mentally retarded children are born in the poorest socioeconomic conditions. It is then assumed by some that the poor socioeconomic conditions *cause* the retardation rather than merely being correlated with it. It is clear in our cases that it is the mental retardation of father or daughter that causes the consanguinity, poor socioeconomic conditions and retarded offspring. If a retarded child has a retarded parent it could hardly escape being born in poor socioeconomic conditions. The fact of a retarded father predicates an uncertain and inadequate income and the presence of a retarded mother indicates a lack of ordinary prudence in managing the family affairs. There will be exceptions but the generalization that a child with a retarded parent will be born into poor socioeconomic conditions seems almost axiomatic. Nonetheless, the majority of the children born to retarded parents are normal, even when both parents are retarded. A few children with one retarded parent were found to be in the superior and gifted IQ ranges. They were raised in a most unsatisfactory socio-economic environment, yet still were highly intelligent.

IQ AND FAMILY SIZE: A PARADOX RESOLVED

Every experienced investigator realizes that it is impossible to get complete information about everyone included in his project. Therefore subsamples have to be taken which include all the desired items, and with each successive restriction the sample size becomes smaller. It is interesting that in our large study including 82,217 persons there were only 1016 families in which the IQ's of both the father and the mother and at least one child were obtained. This was a total of 2032 parents and 2039 children for whom at least one IQ value was available. This group of 4071 persons may not seem like a very large proportion of the total population; however, a glance at the pedigree charts will show why the sample is so small. It is because many people never had any offspring. The last and largest generation was composed, in part, of children who were too young to have been tested, and there were large numbers of persons who were not tested. The fact that so many families qualified for this section of the study is the result of the intensive work of many persons, and of Dr. James V. Higgins in particular. He devoted his doctoral thesis to the study of the IQ values of parents and their children. A description of this work has been published by Higgins, Reed and Reed (1962).

There have been many fears and numerous predictions that our national intelligence level is declining because the larger the family size, the lower the average intelligence of the children in it. Investigations of the situation usually give negative correlations between intelligence and family size of the order of $r = -0.20$ to $r = -0.30$. These negative correlations are large and statistically highly significant. It has been predicted that the average IQ of the population should drop from two to four points per generation because of this negative relationship between the size of the family and the intelligence of the children therein. (Reviewed by Anastasi, 1959, see References.)

The predicted decrease in IQ has not materialized in tests of similar groups of children separated by a time span of ten to 20 years. (Reviewed by Cattell, 1951, see References.) It became clear that there was a striking inconsistency between the predictions and the observations, and it is astonishing that probably the most important reason for this paradox was not established until 1962 by Higgins, Reed and Reed. We realized that, while the relatively large and highly significant negative correlations between intelligence and family size were real, they omitted all those persons in each generation who did not reproduce at all. If the average intelligence of those who failed to reproduce in each generation was significantly different from that of the group who did reproduce, the prediction obtained from the negative correlation between family size and IQ would be invalidated to the extent of the difference in intelligence between the childless and the fertile groups of the parental generation.

It was possible to test this point because the total population of 82,217 persons was so great that our subsample of 1016 families, in which both parents and at least one child had a known IQ value, was still of respectable size. Furthermore, the subsample seemed to be identical with the expectations for an intelligence curve of a normal population in Minnesota. It was a simple matter to include the IQ values for the childless brothers and sisters of the 2032 parents.

It should be reiterated that we are well aware that the accuracy and the value of a single IQ determination for a specific person may be limited. However, in a large collection of IQ values, the errors in the individual tests should to a large extent cancel out. The striking differences to be presented are certainly not due to testing errors. While most of the persons involved in this section of the work are either unrelated to our original probands, except by marriage, or are distant relatives, a very few are close relatives of the probands. It seems appropriate to include these few close relatives because even the institutionalized probands were a part of the population of the state of Minnesota. The latter persons were too trivial a part of the total to have any appreciable effect upon the conclusions obtained. We have an essentially randomly selected "normal" population with which to deal.

The average IQ of the 1016 mothers was 103.22 ± 0.45 and for the fathers it was 100.72 ± 0.48. The mean IQ of the parents was statistically significantly lower than the mean IQ of the children, females 107.67 and males 104.96. The mother's average IQ was 2.5 points higher than the IQ of the fathers, and the female offspring averaged 2.7 points higher than the male offspring. The specific causes for the differences in IQ between the sexes are not known but they result from the differences between males and females which trace back to the fertilization of the egg with an X-bearing sperm to produce a girl, and with a Y-bearing sperm to produce a boy. A more immediate reason for the difference in IQ between the girls and the boys is probably that our culture expects girls to be more diligent in school work and amenable to instruction. However, these sex differences in personality and character are presumably related to the biochemical differences between the sexes which in turn rest upon the genetic differences between the X and the Y chromosomes. Two X chromosomes seem to be advantageous both for longevity and learning, compared with the XY alternative.

The difference between the IQ's of the parents and the children would be reduced if age at testing were considered. The mean age of the parents at testing was 14.24 years, while the mean age of the children was 8.65 years. Higgins fitted a least squares line to the mean IQ's of the children separated according to the age at time of testing. The least squares line dropped from an IQ of 110 at the age of 5 to 97.5 at the age of 18. If the ages of the children were equated via the least squares line to the mean age of the parents at testing, the average IQ of the children would be reduced and would be close to the average of the father and the mother.

Table 47. *Size of Family Compared with Mean IQ of Children* (2039 Children)

Family Size	Mean IQ of Children	Number
1	106.37 ± 1.39	141
2	109.56 ± 0.53	583
3	106.75 ± 0.58	606
4	108.95 ± 0.73	320
5	105.72 ± 1.15	191
6	99.16 ± 2.17	82
7	93.00 ± 3.34	39
8	83.80 ± 4.13	25
9	89.89 ± 2.94	37
10	62.00 ± 7.55	15

It will be well, before continuing with the resolution of the IQ and family size paradox, to point out that we obtained a large negative correlation coefficient (—0.30 ± 0.02) for the relationship of IQ and size of family similar to that which other investigators have found. Table 47 presents the data for the 2039 children of our sample arranged by size of the sibship to which they belonged. The mean IQ's of the children are similar for the family sizes of one to five and then drop significantly from sizes six to ten. One might claim that the reason the children from the large families did so poorly on the tests was that they were the victims of poverty and of social and emotional deprivation. This could be the case, though we have no proof of it.

Table 48. *Size of Family Compared with Mean IQ of Parents*

Size of Family	Number of Families	Mean IQ of Parents	
		Mother	Father
One-child	141	102.29 ± 1.34	99.06 ± 1.40
Two-child	370	104.50 ± 0.69	101.43 ± 0.71
Three-child	287	102.90 ± 0.82	101.17 ± 0.90
Four-child	122	104.93 ± 1.10	102.22 ± 1.28
Five-child	57	103.44 ± 2.07	103.53 ± 2.30
Six-child	21	96.57 ± 4.25	94.90 ± 4.79
Seven-child	7	90.86 ± 9.85	86.57 ± 9.77
Eight-child	4	78.00 ± 15.83	79.25 ± 13.84
Nine-child	5	90.00 ± 11.27	81.00 ± 9.12
Ten-child	2	65.50 ± 17.66	50.50 ± 3.46

Table 49. *IQ Range of Parents Compared with Mean IQ of Parents and Children*

Midparent IQ Range	Mean IQ of Parents	Mean IQ of Children
70 and below	62.24 ± 1.21	75.44 ± 2.29
71 - 85	79.52 ± 1.09	95.64 ± 1.35
86 - 100	94.52 ± 0.40	104.50 ± 0.50
101 - 115	107.03 ± 0.29	109.90 ± 0.40
116 - 130	119.65 ± 0.71	114.41 ± 1.09
131 and above	136.50 ± 3.58	128.33 ± 3.48

It is clear that the parents had the same general kinds of heredity and environment as their children (Table 48). Thus the parents who produced the largest families were the ones who tested lowest when they were school children. Thus the school children with the lower IQ values who reproduced presented their descendants with obviously poor environments and presumably with poor genes for intelligence as well.

The above observation that the negative correlation between the average intelligence of the family of children and its size extends to the IQ's of the parents is another unique feature of our study—with obvious prophylactic indications. It should come as no surprise, however, as we have been aware of the correlation of about + 0.5 between the intelligence of each parent and his child since the time of Sir Francis Galton. The fact that the average IQ values for the parents of the 18 families of seven or more children were rather spectacularly low is somewhat sweetened by the realization that there were only 18 such families in the total of 1016.

It is appropriate to point out that Galton's law of filial regression toward the mean is clearly operating in our population of 4071 parents and children. This means that children of parents who are at the extreme ends of the curve of intelligence will find themselves closer to the mean than their extreme parents. This is shown beautifully in Table 49. The parents whose average IQ was 62.24 ± 1.21 produced children whose IQ averaged 75.44 ± 2.29, a 13 IQ point regression toward the mean. The parents at the other end of the curve had an average IQ of 136.50 ± 3.58 while their children only averaged 128.33 ± 3.48. Thus, Galton's law provides a paradox of a sort, in that the children born in the worst environments and to parents with the poorest heredity, average better than their parents. Conversely, the children born into the best environments and to parents with the best heredity average below their parents. Fortunately, the resolution of this paradox has been understood for many years.

We can turn now to our central problem, which has sometimes been called "Cattell's Paradox" (Cattell, 1951). If we take each of the 2032 parents of our sample and find the average number of children each parent produced, we obtain the data in Table 50, when the parents are grouped according to their IQ range. We see that the parents with IQ's under 70 had 3.81 ± 0.32 children, the highest average for any intelligence grouping. The

Table 50. *Reproductive Rate of Individual Parents*
(IQ Available for Both Husband and Wife)

IQ of Parent	Number of parents	Average Number of Children
70 and below	73	3.81 ± 0.32
71 - 85	180	2.98 ± 0.14
86 - 100	597	2.65 ± 0.05
101 - 115	860	2.68 ± 0.04
116 - 130	287	2.70 ± 0.08
131 and up	35	2.94 ± 0.25
Totals	2032	2.75

Table 51. *Reproductive Rate of Married Siblings, Excluding Spouses* (Single Brothers and Sisters Not Included)

IQ of Married Siblings	Number of Married Siblings	Average Number of Children
55 and below	11	3.64 ± 1.19
56 - 70	64	2.84 ± 0.34
71 - 85	202	2.47 ± 0.13
86 - 100	572	2.20 ± 0.06
101 - 115	763	2.30 ± 0.05
116 - 130	263	2.50 ± 0.09
131 and above	25	2.96 ± 0.34
Totals	1900	2.35

reader will realize that 1016 of these parents were unrelated persons who married into the sibships we wish to study. If we remove the 1016 persons who married into our sibships but include the 884 married siblings for whom we have an IQ value (but without one for their spouse or at least one child), we have 1900 brothers and sisters who were married. The average number of children produced by the married persons in the parental generation still shows an excess of children for the lowest IQ group, as shown in Table 51.

The element still missing in our puzzle is the group of 66 unmarried and childless brothers and sisters of the parental generation. When these 66 childless persons are added to the group of 1900 siblings, the picture changes completely. Now the lowest IQ range produced the fewest children (1.38 ± 0.54 per person) and the highest IQ group produced the most children (2.96 ± 0.34) (Table 52). Thus by including the childless members of a generation as well as the fertile we find that our paradox has been resolved; the lowest IQ group produces the fewest children and the highest IQ group produces the most. When the single and the nonreproductive siblings of the parents are included the negative correlation disappears. The single persons were males of 40 years old or over and females of 35 or over.

Table 52. *Reproductive Rate of all Siblings* (66 Single Brothers and Sisters Added)

IQ of Sibling	Number of Siblings	Average Number of Children
55 and below	29	1.38 ± 0.54
56 - 70	74	2.46 ± 0.31
71 - 85	208	2.39 ± 0.13
86 - 100	583	2.16 ± 0.06
101 - 115	778	2.26 ± 0.05
116 - 130	269	2.45 ± 0.09
131 and above	25	2.96 ± 0.34
Totals	1966	2.27

The above finding must mean that the 66 unmarried siblings had a decidedly lower average IQ than the married siblings did. This is an entirely reasonable prediction and it can be seen from Table 53 that this was the case. Indeed, it is almost shocking to discover that

Table 53. *Number of Unmarried and Married Siblings in the Parental Generation and the Per Cent Who Married for Each IQ Group*

IQ of Sibling	Number of Unmarried	Number of Married	Per Cent Married
55 and below	18	11	37.93
56 - 70	10	64	86.48
71 - 85	6	202	97.12
86 - 100	11	572	98.11
101 - 115	15	763	98.07
116 - 130	6	263	97.77
131 and above	0	25	100.00
Totals	66	1900	96.64
Average IQ	80.46	100.40	

the unmarried siblings in this sample had an average IQ of only 80.46. The reason why the average is so low is, of course, that a large proportion of the single persons in this sample were severely retarded and thus decisively lowered the average IQ for the whole group of single persons.

The discovery of this very large difference between the intelligence of single persons compared with married persons deserves a little further study. There were IQ values available for many other single persons not eligible for inclusion in the Higgins part of the project. If we include them also, we obtain a total of 76 single males over 40 with an average IQ of 68.7 and 58 single females over 35 with an average IQ of 76.4. The average for the 134 single persons of both sexes was 72.01.

It should be pointed out that there may be an important bias here in that we probably have test values for a larger proportion of the retarded single persons than for the normal single persons. This follows because there is a need to test all persons who appear to be retarded which is not present for normal persons. However, it is clear that we have a rule or principle that single persons must *as a group* average lower on intelligence tests than married persons because the unmarried group must always include a significant fraction of severely retarded persons who are not marriageable. A few very low IQ's will thus lower the average drastically. In order to mitigate this circumstance somewhat, the median IQ value for the 134 persons was determined. The median person would be the 67th from the bottom of the IQ range and this person turned out to have an IQ of 74. The median for married persons would have to be over 100 in our project population.

We hope that the finding that the single persons of our country are less intelligent than the married will not be taken out of context and mutilated beyond recognition. The only significance of the finding which we emphasize is that the group of single persons must have a lower average intelligence than the married, because they include an appreciable fraction of persons with such low IQ's as to be unmarriageable. It is hardly necessary to state that there are many single persons of the very highest intelligence, and that our finding is not a reflection upon any person. The large proportion of the severely retarded among our group of 134 single persons beyond the likely age of reproduction is shown in Table 54.

Recently Bajema (1964) has confirmed our findings concerning the resolution of the family size-intelligence paradox. His population included only persons with sufficient intelligence to be enrolled in the sixth grade of the Kalamazoo, Michigan Public School System, which thus omits the mentally retarded in most cases. Nonetheless, only 13.4 per cent of his highest IQ group left no offspring while 30.0 per cent of his lowest IQ group left no offspring. Bajema's study of the direction and intensity of natural selection in relation to intelligence by means of the intrinsic rate of natural increase is recommended to all who are interested in work in this area.

Table 54. *The IQ Distribution of Persons Who Were Still Single and Who Had Not Reproduced by Age 40 for Men and Age 35 for Women*

IQ Range	Number of Persons	Percentage of the Total
25 and below	8	6.0
26 - 55	33	24.6
56 - 70	20	14.9
71 - 85	24	17.9
86 - 100	21	15.7
101 - 115	23	17.2
116 - 130	5	3.7
131 and above	0	0.0
Totals	134	100.0
Average IQ = 72.01		

SUMMARY

1. Our population was composed of 82,217 different individuals. Of these, 79,376 persons survived two years of life and included 2156 retardates, or 2.7 per cent mental retardation. This must be an underestimate of the percentage of retardation because there were many thousands of persons in this population for whom no IQ value or good subjective evaluation was available; these persons were classified as of unknown intelligence, but were always counted as normal in the analyses. Some of them must have been retarded.

2. A population of 1450 retardates that excluded probands, their parents and grandparents and the retarded not in the line of descent was studied. It was designated the "unselected" sample. Only 115 of the 1450 were institutionalized. We found that 43.4 per cent of the 1450 retardates never reproduced. There were 758 known spouses for our 1450 retardates, a total of 2208 persons who produced 2165 children, of whom 214 died before age 2 years and 280 of the survivors were retarded (14.3 per cent). This value of 0.9 surviving children per person is below replacement level, particularly in a pioneer state in which large families were the rule.

3. Fifty-four fertile unions of two retarded persons in our unselected sample produced 215 surviving children, of whom 85 (39.5 per cent) were retarded. The 482 fertile unions of a retarded person with a normal or unknown produced 1736 surviving children of whom 195 (11.5 per cent) were retarded.

4. There were 741 persons of all intelligence ranges for whom there was more than one test score available for different times in their lives. It was found that 4.1 per cent of these persons showed no change in IQ value over the years, 41.8 per cent showed an increase while 54.1 per cent showed a decrease in their IQ values. Thus the changes cancel each other and have no appreciable effect upon the reliability of our study.

5. It was found that 700 of the 1450 unselected retardates (48.3 per cent) had one or both parents retarded. The percentage of our 289 probands who had one or both parents retarded was 49.8, a surprisingly close agreement with the figure for the 1450 unselected retardates. If we eliminated all first and second degree relatives of the probands, in order to decrease such bias as they might introduce, we still find that 36.1 per cent of the retarded had one or both parents retarded. Thus mental retardation in one generation would have been reduced by 36.1 per cent if there had been no reproduction of the retardates in the previous generation.

6. One of the most practical applications of human genetics is that of genetic counseling. The parents of a retarded child can be expected to be seriously perturbed about the possibility of having another retarded child. Predictions for the primarily genetic category can be made with relative confidence, but most cases are not clear cut and force us to resort to empiric risk figures.

Some of the types of premarital risks are as follows:

a. The marriages of normal siblings of a retarded person to a retarded person resulted in 23.8 per cent of the offspring being retarded. This figure is based on only 16 unions and is perhaps a little high.

b. The marriages of normal siblings of a retarded person to a normal person resulted in 2.5 per cent of the offspring being retarded, and each of these persons had a 7.3 per cent chance of having at least one retarded offspring.

c. The marriages of normal persons with only normal siblings and married to normal persons resulted in a mere 0.53 per cent of the offspring being retarded. Such persons had a 1.3 per cent chance of having at least one retarded offspring.

Some of the risks facing parents who have already produced at least one retarded child are as follows:

a. The marriages of two retarded persons resulted in 42.1 per cent retarded children subsequent to the first retarded child.

b. The marriages of a retarded person with a normal (or unknown) resulted in 19.9 per cent retarded children subsequent to the first retarded child.

c. The marriages of a normal person with one or more retarded siblings to a normal person resulted in 12.9 per cent retarded children subsequent to the first retarded child.

d. The marriages of a normal person without retarded siblings to a normal person resulted in 5.7 per cent retarded children subsequent to the first retarded child.

7. One of the interesting findings of the

study was the high degree of assortative mating for intelligence between persons whose IQ values were obtained in school and before their marriages. The correlation coefficient was + 0.464 even though there is always considerable random variation in IQ values, as indicated by the test-retest fluctuations of any one person. In 93 per cent of the unions the spouses were within 31 points of each other in intelligence as measured when they were in school. The great prevalence of close assortative mating for intelligence means that there should be a greater accumulation of the homozygous genotypes for intelligence than if mating were at random. Selection against such homozygotes eliminates a larger proportion of the alleles than in a population at equilibrium. Consequently, a reasonably rapid change in the average intelligence of the population could occur if those at one end of the normal curve of intelligence were encouraged to increase their reproductive rate substantially.

8. The average IQ differences showed greater variability between pairs of siblings than between pairs of twins, as expected. Boys were more variable than girls. Opposite-sex siblings and opposite-sex twins were compared and showed very similar IQ differences, indicating that the factors determining IQ differences in each family affected children born at the same time (fraternal twins) just about the same as children born at any time during the reproductive years.

9. There were 400 children born to consanguineous unions of varying degrees of relationship and 14.5 per cent of them died before age 2 years while 10.2 per cent of the survivors were retarded. Some of the consanguineous unions never would have occurred if the participants had not been retarded in the first place.

10. Probably the major contribution of our study has been the resolution of what has often been called "Cattell's paradox." It has been well established that there is a negative correlation of about — 0.3 between the size of a family and the average IQ of the children in it. The main contributions to the size and strength of the correlation come from the many small families with children having above average intelligence and a few very large families with children averaging well below an IQ of 100. This correlation was confirmed in our study. A possible consequence of this negative correlation would be a gradual drop in intelligence of the population from generation to generation. The failure of such a decrease to be observed provides us with "Cattell's paradox." One of the main goals of our study was to examine this paradox and resolve it, if possible. Fortunately, the key to the situation was easy to find. In previous studies the childless members of each generation were never included, thus giving a false picture of the situation. When the childless members of each generation are included, as well as the fertile siblings, the averages change such that the lowest IQ group of persons produces the fewest children and the highest IQ group produces the most children.

We find that if there is a change in IQ from generation to generation it may well be a slight increase rather than the large decrease predicted only on the basis of the negative correlation between family size and intelligence.

CHAPTER FIVE

SOME IMPLICATIONS OF THE STUDY

The summaries at the ends of the chapters state briefly the results of our longitudinal study of the kinships of 289 mentally retarded persons. It is assumed that these institutionalized retardates had more problems than the retardates who remained in the community. It is also possible that they had more retarded relatives than the community retardates so our sample probably includes what we call an "institutional bias." However, our inclusion of all the known descendants of the grandparents of our 289 probands produced a population of 82,217 persons, so the 289 probands and their close relatives accounted for only a small percentage of our total population. Consequently, we had a large remaining sample that is probably representative of the whole United States west of the Mississippi and north of the Missouri rivers. Our conclusions may be applicable to this area only, but we think that in broad terms they are generally applicable and useful for most western countries.

It is not our intention to repeat the statistics of the chapter summaries again, except where necessary to support our comments as to what seem to be the important conclusions and implications of the whole study.

All family studies show the transmission of mental retardation from one generation to the next, and there is no question about the statistical validity of the transmission.

> *The most obvious implication of these studies is that the greatest predisposing factor for the appearance of mental retardation is the presence of retardation in one or more relatives of the person concerned.*

Perhaps we should mention that the parents do not transmit their retarded brains *intact* to their offspring but transmit their characteristics via their highly specific types of DNA into what may or may not be defective environments. We wish to remind the reader that we found an occasional child born to a retarded parent and brought up in an incredibly poor environment who had superior intelligence. Furthermore, we must never fail to marvel at the strange pseudoparadox known as Galton's law of filial regression toward the mean. Galton's law predicts that the children born to the parents with the lowest intelligence and brought up in the worst environments will average higher on intelligence tests than their severely retarded parents. The prediction also holds for the extremely gifted families at the other end of the normal curve of intelligence. In this case the children of parents with the highest intelligence and best environments average lower than their gifted parents, as may be seen in the classical study of the gifted and their offspring by Terman and Oden (1959). The children of the parents at the bottom end of the intelligence curve will average more than 10 IQ points *above* their parents and the children of parents of extremely high ability will average more than 10 IQ points *below* their gifted parents.

The explanation of the regression toward the mean of the children of parents who are at either end of the normal curve for some trait rests upon the improbability that such unusual situations as the parents experienced will be duplicated for all their offspring. Let us look at two oversimplified examples that should demonstrate the principles involved. If we assume that the mother is retarded because she is homozygous for one pair of genes, say *aa,* but normal for all other genes concerned with intelligence such as *BB,* and the father is normal for *AA* but retarded because he is homozygous for *bb,* all the children would have the genotype *AaBb* and would be normal, or at least nearer the average for the population, than their retarded parents, even if they were reared in the unsatisfactory environment provided by their retarded parents.

Our second fanciful example is a retarded mother who suffered brain injuries as a result of having been dropped down a stairwell a few days after birth, while the father was retarded as a result of an attack of meningitis. The children of this couple would not be likely to be dropped down stairwells or to have meningitis, so therefore they should regress toward the mean in intelligence even though raised under conditions of severe social deprivation.

These two examples are not as far from reality as one might think, though in most cases the situation will be more complicated. It should not be forgotten that it is the *average* intelligence of the children which improves, and some of the children will be found to have lower intelligence than their retarded parents. Furthermore, a significant percentage of the children will be retarded.

We wish to emphasize our fiat of the opening paragraph of the introduction, which stated that *in every case of mental retardation there must be some subnormal behavior of some of the cells of the brain, regardless of the cause of the retardation.* If we will keep in mind that the behavior of the person depends upon the reaction of his brain cells to stimuli, we can speculate about the genetic and environmental factors which condition the appropriate brain cells. There are many ways in which the brain cells can fail to function properly, with usually more than one cause of the failure acting simultaneously. In microcephaly there is a visible lack of brain cells which results in gross retardation. In the families of our study, microcephaly depended upon the presence of a recessive gene in the homozygous condition and the environmental variables were of little importance. Several hundred of the retarded members of our families were retarded because of genetic causes in which the environmental variables were of no importance in the appearance of the trait other than the broad sense that the embryo had to have a uterus in which to develop, and all other requirements for biological existence had to be met.

It is rather exciting to speculate that the primarily genetic traits, such as Down's syndrome, galactosemia and phenylketonuria, may soon be reduced appreciably in the population. The rationale for this opinion is that the types of retardation that have a simple genetic basis can be "cured" by relatively simple means. It is already possible to alleviate the effects of the recessive genes for galactosemia by removing lactose from the diet of the genetically unfortunate baby. The intelligence of the phenylketonuric can be improved significantly by reducing the amount of phenylalanine in the diet soon after birth. The goals of medical research are fairly obvious, and both financial and social support are available for this type of work. It is also probable that the carriers for the genes involved in the classical types of mental retardation can be detected and, hopefully, they would reduce their reproduction. Of course, if they fail to do this, and the "cured" phenylketonurics reproduce, the frequency of the undesirable genes will increase, an unfortunate result of the medical "cure."

A large reduction of the frequency of mental retardation which is caused by syphilis and bacterial invasions of the brain has already occurred and future studies should show even fewer cases of retardation due to obvious environmental variables than we found in our sample.

Let us now consider the mental retardation caused by social deprivation. It is assumed that lack of stimuli during the early years results in the failure of the brain cells to store information and to learn how to use whatever information was stored in the brain cells. Let us imagine a case of a 5 year old child not being able to locate his nose upon demand, but after a year at school the same child was doing as well as the other children. It was assumed that the child was unaware of the name of his nose because his parents had not played the usual children's games with him. Here would be a case of mental retardation at age 5 with normal intelligence at age 6. The "cure" here was simple and consisted merely of the provision of ordinary elementary education. There *are* isolates in this country who are deprived of their share of the usual cultural amenities. It is hard to believe that these inequalities will be perpetuated much longer. Adequate civil and educational rights should be available to them within the next few years. The battle against poverty should be won in the United States within our lifetimes, to the extent that sufficient cultural amenities would be available for every person so that none would be *retarded* because of lack of schooling.

Adequate schooling and community facilities will still fail to prevent retardation due to cultural deprivation in children whose parents are retarded or grossly mentally inadequate in some way. The only solution for these cases is the prevention of births in families in which the parents are clearly inadequate for child rearing. Social agencies will have to assume the initiative if such catastrophes are to be prevented. This is an unpopular type of endeavor because no one wishes to intervene in other people's lives, even though the necessity for the intervention is clear.

One point should be emphasized in our general discussion of cultural deprivation. In isolated groups in which such deprivation is of importance, the percentage of retarded persons is higher than for the population as a whole. However, the curve of intelligence quotients is still of the bell-shaped normal variety, but with the center shifted toward the lower values. The improvement of community standards would shift the whole curve toward the right without any significant change in the shape of the curve. The result of our long-time genetic evolution and our short-time cultural evolution has been to shift the whole curve toward the higher IQ values without, presumably, any important change in the shape of the curve. The intelligence curve for a colony of gorillas would probably have a symmetrical bell shape like our own but with the center considerably to the left of our curve. The point to be made is that these intelligence curves all represent the interaction of multiple genetic and environmental factors and that they always have a tail at the left end of the curve that represents the combinations of the undesirable genetic and environmental factors which give the lowest intelligence. Our goal must be that of eliminating both the genetic and environmental factors which result in the lowest IQ values. The gradual removal of these deleterious factors will not change the shape of the curve but will displace it to the right. The upgrading of intelligence is of particular urgency because the complexity of our society is increasing so rapidly.

It is very well known that the majority of the higher grade retardates are to be found in the lower socioeconomic classes. This means that the majority of the mildly retarded are born to parents who have the least to offer their children. Is this merely a lack of cultural amenities or is a parent retarded in a large proportion of the cases? If one or both parents are retarded, are they transmitting defective genes to the children in addition to an unsatisfactory environment?

We found that 48.3 per cent of our unselected retardates had one or both parents retarded but this included all grades of retardates. An interesting study by Benda et al. (1963) on the cultural-familial type only, was restricted to patients at the Fernald State School who had an IQ of 50 or above on admission and who were without detectable physical or neurological disabilities. They selected 205 patients from 189 sibships. The IQ's ranged from 50 to 83 with a mean of 65.4. Only 13 of the 189 sibships lacked a retarded relative. Thus in 93 *per cent* of the cases there was a retarded relative of the patient, and 92 of the patients (48.7 per cent) had one or both parents retarded. Over 50 per cent of the homes were broken; over 50 per cent made no adequate provision for the children. Obviously, the degree of family adjustment was marginal. It is reasonable to assume that half of the retarded parents also had a retarded parent and that some of the patients would have produced retarded children had they not been institutionalized. In contrast, the 13 families with no retardation presented a markedly different picture. All were intact and functioning. There was no neglect, criminal behavior or social pathology. Reexamination of the 13 patients suggested accidental mental retardation.

The crucial question for the cultural-familial type cases is whether social conditions were bad because of the genetic retardation of the parents or were the parents retarded because of cultural deprivation in the families into which the parents were born. It is entirely clear that socioeconomic conditions will not be satisfactory when one or both parents is retarded. As Benda et al. (1963) point out, there are about 5,000,000 mildly retarded persons in the United States. The problem of how to prevent them from transmitting their retardation to the next generation is a staggering one.

All but three of the 189 families of the Benda study had had contact with social agencies, and the financial expenditures on them must have been mountainous. Most of the families expected financial assistance as their "right," but few felt any compulsion to cooperate in any way in return.

Let us return to a consideration of the normal curve of intelligence. It is abundantly clear from every kind of scientific information available that there is a genetic basis for intelligence which evolved over a long period of time, and which must be polygenic in nature. A necessary consequence of this concept is that some people will have different qualities of genes which result in different degrees of intelligence. Such a situation must give a population in which the great majority of people inherit similar collections of genes for intelligence while fewer and fewer persons inherit the progressively more rare combinations of genes which have the potentials for retardation or giftedness. That is, the normal curve of intelligence reflects a basic normal curve distribution of gene differences. The left hand tail of the normal curve is composed, in part, of persons with gene combinations which can only result in lower intelligence than combinations found further to the right, when the environments are comparable. Thus there must be a very significant proportion of mental retardation which is primarily caused by the combinations of genes for lower intelligence which segregate out at the left end of the normal curve. The importance of this concept has received too little attention. How many investigators have pointed out that the socioeconomic conditions of persons with such genotypes cannot help but be deficient if they are "on their own?" The children of persons with these poor gene combinations will be born into culturally deficient homes and a substantial percentage of them will have similar undesirable gene combinations and be retarded. Assortative mating is of the greatest importance in assuring the transmission of these gene combinations at the left end of the curve from generation to generation. Presumably all the children born into the culturally subnormal homes are subjected to the undesirable aspects of social deprivation but less than half of the children are retarded. It is reasonable to assume that those who are retarded are the ones with the least valuable gene combinations.

What is the magnitude of the problem presented by the retardates resulting from the segregation of gene combinations for lower intelligence at the left end of the curve? We cannot answer the question precisely but we can make a rough estimate. We don't know how many pairs of genes are concerned with intelligence or the relative effect of each pair. However, in view of the facts of evolution, we can be sure that enough pairs of genes are involved to give a smooth and gradual increase of the curve as we proceed from the left end toward the center. We would expect that the retarded persons resulting from the polygenic segregation of the least desirable gene pairs at the left end of the normal curve would be much more numerous than those resulting from the rare isolated events, such as the presence of the extra chromosome which results in Down's syndrome, or the rare recessive traits, such as Tay-Sach's disease or phenylketonuria.

From 2 to 3 per cent of the population is found to have IQ values below 70. We know that about one fifth of 1 per cent of births have Down's syndrome, and if we add to this the list of retardations caused by rare recessives and obvious environmental calamities, such as syphilis, we should have accounted for at least 1 per cent of the population, or about half of the people below an IQ of 70. The remaining 1 per cent of the population that tests below 70 and is not due to obvious defined types of retardation is not too great a part of the population to expect to be retarded because of unfavorable polygenic combinations. Indeed, on any polygenic theory of intelligence we are forced to assume an appreciable fraction of the retarded to be the result of the unfavorable multiple gene combinations. Thus, on theoretical grounds, we have surprisingly little residue of our 2 to 3 per cent of the population which is retarded and which could be ascribed as primarily the result of social deprivation. To be sure, cultural deprivation may be able to lower the intellectual performance of any person but if the polygenic theory of intelligence is valid, there is little opportunity for cultural deficiencies to be the *primary* cause of mental retardation.

We can look at our 289 probands from this point of view. There were 84 probands of the primarily genetic category. Presumably these were due to discrete genetic events and not to either polygenic heredity or social deprivation. There were 27 probands for which there was evidence of a direct environmental insult, such as syphilis, birth injuries and severe falls. Thus, there was a total of 111 retardates (38 per cent) for which neither polygenic inheritance nor social deprivation would seem to be the primary cause. Then there are the troublesome 123 probands whom we were unable to classify. A good number of these are included because the proband was the only retarded person in the kinship; no evidence for either polygenic inheritance or social deprivation was present in some of these families and a fraction of them should be charged to the segregation of single recessive genes in the homozygous condition. If we are permitted to consider half of the 123 probands of unknown origin as not being due to polygenic inheritance or social deprivation, the other half, 62 persons, could be added to the 55 probands of the probably genetic class to give a total of 117 probands (40 per cent) whose retardation was primarily due to cultural deficiencies or polygenic inheritance. We are forced to allot much of this 40 per cent to polygenic inheritance or we must reject the whole science of genetics. The rejection of genetics is unreasonable, so we are left with the conclusion that social deprivation may have a depressing effect upon intelligence but that it is not often the basic or primary cause of mental retardation. We must assume that some cases of mental retardation are due primarily to social deprivation but we don't find a large proportion of our probands who are available for this classification after an allocation has been completed for the other causes which appear to have been present.

Let us return to a subject which has been rather carefully ignored in recent years. This is the importance of the transmission of mental retardation. It is clear from the literature (and amply confirmed by our study) that a significant proportion of the retarded today are the offspring of the retarded of the previous generation. It is not necessary to quarrel about the exact percentage of the retarded who have one or both parents retarded or about the relative importance of genetics and environment in the etiology of the retarded. The fact remains that the retarded of today will produce much more than their per capita share of the retarded of tomorrow. If one is seriously interested in the prevention of mental retardation, the most practical method is that of reducing its transmission. This would be of great value to all concerned.

Most all "normal" traits of man will be of the continuous or graded type which have polygenic inheritance and display a normal curve of variation of the trait. If we think of fatness, as an example, it is obvious that the persons who are extremely thin can only achieve a certain degree of thinness without being at a reproductive disadvantage and, of course, at some degree of expression the trait would be lethal. At the other end of the curve there would be the people with extreme obesity, and it is not difficult to see that there would be a degree of obesity which would be lethal and for which reproduction would fail. Thus the extremes of almost any normal frequent trait would seem to be at a reproductive disadvantage and persons at both extremes of the normal curve would represent genetic lethals.

The normal curve of intelligence seems to depart from the above generalization. The lower end contains the severe cases of retardation who are clearly at a reproductive disadvantage and represent genetic lethals. However, the persons at the extreme upper end of the normal curve of intelligence, the gifted, do not seem to be at a large reproductive disadvantage. The study by Terman and Oden (1959) showed that the gifted were unusually successful in marriage and consistently produced a few children in each of a very high proportion of the marriages. They replaced themselves in the population, at least, so that we have one end of the curve, the lower, at a greater reproductive disadvantage than the upper end. This imbalance would cause the average to move gradually toward the upper end of the curve and account for the evolution of intelligence which would continue as long as this imbalance exists.

> *Thus, there will be continued evolution of higher intelligence as long as the persons at the lower end of the intelligence curve are at a reproductive disadvantage compared with those at the upper end of the curve.*

There are several ways in which the transmission of mental retardation could be reduced. The fight on poverty, the improvement of prenatal care, the reduction of the frequency of venereal diseases and many other such obvious, but difficult, steps can be taken. These desirable advances involve services to people with low risks of having retarded children in the great majority of cases and it may be that many of the retarded persons themselves may get overlooked. Thus, a very large expenditure of effort and resources may result in a relatively small reduction in the frequency of mental retardation. Clearly, the prevention of mental retardation will succeed best if it starts with the retardates themselves.

The most certain way to decrease the transmission of mental retardation is to reduce the reproduction of the retardates. Most retardates are not good material for parenthood. But how can they be persuaded to abstain from parenthood when they succeed in making intimate contacts with the opposite sex? It is unlikely that voluntary abstinence will be very effective with the retarded, and it would be unrealistic to expect the rhythm method to work with any appreciable proportion of them. We would do well to stop evading the issue and admit that institutionalization is a rather undesirable, even if effective, method of birth control. There has been a change in institutional populations in the last few decades, if our observations are correct. There seems to have been a decrease in the proportion of the higher grades of retardation, where the likelihood of reproduction is greatest, and an increase of the severely retarded for whom there is little danger of reproduction. Consequently, the institutions are now less effective in preventing the transmission of mental retardation than they were in the past. It can be seen that those states which have laws permitting the sterilization of patients in mental institutions are not much better off than the states without such laws. This is because so few of the patients are of high enough intelligence to be returned to the community where the sterilization would have prophylactic value. Less than one dozen sterilizations of the retarded are carried out each year in Minnesota. These are almost always high-grade retarded girls who have been unable to control their reproduction before commitment to the institution, but who could get along outside if relieved of the problems of reproduction. The sterilization of these few individuals has no significant effect on the problem for the whole state, though it is of great value to the recipients.

We must recognize that the retarded individual has normal sexual needs, in many cases, and that there are several million retarded persons in the country. Few of them are capable of sustaining a family though a good proportion of them could benefit by marriage if there were no children involved. Few of the latter could manage present day contraceptives which means that voluntary sterilization is the only remaining alternative to numerous children and successive unsuccessful marriages with intervening divorces. There are many reasons why the retarded fail as parents and the reader is referred to the paper by Bass (1963) for a careful review of the subject. She quotes the following interesting statement by Goodenough (1956), "Marriage at an early age between *sterilized* sub-normal cases is desirable and should be encouraged. In this way they are permitted many of the satisfactions of normal life without assuming more of the responsibilities than they are able to handle." (Italics ours.) Voluntary surgical birth control for the retarded, and others with similar problems, seems to be entirely acceptable to the recipients but they seldom have the motivation to initiate it, or, unfortunately, do many of the social workers or other professional personnel who are responsible for the well-being of the retarded.

Part of the reason for the failure of professional personnel to sell the advantages of permanent contraception to the retarded is the fear of inconvenience or adverse repercussions from their solicitude. There does exist a danger to the social worker, or even to the surgeon, particularly since only one state (Virginia) has a law which permits voluntary sterilization outside of institutions (Reed, 1962). Many physicians hesitate to carry out a sterilization operation because there are no laws specifically permitting them to do so.

It is unlikely that the prosecution of a physician who had performed the operation with the consent of the guardians or parents of a retarded person would be successful. However, there is little likelihood of a physician risking a court action no matter how small the chances might be of his being convicted.

One of the important humanitarian implications of our demonstration of the importance of the transmission of mental retardation is that a better legal basis must be provided for the voluntary sterilization of the higher grade retardates in the community.

There has been a myth in circulation during the last few decades that sterilization would not be immediately efficient in reducing the frequency of a trait because if the trait depended upon a recessive there would be so many more carriers of the trait than affected persons, that progress would be imperceptible. This might be true for very rare recessives but we are not concerned with such usually sterile anomalies. We are concerned with a polygenic trait in which assortative mating is high and the trait is transmissible and frequent. With such a trait, even if it has no genetic basis, sterilization will have an important effect which will be greatest in the first generation.

Few people have emphasized that where the transmission of a trait is frequently from parent to offspring, sterilization will be effective and it is irrelevant whether the basis for the trait is genetic or environmental.

There is evidence of the effectiveness of sterilization from Denmark. Kemp (1957) presents data of two types. A study of the children born before women were sterilized shows what could have been expected if their reproduction had been permitted to continue. Thus, of 352 live children of women subsequently sterilized, there were 112 (31.8 per cent) with IQ values less than 75, 127 (36.1 per cent) between 75 to 90 and only 113 (32.1 per cent) above 90. Of these last 113 offspring there were 16 who were psychopathic and 50 with nervous disturbances. Only five seemed to be without mental problems and with IQ's above 100. How could anyone argue that the sterilization was not of benefit to all concerned, the only regret being that it came too late?

Kemp's second type of information resulted from the Danish experience with sterilization from 1930 to 1955 during which time the rate of sterilization increased until approximately one third of the retarded thought to be born each year were sterilized when adult. He estimated that sterilization, segregation in institutions, genetic counseling, and so forth, were reducing the frequency of mental retardation each generation by about 50 per cent. In fact, the *total number* of sterilizations had decreased in the last five years of the period due, in part, to a decreased population of retarded adults in need of it.

Sterilization in Denmark is on a voluntary basis and the best interests of the retarded persons are scrupulously looked after. There is no program in the formal sense, but the whole population is educated regarding the usefulness of the operation for the retarded, so no major difficulties develop. The climate of opinion in the United States should change gradually toward a greater realization of the advantages of voluntary sterilization for the retarded who remain in the community. It was mentioned earlier that only 33 (2.3 per cent) of the unselected retardates were sterilized and only 115 (7.9 per cent) were institutionalized; thus, about 90 per cent of our retarded persons are in the community and about half of them reproduce. Our histories show over and over the undesirability of this reproduction. There was no evidence of any undesirable results of the sterilization of the 33 unselected retardates and the 9 probands of our study. It is true that one cannot tabulate any observed benefits of sterilization, as they are appreciated only by comparing the beneficiaries with those who failed to receive this protection. However, if the number of retarded in the United States could be reduced by 50 per cent each generation by any humane means, the advantages of such methods are clear. This could be achieved with the aid of voluntary sterilization.

When voluntary sterilization for the retarded becomes a part of the culture of the United States, we should expect a decrease of about 50 per cent per generation in the number of retarded persons, as a result of all methods combined to reduce retardation.

One might object that there will still be the same proportion of persons at the left end of the normal curve of intelligence, even though the average intelligence has improved greatly. This is true but it is not an appropriate objection, as a decrease in handicapped persons can only be conceived as beneficial to all.

The reader may wish to doubt the validity of our finding that the 1 to 2 per cent of the population, composed of fertile retardates, produced 36.1 per cent of the retardates of the next generation, while the remaining 98 to 99 per cent of the population produced only 63.9 per cent of the retarded persons of the next generation. He may think that we misclassified normal persons as retarded in order to make our results as frightening as possible. However, such a critic should recall that our data for the unions of normal persons with only normal siblings married to normal persons showed that only 0.53 per cent of the offspring were retarded. Thus, if only this type of union reproduced, only 0.5 per cent of the population would be retarded, instead of the 3 per cent usually assumed to be so affected. In other words, instead of the six million retarded persons now in the United States there would only be five hundred thousand of them, if only normal persons with normal siblings, and married to normal persons, had reproduced in the previous generation.

The reverse of the last statement is that the other five and one half million retarded persons (approximately) are the offspring of a retarded parent or a normal parent with a retarded sibling. Thus five-sixths of the retarded are either first or second degree relatives of another retarded person. This deduction, if correct, pinpoints the area in which social action would be most effective in reducing the prevalence of mental retardation.

One of the most important implications of our study results from the finding that only 0.5 per cent of the children of normal parents with normal siblings were retarded. It follows that the remaining 2.5 per cent (approximately) of the population which is retarded would have at least one parent, or an aunt or uncle, who is or was, retarded. The fact that about five-sixths of the retarded have a retarded parent or a retarded aunt or uncle is of great significance because it demonstrates the large extent to which transmission is involved in the etiology of mental retardation.

It was possible to check the aunts and uncles on both sides of the family for our probands to see whether five-sixths of them did, in fact, have at least one retarded parent or a retarded aunt or uncle. There were 202 probands of the 289 for whom we had information as to the intelligence of their parents and aunts and uncles. There were 174 probands (86.1 per cent) of the 202 who had one or both parents retarded or one or more retarded aunts or uncles. We would expect five-sixths (83.3 per cent) to have such retarded relatives and we were astonished at the closeness of the agreement with the 86.1 per cent observed.

The reduction of social and educational deprivation during the coming decades should result in the improvement of the performance of the retarded to some degree. There is no doubt in our minds that sociological advances will make the greatest differences for the superior and gifted children who are born into impoverished environments. We found that of 102 persons with IQ's above 125, and for whom school achievement was known, only 30 completed college. Seven of these had IQ's over 146 and only one of these completed college. This waste of academic talent was clearly related to below average social conditions and was more striking for the women. The most important single factor seemed to be lack of motivation for schooling which was due in part to unsatisfactory socioenvironmental conditions. We must also mention the exceptions, such as one man with IQ of only 83 who managed to complete college.

The early detection and encouragement of the superior children born in socially impoverished environments would be an excellent investment for the immediate future of the country.

It is also clear that special schooling for gifted children born in good environments would pay off handsomely. The gifted are now less privileged than the retarded in regard to special education provided in the public schools.

Twin studies have been of great value in efforts to determine the relative importance of heredity and environment in causing differences in intelligence. In our study the data for boys (Table 45, page 61), are particularly instructive. The median difference in IQ between 5391 pairs of brothers was 9.64 points while our 57 pairs of boy-boy twins had a median difference of only 5.17 IQ points. About one-half of our pairs of boy twins would be expected to be fraternal twins with greater differences than the identical twin boys. If we account for these fraternal twins the differences between the identical twins could not be more than 4 IQ points, a very small difference indeed. One person will average about 5 points difference when retested, regardless of his social status. It should be clear that identical twins reared together experience no greater environmental fluctuations than a single individual does. The much greater differences of the fraternal twins, compared with the identicals, must therefore be primarily genetic in nature.

It will be recalled that the single persons in our study had an average IQ of only 72.01, at least 28 IQ points below the average for the married persons. One obvious reason for this striking difference is that the unmarried group must always include a significant fraction of severely retarded persons who are not marriageable and must lower the mean, and the median, drastically.

The most enlightening aspect of our study was the resolution of Cattell's paradox. No doubt many people had suspected what the answer to this problem would be and we, with Dr. James V. Higgins, were happy to be able to provide the necessary data to clinch the matter. The paradox is simply that there is a relatively large negative correlation (about − 0.3) between the number of children in a family and their average intelligence as measured by any test; this should result in a decrease in the intelligence of the population each generation—but it doesn't. The explanation of the failure of the intelligence of the population to decline is that while a few of the retarded produce exuberantly large families of children with low average intelligence, most of the retarded produce only one child or no children at all. The persons at the upper end of the curve of intelligence are consistent in their production of smaller families of more intelligent children; thus the children of the smaller, more intelligent families balance, or perhaps outnumber, the children of the larger less intelligent families. The net result of eons of evolution has been an increase in intelligence to the present level.

We end our discussion with the perhaps euphoric opinion that the intelligence of the population is increasing slowly, and that greater protection of the retarded from reproduction will augment the rate of gain. The elevation of the average intelligence is essential for the comprehension of our increasingly complicated world.

REFERENCES

Åkesson, H. O. 1961. Epidemiology and Genetics of Mental Deficiency in a Southern Swedish Population. Uppsala, Almquist and Wiksells, pp. 1-107.

Anastasi, A. 1959. Differentiating effect of intelligence and social status. Eugen. Quart., *6:* 84-91.

Bajema, C. J. 1964. Estimation of the direction and intensity of natural selection in relation to human intelligence by means of the intrinsic rate of natural increase. Eugen. Quart., *10:* 175-187.

Bass, M. S. 1963. Marriage, parenthood and prevention of pregnancy. Amer. J. Ment. Defic., *68:* 318-333.

Benda, C. E., Squires, N. D., Ogonik, M. J. and Wise, R. 1963. Personality factors in mild mental retardation. Amer. J. Ment. Defic., *68:* 24-40.

Böök, J. A. 1963. A genetic and neuropsychiatric investigation of a North Swedish population with special regard to schizophrenia and mental deficiency. Acta Genet., *4:* 1-414.

Böök, J. A., Schut, J. W. and Reed, S. C. 1953. A clinical and genetical study of microcephaly. Amer. J. Ment. Defic., *57:* 637-660.

Brock, L. G. 1934. Report of the departmental committee on sterilization. Sessional Papers, Great Britain, *15:* 1-137.

Brugger, C. 1930. Genealogische Untersuchungen an Schwachsinnigen. Z. ges. Neurol. Psychiat., *130:* 66-103.

Cattell, R. B. 1951. The fate of national intelligence: test of a thirteen year prediction. Eugen. Rev., *42:* 136-148.

Fisher, R. A. 1924. The elimination of mental defect. Eugen. Rev., *16:* 114-116.

Gamble, C. J. 1952. What proportion of mental deficiency is preventable by sterilization? Amer. J. Ment. Defic., *57:*123-126.

Goddard, H. H. 1914. Feeble-mindedness, Its Causes and Consequences. New York, Macmillan & Co.

Goodenough, F. L. 1956. Exceptional Children. New York, Appleton-Century.

Halperin, S. L. 1945. A clinico-genetical study of mental defects. Amer. J. Ment. Defic., *50:* 8-25.

Harlow, H. F. and Harlow, M. K. 1962. Social deprivation in monkeys. Sci. Amer., *207:* 5: 136-146.

Higgins, J. V., Reed, E. W. and Reed, S. C. 1962. Intelligence and family size: a paradox resolved. Eugen. Quart., *9:* 84-90.

Kemp, T. 1957. Genetic-hygienic experiences in Denmark in recent years. Eugen. Rev., *49:* 11-18.

Oliver, C. P. 1940. Recessive polydactylism associated with mental deficiency. J. Hered., *31:* 365-367.

Penrose, L. S. 1938. A Clinical and Genetic Study of 1280 Cases of Mental Defect. His Majesty's Stationery Office, Lond., pp. 1-159.

Punnett, R. C. 1917. Eliminating feeble-mindedness. J. Hered., *8:* 464-465.

Reed, E. W. and Phillips, V. P. 1959. The Vale of Siddem revisited. Amer. J. Ment. Defic., *63:* 699-702.

Reed, S. C. 1961. Counseling in Medical Genetics. De Genetica Medica. Pars. Tertia. Edizioni Instituto Mendel. Roma, pp. 152-177.

Reed, S. C. 1962. New voluntary sterilization law. Eugen. Quart., *9:* 166-167.

Reed, S. C. 1963. Counseling in Medical Genetics, 2nd Ed. Philadelphia, W. B. Saunders Co., p. 278.

Reed, S. C., Reed, E. W. and Higgins, J. V. 1962. The relationship of human welfare to marriage selection. J. Hered., *53:* 153-156.

Reed, S. C., Reed, E. W. and Palm, J. D. 1954. Fertility and intelligence among families of the mentally deficient. Eugen. Quart., *1:* 44-52.

Terman, L. M. and Oden, M. H. 1959. The Gifted Group at Mid-life. Thirty-five Year Follow-up of the Superior Child. Palo Alto, Stanford University Press.

U. S. Department of Labor, Bureau of Employment Security. 1949. Dictionary of Occupational Titles. Vol. 1. Definitions of Titles.

APPENDIX

KEY TO SYMBOLS

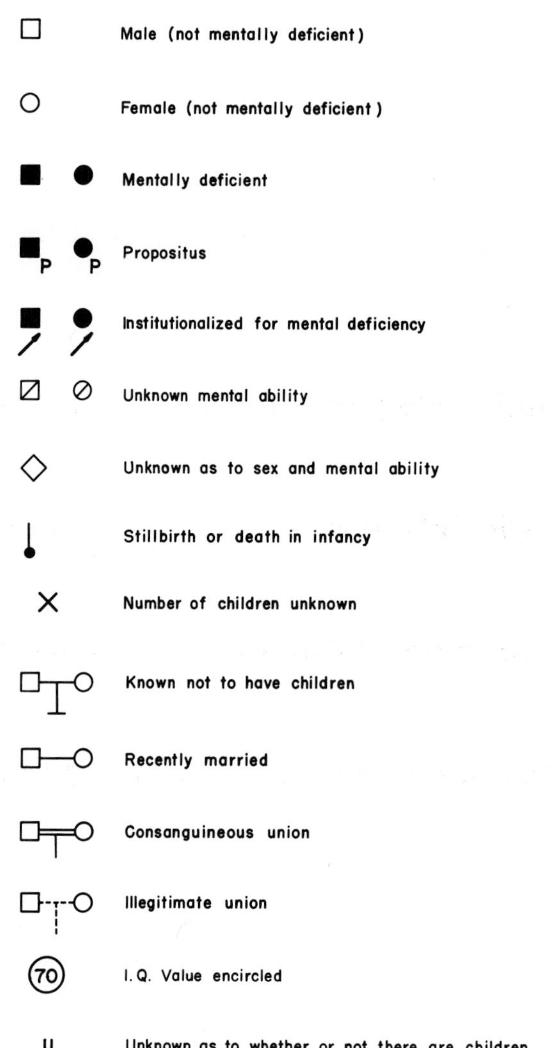

Roman numerals — Indicate generations
Arabic numerals — Indicate individuals
KMD — Original case number
Material below, or external to, continuous dotted line obtained since original study.

INTRODUCTION

The reader may wonder how we justify an appendix that is larger than the text. There are a number of reasons for including this extensive material:

1. The studies of the Danish Institute of Human Genetics have been useful to other workers on many occasions because the pedigrees were published. There is no way of predicting what future scholars may wish to learn from this or any other collection of data; consequently, it is important to include as much of the basic material as possible.
2. The publication of our pedigrees will permit other workers to request the loan of the complete files of data for particular kinships with specific types of retardation, such as Pelizeaus-Merzbacher disease or microcephaly. It is impossible to publish all of the personal, medical and psychological detail for our population of 82,217 persons, because the material occupies 20 correspondence-size file drawers, exclusive of the pedigree charts.
3. Many of the kinships include hundreds of persons with normal intelligence. Intelligence quotients, school records and sociological data of various kinds are available in our files, and more could be obtained. Thus, thousands of normal families are "on tap" and could be used for a variety of research projects. A selection could be made from the published pedigrees of the kinships desired for each project.
4. The large constellations of related families in some of the kinships would allow studies of environmental influences on personality traits. An interesting family for such consideration would be the one in KMD 523, part 3, in which two normal school boys, numbers 854 and 855, lived in a large household of assorted retardates and schizophrenics.

The method of preparing the pedigree charts has been described in Chapter 2. It will be recalled that the IQ score, when known, is enclosed in a circle and placed below the genetic symbol for the person. The scores for the different tests were converted to the base of 100 for the average IQ if the test scores were not already on this basis. Handbooks are available for these conversions. None of the scores is an average score; the rules for selecting the score to be placed on the pedigree chart, when more than one was available, have been given in Chapter 2.

The brief summaries of each kinship included here represent a large publication expense, but still represent only a fraction of the detailed description in our files for each kinship. The detailed family histories with names of persons, dates of birth, death and other statistics amount to several thousands of pages. Therefore, the summaries published are merely abstracts which attempt to give some life to the pedigrees. A short case history of each proband is followed by descriptions of other retardates and nonretardates of special interest. Diagnoses of the kind of retardation or other mental disorders are reported whenever available. It is hoped that the summaries will give the reader an overall view of the family pattern of retardation, of other mental and physical deficits and of the socioeconomic status of the kinship pictured on the pedigree chart.

One of the astonishing differences between the kinships is the prolific reproduction of some compared with the rapid extinction of others. A casual glance at the pedigrees shows an obvious correlation between extensive reproduction and a lower proportion of mental retardation in the kinships compared with smaller kinships in which the proportion of retardation was higher. Much further study should be given to the factors responsible for these manyfold differences in reproductive behavior shown by the total progeny of four grandparents who initiate our kinships. Some of the kinships are so large that in one case as many as nine charts were necessary to include all the persons belonging to that kinship.

THE PRIMARILY GENETIC CATEGORY

There were 84 probands who are classified as having a primarily genetic type of retardation because they had either well defined anomalies, had one or more siblings with IQ's below 50 or were the offspring of consanguineous unions.

On the following pages are reproduced the 121 pedigree charts for the descendants of the grandparents of the 84 probands. A brief summary of the family history for each proband accompanies these charts. Some of the kinships are so large that there is more than one chart for each of these kinships.

The following kinships are included: KMD's 2, 3, 4, 5, 10, 14, 22, 26, 27, 29, 31, 36, 43, 55, 67, 75, 89, 90, 95, 104, 105, 110, 124, 127, 128, 132, 133, 135, 137, 141, 147, 151, 163, 175, 192, 212, 213, 214, 215, 218, 224, 225, 227, 229, 232, 233, 264, 271, 273, 274, 277, 281, 292, 295, 296, 298, 302, 308, 323, 335, 342, 344, 345, 347, 349, 350, 365, 366, 370, 378, 384, 398, 402, 419, 447, 454, 477, 485, 490, 493, 500, 520, 523 and 533.

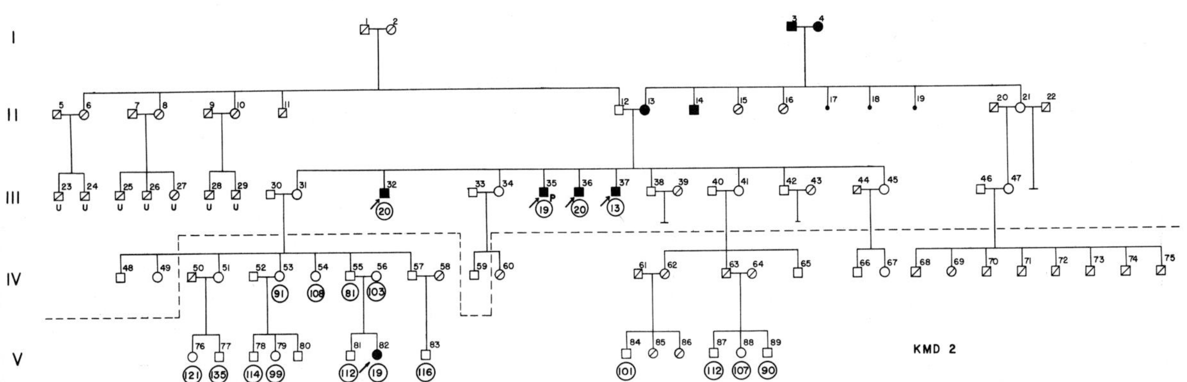

KMD 2

The Proband

The proband (35) was born in 1883, institutionalized at age 11 and has remained in the institution ever since. He was given a physical and neurological examination in 1950 by J. A. Böök, M.D., and John Schut, M.D. No stigmata were found. IQ 19. *Diagnosis:* undifferentiated mental deficiency.

Grandparents

Both maternal grandparents mentally retarded.

Parents

Proband's father (12) was a farmer who was cruel to his wife and family but had normal intelligence.

Proband's mother (13) was mentally retarded. She could not keep house.

Aunts and Uncles

None of the paternal aunts and uncles came to this country. On the maternal side, one retarded uncle (14) died single and childless.

Siblings

Brother (32) was institutionalized at age 14 and died in the institution in 1946 of cardiac insufficiency. IQ 20.

Brother (36) was institutionalized at age 13 and died in the institution in 1946 of lobar pneumonia. IQ 20.

Brother (37) was institutionalized at age 10 and has remained in the institution ever since. He was given a physical and neurological examination in 1950 by J. A. Böök, M.D., and John Schut, M.D. IQ 13. *Diagnosis:* undifferentiated mental retardation. EEG normal during sleep, very moderately abnormally fast during waking.

Six normal siblings, (31), (34), (38), (41), (42) and (45), all of whom married. None had retarded children.

Nieces and Nephews

Not of interest as far as known. Most of them lived outside the United States.

More Distant Relatives

One nephew (55) has an institutionalized child (82) who is not testable, with an estimated IQ of 19. *Diagnosis:* profound mental retardation.

Family Summary

There are four generations of retarded persons, including the maternal grandparents, a maternal uncle, the proband's mother and four of her children. These four siblings all were low-grade retardates as was one of their nephew's children, with no stigmata and no history of difficult birth or early trauma. The other four siblings were normal, as were their own children. The proband's parents had ten children who produced a total of 14 descendants.

Retardation of proband of primarily genetic origin.

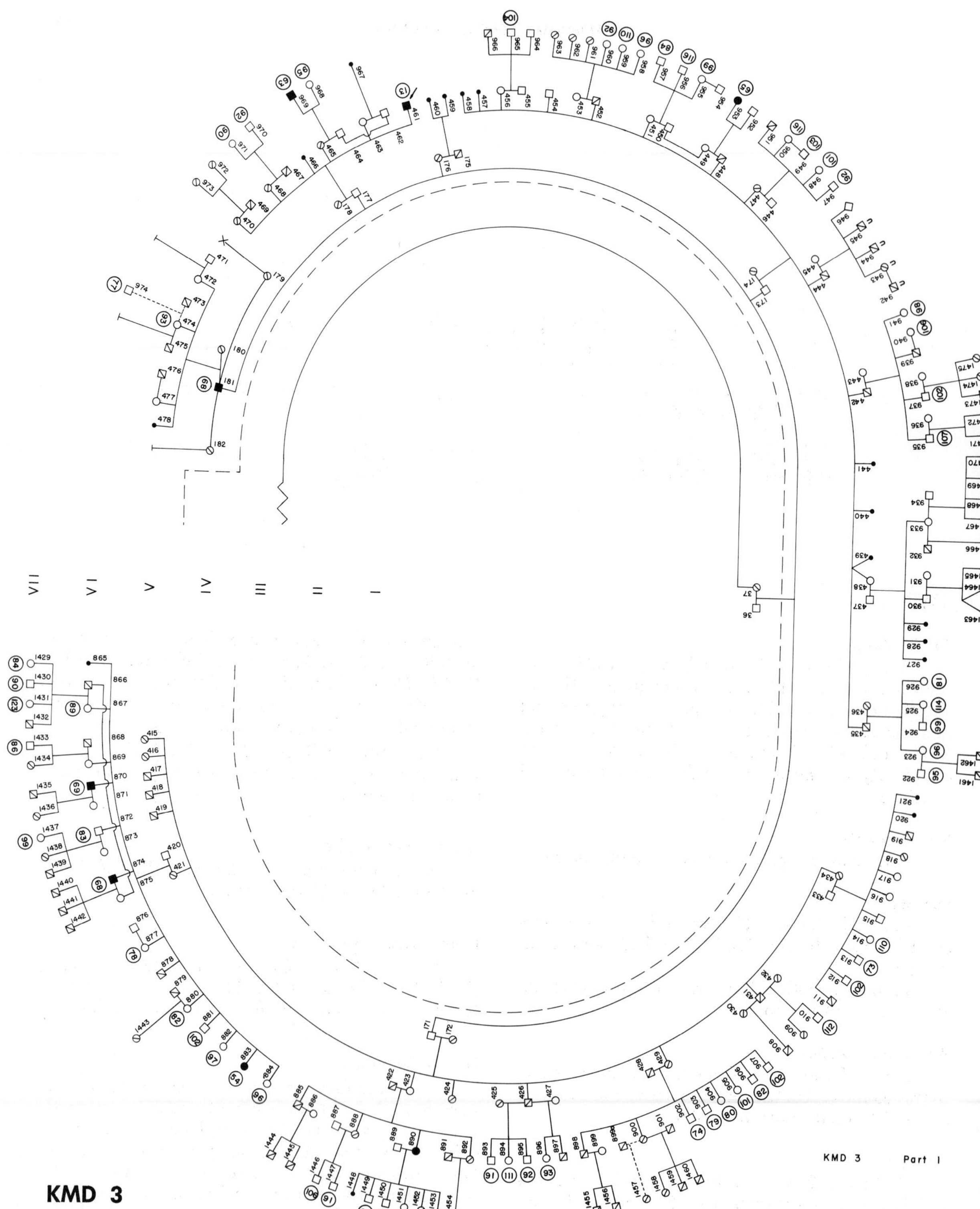

KMD 3 Part I

KMD 3

The Proband

The proband (112) in KMD 3 was an aunt to the proband (351) in KMD 18, so these two histories were combined. The proband (112) was diagnosed after her institutionalization as being epileptic, so (351) has been designated as the proband for the combined histories. However, the grandparents for (112) have been included.

The proband (351) was born in 1884, institutionalized at age 27 years when pregnant and ran away six years later. She supported herself by doing housework until her marriage to a man with normal intelligence (354). She was married twice and in addition had three illegitimate children by three fathers. She was slow in developing but had no stigmata and no history of birth injury or perinatal infection. IQ 60. *Diagnosis:* undifferentiated mental retardation.

Grandparents

Paternal grandparents (18) and (19) were retarded and were first cousins.

Parents

Father (103) was an alcoholic, retarded laborer.

Mother (104) was retarded and a first cousin to her husband.

Aunts and Uncles

Paternal uncles (92), (95) and (98) and paternal aunt (101) were all high-grade retardates. All were married but only two had children.

Maternal aunt (112) was institutionalized at age 34 years, diagnosed as epileptic and retarded and died in the institution. IQ 39.

Maternal aunt (116) was retarded. She married twice, but had no children.

Siblings

Brother (347) died of cholera at 5 years.

Sister (348) was institutionalized in 1901 and was in and out of institutions until her death in 1948 at age 63. She had a diagnosis of mental deficiency with psychosis, depressive type. IQ 66.

Sister (356) was adopted. She had normal intelligence.

Sister (358) was adopted by an aunt. Her intelligence is unknown.

Sister (359) was adopted from the state orphanage. Old records classify her as retarded. She could not be found in the follow-up.

Sister (360) was institutionalized in 1904 at age 7 years and died in the institution in 1927. IQ 52.

Spouses

(349), the first husband of (351), deserted his family. His intelligence is unknown.

(354) was a painter and stationary engineer with normal intelligence.

(350), (352) and (353), fathers of the proband's illegitimate children, unknown.

Children

Son (813), illegitimate, was adopted. He was normal in childhood but had an attack of encephalitis at age 11 years and later became an invalid and "somewhat unbalanced," and was hospitalized in a mental hospital for some time. He died in his early twenties single and childless. It is not known whether or not the encephalitis caused the later mental and physical problems because his IQ of 93 was taken at age 20 years. He had an IQ of 124 at age 7 years, and was reported to have been "a splendid specimen, both mentally and physically."

(814), illegitimate, was a "complete idiot" who died in infancy.

Daughter (815), illegitimate and born in the institution, lived with her aunt. She was something of a delinquent but went to high school and scored an IQ of 107 at age 4 years. She refused to cooperate in the study, but from our information she apparently is single.

Son (816), legitimate, completed the 11th grade and is a refrigerator repairman. His four children (1394), (1395), (1396) and (1397), all have normal intelligence.

Daughter (819), legitimate, graduated from high school and married a normal man. Her two children have not been tested. IQ 101.

Son (820), legitimate, graduated from high school with an equivalence certificate and works for a floor covering firm. He was not tested but is apparently not retarded, and has a son with an IQ of 116.

Daughter (823) completed the 11th grade, married a man with IQ 104 and has a child with IQ 112. IQ 100.

Nieces and Nephews

Only one, (824), who is unknown.

First Cousins

(336) was retarded.

Grandchildren

Eight, six known to have normal intelligence, two have not been tested as yet.

More Distant Relatives

(181) was in prison at one time. IQ 68.

(201), (203) and (205), all siblings and all retarded. Two are childless, but (203) has two children, both normal.

(217), (219), (221) and (223), all siblings and all retarded. Three are childless, one (221) has five children with an IQ range of 78 to 103.

(461) was institutionalized in 1935 at age 31 years. IQ 13.

(870), (874) and (883), siblings, have IQ's of 69, 68 and 54, respectively.

(890) is retarded, but married a normal man and her tested children are normal.

(935) has an IQ of 65.

(969) has an IQ of 63.

(1090) is deaf and has an IQ of 51. He was institutionalized at age 17 years.

(1117) has an IQ of 64.

(1273) has an IQ of 48.

Family Summary

The proband, IQ 60 and a social problem, her paternal grandparents, parents, three paternal uncles, one paternal aunt and two maternal aunts, three siblings, one child, one first cousin and 18 more distant relatives were retarded, all high grade except the proband's child and one more distant relative who were low-grade retardates. Six of the proband's seven children had normal intelligence. Both her paternal grandparents and her own parents were first cousins. The proband's parents had seven children and eight known grandchildren. Four of their seven children were retarded (three were institutionalized) and there is one known retardate (low grade) among the eight grandchildren, seven of whom are the proband's children. The father of four of these latter children had normal intelligence. The proband herself had seven children and eight grandchildren.

Retardation of proband of primarily genetic origin (consanguinity).

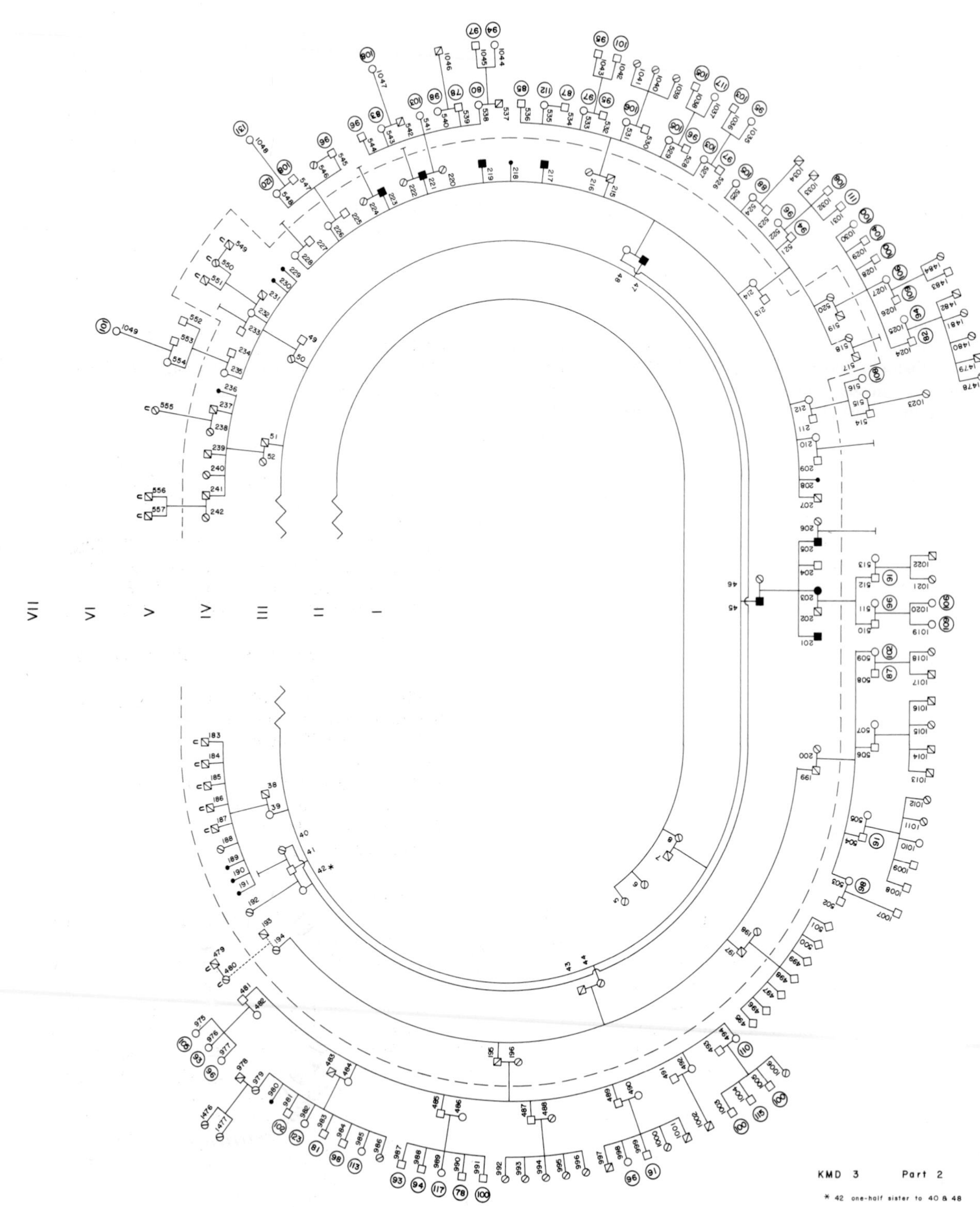

KMD 3 Part 2

* 42 one-half sister to 40 & 48

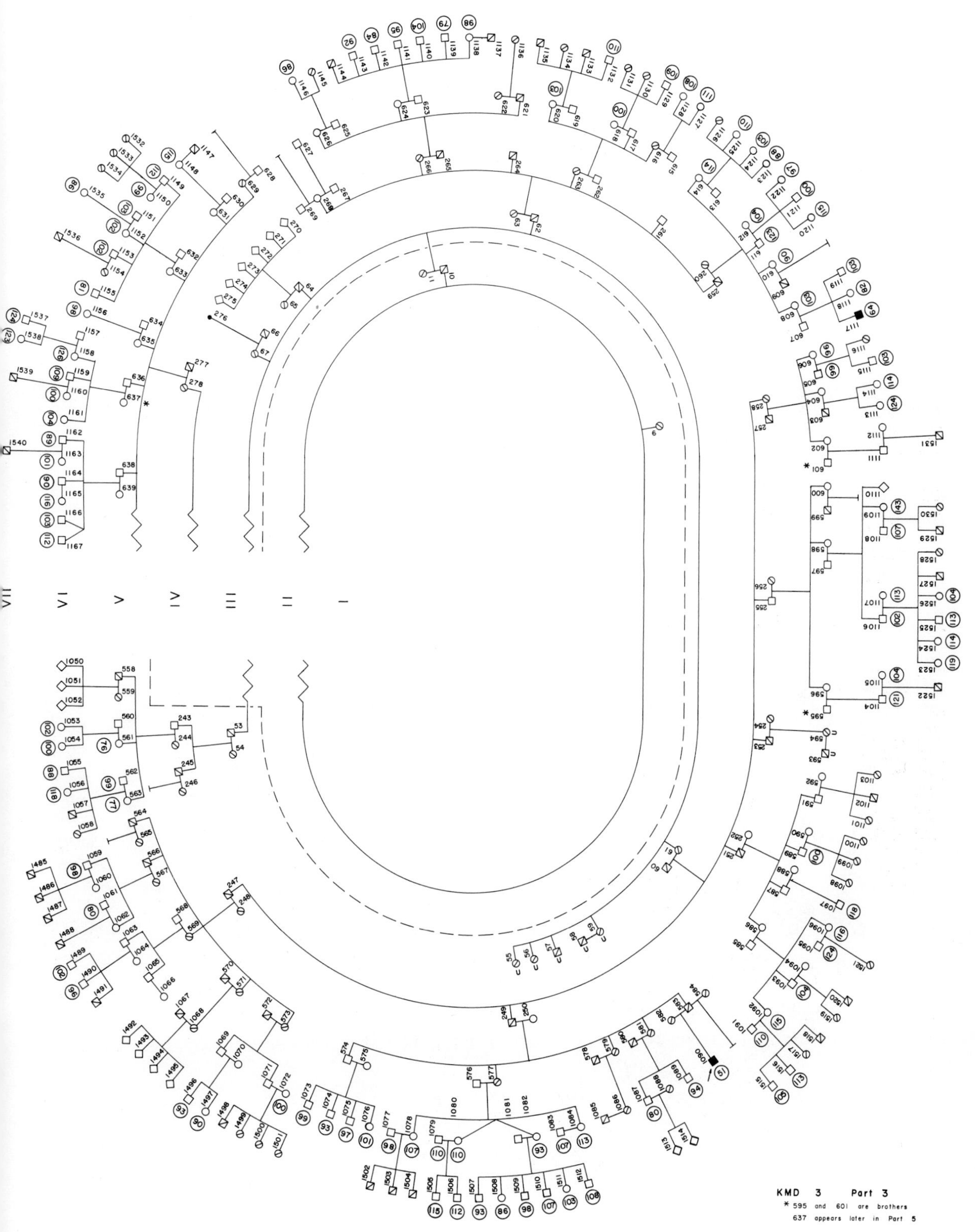

KMD 3 Part 3

* 595 and 601 are brothers
637 appears later in Part 5

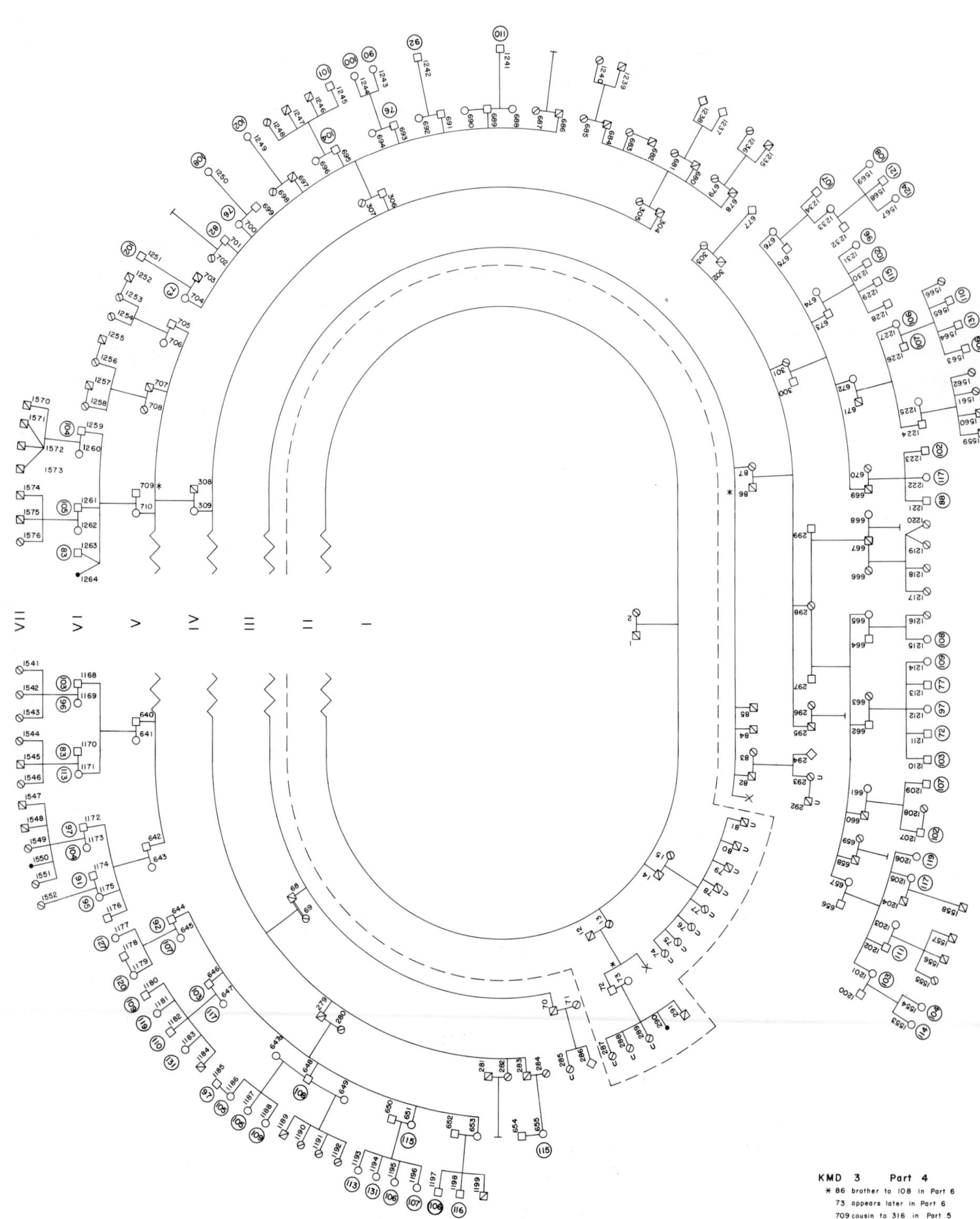

KMD 3 Part 4

* 86 brother to 108 in Part 6

73 appears later in Part 6

709 cousin to 316 in Part 5

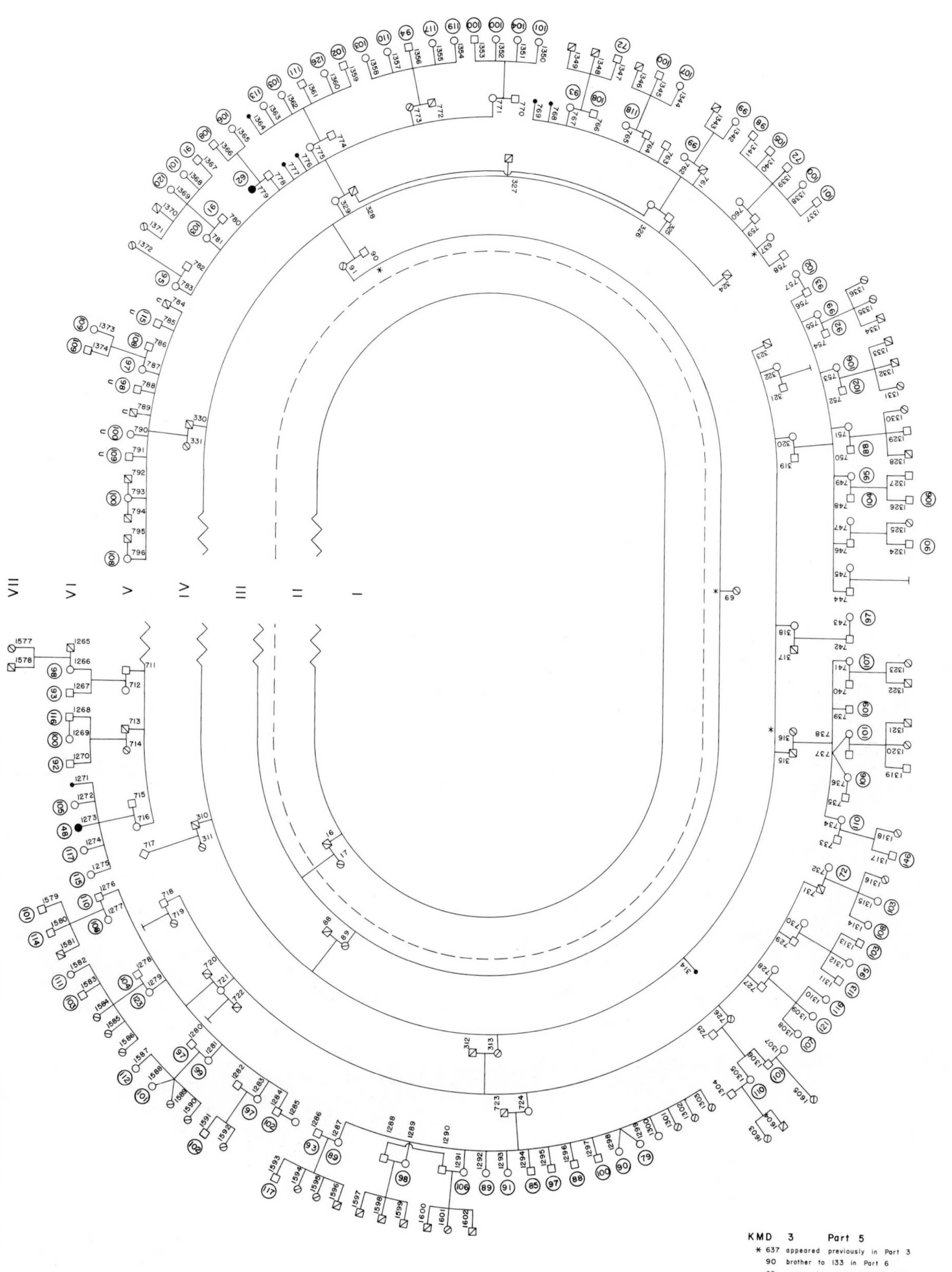

KMD 3 Part 5

* 637 appeared previously in Part 3
90 brother to 133 in Part 6
69 appeared previously in Part 4
316 cousin to 709 in Part 4

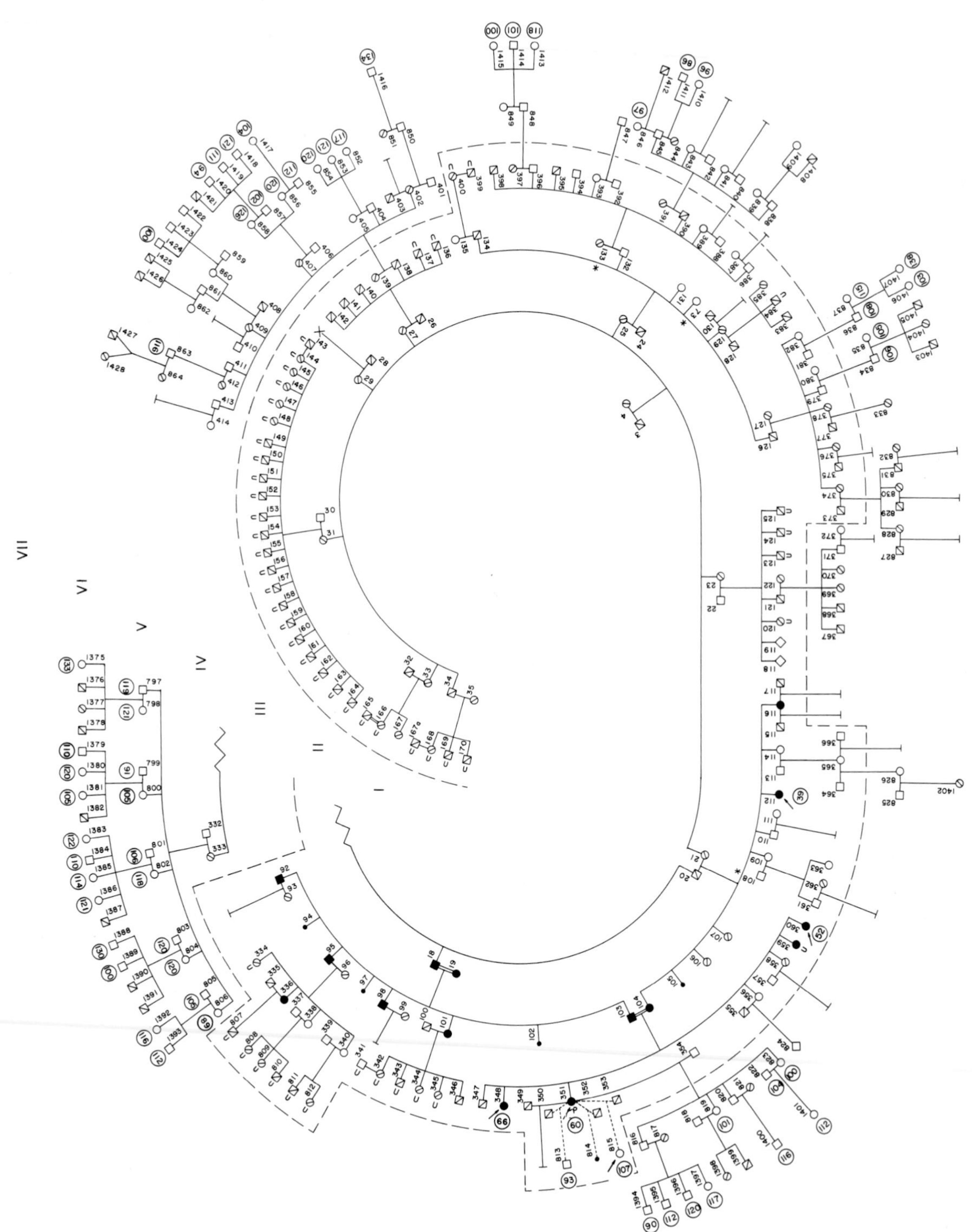

KMD 3 Part 6

* 108 brother to 86 in Part 4

73 appeared previously in Part 4

133 sister to 90 in Part 5

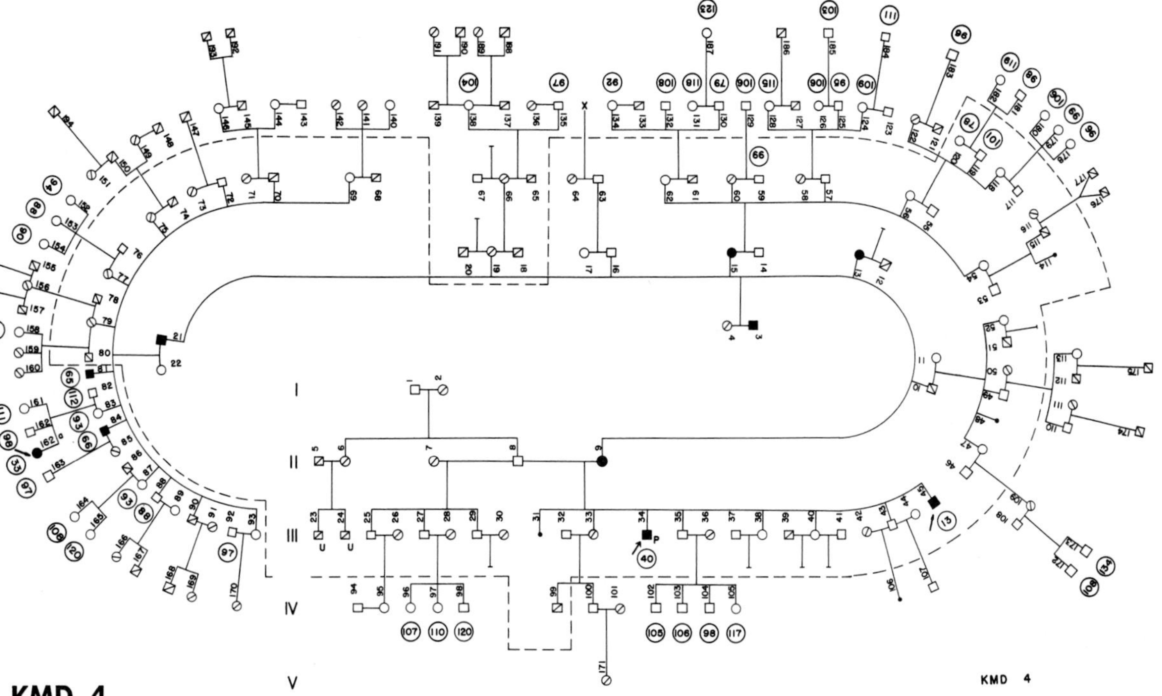

KMD 4

The Proband

The proband (34) was born in 1887, institutionalized at age 13 years and died of arteriosclerotic heart disease in the institution in 1960. He was unmarried and childless. He attended school for five years but learned little. A physical and neurological examination in 1951 by J. A. Böök, M.D., and John Schut, M.D., revealed no definite stigmata; EEG normal, both awake and asleep. IQ 40. *Diagnosis:* undifferentiated mental retardation.

Grandparents

Maternal grandfather was mentally retarded and died of alcoholism.

Parents

Father (8) provided a good home for his family and had normal intelligence.

Mother (9) had many self-induced abortions; died following one at 41 years. She could not keep house. Mentally retarded.

Aunts and Uncles

Two maternal aunts (13) and (15) were retarded. (13) was unable to keep house and was considered "very feebleminded." She was married but childless. (15) was a high-grade retardate who married a normal man and had five normal children.

One maternal uncle (21) was retarded. He often deserted his family and was once imprisoned for rape. His wife was normal but two of their 13 children were retarded.

Siblings

Sister (33) was classified as "somewhat feebleminded." Intelligence unknown, spouse and one son normal, one son unknown.

Four siblings (35), (38), (40) and (43) had normal intelligence. All married, two had children with no retardates.

Brother (45) was institutionalized at age 6 and is still in the institution. The records state he had "brain fever" at 2 years. IQ 13. A physical and neurological examination by J. A. Böök, M.D., and John Schut, M.D., revealed no stigmata.

Half Siblings

Three, all have normal intelligence, as do their children.

Nieces and Nephews

Six of eight survived, all with normal intelligence.

First Cousins

Proband's cousin (81) is single and is a railway station clerk. IQ 65. Proband's cousin (84) was killed in World War II. IQ 66.

More Distant Relatives

Proband's cousin (83) has an institutionalized child (162a) with IQ 33. Psychologist's report states undifferentiated mental retardation.

Family Summary

The proband's father was married twice. His other marriage produced three normal children. The mental retardation is apparent among the proband's maternal relatives only. The proband's own mother had eight children, two of whom were mentally retarded. His retarded maternal uncle had two retarded offspring plus an imbecile grandchild. The family of (8) and (9) of eight children produced only seven offspring.

Retardation of proband of primarily genetic origin.

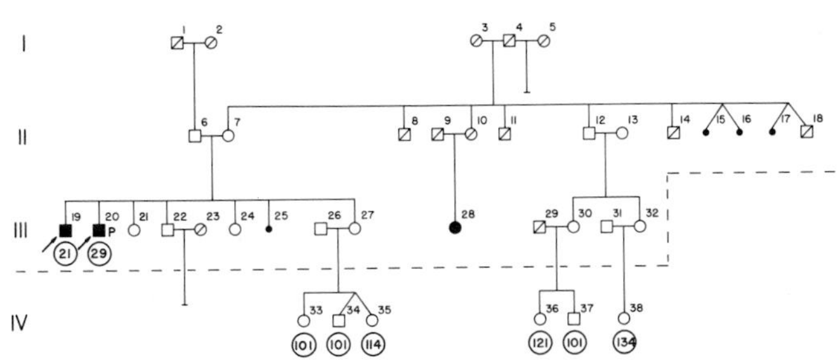

KMD 5

KMD 5

The Proband

The proband (20) was born in 1892, institutionalized at age 8 years, and died of hypertensive cardiovascular disease in the institution in 1954. He was given a physical and neurological examination in 1950 by J. A. Böök, M.D., and John Schut, M.D. No definite stigmata were found and there was no history of disease in infancy. IQ 29. *Diagnosis:* undifferentiated mental retardation.

Grandparents

Not of interest.

Parents

Both parents (6) and (7) had normal intelligence. The father was an engineman on the railroad.

Aunts and Uncles

Not of interest.

Siblings

Brother (19) was institutionalized at 10 years and died in the institution in 1930 of pulmonary tuberculosis. IQ 21.

Four normal siblings and a fifth who died at 1 year of spinal meningitis.

Nieces and Nephews

Only three, all of whom had normal intelligence.

First Cousins

One mentally retarded girl (28) who died single and childless at age 50.

More Distant Relatives

Not of interest.

Family Summary

The proband, his brother and a first cousin were retarded, the two brothers both being rather low-grade retardates of undifferentiated type. The parents and the other siblings were normal, as were the one nephew and two nieces. The proband's parents had seven children who produced a total of three offspring.

Retardation of proband of primarily genetic origin.

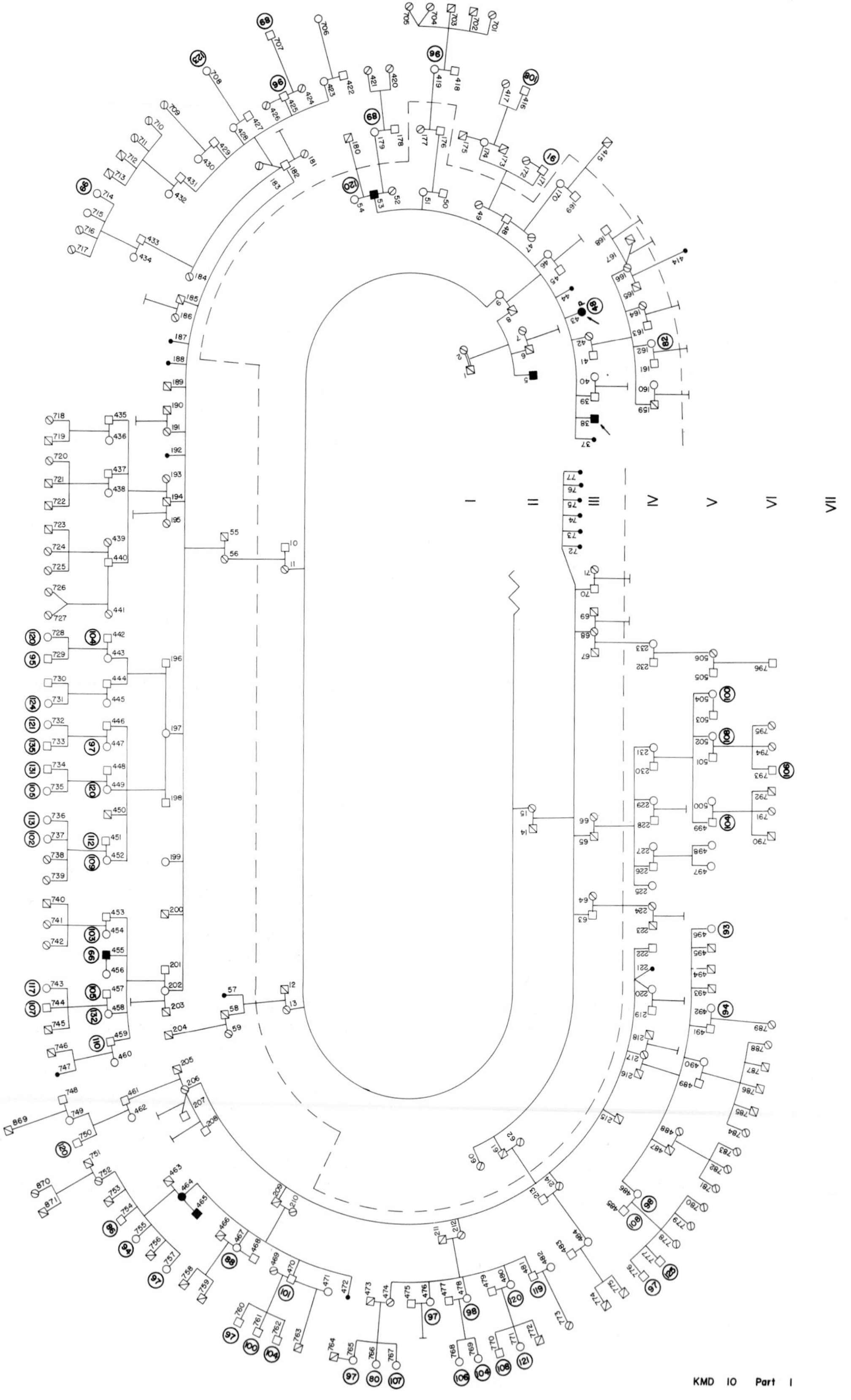

KMD 10

The Proband

The proband (43) was born in 1879. She was institutionalized at age 16, spent the remainder of her life in and out of institutions. She died at age 54 of tuberculosis in an institution. She did not walk until 2½ years old and went to school for about one year but could not learn. She was unmarried and childless. IQ 48. *Diagnosis:* undifferentiated mental retardation.

Grandparents

Paternal grandparents were first cousins.

Parents

Father (8) committed to two mental hospitals as cruel, delusional and religiously fanatic.

Mother (9) was normal and in vigorous health, no suggestion of illnesses or accidents during pregnancies.

Aunts and Uncles

One paternal uncle (5) was mentally retarded, unmarried and childless, and died at age 30.

Siblings

Brother (37) died at 7 months of "spasms."

Brother (38) had a peculiarly shaped head at birth, was institutionalized at age 19 and died age 28. He was epileptic and mentally retarded, middle grade.

Brother (39) was a machinist and carpenter with normal intelligence.

Sister (42) had unknown intelligence. Her husband had normal intelligence and her four children (none retarded) all married but had no surviving offspring.

Brother (44) died of whooping cough at 7 months.

Sisters (46) and (51) and brother (48) all had normal intelligence and normal children.

Brother (53) is mentally retarded. He married twice. His second wife is 25 years younger than he with IQ 120.

Nieces and Nephews

Not of interest.

First Cousins

(122) was mentally retarded. He is also of interest because he developed Huntington's chorea, as did his father (24), his sister (127) and his daughter (357).

(145) with IQ 76, whose divorced first husband had an IQ of 58, had four children by him all with normal intelligence.

More Distant Relatives

A first cousin (98) had eight children who were reared in poor social conditions and produced (551), (552) and (554) who repeated at least two grades of school, were given social promotions and are considered to be mentally retarded. (551) and (554) are single, (552) has a wife (553) with IQ 108. The institutionalized boy (556), first cousin to (551), (552) and (554) is epileptic with an IQ of 39. His normal sister (564) married a retarded man with IQ 68.

(455) is a laborer with IQ 66. His wife (456) graduated from high school and is a bookkeeper.

(464) was classified as retarded because she was in ungraded classes at school. Her second husband (465) was also in ungraded classes.

(615) was institutionalized in 1952 with a diagnosis of undifferentiated mental retardation, schizoid tendencies and sexual delinquency.

Family Summary

The proband was one of ten children of whom two died in infancy, two siblings were mentally retarded (about the same grade) and the five normal siblings only produced a total of eight children. The following generation consisted of only seven children, one of whom, (414) was born dead. Thus the proband's sibship failed remarkably to reproduce itself.

The cluster of five retarded descendants of the eight children of (98) not only failed to reproduce themselves, but also their normal siblings (564) and (574) married retarded men and so far have produced only one child between them. The other normal sections of the family have reproduced themselves several times over.

Because of the retardation of the uncle and two siblings of the proband, it is assumed that her retardation was primarily of genetic origin. The cluster of five retarded descendants of (98) seems also to have genetic basis though it may be different from that of the proband's sibship.

Retardation of proband of primarily genetic origin.

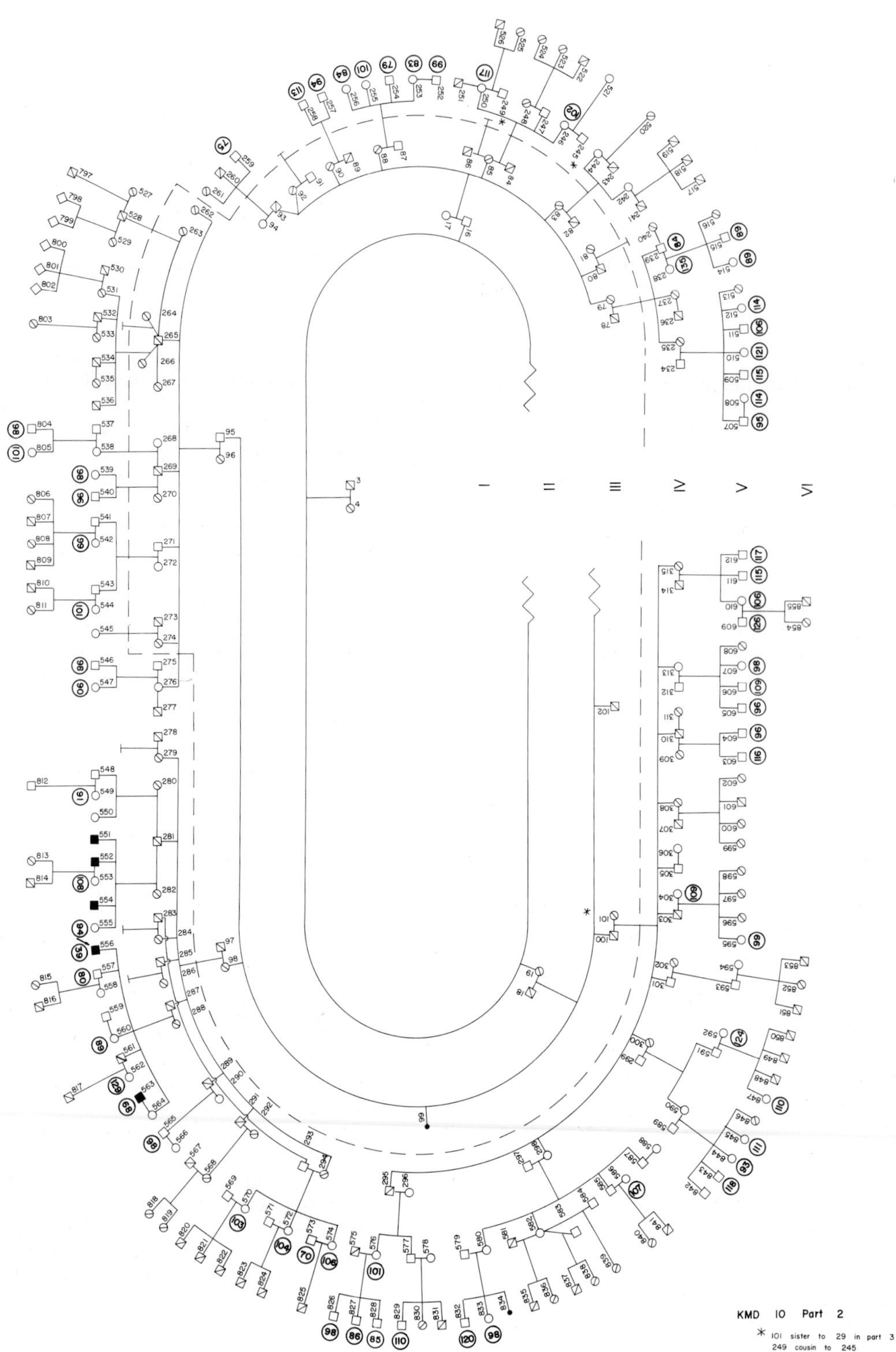

KMD 10 Part 2

* 101 sister to 29 in part 3
249 cousin to 245

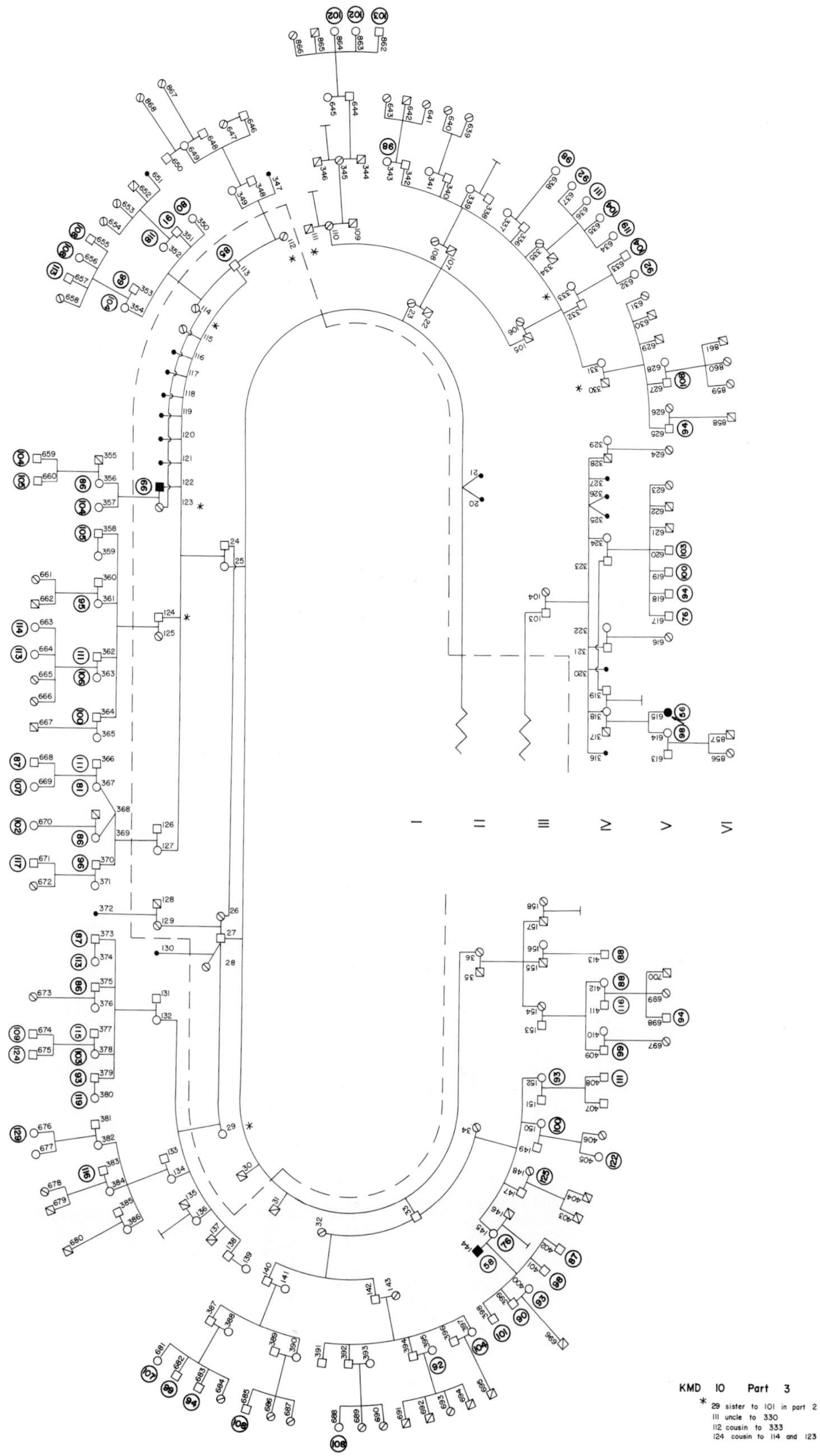
I
II
III
IV
V
VI
KMD 10 Part 3
* 29 sister to 101 in part 2
111 uncle to 330
112 cousin to 333
124 cousin to 114 and 123

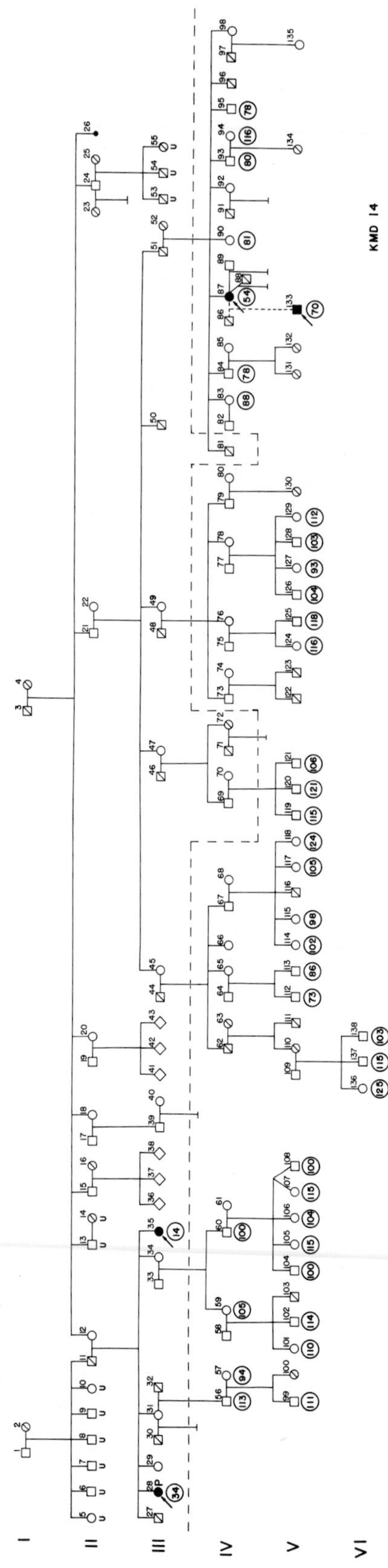
KMD 14

KMD 14

The Proband

The proband (28) was born in 1888, institutionalized at age 10 years and was still in the institution in 1961. Delivery was normal. She was a sickly child who rocked back and forth all the time. She was obviously abnormal as a baby, but had no stigmata. IQ 34. *Diagnosis:* undifferentiated mental retardation.

Grandparents

Paternal grandfather had senile dementia.

Parents

Father (11) had unknown intelligence.

Mother (12) was subject to epileptic attacks for five or six years after the birth of her third child. She had normal intelligence.

Aunts and Uncles

Paternal aunts and uncles, with the exception of one uncle, all remained in Norway. No paternal relatives are known today but they belonged to a wealthy, socially prominent family and had normal intelligence.

One maternal uncle (21) came to this country. He was normal.

Siblings

Brother (27) is unmarried and childless. Relatives say he is a "bum" who lives in a poor section of town. Intelligence unknown.

Sister (29) died single. Normal intelligence.

Sister (31) has normal intelligence.

Sister (34) has normal intelligence as do her husband and children. She and (31) both refused to cooperate.

Sister (35) was institutionalized at age 11 years and died of pulmonary tuberculosis in the institution in 1918. She had no record of perinatal illness or congenital stigmata. IQ 14.

Nieces and Nephews

Not of interest.

First Cousins

Not of interest.

More Distant Relatives

Cousin (51) has an institutionalized retarded daughter (87) with IQ 54 and classified as undifferentiated. The latter had an illegitimate child (133) at age 16. This child was born after the mother had been institutionalized and was also institutionalized. IQ 70. The mother (87) was sterilized, and was later discharged from guardianship. She has been married twice; her present husband is a normal man. IQ range for (87) was 76, 54, 51, 89, 71, 60, 57, 75 and 70 from tests taken over a period of 20 years.

(87) has siblings with borderline and low normal IQ's of 88, 78, 81, 80 and 78. There are ten persons in this sibship of (87); they have produced a total of five children.

Family Summary

The proband and her sister, middle and low grade, were the only retarded persons in their immediate family. One first cousin's family had one retarded person of higher grade. The proband's parents had six children and three grandchildren.

Retardation of proband of primarily genetic origin.

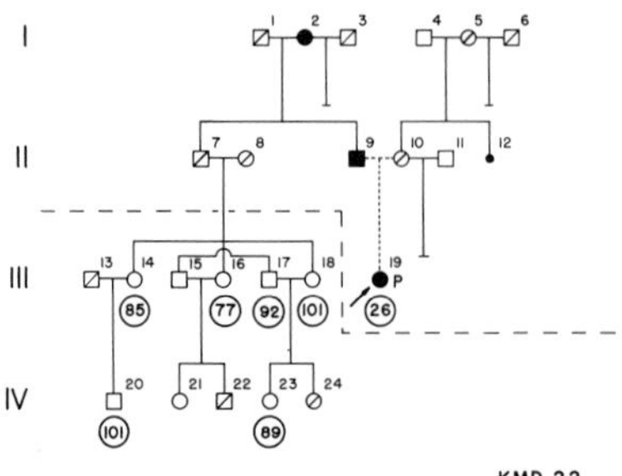

KMD 22

KMD 22

The Proband

The proband (19) was born in 1905, institutionalized at 2 years and died in 1919 of chronic enteritis in the institution. The proband was delivered at 7 months with the right eye congenitally undeveloped and the left eye sightless. She never walked or talked. IQ 26. *Diagnosis:* microphthalmia.

Grandparents

Paternal grandfather was an alcoholic, who refused to support his family and was divorced by his wife. He had normal intelligence.

Paternal grandmother was mentally retarded.

Maternal grandfather became an alcoholic, was divorced by his wife and was imprisoned for larceny. He had normal intelligence.

Maternal grandmother was an alcoholic, an epileptic and became blind from a syphilitic infection. After the birth of her last child she was hospitalized for several months for mental illness. In later life she became "harmlessly insane." Her intelligence is unknown.

Parents

Father (9) was an alcoholic and mentally retarded.

Mother (10) was reared in a very poor environment. She became illegitimately pregnant at age 15. Intelligence unknown.

Aunts and Uncles

Paternal uncle (7) was originally classified as retarded. However, he completed seven years of schooling by age 15 and supported his family as a railroad brakeman until his death in 1917. Intelligence unknown.

Siblings

None.

Nieces and Nephews

None.

First Cousins

Not of interest.

More Distant Relatives

Not of interest.

Family Summary

The proband's family exhibited a great variety of social problems including divorce, alcoholism, crime, venereal disease and promiscuity. The retardation shown in the paternal grandmother and in the proband's father may well have been the product of the environment. The proband's cousins had IQ scores of 85, 77 and 101, and their children are normal in intelligence. This family of the proband's paternal uncle seems to be rising above its poor background.

Retardation of proband of primarily genetic origin (microphthalmia).

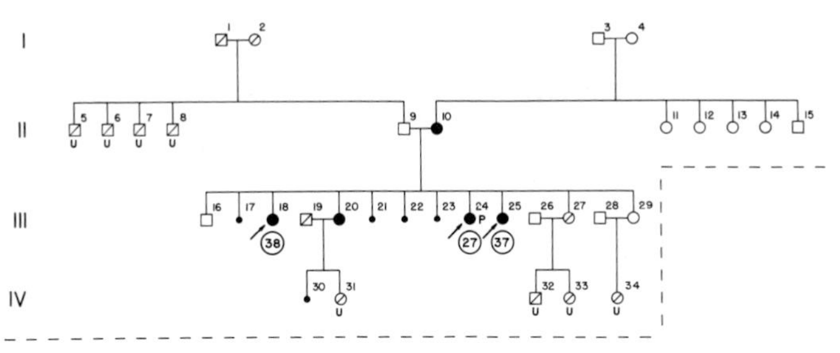

KMD 26

KMD 26

The Proband

The proband (24) was born in 1878, institutionalized at age 18 years and died of a cerebral hemorrhage in the institution in 1939. She went to school but learned little. She was unmarried and childless. IQ 27. *Diagnosis:* undifferentiated mental retardation.

Grandparents

Maternal grandparents had normal intelligence; maternal grandfather committed suicide.

Parents

Father (9) was an alcoholic but had normal intelligence. He was a wheat inspector.

Mother (10) was retarded.

Aunts and Uncles

Paternal aunts and uncles remained in Switzerland.

Maternal aunts and uncles all died young in Switzerland. They had normal intelligence.

Siblings

Brother (16) was a mail carrier and town treasurer who died single and childless.

Brother (17) died at 1 day of prematurity.

Sister (18) was institutionalized in 1915 and has remained in the institution. IQ 38.

Sister (20) has been unknown since 1906. She married a much older man who treated her very cruelly and forced her to support him. She left him and was never heard of again. She was mentally retarded.

(21), (22) and (23) all died in infancy. Causes of death unknown, except for (22), who died of diphtheria.

Sister (25) was institutionalized in 1896 and died of carcinoma of the breast in the institution in 1946. She became paranoid a year before her death. IQ 37.

Sister (27) of unknown intelligence. She married a normal man but her present status is unknown.

Sister (29) had normal intelligence and married a normal man. Her present status is unknown.

Nieces and Nephews

Unknown.

First Cousins

None on the maternal side.

Unknown on the paternal side.

More Distant Relatives

Unknown.

Family Summary

The proband, three sisters and her mother were retarded. The known IQ's are quite similar, 38, 27 and 37. The proband's parents had 11 children and at least five grandchildren.

Retardation of proband of primarily genetic origin.

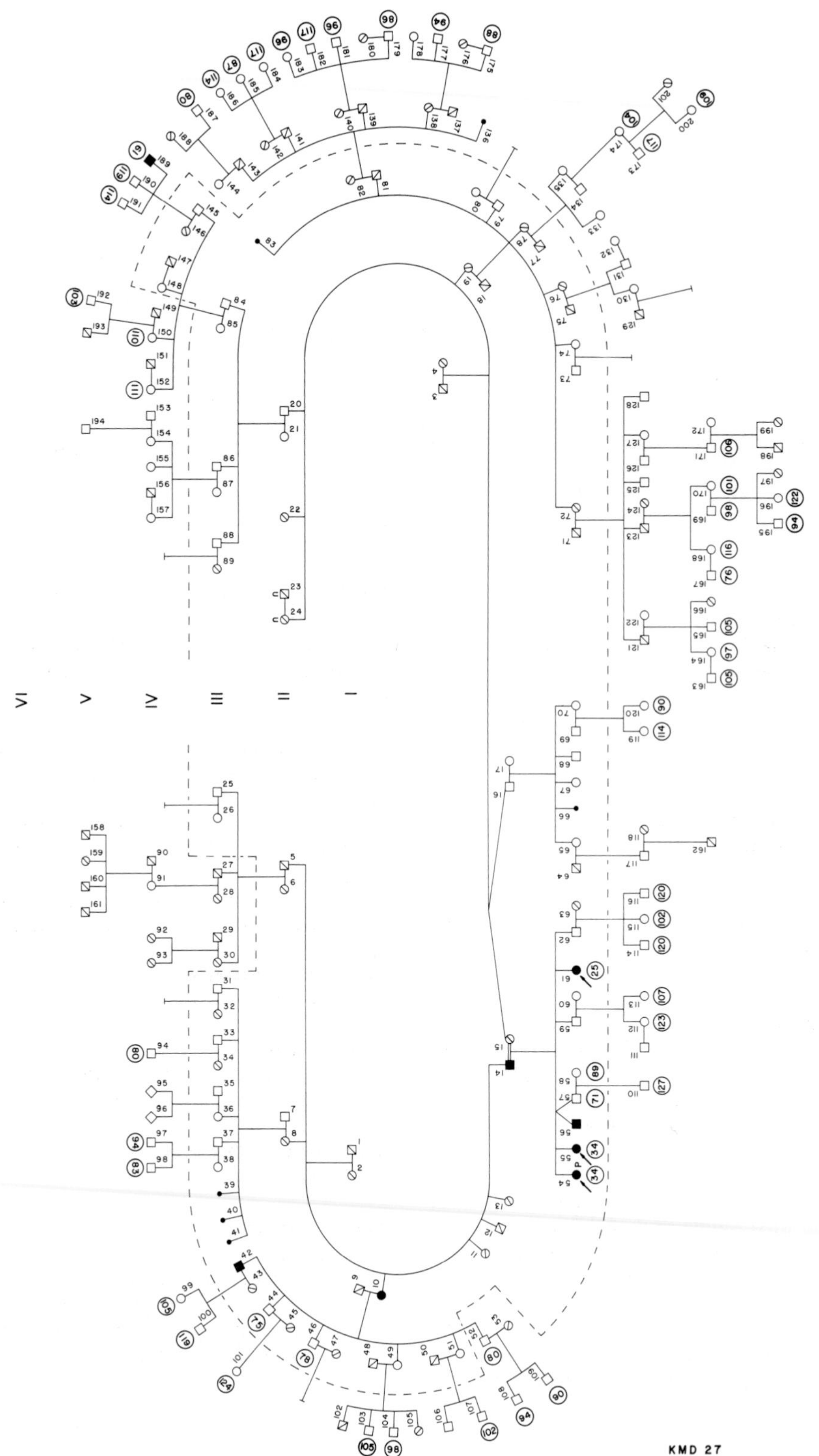

KMD 27

KMD 27

The Proband

The proband (54) was born in 1893, institutionalized at age 18 and discharged to her parents four years later. She was unmarried and childless and lived with relatives until her readmission in 1959. She had a large goiter at birth, which increased in size for several years but in adulthood diminished greatly. Institution records state that the goiter was not thought to be related to the retardation, and was diagnosed as nontoxic, nodular. In recent years the proband has become hyperactive, paranoid and hallucinated. IQ 34. *Diagnosis:* undifferentiated mental retardation.

Grandparents

Maternal grandfather was epileptic.

Parents

The parents were first cousins once removed, the proband's mother being a first cousin to the proband's father's father. The father (14) worked at many occupations but succeeded at none and was mentally retarded. The mother (15) was hospitalized at one time for "climacteric insanity." She had a large goiter. Old records indicate she may have been mentally retarded, but the evidence is so confusing that no reliable estimate of her intelligence could be made.

Aunts and Uncles

A paternal aunt (10) was mentally retarded.

A paternal uncle (12) died of epilepsy.

Siblings

Sister (55) was institutionalized at age 15 years, discharged four years later and now lives with relatives. She also had a large goiter as a young child. It gradually disappeared as she matured. IQ 34.

Brother (56) is an unmarried laborer, mentally retarded.

Twin to (56) has an IQ of 71, wife's IQ 89, one child (110) with IQ 127. The wife (58) was a delinquent with an illegitimate child.

Brothers (59) and (62) are normal, as are their children. (62) has been hospitalized for alcoholism.

Sister (61) had the same institution history as the proband, but died shortly after her return home in 1915. She was described as a "mongolian type." She did not have a goiter. IQ 25.

Nieces and Nephews

All six have IQ scores above 100.

First Cousins

(42) completed the sixth grade and is a farmer. Old records list him as retarded.

More Distant Relatives

One first cousin (84) has a retarded grandchild (189) with IQ 61.

Family Summary

The proband's parents were first cousins once removed. The father and four of his seven children were mentally retarded, while a fifth child had an IQ of 71. Two daughters had very large goiters in childhood; their mother also had a goiter. These growths diminished greatly in size in adulthood. The third daughter was described as a "mongolian type." She did not have a goiter. The proband's parents had seven children and six grandchildren. The grandchildren all have above normal intelligence.

Retardation of proband of primarily genetic origin (consanguinity).

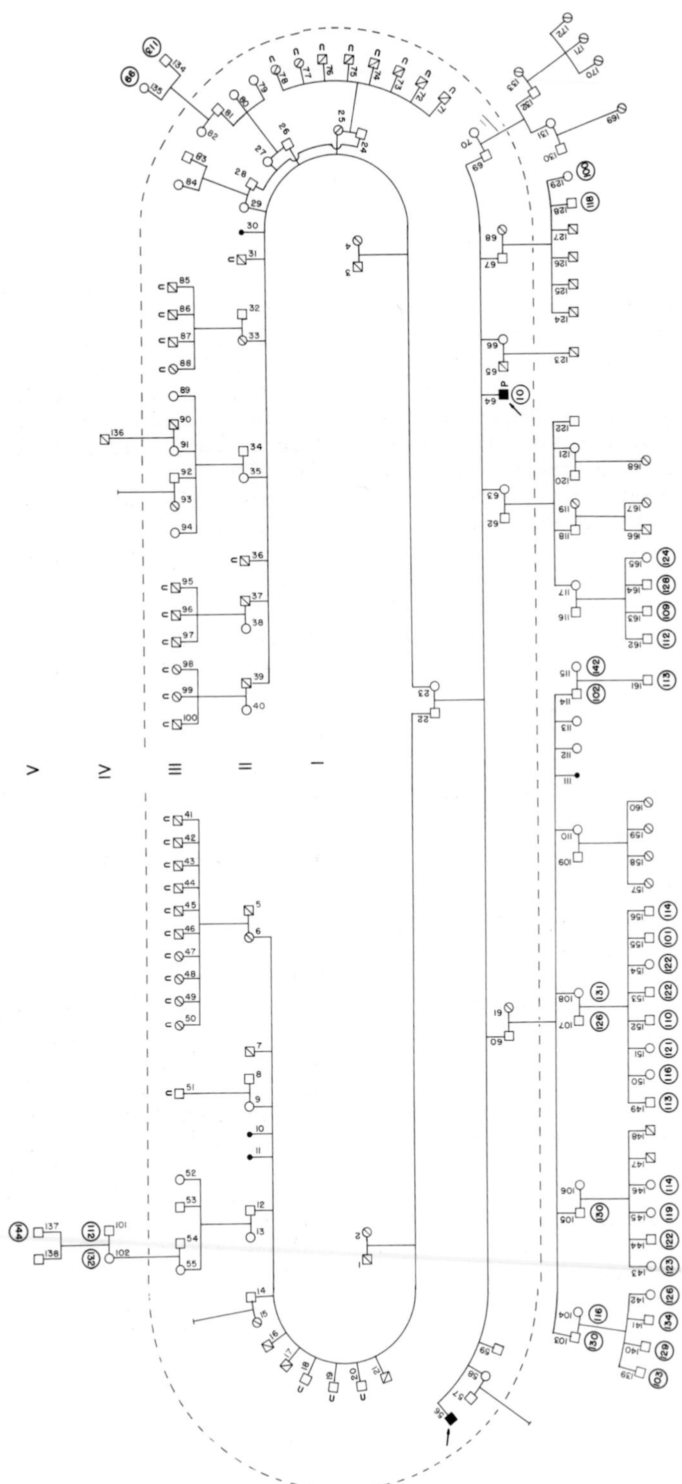

KMD 29

KMD 29

The Proband

The proband (64) was born in 1887, institutionalized at age 7 and died in 1939 of tuberculosis in the institution. He was born blind. The retardation was ascribed by the parents to a fall down a stairway at age 2½ years. He developed epilepsy after his institutionalization. IQ 10. *Diagnosis:* mental retardation with blindness.

Grandparents

Not of interest.

Parents

The father (22) was a wealthy building contractor.

The mother (23) had normal intelligence.

Aunts and Uncles

Not of interest. Nearly all of the paternal and maternal relatives remained in Canada.

Siblings

Brother (56) died in an institution in 1892 at the age of 17 years. He was blind and mentally retarded.

Brother (59) is blind and is now becoming deaf. He attended the State School for the Blind and a music conservatory. He has normal intelligence.

The seven remaining siblings are all well educated, prosperous people with no known retardates in their families.

Nieces and Nephews

Nephew (123) developed an eye tumor which was operated on but he is now blind and epileptic, intelligence unknown.

Two nephews, one niece (103), (105) and (108) have IQ's of 130, 130 and 131.

First Cousins

Not of interest.

More Distant Relatives

Not of interest.

Family Summary

In this socially superior family, the proband (IQ 10) and one brother are both retarded and blind; another brother is blind but normal, and a nephew is blind and epileptic. The proband developed epilepsy after his institutionalization. The proband's parents had nine children and 21 grandchildren. Many of these descendants have IQ scores well above average.

Retardation of proband of primarily genetic origin.

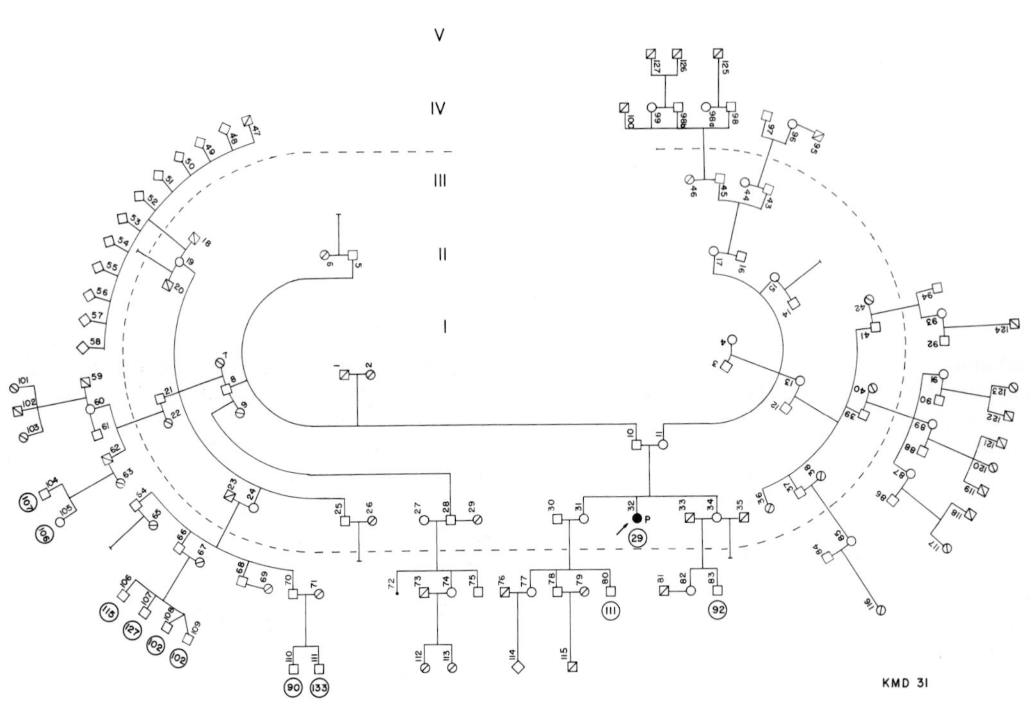

KMD 31

The Proband

The proband (32) was born in 1899, institutionalized at age 8, and died of typhoid fever in the institution in 1917. Her birth was an instrument delivery. IQ 29. *Diagnosis:* Down's syndrome.

Grandparents

Not of interest.

Parents

Both parents (10) and (11) had normal intelligence.

Aunts and Uncles

Not of interest.

Siblings

Two sisters (31) and (34) had normal intelligence.

Nieces and Nephews

Not of interest.

First Cousins

Not of interest.

More Distant Relatives

Not of interest.

Family Summary

The proband was the only retarded person in this family. Her parents had three children and five grandchildren.

Retardation of proband of primarily genetic origin (Down's syndrome).

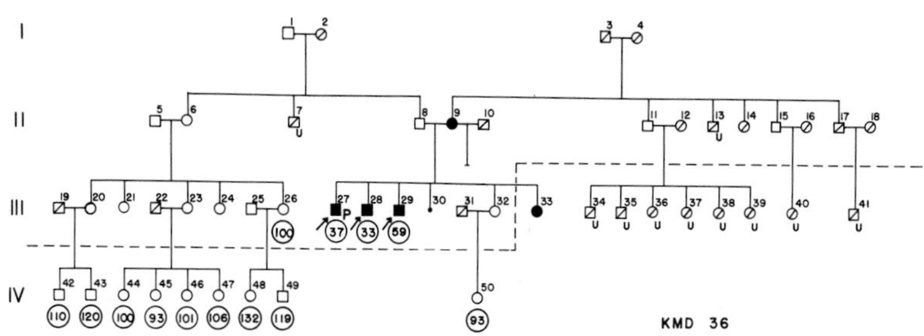

KMD 36

The Proband

The proband (27) was born in 1903, institutionalized at age 9 years and was still in the institution in 1961. He was given a physical and neurological examination in 1950 by J. A. Böök, M.D., and John Schut, M.D. No stigmata were found. IQ 37. *Diagnosis:* undifferentiated mental retardation.

Grandparents

Not of interest.

Parents

Father (8) was a periodic alcoholic and was cruel to his family. He deserted them in 1915 and has not been heard from since. He was a tinsmith and built his own house in his spare time. He had normal intelligence.

Mother (9) was literate but has been rated by various interviewers as a high-grade retardate both in 1912 and 1950.

Aunts and Uncles

Not of interest.

Siblings

Brother (28) was institutionalized at age 8 years and died in the institution in 1926 of epilepsy. IQ 33.

Brother (29) was institutionalized at age 7 years and died in the institution in 1925 of tuberculosis. He had Hutchinson's teeth and slight hydrocephalus. He had a negative Wassermann as did his brothers. IQ 59.

Brother (30) died of convulsions at age 7 months.

Sister (32) was interviewed in 1950 (age 40) and was bright and intelligent. Her only child is normal.

Sister (33) is unmarried, lives at home and is retarded.

Nieces and Nephews

Only a niece (50), IQ 93.

First Cousins

Not of interest.

More Distant Relatives

Not of interest.

Family Summary

The proband, IQ 37, had a retarded mother and three retarded siblings, two of whom had IQ's of 33 and 59. The parents had six children and only one grandchild, IQ 93. The fact that there was one normal girl (32) in the family, suggests that there was no universal infection or single environmental factor responsible for the remarkably similar subnormal intelligence of the three brothers (27), (28), (29) and the sister (33). There were numerous intelligence tests given to the brothers and the tests gave remarkably consistent results.

Retardation of proband of primarily genetic origin.

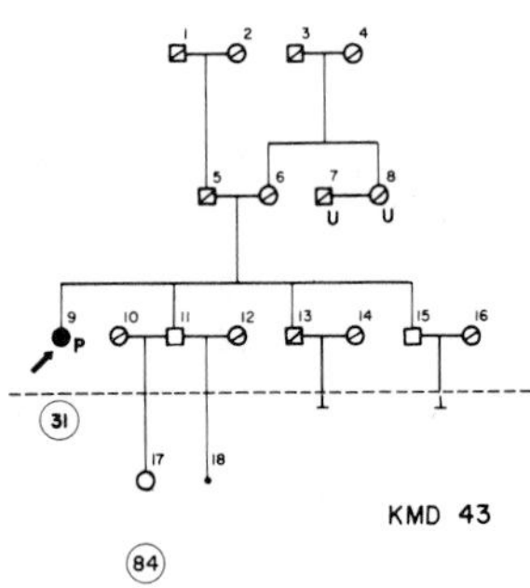

KMD 43

The Proband

The proband (9) was born in 1897, institutionalized at age 12 years and died of tuberculosis in the institution in 1933. IQ 31. *Diagnosis:* cretinism.

Grandparents

Maternal grandfather died of senile dementia.

Parents

Father (5) was thought to have been mentally ill. He abused his family greatly and finally deserted them. Intelligence unknown.

Mother (6) lived in utter squalor. She died in the poorhouse. Intelligence unknown.

Aunts and Uncles

Only one aunt (8), intelligence unknown.

Siblings

Brother (11) is a farmer and is normal despite childhood spent in a poorhouse and an orphanage.

Brother (13) works in a meat packing plant. He has a violent temper. Intelligence unknown.

Brother (15) operates a garage.

Nieces and Nephews

Only two, (17) who had poliomyelitis and is unmarried at age 33, IQ 84; and (18), a boy who died shortly after birth.

First Cousins

Unknown.

More Distant Relatives

Unknown.

Family Summary

The proband's mother and siblings became public charges after the father's desertion. Despite the bad environment, the proband's siblings evinced normal intelligence and became self-supporting. The proband's parents had four children and two grandchildren.

Retardation of proband of primarily genetic origin (cretinism).

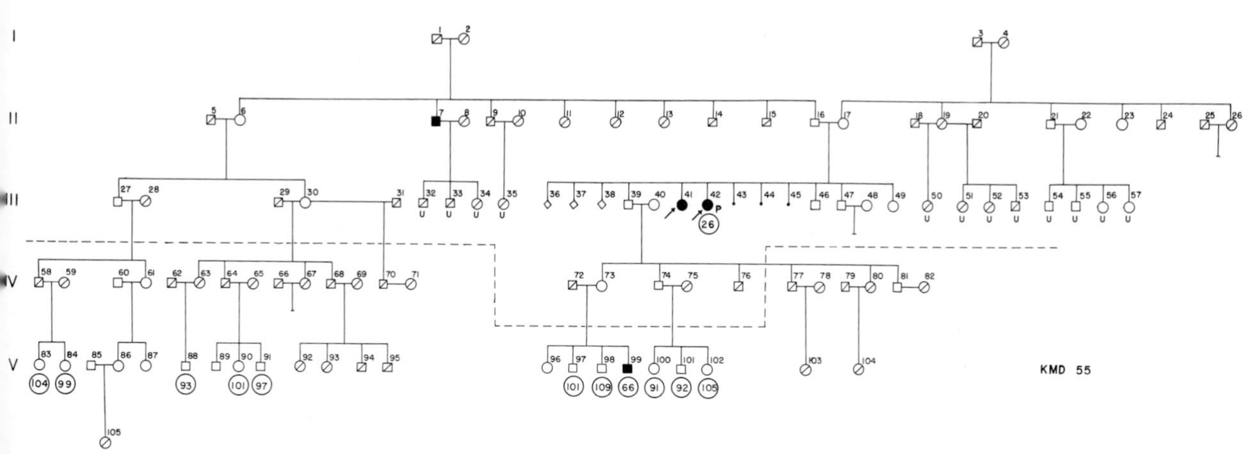

KMD 55

The Proband

The proband (42) was born in 1890, institutionalized at age 8 and died of hypertensive cardiovascular disease and phenylpyruvic oligophrenia in the institution in 1959. She never talked well and never went to school. In 1950 she was given a physical and neurological examination by J. A. Böök, M.D., and John Schut, M.D. No stigmata were found. IQ 26. *Diagnosis:* phenylketonuria.

Grandparents

Not of interest.

Parents

Father (16) operated his own tailor shop.

Mother (17) had normal intelligence.

Aunts and Uncles

Paternal uncle (7) was retarded. He died of alcoholism at age 50.

Paternal aunt (13) was mentally ill.

Siblings

Three siblings (36), (37) and (38) never came to this country and are unknown.

Brothers (39), (46) and (47) had normal intelligence. (39) has a retarded grandchild.

Sister (41) was institutionalized at age 8 and died at age 24 in the institution. She never learned to talk well and was epileptic. She was blonde, blue-eyed and had athetoid movements of her head and hands, indicating that she also had phenylketonuria.

Three siblings died in infancy of "spasms."

Sister (49) has normal intelligence.

Nieces and Nephews

Not of interest.

First Cousins

Not of interest.

More Distant Relatives

Proband's niece (73) has a retarded son (99), IQ 66.

Family Summary

The proband and her institutionalized sister, both low-grade retardates and both phenylketonurics, were the only retardates in the immediate family. One paternal uncle and one great-nephew were high-grade retardates. The proband's parents had 12 children. From their nine children known in this country there are six grandchildren, all descended from one normal son.

Retardation of proband of primarily genetic origin (phenylketonuria).

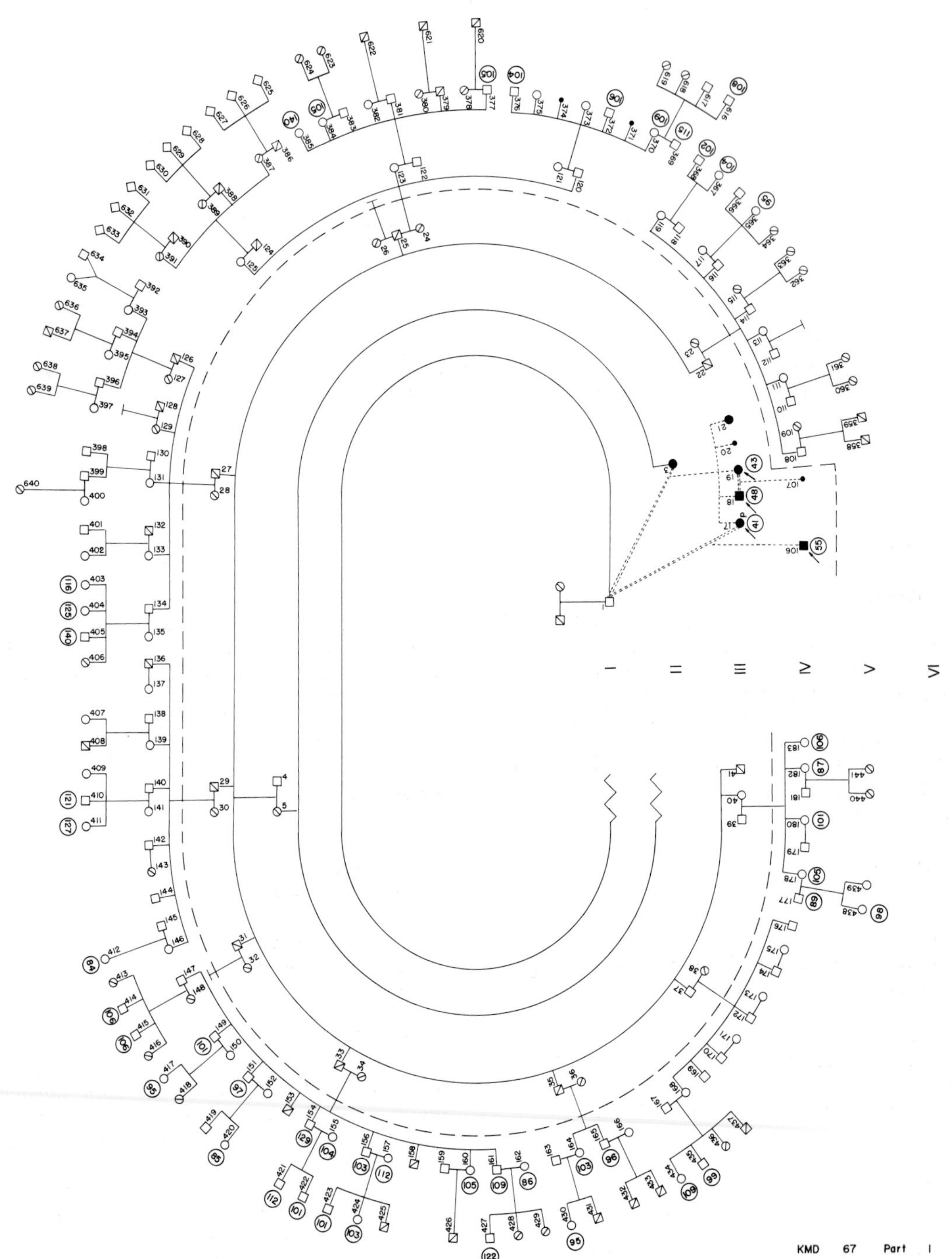

KMD 67

The Proband

The proband (17) was born in 1882, institutionalized at age 30 years and died of adenocarcinoma of the breast in 1951. She was the child of her grandfather by his daughter and she, herself, had a child by him. She was given a physical and neurological examination by J. A. Böök, M.D., and John Schut, M.D., in 1950. No stigmata were found. IQ 41. *Diagnosis:* undifferentiated mental retardation.

Grandparents

Proband's grandfather (1) was also her father. He had normal intelligence.

Parents

Father (1) see above.

Mother (3) was retarded. She was the proband's half sister by the legal wife of (1).

Aunts and Uncles

No paternal aunts and uncles.

Maternal relatives are also half siblings—see below.

Siblings

Brother (18) was institutionalized at age 28 years and died of pulmonary tuberculosis in the institution in 1944. IQ 48.

Sister (19) was institutionalized at age 20 years and died of bronchopneumonia in the institution in 1914. She had a child by her brother (18). IQ 43 and epileptic.

(20) died at birth.

(21) died at 3 years of jaundice. She had a peculiar high palate and was retarded.

Half sister (3), also the proband's mother, retarded.

Half sister (5) died in 1926, intelligence unknown. She married a normal spouse and has no retarded descendants.

Half sister (7) died in 1907 of a "nervous breakdown."

Half brother (8) died in 1920. He was alcoholic and was thought by some to have been retarded. He married a normal woman who supported the family.

Half brother (10) died in 1954 of arthritis. He was an alcoholic and thought by some to be retarded. He married a sister to the wife of (8), a teacher, who had epilepsy.

Half sister (13) died in 1947. Her intelligence was unknown but she married a normal spouse.

Half sister (15) had unknown intelligence.

The mother of the above half siblings had unknown intelligence.

Child

Son (106) was institutionalized at age 12 years and has remained in the institution ever since. He was given a physical and neurological examination by Drs. Böök and Schut in 1950. They reported possible schizophrenia in addition to retardation. IQ 55.

Nieces and Nephews

Only one full niece or nephew (107), sex unknown, who died in infancy.

Half siblings' children not of interest except for (83) who had a retarded son (345) with IQ 60, (79) who had a son (324) with IQ 68, (86) who had normal intelligence but had one illegitimate child (347) with IQ 113 and one legitimate child (348) by a retarded husband with IQ 71.

First Cousins

The same people as half siblings' children.

More Distant Relatives

None of interest.

Family Summary

The proband, her siblings and her child, all retarded, were the result of father-daughter incest, normal father with retarded daughter. Very little retardation appeared in other portions of this rather large family. The proband's parents had five children and two grandchildren, one deceased, one institutionalized. With the eventual death of (106) this incredibly incestuous sibship will have become extinct.

Retardation of proband of primarily genetic origin (consanguinity).

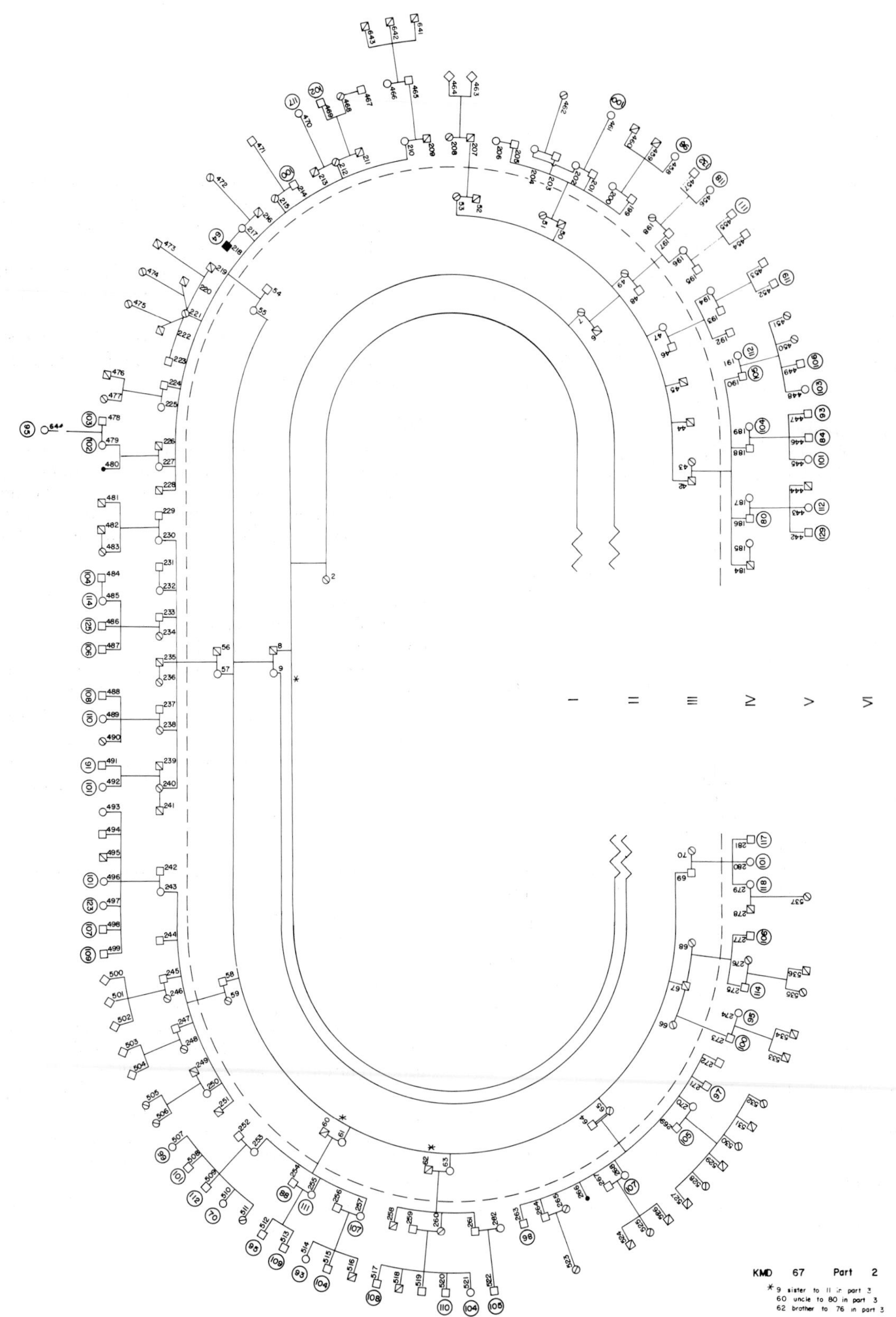

KMD 67 Part 2

* 9 sister to 11 in part 3
60 uncle to 80 in part 3
62 brother to 76 in part 3

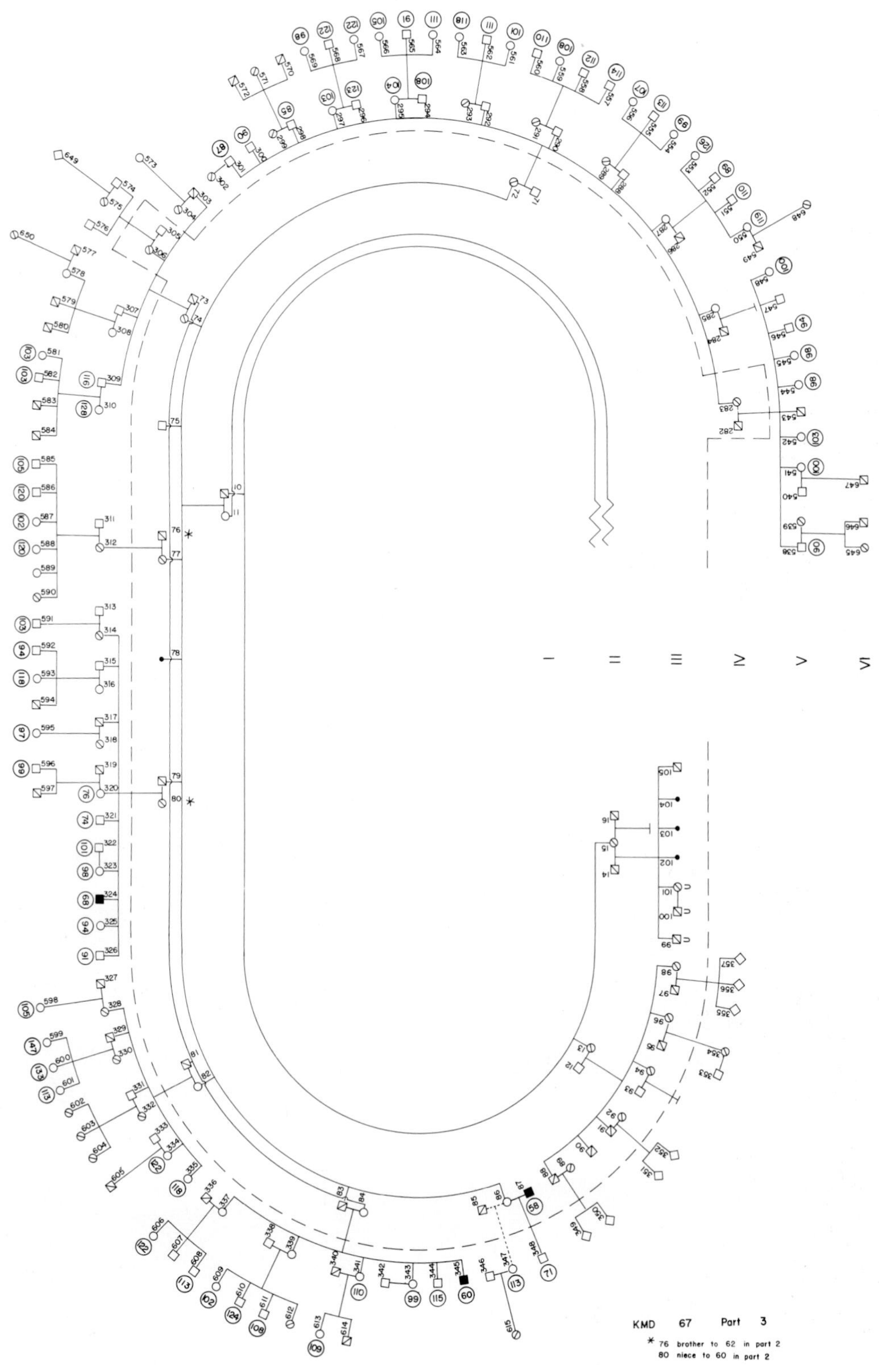

KMD 67 Part 3

* 76 brother to 62 in part 2
80 niece to 60 in part 2

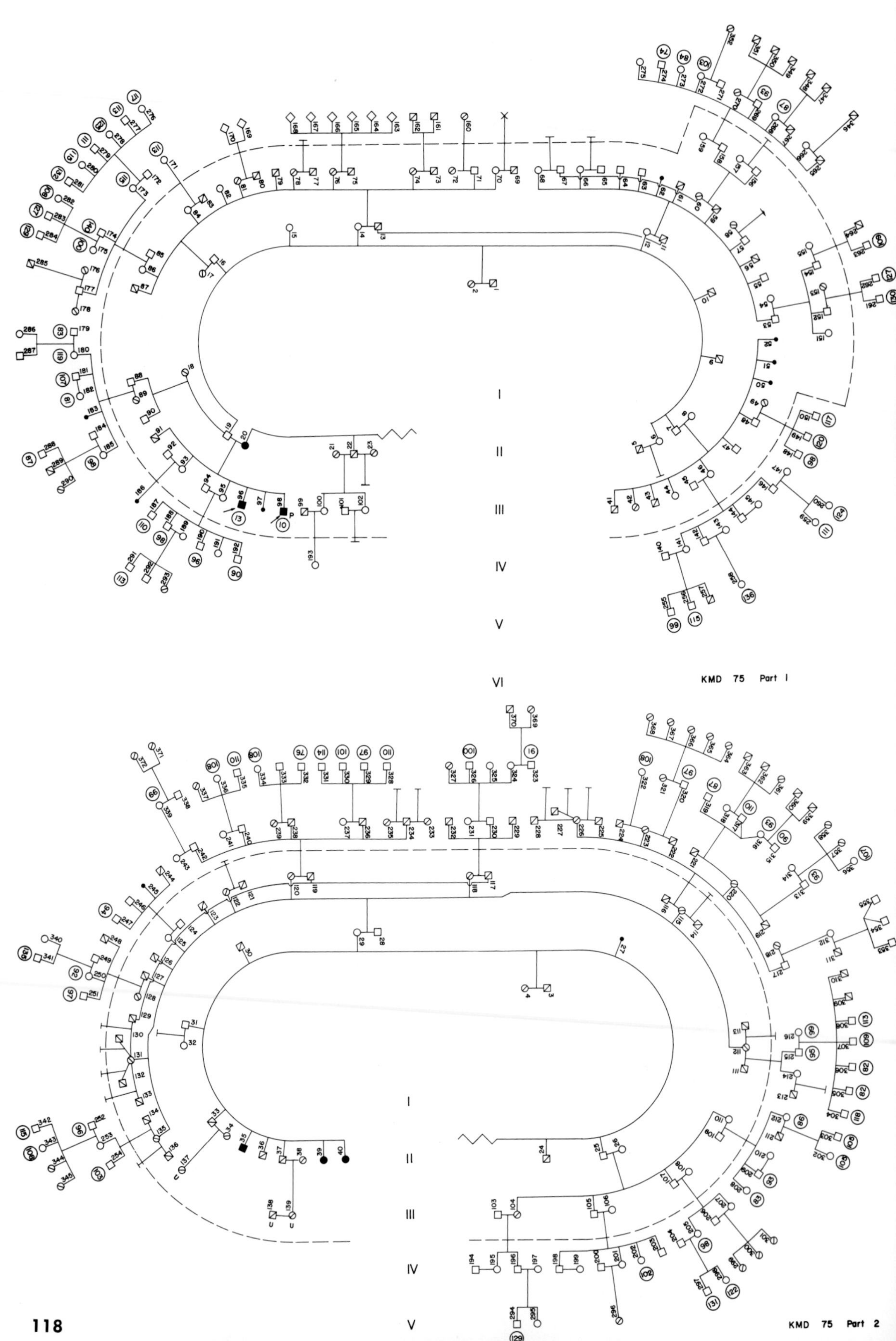

KMD 75 Part 1
KMD 75 Part 2

KMD 75

The Proband

The proband (98) was born in 1897, institutionalized at age 14 years and was still in the institution in 1961. IQ 10. *Diagnosis:* phenylketonuria.

Grandparents

Maternal grandmother had senile dementia.

Parents

Father (19) had normal intelligence but was an alcoholic, cruel to his family and subject to epileptiform attacks.

Mother (20) was retarded.

Aunts and Uncles

Maternal uncle (22) murdered his first wife and attempted suicide but recovered. He had two normal children.

Maternal uncle (33) died of alcoholism, wife and child unknown.

Maternal uncle (35) died single and childless in a mental hospital. He was retarded.

Maternal uncle (37) had a wife (38) who was hospitalized for mental illness. They had one unknown child.

Maternal aunt (39) died at 16 years. She was retarded.

Maternal aunt (40) died at 12 years as the result of a fall. She was retarded.

Siblings

Brother (91) was an unmarried and childless construction worker of unknown intelligence.

Sister (93) is normal and married a normal man. Her only child died at birth.

Sister (95) is illiterate, had very little schooling but helped support the family, married a normal man and had five normal children.

Sister (97) died at 9 days of "spasms."

Brother (96) was institutionalized in 1909 at age 13 years and died of tuberculosis in the institution in 1911. IQ 13. No diagnosis.

Half Siblings

(88) and (90) both normal.

Nieces and Nephews

Not of interest.

Children of Half Siblings

Not of interest.

First Cousins

Not of interest.

More Distant Relatives

Not of interest.

Family Summary

The proband and his brother were low-grade retardates. The proband's mother, a maternal uncle and two maternal aunts were also retarded. The proband's parents had six children and six grandchildren.

Retardation of proband of primarily genetic origin (phenylketonuria).

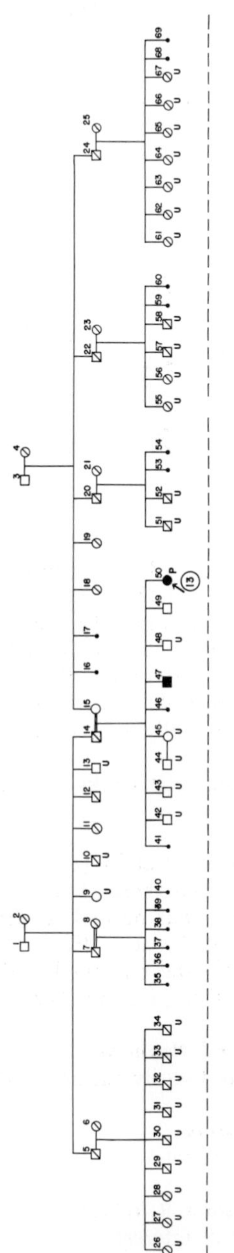

KMD 89

The Proband

The proband (50) was born in 1901, institutionalized at age 11 years and died of lobar pneumonia in the institution in 1919. IQ 13. *Diagnosis:* Down's syndrome.

Grandparents

Maternal and paternal grandmothers were sisters.

Parents

Father (14) had unknown intelligence.

Mother (15) was normal. She was 46 years old when the proband was born. (14) and (15) were first cousins.

Aunts and Uncles

A first cousin marriage of a paternal uncle (7) produced six daughters who died in infancy. All aunts and uncles except (13) remained in Sweden.

Siblings

All normal except for two unknown who died in infancy and a brother (47) who was retarded and had "mongoloid features."

Nieces and Nephews

Unknown.

First Cousins

Unknown. All remained in Sweden.

More Distant Relatives

Unknown.

Family Summary

The proband had Down's syndrome. She had a retarded brother with "mongoloid features." The parents were first cousins and the mother was 46 years old when the proband was born. The proband's parents had nine children; number of grandchildren unknown. Family could not be found for follow-up because the family name was the same as a commonly occurring Scandinavian name.

Retardation of proband of primarily genetic origin (Down's syndrome).

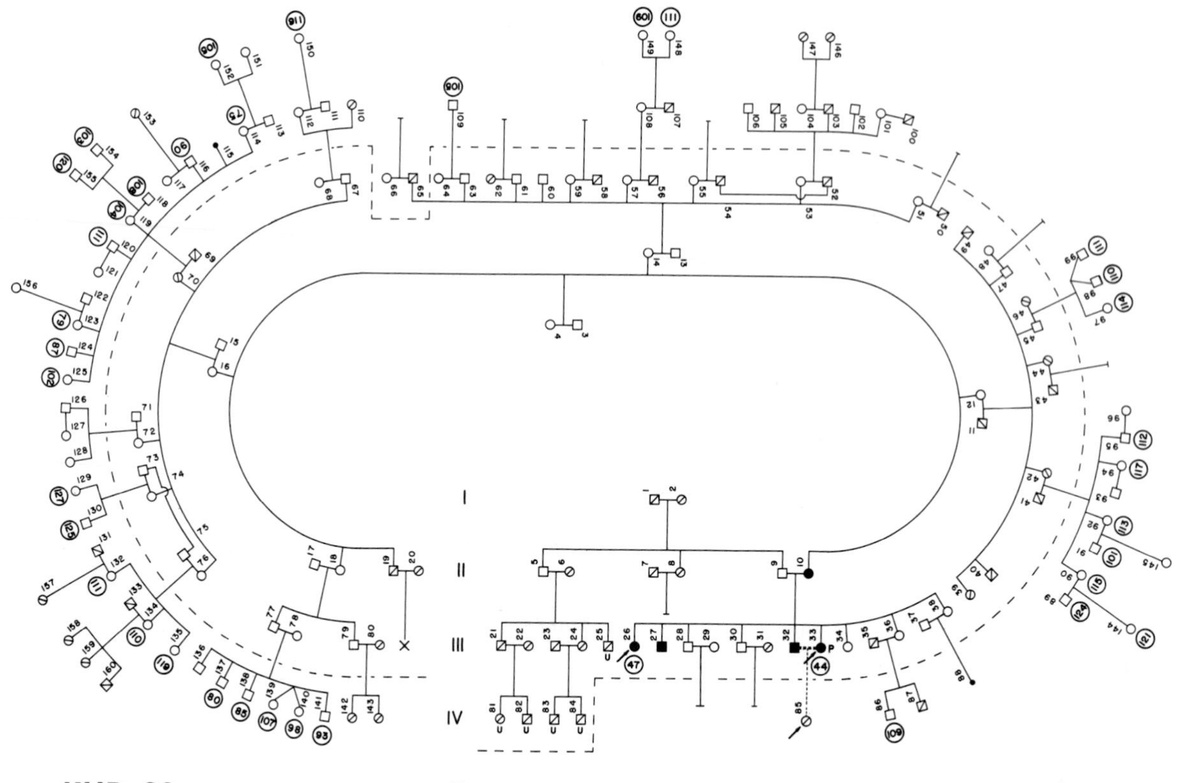

KMD 90

KMD 90

The Proband

The proband (33) was born in 1897, institutionalized at age 19 years, transferred 14 years later to a second state institution where she died of a cerebral hemorrhage in 1949. She had no stigmata and no history of early trauma. She went to school for five years but learned very little. She was institutionalized when she became pregnant by her brother (32). IQ 44. *Diagnosis:* undifferentiated mental retardation.

Grandparents

Not of interest.

Parents

Father (9) was a prosperous farmer.

Mother (10) would not talk except to repeat her husband's statements and was reported to have been very dull.

Aunts and Uncles

Not of interest.

Siblings

Sister (26) was institutionalized in 1905, transferred to a second state institution in 1930 where she died of cirrhosis of the liver in 1958. Between 2 and 3 years of age she had meningitis and the attending physician warned the parents of possible retardation. She developed epilepsy in 1915 at the age of 29 years. IQ 47.

Brother (27) died single at age 31 of heart trouble. He was a farm laborer who could do only the simplest tasks. Retarded, of rather low grade.

Brother (28) is a farmer and community leader.

Brother (30) is a prosperous farmer.

Brother (32) is the father of the illegitimate child of his sister, the proband. He is a single farm laborer who could talk very little and was never allowed to handle machinery.

Sister (34) is a dress designer.

Sister (36) is a housewife of normal intelligence.

Sister (38) works in an office.

Child

Proband's child (85) was born in the institution and died there of pneumonia at the age of 3 years. She was normal at birth and walked before the age of 2 years. Her intelligence is unknown. Apparently she remained in the institution because there was no place for her to go.

Nieces and Nephews

Only two living, one with IQ 109.

First Cousins

Not of interest.

More Distant Relatives

Not of interest.

Family Summary

The proband, her mother and three of her siblings were all at the same level of retardation. The proband's illegitimate child, resulting from incest with a retarded brother, was apparently normal at age 2 years. The proband's parents had nine children and four grandchildren, two of whom died young.

Retardation of proband of primarily genetic origin.

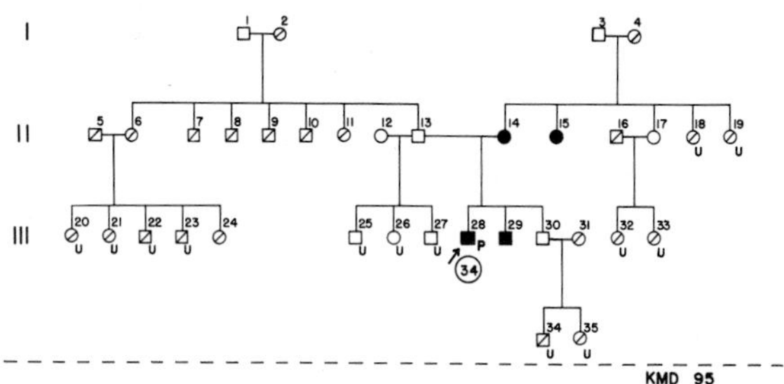

KMD 95

The Proband

The proband (28) was born in 1885, institutionalized at age 21 years and died of tuberculosis in the institution in 1927. His birth and early life were uneventful. He attended school for two years but became more and more excitable and unmanageable. When he tried to kill his brother (he had just witnessed a butchering) he was put into a mental hospital, but escaped. The staff there refused to take him back because they thought he was retarded, so he was transferred to the institution for the retarded. He was taken on trial and proved to be a "good helpful boy." He had a high palate and exaggerated reflexes. IQ 34. *Diagnosis:* undifferentiated mental retardation.

Grandparents

Not of interest except that one set were supposed to have been first cousins. (Whether paternal or maternal unknown.)

Parents

Father (13) was a farmer and storekeeper who had normal intelligence.

Mother (14) had episodes of excitement and anger similar to those of the proband and was retarded.

Aunts and Uncles

Maternal aunt (15) was institutionalized in a mental hospital and is recorded as being both mentally ill and retarded.

Siblings

Brother (29) had quite low intelligence but could do simple tasks around the farm. He did not have the excitable disposition of his mother and brother.

Brother (30) was normal.

Three half siblings (25), (26) and (27) were normal.

Nieces and Nephews

Unknown.

First Cousins

Unknown.

More Distant Relatives

Unknown.

Family Summary

The proband, his mother, brother and maternal aunt were retarded, all of about the same grade. The proband and his mother were also excitable and high tempered, although the proband adjusted well to life in the institution. The children of the proband's father by another marriage were normal. The proband's parents had three children and two known grandchildren. This family could not be found for the follow-up.

Retardation of proband of primarily genetic origin.

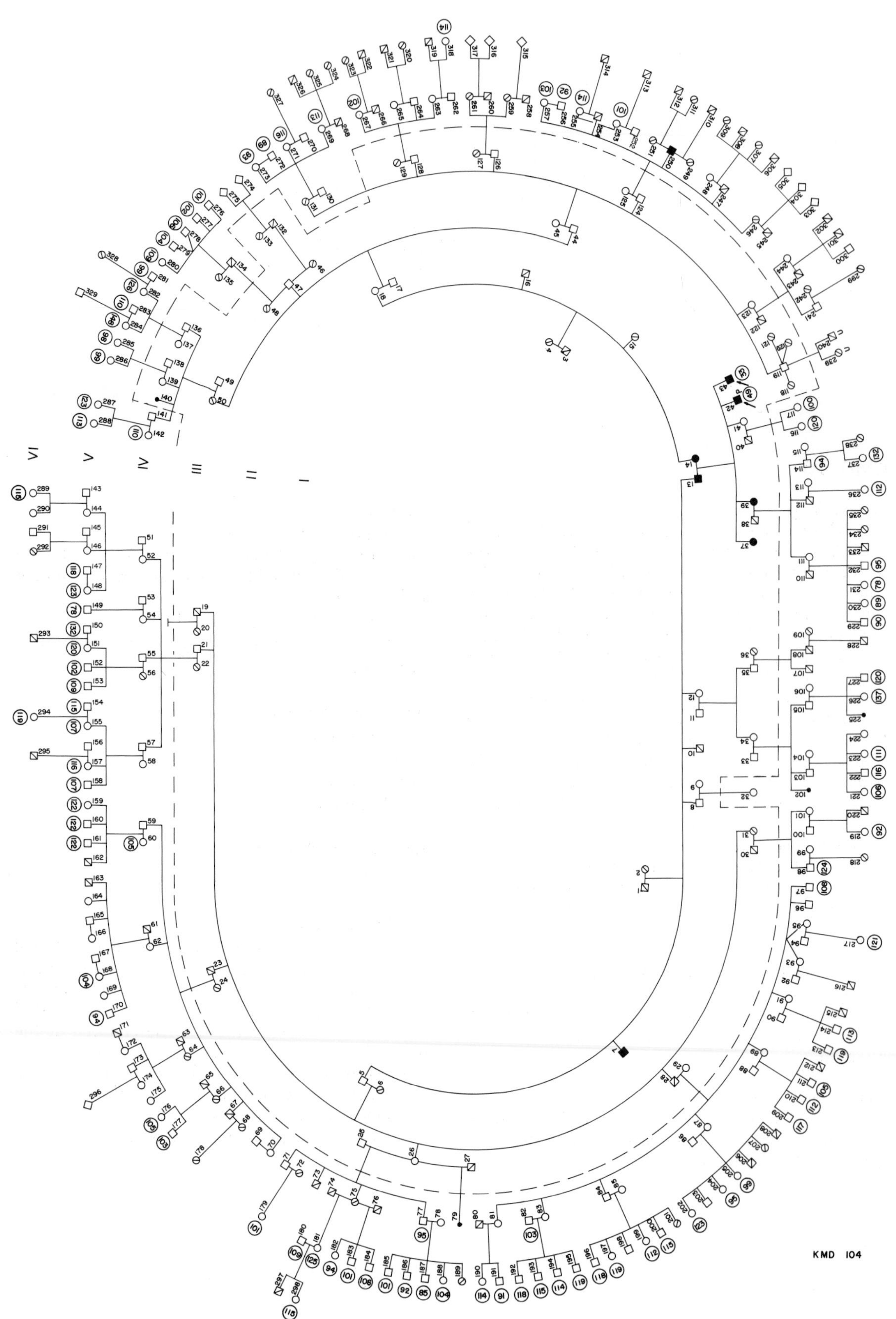

KMD 104

KMD 104

The Proband

The proband (42) was born in 1901, institutionalized at age 11 years and left the institution in 1919. He had no history of difficult delivery or perinatal disease and had no stigmata. In 1923 he was arrested for attempted rape and transferred from the prison to the Faribault institution. He escaped seven years later but reentered the institution a year later and died there of pulmonary tuberculosis in 1935. He walked at 3 years, attended school for four years but learned little. IQ 49. *Diagnosis:* undifferentiated mental retardation.

Grandparents

Not of interest.

Parents

Father (13) was almost illiterate. He was a retarded laborer.

Mother (14) was illiterate and could not keep house. Retarded.

Aunts and Uncles

Paternal uncle (7) was a single, childless farm laborer and was retarded.

Siblings

Sister (37) died at age 24, unmarried and childless. She was obese and retarded.

Sister (39) made little progress in school and is nearly illiterate. She is retarded. Her husband is an immigrant laborer of unknown intelligence, but their three children have normal intelligence.

Sister (41) has normal intelligence as do her children.

Brother (43) was institutionalized in 1912 at age 8 years and died of pneumonia in the institution in 1930. IQ 33.

Nieces and Nephews

Not of interest.

First Cousins

(19) murdered his wife and was transferred from prison to a state mental hospital where he died.

More Distant Relatives

First cousin (44) has a retarded grandchild (250) who was failing the fifth grade at age 13 years.

Family Summary

The proband, IQ 49, both his parents, a maternal uncle and three siblings were retarded. The home environment was poor. However, one of the proband's sisters was above average in some of her studies. She was sensitive about her family and refused to cooperate in this study. The affected persons were all illiterate, or nearly so, and apparently at about the same IQ levels. The proband's parents had five children and five grandchildren. The grandchildren all have normal intelligence including the three children of a retarded sister of the proband.

Retardation of proband of primarily genetic origin.

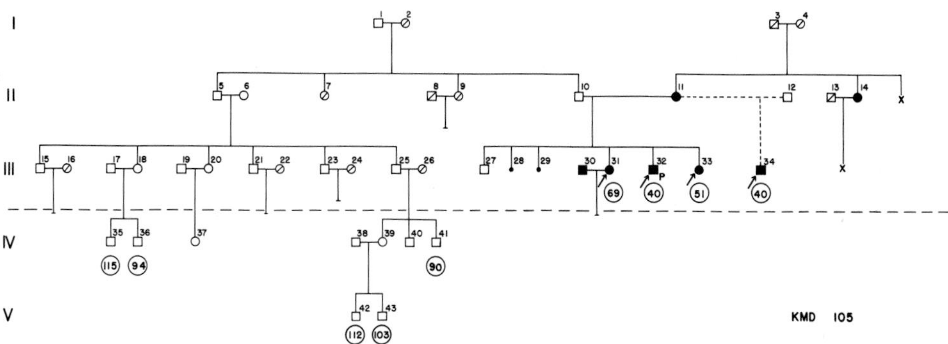

KMD 105

The Proband

The proband (32) was born in 1898, institutionalized at 7 years and was still institutionalized in 1961. He was terribly abused and neglected by his parents, but had no history of trauma. The proband was given a physical and neurological examination by J. A. Böök, M.D., and John Schut, M.D., in 1950. No stigmata were found. IQ 40. *Diagnosis:* undifferentiated mental retardation.

Grandparents

Not of interest.

Parents

Father (10) was forced to marry the proband's mother. He had normal intelligence but after his marriage deteriorated into an alcoholic and a poor provider.

Mother (11) was promiscuous and retarded. She had an illegitimate child before her forced marriage to (10). She and her husband both beat the children until the proband and his siblings were removed from the home and taken to the state orphanage.

Aunts and Uncles

Maternal aunt (14) was promiscuous and retarded. Old records described her as a "terror." Her husband was a thief.

Siblings

Brother (27) was accidently shot at age 9 years. He had been adopted from the orphanage and had normal intelligence.

(28) and (29) were stillbirths.

Sister (31) was institutionalized in 1907 at age 11 years, sterilized in 1931, escaped a year later and married (30) a retarded man. They abducted (33) from the institution and deserted her in California. (31) was discharged from guardianship in 1941 because California refused to extradite her. IQ 77, 71, 69, 72, 69 and 71 (scores obtained over a period of 17 years). Retarded.

Sister (33) was institutionalized at age 6 years and has remained in institutions ever since except for the three months when she was abducted to California by her sister and brother-in-law (31) and (30). She was given a physical and neurological examination by Dr. Böök and Dr. Schut in 1950. No stigmata were found. IQ 51.

Half brother (34) was institutionalized at age 5 years in 1893 and died in status epilepticus in the institution in 1920. IQ 40. His father was a store clerk.

Nieces and Nephews

None.

First Cousins

Not of interest.

More Distant Relatives

Not of interest.

Family Summary

The proband, his mother, a maternal aunt, two full siblings and a half sibling were retarded. The proband's parents abused and neglected their children to such an extent that the authorities put the children in an orphanage. Despite the bad home environment, one child proved to be normal and was adopted. The parents had six children, no grandchildren. Institutionalization and sterilization effectively curtailed the reproduction in this unfortunate family.

Retardation of proband of primarily genetic origin.

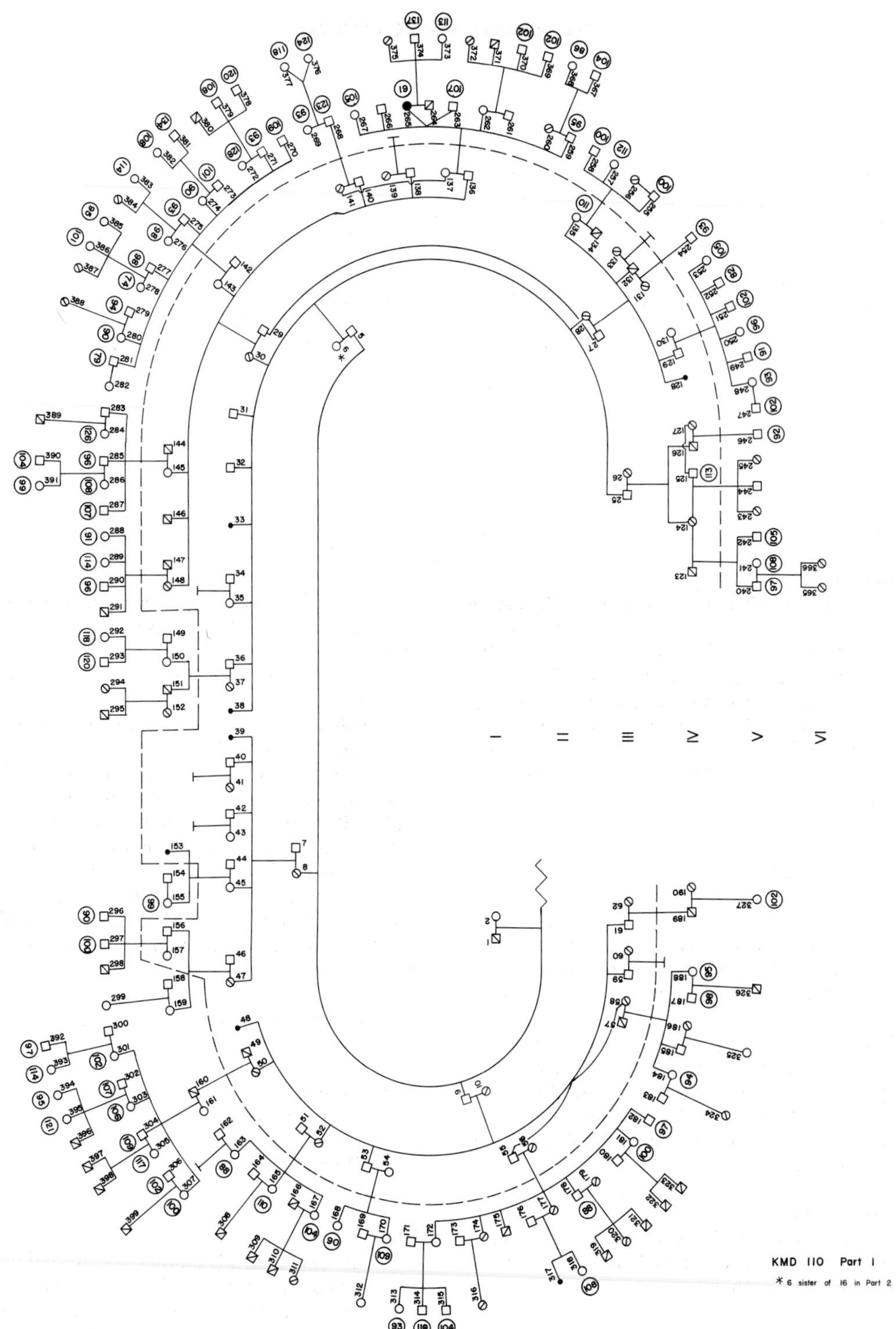

KMD 110

The Proband

The proband (107) was born in 1898, institutionalized at age 11 years, and died of tuberculosis in the institution in 1918. He was obese, polydactylous and nearly blind. IQ 30. *Diagnosis:* Laurence-Moon-Biedl syndrome.

Grandparents

Not of interest.

Parents

Father (19) was a farmer who had normal intelligence.

Mother (20) had normal intelligence.

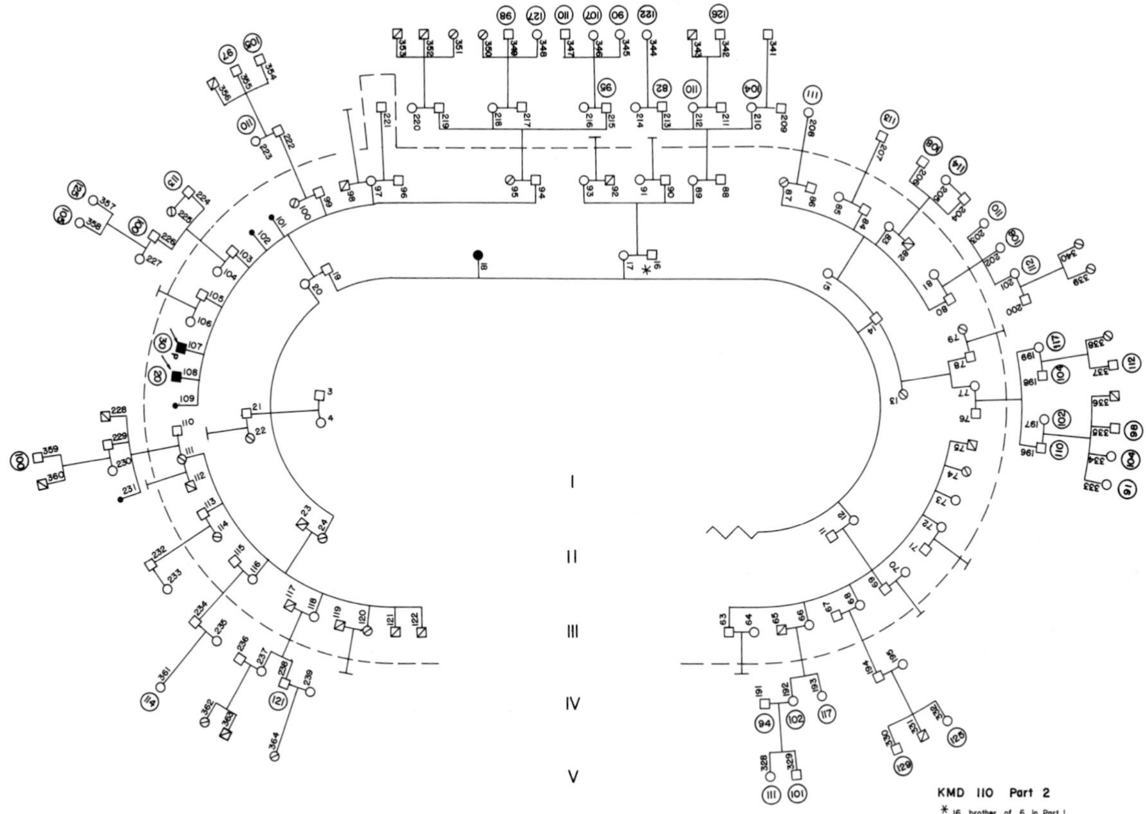

Aunts and Uncles

Paternal aunt (18) died single at age 52 years. She was classified as a low-grade retardate.

Siblings

Brother (94) was obese as a child but became quite slender. He is a salesman of normal intelligence, with normal children.

Sister (97) has normal intelligence, husband and child normal.

Brother (99) is a railroad fireman with normal intelligence and a normal son.

Brother (101) died at 1 year of pneumonia. He was obese and polydactylous.

Sister (102) died of burns at 6 months.

Brother (103) is a barber. He is obese but has normal intelligence as do his wife and children.

Brother (105) is a married but childless railroad station agent. He has normal intelligence and is not obese.

Brother (108) was institutionalized at age 9 years and died of hypopituitarism in the institution at age 23. He was obese and polydactylous but had normal vision. IQ 20.

Brother (109) died of pneumonia at 2 years. He was obese and polydactylous but walked and talked at age 2 years. Old records say, "Seemed all right mentally."

Nieces and Nephews

Not of interest.

First Cousins

Not of interest.

More Distant Relatives

First cousin (30) had a retarded grandchild (265) with IQ 61 who has a daughter (374) with IQ 37.

Family Summary

The proband's parents were normal. They had ten children of whom one was retarded, obese, polydactylous and blind; two were obese and polydactylous but died in infancy with unknown intelligence; two were obese with normal intelligence; three had normal intelligence and no stigmata; one died in infancy, no stigmata. There is no record of consanguinity of the parents. The proband and his retarded brother were so obese that a circus manager wanted them in a side show. The proband's parents had ten children and seven grandchildren.

Retardation of proband of primarily genetic origin (Laurence-Moon-Biedl syndrome).

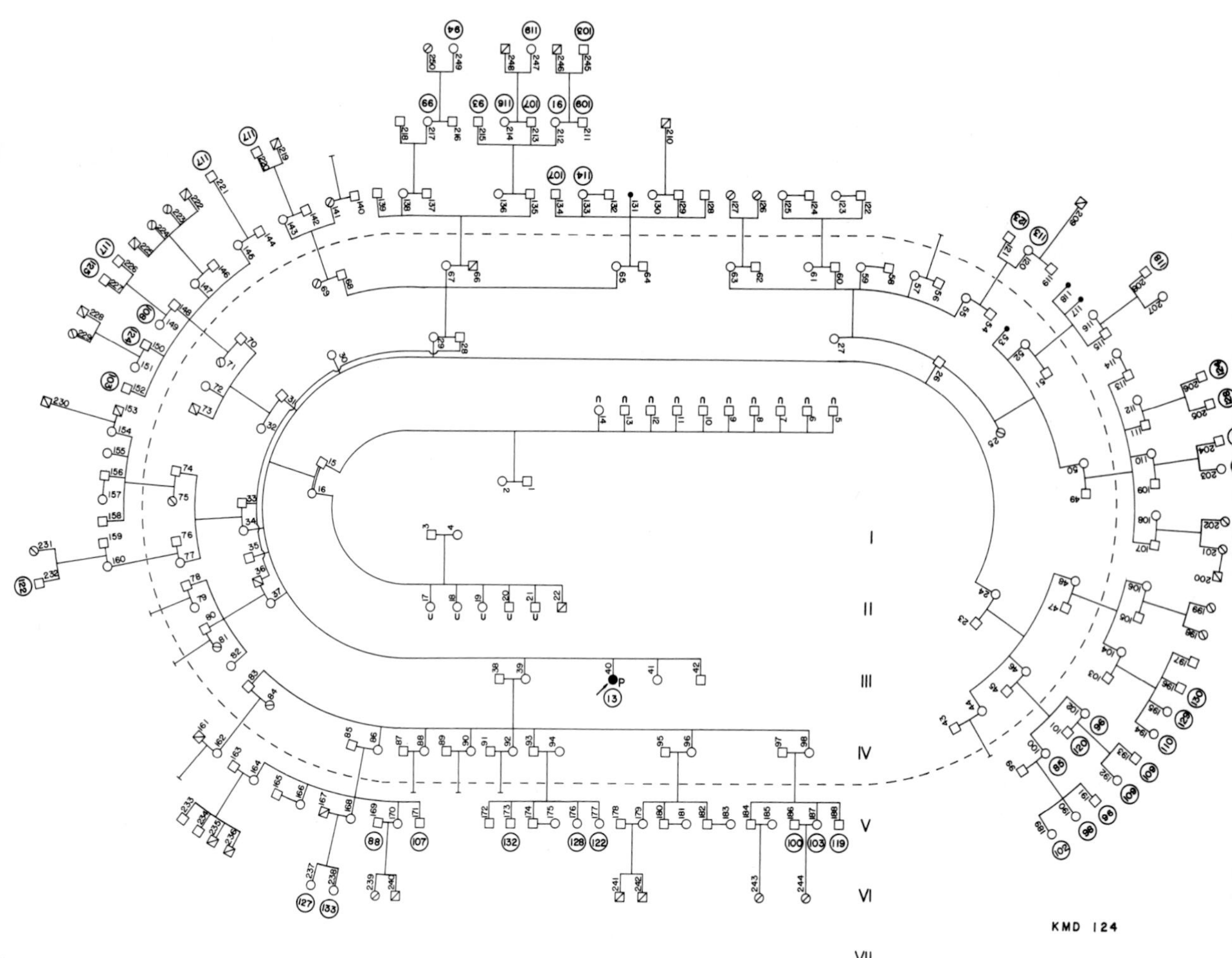

KMD 124

The Proband

The proband (40) was born in 1870, institutionalized at age 36 years and died of arteriosclerosis, chronic nephritis, myocarditis and mitral insufficiency in the institution in 1921. She was unmarried and childless. She seemed normal until the age of 3 when, according to the parents, she had an attack of "brain fever." She had no stigmata. IQ 13. *Diagnosis:* undifferentiated mental retardation.

Grandparents

All had normal intelligence.

Parents

Father (15) and mother (16) were second cousins both with normal intelligence.

Aunts and Uncles

All siblings of both the proband's parents remained in Scotland.

Siblings

All siblings had normal intelligence as do their children and grandchildren.

Nieces and Nephews

Not of interest.

First Cousins

Unknown.

More Distant Relatives

Not of interest.

Family Summary

The proband, IQ 13, was the only retarded person in the family. Her parents attributed her condition to a severe attack of "brain fever" at the age of 3 years. The proband's parents had 12 children and 30 grandchildren.

Retardation of proband of primarily genetic origin (consanguinity).

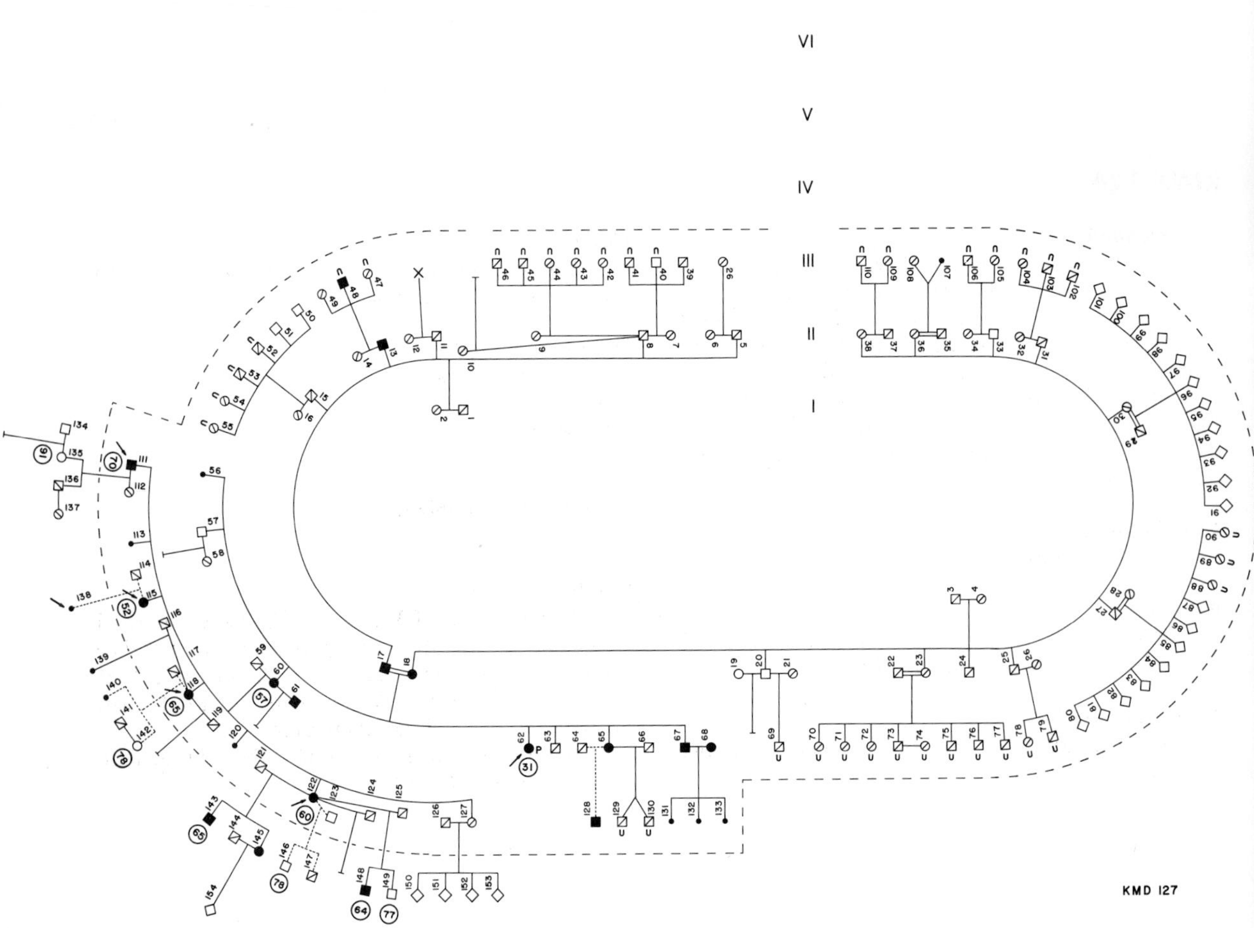

KMD 127

KMD 127

The Proband

The proband (62) was born in 1880, institutionalized at age 35 years and died of tuberculosis in the institution in 1932. Institution records state imbecility with aphasia, ataxic type. She had none of the stigmata of congenital syphilis, had three negative Wassermanns and no history of early trauma. IQ 31. *Diagnosis:* undifferentiated mental retardation.

Grandparents

Not of interest.

Parents

Father (17) was retarded.

Mother (18) was a distant cousin to her husband. She was retarded and syphilitic.

Aunts and Uncles

Paternal uncle (13) was retarded.

Four consanguineous marriages among the maternal relatives.

Siblings

Brother (56) died of "spasms" at two months.

Brother (57) was a married but childless clerk with normal intelligence.

Sister (60) was up for commitment at one time but the court decided she was not retarded. She was blind in one eye from an injury. IQ 57. Her first husband (59) died in a mental hospital. Her second husband (61) was retarded and four of her five surviving children are retarded.

Brother (63) accidentally shot himself. Intelligence unknown.

Sister (65) was retarded and had a retarded, illegitimate child (128) who died at age 2 years. He could not sit up and never attempted to talk.

Brother (67) was a plasterer's helper and was retarded as was his wife. He had a congenitally crippled left foot. His children died in infancy.

Nieces and Nephews

Nephew (111) was institutionalized at age 14 years. He left the institution two years later and joined the Army. IQ 70.

Niece (115) was institutionalized at age 10 years, left the institution two years later, was readmitted at age 14 when pregnant, and died of tuberculosis in the institution at age 28 years. IQ 52. She had signs of congenital syphilis (rhagades) but a negative Wassermann.

Niece (118) was institutionalized at age 20 years, sterilized a year later and after 16 years under outside supervision was discharged from guardianship in 1944. IQ 65.

Niece (122) was institutionalized at age 4 years, discharged two years later. Sterilization was considered but was not done. She married and left the state. She has had two illegitimate children (146) and (147), four legitimate ones (143), (145), (148) and (149) (two of whom are retarded and one borderline) and three husbands. She was sent to the reformatory at one time for neglecting her children. IQ 60.

Nephew (128) was a low-grade retardate who died at age 2 years.

First Cousins

Nearly all unknown, since the proband's maternal and paternal relatives did not come to Minnesota. One (48) is known to have been retarded.

More Distant Relatives

Two great-nephews (143) with IQ 65, and (148) with IQ 64, and one great-niece (145) are retarded.

Family Summary

The proband, her parents, a paternal uncle, three siblings, five nephews and nieces, one first cousin and three great-nephews and nieces were retarded. The other retardates with the exception of the proband and one nephew were high grade. The proband's parents were distant cousins. The proband's mother was syphilitic but none of the children including the proband is recorded as having signs of congenital syphilis or positive Wassermanns. The parents had seven children and 13 grandchildren. Of these 20 persons, five were institutionalized and five died in infancy. Four illegitimate children were born to two of the proband's nieces who had a total of seven spouses between them.

Retardation of proband of primarily genetic origin (consanguinity).

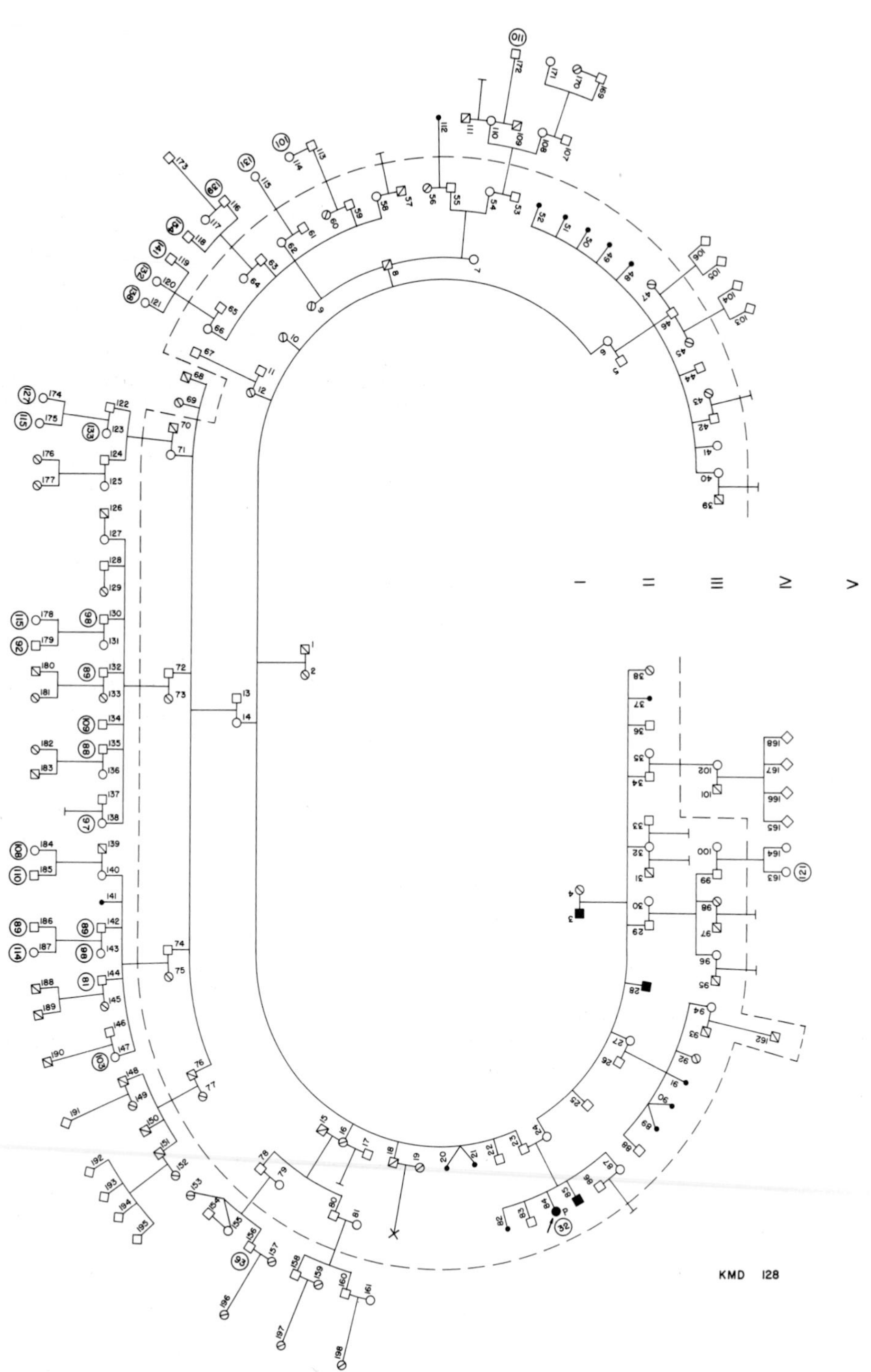

KMD 128

KMD 128

The Proband

The proband (84) was born in 1893, institutionalized at age 17 years and died of bronchopneumonia in the institution in 1937. She had no history of perinatal infection or birth trauma. IQ 32. *Diagnosis:* undifferentiated mental retardation.

Grandparents

Maternal grandfather was retarded.

Maternal grandmother was an alcoholic and left her husband.

Parents

Father (23) and mother (24) both had normal intelligence. The father was a stonecutter.

Aunts and Uncles

Maternal uncle (28), retarded, died single and childless.

Siblings

Brother (82) died at 2 days of "rupture of the bowels."

Brother (83) did not complete grade school, is unmarried and operates a sand and gravel business. Normal intelligence.

Brother (85) died single and childless. He was born crippled, dwarfed and retarded.

Sister (87) married but childless, went to business school and is a typist.

Nieces and Nephews

None.

First Cousins

Not of interest.

More Distant Relatives

Not of interest except for the children of the proband's cousins (62), (63) and (66). These six children, (115), (116), (118), (119), (120) and (121) have IQ's of 131, 139, 154, 141, 132 and 138, respectively.

Family Summary

The proband, her maternal grandfather and a maternal uncle and one sibling were retarded. The proband had an IQ of 32; her retarded brother was a middle-grade, crippled and dwarfed retardate. The proband's parents had five children and no grandchildren.

Retardation of proband of primarily genetic origin.

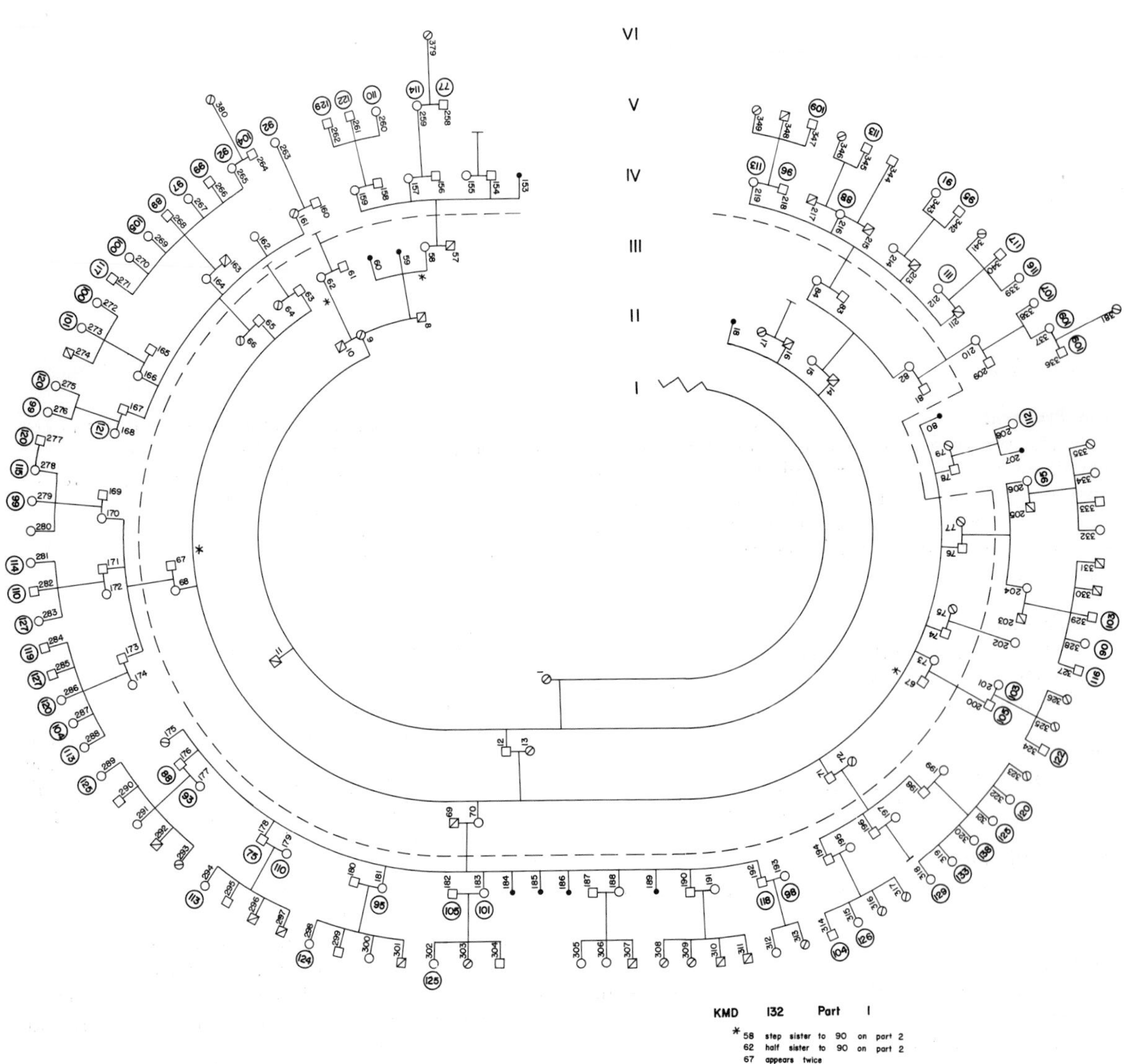

KMD 132

The Proband

The proband (122) was born in 1884, institutionalized at age 11 years and died of arteriosclerosis in the institution in 1940. At birth, the cord was around his neck and he lacked animation and was difficult to resuscitate. IQ 47. *Diagnosis:* Down's syndrome.

Grandparents

Maternal grandfather had senile dementia.

Parents

Both parents (31) and (32) had normal intelligence.

Aunts and Uncles

Paternal uncle (23) was mentally ill for ten years before his death.

Paternal aunt (28) was mentally ill.

Maternal uncle (36) was epileptic.

Siblings

Brother (107) died of appendicitis at 6 years.

Sister (108) died of "inflammation of the lungs" at 18 months.

Sisters (110) and (112), and brothers (116) and (118) had normal intelligence. All married normal spouses but only two had children.

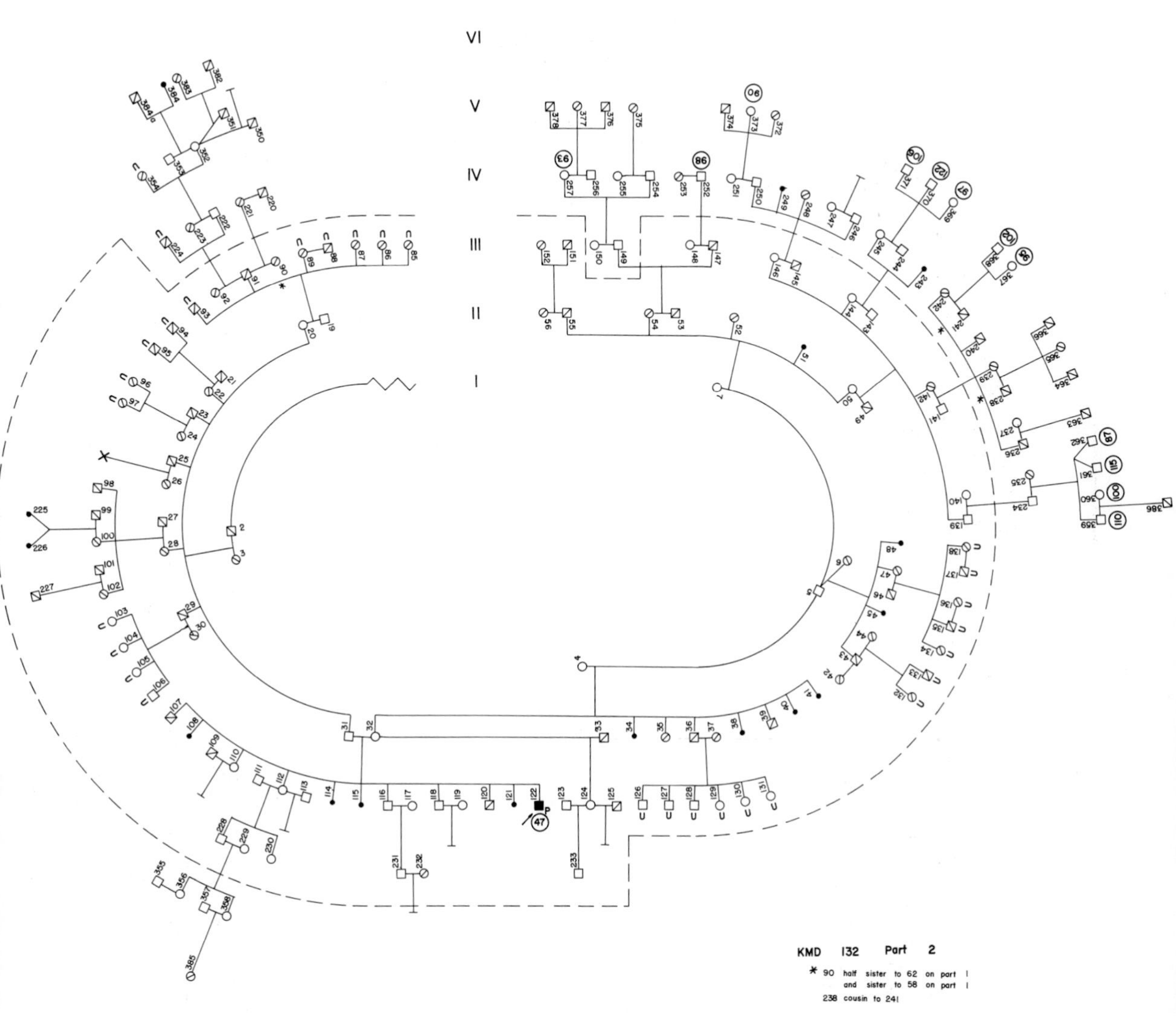

Brother (120) died following a fall downstairs at 3 years.

(114), (115) and (121) were miscarriages.

Half sister (124) had normal intelligence.

Nieces and Nephews

Not of interest.

First Cousins

Not of interest.

More Distant Relatives

Not of interest.

Family Summary

The proband was the only retarded person in the family and the last born of 11 children. The proband's parents only had three grandchildren. Their four married children had only three children.

Retardation of proband of primarily genetic origin (Down's syndrome).

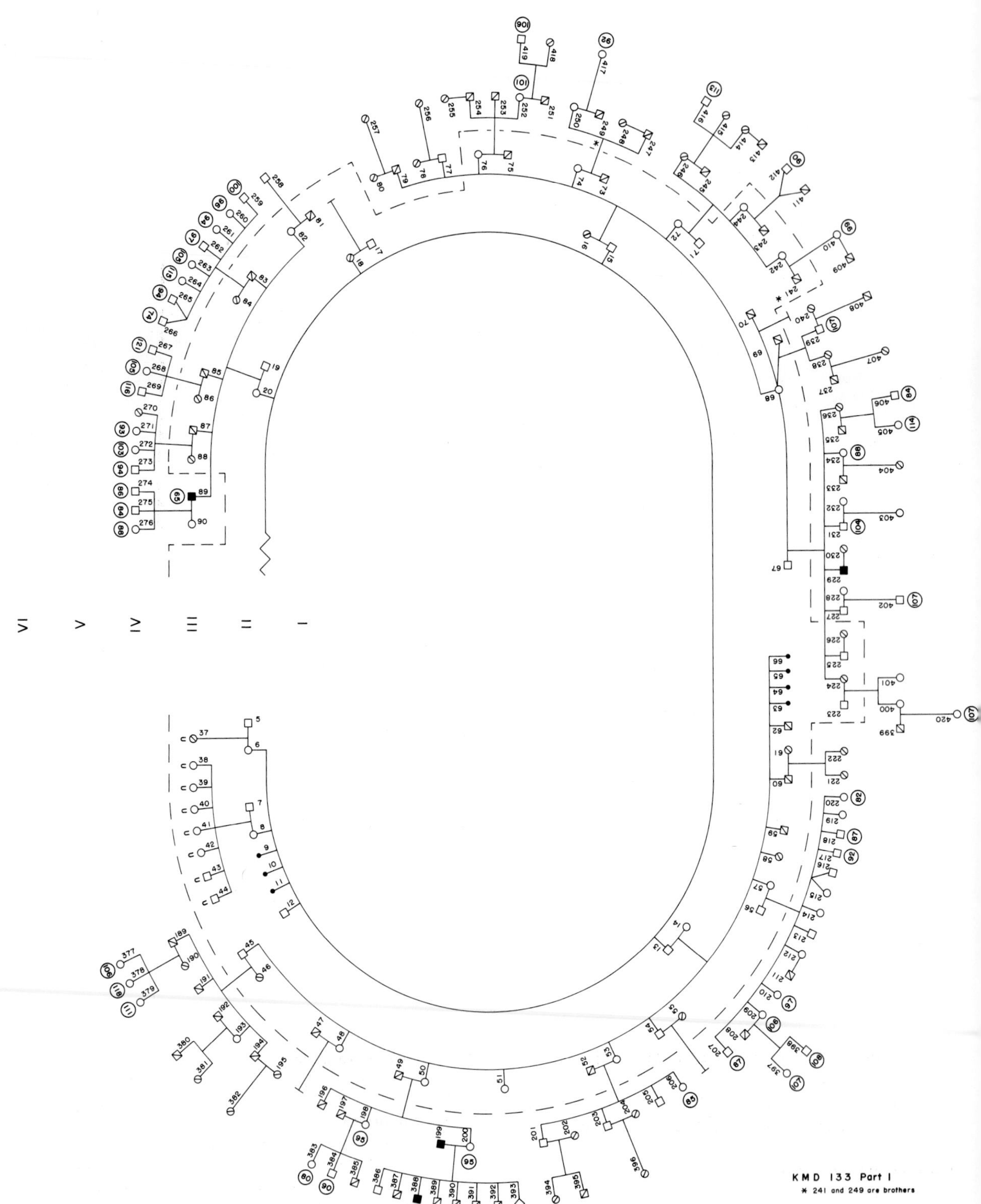

KMD 133 Part I
* 241 and 249 are brothers

KMD 133

The Proband

The proband (111) was born in 1903, institutionalized at age 8 and remained in the institution until her death of pneumonia in 1956. She and her immediate relatives were the subjects of extensive physical, psychological and neurological examinations. (See J. A. Böök, J. W. Schut and S. C. Reed, 1953.) IQ 12. *Diagnosis:* microcephaly and idiocy with general hypofunction of the pyramidal system.

Grandparents

Not of interest.

Parents

The father (25) despite 56 years in this country, spoke only a few words of English. In addition to a physical and neurological examination, he received two psychometric tests. The psychologist felt that his second IQ score of 48 on a Wechsler-Bellevue Test corrected for age was more accurate than his first score of a borderline 75. *Diagnosis:* undifferentiated mental retardation.

The mother (26) had a small head with a shape characteristic of microcephaly. She received an IQ score of 76 on a Wechsler-Bellevue corrected for age. *Diagnosis:* right-sided hemiplegia with organic dementia and mental backwardness.

Aunts and Uncles

Not of interest.

Siblings

An institutionalized identical twin sister (112). IQ 11. *Diagnosis:* microcephaly and idiocy with general hypofunction of the pyramidal system.

Brother (117), IQ 74, considered by the psychologist to be mentally retarded rather than borderline. He exhibited slight pyramidal hypofunction upon examination. He has a retarded child. Another brother (119) exhibited the same slight pyramidal hypofunction, as did brother (126).

Brother (130) institutionalized at age 15, was diagnosed by Dr. Böök and Dr. Schut as having microcephaly and idiocy with general hypofunction of the pyramidal system. IQ 17.

Nieces and Nephews

Nephew (310) has an IQ of 66.

First Cousins

A cousin (89) has an IQ of 65. He has a normal wife and three children, (274), (275) and (276) with low normal IQ's of 86, 84 and 88, respectively.

One cousin (160) completed three years of school and is an unmarried laborer, age 48, and mentally retarded.

More Distant Relatives

First cousin's child (200), IQ 95, married a retarded man and has eight children including one retarded child (388).

First cousin's child (229) went to school for five years and is a janitor despite the fact that all his siblings are college graduates. Mentally retarded.

Family Summary

The immediate family of the proband was reported upon in some detail in Böök et al., 1953. The proband, her identical twin sister and one brother are all institutionalized microcephalic idiots. The father and another brother are retarded. The proband's parents had 12 children. These children had 21 offspring, 12 of whom belong to the retarded brother.

Retardation of proband of primarily genetic origin (microcephaly).

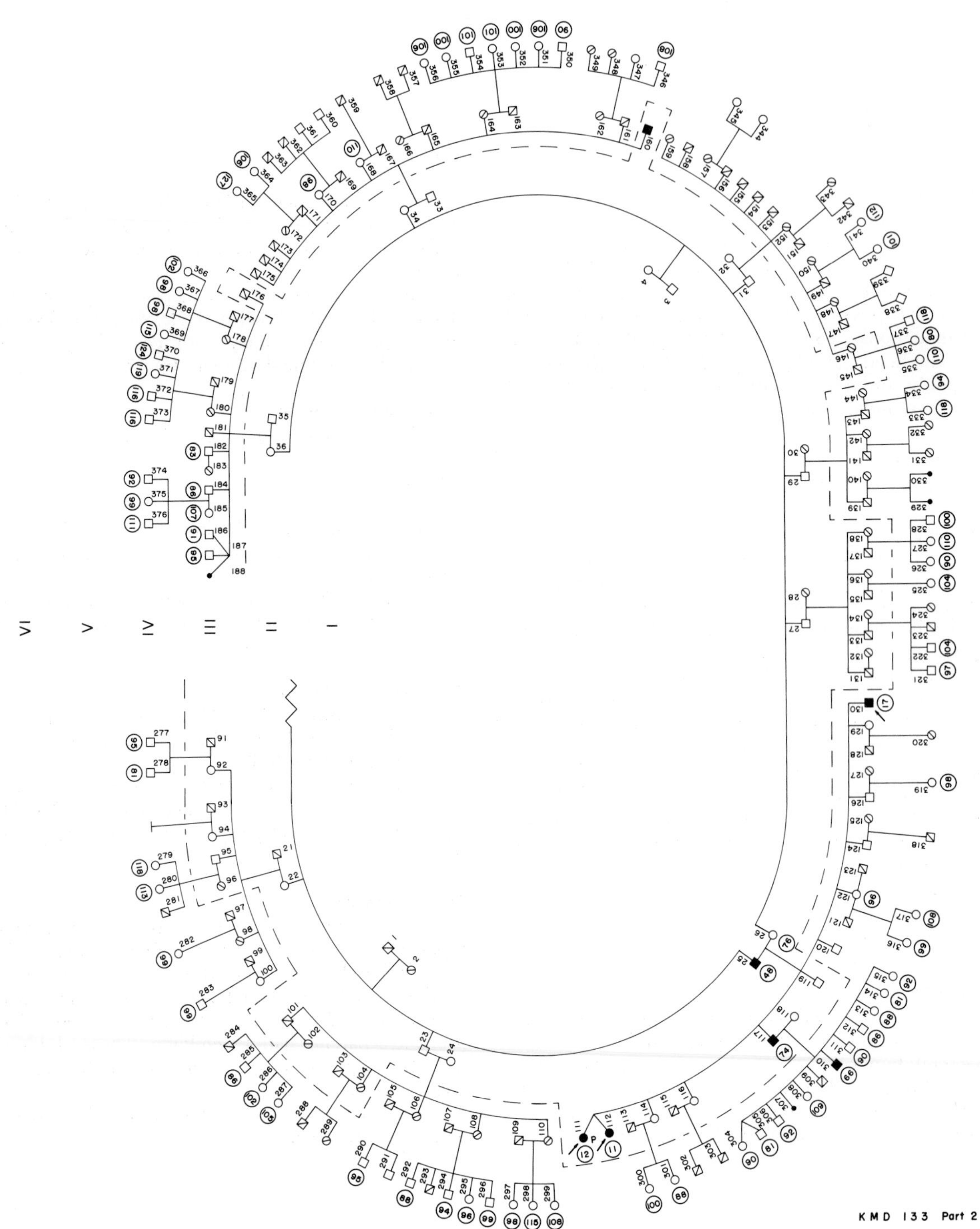

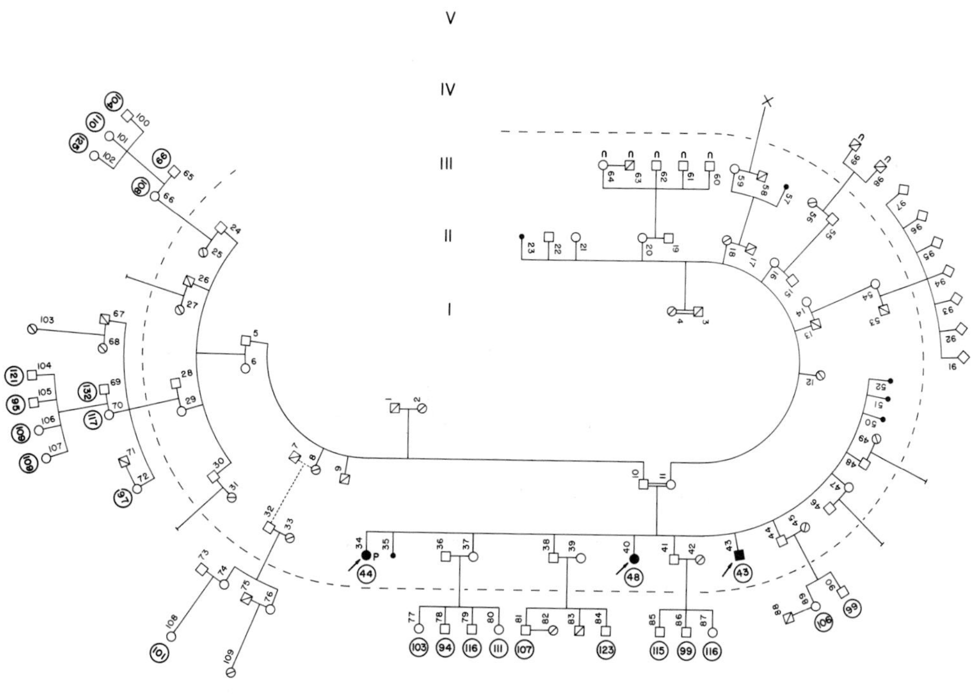

KMD 135

The Proband

The proband (34) was born in 1891, institutionalized at age 9 years and transferred to a mental hospital in 1923 when she developed a psychosis, and died in 1953. She was polydactylous. Her birth and early years were uneventful. IQ 44. *Diagnosis:* mental retardation with polydactyly and subsequent psychosis.

Grandparents

Maternal grandparents were second cousins.

Parents

Father (10) and mother (11), both with normal intelligence, were first cousins.

Aunts and Uncles

Not of interest.

Siblings

Brother (35) died of pneumonia at 7 months.

Sisters (37) and (47) and brothers (38), (41), (44) and (48) have normal intelligence and are not polydactylous. Their children are normal.

Sister (40) was institutionalized in 1951 at age 54 years and is still in the institution. She is polydactylous. IQ 48.

Brother (43) was institutionalized in 1912 at age 11 years, discharged to go home five years later. He is now on the waiting list for readmission. He is polydactylous. IQ 43.

(50) and (51) were miscarriages.

(52) was a stillbirth.

Nieces and Nephews

All have normal intelligence.

First Cousins

Not of interest.

More Distant Relatives

Not of interest.

Family Summary

The proband and two siblings were both polydactylous and retarded with similar IQ's of 44, 48 and 43, respectively. The rest of the adult siblings were neither polydactylous nor retarded. The proband's parents were normal and non-polydactylous, but were first cousins. They had 13 children including two stillbirths, two infant deaths and 12 grandchildren.

This family was the subject of detailed study by Dr. C. P. Oliver in 1940. The findings of physical examinations of the affected persons and a discussion of the probable modes of inheritance are to be found in his paper. (See References, p. 81.)

Retardation of proband of primarily genetic origin (consanguinity).

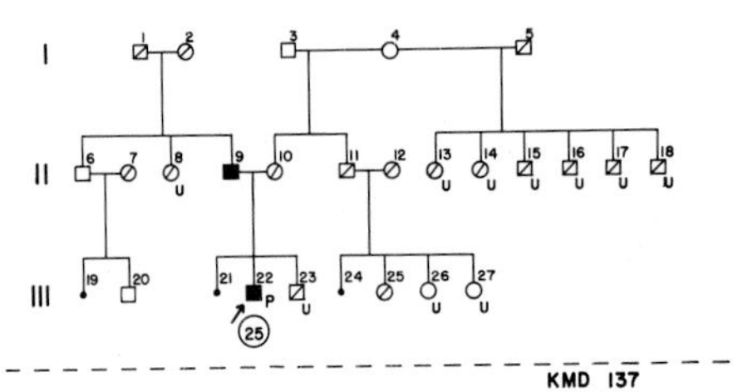

KMD 137

The Proband

The proband (22) was born in 1909, institutionalized at age 4 years and returned home five years later. He was killed in an accident in 1947. He had a large head at birth and later became somewhat paralyzed. IQ 25. *Diagnosis:* hydrocephalus.

Grandparents

Not of interest.

Parents

Father (9) failed at farming and became a laborer. He was almost illiterate. While he was in prison for wife beating, his wife ran away. He was classified as retarded.

Mother (10) became promiscuous after she left her husband and may have contracted syphilis. Intelligence unknown.

Aunts and Uncles

One maternal uncle was mentally ill.

Siblings

Brother (21) died of "summer complaint" and convulsions at 11 months. He was hydrocephalic.

Brother (23) is unknown at the present time. He was not hydrocephalic.

Nieces and Nephews

Not known.

First Cousins

Not of interest.

More Distant Relatives

Unknown.

Family Summary

The proband, IQ 25, and his brother were hydrocephalic. Their father was a high-grade retardate. The proband's parents had three children, grandchildren unknown.

Retardation of proband of primarily genetic origin (hydrocephalus).

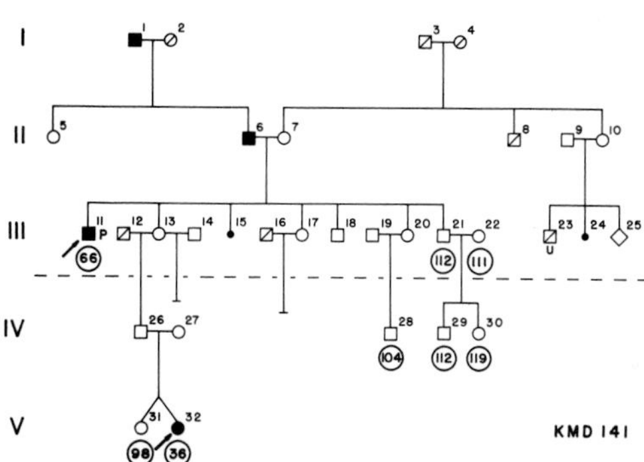

KMD 141

The Proband

The proband (11) was born in 1899, institutionalized at age 4 years and transferred to a church home for retarded in 1926 where he was living in 1961. He was a deaf mute. There was no record of perinatal disease. IQ 66. *Diagnosis:* mental retardation with deaf mutism.

Grandparents

Paternal grandfather was retarded.

Parents

Father (6) was a farmer and was retarded. Mother (7) had normal intelligence.

Aunts and Uncles

Not of interest.

Siblings

Three sisters (13), (17) and (20) and one brother (21) all have normal intelligence, are not deaf mutes and have normal children.

One miscarriage (15).

Nieces and Nephews

Only four, all with normal intelligence.

First Cousins

Not of interest.

More Distant Relatives

Proband's nephew (26) has twin girls, one (31) with IQ 98, the other (32) with IQ 36 and institutionalized. Note from institution states "probably due to defective fetal development, abnormal metabolism."

Family Summary

The proband was a deaf mute and was retarded. His father and paternal grandfather were also retarded. One great-niece is institutionalized, IQ 36. The proband's parents had seven children and four grandchildren.

Retardation of proband of primarily genetic origin (deaf mutism).

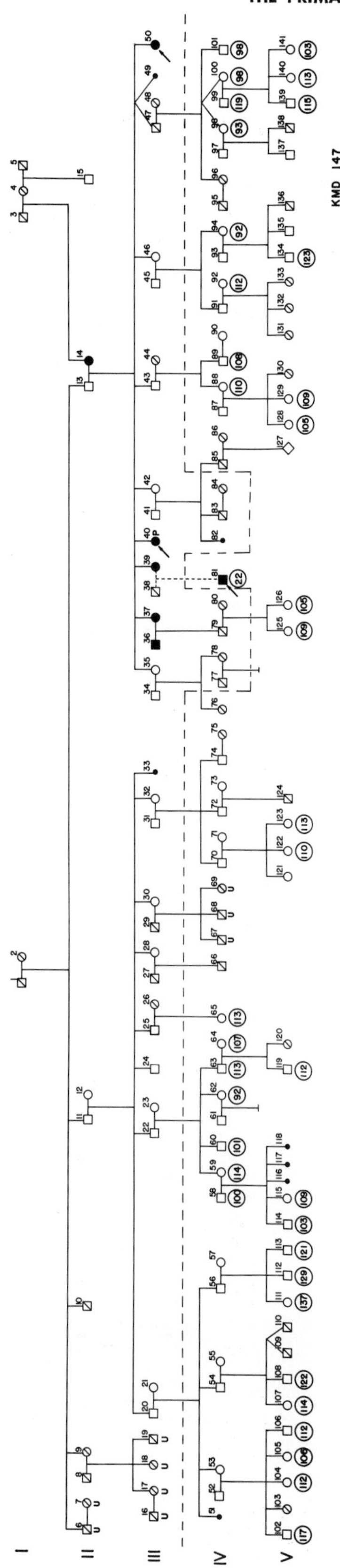

KMD 147

The Proband

The proband (40) was born in 1884, institutionalized at age 20 years and died of pulmonary tuberculosis in the institution in 1911. She had no history of birth injury or perinatal infection. She was a low-grade retardate and had a right lateral curvature of the spine and flattening of the thorax on the right side. No IQ. *Diagnosis:* undifferentiated mental retardation.

Grandparents

Not of interest.

Parents

Father (13) was a farmer of normal intelligence. He was "excessively" alcoholic.

Mother (14) was retarded.

Aunts and Uncles

Not of interest.

Siblings

Sisters (35), (42) and (46) have normal intelligence, with no retardates in their families.

Sister (37) was retarded, married a retarded man and had one child of unknown intelligence and had two normal grandchildren.

Sister (39) was retarded of rather low grade with a slight deformity of the spine. She had an institutionalized, illegitimate child (81).

Brother (43) has normal intelligence and normal children.

Brother (47) is a farmer, intelligence unknown, children apparently normal. His twin died a few minutes after birth.

Sister (50) was institutionalized in 1954 at the age of 54 years. She is a low-grade retardate with a diagnosis of idiot, familial.

Nieces and Nephews

(81) was born in 1903 and institutionalized in 1953. IQ 22. *Diagnosis:* idiot, familial.

First Cousins

Not of interest.

More Distant Relatives

Not of interest.

Family Summary

The proband, two sisters and a nephew were low-grade retardates. The proband's mother and one sister were high-grade retardates. The proband's parents had ten children and 15 grandchildren.

Retardation of proband of primarily genetic origin.

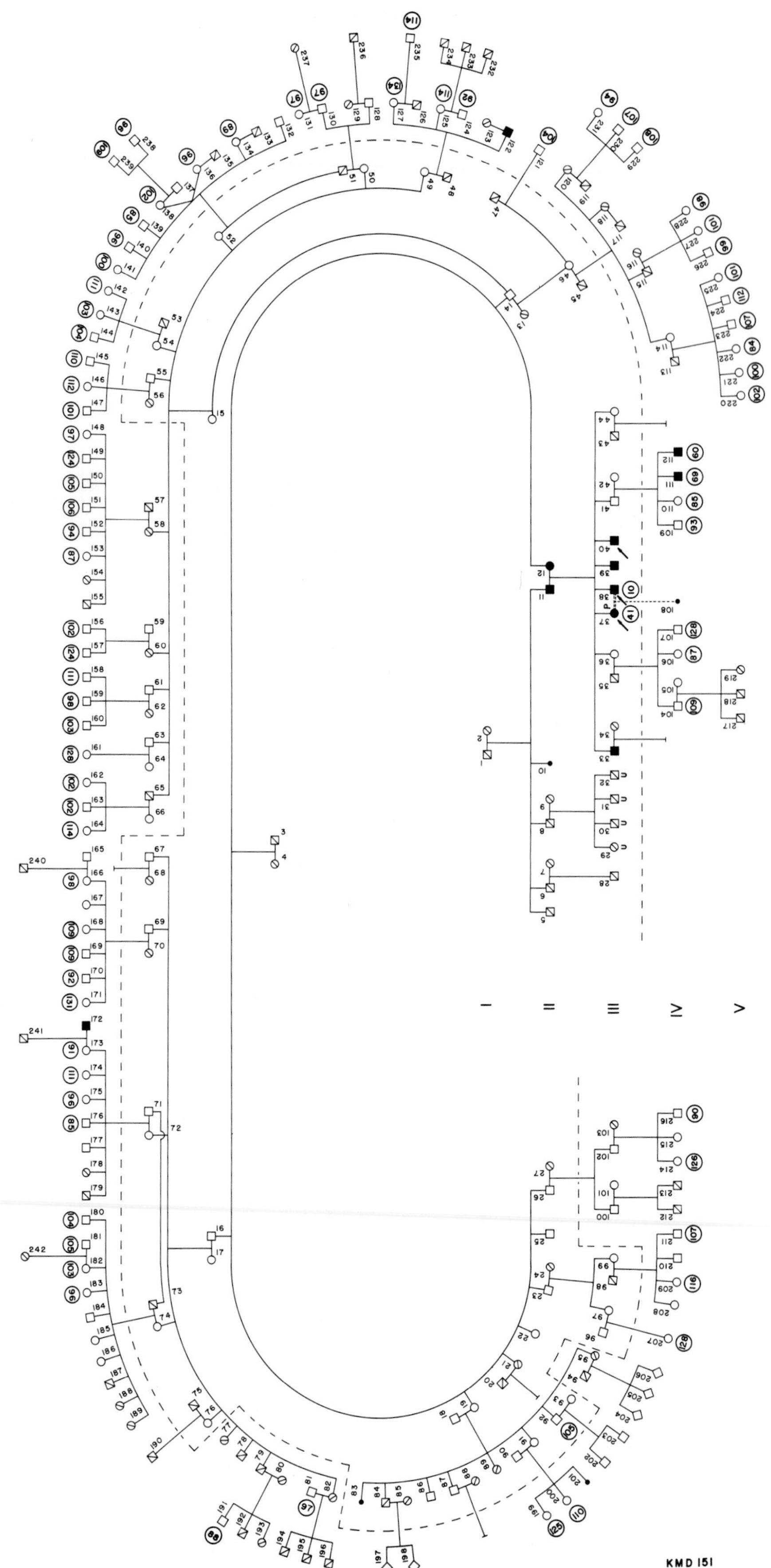

KMD 151

KMD 151

The Proband

The proband (37) was born in 1899, institutionalized at age 12 years and discharged in 1915. She had no history of early trauma. She was readmitted in 1919 [after the birth of a child fathered by her brother (38)], and died in the institution of mitral regurgitation and chronic stenosis in 1928. She had a speech defect and was first sent to the State School for the Deaf but was transferred after three months to the institution for the retarded. IQ 41. *Diagnosis:* undifferentiated mental retardation.

Grandparents

Not of interest except that the maternal grandfather also had a speech defect.

Parents

Father (11) was retarded.

Mother (12) had a speech defect (no uvula, high-arched palate) and was retarded. She was a poor housekeeper.

Aunts and Uncles

Not of interest.

Siblings

Brother (33) is a laborer, married but childless and retarded.

Sister (36) was retarded in school but some of this was ascribed to her home environment. The psychologist reported her as having normal intelligence. She had a high-arched palate and a speech defect. Her children are normal.

Brother (38), father of proband's child, was committed to state guardianship as retarded and violent and institutionalized in 1940. He died of tuberculosis in the institution in 1944. His IQ at age 39 years was "below 10." He had a high-arched palate; no speech.

Brother (39) died of whooping cough at 6 years. He could not walk or talk.

Brother (40) was institutionalized in 1940 and died of perforation of duodendal ulcer in the institution three years later. He was epileptic and a low-grade retardate, but apparently had no defect of the palate.

Brother (41) graduated from business college and is a farmer. He has two retarded children (111) and (112) and two normal ones (109) and (110).

Sister (44) has normal intelligence.

Child

Proband's child (108) died of marasmus with rickets at 7 months.

Nieces and Nephews

Two retarded, (111) with IQ 69 and (112) with IQ 60.

First Cousins

Paternal cousins remained in Germany and are unknown.

Maternal cousins not of interest.

More Distant Relatives

First cousin (49) has a retarded son (122) who was retained in the first, third and fifth grades. He is a plumber's helper and is married but childless.

First cousin (72) has a normal daughter (173) with IQ 91 who married a retarded man.

Family Summary

The proband, both her parents, four siblings, a nephew and niece and one more distant relative were retarded. The proband had a child by her retarded brother. This child died of marasmus in infancy. The proband had an IQ of 41; two siblings were low-grade retardates; the parents, two siblings and a niece and nephew were high grade. The maternal grandfather, mother, proband, one retarded and one normal sibling all had high-arched palates and speech defects. The proband's parents had eight children and eight grandchildren.

Retardation of proband of primarily genetic origin.

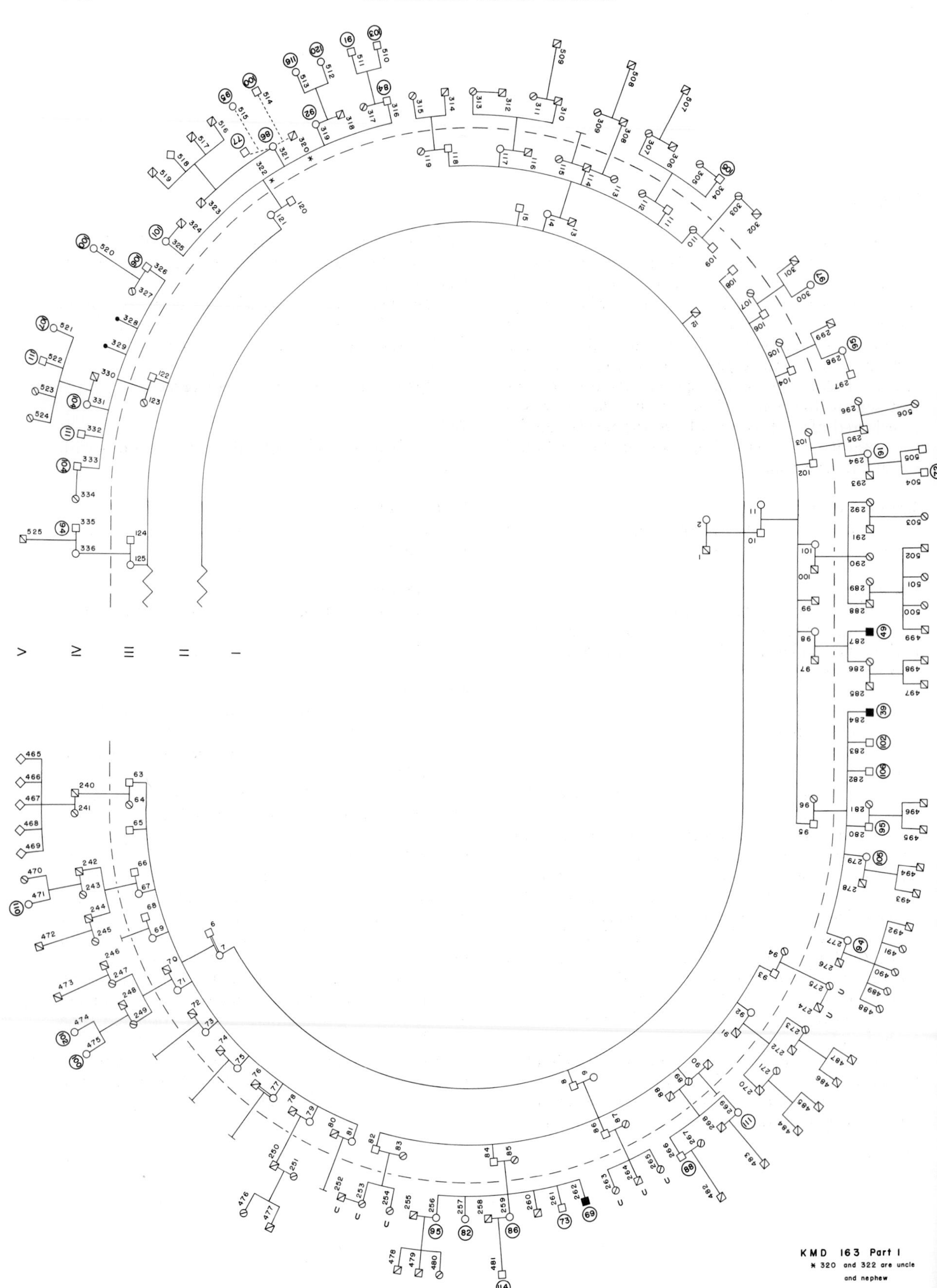
V
IV
III
II
I
KMD 163 Part I
* 320 and 322 are uncle and nephew

KMD 163

The Proband

The proband (147) was born in 1885. First sent to a mental hospital in 1909 she was judged not a proper subject and was institutionalized two years later at age 26 years. She died of pulmonary tuberculosis in the institution in 1922. The proband had no history of birth injury or perinatal infection and no stigmata. She was greatly abused by her father. She had an illegitimate child, father unknown, but relatives suspected her paternal uncle. IQ 34. *Diagnosis:* undifferentiated mental retardation.

Grandparents

Maternal grandfather was retarded.

Maternal grandmother was retarded and had Huntington's chorea.

Parents

Father (24) was an alcoholic, cruel, abusive and retarded. He had nine illegitimate children by another woman (23).

Mother (25) was promiscuous and retarded. She was a second cousin once removed to her husband.

Aunts and Uncles

Paternal aunt (7) married her first cousin. They had ten children, all with normal intelligence.

Paternal aunt (17) married her first cousin once removed. They had four children, all with normal intelligence. (16) developed Huntington's chorea.

Maternal aunt (29) was retarded.

Mother's half-siblings as follows:

(30) had normal intelligence but developed Huntington's chorea.

(40) was retarded.

(43) and (44) were both retarded and both may have had Huntington's chorea.

(45) committed suicide. He was retarded and had Huntington's chorea.

(47) was retarded and had Huntington's chorea.

(49) was retarded.

(59) had Huntington's chorea and was retarded.

(62) has an IQ of 50.

Siblings

No full siblings.

Half Siblings

Nine are the illegitimate children of (24) and (23).

Half brother (131) was an unmarried, childless retardate.

Half sisters (133) and (135) and half brothers (136) and (137) all had normal intelligence.

Half brother (139) was imprisoned for grand larceny. IQ 81.

Three half siblings have unknown intelligence.

Half brother (148), an illegitimate child of the proband's mother, married his double cousin (second cousin once removed and half first cousin) and had 12 children, eight with an IQ range of 71 to 101 and three stillbirths.

Half sister (150), a second illegitimate child of the proband's mother, died at birth.

Child

Son (367) was tried in three boarding homes but did not do well so was institutionalized at age 10 years. He ran away five years later and has not been heard from since. He had no stigmata but had an "insane" temper and a tendency to set fires. His father was unknown although his mother's uncle was suspected. IQ was 75 at age 10 years.

Nieces and Nephews

Only the children of half siblings. Not of interest except for the two children of second cousins (134) and (135), both of whom are normal.

First Cousins

(160), (190) and (191) have Huntington's chorea.

More Distant Relatives

(262) has an IQ of 69.

(284) has an IQ of 39.

(287) has an IQ of 49.

(316) shows symptoms of Huntington's chorea.

(321) has an IQ of 86 but is a welfare problem. She has had two illegitimate children who were placed for adoption and four legitimate ones. She asked for, and was given, a sterilization operation.

(336) has been hospitalized several times for manic depressive psychosis.

(339) with IQ 94 has had three illegitimate children by three fathers. Her sister (345), with IQ 108, has also had an illegitimate child.

Family Summary

The proband, IQ 34, both her parents, her maternal grandparents, a maternal aunt, eight of the proband's mother's half siblings, one half brother and three more distant relatives were retarded, all of middle to high grade. The proband lived in a poor home, was abused by her father and had an illegitimate child with IQ 75. The proband, her father and her son all had "insane" tempers. The proband was hospitalized at one time for suspected mental illness and her son set fires. The proband's parents were second cousins once removed. In addition to the retardation in this family and sometimes concurrent with it, is the disease of Huntington's chorea. The early symptoms of this affliction may have caused some of the subjects to have been mistakenly classified as retarded by the early workers. The proband's parents had one child and one grandchild.

Retardation of proband of primarily genetic origin (consanguinity).

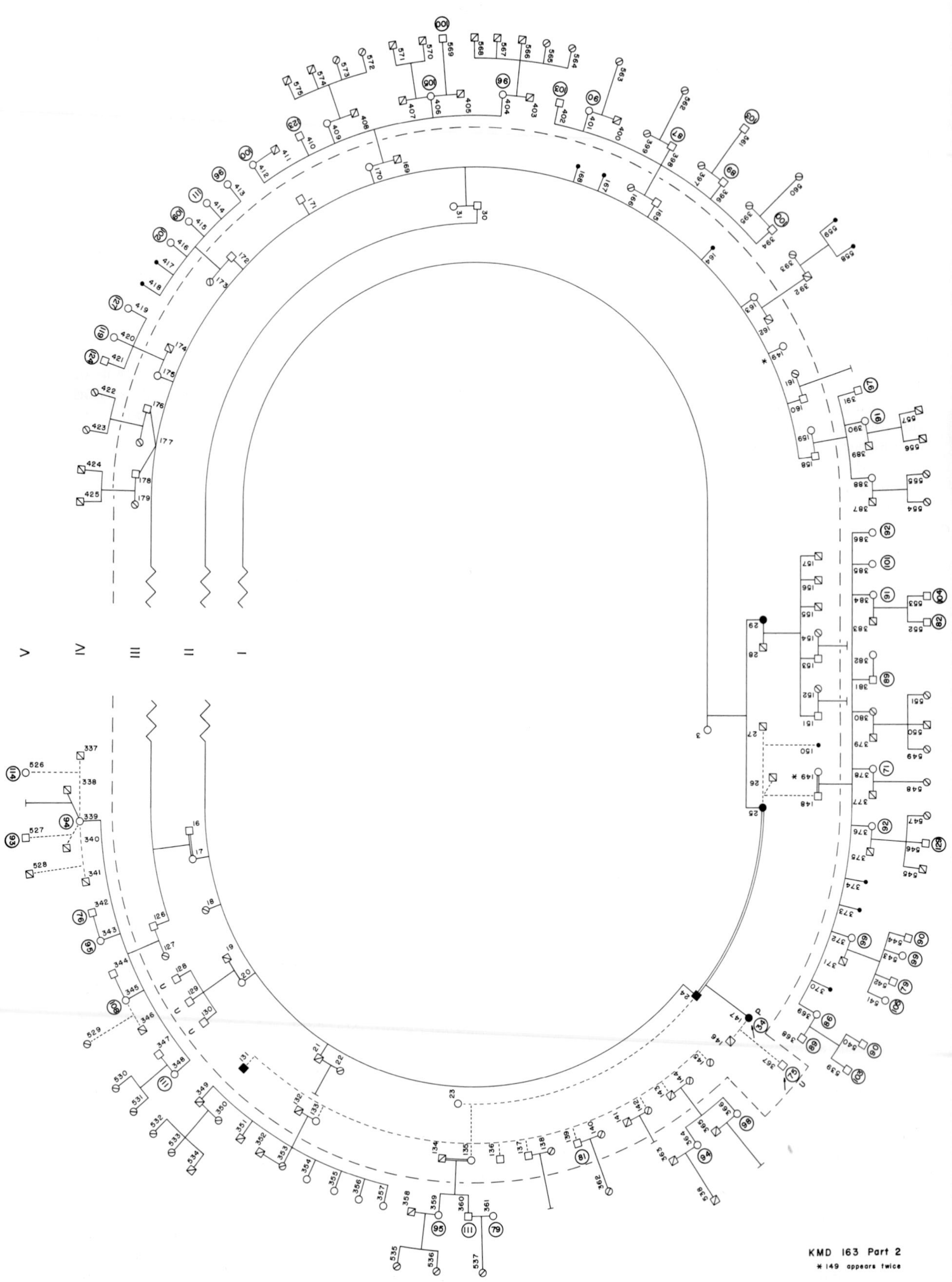

KMD 163 Part 2

* 149 appears twice

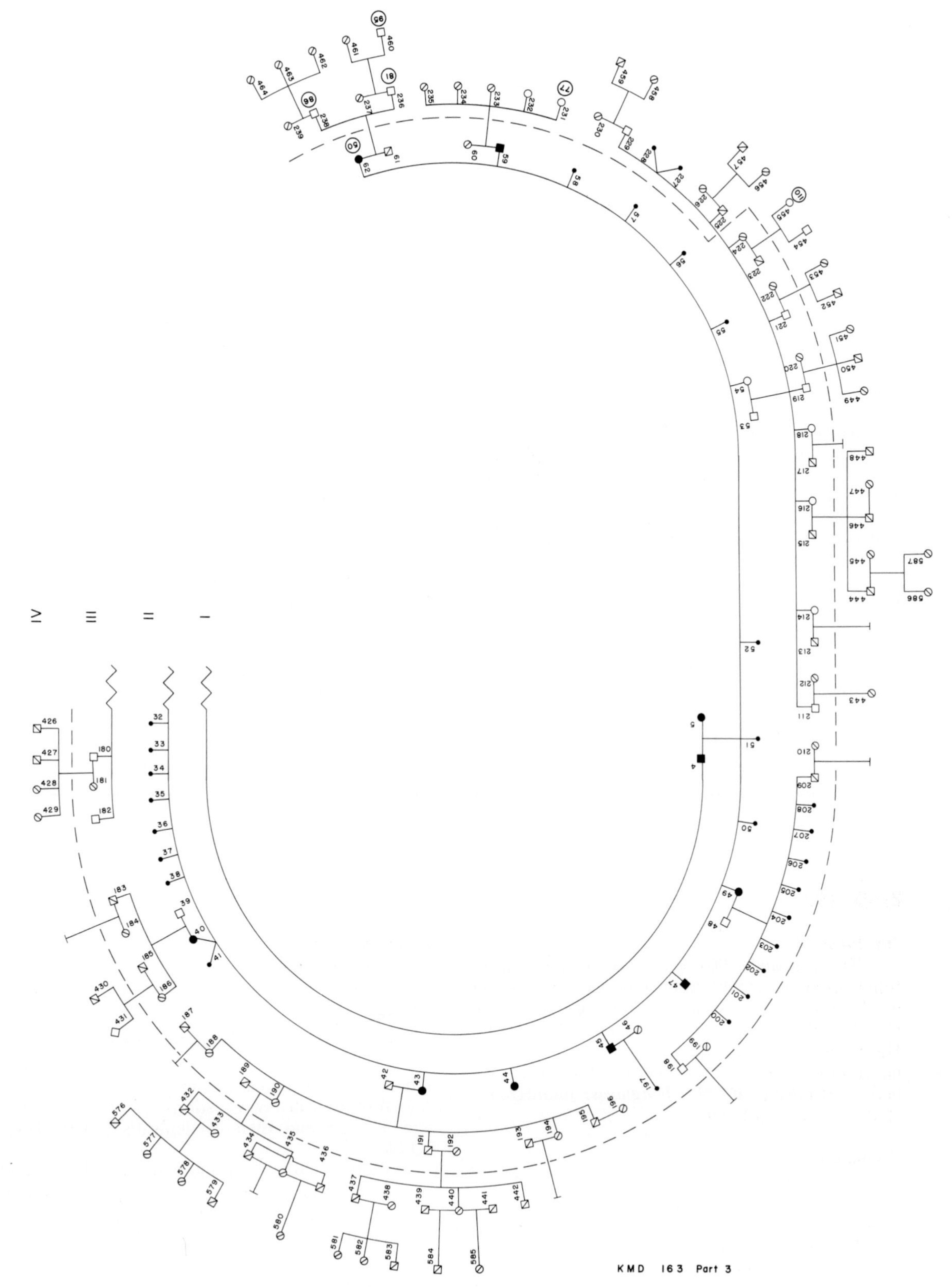
I
II
III
IV
V
KMD 163 Part 3

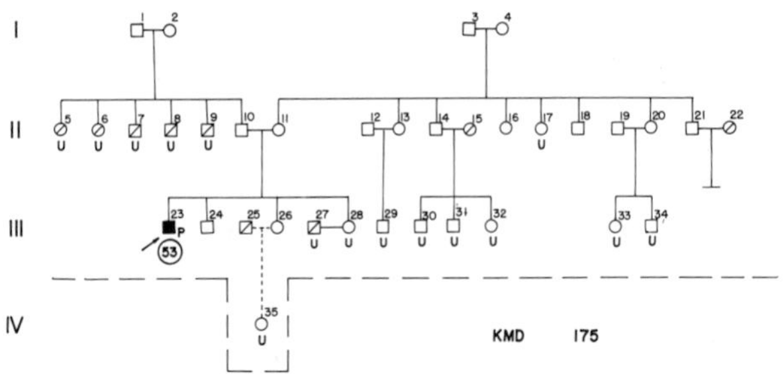

KMD 175

The Proband

The proband (23) was born in 1884, institutionalized at age 12 years and died of pneumonia in the institution in 1918. He was hydrocephalic at birth and had a bad rash on his face. The attending doctor diagnosed hydrocephalus. There was no evidence of syphilis in the family. He developed epilepsy after his institutionalization. IQ 53. *Diagnosis:* hydrocephalus.

Grandparents

All normal.

Parents

Father (10) had normal intelligence, but was an alcoholic, did not support his family and disappeared when the children were small.

Mother (11) had normal intelligence.

Aunts and Uncles

All remained in Sweden.

Siblings

Brother (24) died of diphtheria at 17 years of age. Normal intelligence.

Sister (26) had an illegitimate child. Normal intelligence.

Sister (28) had normal intelligence.

Nieces and Nephews

One illegitimate niece (35). It is not known whether there are any other relatives in this group.

First Cousins

Unknown since all remained in Sweden.

More Distant Relatives

Unknown.

Family Summary

The proband was hydrocephalic, IQ 53. His three siblings all had normal intelligence. This family could not be found in the follow-up. The parents had four children, unknown number of grandchildren.

Retardation of proband of primarily genetic origin (hydrocephalus).

KMD 192

The Proband

The proband (60) was born in 1903, institutionalized at age 6 years and was in and out of the institution several times before his death of tuberculous meningitis and peritonitis in 1915. His birth was an instrument delivery but there is no record of injury or of perinatal disease. He had no stigmata. IQ 50. *Diagnosis:* undifferentiated mental retardation.

Grandparents

Not of interest.

Parents

Father (15) was subject to epileptiform attacks but had normal intelligence. He was a carpenter.

Mother (16) had normal intelligence.

Aunts and Uncles

Not of interest.

Siblings

Sister (56) completed two years of college.

Brother (57) completed two years of high school and is a lumber dealer.

Brother (59) was institutionalized in 1910 at age 9 years and died of nephritis a year later. IQ 56.

Brother (61) was institutionalized in 1930 at age 25 years and has remained in the institution ever since. He has defective vision and speech, poor control over hands and arms. IQ 45.

Nieces and Nephews

Only one, a nephew with IQ 98.

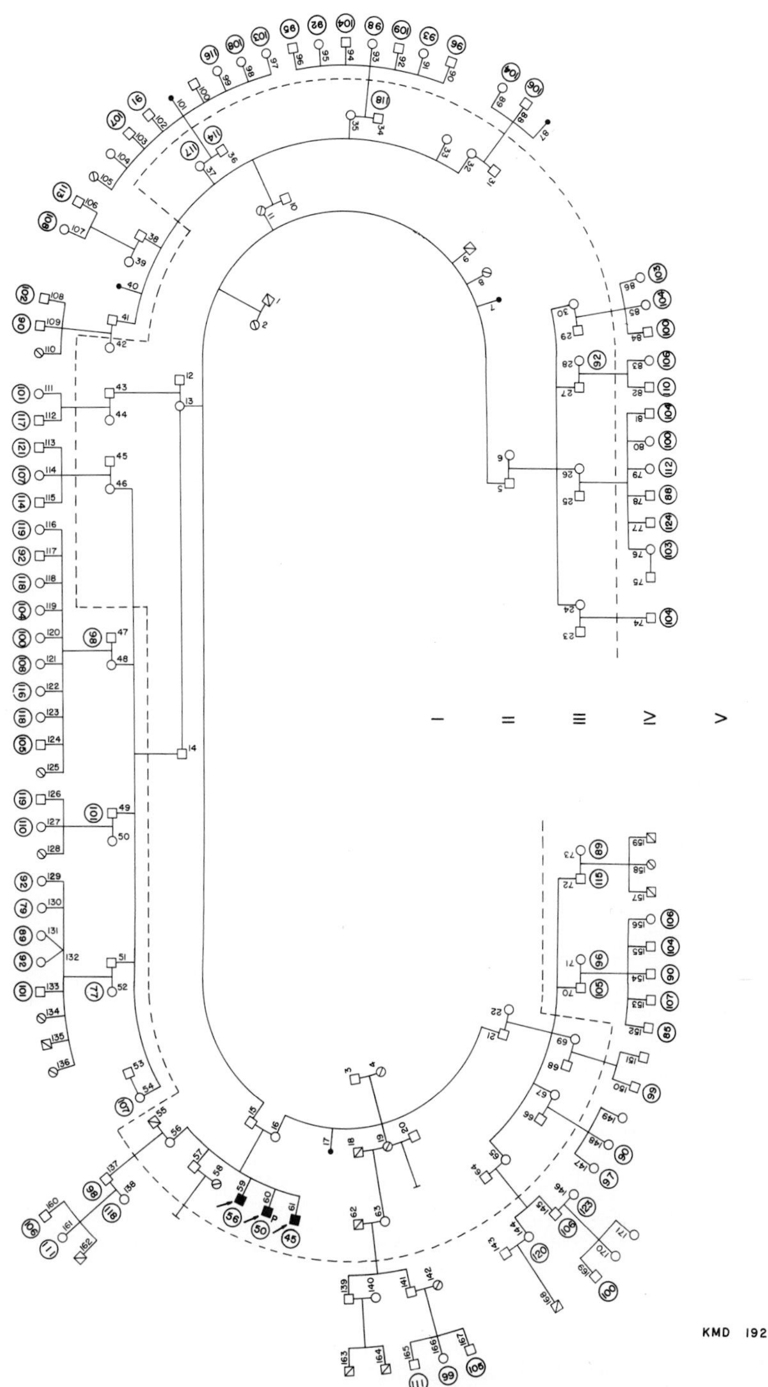

KMD 192

First Cousins

Not of interest.

More Distant Relatives

Not of interest.

Family Summary

The proband and two of his siblings, IQ's 50, 56 and 45 respectively, were institutionalized. The home environment was good and both parents had normal intelligence, although the father had epileptiform attacks and one of the retarded brothers was also epileptic. There were no other retarded persons in this kindred. The proband's parents had five children and one grandchild.

Retardation of proband of primarily genetic origin.

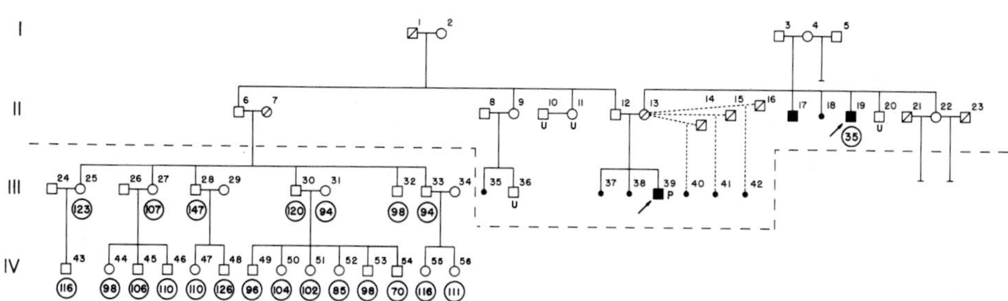

KMD 212

The Proband

The proband (39) was born in 1910, institutionalized at age 3 years and died of miliary tuberculosis in the institution in 1914. He was a breech delivery with instruments. He could never hold his head up and was classified as a low-grade retardate and hydrocephalic. *Diagnosis:* hydrocephalus.

Grandparents

Both paternal and maternal grandfathers deserted their families.

Parents

Father (12) had normal intelligence.

Mother (13) was promiscuous and an alcoholic. She deserted her family. Her intelligence is unknown.

Aunts and Uncles

Paternal relatives all had normal intelligence.

Maternal uncle (17) died at age 4 years. He was hydrocephalic.

Maternal uncle (18) died at 3 months. He was hydrocephalic.

Maternal uncle (19) was institutionalized at age 38 years and died in the institution in 1940 at age 49 years. He was paraplegic. IQ 35.

Maternal uncle (20) was choreic but had normal intelligence.

Maternal aunt (22) had normal intelligence but was almost a dwarf and had "double joints" in her hips so that she had difficulty in walking. She was married twice but had no children.

Siblings

Sister (37) died at 6 months. She was hydrocephalic.

(38) was a criminal abortion, as were half siblings (40), (41) and (42).

Nieces and Nephews

None.

First Cousins

All normal.

More Distant Relatives

Not of interest.

Family Summary

The proband, a sister and two maternal uncles were diagnosed hydrocephalics. Another maternal uncle was paraplegic and a maternal aunt was crippled and "double jointed." This family also had cases of desertion, alcoholism and mental illness. The proband's grandparents had ten children but only 14 grandchildren, five of whom reproduced. The proband's parents had three pregnancies, no grandchildren.

Retardation of proband of primarily genetic origin (hydrocephalus).

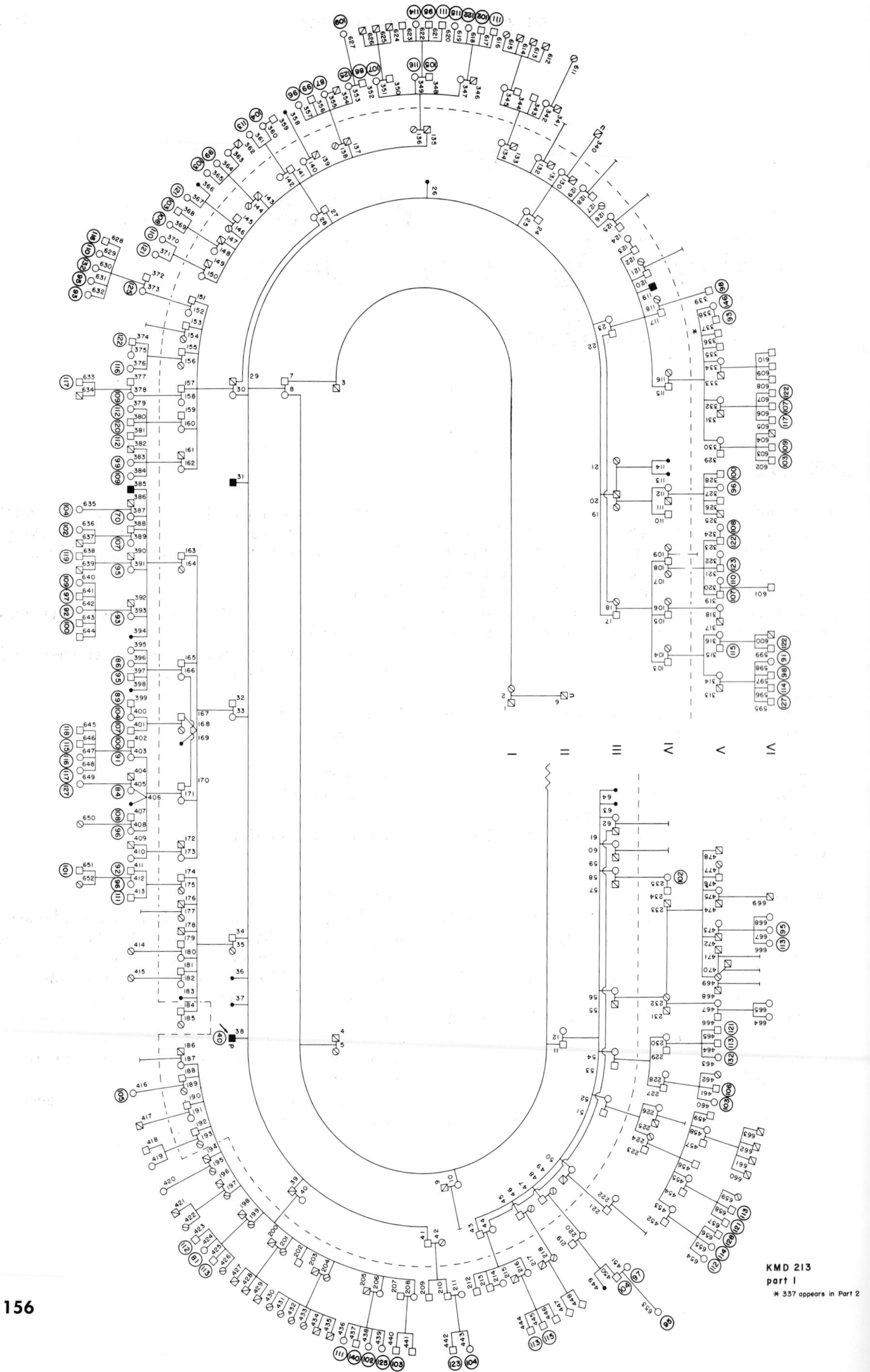

KMD 213
part I
* 337 appears in Part 2

KMD 213

The Proband

The proband (38) was born in 1878, institutionalized at age 16 years and died of typhoid fever in the institution in 1915. He was well taken care of in a prosperous home. IQ 40. *Diagnosis:* Down's syndrome.

Grandparents

Not of interest.

Parents

Father (7) was an alcoholic but was a prosperous farmer.

Mother (8) had normal intelligence.

Aunts and Uncles

Not of interest.

Siblings

Brother (17) was an alcoholic who at one time was considered for hospitalization, but had normal intelligence.

Brother (20) was an alcoholic. His intelligence was unknown.

Sisters (23), (25), (30) and (33) all had normal intelligence.

Brother (26) died three hours after birth.

Brothers (27), (34) and (41) had normal intelligence. (34) was an alcoholic.

Brother (31) was a low-grade retardate who died at age 2 years. He never sat up.

(36) and (37) were miscarriages.

Brother (39) had unknown intelligence.

Nieces and Nephews

Nephew (119) was an unmarried and childless farm laborer who was retarded.

First Cousins

Not of interest.

More Distant Relatives

(385) proband's great-nephew is retarded. (385) left school at 16 years when he failed the sixth grade for the second time.

(698) has an IQ of 53.

Family Summary

The proband, IQ 40, a low-grade retarded brother, a high-grade retarded nephew and one high-grade retarded great-nephew comprise the affected persons in the immediate family. The proband himself was diagnosed as having Down's syndrome. The other retardates in his immediate family and those among more distant relatives were undifferentiated types. The proband's parents had 15 children and 59 grandchildren.

Retardation of proband of primarily genetic origin (Down's syndrome).

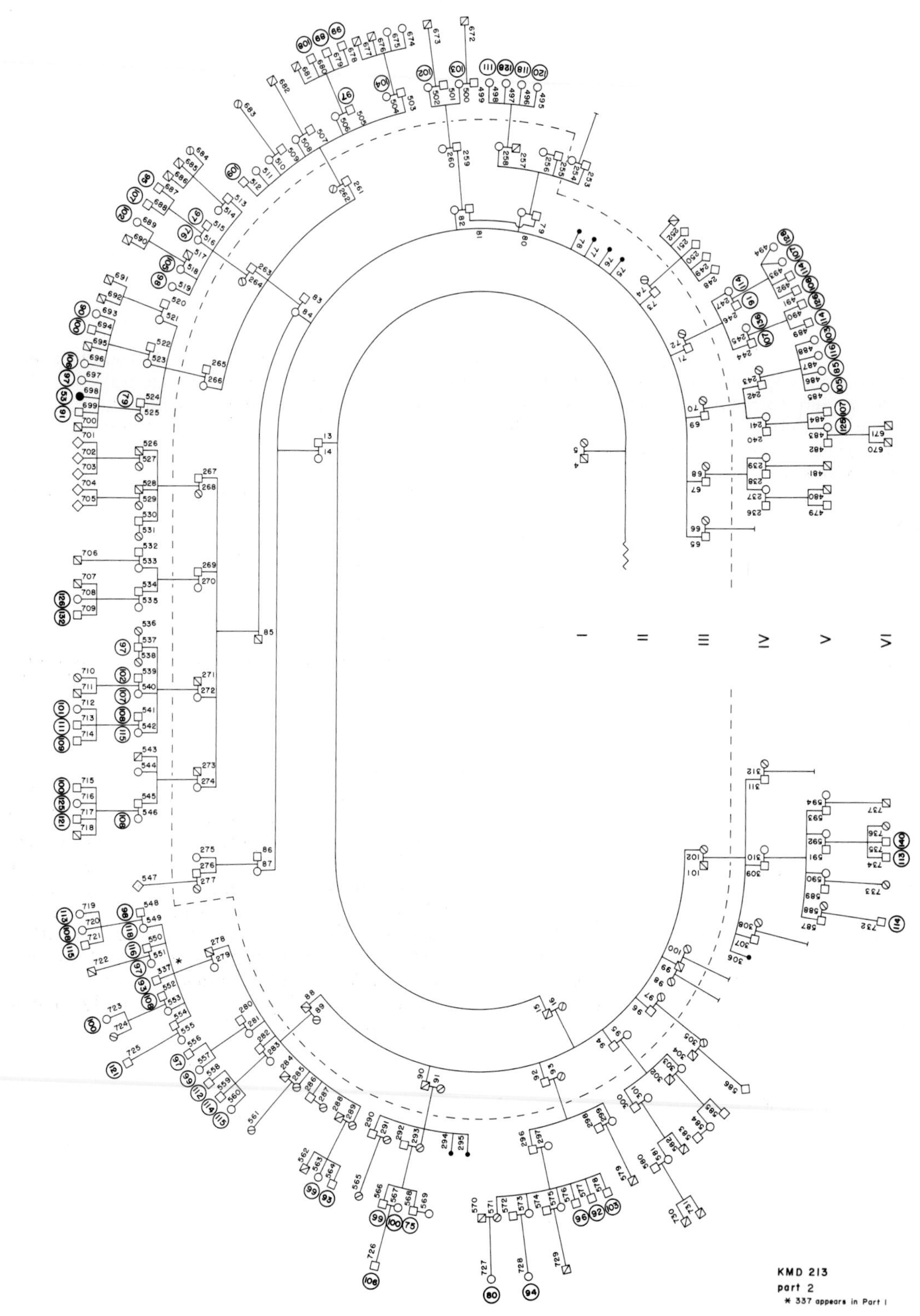
I
II
III
IV
V
VI
KMD 213
part 2
* 337 appears in Part I

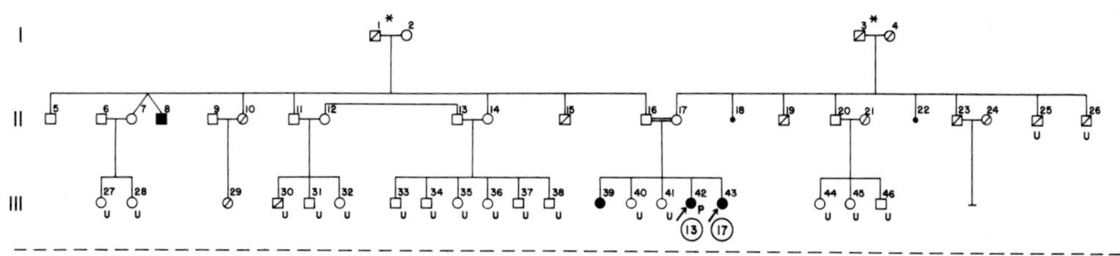

KMD 214

The Proband

The proband (42) was born in 1893, institutionalized at age 9 years and died of pulmonary tuberculosis in the institution in 1925. She did not grow well and was always small and weak. There was no history of trauma but she had talipes equinovarus of the left foot. Her home environment was good. IQ 13. *Diagnosis:* undifferentiated mental retardation.

Grandparents

Maternal grandmother died in a mental hospital. Her parents were cousins. Proband's paternal and maternal grandfathers were half brothers.

Parents

Both the father (16) and mother (17) had normal intelligence. They were the children of half brothers.

Aunts and Uncles

Paternal uncle (8) died of typhoid fever at 2½ years. He never stood, walked or talked.

Maternal uncles (19) and (25) were both mentally ill, but were never hospitalized. (19) was thought to have committed suicide.

Siblings

Sister (39) died at age 3 years, retarded and epileptic.

Sisters (40) and (41) had normal intelligence.

Sister (43) was institutionalized at age 8 years and died of pulmonary tuberculosis in the institution in 1926 at age 23 years. She was a large baby but did not grow well. She had a crippled right foot, described as "turning out." Epileptic. IQ 17.

Nieces and Nephews

Unknown.

First Cousins

Not of interest.

More Distant Relatives

Unknown.

Family Summary

The proband, IQ 13, and two sisters were retarded. One of these sisters was institutionalized, IQ 17. She and the proband each had a crippled foot. The proband's parents were cousins. They had five children, grandchildren unknown. This family could not be found for the follow-up since the family name is a commonly occurring Scandinavian name.

Retardation of proband of primarily genetic origin (consanguinity).

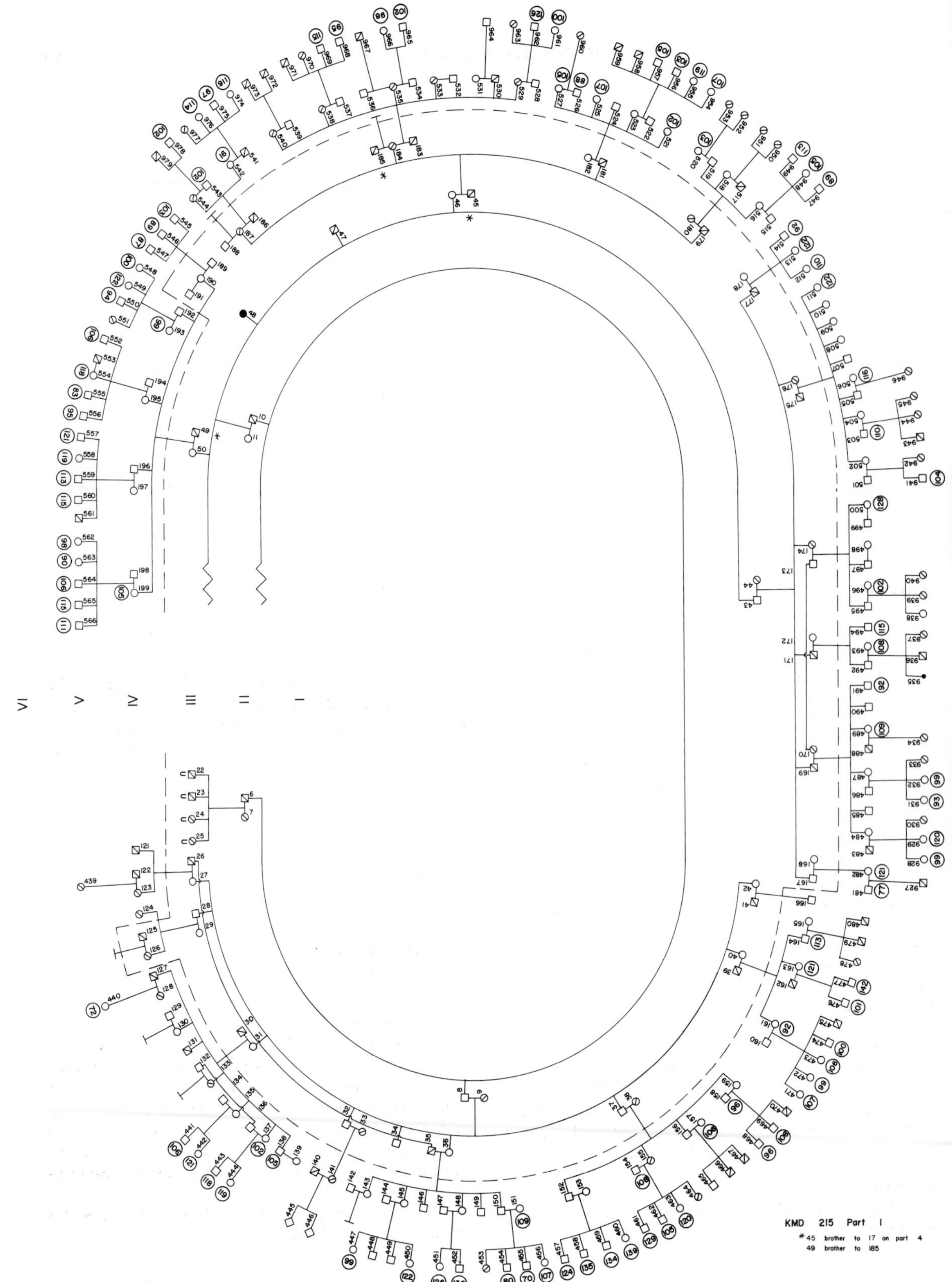

KMD 215

The Proband

The proband (103) was born in 1886, institutionalized at age 15 years and died of septicemia in the institution in 1915. He was slow to talk, and had difficulty in walking which became more pronounced as he grew older because he developed a tendency to pitch forward and would then creep. He was a low-grade retardate. *Diagnosis:* Pelizaeus-Merzbacher disease.

Grandparents

Not of interest.

Parents

Father (18) had normal intelligence.

Mother (19) had unknown intelligence.

Aunts and Uncles

Maternal aunt (21), twin to the proband's mother, had a son (120) who was a retarded cripple.

Siblings

Sisters (100) and (102) had normal intelligence. Their children are normal.

Sisters (105) and (107) had unknown intelligence. All three sons of (105) had Pelizaeus-Merzbacher disease. One son and four grandsons of (107) are also affected.

Half Siblings

Half sisters (91), (94) and (98) had normal intelligence.

Half sister (93) and half brother (95) had unknown intelligence.

Nieces and Nephews

Nephews (404), (405) and (406), all brothers, were institutionalized for mental retardation and all died in the institution. (404) and (405) both died of aplasia axialis extracorticalis congenita; both had defective speech, partially paralyzed limbs and IQ's of 57 and 60, respectively. (406), with an IQ of 45, had the same symptoms and died of an acute upper respiratory infection. Hospital records reported these three patients to have "a progressive spastic paralysis." Apparently, all three had Pelizaeus-Merzbacher disease.

Nephew (416) is institutionalized with an estimated IQ of 10 to 15. He was examined by a neurologist, G. S. Frank, M.D., in 1958, who reported that he presented a picture of "chronic, progressive degenerative or demyelinating disease of the central nervous system, familial and probably congenital but at least present early in life, clinically compatible with Pelizaeus-Merzbacher's diffuse sclerosis."

First Cousins

(120) was a retarded cripple who could move only by creeping on his stomach. While his condition was attributed by his parents to poliomyelitis at 7 months, his aunt reported that he had been born that way. Presumably he also had Pelizaeus-Merzbacher disease. His mother was a twin to the proband's mother.

(48) died single and childless and was retarded. (Not Pelizaeus-Merzbacher disease.)

(62) was a high-grade retardate. (Not Pelizaeus-Merzbacher disease.)

More Distant Relatives

Proband's niece (409) has two sons (896) and (897) who were examined by neurologist Daniel E. Stalker, M.D., in 1956. Dr. Stalker reported that (896) had severe spasticity in the lower limbs while the upper limbs appeared to be normal. He has had two operations to correct this condition and has been placed in braces but is unable to manage crutches and has difficulty holding on to parallel bars to walk. He speaks only a few words and is mentally retarded, IQ 68. His brother (897) was examined at the same time. He had some spastic involvement of all extremities, mild in the upper ones but scissoring in the lower ones. He was also operated upon and placed in leg braces. He is being taught to walk, and is succeeding better than his brother. He appeared to be brighter, and has an IQ of 72. Both boys attend a special school. (Presumably Pelizaeus-Merzbacher disease.)

Proband's niece (411) has two sons (898) and (901) who were examined by Dr. Frank in 1958. For (898) Dr. Frank reported "bilateral diffuse congenital cerebral damage, probably, but not definitely progressive. History of instrumentation at birth with poor respiration in a large infant. This might be cerebral palsy secondary to birth injury, one of the chronic diffuse scleroses such as Pelizaeus-Merzbacher disease or a typical form of spastic paraplegia, congenital. However, in view of the family history, I would favor Pelizaeus-Merzbacher's diffuse sclerosis." (898) is institutionalized, IQ estimated at 25. His brother (901) was also examined by Dr. Frank. Regarding this case, Dr. Frank reported "very slow progressive familial diffuse degenerative or demyelinating process—most compatible with a clinical diagnosis of Pelizaeus-Merzbacher's diffuse sclerosis." (901) was operated upon for spastic paraplegia and scissoring. He can walk with crutches and attends a school for crippled children. His IQ is 84.

Proband's cousin (71) has a daughter (297) who was institutionalized as a low-grade retardate.

(618) and (620), two brothers, have IQ's of 64 and 57, respectively. (618) is a nonreader; (620) has hemiplegia and difficult speech. (Not Pelizaeus-Merzbacher disease.)

(624) has an IQ of 68 with no physical handicap.

(990) has an IQ of 69.

Family Summary

The proband, his first cousin, four nephews and four great-nephews, all exhibit a common syndrome of speech defect, motor paralysis of the lower limbs and mental impairment. Two of the nephews died of aplasia axialis extracorticalis congenita, or Pelizaeus-Merzbacher disease. All the affected persons were males. The disease did not appear in the descendants of the proband's father's second marriage, but in the descendants of the proband's mother and her twin sister. The proband's parents had five children and 24 grandchildren.

Retardation of proband of primarily genetic origin (Pelizaeus-Merzbacher disease, sex-linked recessive).

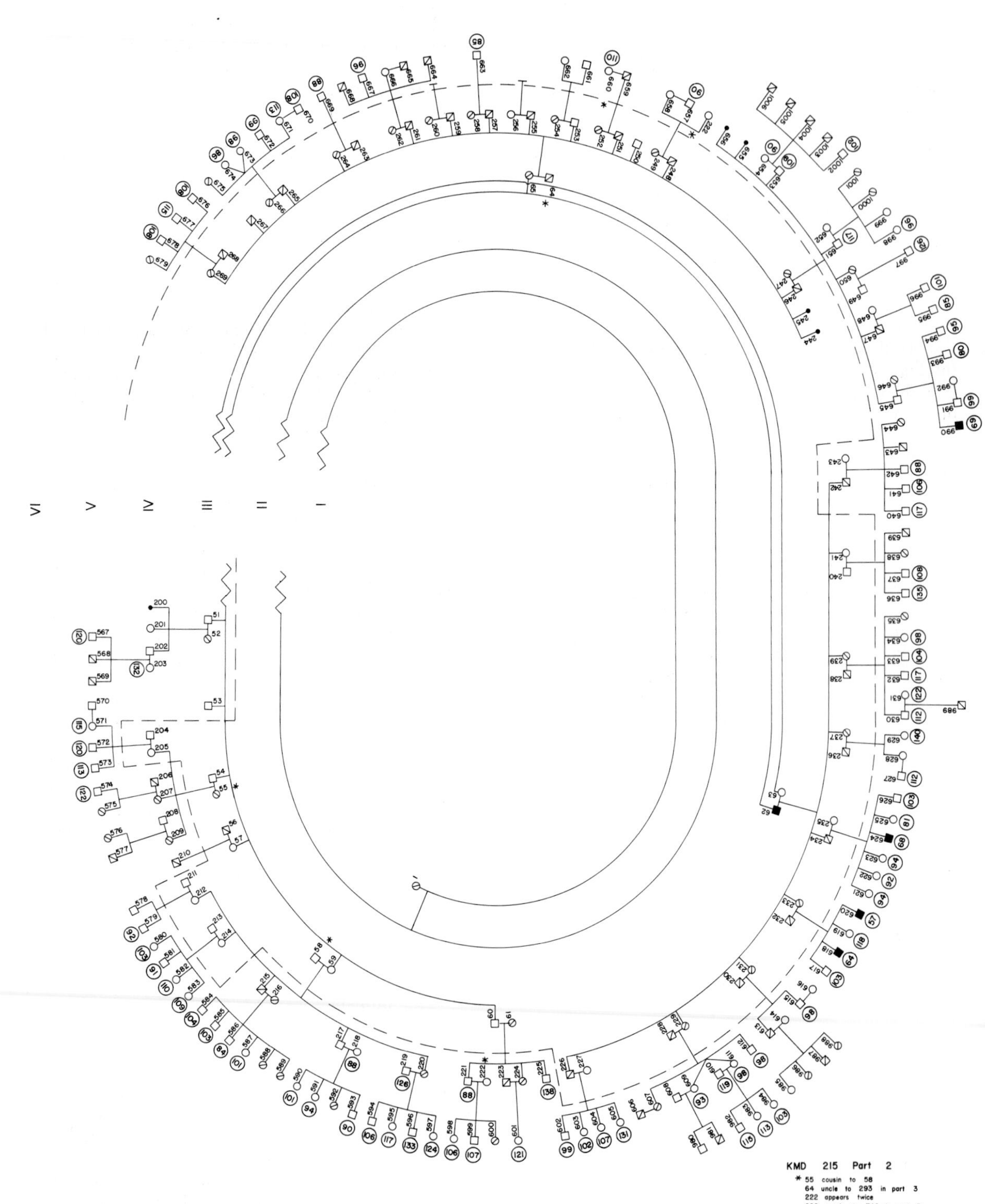
VI
V
IV
III
II
I
KMD 215 Part 2
* 55 cousin to 58
64 uncle to 293 in part 3
222 appears twice
660 cousin to 746 in part 3

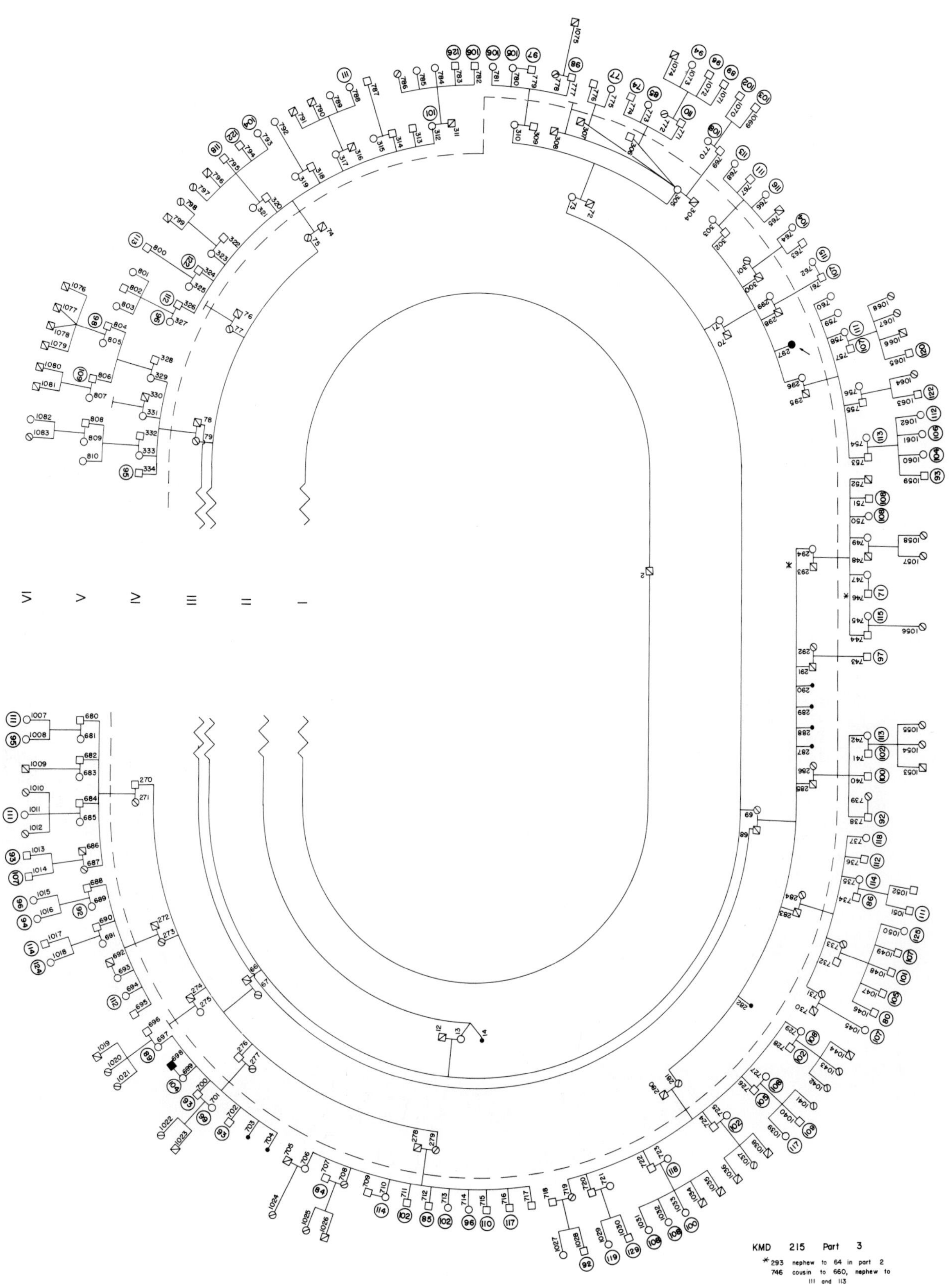

KMD 215 Part 3

*293 nephew to 64 in part 2
746 cousin to 660, nephew to 111 and 113

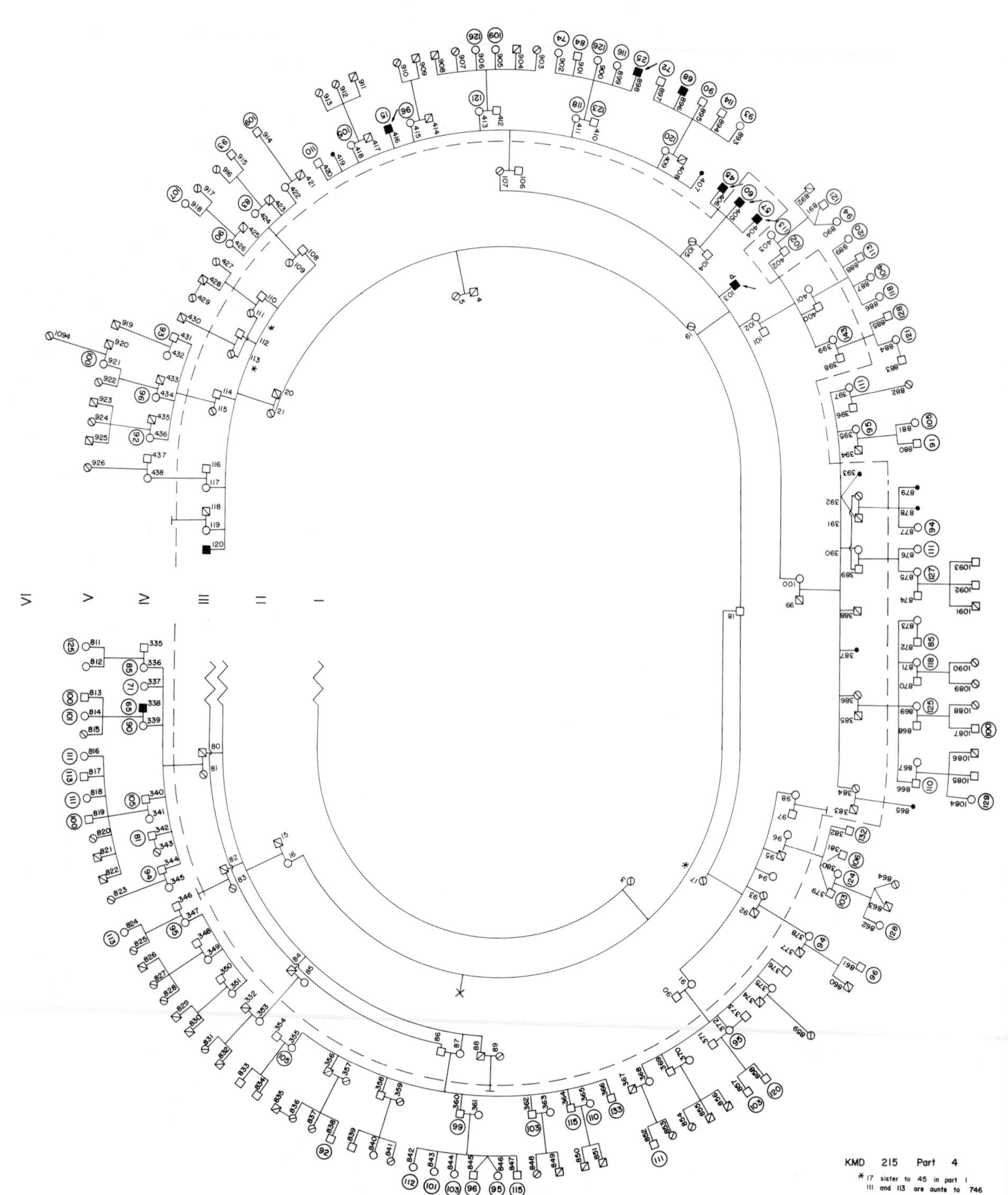

KMD 215 Part 4

* 17 sister to 45 in part I
111 and 113 are aunts to 746

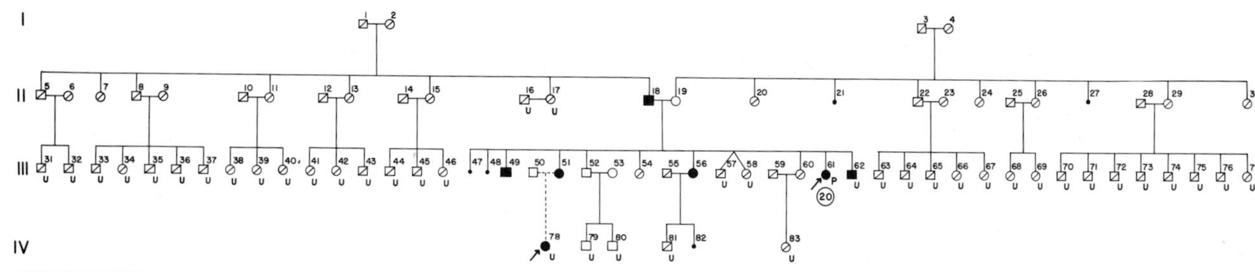

KMD 218

KMD 218

The Proband

The proband (61) was born in 1887, institutionalized at age 22 years, discharged to her parents in 1914 and died of pulmonary tuberculosis in 1923. She walked at age 4 years and talked at age 10. She developed epilepsy at age 25 years. She was the eleventh born in a sibship of 12, and had epicanthal eye folds, short, stubby fingers and toes and a prominent fissured tongue. IQ 20. *Diagnosis:* Down's syndrome.

Grandparents

Not of interest.

Parents

Father (18) was retarded.

Mother (19) had normal intelligence but an "ungovernable temper, bordering almost on insanity." Her home was well kept.

Aunts and Uncles

Not of interest.

Siblings

Sister (47) was a stillbirth.

Brother (48) died at 5 weeks. He had a rash and blister-like sores on his body.

Brother (49) was thought to have drowned at age 21. He was retarded.

Sister (51) had a retarded illegitimate child. She was epileptic and retarded and committed suicide at age 20.

Brother (52) had normal intelligence.

Sister (54) died of blood poisoning at age 20 years.

Sister (56) was a high-grade retardate.

Brother (57), sisters (58) and (60) had unknown intelligence.

Brother (62) was retarded.

Nieces and Nephews

Niece (78) was institutionalized for mental retardation attributed to injury from the kick of a horse. After this head injury she developed epilepsy.

First Cousins

Unknown. All the paternal and maternal relatives remained in Europe except for (26) who lived in Florida.

More Distant Relatives

Unknown.

Family Summary

The proband, IQ 20, her father, two brothers, two sisters and a niece were retarded. The mother was belligerent and bad tempered. Both parents abused the children. The proband's parents had 12 children and an unknown number of grandchildren—at least six. The proband's normal brother had two normal children. This family could not be found for follow-up since they had a commonly occurring Scandinavian name and moved often from farm to farm.

Retardation of proband of primarily genetic origin (Down's syndrome).

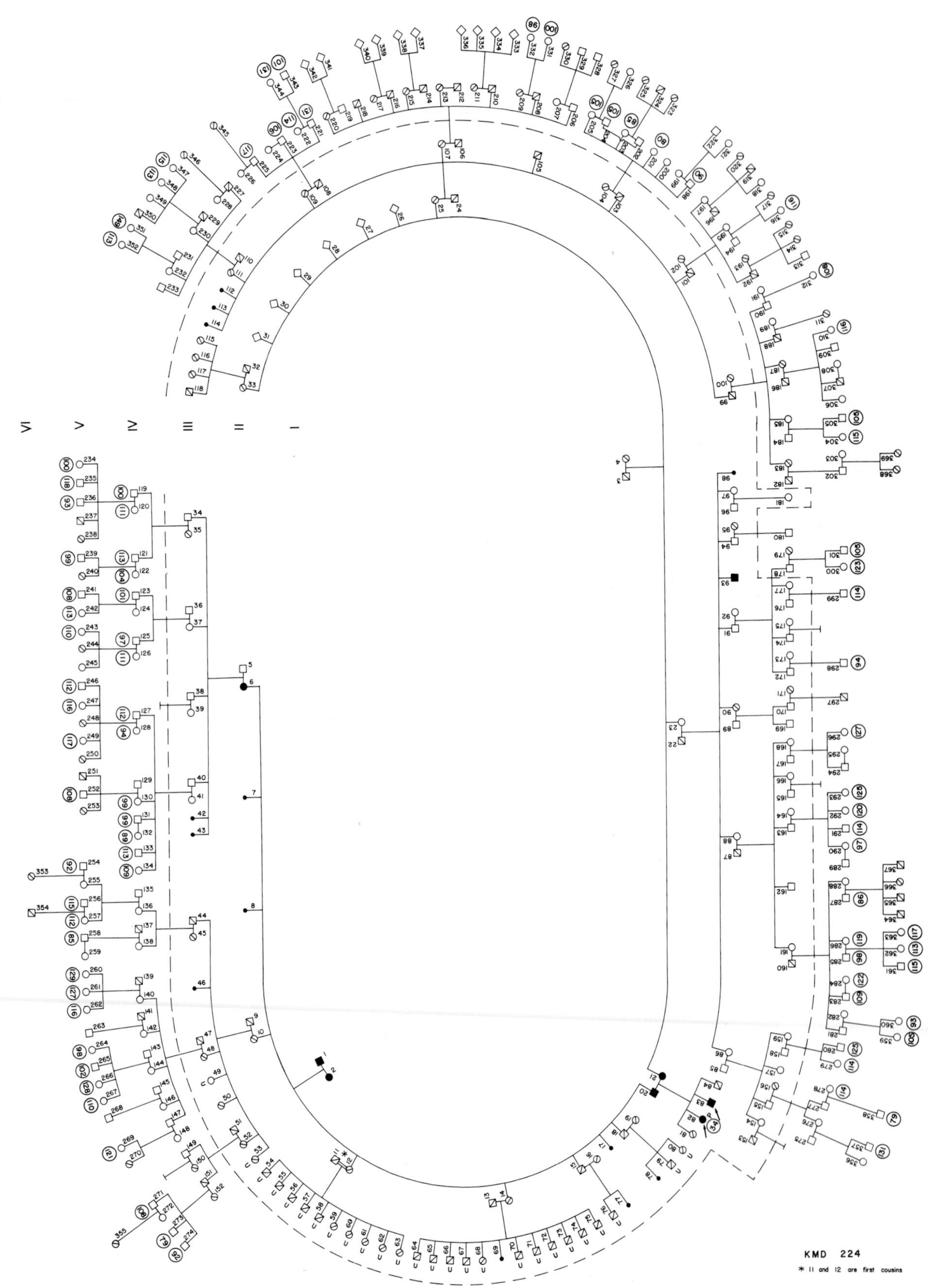
VI
V
IV
III
II
I
KMD 224
* 11 and 12 are first cousins

KMD 224

The Proband

The proband (82) was born in 1885, institutionalized at age 25 years and died of pulmonary tuberculosis in the institution in 1929. She grew up in abject poverty and neglect. Both parents were cruel to their children. The proband was promiscuous but never became pregnant. IQ 34. *Diagnosis:* undifferentiated mental retardation.

Grandparents

Paternal grandparents were retarded.

Parents

Both father (20) and mother (21) were retarded, alcoholic and cruel to the children who were usually hungry and unclothed.

Aunts and Uncles

Paternal aunt (6) was retarded. Her husband had normal intelligence as did her children and grandchildren.

Siblings

Sister (81) of unknown intelligence who died of diphtheria at 3 years of age.

Brother (83) was institutionalized at age 20 years and died of pulmonary tuberculosis in the institution a year later. He was a low-grade retardate.

Brother (84) of unknown intelligence who died of diphtheria at 3 years of age.

Nieces and Nephews

None.

First Cousins

(93) is an unmarried, retarded farm laborer.

More Distant Relatives

Not of interest.

Family Summary

The proband, IQ 34, and her brother, a low-grade retardate, were institutionalized. They grew up in a poor home in which they were abused and neglected. The proband's paternal grandparents, parents, a maternal aunt and a first cousin were also retarded, but of a higher grade. The proband's parents had four children, no grandchildren.

Retardation of proband of primarily genetic origin.

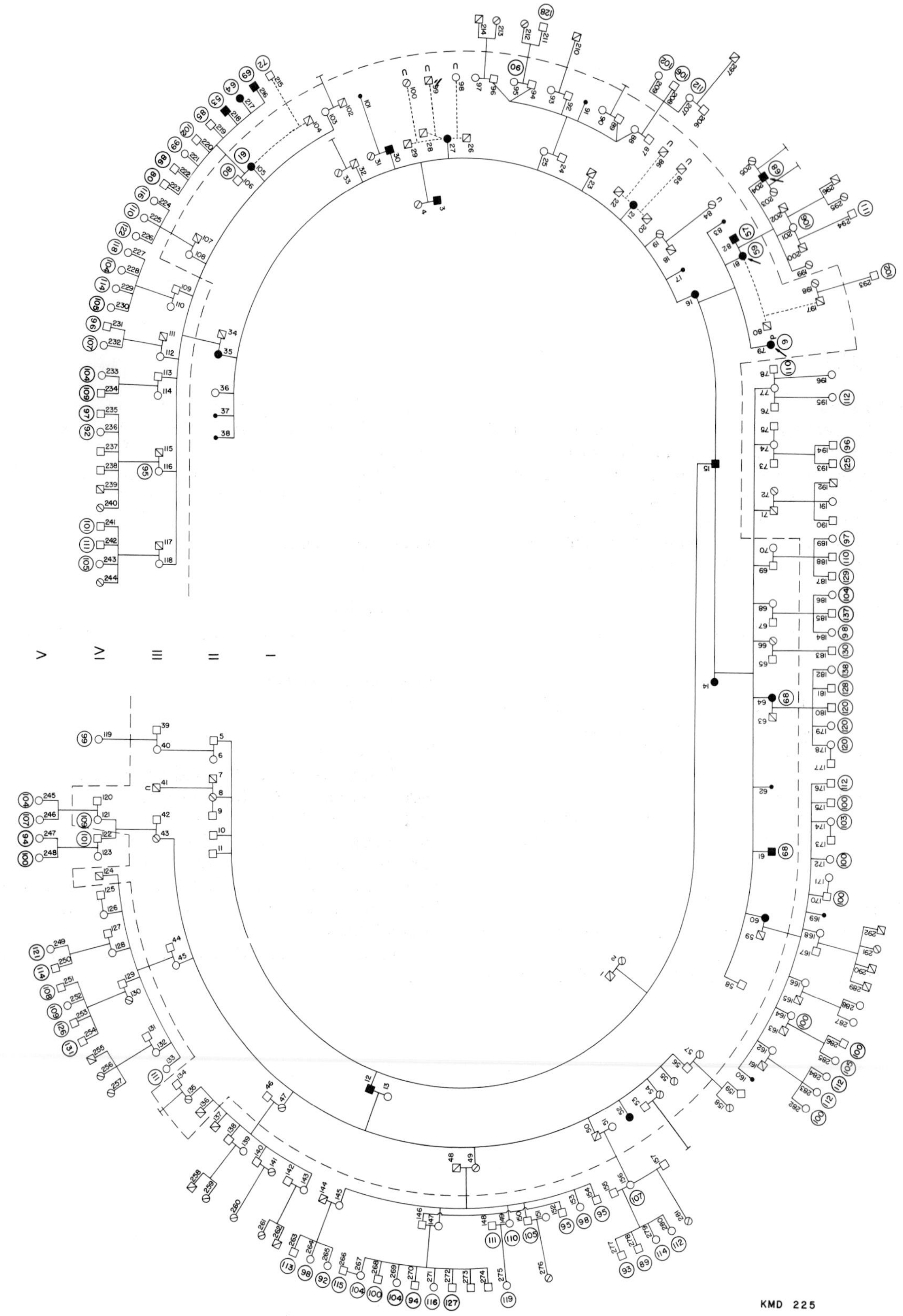

KMD 225

KMD 225

The Proband

The proband (79) was born in 1889, institutionalized at age 24 years and died of ulcers of the jejunum in the institution in 1931. She grew up in a poor environment. She did not walk or talk until 6 years of age. IQ 9. *Diagnosis:* cretinism.

Grandparents

Paternal grandfather was epileptic.

Maternal grandfather was an alcoholic and retarded.

Maternal grandmother was an alcoholic and promiscuous.

Parents

Father (15) was married twice, both times to retarded women. He was forced to marry the proband's mother after the birth of the proband. He was retarded.

Mother (16) was retarded.

Aunts and Uncles

Paternal uncle (5) was an alcoholic and committed suicide while taking the Keely cure for alcoholism.

Paternal uncle (12) was retarded.

Maternal aunt (21) had two illegitimate children. She was retarded.

Materanl aunt (27) had three illegitimate children. She was retarded. (27) and (21), together with their children, lived at a "poor farm" in Sweden and never came to this country.

Maternal uncle (30) was an alcoholic and retarded.

Maternal aunt (35) was retarded.

Siblings

Sister (81) was institutionalized in 1926 at age 35 years, sterilized in 1927 and now lives under outside supervision. She married a retarded man (82), IQ 57, who abandoned her. She has one child of unknown intelligence, one with IQ 106 and one with IQ 68.

(83) was a stillbirth.

Half Siblings

Half brother (58) operates a gravel pit. He has normal intelligence.

Half sister (60) is retarded. She married a man of unknown intelligence (59) and had 11 children, the nine survivors of whom all have normal intelligence.

Half brother (61) is an unmarried, childless truck driver, IQ 68.

Half brother (62) died at 3 months of "spasms."

Half sister (64) has an IQ of 68. Her husband (63) has unknown intelligence; her children have remarkably high IQ's of 120, 120, 120, 128 and 138, respectively.

Half sister (66) has unknown intelligence.

Half sisters (68), (74) and (77), and half brother (69) have normal intelligence.

Half brother (71) has unknown intelligence.

Nieces and Nephews

Nephew (204) was adopted but was institutionalized, first in a mental hospital and later in the institution for the retarded. He was sterilized and is still in the institution. IQ's 71, 77, 93, 68, 74, 75, 67 and 59, the results of tests administered over a period of 17 years. He was married twice.

Children of Half Siblings

None was retarded. The two retarded women (60) and (64) married men of unknown intelligence and had 16 children. (64) with an IQ of 68 had five children with IQ's of 120, 120, 120, 128 and 138, respectively.

First Cousins

(52) died as a young woman. She completed the fourth grade at 14 years. She stayed in bed most of the time because she was "afraid of everybody."

(105), IQ 61, had an illegitimate child, was hospitalized for neurosis with the recommendation for her commitment as retarded and for her sterilization. Her husband refused his consent. The husband is an "invalid" and neurotic, IQ 80. The school reported that (105) and her siblings came from a family of "very low intelligence." Of her nine children, three are retarded, one borderline, one unknown and three normal.

More Distant Relatives

(216), (217) and (218), all siblings, have IQ's of 69, 64 and 53, respectively. Only one child in this sibship of nine has an IQ of 100 or above. (220) has an IQ of 101.

Family Summary

The proband, IQ 9, was a cretin. In addition she had a maternal grandfather, one paternal uncle, three maternal aunts and a maternal uncle, both parents, one full sibling and three half siblings, a cousin and three more distant relatives who were higher-grade retardates, at least two of whom had associated neuroses. The children of the proband's retarded half sibling were normal, but three of the nine children of her retarded cousin are retarded. The proband's parents had three children and three grandchildren. The proband's sister's family (81) indicates a probable genetic basis for their undifferentiated retardation as does the family of the maternal aunt (35). The proband's father had 11 children by his second marriage. Of these, three were retarded, five normal and three of unknown intelligence. He also had 30 grandchildren of whom nine have IQ's of 120 or above and none is retarded.

Retardation of proband of primarily genetic origin (cretinism).

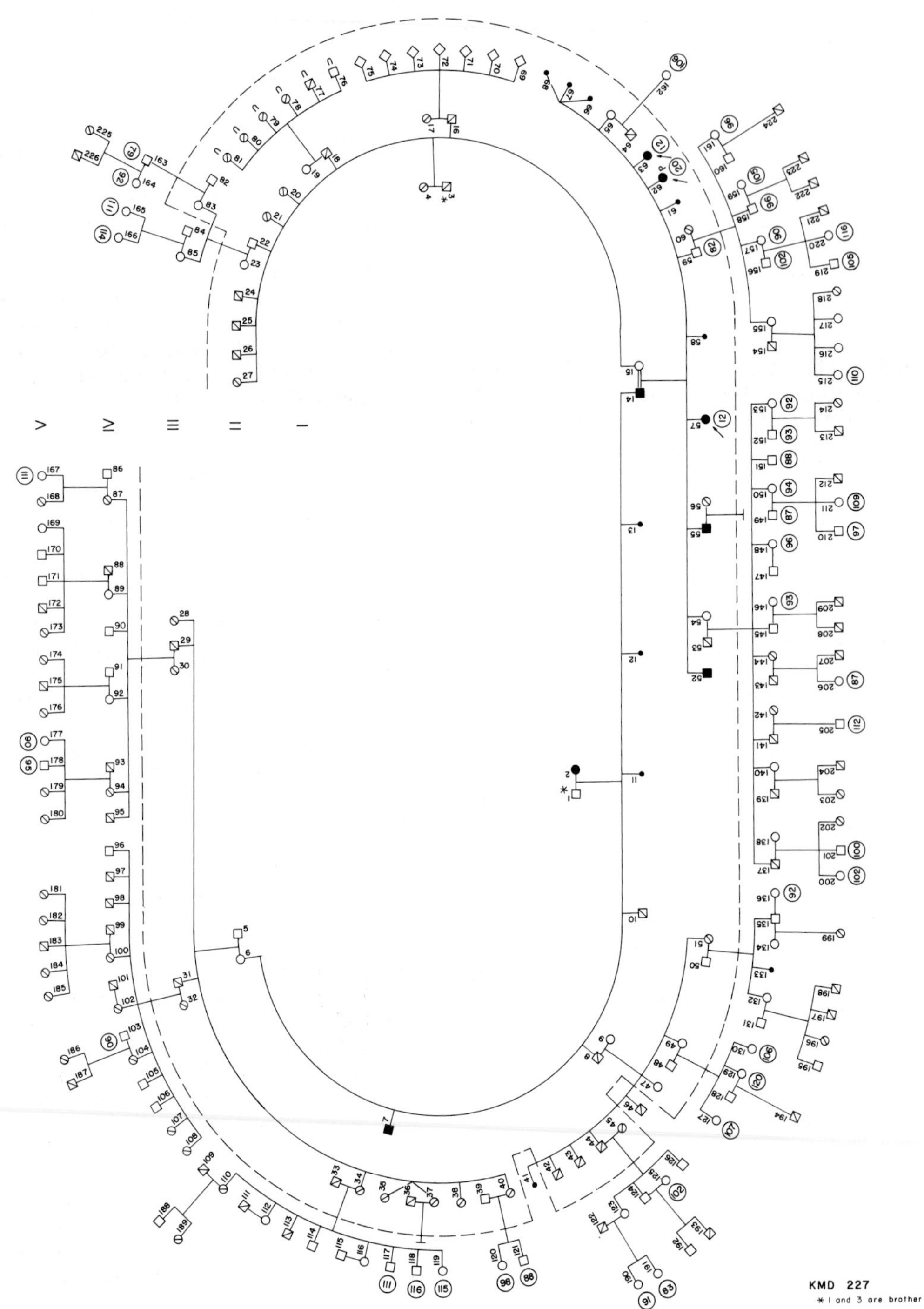

KMD 227

* 1 and 3 are brothers

KMD 227

The Proband

The proband (62) was born in 1904, institutionalized at age 5 years and died of bronchopneumonia and measles in the institution in 1913. Her birth was normal. She was choreic, had no locomotion and very limited speech. IQ 20. *Diagnosis:* undifferentiated mental retardation.

Grandparents

Paternal and maternal grandfathers were brothers.

Paternal grandmother was retarded.

Parents

Father (14) was retarded and an alcoholic. He was kind to his family but could not work without supervision.

Mother (15) operated the family farm. She had normal intelligence and was first cousin to the proband's father.

Aunts and Uncles

Paternal uncle (7) died unmarried and childless. He was an alcoholic and retarded.

Paternal uncle (10), intelligence unknown, died of alcoholism.

Siblings

Brother (52), unmarried and childless, was killed in an accident at age 47. He was retarded (high or middle grade).

Sisters (54) and (65) have normal intelligence and normal children.

Brother (55) was a plasterer and a high-grade retardate. He was married but childless.

Sister (57) was institutionalized in 1909 at age 11 years and died of bronchopneumonia in the institution in 1913. She had crying spells and "fits." She had no locomotion, very little speech and was choreic. IQ 12.

Sister (58) died at age 18 weeks of "spasms."

Brother (59) was a laborer with IQ 82 and normal children.

(61) was a miscarriage.

Sister (63) was institutionalized in 1913 at age 8 years and died of pulmonary tuberculosis at age 18 years. She had no locomotion and very little speech. IQ 12.

(66), (67) and (68) were triplets who died in infancy.

Nieces and Nephews

Not of interest.

First Cousins

Not of interest.

More Distant Relatives

Not of interest.

Family Summary

The proband, IQ 20, and two sisters were institutionalized, all rather low-grade retardates with no locomotion and very little speech and choreic movements. In addition, the proband's paternal grandmother, paternal uncle, father and two brothers were high-grade retardates. The proband's parents were first cousins. They had 13 children and 14 grandchildren, all the offspring of the three normal children.

Retardation of proband of primarily genetic origin (consanguinity).

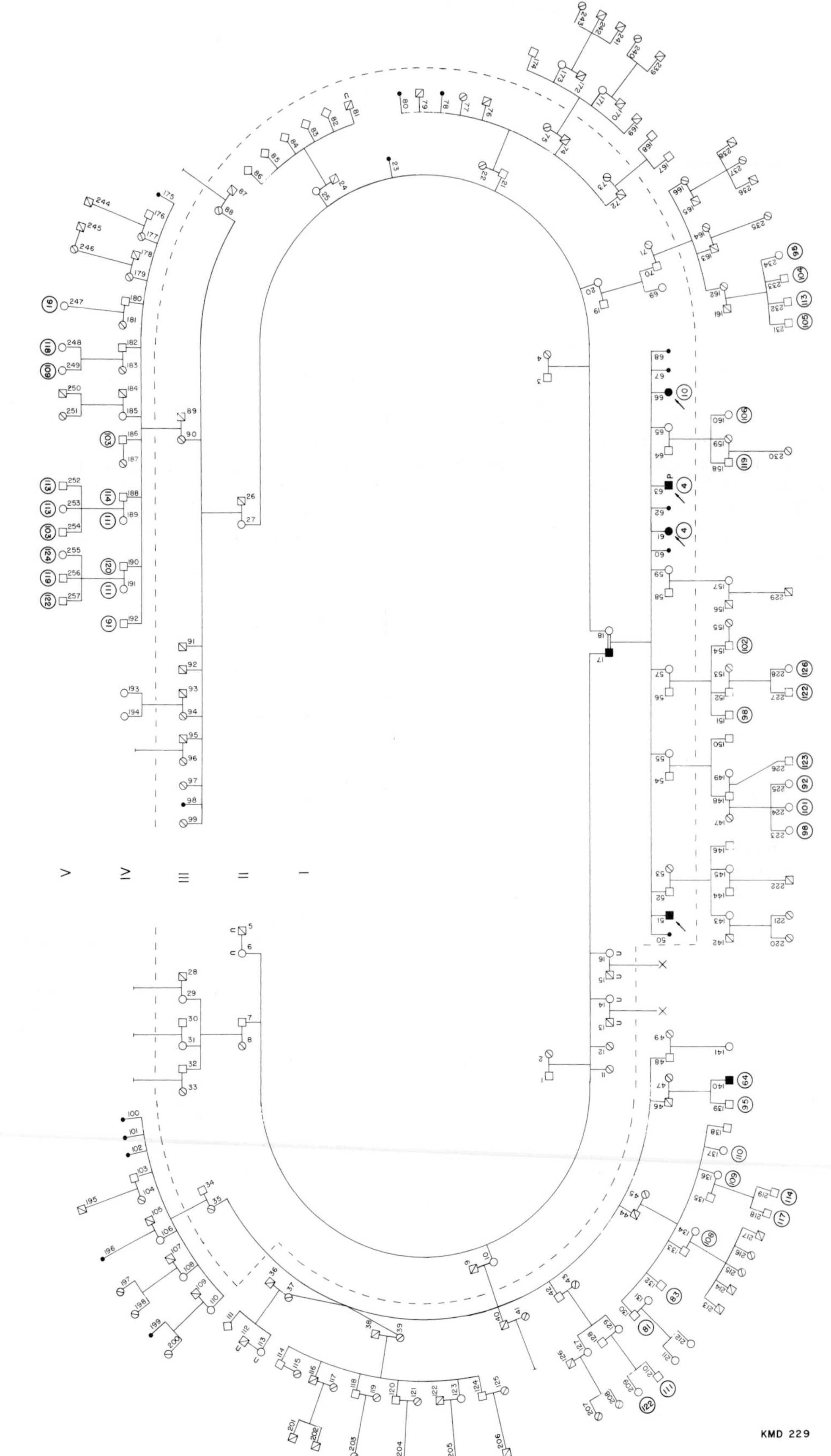

KMD 229

KMD 229

The Proband

The proband (63) was born in 1897, institutionalized at age 13 years and died of pulmonary tuberculosis in the institution in 1913. At age 10 months he had an attack of "infantile paralysis." In 1913 at age 13 years he had a positive Wassermann test. He showed poor locomotion, limited speech and had lateral scoliosis. IQ 4. *Diagnosis:* undifferentiated mental retardation.

Grandparents

Paternal and maternal grandfathers were brothers.

Parents

Father (17) was an alcoholic and syphilitic. He was an unsuccessful blacksmith and was retarded.

Mother (18) had normal intelligence but was syphilitic. She and (17) were first cousins.

Aunts and Uncles

Not of interest.

Siblings

Brother (50) died of bronchopneumonia at age 3 months.

Brother (51) was institutionalized at age 25 years in 1911 and died of hypostatic pneumonia and tuberculosis in the institution in 1912. He was a low-grade retardate who was pigeon breasted and paraplegic.

Brother (52), sisters (55), (57), (59) and (65) had normal intelligence and normal children.

Brother (60) died shortly after birth.

Sister (61) was institutionalized at age 13 years and died of pulmonary tuberculosis in the institution in 1913. She was epileptic and a low-grade retardate with a mental age of 6 months.

Sister (62) died of pneumonia at 18 months.

Sister (66) was institutionalized in 1934 at age 29 years and died of carcinoma of the uterus in the institution in 1936. She could not walk, only crawled, and could not speak. IQ 10.

Brother (67) died of cholera infantum at 5 months.

Sister (68) died a few minutes after birth.

Nieces and Nephews

Not of interest.

First Cousins

Not of interest.

More Distant Relatives

First cousin (46) has a son (140) with IQ 64.

Family Summary

The proband, IQ 4, and three of his siblings were low-grade, institutionalized retardates. The proband's parents were first cousins, and they and the proband were syphilitic. None of the institutionalized siblings showed any signs of congenital syphilis. Five of the proband's siblings had normal intelligence and five died in infancy of various causes. One first cousin had a high-grade retardate son. The proband's parents had 14 children and 11 grandchildren. Despite the fact that the proband was reported to have had infantile paralysis at 10 months, the general pattern of retardation appearing in a similar form in the siblings from a cousin marriage indicates that genetic factors are involved in the retardation.

Retardation of proband of primarily genetic origin (consanguinity).

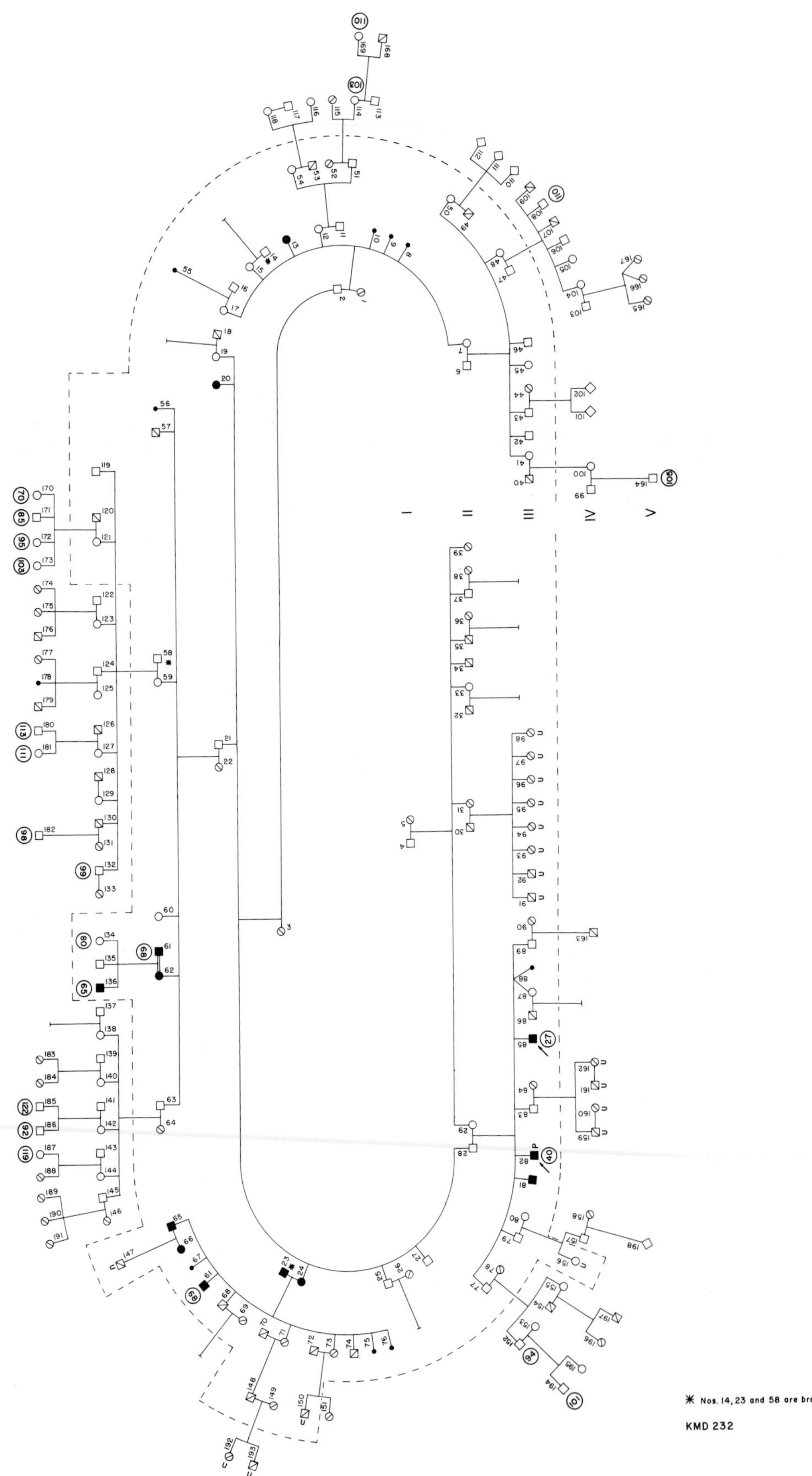

✱ Nos. 14, 23 and 58 are brothers

KMD 232

KMD 232

The Proband

The proband (82) was born in 1887, institutionalized at age 16 years and died of bronchopneumonia in the institution in 1952. He was reared in a good environment but was backward from birth and very slow to walk and talk. He was given a physical and neurological examination by J. A. Böök, M.D., and John Schut, M.D., in 1950. They reported acromegaly in addition to the retardation. EEG moderately abnormal during the waking state, normal during sleep. IQ 40. *Diagnosis:* mental retardation with acromegaly.

Grandparents

Maternal grandfather died in a mental hospital.

Parents

Father (28) and mother (29) both had normal intelligence. The father was a farmer.

Aunts and Uncles

Paternal aunt (20) was retarded, later became mentally ill and died single and childless in a mental hospital.

Paternal aunt (24) was retarded and her husband was an alcoholic and retarded. They had nine children of whom three died in infancy, two were retarded and four had unknown intelligence.

Paternal uncle (27) had normal intelligence and died of alcoholism.

Proband's Father's Half Sibling

(13) was retarded, also mentally ill, and died in a mental hospital.

Siblings

Brothers (77), (79), (83) and (89), and sister (87) all had normal intelligence.

Brother (81) is an unmarried, childless, farm laborer and is retarded.

Brother (85) was institutionalized at age 10 years and is still in the institution. He was given a physical and neurological examination by Dr. Böök and Dr. Schut in 1950. They reported some acromegaly, but not quite as much as the proband. IQ 27.

Sister (88) died of whooping cough at 4 months.

Nieces and Nephews

Not of interest.

First Cousins

(62), retarded, married her retarded first cousin (61) with IQ 68 [(61) appears twice] and had three children, (134) with IQ 80, (135) who left school in the ninth grade with a D average and (136) with IQ 65.

(65) abandoned his pregnant wife and has not been heard of since that time. He was retarded, as was his wife.

(75) died of convulsions at age 18 months.

More Distant Relatives

First cousin's child (136) is an unmarried farm laborer with an IQ of 65.

Family Summary

The proband, IQ 40, and his brother, IQ 27, were acromegalic and were the only retarded persons in the immediate family except for a high-grade retarded brother. In addition, they had two paternal aunts, one half-aunt, three first cousins and two more distant relatives who were retarded, but of the high retardate level.

Both the proband's parents had normal intelligence and provided a good home for their children. They had nine children and seven grandchildren. The proband's other retarded relatives grew up in very poor environments.

Retardation of proband of primarily genetic origin.

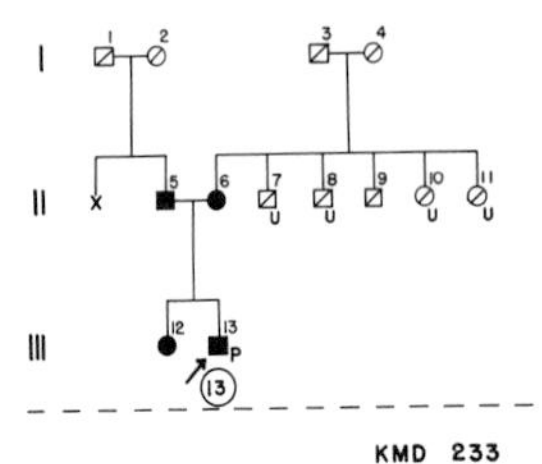

KMD 233

The Proband

The proband (13) was born in 1872, institutionalized at age 29 years and died of myocardial degeneration in the institution in 1945. He was born with a deformed foot and was reared in a dugout by his retarded parents who made a living by stealing and begging. IQ 13. *Diagnosis:* undifferentiated mental retardation.

Grandparents

Unknown.

Parents

Father (5) had such poor mentality that he could not do simple manual labor without continual supervision. He never learned to speak English. "It is not understood how he passed the immigration officers."

Mother (6) would not have tested "over four years." She and her daughter died in the "poor house."

Aunts and Uncles

All relatives remained in Germany.

Siblings

Sister (12) could speak only a few words.

Nieces and Nephews

None.

First Cousins

Unknown.

More Distant Relatives

Unknown.

Family Summary

The proband, IQ 13, his sister (who could not talk) and both his parents were retardates of low or middle grade. The family home was poor. The proband's parents had two children, no grandchildren.

Retardation of proband of primarily genetic origin.

KMD 264

The Proband

The proband (55) was born in 1881, institutionalized at age 20 years and died of lobar pneumonia and arteriosclerotic heart disease in the institution in 1959. He was given a physical and neurological examination in 1950 by J. A. Böök, M.D., and John Schut, M.D. They found no stigmata and gave a diagnosis of idiocy. IQ 20. *Diagnosis:* undifferentiated mental retardation.

Grandparents

Not of interest.

Parents

Father (20) and mother (21) both had normal intelligence.

Aunts and Uncles

Paternal relatives not of interest except that (18) married his niece (19). They had two children, both with normal intelligence.

Maternal uncle (22) was a single, childless, retarded farm laborer.

Maternal aunt (33) with normal intelligence married a retarded, partially blind cripple.

Siblings

Sister (54) was institutionalized in 1902 at age 24 years and died of a cerebral hemorrhage in the institution in 1945. She had convulsions. IQ 39.

Sister (57) was classified as "mentally slow" by the early workers. Her husband and children have normal intelligence except for (124) who is unknown and (131) with IQ 74.

Brother (58) was institutionalized in 1902 at age 15 years and has remained in the institution ever since. He was given a physical and neurological examination in 1950 by Dr. Böök and Dr. Schut. They found no stigmata and gave a diagnosis of imbecility. IQ 40.

Sister (59) was institutionalized in 1902 at age 13 years and died of rheumatic heart disease in the institution in 1942. IQ 35.

Sister (61) had normal intelligence.

Nieces and Nephews

Not of interest.

First Cousins

Not of interest.

More Distant Relatives

(189) is an institutionalized microcephalic.

Family Summary

The proband, IQ 34, one maternal uncle, three siblings and one more distant relative were retarded. The uncle was a high-grade retardate,

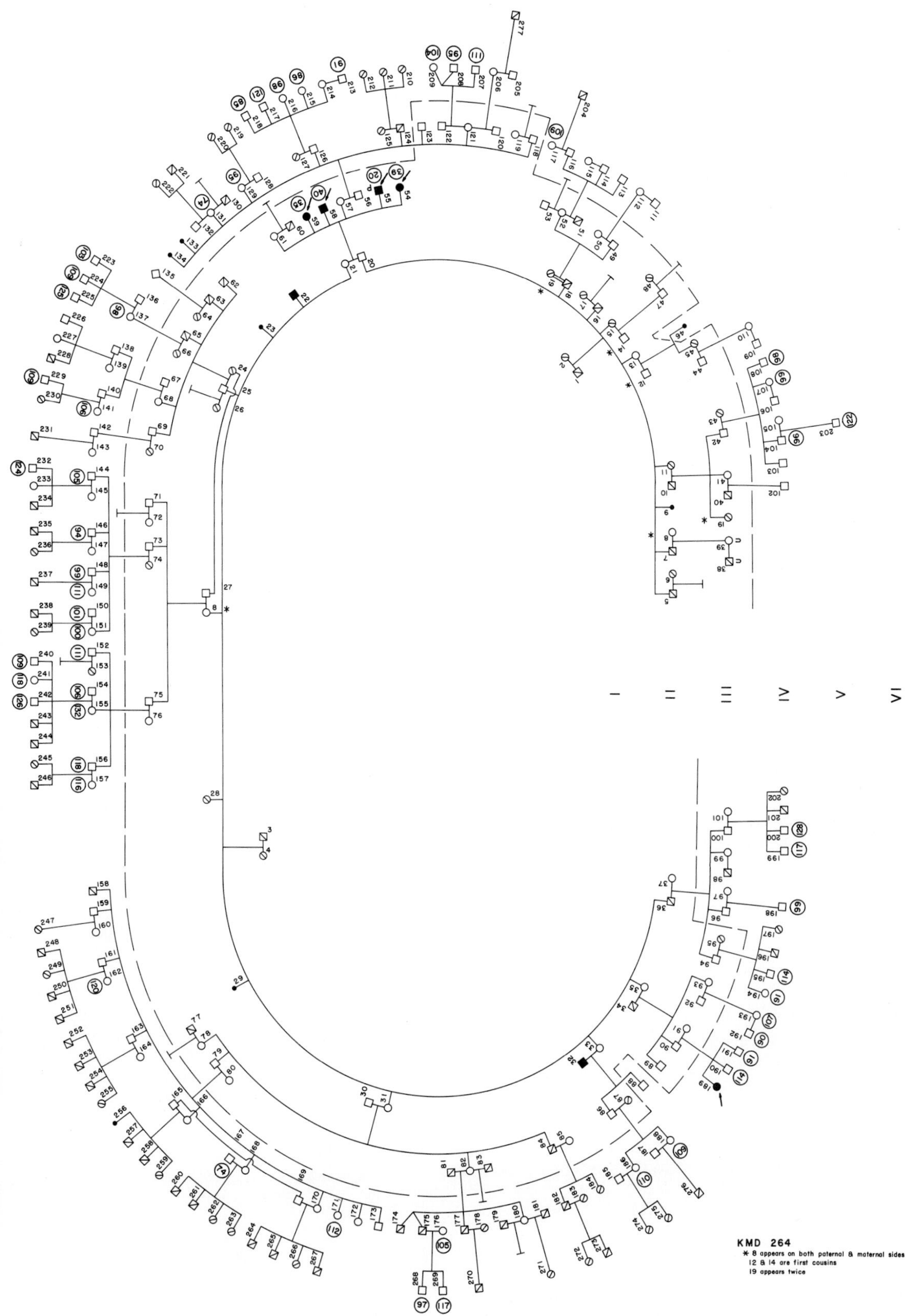

the distant relative a microcephalic, while the proband and his three siblings were low- and middle-grade retardates, all institutionalized and all without stigmata or any history of trauma. The proband's parents had six children and nine grandchildren, all the children of one normal daughter.

Retardation of proband of primarily genetic origin.

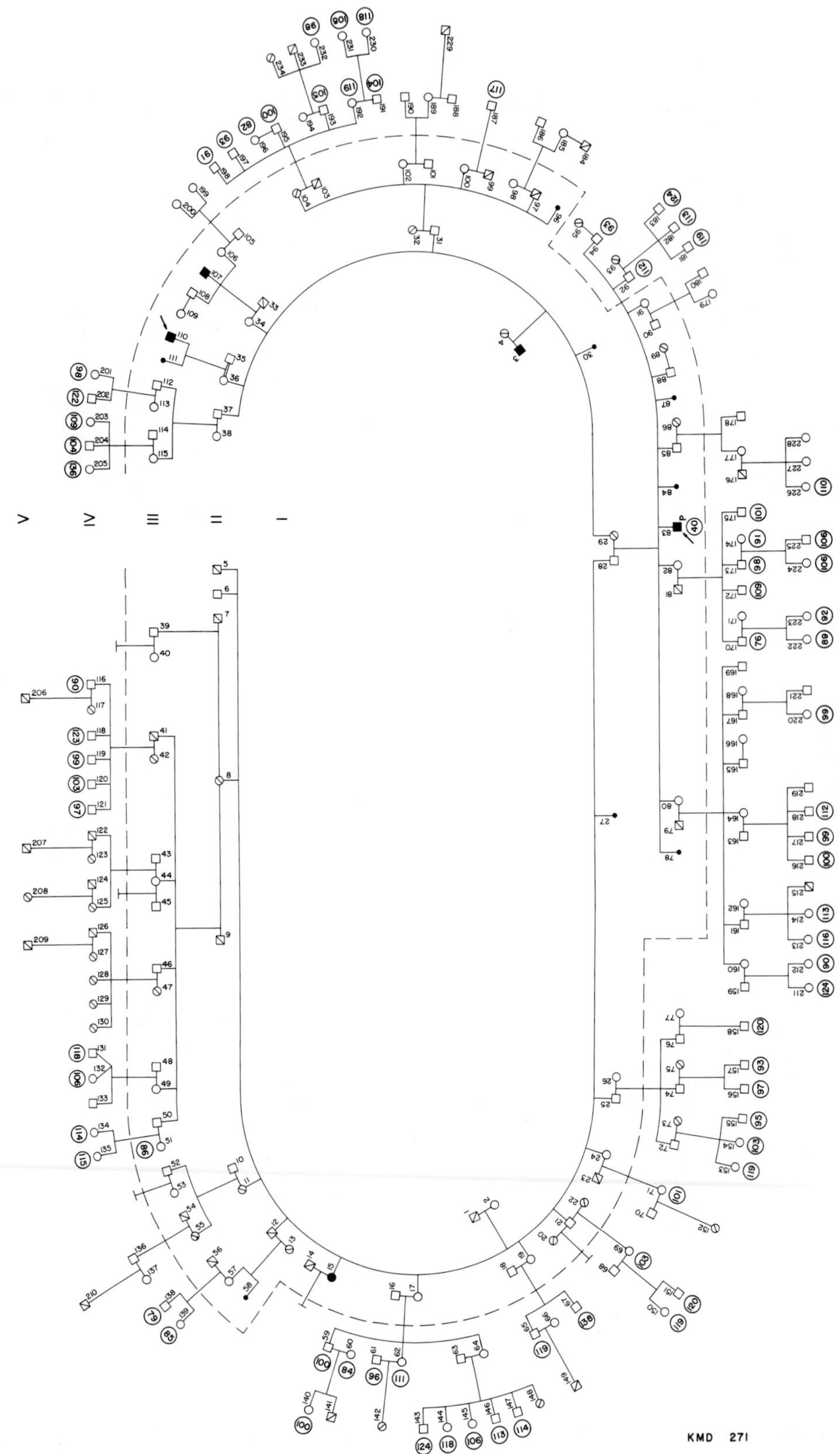
KMD 271

KMD 271

The Proband

The proband (83) was born in 1903, institutionalized at age 9 years, discharged to his parents in 1917 and died of scarlet fever while at home in 1918. He was a weak, sickly baby who never learned to talk well. The old institution records classify him as a "mongol." IQ 40. *Diagnosis:* Down's syndrome.

Grandparents

Maternal grandfather was retarded.

Parents

Father (28) was a plasterer with normal intelligence.

Mother (29) was subject to "fainting spells." Her intelligence was unknown.

Aunts and Uncles

Paternal aunt (15), married but childless, was retarded.

Siblings

Brother (78) was a "seven months" baby. He died at 4 months of "summer complaint."

Sisters (80), (82) and (91) have normal intelligence as do their children.

(84) and (87) were miscarriages.

Brothers (85), (88), (92) and (94) have normal intelligence as do their children.

Nieces and Nephews

All known to have normal intelligence.

First Cousins

(107) is a high-grade retardate, unmarried and childless.

(110) was an institutionalized, low-grade retardate.

(111) was a low-grade retardate who died at 18 months.

More Distant Relatives

Not of interest.

Family Summary

The proband, IQ 40, his maternal grandfather, a paternal aunt and three first cousins were retarded. The first cousins were low-grade retardates, the grandfather and aunt were high grade. The proband's parents had 11 children and 17 grandchildren.

Retardation of proband of primarily genetic origin (Down's syndrome).

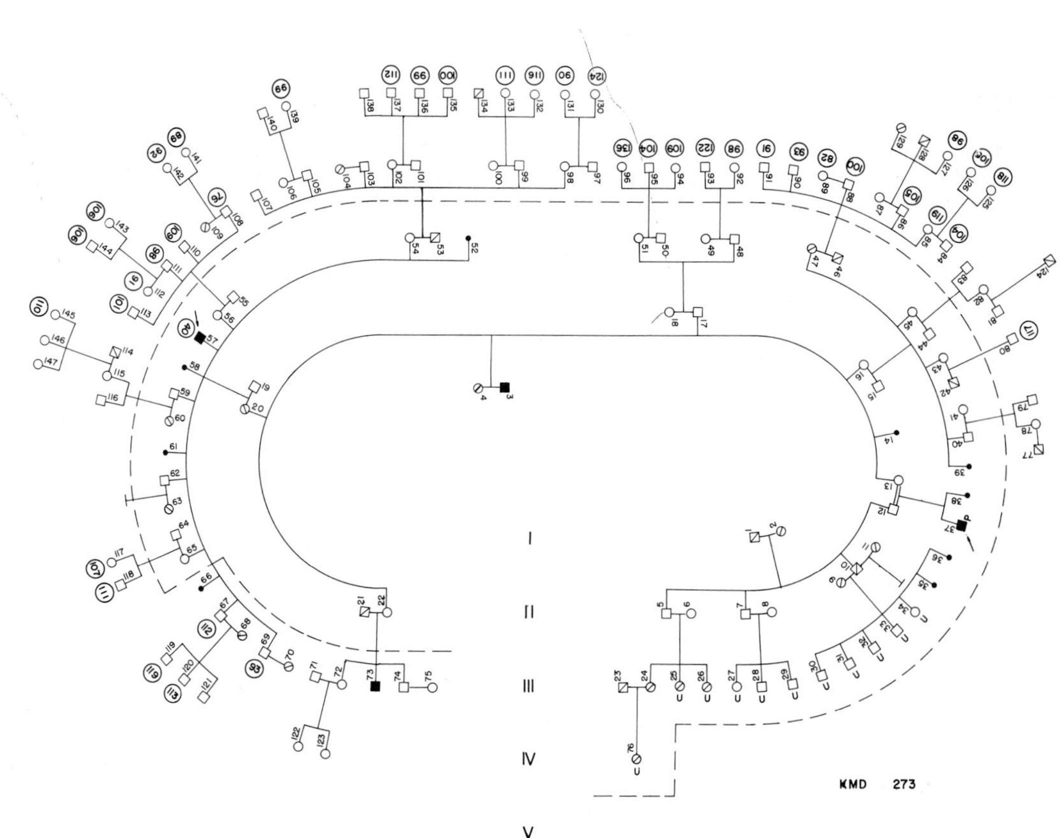
I
II
III
IV
V
KMD 273

KMD 273

The Proband

The proband (37) was born in 1899, institutionalized at age 6 years and died of bronchopneumonia in the institution in 1911. His birth was difficult and he was a large baby "much puffed up" with a lump the size of an egg on the side of his head just back of the crown. Medical examination upon admission reports a high occipital bone. The attending physician diagnosed Buhl's disease, an acute fatty degeneration of the viscera of the newborn with hemorrhages in various parts of the body. The home environment was good. The proband could never talk and was described as a low-grade retardate. *Diagnosis:* Buhl's disease.

Grandparents

Maternal grandfather was retarded. His condition was attributed to sunstroke.

Parents

Father (12) and mother (13) both had normal intelligence. They were first cousins once removed.

Aunts and Uncles

Not of interest.

Siblings

Brother (38) died of pneumonia at 18 months. His birth was uneventful but he was a large baby and was retarded.

Nieces and Nephews

None.

First Cousins

(57) was institutionalized at age 9 years. He was classified as "Mongolian type." IQ 40.

(73) is an unmarried, childless laborer who repeated the fifth grade twice and failed the sixth grade at age 16 years.

Family Summary

The proband and his brother were low-grade retardates. The parents had normal intelligence but were first cousins once removed. They had two children, no grandchildren. Two of the proband's cousins were retarded; one was a high-grade retardate, one probably had Down's syndrome.

Retardation of proband of primarily genetic origin (consanguinity).

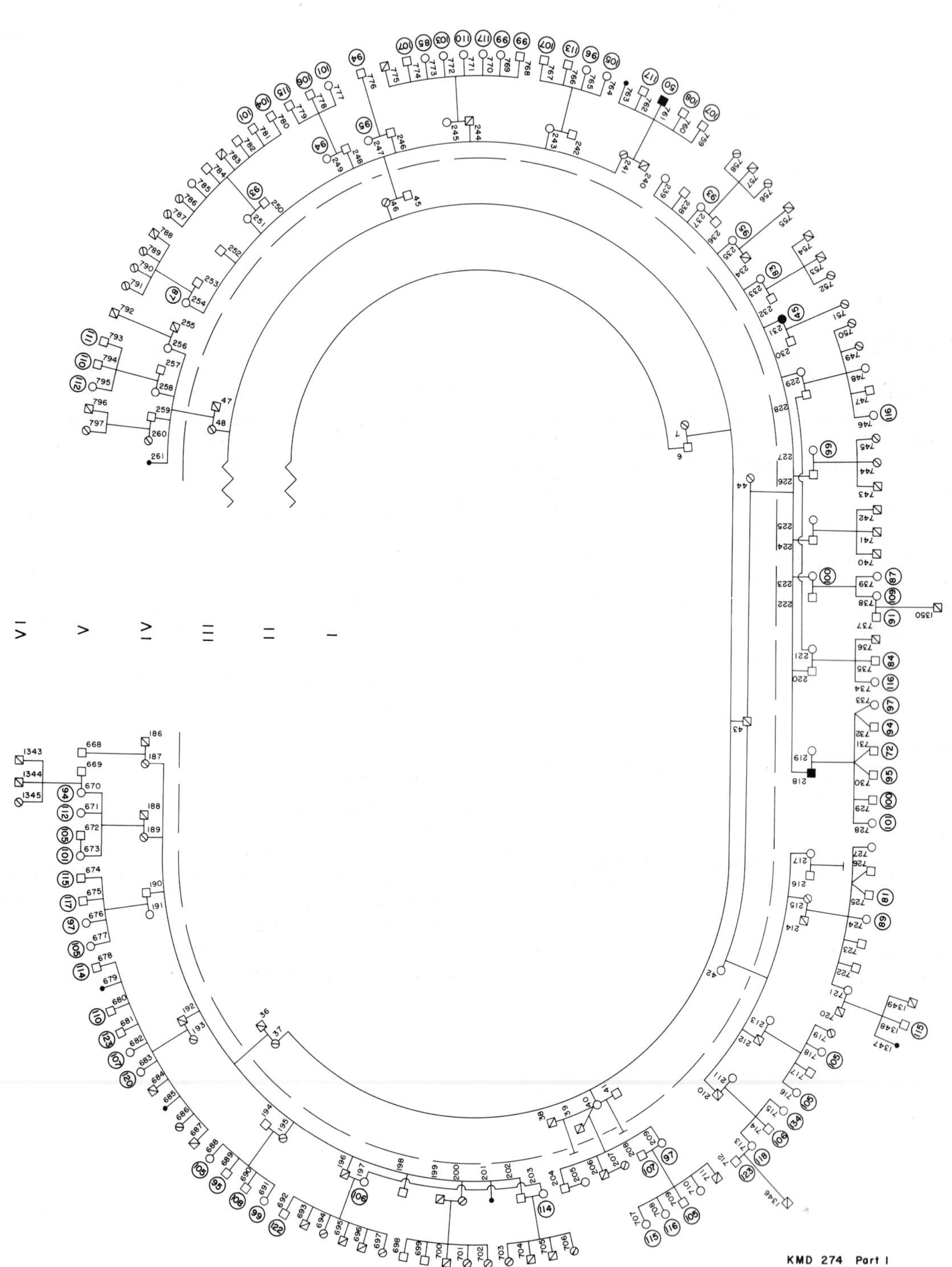

KMD 274 Part I

KMD 274

The Proband

The proband (89) was born in 1889, institutionalized at age 17 years and died of lobar pneumonia in the institution in 1937. While in the institution she had an illegitimate child by a retarded man. No data could be obtained about the early life of the proband and her siblings because the mother was too retarded to be able to give the details. She had no stigmata. The father deserted his family and the older children went to foster homes while the younger ones were taken to the state orphanage. IQ 47. *Diagnosis:* undifferentiated mental retardation.

Grandparents

Paternal grandfather died of alcoholism. He was retarded.

Parents

Father (18) was an alcoholic, retarded man who deserted his family.

Mother (19) had an IQ of 45 (approximate) and was an alcoholic.

Aunts and Uncles

Paternal relatives (6), (8), (10), (12), (14) and (16) were all described as brighter than the proband's father (18) but were also characterized as "lazy," "shiftless" and "dull." (14) kept a hotel but was "too lazy to cook food for the boarders."

Maternal uncle (23) died of alcoholism. He abandoned his wife, a normal woman, who was childless. He was retarded.

Maternal uncle (27) was an alcoholic and retarded. He was unmarried and childless.

Maternal aunt (33) was retarded; her husband was normal. They had a retarded child and two retarded grandchildren.

Maternal uncle (34) was an alcoholic and retarded; his wife was normal.

Siblings

(84), (85) and (86) all died of unknown causes in infancy.

Brothers (87) and (88) were unknown at the time the original history was written when they were 29 years and 27 years old, respectively.

Brother (90) was adopted and taken out of the state. He had normal intelligence.

(91) was a miscarriage.

Brother (92) was institutionalized at age 10 years and escaped ten years later. His present status is unknown. IQ 47.

Child

(374a) born in the institution and died at age 3 years of pneumonia. She was apparently normal.

Nieces and Nephews

Unknown.

First Cousins

(53) died in a mental hospital with a diagnosis of schizophrenia, catatonic type.

(105) was retarded.

(118) refused to cooperate because she was a "nerves reck."

(136) died in a mental hospital, diagnosis of senile psychosis, simple deterioration.

(143) was reported in recent welfare records as retarded. She has four retarded children (524), (528), (535) and (537) by a normal husband.

(176) completed the third grade and is retarded.

(181) died in a mental hospital, diagnosis dementia praecox, paranoid type.

More Distant Relatives

(218) was retained in the fifth and seventh grades.

(231), a sibling to (218) has an IQ of 45.

(474) is an unmarried farm laborer with IQ 66.

(486), a sibling to (474), has an IQ of 31.

(524) completed the fifth grade and worked in a laundry. She was committed as retarded but was never institutionalized. She had an illegitimate child with IQ 96. Her IQ was 52.

(528), a sibling to (524), (535) and (537), was committed as retarded in 1942 at age 38 years, imprisoned in 1944 for drunkenness and molesting women. He was placed under outside supervision in 1946 and is on the waiting list for institutionalization. IQ 61. His wife (529) was institutionalized and sterilized in 1943. IQ 58. All three children of this couple (1177), (1178) and (1179) are retarded with IQ's of 53, 70 and 66, respectively, and are in a special school for the retarded.

(535) was institutionalized in 1930 at age 18 years but escaped two months later and is under outside supervision. His IQ is 56. His wife (536) neglected her children so badly that neighbors complained to county officials. Her IQ is 74. The children's IQ's range from 77 to 104.

(537) was institutionalized in 1930 at age 16 years, escaped in 1945 and was discharged from guardianship. His IQ is 59.

(556) was institutionalized in 1921 at age 19 years because of "vicious assaults on little girls." IQ 39.

(559), a sibling to (556), was institutionalized in 1933 at age 26 years. He was put in the Annex for Defective Delinquents in 1945, released under custody in 1948 but returned to the Annex for Defective Delinquents permanently in 1955, after

Continued on page 185

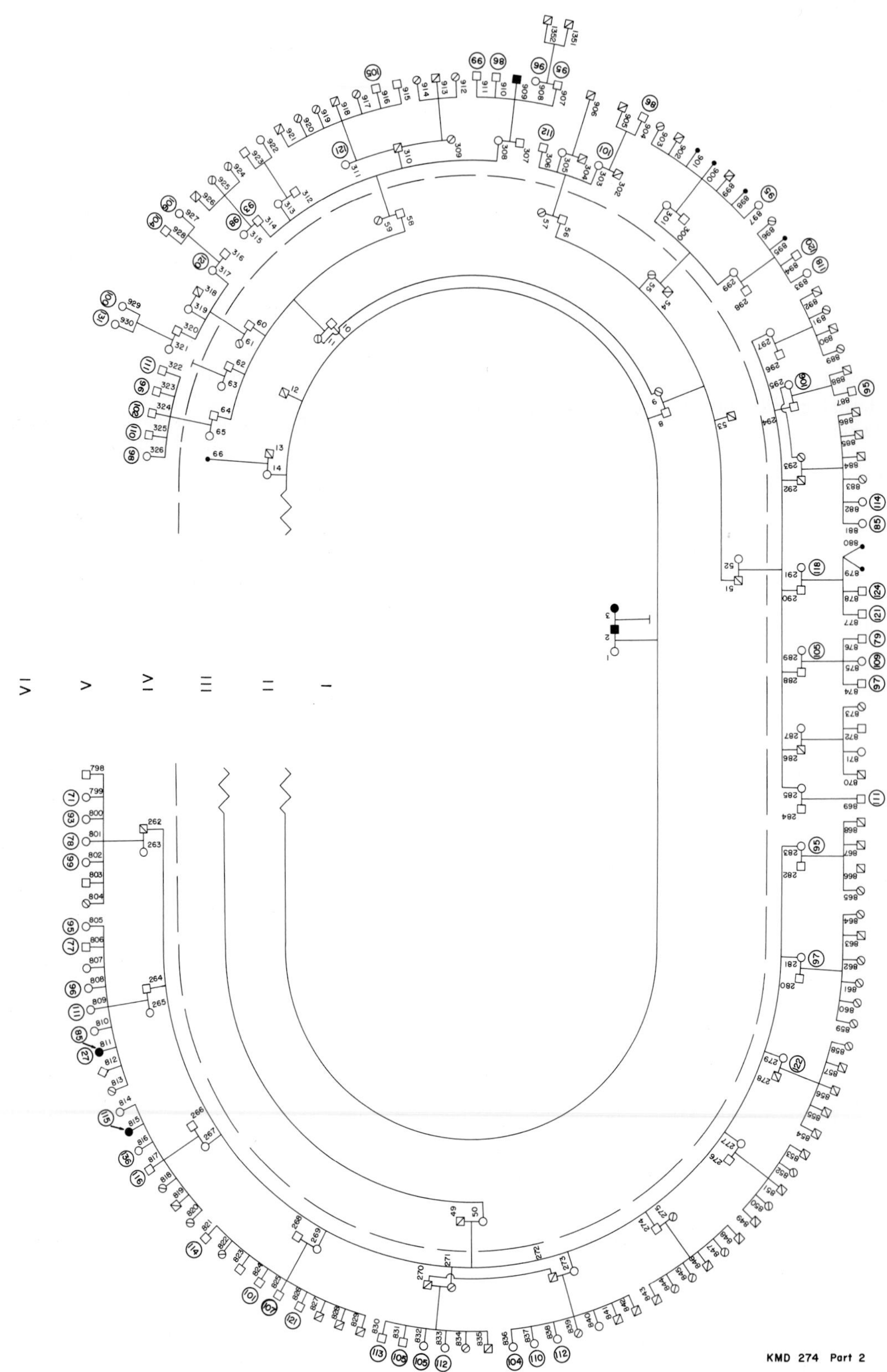

KMD 274 Part 2

KMD 274 – *Continued*

having been picked up eight times for approaching little girls. IQ 70. He had an illegitimate child by (560). (560) was institutionalized in 1925 at age 11 years and is still in the institution. She has an IQ of 42. Her child was conceived and born in the institution because (559) accidentally found a key which opened a door to the women's quarters. The child (1216) has an IQ of 89.

(577) was imprisoned for burglary. IQ 76.

(581) had an illegitimate child with IQ 84. She is described in welfare records as "very maladjusted and of questionable intellect, probably will never be self supporting."

(All persons from [524] through [581] are the children of three sisters.)

(647) is a cretin.

(649), a sibling to (647), has an IQ of 68.

(761) has an IQ "below 50."

(811) is microcephalic with an IQ of 27.

(815) is institutionalized with a diagnosis of undifferentiated mental retardation with a "very low" IQ.

(909) failed all subjects in junior high school except shop and left because of age. He is unemployed.

(910) is in a boys' reformatory. IQ 86.

(948) is institutionalized for phenylketonuria, with IQ 50.

(950) has an IQ of 62 with no diagnosis. She is a sister to (948).

(953) is institutionalized for phenylketonuria, IQ 2.

(954), a sibling to (953), is institutionalized for phenylketonuria, IQ 2.

(948), (950), (953) and (954) are children of two sisters who married two brothers.

(1001) has an IQ of 66 with "some indication of a central nervous system impairment."

(1096) is a single laborer who had a D average in the fifth grade at age 12 years.

(1097), sibling to (1096), is a single laborer who had a D average in the seventh grade at age 14 years.

(1170) was considered unsuitable for adoption although her IQ is 96. She has been in a girls' reformatory.

(1177) is in a special school. Her IQ is 53.

(1178) is in a special school. His IQ is 70.

(1179), sibling to (1177) and (1178), is in a special school. Her IQ is 66.

(1225) has an IQ "below 70."

(1228) has been in a girls' reformatory for incorrigibility. IQ 88.

(1230) was sent to a special school in 1953 at age 8 years and institutionalized five years later. IQ 65.

(1231), sibling to (1230), has an IQ of 63.

(1232) is in a reformatory, IQ 108.

(1233) is promiscuous. IQ 88.

(1234) has an IQ of 65.

(1238), sibling to (1234), has an IQ of 74 and is in an ungraded room for the retarded.

(1308) completed the fourth grade at age 12 with poor grades. He is a single farm laborer.

Family Summary

The proband, IQ 47, paternal grandfather, three maternal uncles, one maternal aunt, both parents, one sibling, two first cousins and 31 more distant relatives were retarded. In addition to the undifferentiated retardation, there were three cases of phenylketonuria, one cretin, one microcephalic and one with a "central nervous system impairment." There were also several who were mentally ill and at least six with some kind of prison record. Including retarded spouses, there is a total of 48 retarded persons known in this family. The offspring of three sisters, cousins to the proband, contributed 17 of the retardates to this total of 48 and all the six with prison records. The proband's parents had nine children, grandchildren unknown.

Retardation of proband of primarily genetic origin.

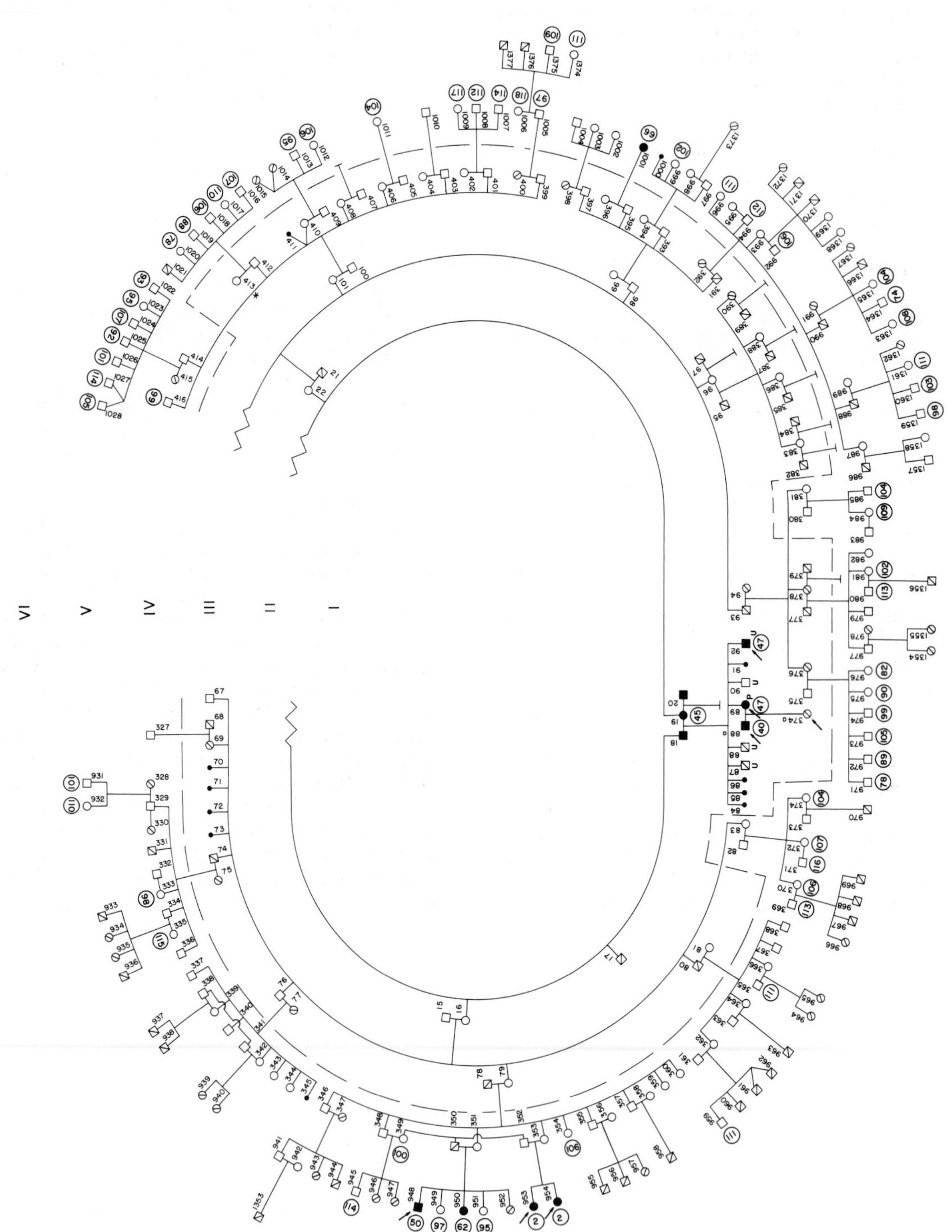

KMD 274 Part 3
* 413 is second cousin to 429 in Part 4

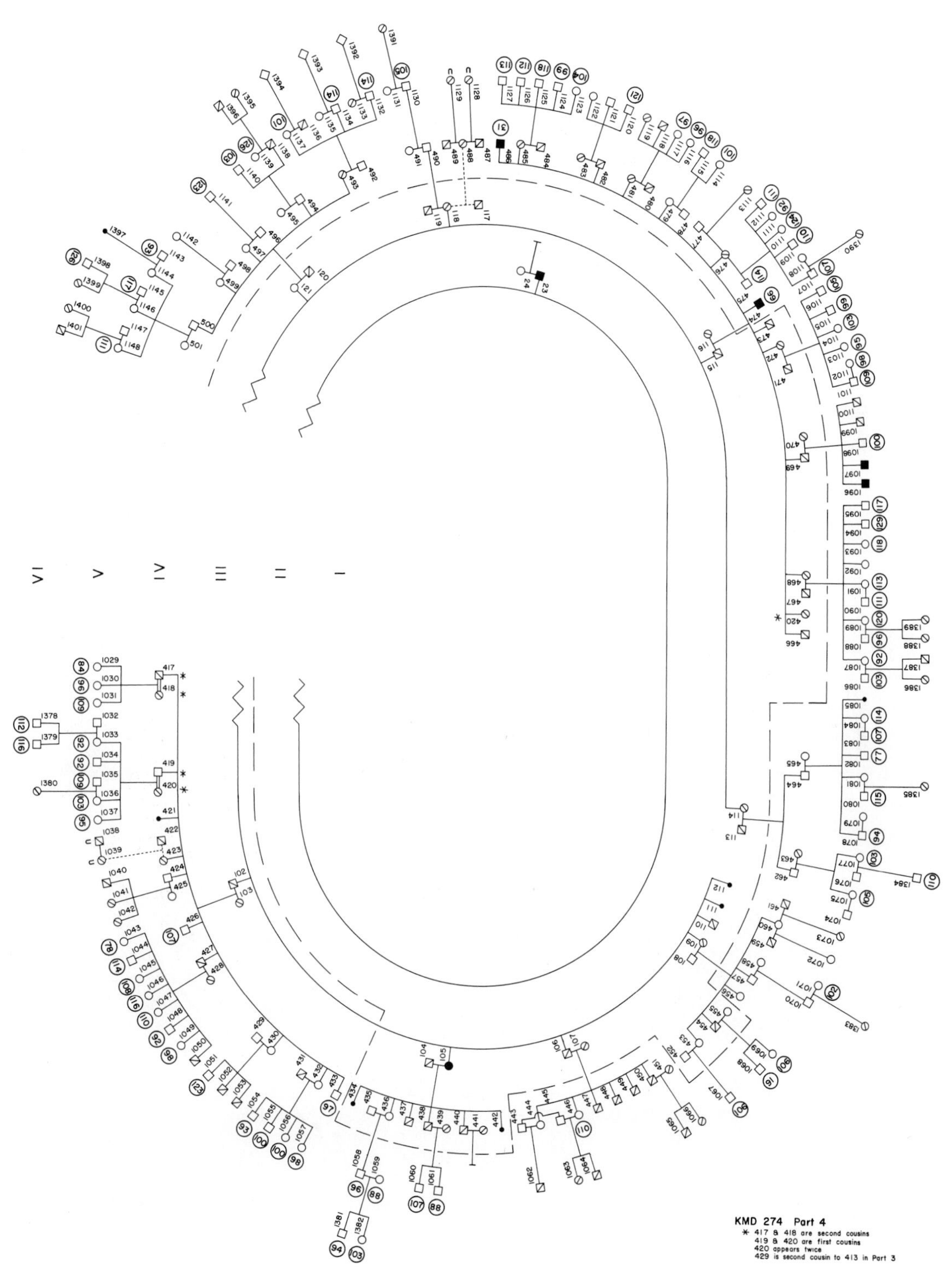

KMD 274 Part 4

* 417 & 418 are second cousins
419 & 420 are first cousins
420 appears twice
429 is second cousin to 413 in Part 3

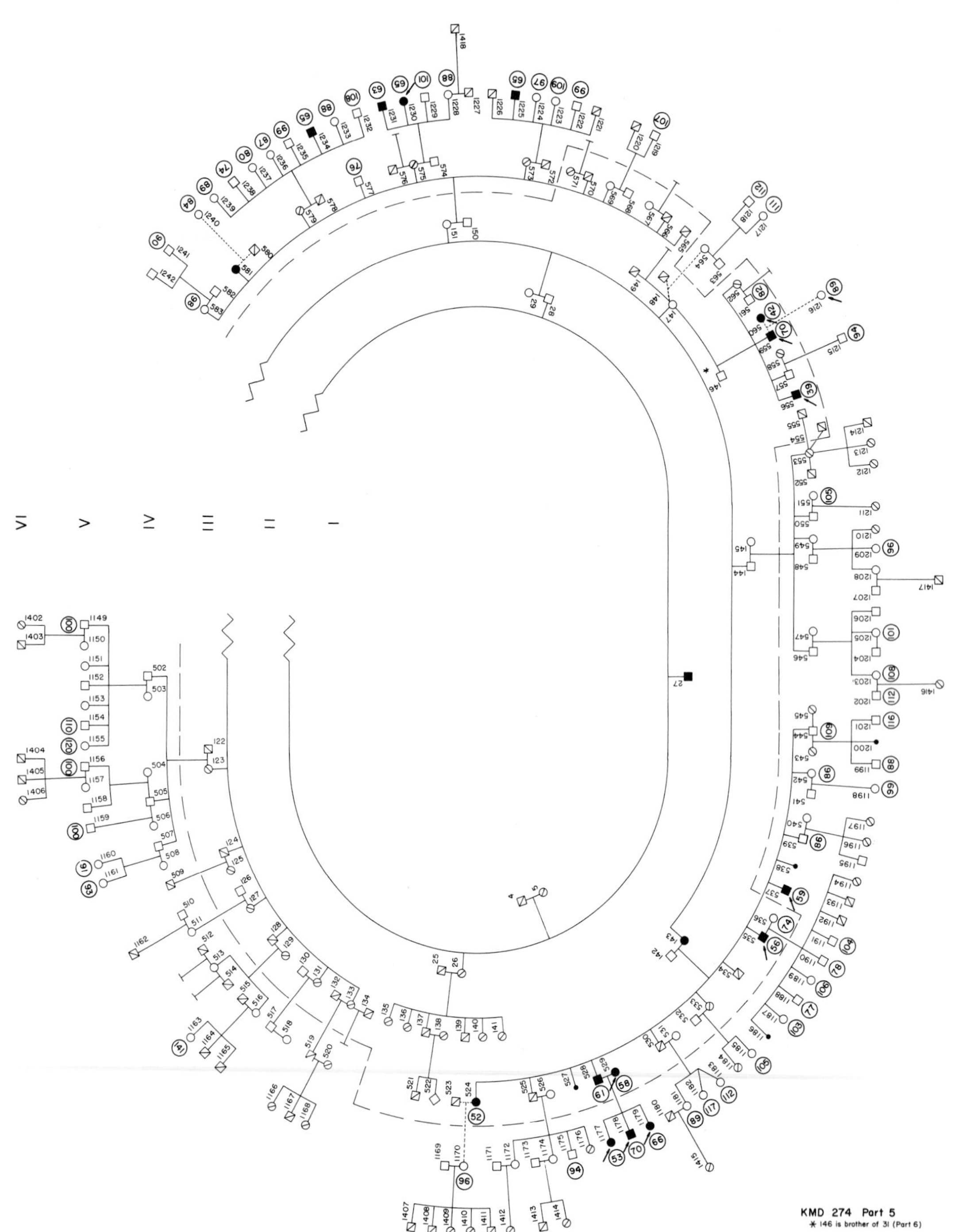

KMD 274 Part 5
* 146 is brother of 31 (Part 6)

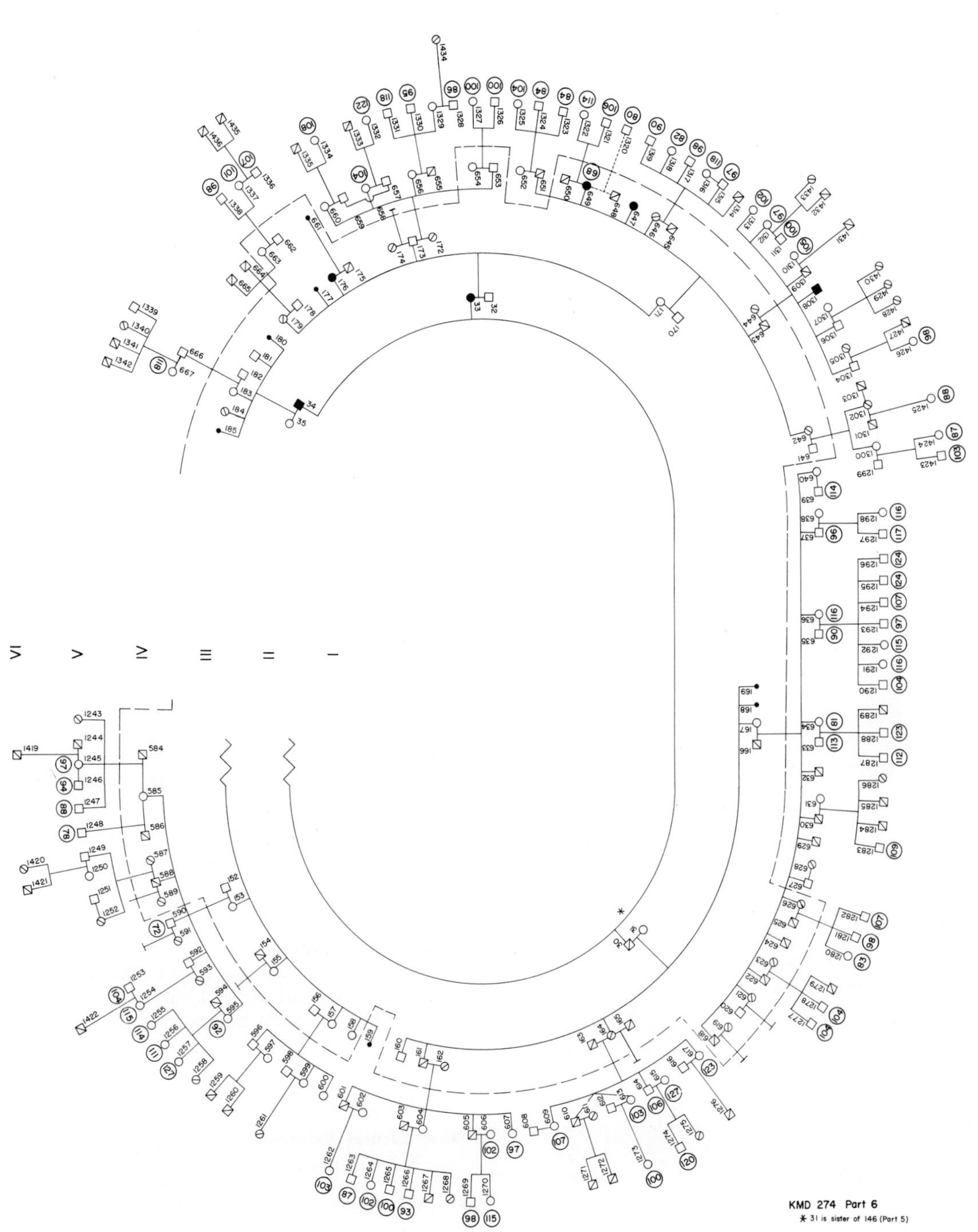

KMD 274 Part 6

* 31 is sister of 146 (Part 5)

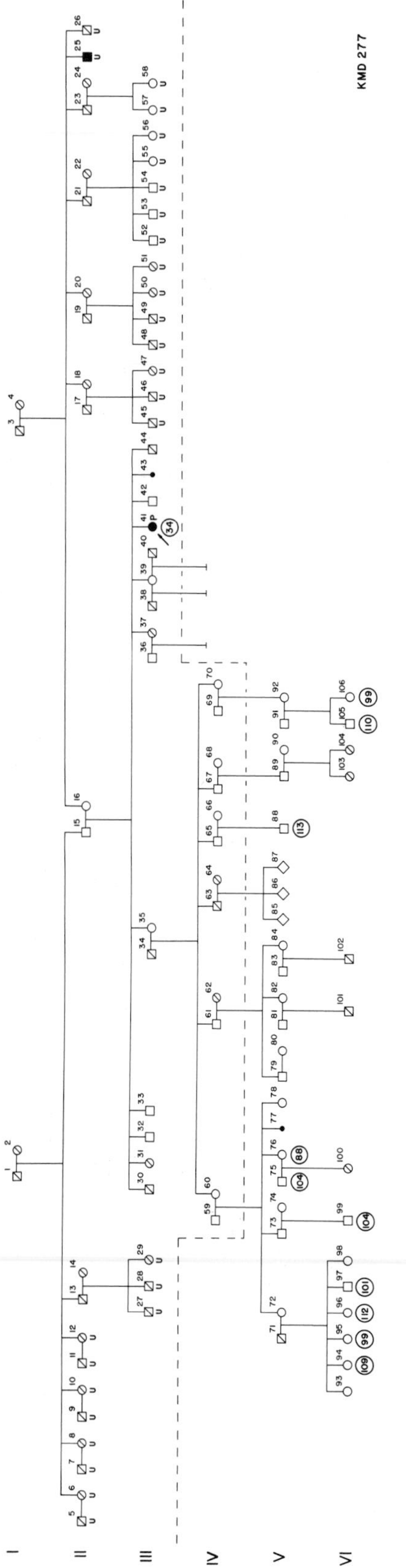

KMD 277

The Proband

The proband (41) was born in 1874, institutionalized at age 13 years and transferred to a mental hospital (because they had facilities for tubercular patients) in 1935 and died there in 1936. She had a rachitic broad, flat nose and was polydactylous. At age 18 months she fell from a second story window and they had trouble reviving her. She walked at 13 months, but never talked plainly. She went to school for two years but learned little. Her home environment was good. Neither the proband's parents or her siblings were polydactylous. IQ 34. *Diagnosis:* mental retardation with polydactyly.

Grandparents

Not of interest.

Parents

Father (15) and mother (16) both had normal intelligence. The father was a blacksmith.

Aunts and Uncles

Paternal relatives remained in Germany.

Maternal uncle (25) was retarded.

Siblings

Brother (30) drowned at age 25 years. His intelligence was unknown.

Sister (31) died of diphtheria at 5 years.

Brothers (32), (33) and (42) all remained unmarried. All had normal intelligence.

Sisters (35) and (39) had normal intelligence. (35), spouse unknown, had five normal children, one unknown. (39) was married twice but was childless.

The intelligence of (37) and (44) was unknown. Neither have children.

Sister (43) died of "brain fever and spasms" at age 2 years.

Nieces and Nephews

Only one of the proband's siblings (35) reproduced. She had six children, five with normal intelligence, one with unknown intelligence.

First Cousins

Unknown.

More Distant Relatives

Not of interest.

Family Summary

The proband, IQ 34, and polydactylous, and one paternal uncle were the only retarded persons in this kindred. Her parents had 11 children, only one of whom reproduced, so there were only six grandchildren.

Retardation of proband of primarily genetic origin.

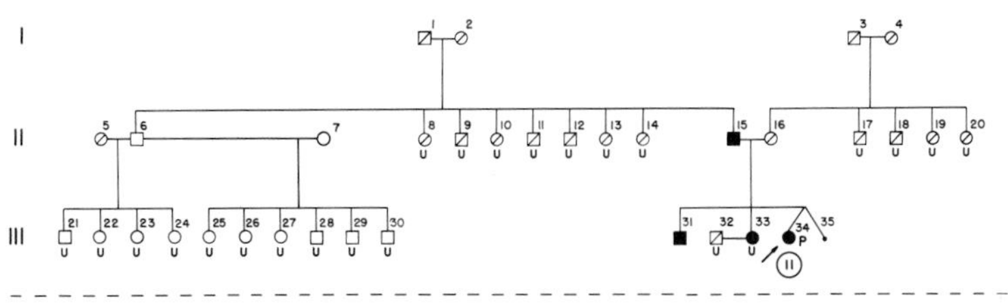

KMD 281

KMD 281

The Proband

The proband (34) was born in 1897, institutionalized at age 11 years, transferred to a second institution 20 years later and was still there in 1961. She is completely dependent and helpless. The proband was a twin. She developed epilepsy after her first institutionalization. IQ 11. *Diagnosis:* undifferentiated mental retardation.

Grandparents

Maternal grandmother committed suicide. She had been mentally ill for many years.

Parents

Father (15) could never support his family. He had always been a public charge and was moved to a "poor farm" when he developed senile dementia.

Mother (16) could not care for her home. She would hide herself when anyone approached the house. She was hospitalized for mental illness at age 53 years in 1908 and died in the hospital in 1932.

Aunts and Uncles

Not of interest.

Siblings

Brother (31) left home at age 23 to go to work but never arrived at his destination. Town officials tried to locate him and a newspaper notice was found concerning a man with his name who was found dead in the woods of northern Minnesota. The identification was never verified for death records, but it is likely that this was the proband's brother. He was quite retarded and "very peculiar."

Sister (33) learned to read and write and could work under supervision. She left the state in 1911 and could not be found for the follow-up. She was a high-grade retardate.

Brother (35), twin to the proband, died at 2 months.

Nieces and Nephews

Unknown.

First Cousins

Unknown. Maternal relatives remained in Europe. Paternal relatives were in other states and could not be located because they had a commonly occurring Scandinavian family name.

More Distant Relatives

Unknown.

Family Summary

The proband, IQ 11, was a low-grade retardate who developed epilepsy. Her father and brother were rather low-grade retardates, her sister was a higher grade retardate who learned to read and write. The proband's mother was mentally ill for many years. The proband's parents had four children, grandchildren, if any, are unknown.

Retardation of proband of primarily genetic origin.

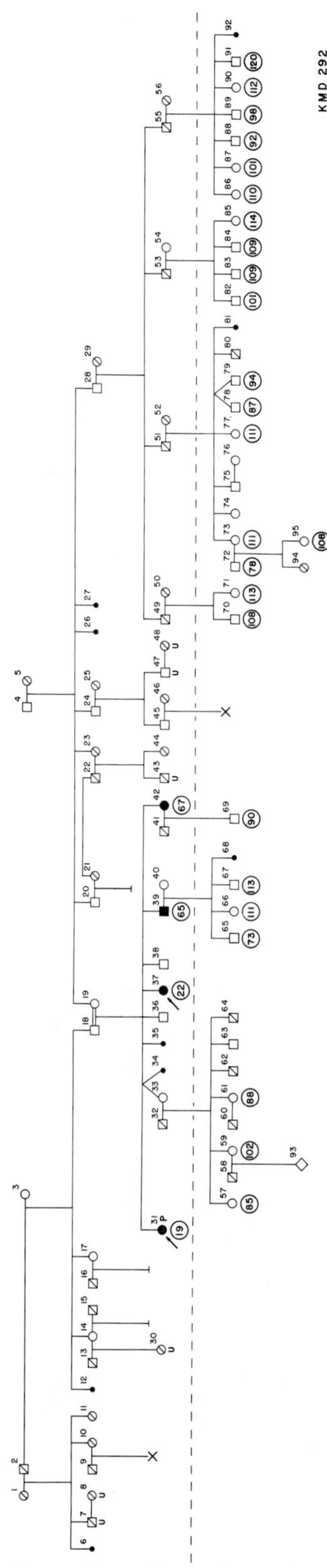

KMD 292

The Proband

The proband (31) was born in 1895, institutionalized at age 17 years and died of cretinism in the institution in 1960. She was given a physical and neurological examination in 1950 by J. A. Böök, M.D., and John Schut, M.D. IQ 19. *Diagnosis:* cretinism.

Grandparents

Not of interest.

Parents

Father (19) and mother (20) both had normal intelligence but were second cousins.

Aunts and Uncles

Not of interest.

Siblings

Sister (33) has normal intelligence, four children normal, two children and spouse of unknown intelligence.

Brothers (34), a twin to (33), and (35) both died in infancy.

Brothers (36) and (38) both died single and childless and both had normal intelligence.

Sister (37) was institutionalized at age 7 years and is still in the institution. She was also examined by Dr. Böök and Dr. Schut. She is a cretin with IQ 22.

Brother (39) has an IQ of 65, wife with normal intelligence, one child with a borderline IQ of 73, two normal children.

Sister (42) has an IQ of 67, husband of unknown intelligence, one child has IQ of 90.

Nieces and Nephews

Nephew (65) has a borderline IQ of 73.

First Cousins

Paternal relatives unknown.
Maternal relatives not of interest.

More Distant Relatives

Not of interest.

Family Summary

The proband, IQ 19, and her sister, IQ 22, were both institutionalized cretins. They had two high-grade retardate siblings with IQ's of 65 and 67, respectively. The proband's parents were second cousins. They had nine children and 11 grandchildren.

Retardation of proband of primarily genetic origin (consanguinity).

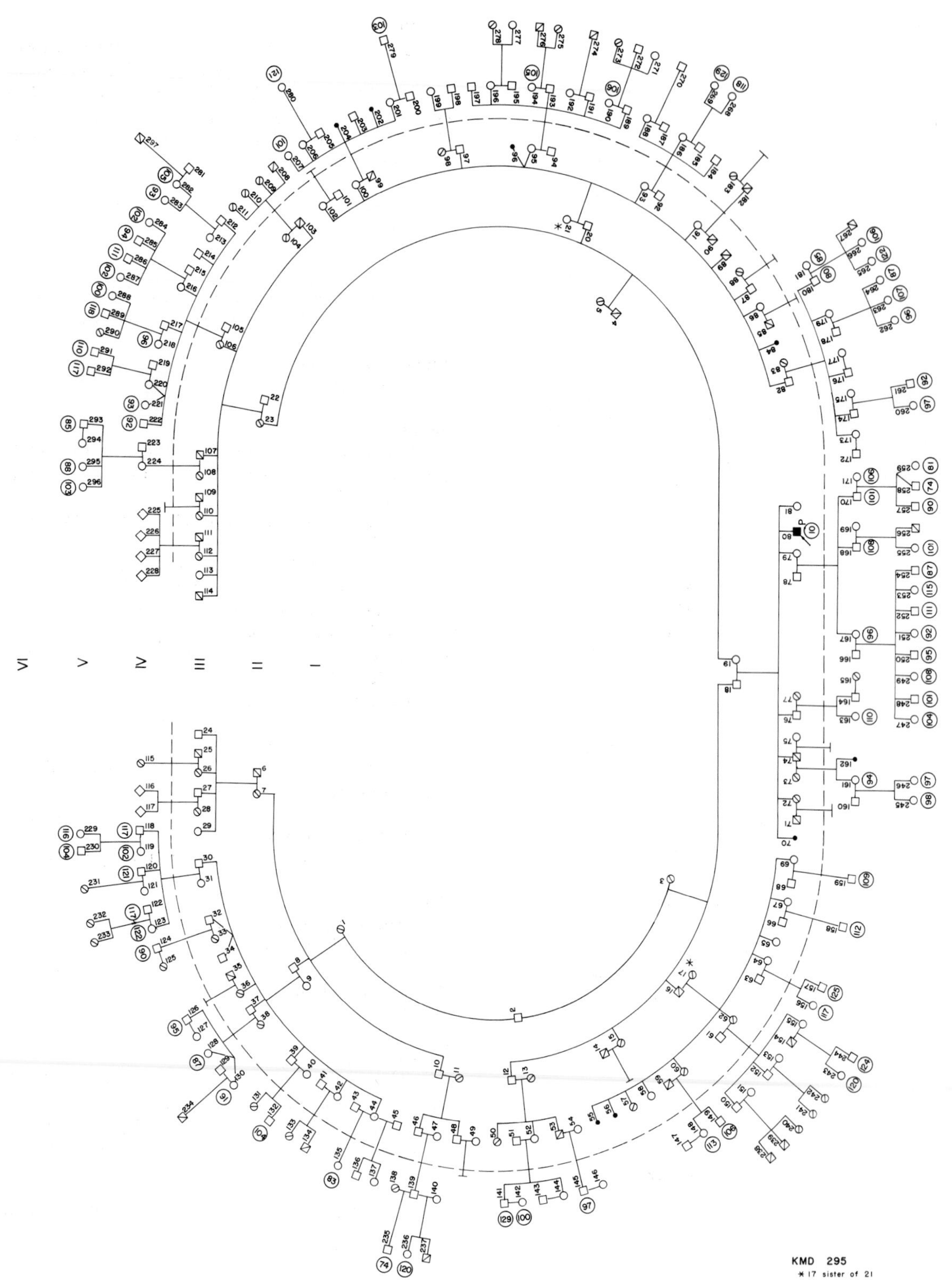

KMD 295
* 17 sister of 21

KMD 295

The Proband

The proband (80) was born in 1902 and institutionalized at age 10 years. He was discharged to his parents two years later and died in 1928 of ulcerating pharyngitis, edema of larynx, asphyxia, scarlet fever, atrophy of the brain and mental deficiency. He was born blind and was always sickly. Institution records state he was a mongoloid. IQ 10. *Diagnosis:* Down's syndrome.

Grandparents

Not of interest.

Parents

Father (18) and mother (19) both had normal intelligence.

Aunts and Uncles

Not of interest.

Siblings

Brother (70) died of convulsions at 6 months.

Sister (72) works in a state hospital. Her intelligence is unknown.

Brother (74) completed the sixth grade and is a plumber, wife unknown, child normal.

Brother (76) owns and operates a farm, wife unknown, children normal.

Sisters (79) and (81) both have normal intelligence. (79) has a normal spouse and three normal children.

Nieces and Nephews

All have normal intelligence.

First Cousins

Not of interest.

More Distant Relatives

Not of interest.

Family Summary

The proband, IQ 10 and blind, was the only retarded person known in this kindred. He was the sixth child in a sibship of seven. The proband's parents had seven children and seven grandchildren.

Retardation of proband of primarily genetic origin (Down's syndrome).

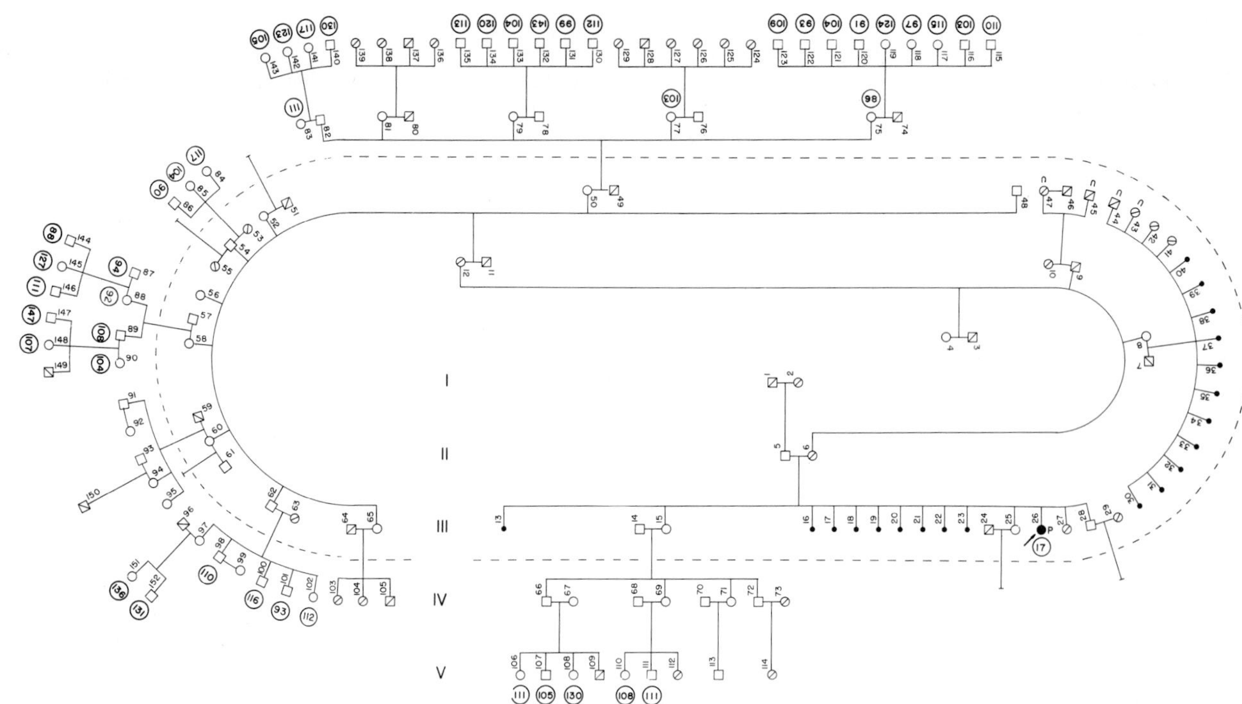

KMD 296

KMD 296

The Proband

The proband (26) was born in 1897, institutionalized at age 14 years, discharged in 1912, readmitted in 1920 and died of influenza, myocardial insufficiency and mongolism in the institution in 1922. IQ 17. *Diagnosis:* Down's syndrome.

Grandparents

Not of interest.

Parents

Father (5) had normal intelligence.

Mother (6) was obese. Her intelligence was unknown.

Aunts and Uncles

No paternal relatives. The proband's father was an only child.

Maternal aunt (8) had 11 miscarriages in 15 pregnancies.

Siblings

Sister (13) died at age 3 months.

Sister (15) is obese. She has normal intelligence, normal spouse and children.

(16) through (23) were miscarriages of 1 or 2 months.

Sister (25) died at age 45 years married but childless. She was obese. She had normal intelligence.

Sister (27) died of diphtheria at age 10 years.

Brother (28) is obese. He is a mechanic with normal intelligence, married but childless.

Nieces and Nephews

Only four, all with normal intelligence.

First Cousins

Not of interest.

More Distant Relatives

Not of interest.

Family Summary

The proband, IQ 17, was the only retarded person known in this kindred. The proband's mother was obese, as were her children. Of her 14 pregnancies, eight terminated in miscarriages, one child died in infancy, and of the five survivors, three married but only one had children, giving the proband's parents a total of four grandchildren. The proband's maternal aunt also had a reproductive history of miscarriage—11 miscarriages in 15 pregnancies.

Retardation of proband of primarily genetic origin (Down's syndrome).

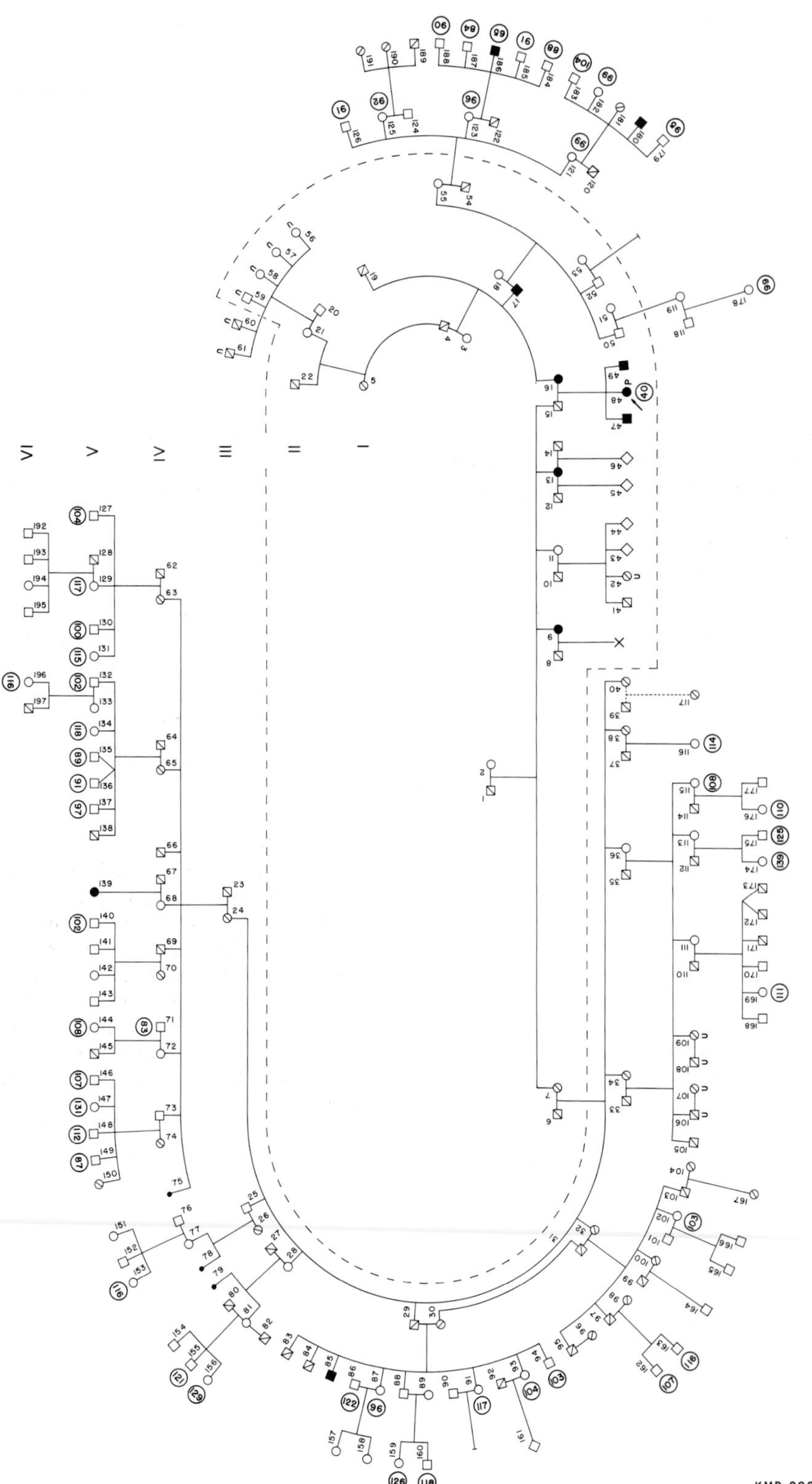

KMD 298

KMD 298

The Proband

The proband (48) was born in 1895, institutionalized at age 16 years and was still in the institution in 1961. She was dwarfish, blind and had one eye missing. She was always neglected and after her mother's death she was forced into incestuous relations with her father. The authorities then arrested her father and sent her to the institution. IQ 40. *Diagnosis:* anophthalmia.

Grandparents

Not of interest.

Parents

Father (15) died in a mental hospital in 1930 with a diagnosis of "senile delirious and confused states." His intelligence was unknown. He was an alcoholic, promiscuous and was arrested at one time for incest with the proband.

Mother (16) never took care of her home and was retarded. She had severe convulsions as a baby.

Aunts and Uncles

Paternal aunts (9) and (13) were retarded, children and spouses unknown. (13) also had "chorea."

Maternal uncle (17) was retarded but married a normal woman. His three children have normal intelligence.

Siblings

Brothers (47) and (49) are unmarried, childless, retarded farm laborers.

Nieces and Nephews

None.

First Cousins

Not of interest.

More Distant Relatives

First cousin (29) has a child (85) who completed the sixth grade after being retained in grades one, three and six. He has no occupation and is retarded.

First cousin (24) has a grandchild (139) who has a diagnosis of multiple congenital defects as a result of the mother having had rubella in the first trimester of pregnancy.

First cousin (55) has a grandchild (180) with Down's syndrome and another grandchild (186) with IQ 65, undifferentiated type.

Family Summary

The proband, IQ 40, her mother, two paternal aunts, one paternal uncle, two siblings and four more distant relatives (one of these had Down's syndrome, one was retarded as the result of rubella in the mother) were retarded. The proband was taken from the home after the death of her mother, and her father was arrested for incest. The proband's parents had three children, no grandchildren.

Retardation of proband of primarily genetic origin (anophthalmia).

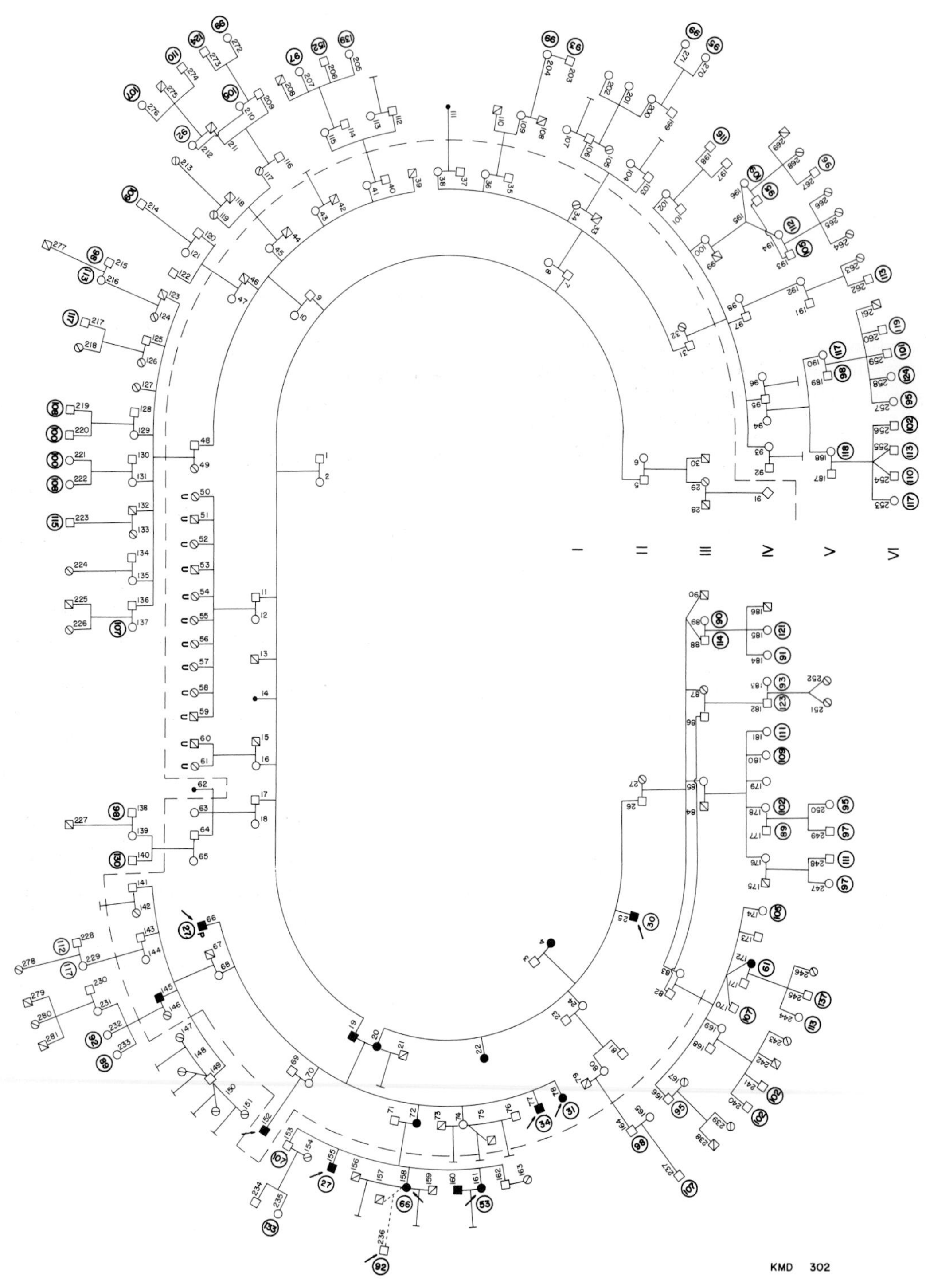

KMD 302

KMD 302

The Proband

The proband (66) was born in 1887, institutionalized at age 24 years and died of cerebral hemorrhage in the institution in 1945. His birth was uneventful and he had no history of perinatal disease. He was reared in a poor home, attended school for two years with little result. He was obese. IQ 27. *Diagnosis:* mental retardation with obesity.

Grandparents

Paternal grandfather had normal intelligence but was erratic and peculiar.

Maternal grandmother was retarded.

Parents

Father (19) and mother (20) were both retarded.

Aunts and Uncles

Maternal aunt (22) was a low-grade retardate.

Maternal uncle (25) was institutionalized in 1923 at age 48 years and died of arteriosclerotic heart disease in the institution in 1941. He could talk very little and performed only the simplest tasks. IQ 30.

Siblings

Sisters (68), (70) and (74) were classified as "mentally slow" by the original workers. Apparently they were above the retarded level of IQ 69. (74) was married three times but had no children. (70) had a normal husband but one child who was a low-grade retardate. (68) had one high-grade retardate child in a family of four, husband unknown.

Sister (72) completed the sixth grade, works in a laundry and is classified as retarded by all workers who saw her. Her husband is a man of normal intelligence who was instrumental in the commitment of his retarded son and daughters (155), (158) and (161).

Brother (77) was institutionalized in 1917 at age 18 years and died of bronchopneumonia in the institution in 1930. He was obese, did not coordinate well and had an IQ of 34.

Sister (78) was institutionalized in 1917 at age 11 years and died of pulmonary tuberculosis and Down's syndrome in the institution in 1920. IQ 31.

Nieces and Nephews

Nephew (145) is a factory worker. He was retained in the first, second, third and fifth grades, leaving school when in the fifth grade at age 13 years. His three siblings manage business enterprises. His wife is unknown but his children are normal.

Nephew (152) was institutionalized in 1922 at age 8 years and has remained in the institution ever since. He is obese, has coarse skin, "droopy" eyes, lateral and rotary nystagmus and ophthalmia neonatorum. He talks very little and is "rather low grade."

Nephew (155) was institutionalized in 1923 at age 6 years and died of coronary disease in the institution in 1955. He had defective speech. IQ 27.

Niece (158) was institutionalized in 1942 at age 23 years. After the birth of her illegitimate child she was sterilized. She was discharged from guardianship because she is now married and living out of the state. IQ 66.

Niece (161) was institutionalized in 1942 at age 18 years. She was sterilized and has been under outside supervision. She has an IQ of 53. Her husband (160) is less capable mentally than his wife and has been in a mental hospital with a diagnosis of schizophrenic reaction, schizo-affective type.

First Cousins

(172) has an IQ of 61.

More Distant Relatives

Not of interest.

Family Summary

The proband, IQ 27, one sibling, a maternal uncle and two nephews were middle- and low-grade institutionalized retardates with associated speech defects, poor coordination, obesity and eye anomalies. In addition, a maternal aunt was a low-grade retardate. The proband's maternal grandmother, both parents, one sibling, a nephew, two nieces and one first cousin were high-grade retardates. One sibling of the proband had Down's syndrome. A normal sister produced an obese low-grade retardate with eye anomalies and poor speech; a retarded sister produced a low-grade retardate with defective speech, and two high-grade retardates. With the exception of one retarded first cousin who has three children, two with IQ's of 113 and 137, respectively, and one too young to test, no retardation has appeared in the rest of the family. The proband's parents had seven children, four of whom were retarded (two low grade with anomalies, one with Down's syndrome and one high grade) and 12 grandchildren, five of whom were retarded (three high grade, two low grade).

Retardation of proband of primarily genetic origin.

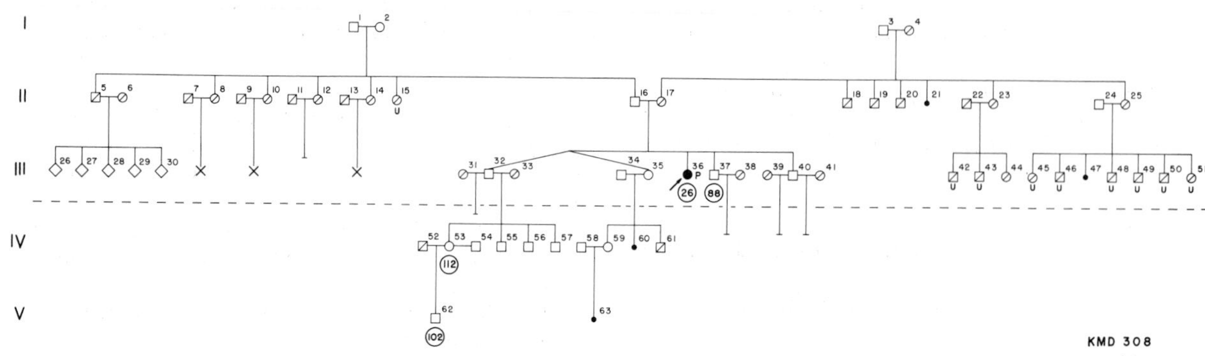

KMD 308

The Proband

The proband (36) was born in 1905, institutionalized at age 7 years and discharged to her parents in 1917. She lived with her mother in 1961 and was single and childless. There was no record of difficult birth or perinatal infection and no evidence of syphilis except notched vertebral borders of the scapulae. She was undersized, had a head flattened in the back, a protruding tongue and was dull and apathetic. There was a tentative diagnosis of cretinism when she was admitted. IQ 26. *Diagnosis:* cretinism.

Grandparents

Not of interest.

Parents

Father (16) was a butcher. He had normal intelligence.

Mother (17) could barely speak English. Social welfare records stated she was "not considered mentally fit." Her intelligence is unknown.

Aunts and Uncles

All paternal and maternal relatives remained in Europe.

Siblings

Brother (32) owns and operates a grocery and meat market, children normal, wife of unknown intelligence.

Sister (35) drowned at age 35 years. She had normal intelligence, as did her husband and one child; one child died in infancy, one has unknown intelligence.

Brother (37) completed the seventh grade and is a sausage maker. He has been arrested twice, once for breaking and entering and once for using a car without the owner's permission. IQ 88. He is married, but childless.

Brother (40) completed the eighth grade and puts advertising cards in busses. He was interviewed and was thought to have low normal intelligence. He has been married twice, but is childless.

Nieces and Nephews

All known to have normal intelligence except (61) who is of unknown intelligence because he drowned at age 3 years.

First Cousins

Unknown.

More Distant Relatives

Not of interest.

Family Summary

The proband, IQ 26, was the only retarded person in the family. In one welfare record she is described as a helpless cripple, but this was apparently not her condition in childhood, according to the old medical records which included a review of her stigmata and a tentative diagnosis of cretinism. The proband's parents had five children and seven grandchildren. All four of the proband's normal siblings married, but only two reproduced.

Retardation of proband of primarily genetic origin (cretinism).

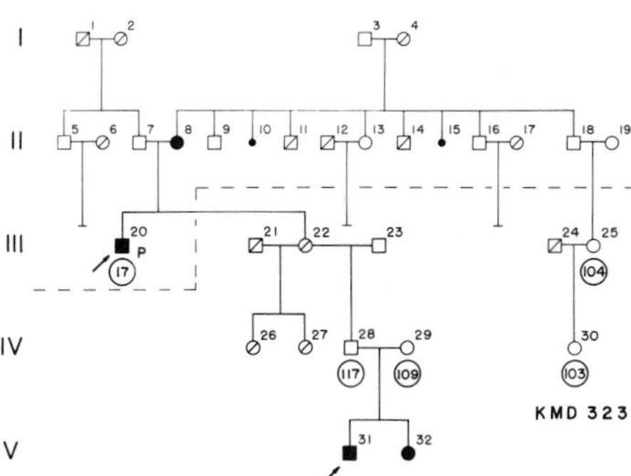

KMD 323

The Proband

The proband (20) was born in 1908, institutionalized at age 6 years, discharged to his parents in 1914 and died in a diabetic coma in 1924. He was slow to walk and talk, had a double thumb on one hand, was strabismic and was listed as a mongol. IQ 17. *Diagnosis:* Down's syndrome.

Grandparents

Not of interest.

Parents

Father (7) had syphilis at age 18 (seven years before birth of proband). He had a violent temper but normal intelligence.

Mother (8) left school at the age of 17 years when in the eighth grade. She was classified as retarded.

Aunts and Uncles

Paternal uncle (5) attended business college and operates a restaurant but had a "violent, insane temper." When telephoned he castigated the interviewer for wasting money, said he paid taxes and went to church, and refused to cooperate.

Siblings

Sister (22) deserted her second husband and their child and has been described as a schizophrenic, but no hospital record was found for her.

Nieces and Nephews

Nephew (28), a college graduate, has two retarded children, (31) an institutionalized boy who is blind, deaf, epileptic and severely retarded. He has a right bifid thumb as did the proband.

(32), sister to (31), has a less severe form of the neurological disorders affecting her brother. She has microcephaly, deafness, optic nerve atrophy, epilepsy and mental retardation.

First Cousins

Only one, IQ 104. Seven adult maternal aunts and uncles, four of whom were married, only produced one child among them.

More Distant Relatives

Only one, IQ 103.

Family Summary

The proband, IQ 17, his mother and a great-nephew and great-niece were the only retarded persons in this small kindred. The great nephew and niece exhibit a complex syndrome of neurological disorders. The proband's parents had two children, three grandchildren. The proband's two sets of grandparents had a total of 11 children, the next generation only three, the generation after that has only four persons. This family was noted for their violent tempers and other personality problems.

Retardation of proband of primarily genetic origin (Down's syndrome).

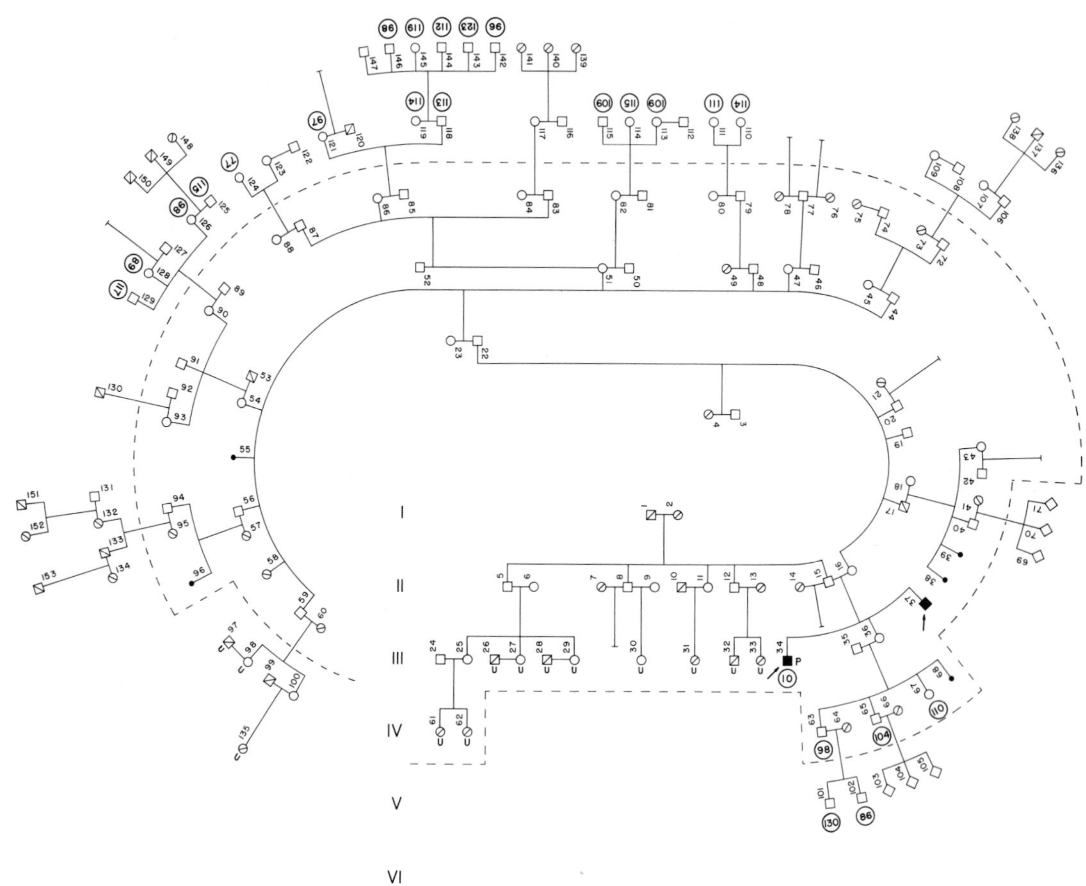

KMD 335

KMD 335

The Proband

The proband (34) was born in 1866, institutionalized at age 7 years and died of chronic interstitial nephritis in the institution in 1922. He was slow to develop but had no history of difficult birth or perinatal infection and had no stigmata. He was destructive. IQ 10. *Diagnosis:* undifferentiated mental retardation.

Grandparents

Not of interest.

Parents

Father (15) and mother (16) both had normal intelligence.

Aunts and Uncles

Not of interest.

Siblings

Sister (36) had spinal meningitis at age 12 years and never walked again but went around in a wheelchair. She had normal intelligence and married a contractor. Both (36) and her husband (35) were religious fanatics. Their children have normal intelligence.

Brother (37) was institutionalized at age 17 years and died of pneumonia and tuberculosis in the institution in 1907. He was a low-grade epileptic retardate.

Nieces and Nephews

Not of interest.

First Cousins

Not of interest.

More Distant Relatives

Not of interest.

Family Summary

The proband, IQ 10, and his brother, an epileptic low-grade retardate, were the only retarded persons in this kindred. There was no history of birth injury or serious disease. The proband's parents had three children and four grandchildren.

Retardation of proband of primarily genetic origin.

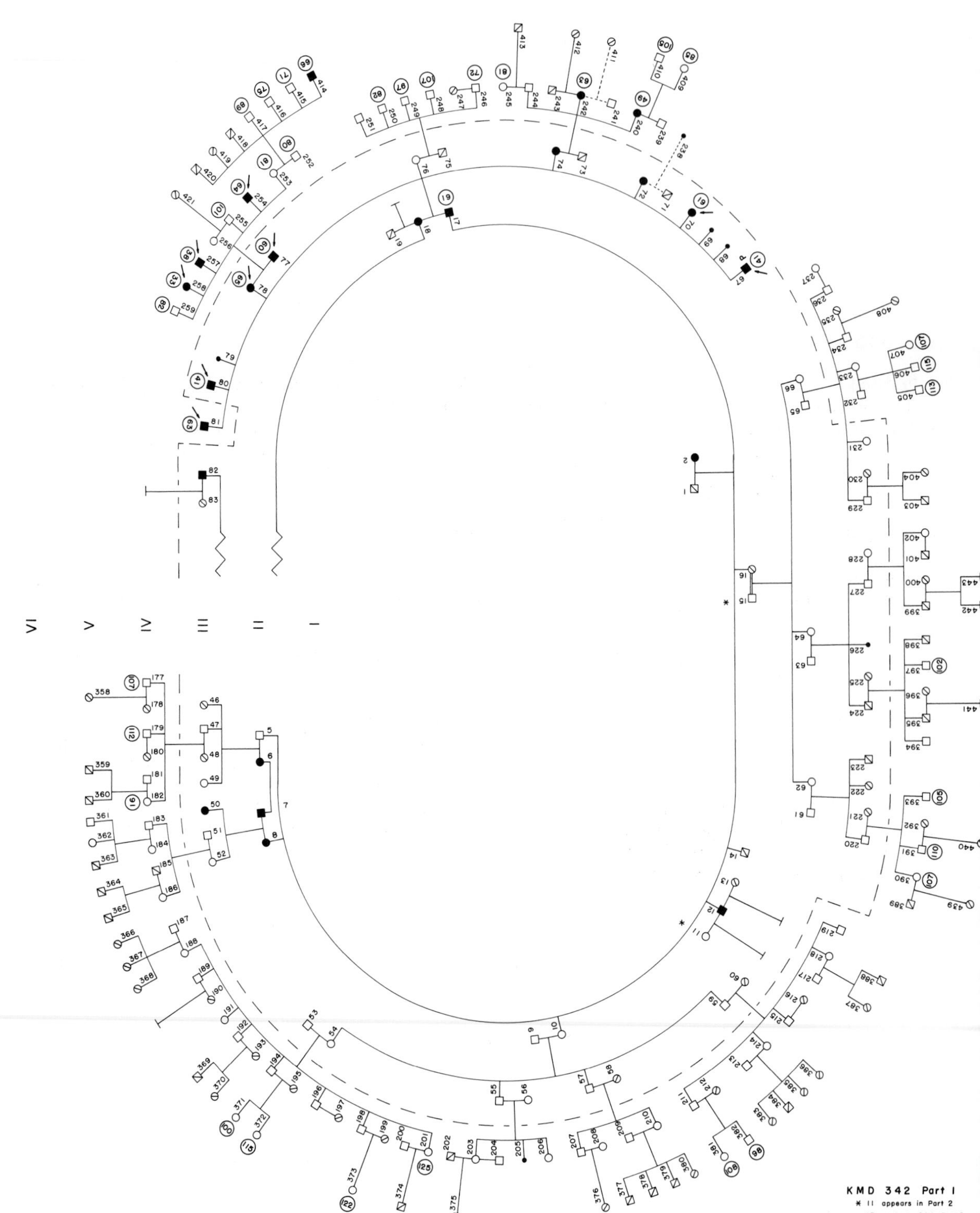

KMD 342 Part I
* 11 appears in Part 2
15 uncle to 20 in Part 2

KMD 342

The Proband

The proband (67) was born in 1896, institutionalized at age 17 years, escaped twice, was discharged in 1919 but was on the waiting list for readmittance when he was imprisoned in 1938. He was then readmitted to the institution but escaped in 1939. He was reinstitutionalized in a mental hospital in 1942, discharged in 1947 and in 1961 was in a "home" in another state. He never married or had children. He was reared in a one room dugout in extreme filth and poverty, but had no record of difficult delivery or perinatal infection. IQ 41. *Diagnosis:* undifferentiated mental retardation.

Grandparents

Paternal grandfather was an alcoholic, lazy and shiftless.

Paternal grandmother was an alcoholic and retarded.

Maternal grandfather was epileptic.

Parents

Father (17) was an ignorant laborer who could not provide for his family. IQ 61.

Mother (18) was retarded. Both parents were alcoholics until they joined the Salvation Army. After that they both improved considerably in their mode of living.

Aunts and Uncles

Paternal aunt (8), retarded, married a retarded man. One of her two children was retarded.

Paternal uncle (12) was a retarded, illiterate man who developed a psychosis with cerebral arteriosclerosis and was placed in a mental hospital. He was married twice but had no children.

Paternal uncle (14) was an alcoholic lumberjack who burned to death in his shanty when a lamp overturned.

Paternal aunt (16) married her normal half cousin. Their children are normal.

Maternal aunt (21) was retarded, as were her husband and three of her seven surviving children.

Maternal uncle (22) was an unmarried, childless, retarded alcoholic.

Maternal uncle (25) died at 17 months. He never walked or talked, and was severely retarded.

Maternal uncle (31) was an illiterate public charge who was married three times. He had 22 children (three by his own daughters) and was charged with incest and family neglect in court, but was never convicted. He was retarded, wives' intelligence unknown.

Maternal uncle (36) was an alcoholic until he joined the Salvation Army. He could perform only the simplest tasks and was retarded. His second wife (the mother of his children) had normal intelligence.

Maternal uncle (38) was epileptic and retarded.

Siblings

Sister (68) died of "consumption of the bowels" at age 14 months.

Sister (69) died at age 2 years. She was a cripple of unknown intelligence.

Sister (70) was sent to the State Orphanage at age 6 years in 1906, institutionalized at age 12, and has been under outside supervision for many years. She is an unmarried, childless domestic. IQ 61.

Sister (72) was sent to the State Orphanage, later placed in a boarding home and died during an illegitimate pregnancy. She was retarded.

Sister (74) was reared from the age of 3 in a prosperous farm home but was retarded and married an unemployed, alcoholic laborer. Two of her three children have IQ's of 49 and 63 and have been committed to state guardianship as retarded.

Sister (76), the only person with normal intelligence in this sibship, was reared in a foster home. She had five children, four with normal intelligence, one with borderline IQ of 72 and a delinquent. Husband has unknown intelligence.

Sister (78) was institutionalized in 1906 at age 21 years after she had had five children (three of whom were retarded), sterilized a year later and escaped in 1928 to rejoin her husband. She had one child born after the operation whose birth was verified by welfare agencies. Her husband (77) was institutionalized in 1932, but escaped a year later. (77) and (78) traveled across the continent from one welfare agency to the next and now live in a western state. They were discharged from guardianship.

Sister (79) died at age 4 months.

Brother (80) was institutionalized in 1923 at age 14 years and is still in the institution. He was given a physical and neurological examination in 1950 by J. A. Böök, M.D., and John Schut, M.D. Their diagnosis was imbecility. They found no stigmata. IQ 41.

Sister (81) was institutionalized in 1926 at age 10 years and died of lobar pneumonia in the institution in 1926. IQ 63.

Nieces and Nephews

Niece (240) has been committed to state guardianship as retarded and placed under outside supervision. IQ 49. Her husband is a mechanic and probably has normal intelligence.

Niece (242) has been committed to state guardianship as retarded, and placed under outside supervision. She has had one illegitimate child and one legitimate one. IQ 63.

Nephew (246) was a problem student, and has been reported for wife beating. IQ 72.

Niece (253) has been a continuous problem to social workers since her school years. She has a low normal IQ of 81, and married a thief with a prison record who has an IQ of 80. They are repeating the family pattern in the fourth generation.

Nephew (254) was institutionalized in 1932 at age 9 years and has remained in the institution ever since. He was examined by Dr. Böök and Dr. Schut in 1950. They reported a diagnosis of moron with schizophrenia. His IQ scores declined

Continued on page 209

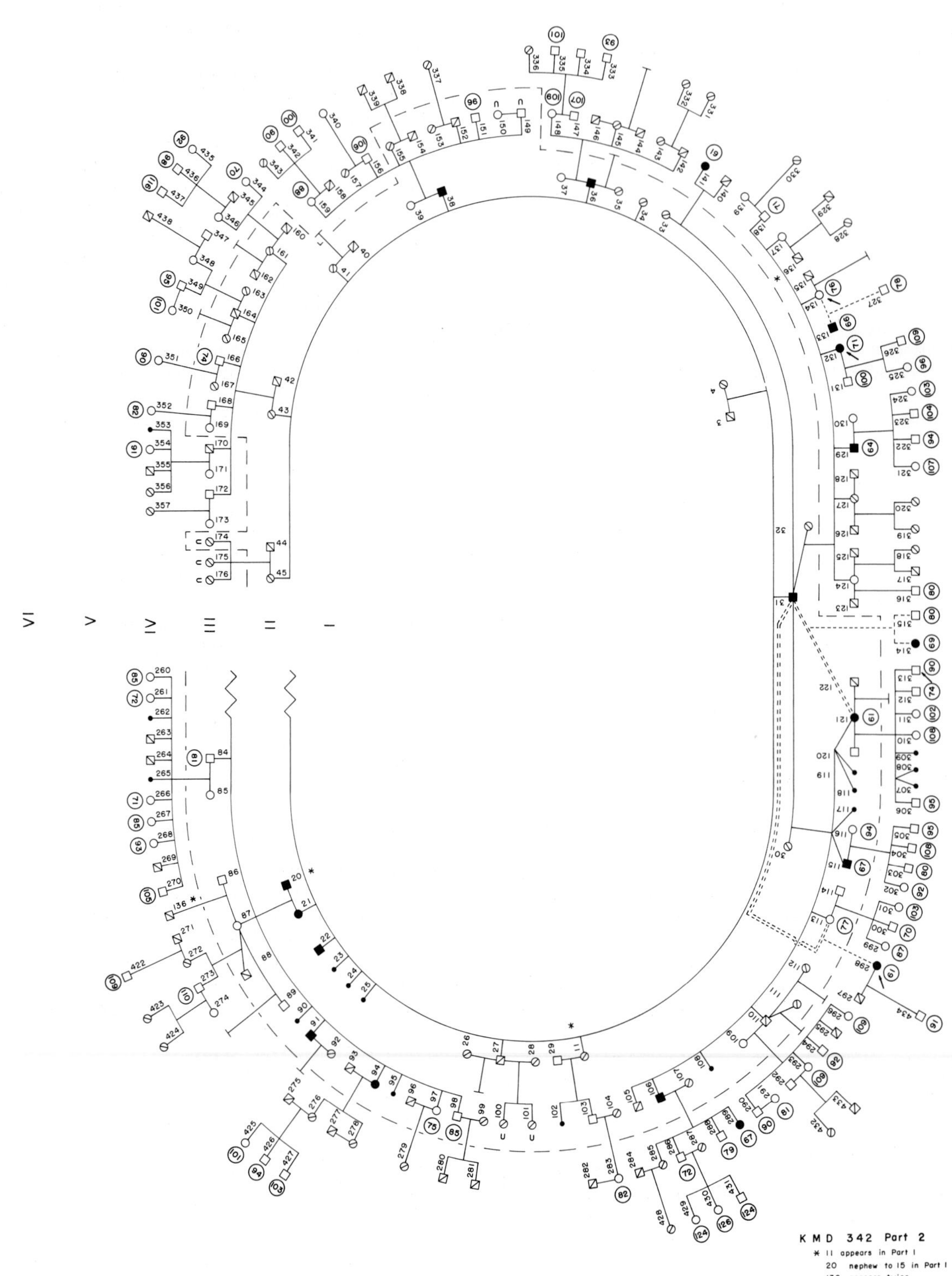

KMD 342 Part 2
* 11 appears in Part I
20 nephew to 15 in Part I
136 appears twice

from 94 in 1928 to 71 in 1932, 53 in 1938 and 49 in 1938, with a rise to 64 in 1950 on the Stanford-Binet. Dr. Böök and Dr. Schut thought the declination could be attributed to the schizophrenia. The higher IQ was obtained after the examination had been completed and the case closed.

Nephew (255) is mentioned because of his normal intelligence and good adjustment, especially considering his background. He was so abused and neglected that the neighbors complained and he was placed in boarding homes until he entered the Army in World War II as a paratrooper. He completed high school and married a registered nurse who ranked in the 99 percentile on college aptitude tests.

Nephew (257) was institutionalized in 1930 at age 4 years, and is still in the institution. He was examined by Dr. Böök and Dr. Schut in 1950. They found imbecility with left hemiplegia which was attributed to poliomyelitis at the age of 6 years. IQ 38.

Niece (258) was institutionalized at age 5 years and is still in the institution. She was examined by Dr. Böök and Dr. Schut in 1950, with a report of imbecility with no psychotic signs or symptoms. IQ 33.

First Cousins

(50) died unmarried and childless. She was retarded.

(82) could not talk well, was an illiterate laborer who was married but childless.

(84) had served prison terms. IQ 81.

(91) was a married, childless retardate.

(94) is retarded. Her two children and her husband have unknown intelligence.

(106) was a retarded man who was in the second grade at the age of 12 years. He served some time in the reformatory. His children have IQ's of 72, 79 and 67, respectively.

(113) has been in court twice for commitment but was found not to be retarded. She had a retarded child by her father, two normal and one retarded (298) (and institutionalized), by a husband with normal intelligence. IQ 65 in 1924 at age 12 years and 77 in 1936 at age 28 years.

(115) has served time for robbery. He is a truck driver with IQ 67. His wife has an IQ of 94 and the children's IQ's are 92, 80, 108 and 95.

(121), the only survivor of seven-month triplets, was institutionalized in 1940 at age 25, sterilized, placed under outside supervision in 1941 and discharged from guardianship in 1953. IQ 61. She divorced her first husband, an abusive and unbalanced person, who is a mechanic. (121) has two children by her father, one (314) with IQ 69 in a boarding home, and one (315) with IQ 80. He (315) was incorrigible, his IQ was too high for commitment as retarded, and he has been unresponsive to psychiatric treatment.

(129) was a juvenile delinquent. He is a glass cutter, IQ 64. He married a woman with normal intelligence and has four children with IQ's of 107, 94, 104 and 103.

(132) was institutionalized in 1939 at age 18 years. She escaped, married a man with IQ 100 and was living under outside supervision until her discharge from guardianship in 1951. IQ 71. Her two children have IQ's of 96 and 109. The child (325) has achieved a rise in IQ scores from 66 to 89 to 96 by the age of 11 years.

(134) was institutionalized in 1941, sterilized and placed under outside supervision the same year. She has been discharged from guardianship and restored to capacity. She had an illegitimate child (327) by a convict with IQ 66. This child has a borderline IQ of 78.

(138) is a glass cutter with IQ 71.

(141) has an IQ of 61.

(166) was in the State Reformatory. IQ 74.

More Distant Relatives

Great-nephew (414) is a school behavior problem and has an IQ of 66.

Great-nephew (415) is a school behavior problem and has IQ scores of 81 and 71 at ages 10 and 11 years. He is probably retarded.

(286), IQ 72, is of interest because his three children (429), (430) and (431) have IQ scores of 124, 126 and 124, respectively.

The families of (9) and (10) and of (15) and (16) are of interest because no retardation has appeared in them in four generations.

Family Summary

The proband, IQ 41, his paternal grandmother, both parents, a paternal aunt and uncle, a maternal aunt and four maternal uncles, six siblings, five nieces and nephews, 11 first cousins and four more distant relatives were retarded. In the proband's own line of descent there are four generations who have been given intelligence tests. In addition to the retardation, this family presents a continuing record of mental illness, delinquency and crime, illegitimacy, incest and poverty. Despite community and welfare efforts dating from 1912 the last generations are still community problems. However, the proportion of retardates is decreasing in the later generations of the proband's family partly as the result of institutionalizations and sterilization. The proband's parents had 11 children and 15 grandchildren, of whom one was stillborn and three are institutionalized, so that there are only 11 grandchildren capable of reproducing. One of these 11 (253) has had seven children and seems to be perpetuating the family pattern of retardation and delinquency, despite her location in a prosperous community and the aid of school and welfare workers.

The proband's maternal uncle, a retarded, illiterate man, had 22 children, of whom four died in infancy. Of the 18 survivors, nine were retarded. The nine retarded had 25 children with two retarded, the nine with borderline, normal or unknown intelligence had only 17, with two retarded. Two of these four retardates were offspring of father-daughter incest. A great many social problems and four institutionalizations could have been avoided if the proband's maternal uncle, the original progenitor who never supported his 22 children, had been institutionalized or sterilized as a young man. His descendants now number 68 persons, seven of whom died in infancy. Eleven of the 61 survivors are known to be retarded.

Retardation of proband of primarily genetic origin.

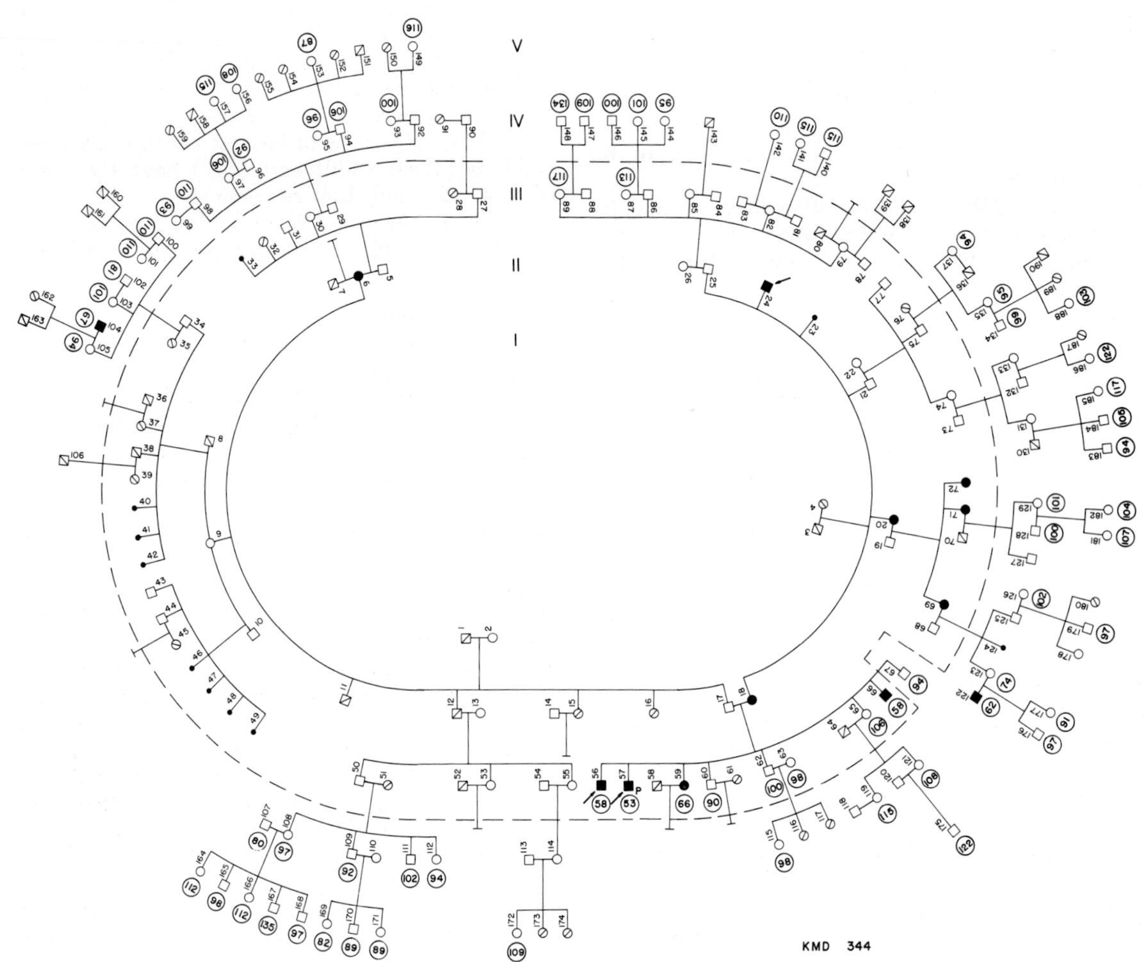

I
II
III
IV
V
KMD 344

KMD 344

The Proband

The proband (57) was born in 1900, institutionalized at age 12 years, discharged in 1920 but readmitted in 1936 and was in the institution in 1961. His environment was poor but there is no record of birth injury or perinatal infection. He walked at age 4 years and was sent to a school for the deaf for four years before he was institutionalized. He was held in jail in 1936 when his father died as a result of a kick by the proband. No charge was placed because of his low mentality, and he was readmitted to the institution. He was given a physical and neurological examination in 1950 by J. A. Böök, M. D., and John Schut, M. D. Their diagnosis was imbecility with deaf mutism. IQ 53. *Diagnosis:* mental retardation with deaf mutism.

Grandparents

Not of interest.

Parents

Father (17) was an excellent shoemaker who owned considerable property. He was killed by the proband when he teased him. Both (17) and (18) were alcoholic.

Mother (18) could not keep house and did not know the dates of birth of her children. She was retarded, and also had a deaf mute brother and great-grandfather. The parents of (17) were greatly opposed to his marriage because of the deaf mutism in the family of (18).

Aunts and Uncles

Paternal aunt (6) was a high-grade retardate, husband and children normal.

Maternal aunt (20) could not keep house or take care of her children, husband normal, all three children retarded but grandchildren all have IQ's above 70.

Maternal uncle (24) was institutionalized in 1904 at age 22 years when he kept running away. He was discharged to his mother in 1909, hospitalized in a mental hospital in 1957 where he is at the present time. He is a deaf mute (attributed to typhoid fever at age 5 years) with a diagnosis of "mild mental deficiency with psychotic reaction."

Siblings

Brother (56) was sent to a school for the deaf before being institutionalized in 1915 at age 17 years. He was paroled to his mother in 1920, appeared twice in Juvenile Court for stealing; was found to be insane (he was homicidal) and has been reinstitutionalized since 1924. He was given a physical and neurological examination by Dr. Böök and Dr. Schut in 1950. They diagnosed imbecility with deaf mutism. His EEG was moderately abnormal, slow during waking state, normal during sleep. IQ 58.

Sister (59) is a deaf, retarded woman who is blind in one eye and crippled from tuberculosis of the hip. She completed the fifth grade and is a poultry checker. She married a junk picker many years older than she and is childless. She has an IQ of 66.

Brother (60) has normal hearing and an IQ of 90. He served a work house sentence for beating his mother and has lost good jobs because of his alcoholism. He is married but childless.

Brother (62) is a plumber with normal hearing and seventh grade education. He married "so he could get on relief" and later divorced his wife. He has two prison records, IQ 100. Two children have unknown intelligence, one is normal.

Sister (65) completed the eighth grade and works in a candy factory. She has normal hearing and an IQ of 106, husband unknown, children normal.

Brother (66) is an unmarried and childless deaf mute. A petition to commit him as retarded was withdrawn. IQ 58.

Brother (67) completed the eighth grade and is an unmarried laborer. He is not deaf. IQ 94.

Nieces and Nephews

Not of interest.

First Cousins

(69), (71) and (72), siblings, all are retarded. (69) completed the third grade at age 15 years, (71) was in the fourth grade at age 14 years, spouse unknown, two normal children, and (72) died at age 12 years when in the third grade. Old records state this family was known as the "stupids of the school." (69) has a normal spouse and a daughter with IQ 74 who married a retarded man, IQ 62. This couple has two children, (176) and (177), with IQ's of 97 and 91, respectively. There is no deafness in this family, the descendants of the proband's maternal aunt (20) who is described as "having no judgment." Her husband (19) was a tailor.

More Distant Relatives

Not of interest except for the marriage of (105) with IQ 94, to (104) a retarded laborer with an IQ of 67.

Family Summary

The proband, a deaf mute with IQ 53, had two deaf, retarded brothers, one deaf, retarded sister, and a deaf maternal uncle who was retarded. The proband's mother, one paternal aunt, one maternal aunt and three cousins were retarded, but not deaf. None of the proband's normal siblings was deaf. The proband's parents had eight children and five grandchildren.

Retardation of proband of primarily genetic origin.

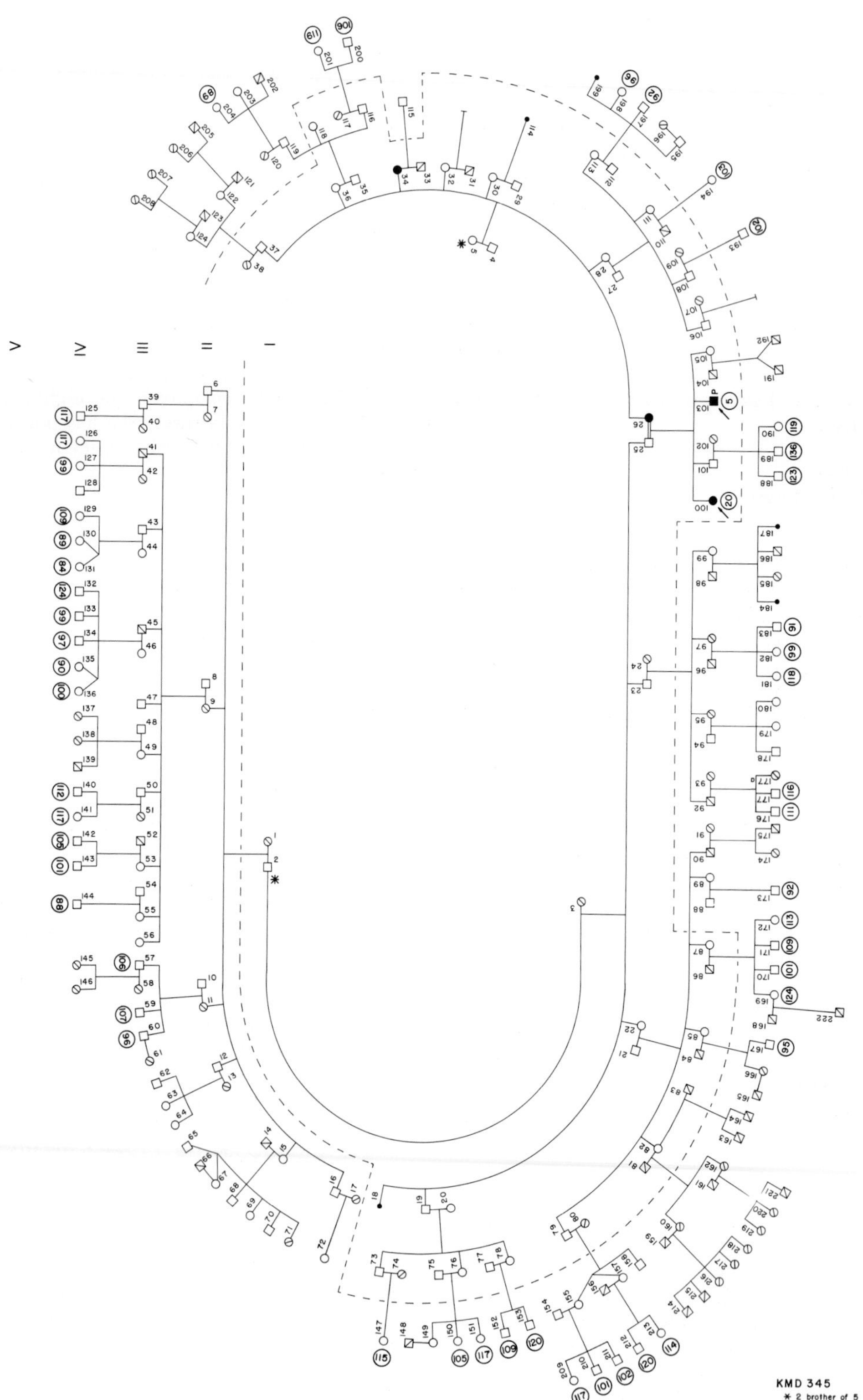

KMD 345
* 2 brother of 5

KMD 345

The Proband

The proband (103) was born in 1911, institutionalized at age 5 years and died of enteritis in the same year. He never sat up alone. The flexors in his extremities were contracted and he made choreic movements at times. IQ 5. *Diagnosis:* undifferentiated mental retardation.

Grandparents

Maternal grandmother was "very neurotic and hysterical." She was a sister of the paternal grandfather.

Parents

Father (25) was a reformed alcoholic. He had normal intelligence.

Mother (26) was neurotic, a high-grade retardate, and first cousin to her husband.

Aunts and Uncles

Maternal aunt (34) was retarded, husband unknown, only child normal.

Siblings

Sister (100) was institutionalized in 1912 at age 7 years and died of tubercular peritonitis in the institution in 1916. She was not walking at age 18 months when she began to have convulsions occasionally. She walked at age 3 years, never talked and had an IQ of 20.

Brother (101) graduated from college and is an insurance agent, wife unknown, three children all with IQ's above 100.

Sister (105) completed one year of college, husband and children of unknown intelligence.

Nieces and Nephews

One sibship of three (188), (189) and (190) has IQ's of 123, 136 and 119, respectively.

First Cousins

Not of interest.

More Distant Relatives

Not of interest.

Family Summary

The proband, IQ 5, and a sister, IQ 20, were low-grade retardates. The proband's mother and a maternal aunt were high-grade retardates. The proband's parents were first cousins and had four children and five grandchildren.

Retardation of proband of primarily genetic origin (consanguinity).

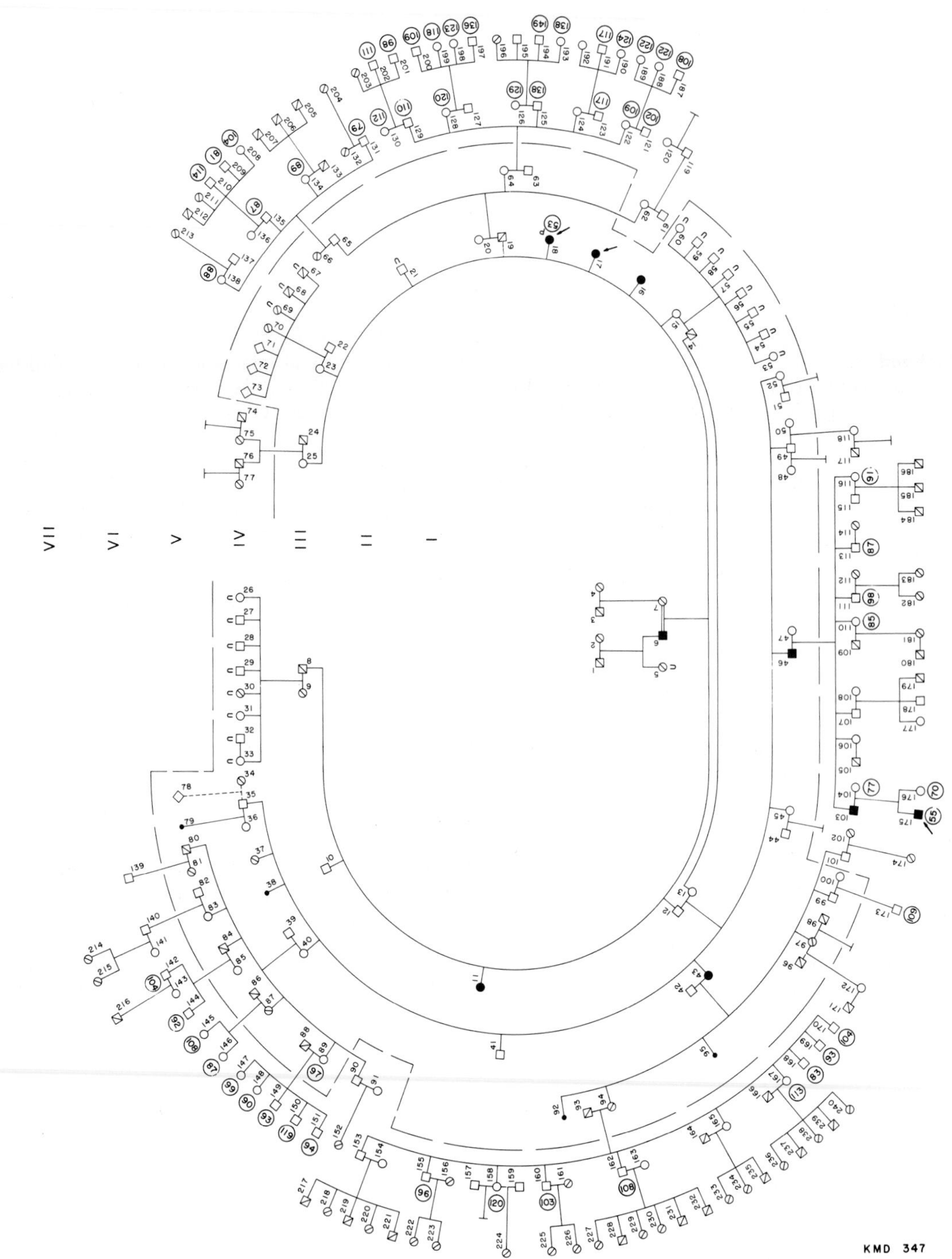

KMD 347

KMD 347

The Proband

The proband (18) was born in 1871, institutionalized at age 11 years and died of cerebral hemorrhage in the institution in 1933. Her birth and early life were uneventful. She had some sort of an "attack" at age 13 years, but there is no record of her ever having any others. She was said to have deteriorated mentally after age 11 years but there is no confirmation of this in institution records. IQ 53. *Diagnosis:* undifferentiated mental retardation.

Grandparents

Unknown.

Parents

Father (6) lacked judgment and foresight, and never took care of his family. He died in the county poorhouse.

Mother (7) was mentally ill for some years before her death. She was a second cousin to her husband.

Aunts and Uncles

Unknown.

Siblings

Brother (8) was an alcoholic, a gambler and deserted his family.

Brother (10) died of spinal meningitis at age 17 years. He had normal intelligence.

Sister (11) was retarded. She lived in the county poorhouse with her parents.

Brother (12) was considered to be quite peculiar, but made a good living as a contracting carpenter. His wife (13) was ignorant and emotional, a religious fanatic, but was classified as having normal intelligence; two of her ten children were retarded. She and (14) were siblings and came from a family with psychotic members.

Sister (15) had normal intelligence, as did her eight children.

Sister (16) died in a mental hospital of "epileptic dementia." She was also considered retarded.

Sister (17) was institutionalized at the time of her death of pulmonary tuberculosis at age 16 years. She was a low-grade retardate with no stigmata.

Brother (19) was an alcoholic and "shrewd."

Brother (21) had normal intelligence. His present status is unknown.

Sister (23) had normal intelligence. Her family could not be found for the follow-up.

Sister (25) had normal intelligence.

Nieces and Nephews

Nephew (35) was a stonemason but became a "preacher," deserted his wife and went to live with a girl who was pregnant by him. He was described as "unbalanced but having average intelligence."

Niece (43) was obese, epileptic and retarded. She married an ex-convict with normal intelligence.

Niece (45) was obese but had normal intelligence. She also married an ex-convict with normal intelligence.

Nephew (46) is retarded, wife and six of his seven children normal, one retarded.

First Cousins

None who is known.

More Distant Relatives

Nephew (46) has a son (103) who deserted his family. He is retarded. His wife (104) with IQ 77 was hospitalized for manic depressive psychosis, manic type. A second hospitalization gave a new diagnosis of dementia praecox, hebephrenic type. She is in the hospital at the present time and her condition is deteriorating. She and her husband (103) have one child (175) who is retarded. (175) is in a school for educable retarded, IQ 55.

Family Summary

The proband, IQ 53, her father, three siblings, a niece and nephew and two more distant relatives were retarded. There was also considerable mental illness and antisocial behavior among the relatives. The proband's mother was mentally ill. Her parents, who were second cousins, had 12 children and 37 grandchildren.

Retardation of proband of primarily genetic origin (consanguinity).

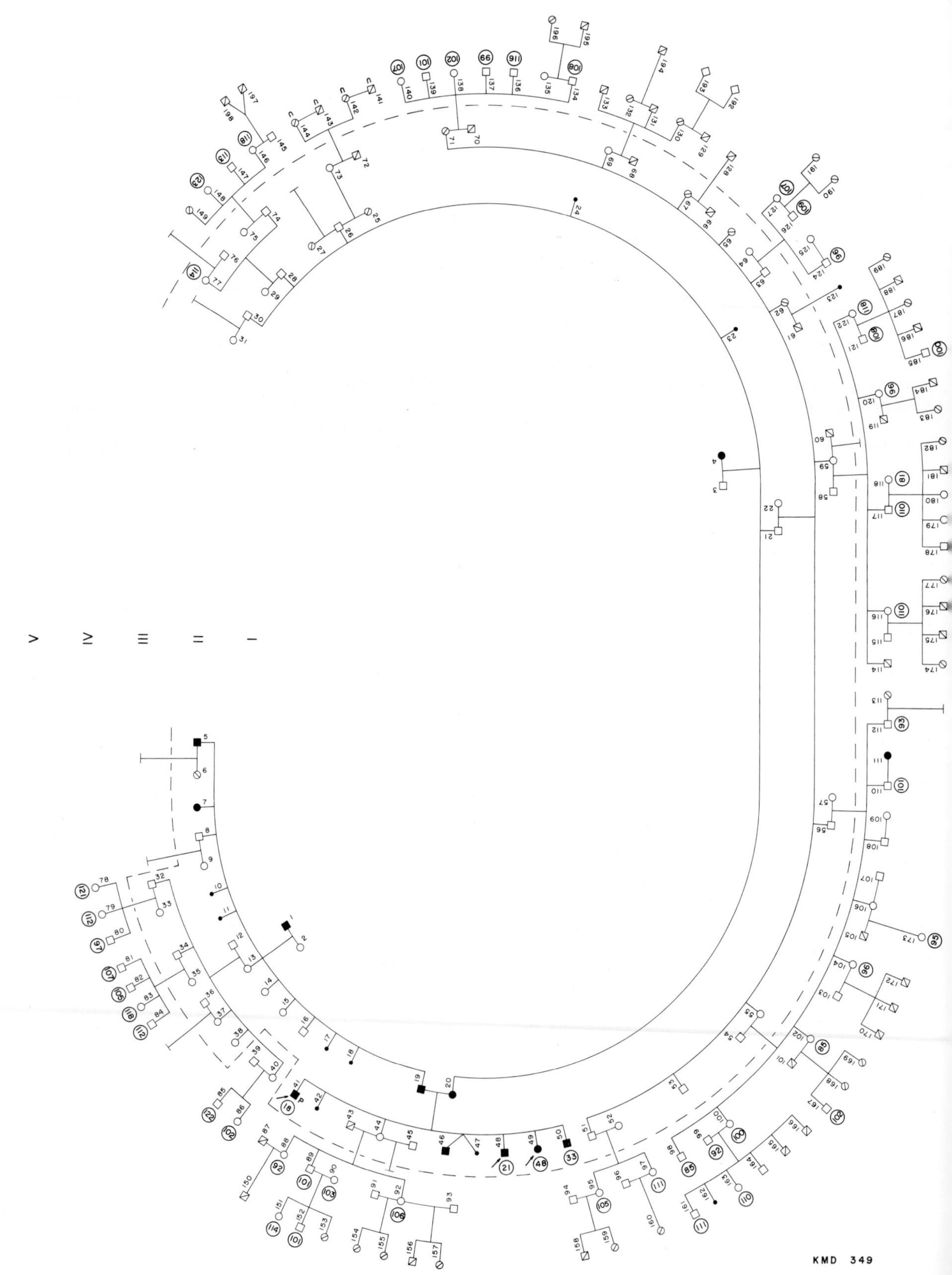
V
IV
III
II
I
KMD 349

KMD 349

The Proband

The proband (41) was born in 1897, institutionalized at age 7 years and died of pulmonary tuberculosis in the institution in 1927. He was a large baby whose head was bruised at birth. He had no history of perinatal infection and no stigmata. His home environment was rather poor. IQ 18. *Diagnosis:* undifferentiated mental retardation.

Grandparents

Paternal grandfather did not talk until age 7 years and was slow and dull, although a good worker. Paternal grandmother had normal intelligence but had epileptiform attacks.

Maternal grandmother was peculiar and excitable and was retarded.

Parents

Father (19) was an iron moulder with a fair income, classified as not retarded in the institution records but described as retarded by the early workers who saw him.

Mother (20) was also classified as not retarded in the institution records but was described as a high-grade moron by the early workers who saw her.

Aunts and Uncles

Paternal uncle (5) could not talk well and was retarded. He was married but childless.

Paternal aunt (7) was retarded and childless.

Paternal aunt (10) and paternal uncle (11) both died of convulsions in infancy.

Siblings

(42) was a miscarriage.

Sister (44) was originally classified as retarded. She was our chief source of information and was interviewed by telephone. Despite her poor school record—seventh grade at age 16 years, probably the result of her family problems—we have reclassified her as having low normal or normal intelligence. She works as a nursemaid and has been married twice. Her three children have normal intelligence.

Brother (46) could do only third grade work in school. He is an unmarried, childless laborer.

Sister (47), twin to (46), died of pneumonia at age 3 months.

Brother (48) was institutionalized in 1912 at age 10 years and died of adenocarcinoma of the liver in the institution in 1951. He was given a physical and neurological examination in 1950 by J. A. Böök, M.D., and John Schut, M.D. They found no stigmata except a depressed posterior fontanel and sagittal suture up to vertex of head. Their diagnosis was low-grade idiot. IQ 21.

Sister (49) was institutionalized in 1912 at age 8 years, discharged to her parents in 1917 but readmitted in 1950 and is still in the institution. She was given a physical and neurological examination in 1950 by Dr. Böök and Dr. Schut. They found no stigmata and gave a diagnosis of low-grade idiocy. They thought her IQ of 48 was too high.

Brother (50) has an IQ of 33. He lives with his sister (44).

Nieces and Nephews

Only three, (88) with IQ 92, (89) with IQ 101 and (92) with IQ 106. (88) is crippled but works as a certified psychiatric aide. Her husband (87) also works as a psychiatric aide but has been arrested for drunkenness and has an unstable personality.

First Cousins

(65) was hospitalized for catatonic schizophrenia.

(73) died in a mental hospital with Alzheimer's disease.

More Distant Relatives

Not of interest.

Family Summary

The proband, IQ 13, and four siblings were all low- to middle-grade retardates of undifferentiated type. The parents were high grade to borderline in intelligence, as were the paternal grandfather, maternal grandmother and a paternal aunt and uncle. Careful physical and neurological examinations of two of the proband's siblings revealed no specific anomalies. The proband's parents had eight children and only three grandchildren, all the offspring of the one normal individual in the proband's sibship. Despite this girl's poor home with two retarded parents and five retarded siblings she completed the seventh grade, has supported herself and takes care of her retarded brother.

Retardation of proband of primarily genetic origin.

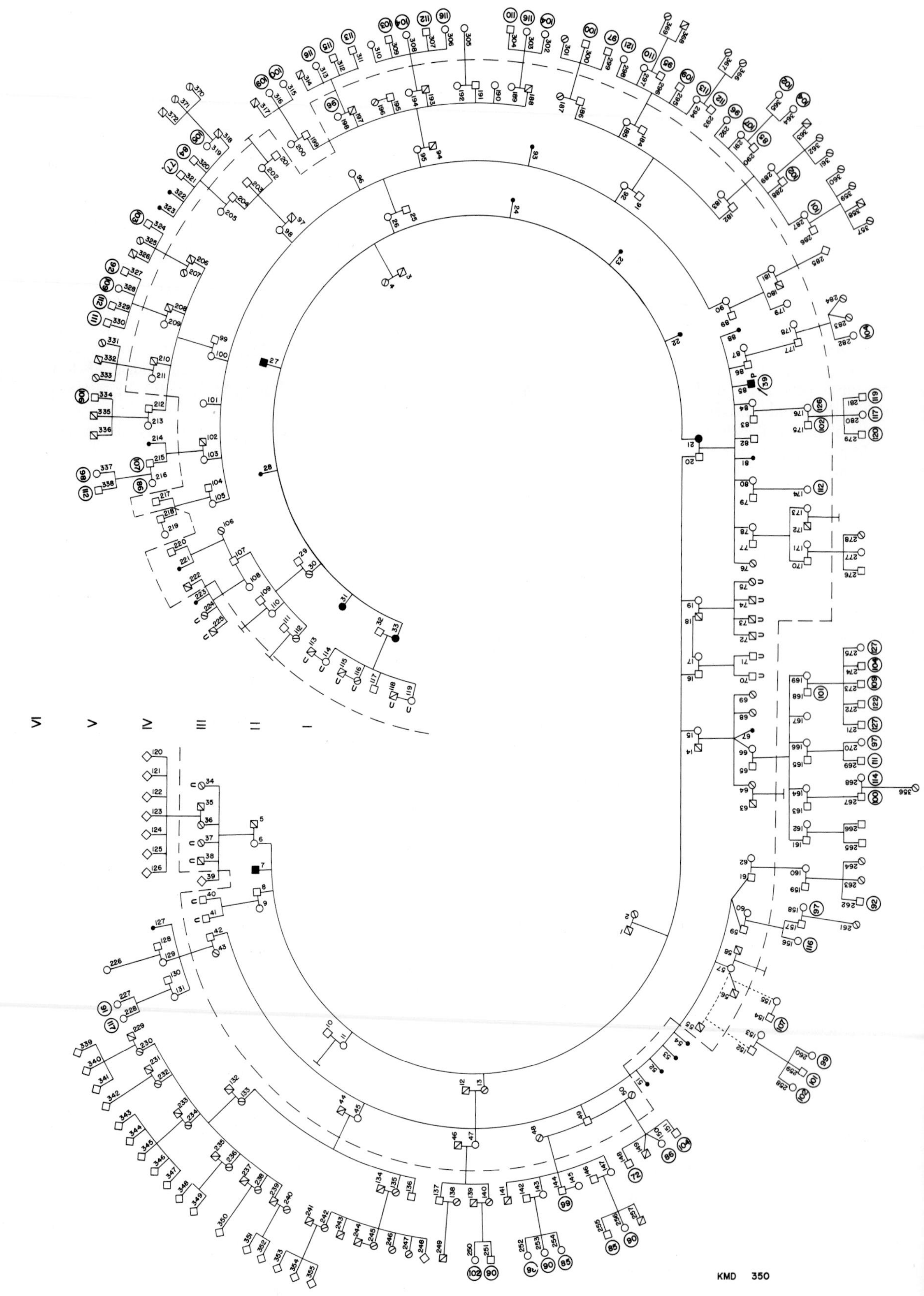

KMD 350

KMD 350

The Proband

The proband (85) was born in 1890, institutionalized at age 9 years and died of pulmonary tuberculosis in the institution in 1945. He was born prematurely at 7 months, showed no signs of trauma, did not speak clearly until the age of 6 years, and attended school for two years with poor results. The home environment in which he lived with his father and sister was good. IQ 39. *Diagnosis:* microcephaly.

Grandparents

Not of interest.

Parents

Father (20) was a contractor.

Mother (21) did not take care of her home or family. She was retarded and died when the proband was 5 years old.

Aunts and Uncles

Paternal uncle (7) was an "excitable idiot" who died at age 2½ years.

Maternal uncle (27) died single and childless. He was a retarded farm laborer.

Maternal aunt (31) was unmarried at age 46 years. She was retarded and had a "severe form of chorea." She was paralyzed from the hips down.

Maternal aunt (33) was retarded.

Siblings

Sister (76) died of pulmonary tuberculosis at age 21 years.

Sister (78) graduated from high school, husband and children normal.

Sister (80) completed two years of college, husband and child normal.

Sister (81) died at 14 months, cause unknown.

Brother (82), unmarried and childless, is a railway clerk with normal intelligence.

Sister (84) graduated from high school, husband and child normal.

Brother (86) completed the tenth grade, is an electrical foreman and has a normal wife and child.

Sister (88) died at 14 months of "summer complaint."

Nieces and Nephews

All have normal intelligence.

First Cousins

Not of interest.

More Distant Relatives

Not of interest.

Family Summary

The proband, IQ 39 and microcephalic, one paternal uncle, a maternal uncle, two maternal aunts and his mother were retarded. One uncle was a low-grade retardate, one retarded aunt had "chorea" and was paralyzed from the hips down. The proband was a premature birth but had no history of trauma or illness. The proband's parents had nine children and five grandchildren.

Retardation of proband of primarily genetic origin (microcephaly).

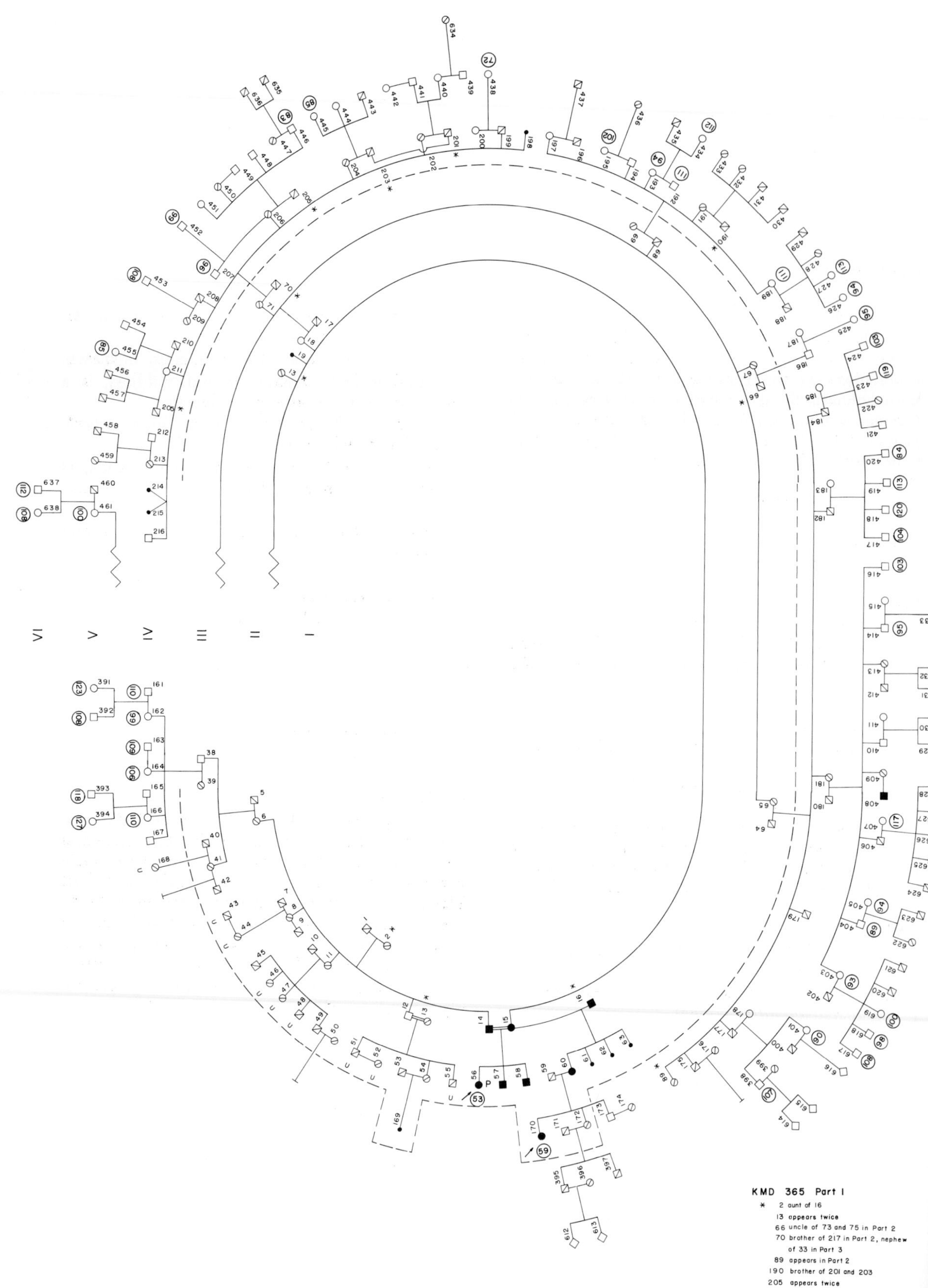
KMD 365 Part I
* 2 aunt of 16
13 appears twice
66 uncle of 73 and 75 in Part 2
70 brother of 217 in Part 2, nephew of 33 in Part 3
89 appears in Part 2
190 brother of 201 and 203
205 appears twice

KMD 365

The Proband

The proband (56) was born in 1874, institutionalized at age 16 years and died of hypertensive cardiovascular disease and paralysis agitans in the institution in 1950. In 1950 she was given a physical and neurological examination by J. A. Böök, M.D., and John Schut, M.D. They reported a diagnosis of Parkinson's disease and imbecility. They also noted an extensive syphilitic infection in this family. The proband's father died of general paresis and two siblings had syphilis, probably congenital. They found it impossible to determine which, if any, of the proband's symptoms might be due to syphilis. The proband had no history of birth injury or any stigmata. Her home environment was poor. IQ 53. *Diagnosis:* mental retardation with Parkinson's disease.

Grandparents

Not of interest.

Parents

Father (14) was retarded and died in a mental hospital of paresis, the result of a syphilitic infection. He deserted his family.

Mother (15) was a retarded woman who neglected her family. She was a first cousin to (14). Her second husband (16) was also retarded.

Aunts and Uncles

Maternal aunt (23) was retarded. She was married twice to men of unknown intelligence and had six children, none known to be retarded.

Maternal uncle (25) was a married, childless, alcoholic retardate who drowned.

Maternal uncle (27) was retarded, wife normal, at least one child retarded.

Maternal uncle (31) was an alcoholic and retarded, wife normal, at least one child retarded.

Maternal aunt (34) was retarded, husband unknown, one of her three children is retarded.

Siblings

Brother (57) is a syphilitic, retarded and childless farm laborer.

Brother (58) never went to school and was retarded. He died at age 23 of "ulcers," probably syphilis.

Half Siblings

Half sister (60) was retarded and possibly syphilitic. Her husband (59) was imprisoned and later was hospitalized for mental illness with a diagnosis of dementia praecox, paranoid type.

(61), (62) and (63) were girls who died shortly after birth.

Nieces and Nephews

No full nieces and nephews.

The proband's half sister (60) had three children, (170) an institutionalized retardate with IQ 59, and a diagnosis of mental retardation due to cerebral birth trauma, (172) who refused to cooperate and does not communicate with her brother (173), a normal man.

First Cousins

(97) has served two prison sentences. IQ 78.

(101) was a childless retardate.

(146) attended special classes in school.

(150) deserted his family. He was retarded. Not all the proband's cousins on either side of the family are known. The mental status of these relatives was difficult to evaluate because of their meager schooling, low social class and unskilled occupations.

More Distant Relatives

(307) was in special classes.

(370) died in the institution of epilepsy and cerebral palsy at age 5 years. He had been committed as mentally retarded.

(385) has an IQ of 68.

(408) completed the second or third grade and is a janitor.

Family Summary

The proband, IQ 53, both her parents, five maternal aunts and uncles, two siblings, one half sibling and that half sibling's child, three first cousins and four more distant relatives were retarded. The proband's parents were first cousins. The proband had Parkinson's disease, her father and her two siblings also had syphilis. The home environment was poor. The proband's parents had three children, no grandchildren.

Retardation of proband of primarily genetic origin (consanguinity).

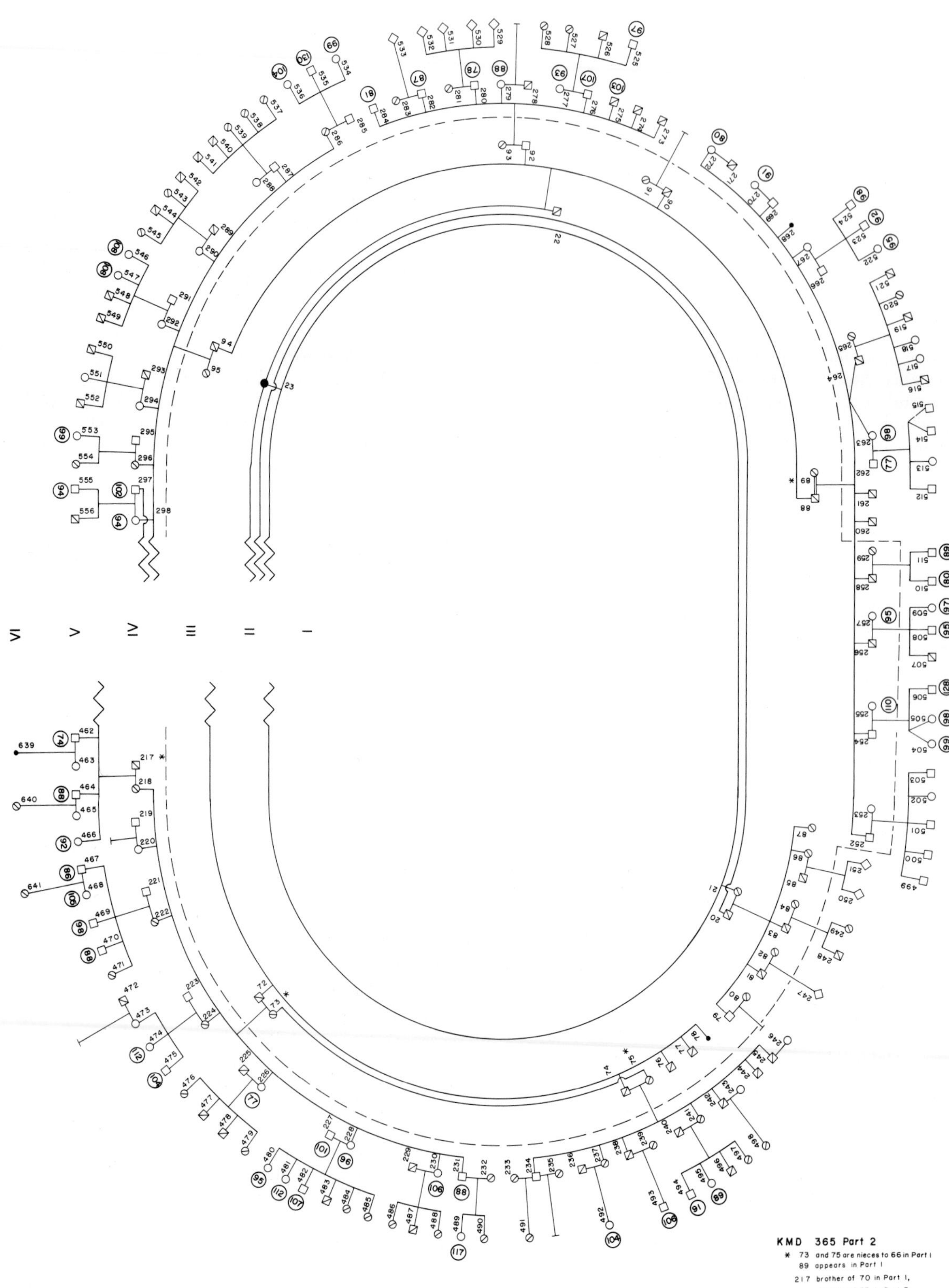

KMD 365 Part 2

* 73 and 75 are nieces to 66 in Part I
89 appears in Part I
217 brother of 70 in Part I,
nephew of 33 in Part 3

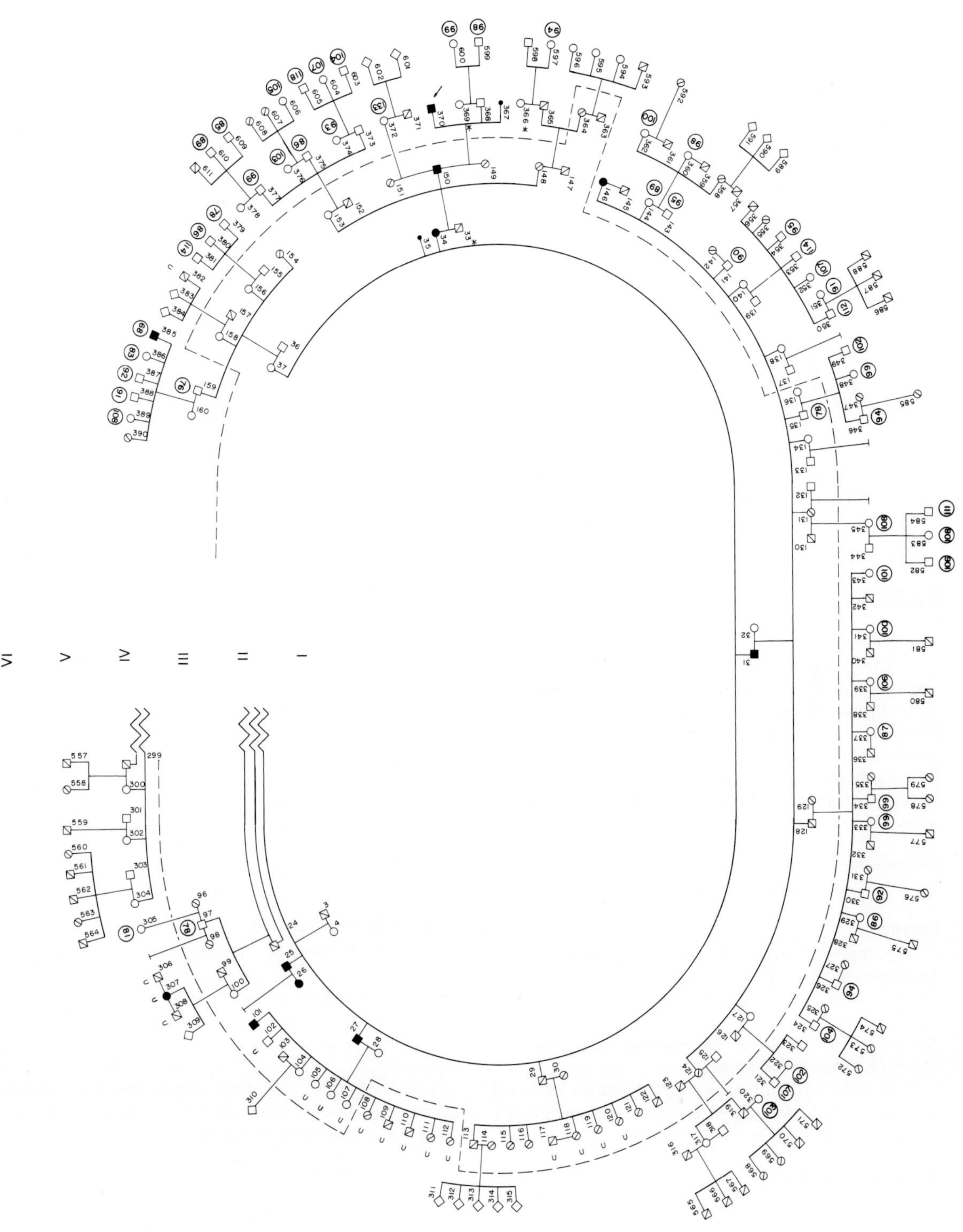

KMD 365 Part 3
∗33 uncle of 70 in Part I and 217 in Part 2
369 and 366 are sisters

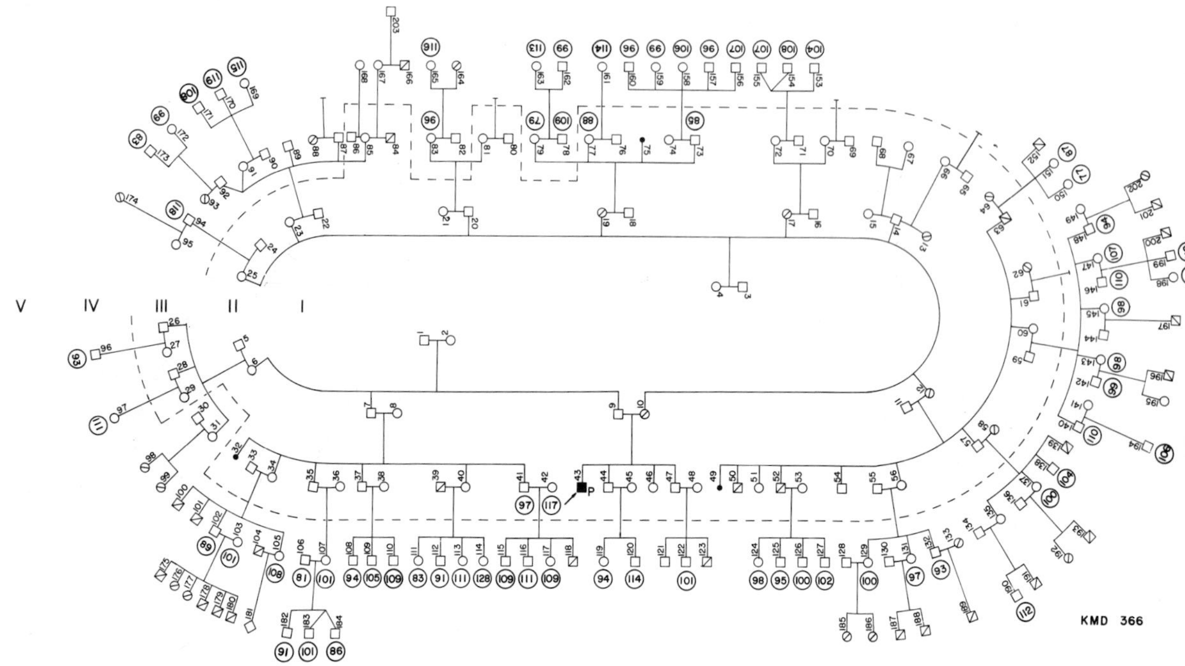

KMD 366

The Proband

The proband (43) was born in 1900, institutionalized at age 11 years and died of septicemia and chronic nephritis in the institution in 1913. He had a large head at delivery which enlarged greatly after birth. The institution records describe him as hydrocephalic with spina bifida and the lower limbs paralyzed and diseased. No IQ. *Diagnosis:* hydrocephalus.

Grandparents

All had normal intelligence.

Parents

Father (9) was a farm laborer with normal intelligence. He had an active case of syphilis with open lesions during the time of the gestation and birth of the proband. According to the doctor, his case was arrested by treatment before the other children were born.

Mother (10) divorced (9) because of cruel treatment and non-support. She supported her family by taking in washings.

Aunts and Uncles

Maternal aunt (12) had convulsions.

Siblings

Brother (44) graduated from high school, is a store manager, and has a normal wife and two normal children.

Sister (46) graduated from high school, is single, and is a cashier.

Brother (47) graduated from college, is a military finance officer and has a normal wife, two normal children and one of unknown intelligence.

Nieces and Nephews

Not of interest.

First Cousins

Not of interest.

More Distant Relatives

Not of interest.

Family Summary

The proband was the only known retarded person in this kindred. He had hydrocephalus, spina bifida, paralyzed limbs and probably also an early syphilitic infection, since he had ulcers before he was a year old. The proband's father had an active case of syphilis during the time of his gestation and birth. The proband's parents had four children and five grandchildren.

Retardation of proband could be genetic, or could be environmental as a result of an acute syphilitic infection. Since the hydrocephalus was present at birth and was accompanied by spina bifida, the genetic origin seems to be the primary cause.

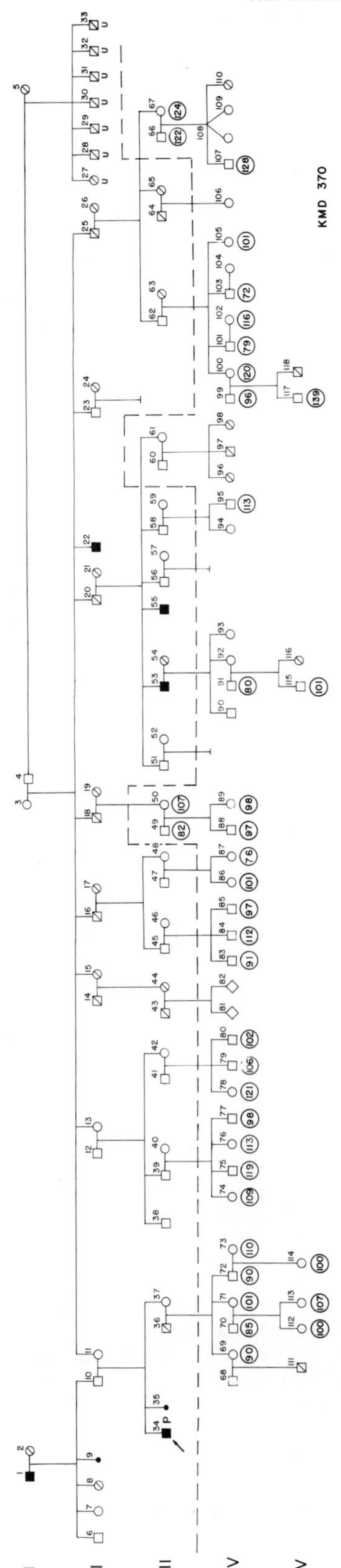

KMD 370

The Proband

The proband (34) was born in 1899, institutionalized at age 12 years, discharged to his parents in 1912, readmitted in 1923 and died of cardiac failure and tuberculosis in 1932. He was obese, had ichthyosis and was a cretin who improved physically after the administration of thyroid extract. He was a low-grade retardate. *Diagnosis:* cretinism with ichthyosis.

Grandparents

Paternal grandfather was said to have been normal until he suffered a sunstroke at age 30 years. After this occurrence he became "very childish and silly."

Maternal grandmother was hospitalized for mental illness.

Parents

Father (10) was a rural mail carrier.

Mother (11) was "below par" mentally.

Aunts and Uncles

Maternal uncle (22) was retarded. He died single and childless.

Siblings

(35) was a stillbirth.

Sister (37) completed the tenth grade and works in a factory. She does not have ichthyosis, nor did her parents. Her three children are normal.

Nieces and Nephews

Not of interest.

First Cousins

(53) left school in the seventh grade at 15 years. He is a baker and was considered retarded.

(55) died of influenza at age 18 years. He was in special classes at school.

More Distant Relatives

Not of interest.

Family Summary

The proband was a low-grade retardate with a diagnosis of cretinism. His physical symptoms improved after treatment with thyroid extract, but his mental condition remained unchanged. He also had ichthyosis. The proband's paternal grandfather, a maternal uncle and two first cousins were high-grade retardates. The proband's parents had three children and three grandchildren.

Retardation of proband of primarily genetic origin (cretinism).

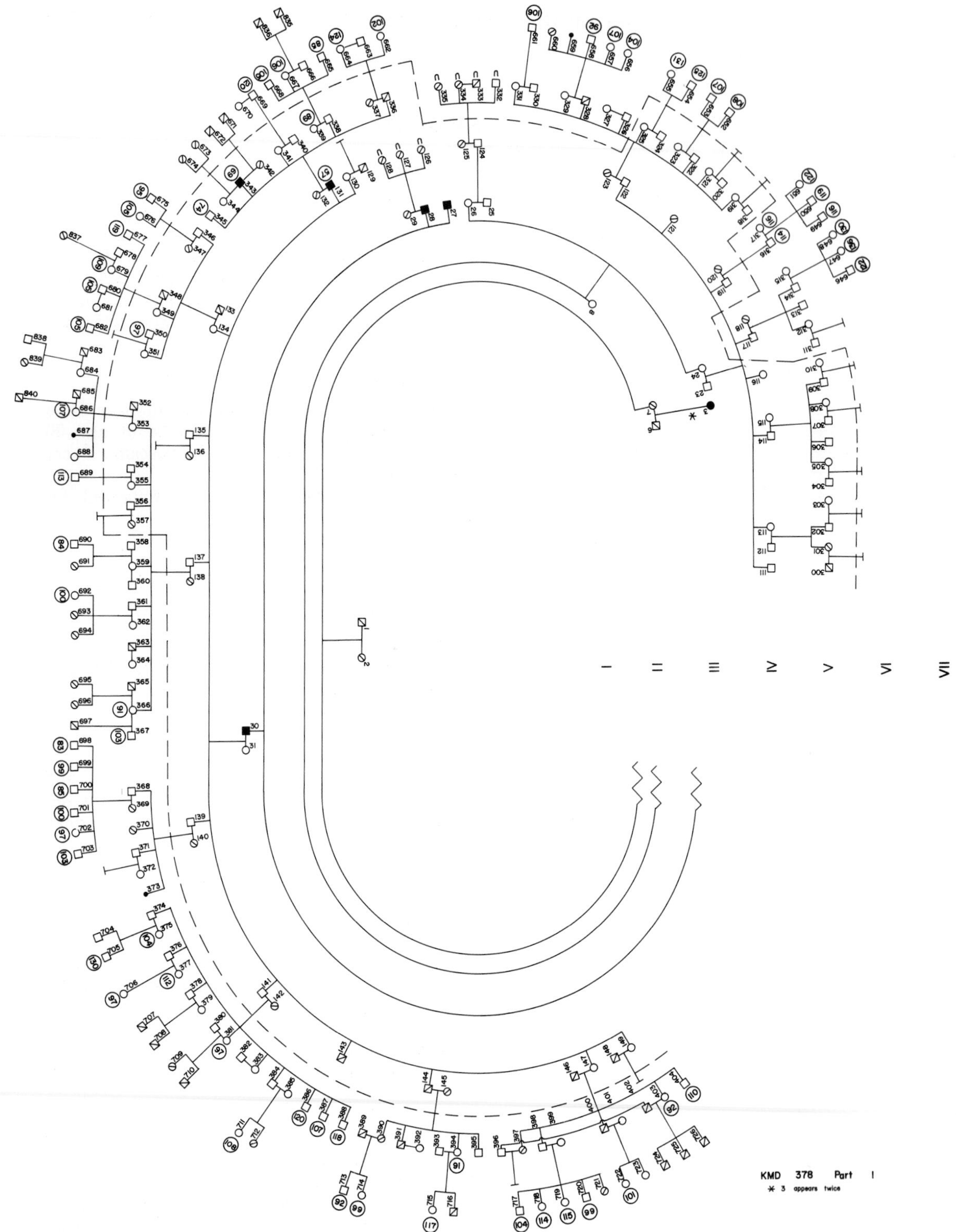

KMD 378

The Proband

The proband (44) was born in 1888, institutionalized at age 8 years and left the institution in 1920. She married a contractor and had five children. There was no history of birth injury or perinatal infection. She had ichthyosis. IQ not given. *Diagnosis:* mental retardation with ichthyosis.

Grandparents

Maternal grandmother was retarded.

Maternal grandfather died in a mental hospital.

Parents

Proband's father (10) was also her great great-uncle (great-uncle to proband's mother and age 70 when proband was born). This was a forced marriage because of the illegitimate pregnancy. (10) was a prosperous farmer who developed senile dementia in old age.

Proband's mother (11) divorced (10) and married a second normal man. She gave her children away to strangers. She had ichthyosis and was retarded.

Aunts and Uncles

Proband's paternal aunt (7) was also her great-grandmother.

Maternal uncle (13) was retarded. Only one retarded person has appeared among his 77 descendants.

Maternal aunt (16) married her first cousin once removed (15). She was retarded but the children and grandchildren of this marriage are all apparently normal.

Maternal aunt (19) had an illegitimate child, later married a retarded man. She was retarded. One case of retardation has appeared among her 47 descendants.

Siblings

Brother (40) drowned at age 30 years, single and childless. He was a deaf mute and was retarded.

Brother (41) is a gardener at an institution. Normal intelligence, wife unknown, children normal.

Sister (46) was adopted. She completed ten years of school. She married a normal spouse and has normal children. Normal intelligence but has ichthyosis.

Four miscarriages (47), (49), (55) and (56).

Brother (48) was adopted but was sent to a "Catholic Home" and died unmarried and childless of influenza in 1918. Retarded.

Brother (51) was adopted. He was an Army captain and is childless. Normal intelligence.

Brother (53) was adopted. He is a truck driver, has normal intelligence and a normal wife and children.

Half Siblings

(27) died unmarried and childless at 38 years, probably of syphilis. Retarded.

(28) was retarded, wife's and children's intelligence unknown.

(30) was retarded but married a normal woman. He had one retarded child (131) in a family of 11.

(32) was retarded. Spouse was a registered nurse.

(35) was retarded, husband normal intelligence. Of her nine children, one (163) was retarded.

(37) was retarded, husband and children of unknown intelligence.

(38) was retarded, spouse and six of their ten surviving children are retarded.

Children

Son (195) completed the eighth grade and is a chauffeur. His wife, intelligence unknown, divorced him. IQ 84.

Son (197) completed the tenth grade and is a policeman. His wife and children have normal intelligence. IQ 89.

Son (199) completed the tenth grade and is a salesman. His wife and children have normal intelligence. IQ 98.

Son (201) completed the fifth grade and is a laborer. IQ 88. He has a retarded child (wife's intelligence unknown).

Daughter (204) deserted her family. Both her husbands had unknown intelligence and her children are unknown. IQ 90.

Grandchildren

(519) is in special classes. IQ 64.

Nieces and Nephews

Not of interest.

Children of Proband's Half Siblings

(131) has an IQ of 57. One of his five children (343) has an IQ of 69, one (345) is borderline, IQ 74.

(163) has two illegitimate children and is retarded. One of her nine children (451) has IQ 59, three have low normal IQ's.

(169) completed the fourth grade, is retarded, but married a normal woman and has two children with IQ's of 117 and 95, respectively.

(172) is retarded, wife's intelligence unknown, son has IQ of 119.

(176) is retarded, husband unknown, children all have normal intelligence.

(178) is retarded, husband normal intelligence, children all have normal intelligence.

(179) was retarded, wife normal intelligence, son with IQ 106.

(181) is unmarried, childless and retarded.

First Cousins

Not of interest.

More Distant Relatives

Half sibling (35) has a retarded grandchild (451) who is a laborer. IQ 59.

Half sibling (30) has a retarded grandchild (343), IQ 69.

Cousin (70) has a retarded grandchild, IQ 67.

Cousin (95) has a retarded grandchild, IQ 68.

Family Summary

The proband was the child of a great-uncle–great-niece marriage. Her father was a prosperous farmer. She, her mother, two aunts and an uncle, two siblings, seven half siblings, eight children of half siblings, one grandchild and four more distant relatives were retarded, all fairly high-grade retardates. The proband, her mother and her two normal sisters had ichthyosis. Also, one retarded brother was a deaf mute. The proband's parents had 11 children, including four stillbirths, and 15 grandchildren.

Retardation of proband of primarily genetic origin (consanguinity).

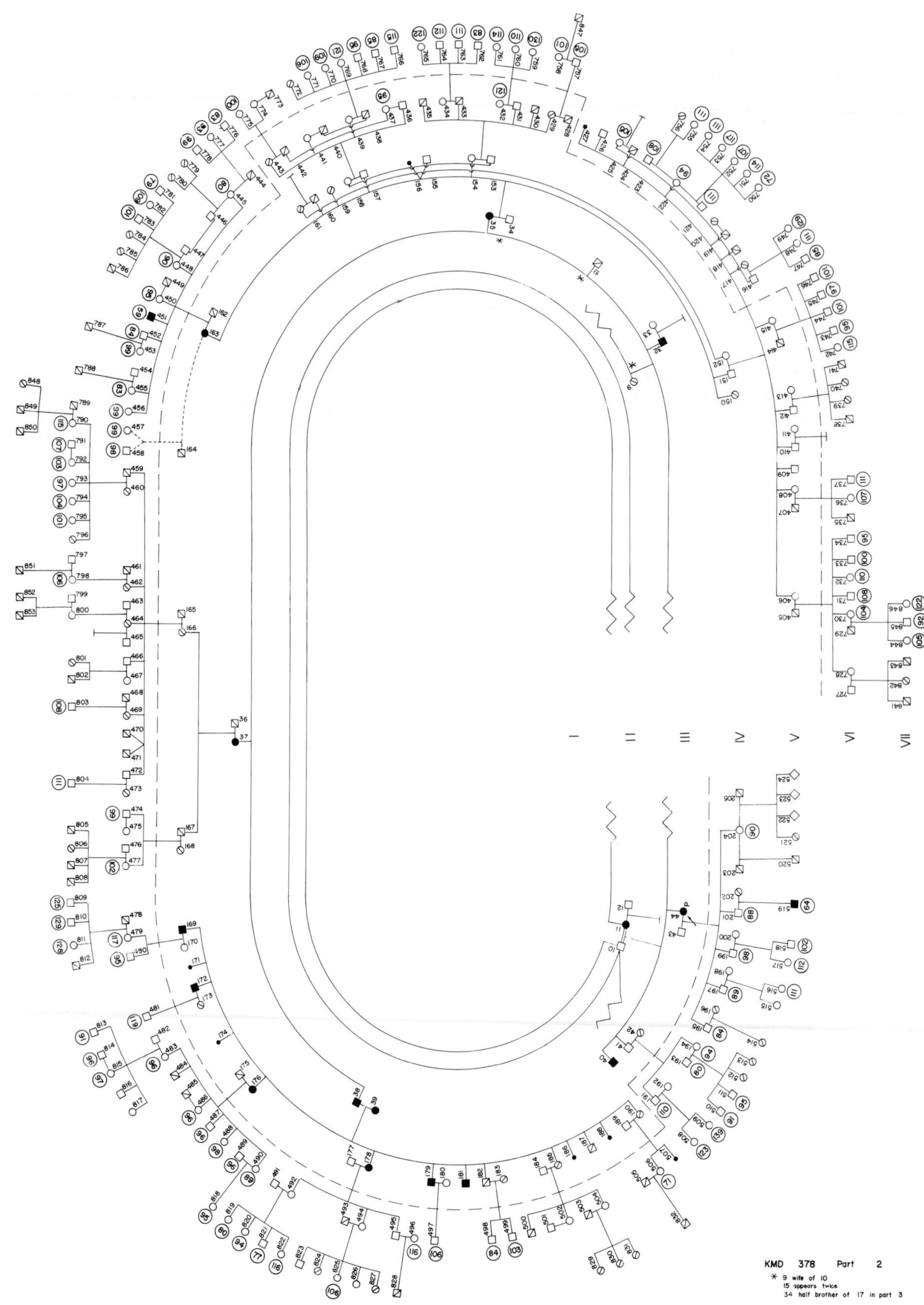
I
II
III
IV
V
VI
VII
KMD 378 Part 2
* 9 wife of 10
15 appears twice
34 half brother of 17 in part 3

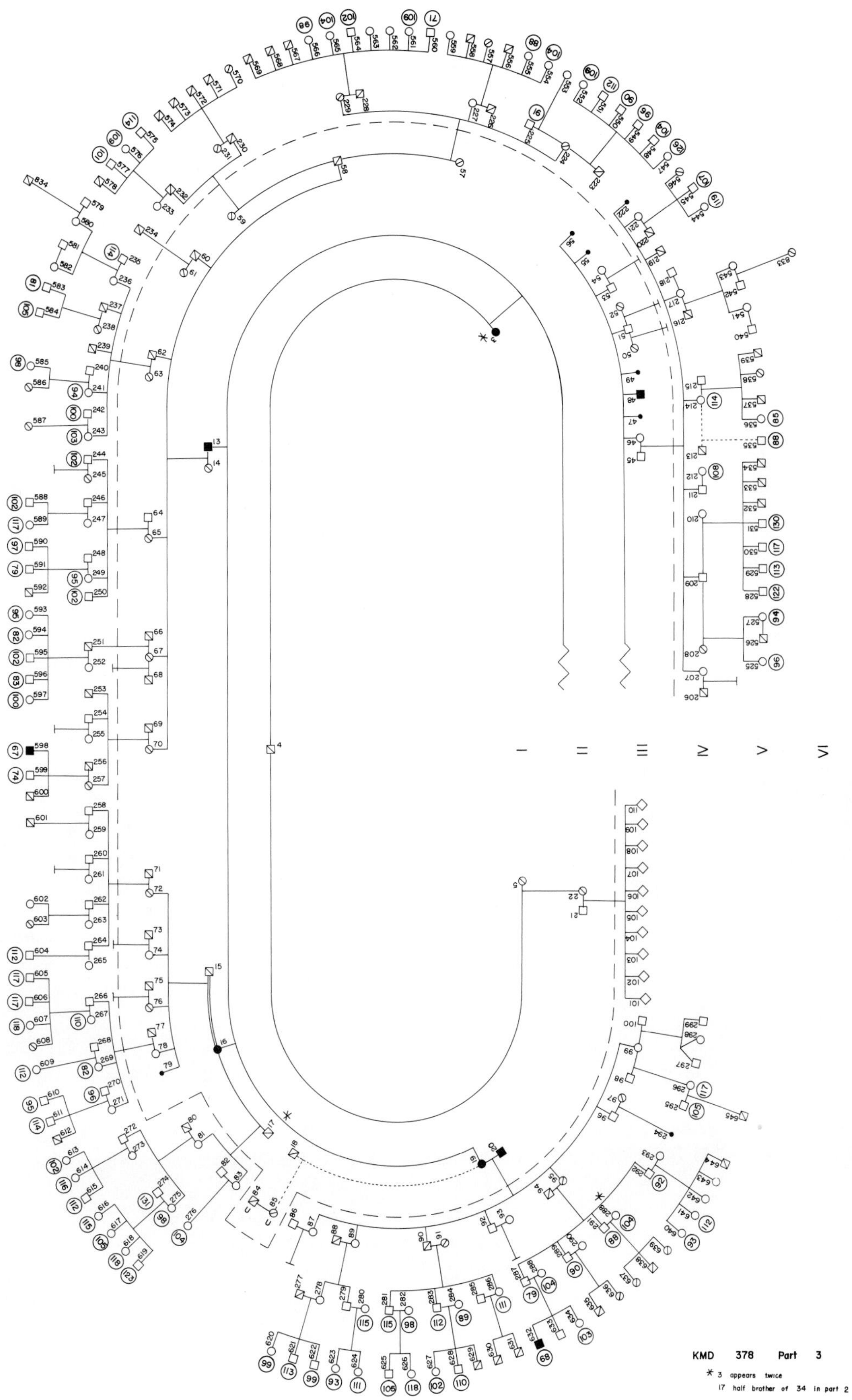

KMD 378 Part 3

* 3 appears twice
17 half brother of 34 in part 2

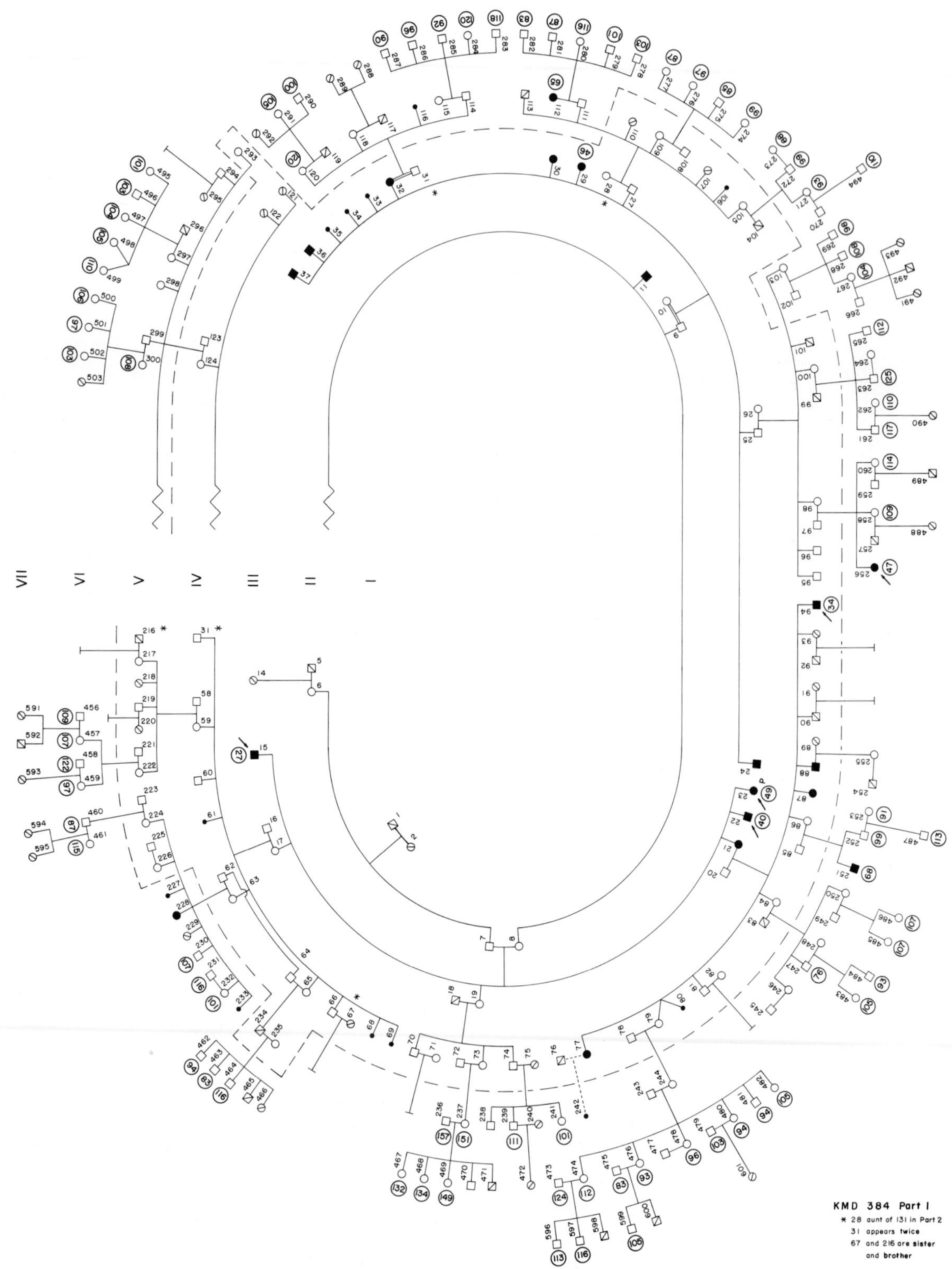

KMD 384 Part I

* 28 aunt of 131 in Part 2
31 appears twice
67 and 216 are sister and brother

KMD 384

The Proband

The proband (23) was born in 1871, institutionalized at age 16 years and died of influenzal pneumonia in the institution in 1933. She was a healthy child without stigmata and her birth was uneventful. She was described in institution records as a "good faithful helper." IQ 49. *Diagnosis:* undifferentiated mental retardation.

Grandparents

Not of interest. They died in Europe and were unknown to the early workers.

Parents

Father (7) was a prosperous farmer.

Mother (8) had normal intelligence.

Aunts and Uncles

Maternal uncle (9) and his wife (10) had normal intelligence, but were first cousins. Of their 11 children, six were retarded and three died shortly after birth of unknown causes.

Maternal uncle (11) was a retarded, childless farm laborer.

Siblings

Brother (15) was institutionalized in 1889 at age 33 years and died in the institution of pulmonary tuberculosis in 1919. He had no stigmata. He was a "good farm helper" with IQ 27.

Sister (17) and her husband both had normal intelligence, as did their children.

Sister (19) had normal intelligence, husband's unknown, children normal.

Sister (21) was a high-grade retardate, husband normal, four of their ten surviving children retarded.

Brother (22) was institutionalized in 1887 at age 18 years and died in the institution of primary carcinoma of the liver in 1935. He had no history of trauma or illness, no stigmata and was "a good farm helper" with IQ 40.

Nieces and Nephews

Niece (77) was retarded. She died in childbirth with an illegitimate child who also died.

Niece (79) and her husband (78) had a forced marriage. (79) has a diagnosis from a mental hospital of involutional psychosis, melancholia, probably associated with cerebral arteriosclerosis, dull but not mentally deficient.

Niece (87) was a high-grade retardate who died childless at age 21 years.

Nephew (88) is a retarded laborer, wife's intelligence unknown, only child normal.

Nephew (94) was institutionalized in 1920 at age 8 years and is still in the institution. IQ 34.

First Cousins

(24) could not talk and was retarded.

(25) was a teacher who became mentally ill.

(29) cannot talk and has an estimated IQ of 46.

(30) does not talk plainly and is retarded.

(32) does not talk plainly and is retarded. She married her first cousin once removed, a normal man. Their three surviving children are normal.

(36) was a deaf mute who was transferred from the school for the deaf to a mental hospital, in which he died of accidental drowning. He was psychotic and retarded.

(37) was an idiot who never walked or talked. All the above including (24) are siblings and the offspring of a cousin marriage of two normal persons.

More Distant Relatives

(161) was institutionalized in 1919 at age 13 years, remained for two years, was readmitted in 1936 and died of influenza in the institution in 1946. Her diagnosis was "imbecile with engrafted schizophrenia of the catatonic type." IQ 44.

(228) died of a "nervous condition" resulting from a fall at age 16 years. She failed all the first three grades in school but was never institutionalized.

(251) was killed in World War II. IQ 68.

(256) is institutionalized with a diagnosis of severe idiopathic mental deficiency. IQ 47.

(564) has an IQ of 67.

The family of (237) is of interest because of the high IQ's in the family: wife (237) with IQ 151, husband (236) with IQ 157 and three tested children, (467), (468) and (469) with IQ's of 132, 134 and 149, respectively.

Family Summary

The proband, IQ 49, three siblings with similar IQ's, a maternal uncle, two nieces and two nephews, six first cousins and five more distant relatives were retarded. There was a sibship with deafness and retardation from consanguineous parents, and several sporadic cases of mental illness. The proband had no history of trauma, her parents had normal intelligence and were not known to have been related. The proband's parents had six children with four retarded, and 23 grandchildren with four retarded and four who died in infancy.

Retardation of proband of primarily genetic origin.

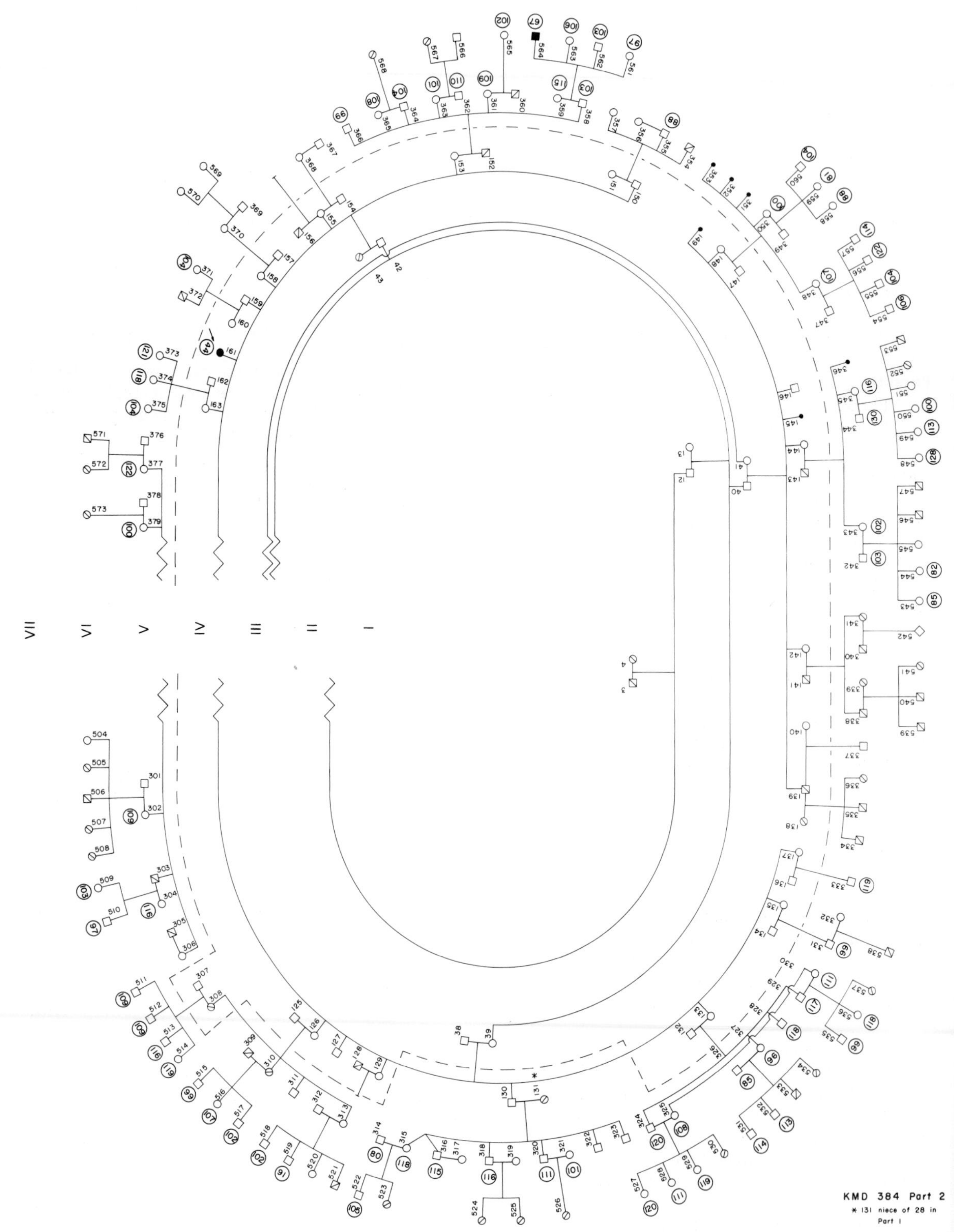

KMD 384 Part 2
* 131 niece of 28 in Part I

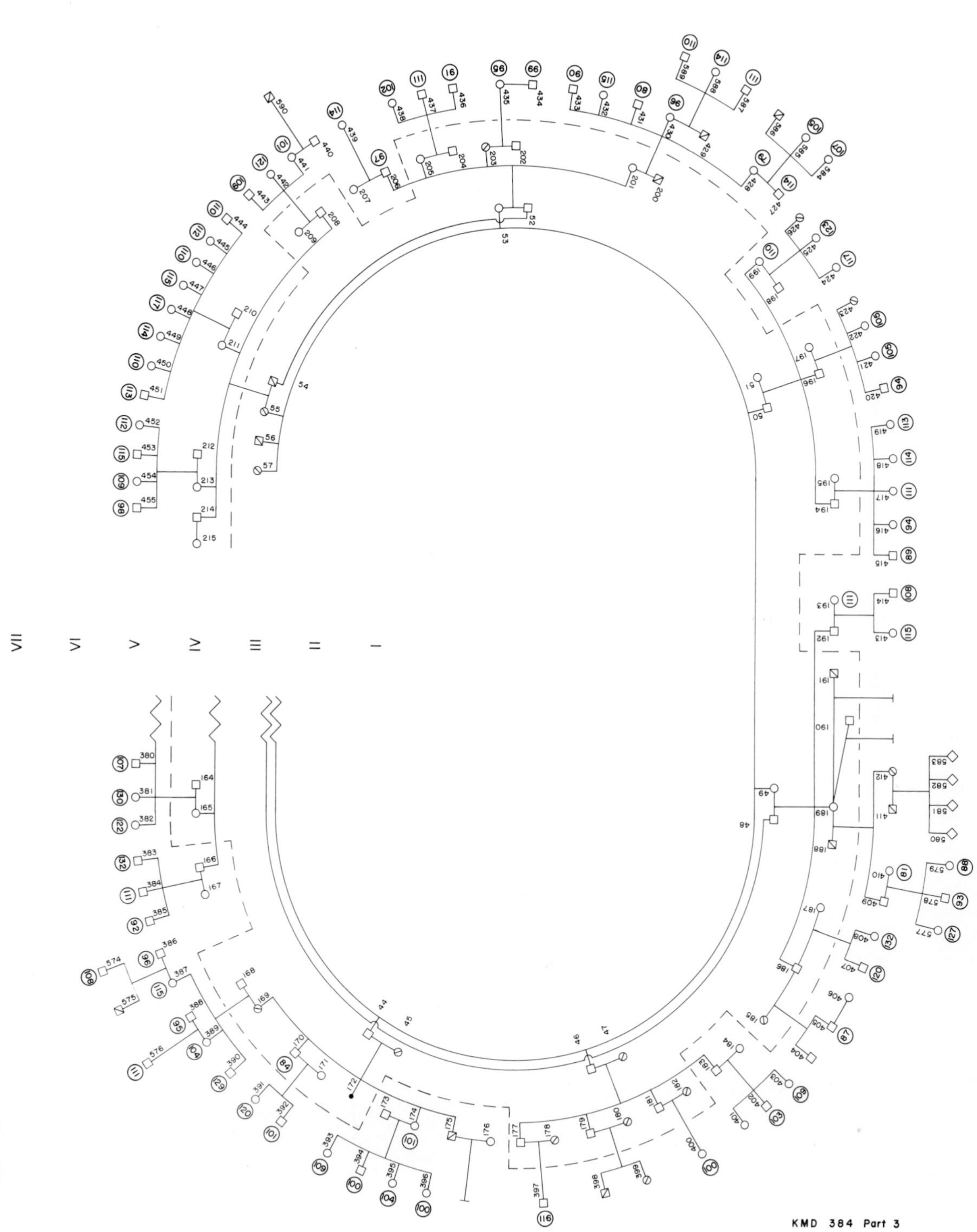

KMD 384 Part 3

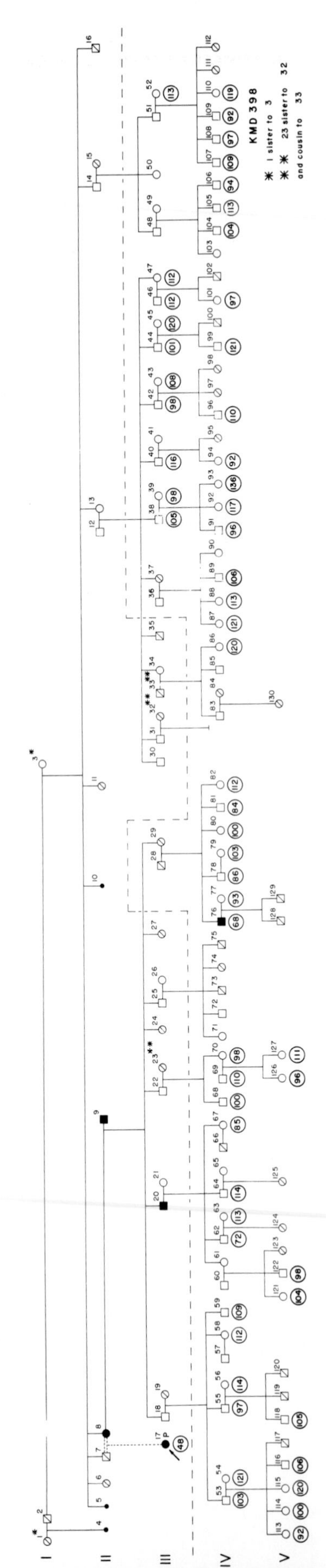
KMD 398
✱ I sister to 3
✱✱ 23 sister to 32 and cousin to 33
I
II
III
IV
V

KMD 398

The Proband

The proband (17) was born in 1892, institutionalized at age 8 years and died of hypertensive cardiovascular disease in the institution in 1952. She was a child of a brother-sister union. She was born blind, had diabetes and was a restless, excitable retardate. IQ 48. *Diagnosis:* mental retardation with blindness.

Grandparents

Paternal (and maternal) grandfather (2) was a "poor manager" and "always ailing."

Parents

Father (7) died of cancer at age 21 years. He was classified as a "borderline" case.

Mother (8) and sister to her husband completed the third grade and was retarded. She was 16 years old when the proband was born. She later married a foreign born man who was about 30 years older than she and also retarded.

Aunts and Uncles

Not of interest.

Siblings

None.

Half Siblings

Half brother (18) was classified as retarded in the old records, but he operates a farm implement business and probably has normal intelligence, as do his children.

Half brother (20) completed the second grade and is a retarded laborer. His wife has normal intelligence and none of his four children is retarded, but one has a borderline IQ of 72.

Half brother (22) was also classified as retarded in the old records, but is rated as a first class millwright, a skilled occupation, and has normal children.

Half sister (24) died at age 17 years. Her intelligence was unknown.

Half brother (25) has normal intelligence and no retarded children.

Half sister (27) died of scarlet fever at age 10 years. Her intelligence was unknown.

Half sister (29) completed the seventh grade and worked as an aide in an institution for the retarded. She passed the psychiatric aide test but was on probation and was asked to leave because her work was unsatisfactory. She was rated by supervisors as "below normal." She has a retarded son with IQ 68, and four normal children.

Nieces and Nephews

No full nieces and nephews. Of the children of half siblings, (76) has an IQ of 68 and is a laborer. Also (62) has a borderline IQ of 72 and (67), (78) and (81) have low normal IQ's of 85, 86 and 84, respectively.

First Cousins

Not of interest.

More Distant Relatives

Not of interest.

Family Summary

The proband, IQ 48 and blind, was the child of a brother-sister union. One half sibling and one half nephew were high-grade retardates, as was the proband's mother and the father of the half siblings. The proband's parents had one child, no grandchildren.

Retardation of proband of primarily genetic origin (consanguinity).

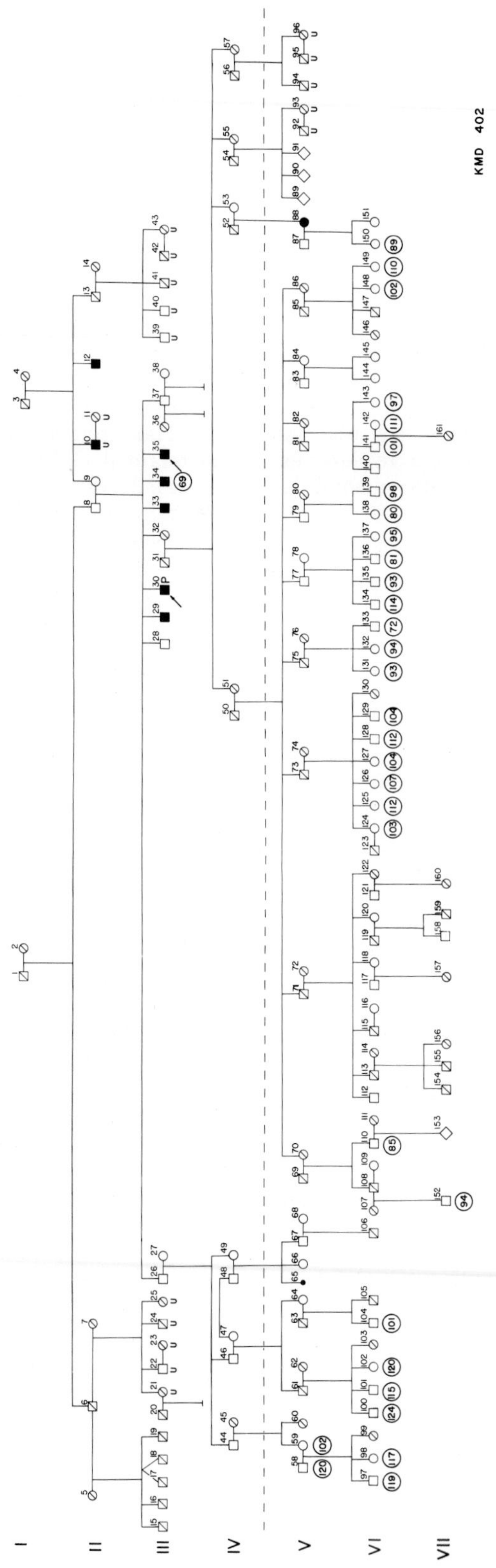
KMD 402

KMD 402

The Proband

The proband (30) was born in 1864, institutionalized at age 51 years and died of pulmonary tuberculosis, myocarditis and progressive muscular dystrophy in the institution in 1913. He never walked well and was always "weak mentally and physically," and by the age of 20 years had deteriorated greatly in both respects. He was retarded, degree unknown. *Diagnosis:* mental retardation with sex-linked progressive muscular dystrophy.

Grandparents

Unknown.

Parents

Father (8) was epileptic but had normal intelligence.

Mother (9) had normal intelligence.

Aunts and Uncles

Maternal uncles (10) and (12) were retarded.

Siblings

Brothers (26) and (28) had normal intelligence. (26) had a normal wife and children, (28) was never married.

Brother (29) died of cholera morbus at age 14 years and "had the same trouble as the others" (progressive muscular dystrophy and mental retardation).

Sister (32) died of pneumonia at age 30 years. Her intelligence was unknown. One retardate has appeared among her descendants (granddaughter).

Brother (33) died of lobar pneumonia and progressive muscular dystrophy in 1922 in the County Poor Farm. He left school at age 19 years when in the fifth grade. He was "peculiar from birth" and the acute muscular symptoms appeared at age 20 years.

Brother (34) died in 1914 of progressive muscular dystrophy. He was "always weak physically and mentally," but deteriorated rapidly physically after the age of 32 years. He attended school until age 19 and was then in the fifth grade. IQ 69 (taken at age 45 years).

Brother (35) was institutionalized in 1912 at age 40 years, and died two years later of pulmonary tuberculosis. He did "fairly well" in school until age 15 or 16 years and left at age 19 years when in the fifth grade. He "went all to pieces" after about age 16 years.

Brother (37) was a good business man but had epilepsy. He was married twice but had no children.

Nieces and Nephews

Not of interest.

First Cousins

(24) was described in the old records as being like the patient only "not so bad." He could not be found for the follow-up.

More Distant Relatives

Niece (53) has a retarded daughter (88) who repeated the first, fourth, sixth and eighth grades and left school when in the eighth grade at age 18 years.

Family Summary

The proband and four of his brothers were retarded and had progressive muscular dystrophy. One paternal first cousin was said to have been affected but this could not be verified. Two maternal uncles and one great-niece were retarded. The proband's parents had nine children and seven grandchildren. None of the proband's sister's male descendants has progressive muscular dystrophy.

Retardation of proband of primarily genetic origin (sex-linked progressive muscular dystrophy).

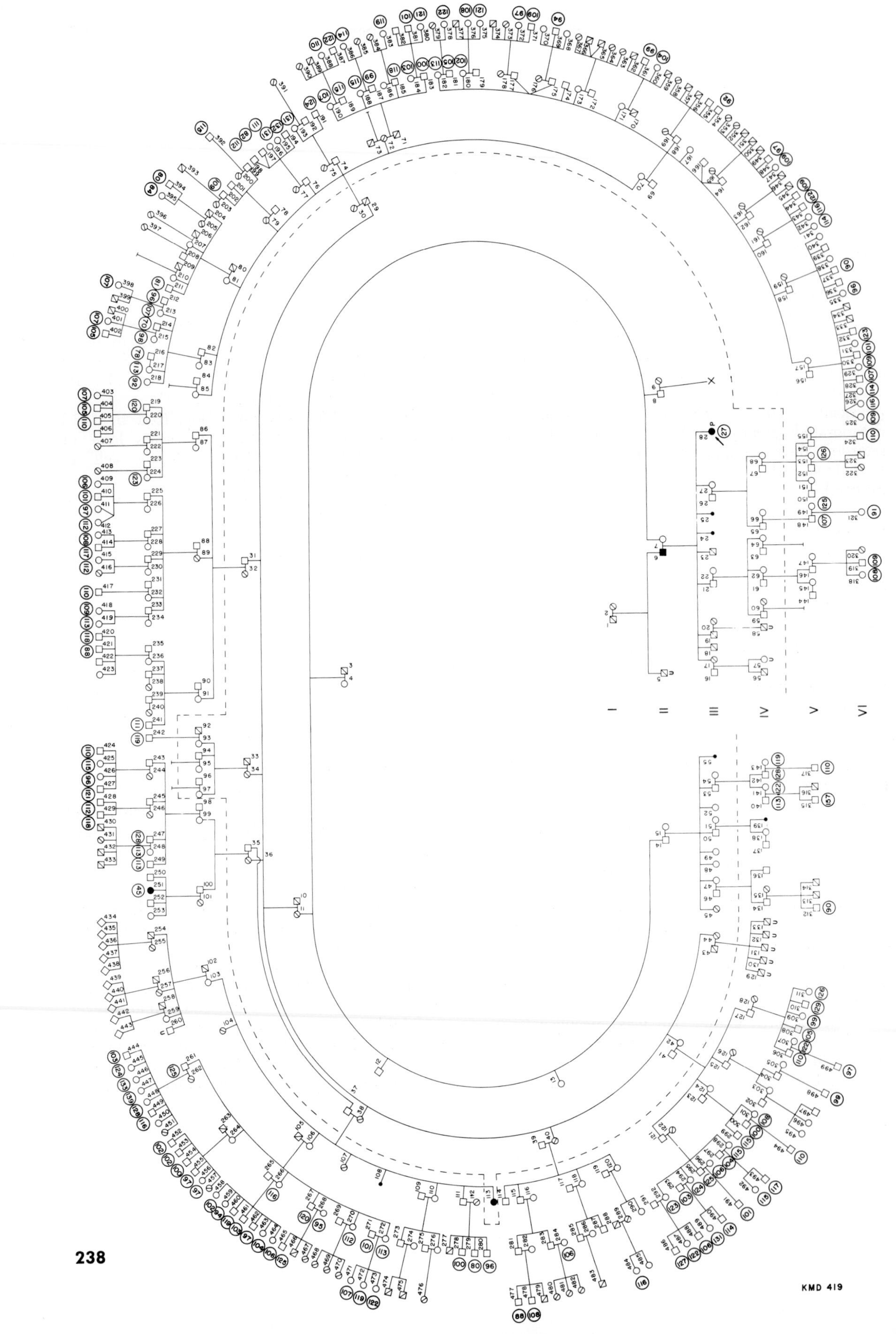

KMD 419

KMD 419

The Proband

The proband (28) was born in 1879, institutionalized at age 36 years and died of pulmonary tuberculosis in the institution the same year. She was the last born in her fraternity of nine. She walked at age 5 years, talked at age 10 years. IQ 27. *Diagnosis:* Down's syndrome.

Grandparents

Not of interest.

Parents

Father (6) was an alcoholic and retarded, "wholly worthless."

Mother (7) was a dressmaker. She left her husband in Europe and came to this country with her children. She supported her family.

Aunts and Uncles

Only one paternal relative, an unknown uncle.

Maternal relatives not of interest.

Siblings

Sister (17) and brothers (18), (19) and (23) had unknown intelligence.

Brother (21) had normal intelligence but committed suicide at age 25 years. He was an alcoholic and abused his wife and family who were all normal.

(24) and (25) died in infancy, causes unknown.

Sister (27) had normal intelligence, as did her husband and children.

Nieces and Nephews

Not of interest.

First Cousins

Not of interest.

More Distant Relatives

(113), child of first cousin (38), was retarded. She died single and childless.

(251) has an IQ of 45. She was recommended for institutionalization because she was not considered trainable. She has a short attention span and is hyperactive.

Family Summary

The proband, IQ 27, her father and three more distant relatives were the only known retarded persons in this family. The proband's parents had nine children and eight grandchildren.

Retardation of proband of primarily genetic origin (Down's syndrome).

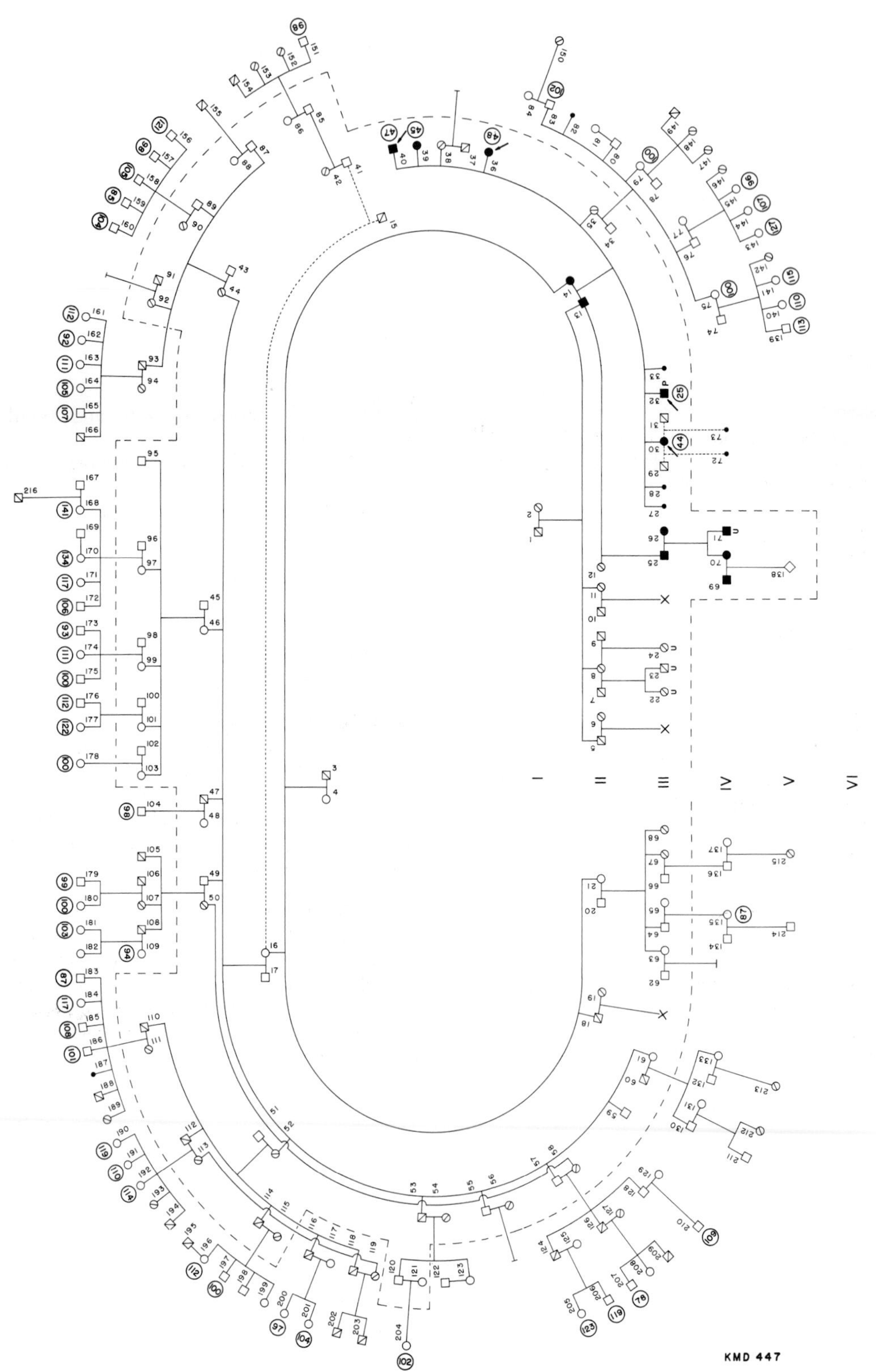

KMD 447

KMD 447

The Proband

The proband (32) was born in 1896, institutionalized at age 12 years, transferred to a second institution in 1941 because of tuberculosis and died there of pulmonary tuberculosis in 1952. He talked at age 2 years, did not walk until age 3 years. He attended school for two years but learned very little. The parents stated he had "very bad chills and fever" at age 1 year. He had no stigmata. The home was broken up when the proband's parents went to the county poorhouse. IQ 25. *Diagnosis:* undifferentiated mental retardation.

Grandparents

Not of interest.

Parents

Father (13) was shiftless and retarded. He lived in the county poorhouse for 32 years.

Mother (14) did not take care of herself or her family. She was retarded.

Aunts and Uncles

Paternal relatives are unknown. They all remained in Germany.

Maternal relatives not of interest.

Siblings

Brother (27) died of convulsions at 11 days.

Sister (28) died of convulsions at 3 months.

Sister (30) had convulsions in infancy. She was institutionalized in 1913 at age 21 years after two illegitimate miscarriages. She was given a physical and neurological examination in 1950 by J. A. Böök, M.D., and John Schut, M.D. They found no stigmata and gave a diagnosis of imbecility. An EEG taken June 6, 1951 was abnormal with slow basic activity and generalized bursts of slow waves of high voltage. IQ 44.

Brother (33) died of convulsions at age 3 months.

Sister (35) was in the state orphanage at one time. Her intelligence was unknown. Her husband and children have normal intelligence.

Sister (36) was institutionalized in 1915 at age 12 years after seven years in the state orphanage. She was sterilized in 1929 and placed under outside supervision for a time but was readmitted a year later. She is now living in a boarding home. IQ 48.

Sister (38) was adopted. Her intelligence is unknown. She is married but childless.

Sister (39) is unmarried and childless. Her IQ is 45.

Brother (40) was institutionalized in 1924 at age 10 years, and has remained in the institution ever since. In 1950 he was given a physical and neurological examination by Dr. Böök and Dr. Schut. They found no stigmata and gave a diagnosis of imbecility. IQ 47. An EEG taken June 20, 1951 revealed a moderately abnormal pattern during the waking state with mixed activity that was too fast and too slow.

Half Siblings

Half brother (25) was retarded and married a retarded, promiscuous woman who deserted him after the birth of two retarded children. His mother (12) had unknown intelligence.

Nieces and Nephews

Only five surviving full nephews and nieces, (75), (76), (79), (80) and (83), all the children of one sister and all with normal intelligence. The two children of the half brother are both retarded.

First Cousins

Not of interest.

More Distant Relatives

Not of interest.

Family Summary

The proband, IQ 25, both his parents, four siblings, one half brother and two children of the half brother were all retarded. The family of the half brother is in the probably genetic category with three generations of retardates. In addition, three siblings died of convulsions in infancy. The home conditions were poor. The five children and 12 grandchildren of the proband's only sibling who had surviving children, a sister of unknown intelligence with a normal spouse, all are apparently normal. The proband's parents had ten children and eight grandchildren, including two stillbirths and one who died in infancy.

Retardation of proband of primarily genetic origin.

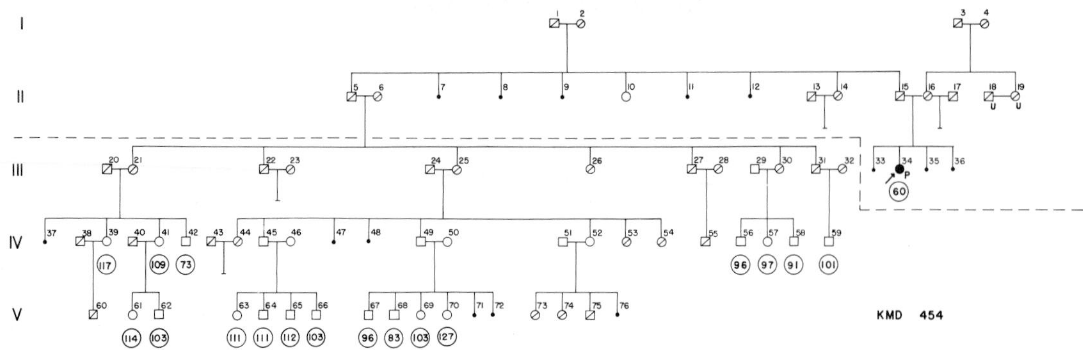

KMD 454

The Proband

The proband (34) was born in 1895, institutionalized at age 15 years and was discharged to her family in 1912. She was single, childless and died of cancer in 1949. Her birth was uneventful but she was born "with a hole in her back." One of her legs was shorter than the other and her arms were bent. IQ 60. *Diagnosis:* mental retardation with spina bifida.

Grandparents

Not of interest.

Parents

Father (15) was a lumberman of unknown intelligence.

Mother (16) was thought to have been murdered by her second husband. She was of unknown intelligence and was possibly syphilitic.

Aunts and Uncles

Five of the proband's father's eight siblings died in infancy. Only one (5) reproduced.

The proband's mother had only one sibling, an unknown sister (19).

Siblings

Brother (33) died in convulsions at age 6 months. He was hydrocephalic and had "sores on his body."

Brother (35) died in convulsions at 1 year.

Sister (36) died in convulsions at 3 weeks. She had "abscesses on her body."

Nieces and Nephews

None.

First Cousins

Not of interest.

More Distant Relatives

Not of interest.

Family Summary

The proband, IQ 60, was the only known retarded person in the family. She had spina bifida. One brother had hydrocephalus and all three of her siblings died of convulsions in infancy. There was some indication that the mother may have been syphilitic but there is no medical record of this. The proband and two of her siblings had "sores," but these were not diagnosed as syphilitic. The proband showed no later development of syphilis. The proband's parents had four children, no grandchildren.

Retardation of proband of primarily genetic origin (hydrocephalus).

KMD 477

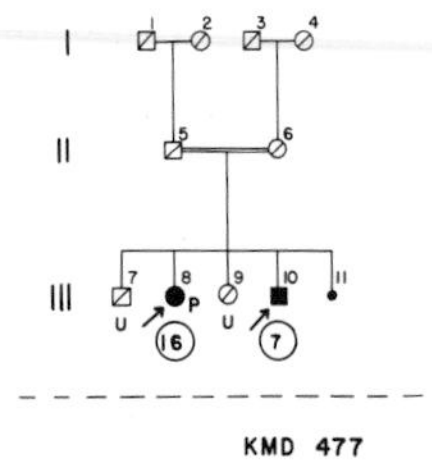

The Proband

The proband (8) was born in 1870, institutionalized at age 17 years and died of pneumonia and a fractured femur in 1913. No medical history was available for her. IQ 16. *Diagnosis:* undifferentiated mental retardation.

Grandparents

Not of interest.

Parents

Father (5) was "not up to par mentally." He could not support his family and was a cattle thief. He was a first cousin to his wife (6), a degenerate woman of unknown intelligence.

Aunts and Uncles

None.

Siblings

Brother (7) and sister (9) were unknown to the original workers.

Brother (10) was institutionalized at age 12 years and died of carcinoma of the liver in the institution in 1925. IQ 7.

(11) was a stillbirth.

Nieces and Nephews

Unknown.

First Cousins

None.

More Distant Relatives

Unknown.

Family Summary

The proband, IQ 16, and her brother were institutionalized low-grade retardates. They lived in a poor home with degenerate parents who were first cousins. The proband's parents had five children, grandchildren unknown.

Retardation of proband of primarily genetic origin (consanguinity).

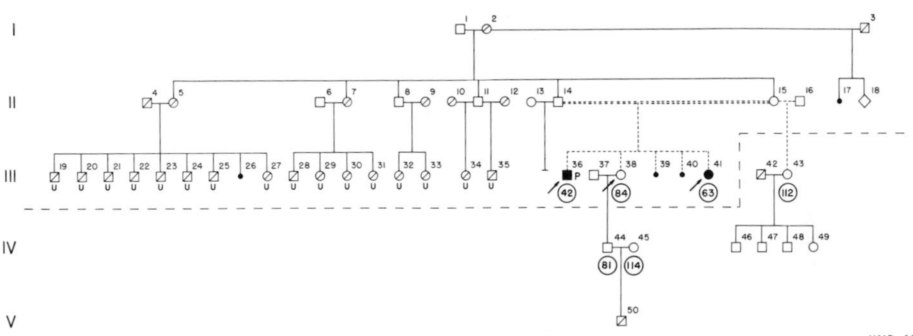

KMD 485

KMD 485

The Proband

The proband (36) was born in 1901, institutionalized at age 10 years and was still in the institution in 1961. His birth and early life were uneventful. When the proband's mother abandoned her family for another man, the neighbors complained to the Humane Society. A social worker found the home neglected and had all three children institutionalized. The proband was given a physical and neurological examination in 1950 by J. A. Böök, M.D., and John Schut, M.D. They found no stigmata and gave a diagnosis of imbecility. IQ 42. *Diagnosis:* undifferentiated mental retardation.

Grandparents

Not of interest.

Parents

Father (14) was a steam fitter and assistant engineer. He was a brother to his wife (15).

Mother (15) had normal intelligence but abandoned her family several times to go with other men. After the proband's parents were separated, (15) married (16) who was never divorced from his first wife and who later abandoned her and their child.

Aunts and Uncles

Not of interest.

Siblings

Sister (38) was institutionalized at age 13 years and paroled to her mother two years later. IQ 84. In 1924 she was discharged from guardianship when she was found not to be mentally retarded. She married a mechanic (37) who graduated from high school and a technical course.

(39) and (40) were miscarriages.

Sister (41) was institutionalized at age 5 years and discharged four years later. She was readmitted in 1923, sterilized in 1930 and paroled to her mother in 1931. She was discharged from guardianship in 1946, and is living with her mother and working in a laundry. IQ 63.

Half Siblings

Half sister (43) has an IQ of 112.

Nieces and Nephews

Only one, (44), with IQ 81. His divorced wife has an IQ of 114.

The proband's half sister (43) has four normal children.

First Cousins

Unknown. Since the proband was the offspring of siblings, the rest of the family could not be found. All connections with relatives had been broken up at the time of the original study. The proband's mother became pregnant while living at home and she and her brother ran away together.

More Distant Relatives

Unknown.

Family Summary

The proband, IQ 42, and his sister, IQ 63, were the offspring of a brother-sister union. Both parents had normal intelligence. They had five pregnancies (including two miscarriages) and only one grandchild. Because of the incest it was impossible to find out anything about the other relatives.

Retardation of proband of primarily genetic origin (consanguinity).

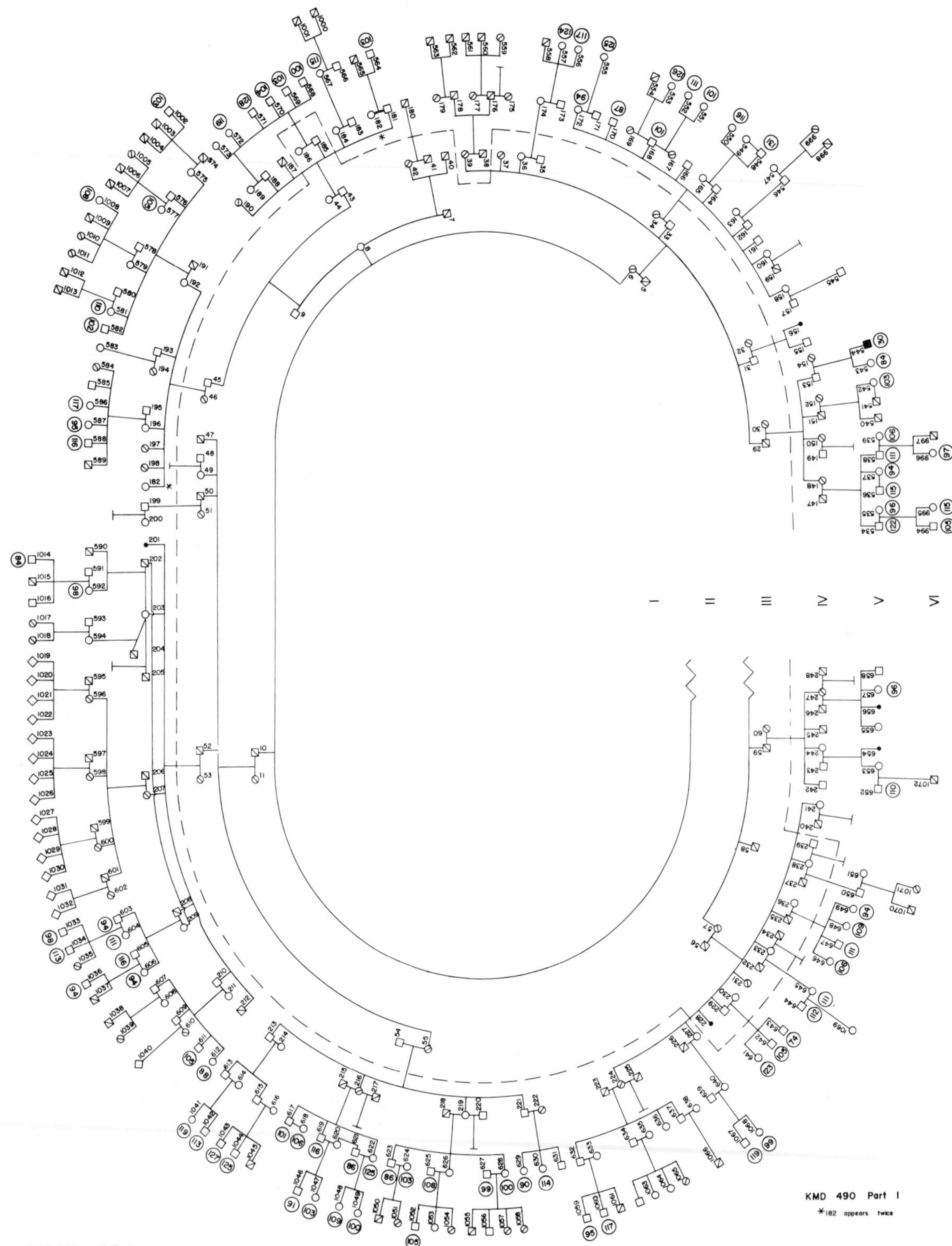

KMD 490

The Proband

The proband (119) was born in 1897, institutionalized at age 16 years and died of bronchopneumonia in the institution in 1917. She walked at 5 years, never talked well and was diagnosed as a mongoloid. IQ 20. *Diagnosis:* Down's syndrome.

Grandparents

Not of interest.

Parents

Father (17) was an alcoholic. He was retarded and abused his first wife and had a child by her niece (18).

Mother (18) was a retardate whose first husband (20) had normal intelligence.

Aunts and Uncles

Not of interest.

Siblings

Brother (120) was an unmarried, childless laborer who died of cancer of the liver at age 54 years.

Half Siblings by First Wife of Proband's Father

Half brother (89) was an alcoholic farmer.

Half sister (92) was a nurse.

Half sisters (94), (96), (107) and (116) had unknown intelligence.

Half brothers (97), (99), (100), (101), (104) and (108) had unknown intelligence. (104) married a retarded woman (105) and three of his eight children are retarded.

Half brother (102) has normal intelligence.

Half Siblings by First Husband of Proband's Mother

Half sister (122) of unknown intelligence, was married three times, first to (121) a retarded man, and then to two men of unknown intelligence. (122) has two retarded children (369) and (443).

Half sister (98) appears first as a spouse of (97). She has normal intelligence.

Half brother (125) is a plasterer of unknown intelligence.

Half sisters (90) and (128) have unknown intelligence. (90) appears first as a spouse, hence her lower number, as in the case of (98) above.

(128) has a retarded child (471) with IQ 68 and her twin (90) has a child (367) with IQ 71.

Nieces and Nephews

None.

Children of Half Siblings

(367) with IQ 71 had an illegitimate child (782) with IQ 85, by a man with IQ 60 who was sent to prison for carnal knowledge. Her second illegitimate child (783) has an IQ of 39, father unknown. (367) has had no children by her first cousin, a retarded ex-convict.

(423), (424) and (427), all siblings with a retarded mother have IQ's of 62, 68 and 50, respectively. (423) was institutionalized at age 18 years in the Annex for Defective Delinquents for incest with his sister and for arson. (424) was institutionalized at age 17 years after a conviction for arson. Their five siblings have IQ's of 82, 94, 77, 76 and 93, respectively.

(369) and his twin (443) have different numbers because (369) appears first on the chart as a spouse. He has been in several penal institutions.

(443) is in a mental hospital with a diagnosis of imbecile with psychosis. His IQ is 54.

(471) has an IQ of 68, husband (470) with IQ 110.

(492) is blind, partly deaf and has an IQ of 27. He was institutionalized at age 14 years but discharged to his parents two years later. His brother (490) is a millwright's helper with a borderline IQ of 75. Brother (493) has an IQ of 111 but is blind as a result of optic atrophy, and is also totally deaf. Brother (496) is deaf and blind (from ophthalmia neonatorum) with an IQ of 75 and is in a state hospital with a diagnosis of paranoia. Sister (499) was blind and died of asthma and cardiac failure at age 8. Brother (500) is deaf and blind from congenital glaucoma and has an IQ of 87. Both parents had normal intelligence and none of the eye and ear defects and the children were well taken care of. The father was syphilitic but two of the blind and deaf sons had negative Wassermanns (only two of the children were tested). However, it is possible that all the abnormalities in this sibship may have resulted from syphilitic and gonorrheal infections.

First Cousins

Not of interest.

More Distant Relatives

(544) is committed as retarded, but not institutionalized. His IQ is 30.

(713) is blind with IQ 75 at age 7 years.

(746) has an IQ of 62.

(783) has an IQ of 39.

(820) was institutionalized at age 8 years but discharged a year later. He threw a stone that killed a boy. IQ 83.

(832), a janitor with IQ 74, married a woman with IQ 62.

(956) attends a special school. His IQ is 52.

Family Summary

The proband had an IQ of 20 and a diagnosis of Down's syndrome. Her parents were high-grade retardates. Her half siblings had seven retarded children, all high-grade retardates except one who was blind, deaf and had an IQ of 27. Three of the others were siblings and of the remaining three, there was a set of twins and one was a first cousin to them. Five more distant relatives were retarded, giving a figure of 15 retardates in the line of descent plus three retarded spouses, a total of 18 retarded persons in this large family of 1195 persons. Two families which included retarded persons also had extensive histories of delinquency and imprisonment. The proband's parents had two children, no grandchildren.

Retardation of proband of primarily genetic origin (Down's syndrome).

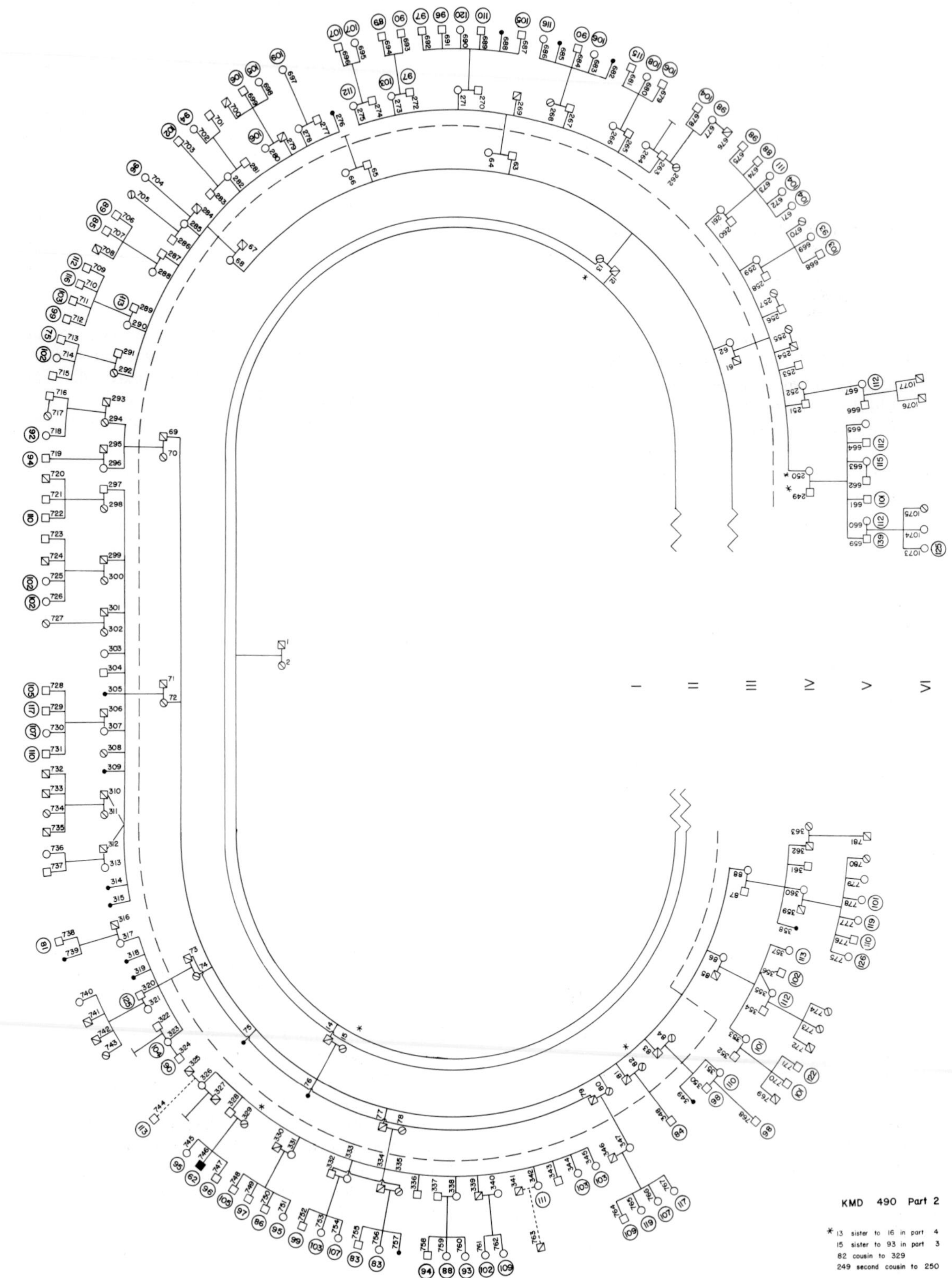
I
II
III
IV
V
VI
KMD 490 Part 2
* 13 sister to 16 in part 4
15 sister to 93 in part 3
82 cousin to 329
249 second cousin to 250

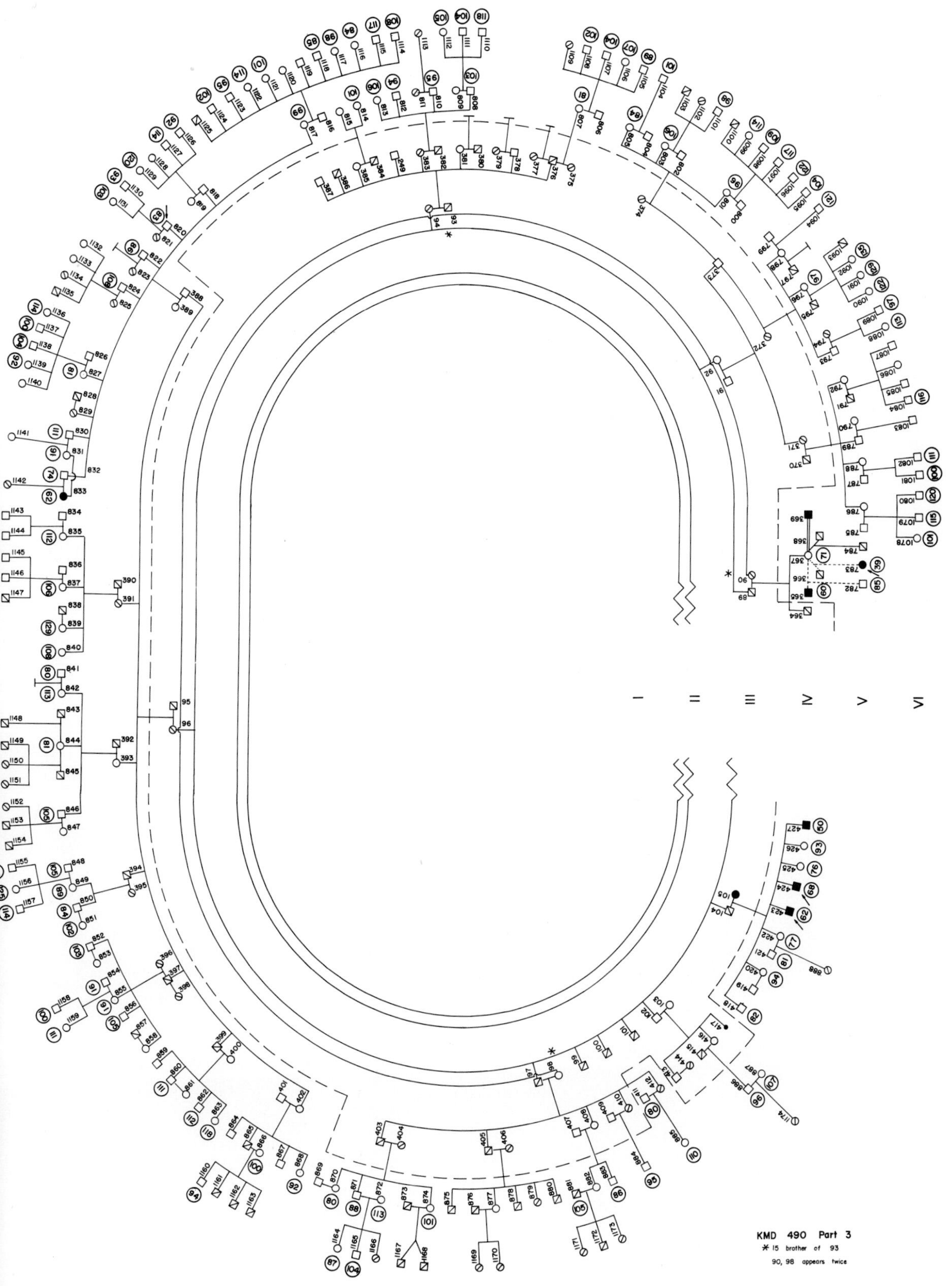

KMD 490 Part 3

* 15 brother of 93

90, 98 appears twice

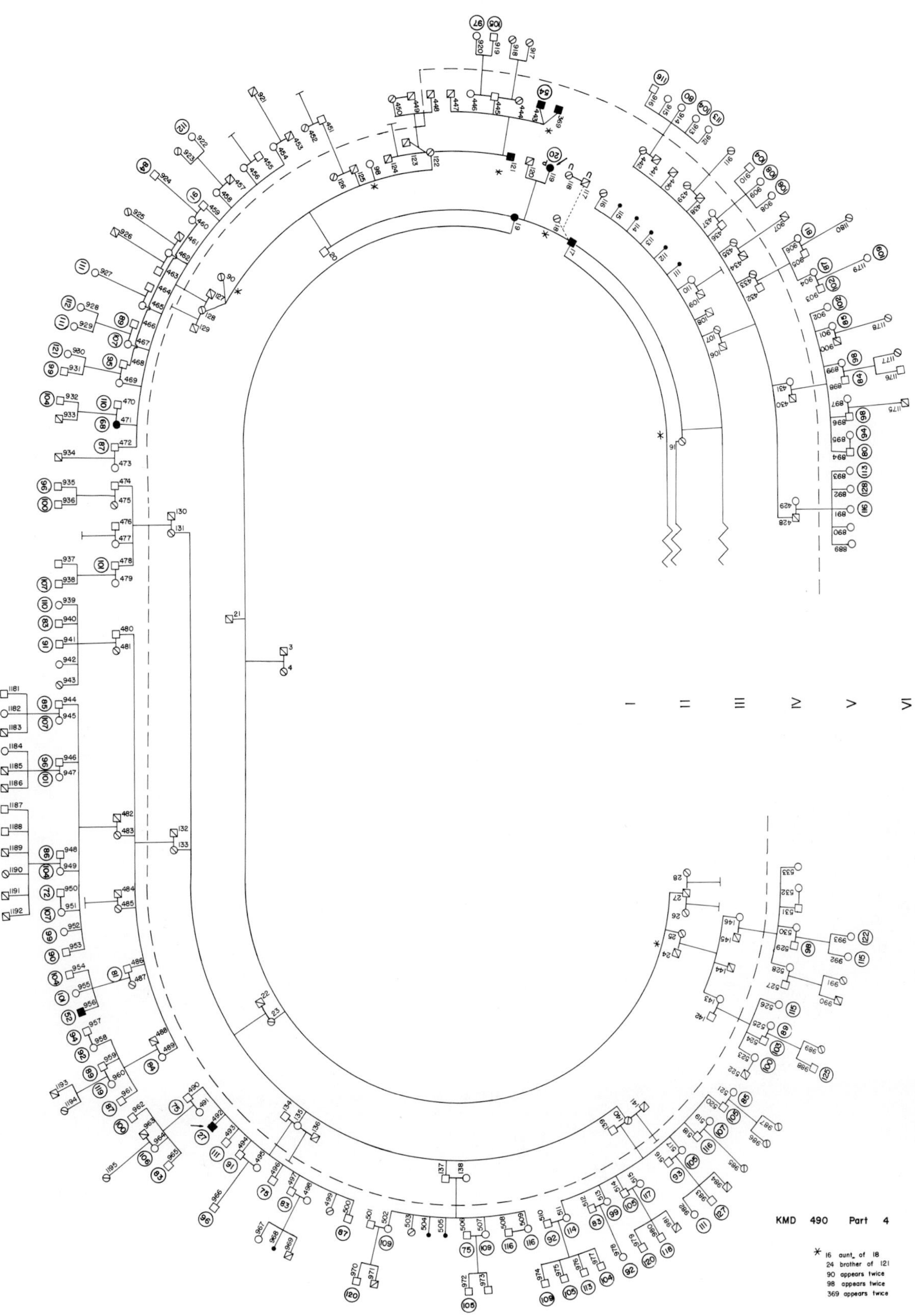
I
II
III
IV
V
VI
KMD 490 Part 4
* 16 aunt of 18
24 brother of 121
90 appears twice
98 appears twice
369 appears twice

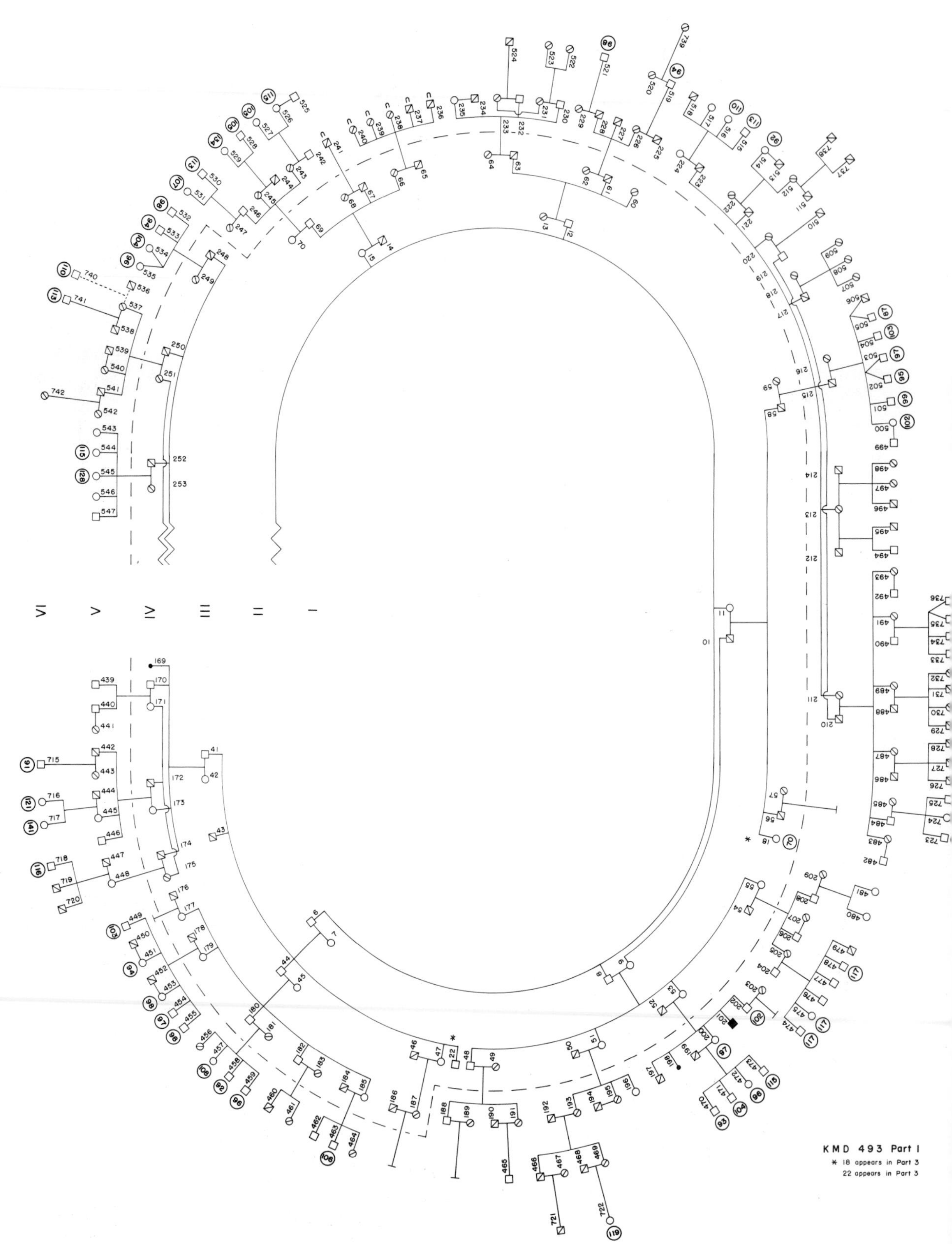

KMD 493 Part I
* 18 appears in Part 3
22 appears in Part 3

The Proband

The proband (111) was born in 1898, institutionalized at age 12 years and died of "insufficiency and nephritis" in the institution in 1915. She had poor muscular coordination, a spastic gait and was microcephalic. IQ 7. *Diagnosis:* microcephaly.

Grandparents

Not of interest.

Parents

Father (20) was described as "dull and slow."

Mother (21) was an illegitimate child and, according to relatives and friends, related to her husband (probably cousins). She died in a mental hospital but had low-normal to normal intelligence.

Aunts and Uncles

Paternal uncle (17) was married twice, the second time it was a forced marriage to his own niece (18) who had an IQ of 70 and was illegitimately pregnant by him. They had 12 children of whom two were stillbirths, one died in infancy and four were retarded.

The proband's mother had only half siblings. One half sister (32) was epileptic and retarded.

Siblings

Sister (112) was institutionalized in 1909 at age 9 years and died of bronchopneumonia and measles in the institution in 1913. She had a double congenital dislocation of the hips, was microcephalic and had a mental age of 6 months.

Sister (114) was above average intelligence despite the fact that she and her normal sister had to help take care of five microcephalic idiots during their childhood. Her husband is normal, children of unknown intelligence but grandchildren are normal.

Sister (115) was institutionalized in 1931 at age 27 years and died of influenza and pneumonia in the institution in 1932. She was unable to walk and had a spastic paralysis of spine and limbs. She had a deformed head (microcephalic) and an IQ of approximately 3.

Sister (117)has an IQ of 83, a husband and child with unknown intelligence and a retarded child (396) with IQ 55.

Brother (118) was institutionalized in 1925 at age 14 years and died the same year of bronchopneumonia. He had a deformed head (microcephalic) and general dwarfism and frailty. He was considered amental.

Sister (119) was institutionalized in 1925 at age 11 years and is still in the institution. She was given a physical and neurological examination in 1950 by J. A. Böök, M.D., and John Schut, M.D. They reported pithecoid posture and petit mal seizures, and gave a diagnosis of microcephaly and idiocy with convulsive disorders and pyramidal hypofunction. IQ 6.

Half Siblings

Half brother (104) died of typhus at age 14 years. He had normal intelligence.

Half brother (105) is a farmer and "about up to par."

Half sister (108) has normal intelligence.

Half brother (109) died at age 1 day.

Half sister (110) died in infancy.

Nieces and Nephews

Niece (396) has an IQ of 55.

Children of Half Siblings

Not of interest.

First Cousins

(18) has an IQ of 70. She appears in two generations, once as a spouse of her uncle (17).

(85) was at one time considered for commitment. Her IQ is 63, her husband's IQ is 71. Two of their nine children are retarded.

(90), (91) and (93) are high-grade retardates. (90) has five children with IQ's of 87, 96, 82, 90 and 81, respectively. Her husband's intelligence is unknown. A normal sister (96) to (90), (91) and (93) has children with IQ's of 77, 84, 74, 107 and 77, respectively. The father of these latter children is a brother to the father of the children of (90). The old records stated that (96) appeared to be retarded but her school attendance was so poor that they thought she really had normal intelligence.

More Distant Relatives

(201) is retarded.

(338) has been committed to state guardianship as retarded. IQ 47.

(339), brother to (338), has been committed to state guardianship as retarded. He is a farm laborer, IQ 51. The IQ's of their siblings are 82, 73, 93, 95, 92 and 96, respectively.

(621) has an IQ of 63.

(626) has an IQ of 62.

Family Summary

The proband, IQ 7 and microcephalic, had four siblings similarily affected, all with very low IQ's. One of the two normal siblings has an IQ of 83 and a child with IQ 55. The proband's parents had normal intelligence but were related. The proband's half siblings by another mother all have normal intelligence. The proband's parental uncle of normal intelligence was married twice, once to his niece with IQ 70, by whom he had 12 children, including two stillbirths, one infant death and four retardates. In addition to the five microcephalics, there were 12 other retardates in this family, all of undifferentiated high or middle grade. The proband's parents had seven children and four grandchildren. The proband and her immediate family were the subjects of extensive physical and neurological examinations (see J. A. Böök, J. W. Schut and S. C. Reed, 1953).

Retardation of proband of primarily genetic origin (microcephaly).

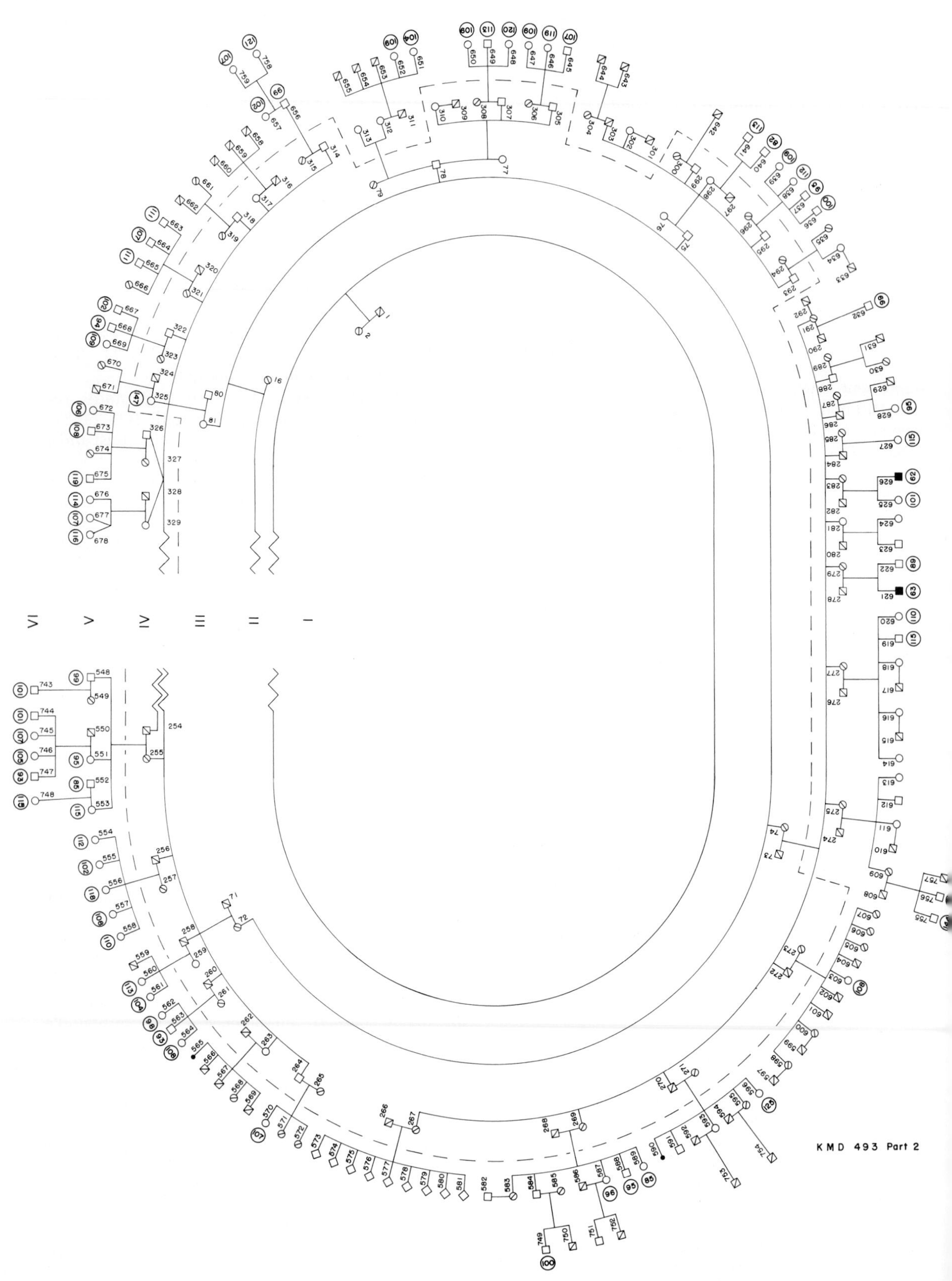

KMD 493 Part 2

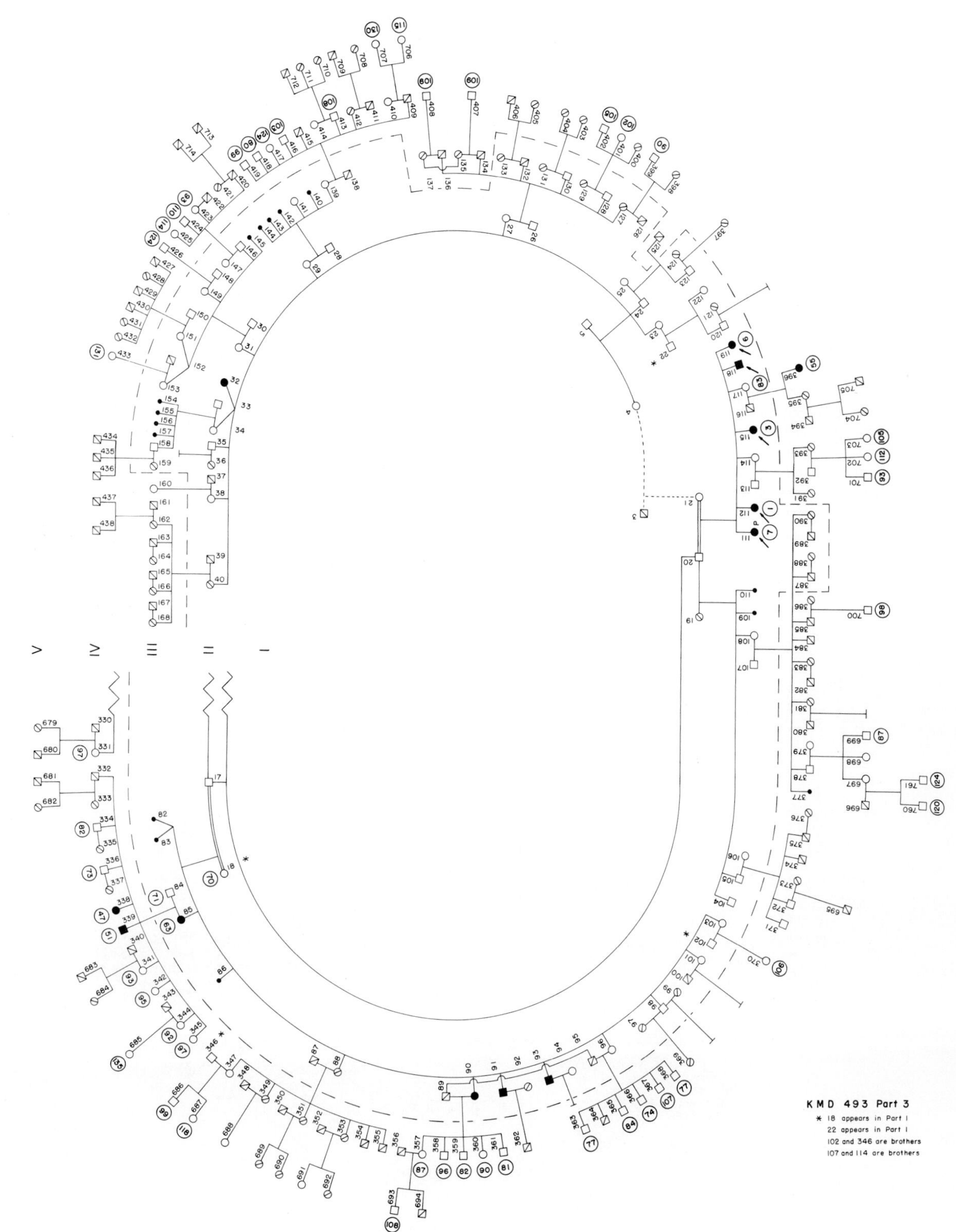

KMD 493 Part 3

* 18 appears in Part I
22 appears in Part I
102 and 346 are brothers
107 and 114 are brothers

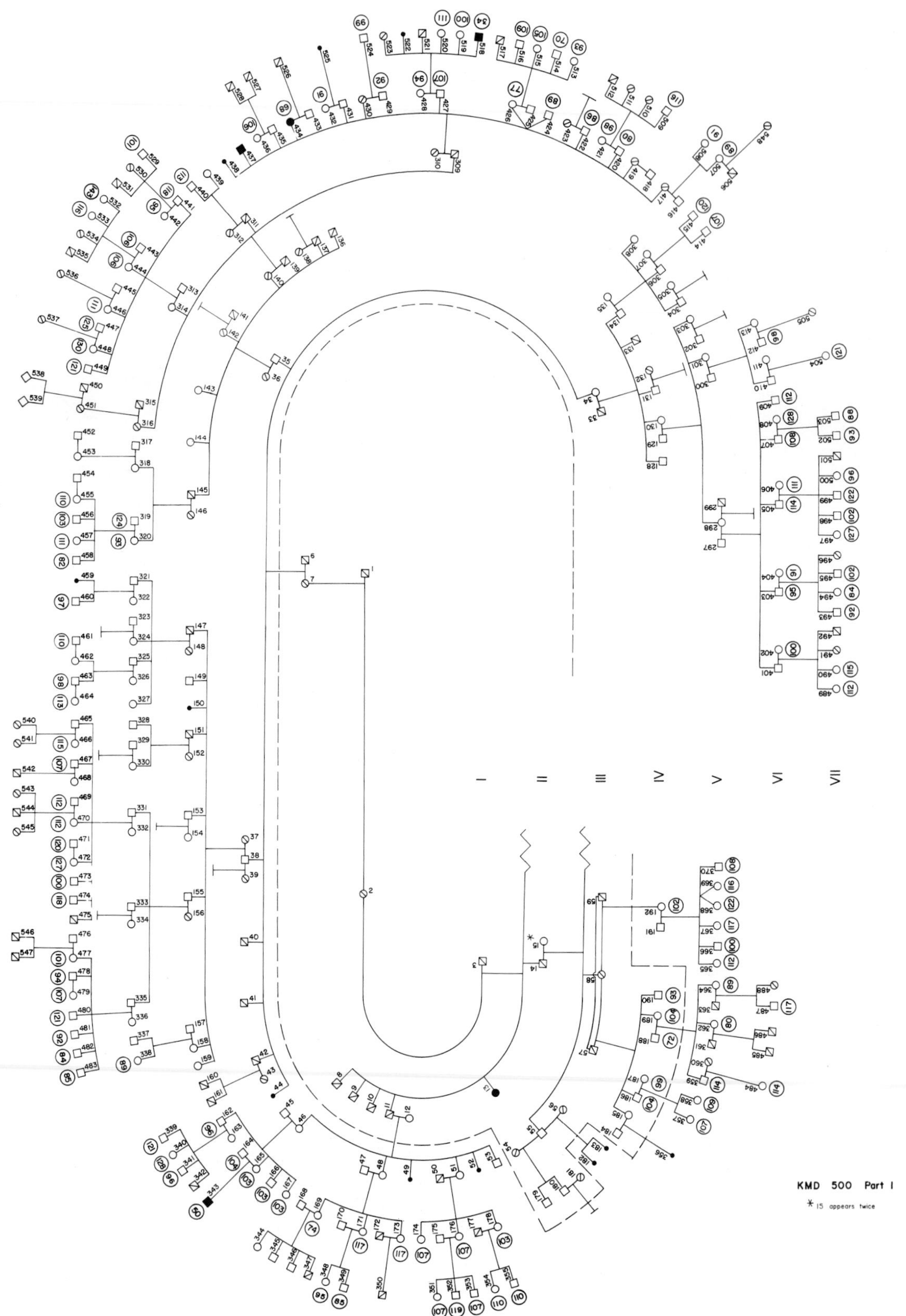

KMD 500 Part I

* 15 appears twice

KMD 500

The Proband

The proband (68) was born in 1895, institutionalized at age 21 years and died of bronchopneumonia in the institution in 1948. He did not talk well and dragged his feet. His birth and early life had no record of injury or illness except pneumonia at age 2 years. His responses to tests resembled those of an epileptic, but he had never had any symptoms of convulsive disorder and he had no stigmata. IQ 25. *Diagnosis:* undifferentiated mental retardation.

Grandparents

Not of interest except that there is some possibility that the proband's parents might have been related. Both sides of the family had the same name but came from different, although adjoining, counties in Ireland. The proband's mother said she did not think she was related to her husband, but if so, "the old people way back may have been."

Parents

Father (16) was so continuously intoxicated that the early workers could learn nothing about his mental status. He was abusive and spent all his earnings for alcohol so that his family lived in great poverty. He seldom spoke to his children but used signs instead.

Mother (17) had normal intelligence but became an alcoholic after her marriage.

Aunts and Uncles

Paternal aunt (13), unmarried, was a janitress in a theater and was retarded.

Paternal uncle (14) died in a mental hospital of senile psychosis. He was an alcoholic, abusive and epileptic. He married the proband's mother's sister (15), an alcoholic woman of normal intelligence. Their children (55), (58), (61), (63), (64), (65) and (67), double cousins to the proband and his siblings, showed none of the retardation, speech or posture defects present in the proband's own family. The children of (14) were greatly neglected and had much the same environmental deprivations as the proband and his siblings.

Maternal uncle (25) died in a mental hospital. He had senile psychosis.

Siblings

Brother (69) died of pneumonia at age 3 months.

Brother (70) was institutionalized in 1916 at age 20 years and died of heart and kidney disease due to high blood pressure in the institution in 1937. He had poor articulation, dragged his feet and had an IQ of 20. He also was reported as responding to tests in the manner of an epileptic but he never had seizures.

Brother (71) was institutionalized in 1916 at age 18 years and is still in the institution. He was given a physical and neurological examination in 1950 by J. A. Böök, M.D., and John Schut, M.D. They found a poor gait, pithecoid posture, poor speech and idiocy. His IQ is 27.

Brother (72) was institutionalized in 1916 at age 14 years and died of epilepsy in the institution in 1929. He also walked and talked poorly. IQ 26.

Nieces and Nephews

None.

First Cousins

Not of interest.

More Distant Relatives

(343) is blind and classified as uneducable at the Braille and Sight Saving School. IQ 50.

(434) has an IQ of 68, husband with normal intelligence.

(437), sibling to (434), had convulsions at age 9 months and was given no IQ score on a Kuhlmann-Anderson test, with a note "below scale."

(518) has an IQ of 34 and has Down's syndrome.

Family Summary

The proband, IQ 25, and his three brothers were all institutionalized with the same defects of poor speech, poor gait and low IQ's. No other stigmata could be found when the surviving sibling was given a physical and neurological examination by Dr. Böök and Dr. Schut. There was no evidence of birth infections or congenital syphilis. The proband's mother was known to have had normal intelligence. Both she and her husband were excessively alcoholic and there is a possibility that they were related. A marriage of the proband's father's brother to the proband's mother's sister did not result in the production of any known defective persons, although the home environment was similarly unfavorable. The only other retarded persons known in this kindred of 548 persons, with the exception of a paternal aunt, were distant relatives of the proband, one with Down's syndrome, one blind retardate, one untestable, low-grade retardate and one high-grade retardate. The proband's parents had five children, no grandchildren.

Retardation of proband of primarily genetic origin.

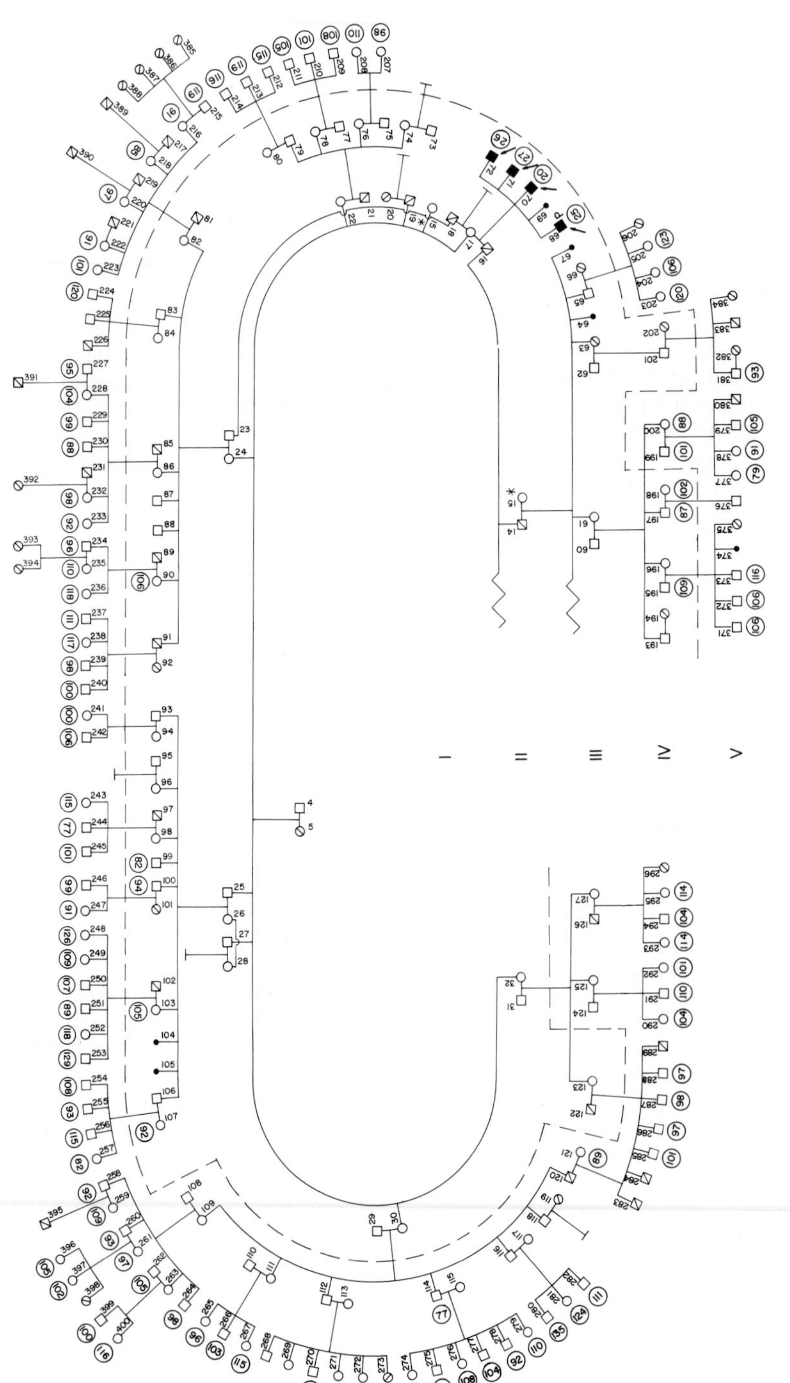

KMD 500 Part 2

* 15 appears twice

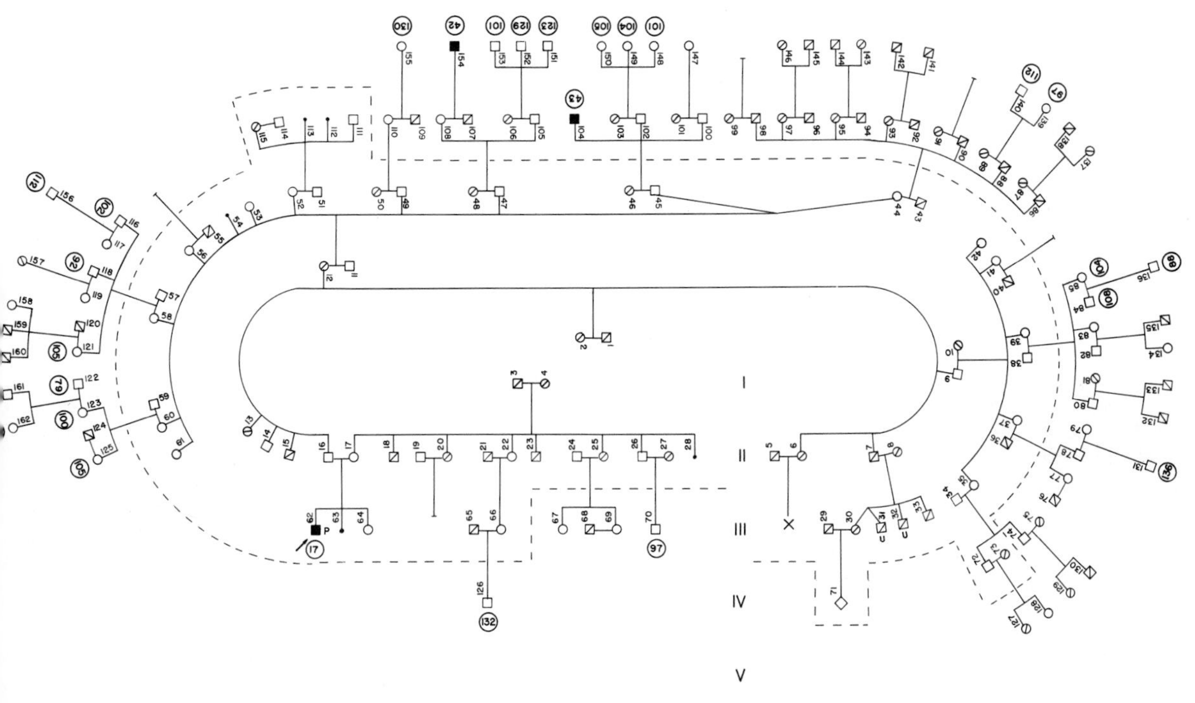

KMD 520

KMD 520

The Proband

The proband (62) was born in 1896, institutionalized at age 6 years and died of pulmonary tuberculosis in the institution in 1929. He was premature (7 months) and had a spine injury, "vertebrae not developed and membrane too weak to stand the strain." There was no diagnosis of spina bifida. His head was asymmetrical. He was reared in a good home and received a great deal of expert medical attention. IQ 17. *Diagnosis:* unknown.

Grandparents

Maternal grandmother died in a mental hospital, cause of illness given as "chronic uterine disease, cause predisposing epilepsy (probably)."

Parents

Father (16) was a successful merchant.
Mother (17) had normal intelligence.

Aunts and Uncles

Paternal uncle (7) developed epilepsy at age 22 years after he was kicked by a horse.

Paternal uncle (14) had a "crippled spine" but normal intelligence. He died at age 14 years.

Siblings

(63) was a miscarriage.

Sister (64), a college graduate, was killed in an accident at age 40 years.

Nieces and Nephews

None.

First Cousins

Not of interest.

More Distant Relatives

(104), child of first cousin (45), has an IQ of 43, apparently undifferentiated retardation. He "helps around the house."

(154) has an IQ of 42 with no diagnosis.

Family Summary

The proband, IQ 17 and with apparent spina bifida, and two distant relatives with IQ's of 43 and 42 (undiagnosed) were the only retarded persons in this family. The proband's parents had two live births and one miscarriage, no grandchildren.

Retardation of proband of primarily genetic origin (probable central nervous system anomaly).

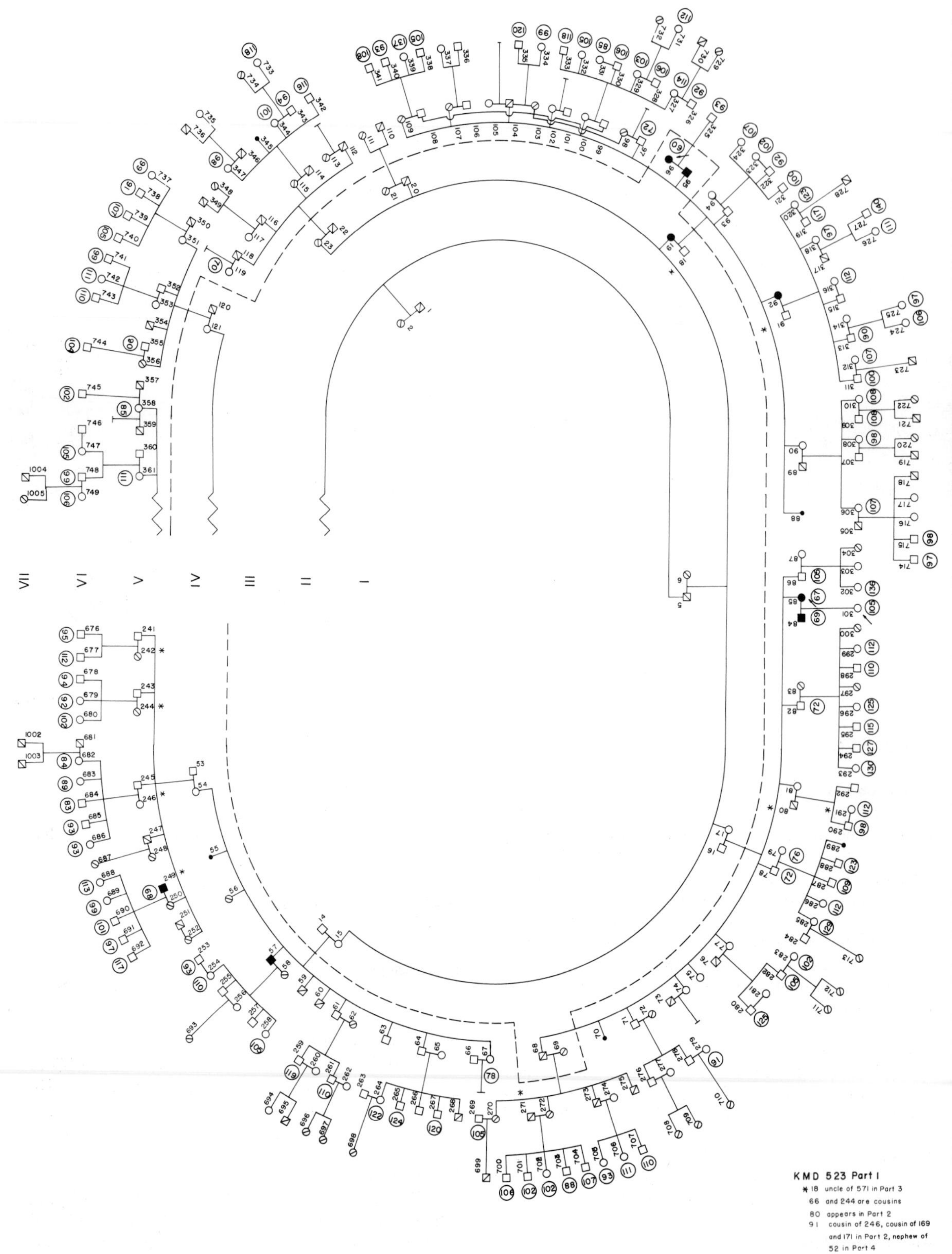

KMD 523 Part I

* 18 uncle of 571 in Part 3
66 and 244 are cousins
80 appears in Part 2
91 cousin of 246, cousin of 169 and 171 in Part 2, nephew of 52 in Part 4
242 and 271 are brother and sister
246 cousin of 91, sister of 169 and 171 in Part 2, niece of 52 in Part 4
249 nephew of 28 in Part 2
291 niece of 26 in Part 2

KMD 523

The Proband

The proband (38) was born in 1875, institutionalized at age 41 years and died of pulmonary tuberculosis in the institution in 1919. He had no history of birth injury or perinatal infection and no stigmata. He worked as a farm laborer. His home environment was fairly good. IQ 34. *Diagnosis:* undifferentiated mental retardation.

Grandparents

Not of interest.

Parents

Father (7) was a successful farmer.

Mother (8) was retarded. The proband's parents were first cousins.

Aunts and Uncles

Maternal uncle (10) was retarded. Wife and children were normal.

Siblings

Brother (24) had unknown intelligence. He has a retarded grandchild.

Sister (27) left school at age 14 years when in the second grade. Her husband's intelligence is unknown. Children and grandchildren have normal intelligence.

Sister (29) and brother (32) have normal intelligence as do their spouses and children.

Sister (31) was retarded. Her only child has normal intelligence. The father's intelligence is unknown.

Sisters (34), (36) and (37) and brother (35) all died of diphtheria in childhood.

(39) and (40), siblings who died in infancy, causes unknown.

Sister (41), retarded, married her normal first cousin. One of their eight surviving children (154) is retarded, IQ 63, and one (152) was hospitalized for a paranoid psychosis.

Nieces and Nephews

Niece (152) was hospitalized for a paranoid psychosis.

Nephew (154) has IQ 63.

First Cousins

(19) was retarded, husband normal, two of her ten surviving children are retarded.

(47) was a retarded farmer, and three of his 11 children (173), (177) and (189) are known retardates.

More Distant Relatives

(57) was a retarded carpenter.

(85) was institutionalized in 1939 when pregnant and sterilized after delivery at age 28 years. She was discharged from guardianship in 1956. Her IQ was 67. Her husband (84), with IQ 69 married her a few days before their child was born. They were later divorced. Their child (301) has an IQ of 105.

(92) has a mental age of "about eight years," husband and children normal.

(95), brother to (92), completed the fourth grade and is a laborer. His wife (96) was institutionalized and sterilized at age 20 years, IQ 60. Her mother had also been institutionalized and all five siblings of (96) are retarded.

(173) has an IQ of 48. One of his three children has an IQ of 65. His wife's intelligence is unknown.

(177) is a midget and has the intelligence of "a child of four."

(189), sister to (173) and (177), has produced a family with more mental and social problems than any other single family in this study. (189) has an IQ of 58 and is schizophrenic. Commitment and institutionalization were recommended but the county board refused to consider it. (189) then married (188) a laborer with IQ 57. They had seven children as follows:

(514) with IQ 62, wife's IQ 82, one child (854) with IQ 92. The wife of (514) had received special schooling because of heart trouble.

(517) was considered for commitment as schizophrenic after she attacked a man with a knife. Her IQ is 57. Her father refused to commit her. She married a laborer (516) with normal intelligence and has one child (855) with IQ 100. (517) usually lives in a car parked outside her home. It is remarkable that her neglected child can score 100 on an Otis test at age 9 years.

(519) with IQ 68, married and divorced (518) with IQ 67 and a delinquent. Two of their children (856) and (857) have IQ's of 51 and 69. The youngest (858) has a borderline IQ of 77. (856) is a delinquent and has been institutionalized. All three children are wards of the state as dependent and neglected. (519) was institutionalized and sterilized in 1945 at age 20 years.

(521) with IQ 72 and illiterate was forced to marry (522) a girl with IQ 65 and a delinquent who had been considered for commitment at one time. Her brother (520) with IQ 95 is the second husband of (519).

(523) with IQ 79 (the highest in the sibship) is a single laborer.

(524) has an IQ of 56.

(525) has an IQ of 40. Both these adults and (523) all live at home with the parents. In this family of seven, there are only seven descendants so far. The family of (189) has had contact with nearly every social agency in the county for retardation, mental illness, child neglect and delinquency (both for court offenses and for unwed motherhood). They support themselves fairly well by working in a large meat

Continued on page 261

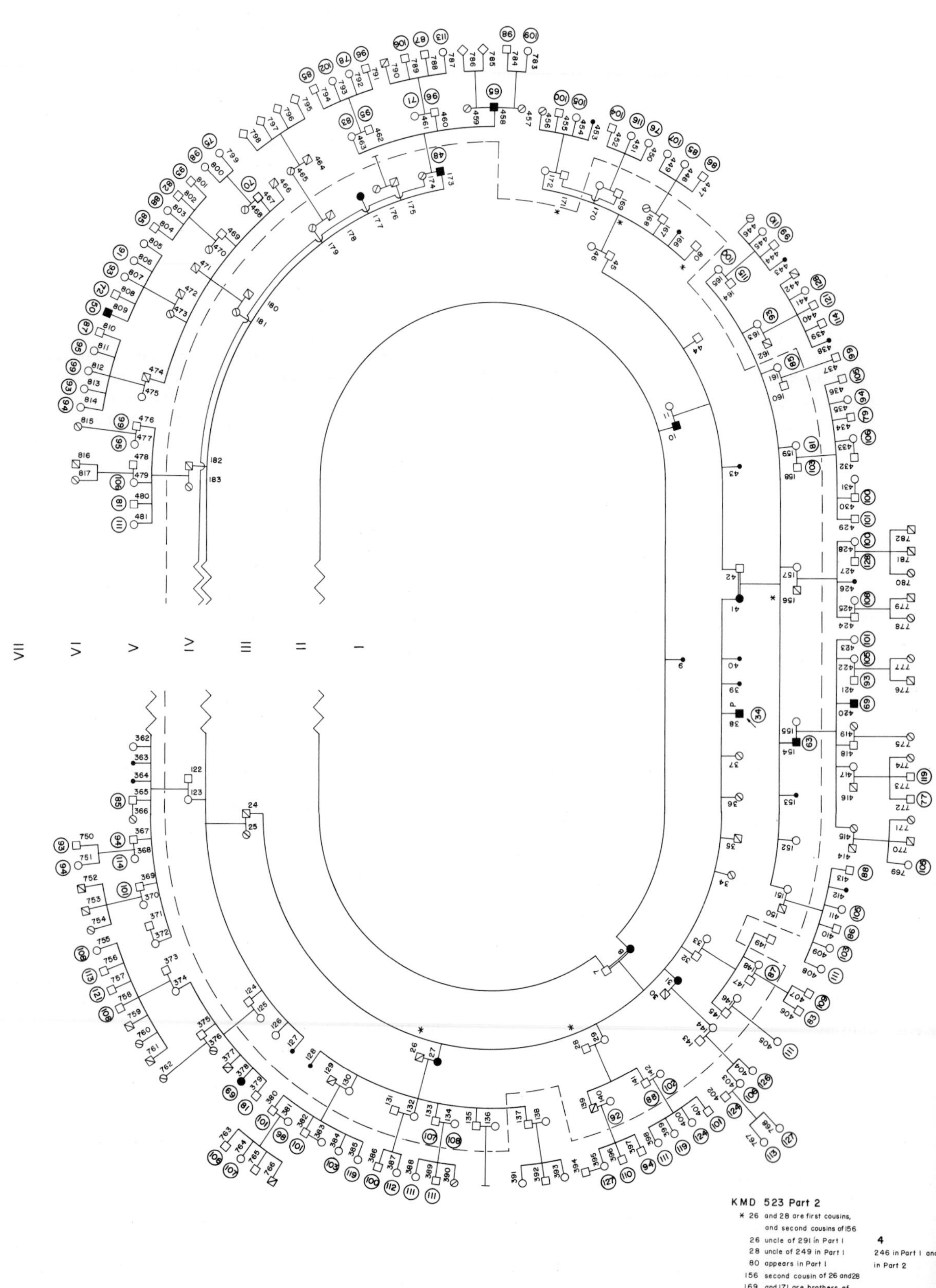

KMD 523 Part 2

* 26 and 28 are first cousins, and second cousins of 156
26 uncle of 291 in Part I
28 uncle of 249 in Part I
80 appears in Part I
156 second cousin of 26 and 28
169 and 171 are brothers of 246 in Part I, cousins of 91 in Part I, nephews of 52 in Part 4

4
246 in Part I and in Part 2

KMD 523 – *Continued*

packing plant, but continually give rise to an endless series of social problems. One wonders what will become of the two apparently normal grandchildren, (854) and (855), in such an environment.

(228) was in the second grade at age 14 years. She was married twice but is childless.

(234) has an IQ of 68, husband and child normal.

(235) is an unmarried laborer with IQ 60.

(236) brother to (228), (234) and (235) has an IQ of 64, wife's IQ 103, three children all normal.

(378) has an IQ of 69.

(420) is unemployed with IQ 69.

(458) is a painter with IQ 65.

(514), (517), (519), (524), (525) see above.

(622) with normal intelligence married an illiterate, retarded laborer 22 years older than herself and has three retarded children in a family of five.

(674) has an IQ of 63.

(809) has a speech defect and an IQ of 50.

(823) had "social promotions" in school.

(856) see above. He is apparently both retarded and psychotic. He is very much interested in sex, attacked a man with a knife and has been involved in several thefts. IQ 51. His brother (857) is "very maladjusted" and is a thief. IQ 69. Sister (858) is regarded as probably retarded by social workers (IQ 77 at age 11 years, dropping from 99 at age 6 years).

(951) is a farm laborer who left school at age 16 when in the fifth grade.

(953) is a farm laborer who left school at age 16 when he completed the fifth grade.

(954), brother to (951) and (953), is a farm laborer with IQ 68.

Family Summary

The proband, IQ 34, his mother, one maternal uncle, three siblings, one nephew, two first cousins and 28 more distant relatives were retarded, all of middle to high grade and undifferentiated type. In addition one niece and several more distant relatives were psychotic. The proband's parents were first cousins. Attention is called to the family of (189) which combines mental retardation with psychosis. This combination gives rise to an incredible number of social problems. Despite the poor genetic background and the obviously bad environment, two grandchildren score within the normal range on intelligence tests. The proband's parents had 13 children and 26 grandchildren.

Retardation of proband of primarily genetic origin (consanguinity).

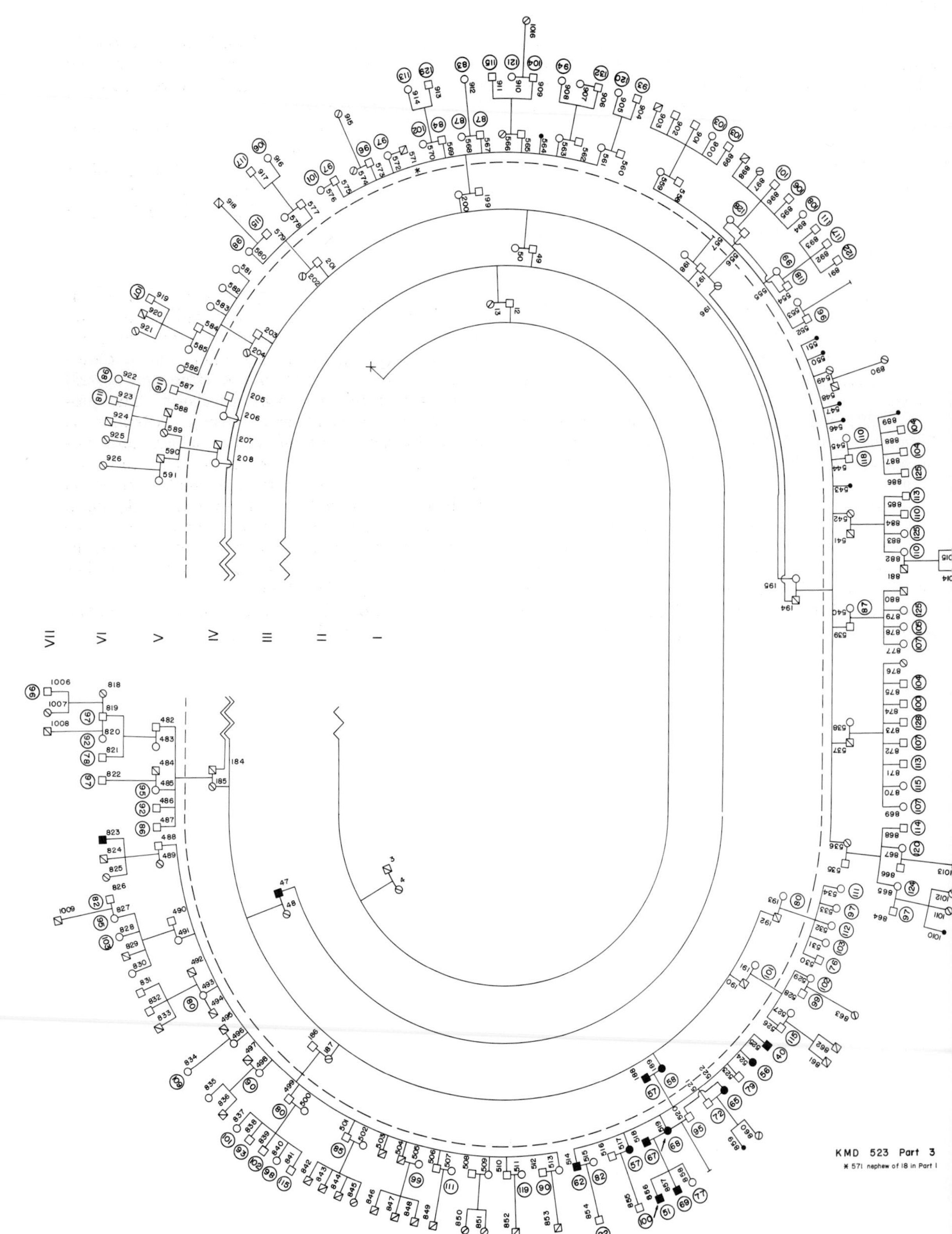

KMD 523 Part 3

✱ 571 nephew of 18 in Part I

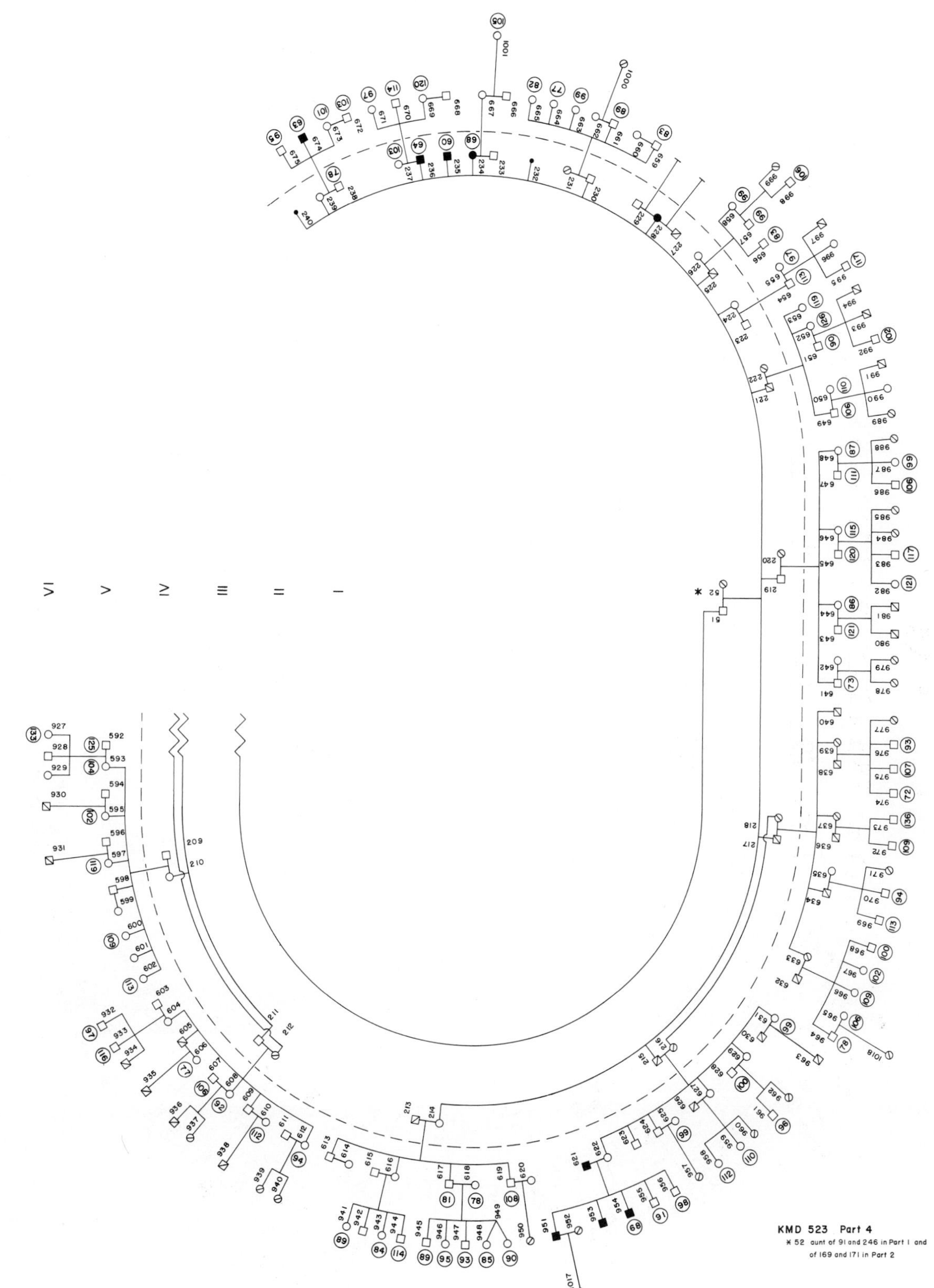

KMD 523 Part 4

* 52 aunt of 91 and 246 in Part 1 and of 169 and 171 in Part 2

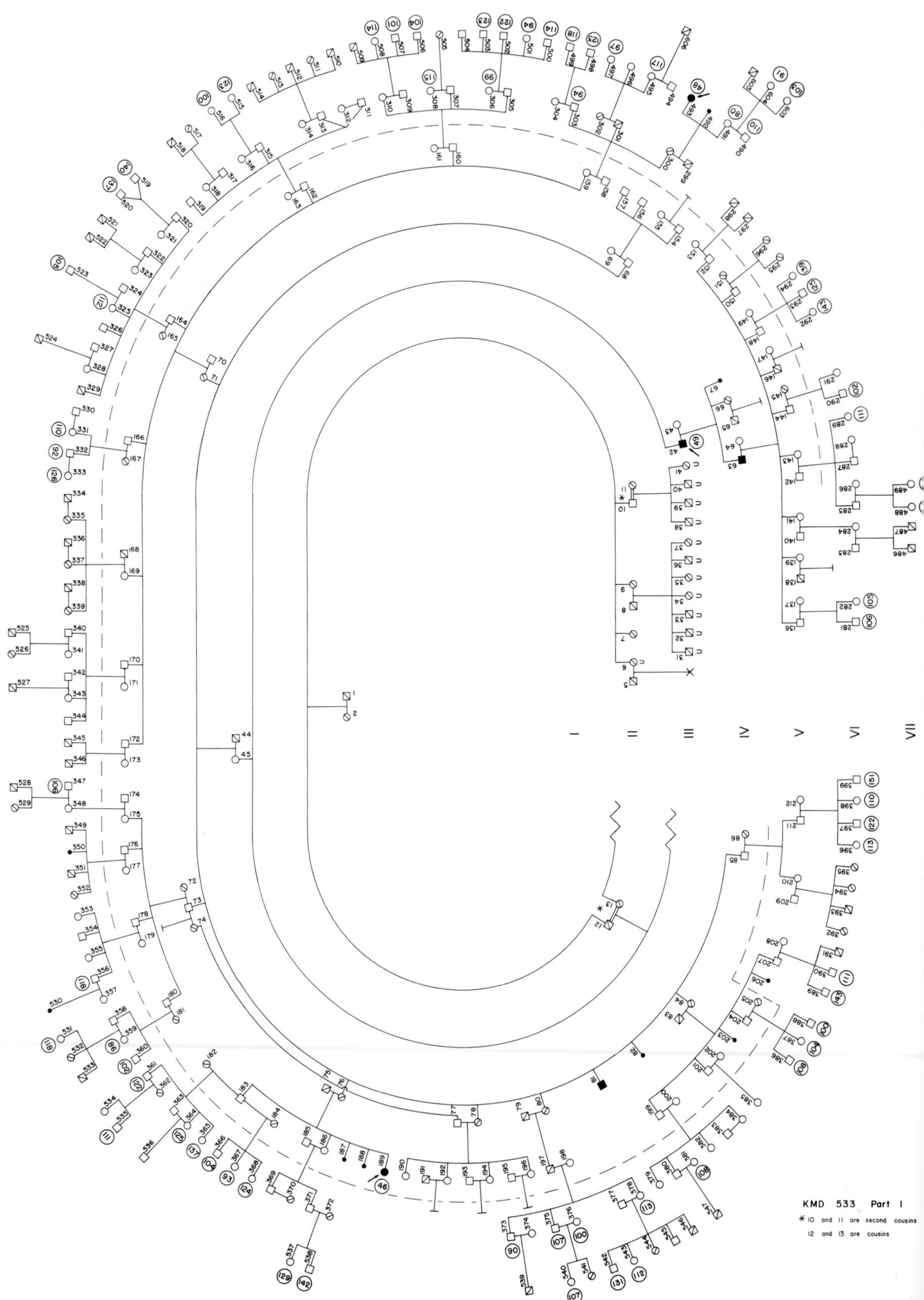

KMD 533 Part I

* 10 and 11 are second cousins
12 and 13 are cousins

KMD 533

The Proband

The proband (50) was born about 1849, institutionalized at age 64 years and died of general debility and bronchitis in the institution in 1914. There is no record of birth injury or illness. He had a staggering gait and was blind in one eye. IQ 23. *Diagnosis:* undifferentiated mental retardation.

Grandparents

Maternal grandparents were first cousins.

Parents

Father (12) and mother (13) had unknown intelligence. They were second cousins.

Aunts and Uncles

Both sides of the family are unknown because only the proband's parents came from the old home in Maine in about 1870. They lost contact with their siblings.

Siblings

Brother (42) was institutionalized in 1916 at age 69 years and died of bronchopneumonia in the institution the same year. He had a wife (43) who was industrious and prosperous and three children, (63) retarded, (66) of unknown intelligence who was hospitalized for schizophrenia after an attempted suicide and (67) who died at age 18 months. The IQ of (42) was 49.

Sister (45) had normal intelligence. Her husband (44) never went anywhere alone because he thought he was going to die. He was hospitalized at one time. No retardation has appeared among her descendants.

Sister (47) had unknown intelligence. No retardation has appeared among her descendants.

Brother (49) of unknown intelligence, married a relative (50), degree of relationship unknown. One child (101) died of "water on the brain." (102) died of convulsions at age 6 weeks, (103) and (104) died at birth, the other four had normal intelligence.

Brother (51) was retarded and was also hospitalized at one time for mental illness. One of his children was retarded, one normal, three died in infancy.

Brother (53) was an unmarried and childless, retarded farm laborer.

Sister (54) died of typhoid fever at age 7 years.

Brother (55) was a mine superintendent with normal children.

Brother (57) was a farmer of unknown intelligence. His wife (58) deserted her family. He had a retarded grandchild.

Sister (60) was retarded, child unknown.

Brother (61) was a retarded, childless laborer.

Brother (62) was a premature baby who died shortly after birth.

Nieces and Nephews

Nephew (63) was a high-grade retardate. Wife had normal intelligence as did their nine children.

Niece (66), sister to (63), was hospitalized for schizophrenia in 1916 at age 38 years.

Nephew (81) was an unmarried, childless retardate.

Nephew (82) died of convulsions at age 18 months.

Niece (95) died of epilepsy at age 30 years.

Nephew (101) died of convulsions at age 9 months. He was hydrocephalic.

Niece (102) died of convulsions at age 6 weeks.

Nephew (113) was retarded, wife's intelligence unknown. Of his four children, (255), (256), (258) and (259), three have IQ's of 85, 113, and 100, respectively. (256) died in childhood.

First Cousins

Unknown.

More Distant Relatives

(189), great-niece, was institutionalized in 1917 at age 16 years. Her IQ is 46.

(276), a great-niece, was in special classes. IQ 68. Her husband (275) has an IQ of 95 but her three children (481), (482) and (483) have IQ's of 76, 72 and 98, respectively.

(493) was institutionalized in 1950 at age 18 years with IQ 48. She has a half sibling, not related to the proband, who was also institutionalized for retardation and epilepsy.

Family Summary

The proband, IQ 23, five siblings, three nieces and nephews and three more distant relatives were retarded, all of middle or high grade except for the proband. The proband's maternal grandparents were first cousins and his parents were second cousins. Two of the three married retarded siblings had a retarded child each, the offspring of the third are unknown. There were also several cases of epilepsy and mental illness. The immediate family of the proband comprises nearly all the members of this family since the collateral relatives could not be found for the follow-up. The proband's parents had 13 children with six retarded and 43 grandchildren, 12 of whom died in infancy and three of whom were retarded.

Retardation of proband of primarily genetic origin (consanguinity).

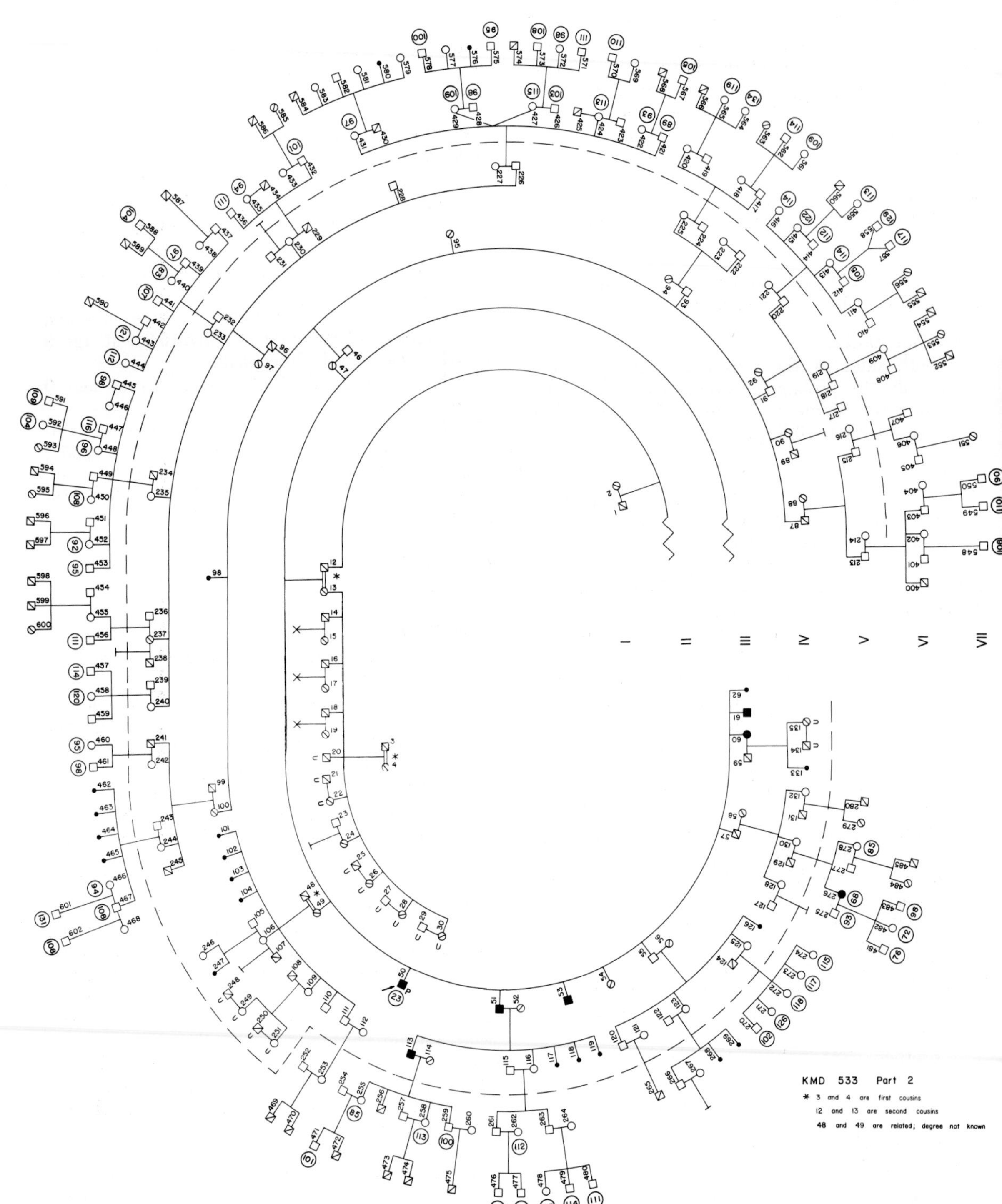

KMD 533 Part 2

* 3 and 4 are first cousins
12 and 13 are second cousins
48 and 49 are related; degree not known

THE PROBABLY GENETIC CATEGORY

There are 55 probands in this group for which the cause of the retardation was apparently some kind of heritable disorder. They are included here either because the retardation persisted for at least three generations in the direct line of descent (50 families), or because the parent and one or more children had IQ scores below 50 (5 families).

A brief family summary for each of the proband's families accompanies the 95 pedigree charts of the entire kinships. This group of charts demonstrates quite clearly the "clustering" of retarded individuals within otherwise normal family groups.

The following kinships are included:

KMD's 24, 32, 42, 51, 68, 71, 73, 74, 76, 91, 100, 126, 129, 140, 185, 186, 194, 202, 204, 210, 230, 240, 251, 252, 258, 267, 269, 289, 307, 320, 325, 339, 340, 343, 364, 380, 381, 403, 404, 408, 410, 421, 425, 428, 432, 444, 448, 464, 468, 478, 496, 498, 512, 513 and 544.

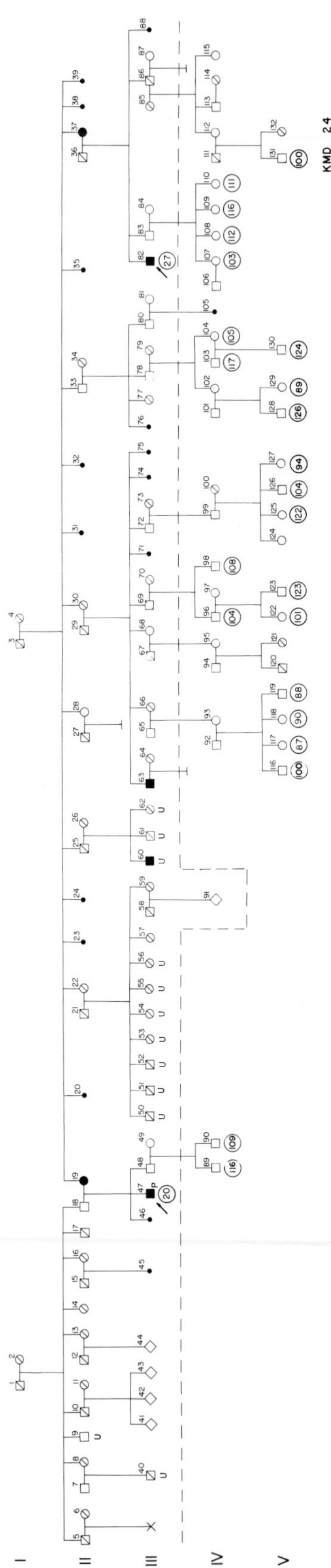

KMD 24

The Proband

The proband (47) was born in 1896, institutionalized at age 9 years, was transferred to a second institution in 1951 and died in a third in 1956. The parents reported he had been severely ill for a year between 2 and 3 years of age. He talked at 3 years, walked at 4 but never attended school. Institution records do not report evidence of serious illness or presence of stigmata. IQ 20. *Diagnosis:* undifferentiated mental retardation.

Grandparents

Not of interest.

Parents

Father (18) was an alcoholic. He abused his family and did not support them, but had normal intelligence.

Mother (19) was retarded of a "rather low grade." She could not keep house.

Aunts and Uncles

Paternal relatives remained in Germany.

Maternal aunt (37) was retarded of a rather low grade, "very retarded." Her husband (36) died in a mental hospital. Eight siblings of the proband's mother died in infancy of unknown causes; six survived to adulthood.

Siblings

Sister (46) died of "weakness" at seven weeks.

Brother (48) is a clerk with normal wife and children.

Nieces and Nephews

(89) with IQ 116 and (90) with IQ 109.

First Cousins

(60) remained in Germany. He was retarded.

(63) is unemployed, married but childless and is retarded.

(82) was institutionalized at age 9 years and has remained in the institution. The diagnosis is low-grade retardation, cause undiagnosed, although he had a history of severe illness at age 2 years. IQ 27.

(88), brother of (82), died in convulsions at 5 months.

More Distant Relatives

Not of interest.

Family Summary

The proband and one cousin are low-grade retardates. The proband also had a sister (who died of "weakness") who might possibly have been a low-grade retardate. Two other cousins are also retarded, as were the proband's mother and aunt. The home environment was poor. However, the proband's normal brother, although in the third grade at the age of 10 (two years behind his age group), managed to graduate from high school and to take some college courses. Both of the retarded mothers (proband's mother and a maternal aunt) produced a retarded child, and each had a child who died in infancy at possible low-grade retardate level—one of "weakness," one of convulsions.

Retardation of proband of probably genetic origin.

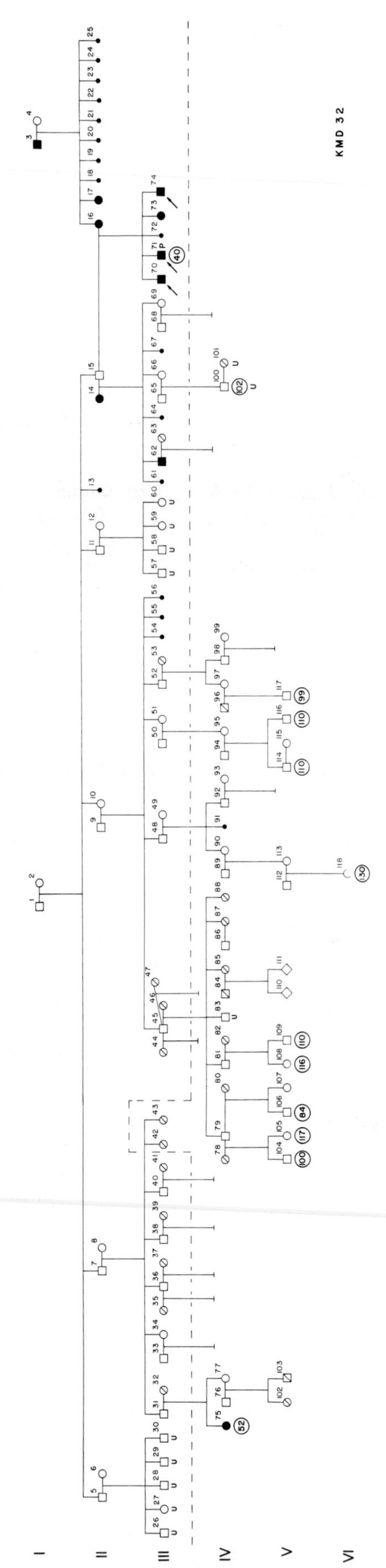
KMD 32

KMD 32

The Proband

The proband (71) was born in 1871, institutionalized at age 8, and discharged in 1944 to enter a county home for the aged. At his birth, labor was prolonged (four days) and proband was deficient in animation for three hours. He was a good farm worker. IQ 40. *Diagnosis:* undifferentiated mental retardation.

Grandparents

Maternal grandfather was mentally retarded and epileptic.

Parents

The father (15) was hospitalized twice for "alcoholic insanity" but had normal intelligence.

The mother (16) was mentally retarded and epileptic. She could not keep house.

Aunts and Uncles

Maternal aunt (17) was mentally retarded and died single and childless at age 40 of epilepsy. The eight remaining maternal aunts and uncles all died in infancy. Causes of the deaths unknown.

Siblings

Brother (70) was institutionalized for mental retardation and died of pneumonia in the institution in 1884.

Sister (72) died of "summer complaint" at 6 months.

Sister (73) became addicted to paregoric and was thought to have committed suicide at age 28 with an overdose. She was mentally retarded and also became disturbed to the point where she tried to poison various people. She was unmarried and childless.

Brother (74) was institutionalized for low-grade mental retardation, and died of tuberculosis in the institution in 1903.

Half Siblings

Half brother (62) completed the sixth grade at age 20 and is mentally retarded. He served a prison sentence for forgery. He is married, but childless, and works as a steward.

Half siblings (64) and (67) were miscarriages.

Half siblings (66) and (69) have normal intelligence. The mother (14) of these half siblings was a promiscuous retardate who came from a family with a long social history of crime, alcoholism and promiscuity.

Nieces and Nephews

No full nieces or nephews. Half sister (66) had one child (100) with an IQ of 102.

First Cousins

Not of interest.

More Distant Relatives

A cousin (31) had a retarded child (75), IQ 52.

Family Summary

The proband, IQ 40, his mother, his maternal grandfather, three siblings, one half brother and one more distant relative were all retarded. The proband was born after a prolonged labor and was deficient in animation for three hours after birth. The proband's father married two retarded wives. He and the proband's own mother had five children, four retarded and one who died in infancy. By his second wife he had six children, one retarded, two normal, one who died in infancy and two miscarriages. There is only one grandchild resulting from both marriages of the proband's father. The maternal grandfather, the proband's mother and aunt were epileptic and eight of the proband's mother's siblings died in infancy.

Retardation of proband of probably genetic origin.

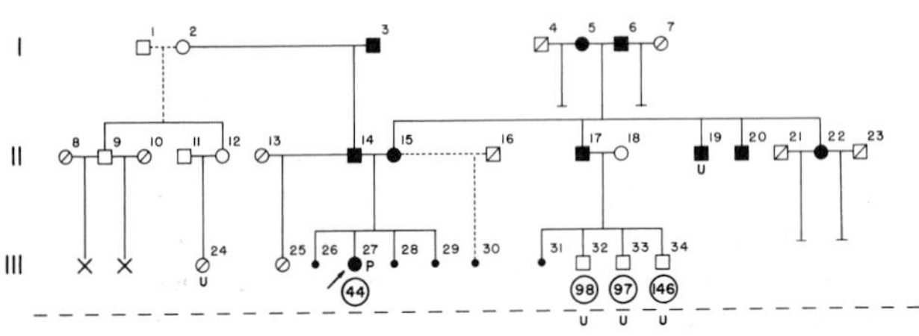

KMD 42

KMD 42

The Proband

The proband (27) was born in 1906, institutionalized at age 5 years and died of carcinoma of lungs and right kidney in the institution in 1941. She was delivered by instruments and had a "mild degree of hydrocephalus and rachitis." The home was squalid and poor and the proband was poorly cared for and undernourished. While the mother was thought to have been syphilitic, there is no evidence that the proband had the disease. The institution diagnosis was imbecile, familial. IQ 44. *Diagnosis:* undifferentiated mental retardation.

Grandparents

Paternal grandfather was retarded.

Maternal grandparents both retarded. Maternal grandfather deserted his family.

Parents

Father (14) was an itinerant, alcoholic laborer and was retarded.

Mother (15) was a prostitute, retarded, and probably syphilitic. Both parents were described as "defective almost to the degree of idiocy."

Aunts and Uncles

All maternal aunts and uncles, (17), (19), (20 and (22), retarded.

Siblings

(26) died 8 hours after birth of injuries caused by an instrument delivery.

(28) died of convulsions at 2 months.

(29) died of marasmus at 1 month.

Half Siblings

Half sister (25) died young. Intelligence unknown.

Half sibling (30) was an illegitimate child of unknown sex, born at the Poor Farm. It died at 6 months.

Nieces and Nephews

None.

First Cousins

(34) has an IQ of 146 which was taken at age 4 years.

More Distant Relatives

Unknown.

Family Summary

The social history of the maternal side of this family is a long, detailed one of alcoholism, squalor, degeneracy and vagrancy. The paternal grandmother was a normal woman who became involved with a priest and had two normal children by him before her forced marriage to the proband's paternal grandfather. The proband's parents had four children, no grandchildren.

Retardation of proband of probably genetic origin.

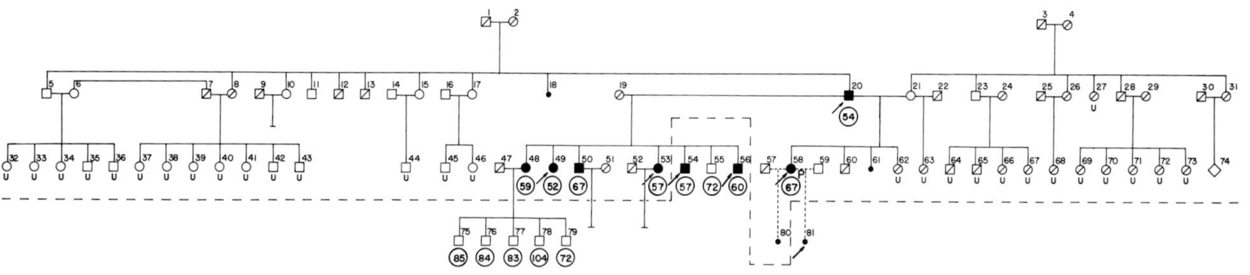

KMD 51

The Proband

The proband (58) was born in 1894, institutionalized at age 17 years when pregnant. There was no record of difficult delivery or perinatal infection. She was later discharged but after she had a second illegitimate child in 1925 she was readmitted and sterilized in 1928. She lived outside the institution for three years, was readmitted and later transferred to a mental hospital from which she was discharged in 1952 with a diagnosis of mental retardation only. IQ 67. *Diagnosis:* undifferentiated mental retardation.

Grandparents

Not of interest.

Parents

The father (20) was born in 1857, institutionalized at age 60 and died of senility in the institution in 1931. He had Parkinson's disease. He was a handyman and railroad flagman. IQ 54.

The mother (21) had normal intelligence. She died when the proband was 5 years old.

Aunts and Uncles

Not of interest.

Siblings

Brothers (60) and (61) died of diphtheria in childhood. Unknown intelligence.

Sister (62) was adopted from an orphanage. Unknown intelligence.

Half Siblings

Half sister (48) is a maid. At one time there was a petition for her commitment as mentally retarded but it was dismissed. IQ 59. Her five children have IQ's of 85, 84, 83, 104 and 72, respectively. The father's intelligence is unknown.

Half sister (49) was institutionalized and sterilized at age 22. She left the institution 16 years later. IQ 52. She had "dizzy spells and stupors."

Half brother (50) has a prison record. IQ 67.

Half sister (53) was institutionalized and sterilized at age 18, later left the institution, married and was discharged from guardianship because she was out of the state. IQ 57.

Half brother (54) was institutionalized at age 17 years and has remained in institutions ever since. IQ 57 with a diagnosis of mental retardation with psychosis and convulsive disorder.

Half brother (55) died in a railroad accident at age 18. IQ 72.

Half brother (56) is institutionalized. IQ 60.

Half sister (63) is unknown. She belonged to a different father. The mother (19) of the above half siblings had an illegitimate child before her marriage to the proband's father. She was an alcoholic and cruel to her family.

Children

(80) illegitimate stillbirth, an acephalic girl.

(81) illegitimate child born in the institution, died of influenzal pneumonia at 5 months.

Nieces and Nephews

Not of interest, except for the interesting array of IQ's in the sibship (75) through (79) of 85, 84, 83, 104 and 72.

Family Summary

The proband's father was married twice. His first wife had an illegitimate child before this marriage. She refused to take an intelligence test. She was classified as "subnormal." The proband's own mother was a prosperous widow with one child. The proband's father himself was an alcoholic laborer who was institutionalized at age 60 with IQ 54. He also had Parkinson's disease. In addition to the mentally retarded father and the proband, there were six retarded half siblings. The proband's nieces and nephews, all the children of one sister, have an IQ range of 72 to 104. The proband's parents had four children and two grandchildren (both of whom were the children of the proband), one an acephalic stillbirth and the other a child who died in infancy of pneumonia. This is a family whose continued propagation of bad environment and poor genetic endowment was effectively curtailed by institutionalization and sterilization.

Retardation of proband of probably genetic origin.

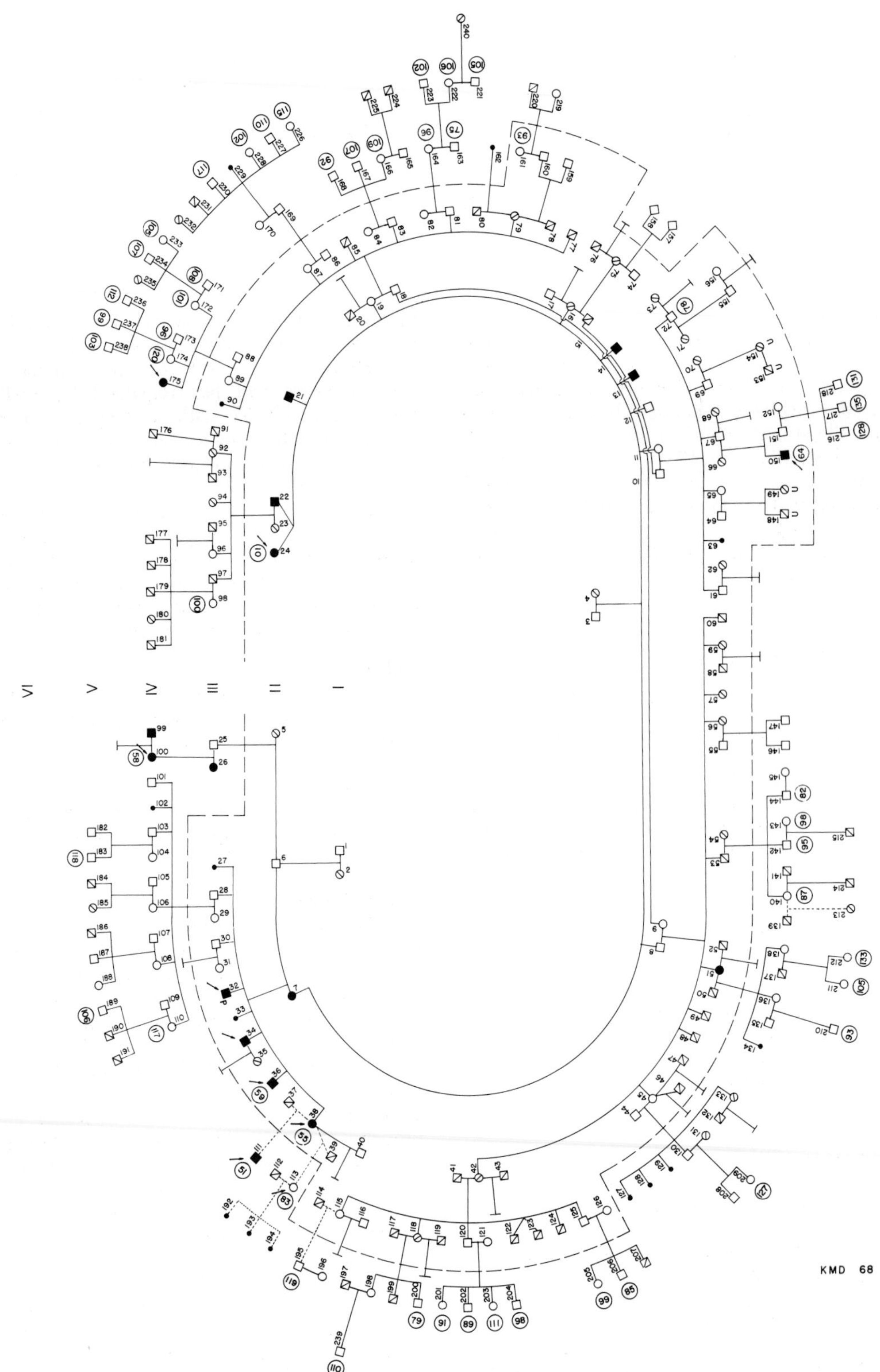
VI
V
IV
III
II
I
KMD 68

KMD 68

The Proband

The proband (32) was born in 1886, institutionalized at age 14 years, ran away in 1908 but returned of his own accord four years later. He remained in the institution until 1917 when he ran away again. He was also in a mental hospital at one time. In 1961 he was an unmarried, childless farm laborer, who although illiterate, was self supporting. The parents reported he fell down a long flight of steps as an infant. He went to school for eight years but learned very little. No IQ was recorded for him but he was described as a middle-grade retardate. *Diagnosis:* undifferentiated mental retardation.

Grandparents

Not of interest.

Parents

Father (6) was a reformed alcoholic, a successful cooper and part time preacher. He had normal intelligence.

Mother (7) was retarded, "should have never been allowed to marry." She could not keep house.

Aunts and Uncles

Maternal uncle (13) died in a mental hospital in a terminal dementia. He was unmarried, childless and retarded.

Maternal uncle (14) was a single, childless, itinerant hunter and trapper and was considered retarded.

Maternal uncle (21) was a single, childless laborer and was retarded.

Maternal uncle (22) is retarded.

Maternal aunt (24) was institutionalized as a young woman and died in the institution in 1948 at age 59 years. IQ 10.

Siblings

Sister (27) died of diphtheria in infancy.

Brother (28), although forced to leave school at age 14 years to go to work, educated himself at night school, supported his wife and children and also supported a separate home for his retarded mother and his four retarded siblings. He became an ordained minister and traveled for years as a mission secretary. He married a normal spouse and has normal children. His history is a real "Horatio Alger" success story.

Brother (30) also went to night school and became a ship engineer.

Brother (33) died in infancy.

Brother (34) was institutionalized at age 13 years, discharged three years later, served two years in a reformatory and is now a self supporting farm laborer. He is divorced and childless.

Brother (36) was institutionalized at age 14, ran away from the institution twice in two years, was in a reformatory for a time at age 15 years, and worked in a bottling firm until he was murdered in 1925 by the husband of his girl friend. IQ 59.

Sister (38) with IQ 55 had two illegitimate children, then was institutionalized at age 23, sterilized and placed under outside supervision ten years later. In 1940 she was discharged from guardianship and restored to competency. Shortly after she married a foreign born man who went to night school and is a good carpenter.

Half Siblings

Half brother (25) had normal intelligence but married and was divorced by a retarded spouse.

Nieces and Nephews

Nephew (111) was institutionalized in 1928 at age 4 years. He has remained in the institution ever since. IQ 51.

Niece (113) was born in the institution. She has had three illegitimate miscarriages, is single and works at a lunch counter. IQ 83.

Half brother's child (100) was institutionalized at age 15 years in 1933, sterilized, and placed under supervision in 1935. She married a retarded man who abused her, was in jail for vagrancy in 1948, was transferred to the institution and remained there until her discharge in 1951. IQ 58.

First Cousins

(51) is retarded.

More Distant Relatives

First cousin (67) has an institutionalized child (150) who was sent to the State School for the Deaf in 1916 and was expelled for theft in 1924. He was then admitted to the institution in 1926, sterilized in 1937 and now lives with his mother. He was difficult to manage and a "sex menace." He is deaf and dumb. IQ 64.

First cousin's child (175) is blind and hydrocephalic and is institutionalized.

Family Summary

The proband, his mother, four siblings, a nephew and a half niece as well as four maternal uncles, an aunt and a cousin were retarded. Six of these persons were institutionalized. All were middle- or high-grade retardates except for the aunt who had an IQ of 10. Two more persons in the fourth generation have been institutionalized, including a blind hydrocephalic first cousin's child. The proband's two normal brothers both managed to overcome the handicaps of a retarded mother and an alcoholic father and poor education to achieve success. Both married normal women. The more successful of the two has five adult children, all well educated, professional persons. The other is childless. The normal half brother married a retarded woman and has one child who is retarded. The proband's parents had eight children and eight grandchildren.

Retardation of proband of probably genetic origin.

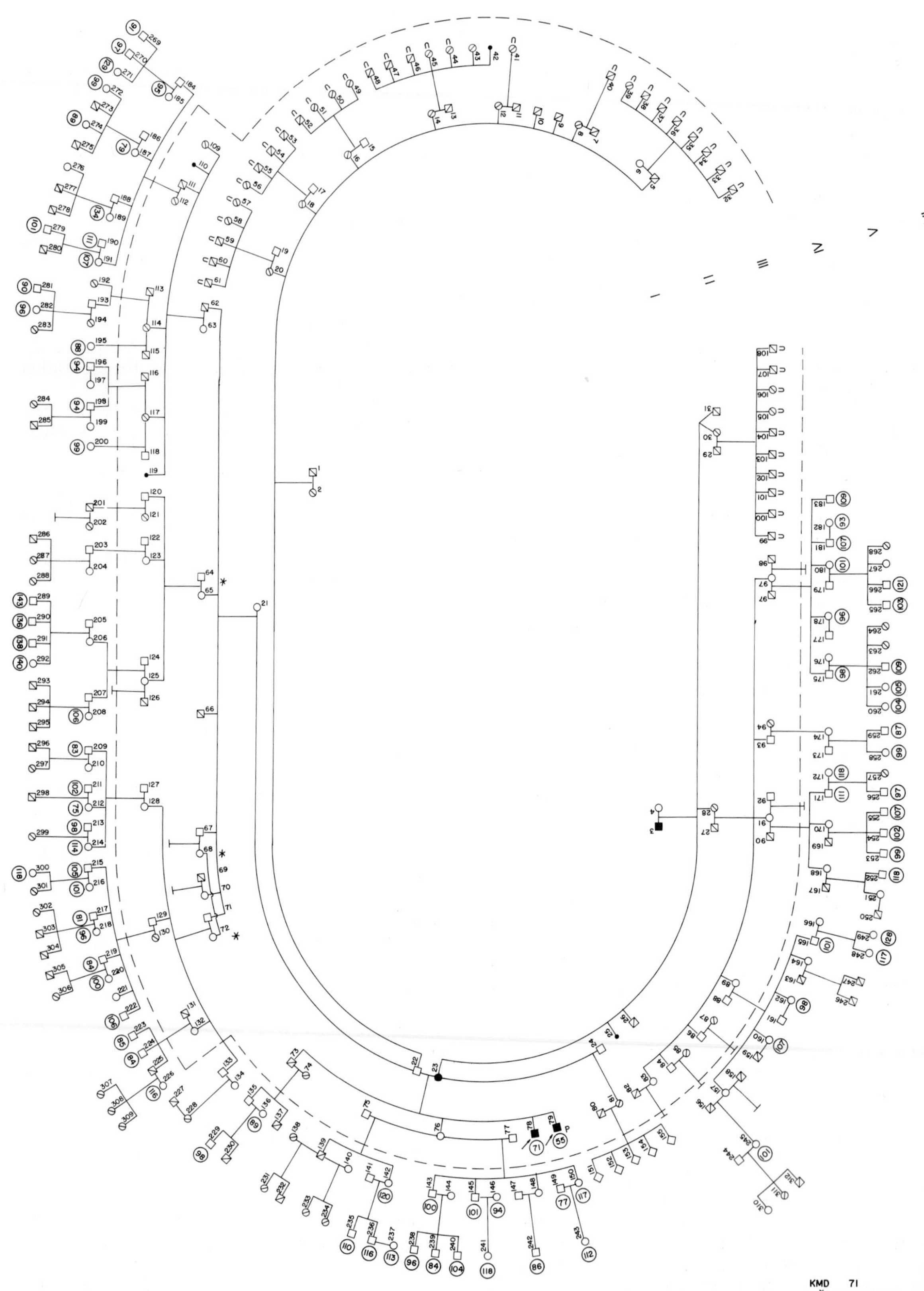
KMD 71
* 64 cousin to 68, 72

KMD 71

The Proband

The proband (79) was born in 1900, institutionalized at age 7 years and escaped in 1922. When last heard of he was single and was in the Army in World War II. He had a high, narrow palate and left-sided scoliosis. IQ 55. *Diagnosis:* undifferentiated mental retardation.

Grandparents

Maternal grandfather was retarded.

Parents

Father (22) had normal intelligence. He was a clerk.

Mother (23) was retarded.

Aunts and Uncles

Not of interest except that maternal aunt (25) died of "brain trouble" at age 2 years.

Siblings

Brother (73) was a farmer of unknown intelligence, who committed suicide.

Sister (76) had normal intelligence. No retardates have appeared among her descendants.

Brother (78) was institutionalized at age 9 years, escaped at age 24 years in 1922 and was a single and childless farm laborer. He now lives in a rest home. He has right-sided scoliosis. IQ 71.

Half Siblings

Two half brothers (62) and (66) of unknown intelligence.

Two normal half sisters (65) and (70).

Two normal half brothers (67) and (71).

One half sister (81) of unknown intelligence.

Nieces and Nephews

Not of interest.

Children of Half Siblings

Not of interest.

First Cousins

Not of interest.

More Distant Relatives

Not of interest.

Family Summary

The proband, his brother, mother and maternal grandfather were retarded. Both the proband and his brother had similar stigmata of scoliosis. The proband and his siblings were reared in an orphanage and in foster homes after the death of their mother. The proband's parents had four children and eight grandchildren.

Retardation of proband of probably genetic origin.

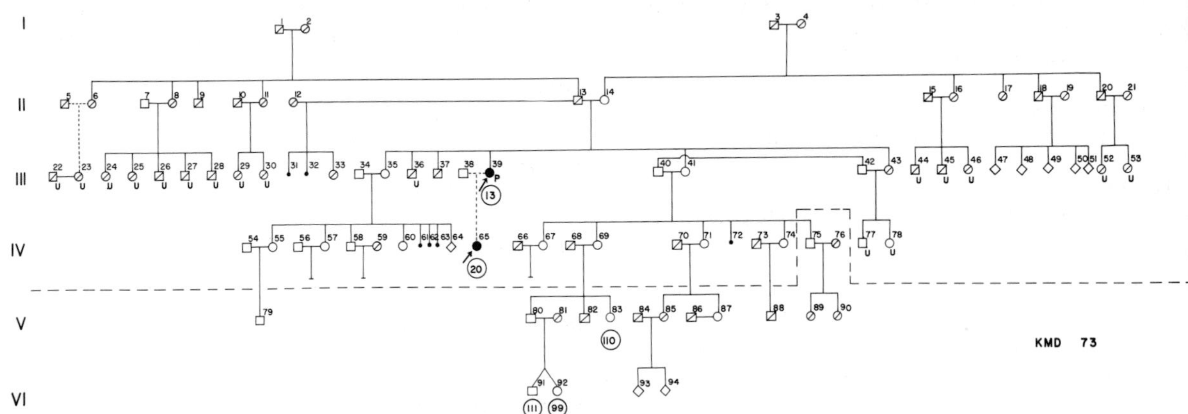
I
II
III
IV
V
VI
KMD 73

KMD 73

The Proband

The proband (39) was born in 1877, institutionalized at age 26 years and died of fracture of the femur in the institution in 1930. She had no speech. There was no history of birth injury or perinatal infection. She had an illegitimate child (65) who was also retarded. IQ 13. *Diagnosis:* undifferentiated mental retardation.

Grandparents

Not of interest.

Parents

Father (13), unknown intelligence.

Mother (14) had normal intelligence.

Siblings

Sisters (35) and (41) both normal, married normal men and had normal children.

Brother (36) is unknown to relatives.

Brother (37) died single and childless.

Sister (43) died of appendicitis at 25 years. Intelligence unknown. Her husband returned to Sweden with their two children.

Half Siblings

Half siblings (31), (32), (33). First two died in infancy, third died at age 24 years.

Child

(65) was institutionalized at 2 months, transferred to a second institution in 1935 at age 32 and died there of tuberculosis in 1939. She had a harelip and IQ 20. Her father had normal intelligence.

Nieces and Nephews

Not of interest.

First Cousins

Not of interest.

More Distant Relatives

Not of interest.

Family Summary

The proband and her illegitimate child were low-grade retardates, IQ's 13 and 20, respectively. The proband's retarded child had a normal father. The proband's parents had six children and 17 known grandchildren.

Retardation of proband of probably genetic origin.

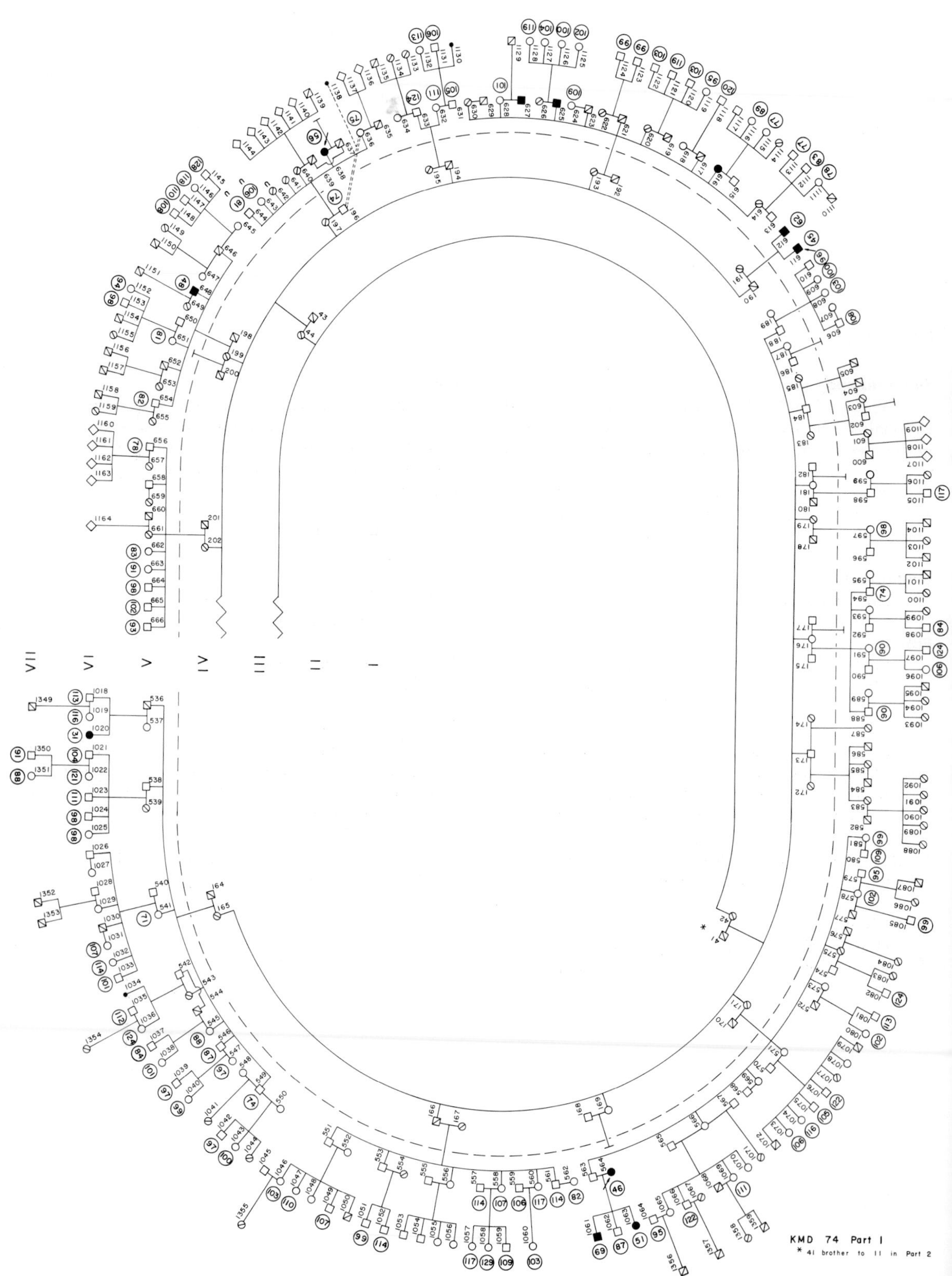
KMD 74 Part I
* 41 brother to 11 in Part 2

KMD 74

The Proband

The proband (153) was born in 1899, institutionalized at age 12 years, moved to a mental hospital in 1923 and was still in that institution in 1961. Her birth and early development were uneventful. She apparently developed a psychosis as a young adult. She had no stigmata. The mental hospital reported a diagnosis of mental deficiency with psychosis. IQ 63. *Diagnosis:* undifferentiated mental retardation with subsequent psychosis.

Grandparents

Paternal grandfather was retarded and had senile dementia for "many years."

Maternal grandmother (4) was retarded. She had four husbands, three of whom she divorced.

Parents

Father (34) was a retarded indigent laborer who was hospitalized following an "attack" of hallucinations.

Mother (35) was institutionalized at age 36 years. She was epileptic with IQ 67.

Aunts and Uncles

Paternal uncle (8) was an alcoholic and retarded. He married his first cousin (9) of unknown intelligence and had 13 children, one (56) known to have been retarded. Only five of the 13 reproduced.

Paternal aunt (20) was "very peculiar and eccentric."

Paternal aunt (27) was retarded.

Paternal uncle (28) was an alcoholic, retarded and subject to epileptoid attacks.

Paternal uncle (32) "became unbalanced" and attempted suicide.

The proband's mother had no full siblings, only three half sibs, one with normal intelligence and no mental illness and two who died young.

Siblings

Brother (154) was tried in six boarding homes but was sent to a reformatory at age 16 years for "incorrigibility, larceny and vile language." After his release he went to work on a farm. Relatives think he was killed in the service. IQ 78.

Brother (155) died of tuberculosis at age 5 years.

Sister (156) died of heart trouble at 13 months.

Sister (157) was institutionalized at age 17 and has remained in the institution ever since. She was given a physical and neurological examination by J. A. Böök, M.D., and John Schut, M.D. in 1950. They found no stigmata and reported a diagnosis of moron. A psychologist's report in 1958 stated she worked well but could not adjust to the outside for she is suspicious and distrustful of anything new. The institution diagnosis is moron. IQ 70.

Nieces and Nephews

Unknown, but it is likely there are none. If so, they would be only the children of the proband's brother (154) who relatives think was killed in action.

First Cousins

Maternal ones unknown.

(47) has been imprisoned for grand larceny twice. IQ 88.

(56) was retarded. She died single at age 18 years.

(73) is retarded, but had two normal wives. Of his nine children, all married, only two have reproduced. None is retarded.

(75) is retarded, wife of unknown intelligence. All of his children are apparently normal.

(105) was retarded.

More Distant Relatives

(392) was imprisoned for theft and had an IQ of 58. His wife has normal intelligence but one of his four children, (874), has an IQ of 62 and one, (679), has a borderline IQ of 78.

(394), brother to (392), has an IQ of 56, wife of unknown intelligence, and children with IQ's of 75 to 97.

(398), sister to (392) and (394), died of "spasms" at age 1 year.

(399), brother to the three preceding, was retarded and had a retarded son.

(422) has an IQ of 67, wife with IQ 94 and has a diagnosis of "symptoms of early nervous disorder."

(480) attends a school for the retarded. IQ 71.

(563) completed the tenth grade but has been hospitalized twice, once with a diagnosis of manic depressive, the second time with a diagnosis of schizophrenia. He married (564) with an IQ of 46. She has been institutionalized. Two of their three children, (1061) and (1063), are retarded. (564) also had two illegitimate children by other men.

(611) was institutionalized at age 8 years and died in the institution at age 20. He had progressive muscular dystrophy and an IQ of 45.

(612), brother to (611), died at age 19 years just before his institutionalization. He had progressive muscular dystrophy and an IQ of 62.

(616) completed the fifth grade at 16 years.

(625), brother to (616), is a high-grade retardate.

Continued on page 283

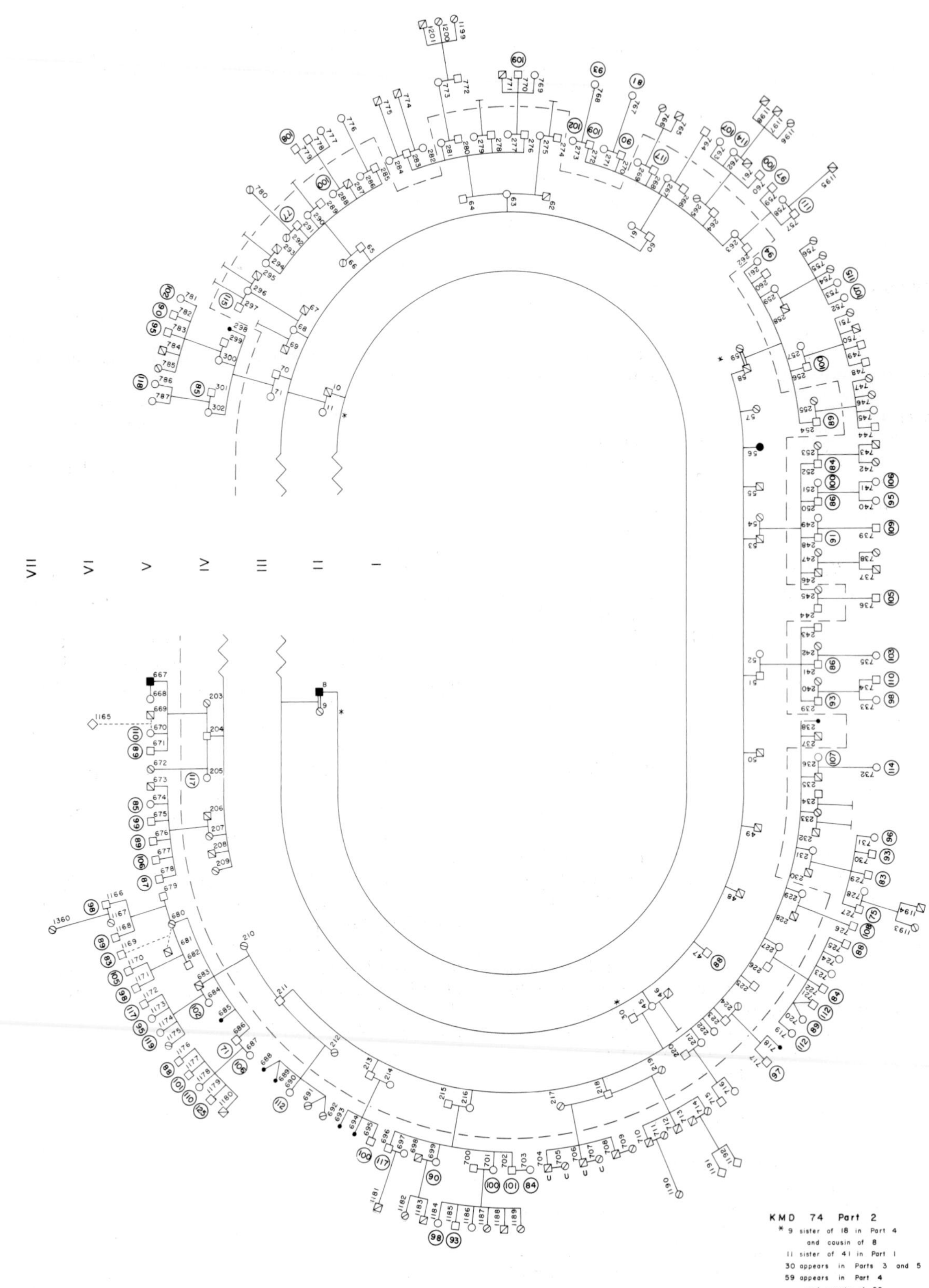

KMD 74 Part 2

* 9 sister of 18 in Part 4 and cousin of 8
11 sister of 41 in Part 1
30 appears in Parts 3 and 5
59 appears in Part 4 and cousin of 58

KMD 74 – *Continued*

(628), sister to (616) and (625), has an IQ of 101 but married a retarded laborer.

(636), IQ 75, had a child by her father (196), IQ 74. This child (1138) was a stillbirth.

(638) was institutionalized at age 5 years, sterilized at age 23 years, IQ 56.

(648) is a carpenter's helper with IQ 48.

(667) is a high-grade retardate.

(820), with IQ 120, married a retarded farmer.

(874) was imprisoned twice for grand larceny and has an IQ of 62.

(899) has an IQ of 68.

(903) has an IQ of 68.

(913) tested at the fourth grade level at the age of 12 years.

(959) is institutionalized with IQ 55. No diagnosis was available.

(1020) has an IQ of 31 with no diagnosis.

(1061) and (1063), siblings, have IQ's of 69 and 51, respectively.

(1311) has an IQ of 65.

(1331), an illegitimate child, is institutionalized with an IQ of 12 and a diagnosis of congenital cerebral spastic paraplegia (defective fetal development due to other causes); epilepsy (generalized seizures, petit mal).

Family Summary

The proband, IQ 63 and with an associated psychosis, her paternal grandfather, maternal grandmother, both her parents and one sibling were retarded, all of high grade. In addition, one paternal aunt, two paternal uncles, four first cousins and 20 more distant relatives were retarded. Two of these latter persons had progressive muscular dystrophy and one has spastic paraplegia and epilepsy. The retardation in the proband's own family was not transmitted because of the institutionalizations. The other cases of retardation are not randomly distributed among the descendants but appear in constellations, for example, in the grandchildren of (44) and in the children, grandchildren and great-grandchildren of (92). This family is chiefly comprised of many poorly educated, low social class persons, especially in the older generations. There were few high school graduates and almost no college students, although the family level is rising somewhat in the later generations. The proband's parents had five children and no known grandchildren.

Retardation of proband of probably genetic origin.

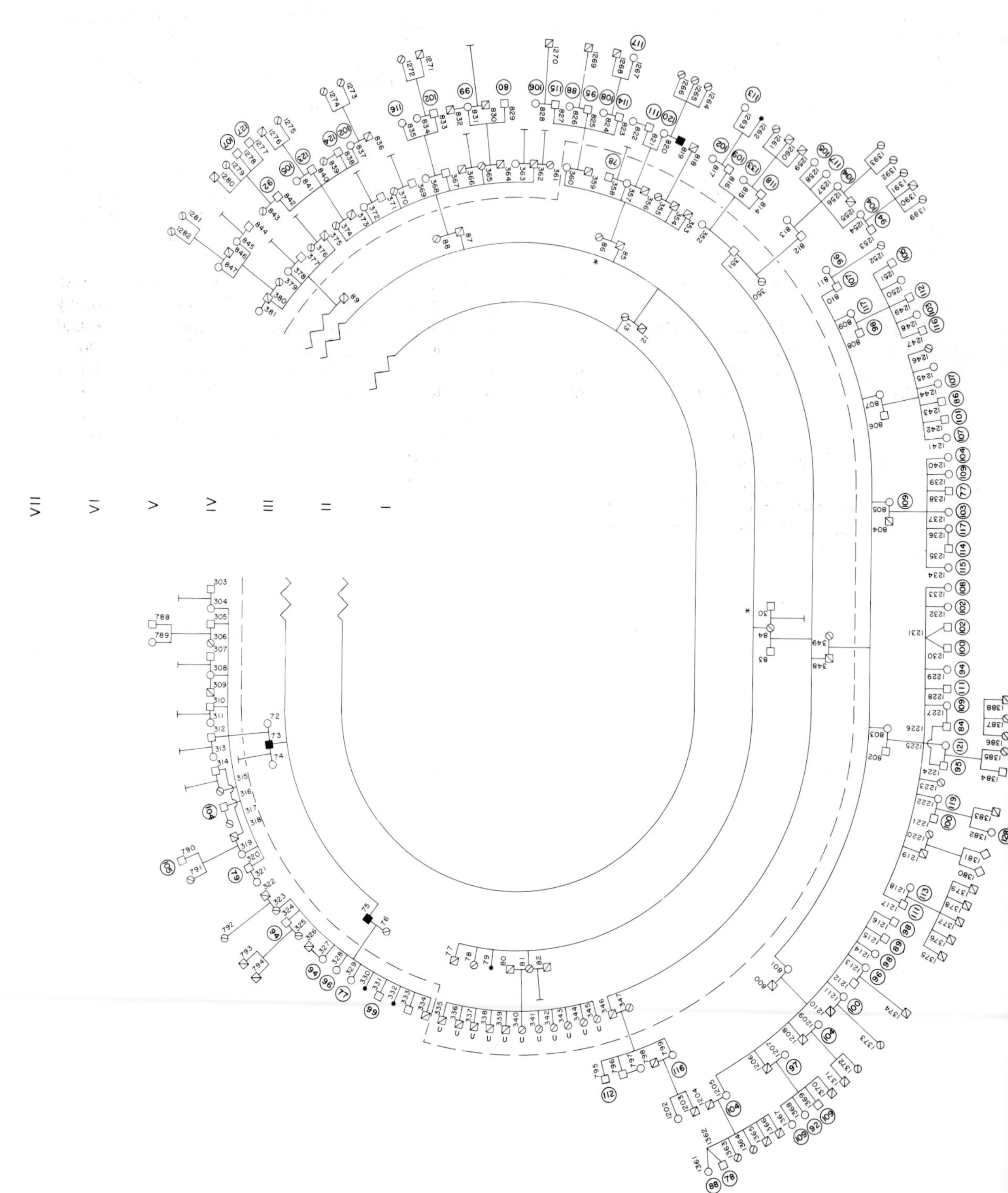

KMD 74 Part 3
* 30 appears in Parts 2 and 5
86 daughter of 91 in Part 4

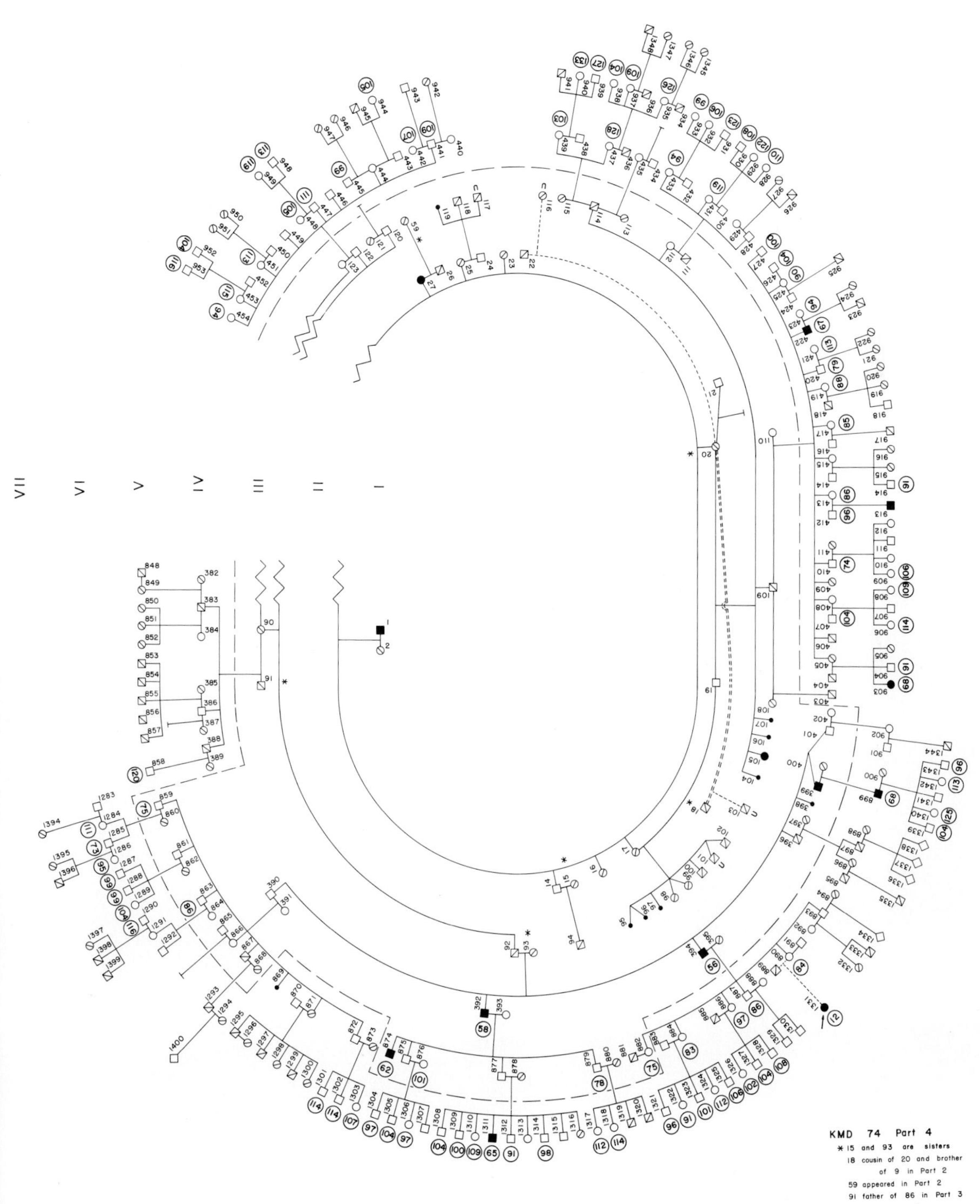

KMD 74 Part 4
* 15 and 93 are sisters
18 cousin of 20 and brother of 9 in Part 2
59 appeared in Part 2
91 father of 86 in Part 3

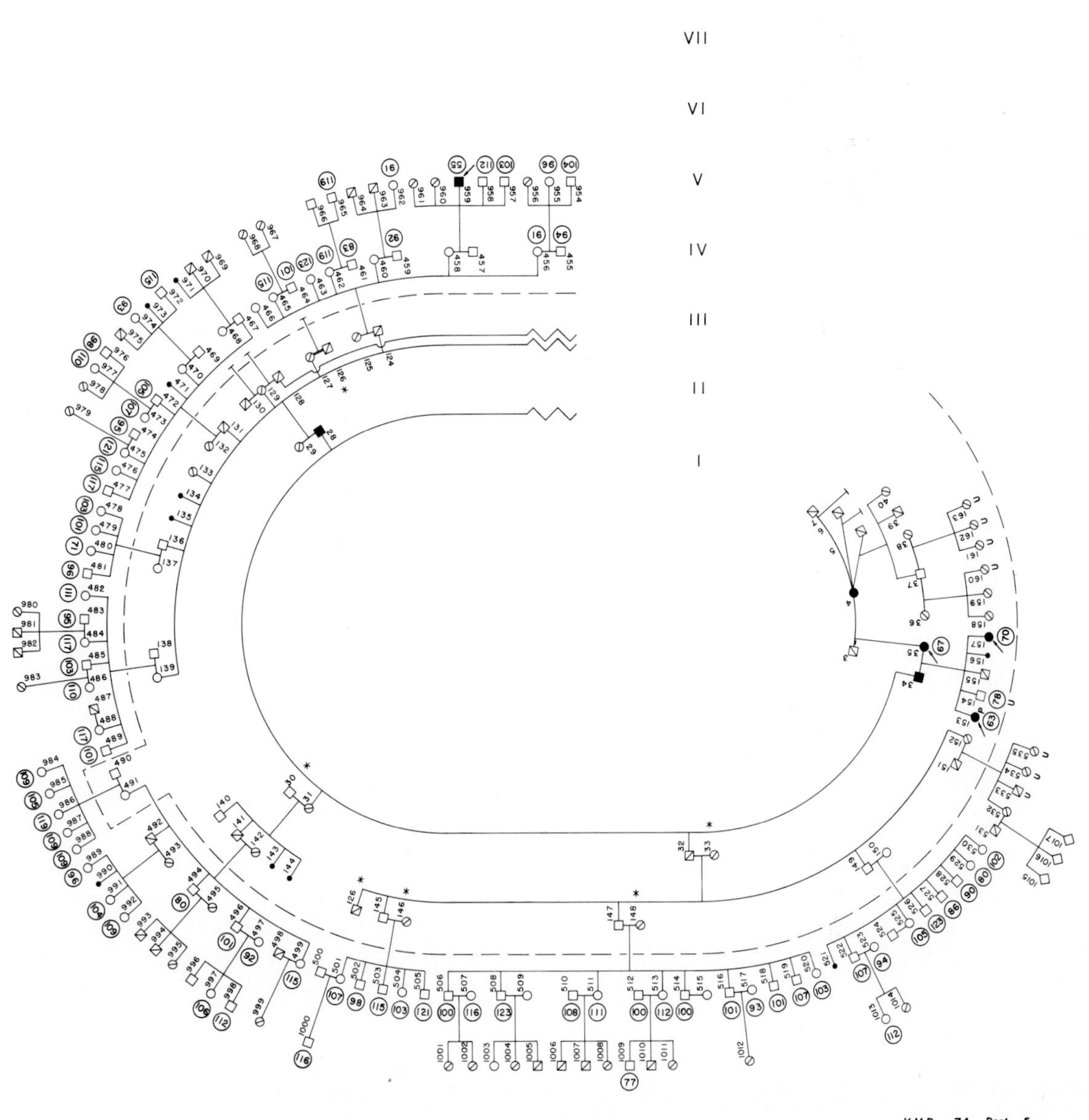

KMD 74 Part 5
* 30 appeared in Parts 2 and 3, uncle of 33
126 appears twice
146 aunt of 148

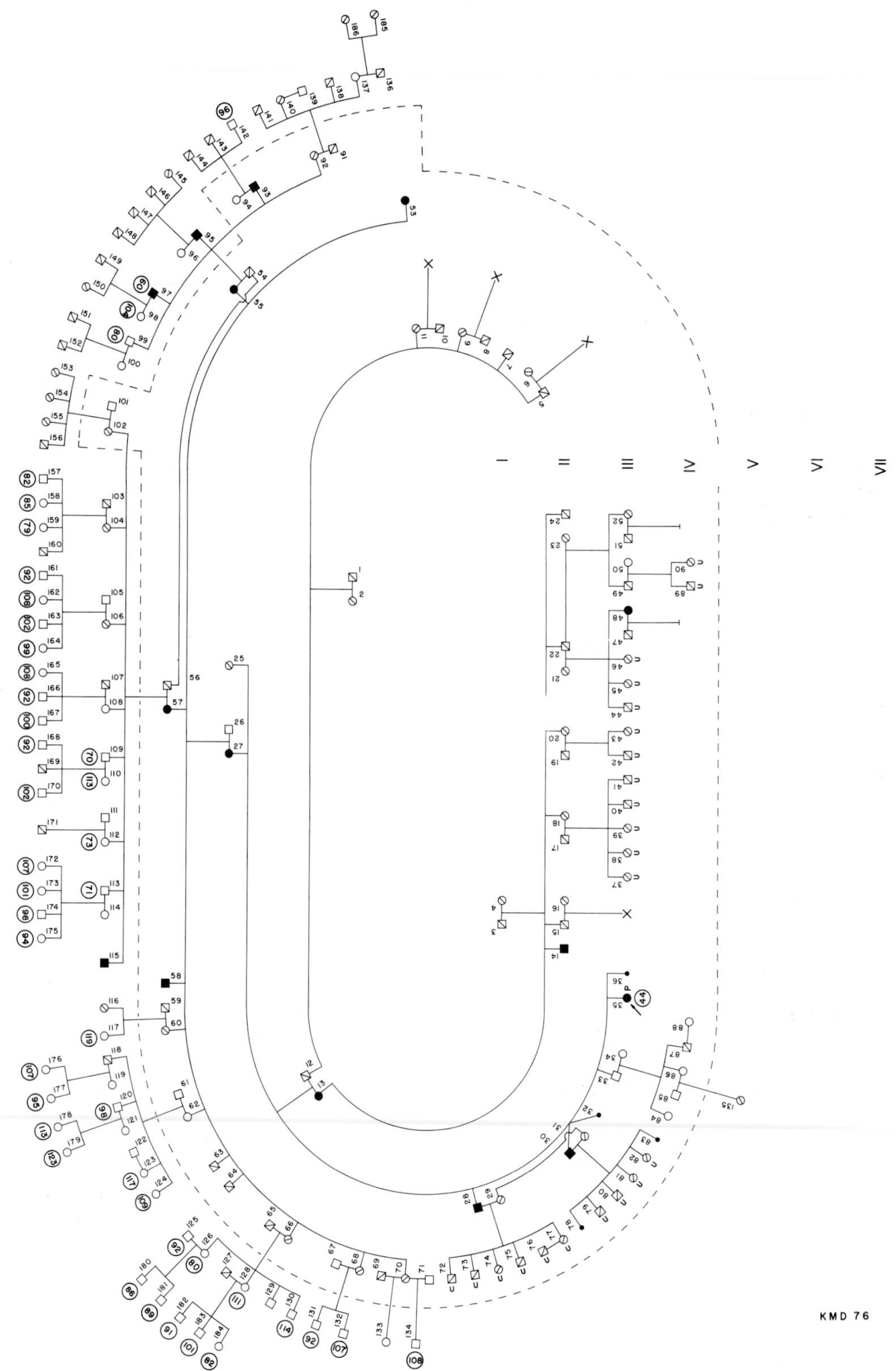

KMD 76

KMD 76

The Proband

The proband (35) was born in 1884, institutionalized at age 28 years and was in and out of the institution until her death there of a ruptured gallbladder in 1923. She had no history of difficult birth or perinatal infection. She had an attack of scarlet fever with prolonged aftereffects at age 6 years. IQ 44. *Diagnosis:* undifferentiated mental retardation.

Grandparents

Not of interest.

Parents

Father (12) was an alcoholic and "not up to par mentally." Old chart shows him as retarded. Intelligence unknown.

Mother (13) was epileptic and retarded.

Aunts and Uncles

Maternal uncle (14) committed suicide. He was retarded.

Siblings

Sister (25) died of scarlet fever in childhood.

Sister (27) was retarded, husband normal, but four of her 11 children were also retarded.

Brother (28) was institutionalized for a few months in a mental hospital. Old records classify him as retarded.

Brother (30) was retarded. His twin (32) died at birth.

Brother (33) probably was normal. He was "brighter than his brothers." He married a normal woman.

Brother (36) died of convulsions at 6 months.

Nieces and Nephews

Nieces (53), (55), (57) and nephew (58) are retarded.

First Cousins

(48) was retarded.

(49) died of epilepsy.

More Distant Relatives

Retarded niece (55) has three retarded children (93), (95) and (97). (93) spent two years in the fourth grade and two in the fifth—his last year in school. He is a welder. (95) spent two years in the first grade, two in the second and two in the seventh, which he failed to pass the second time. He is a laborer. (97) is a laborer with IQ 60. All three of these men have normal spouses.

Retarded niece (57) has a retarded child (115) who completed the fifth grade, is unmarried and works in a mine. This niece (57) also has three children (109), (112) and (113) with borderline IQ's of 70, 73 and 71, respectively.

Family Summary

The proband, IQ 44, her mother, her maternal uncle, three siblings, four nephews and nieces, five great-nephews and one first cousin were retarded. These persons were middle- or high-grade retardates. The proband's parents had eight children and 25 grandchildren.

Retardation of proband of probably genetic origin.

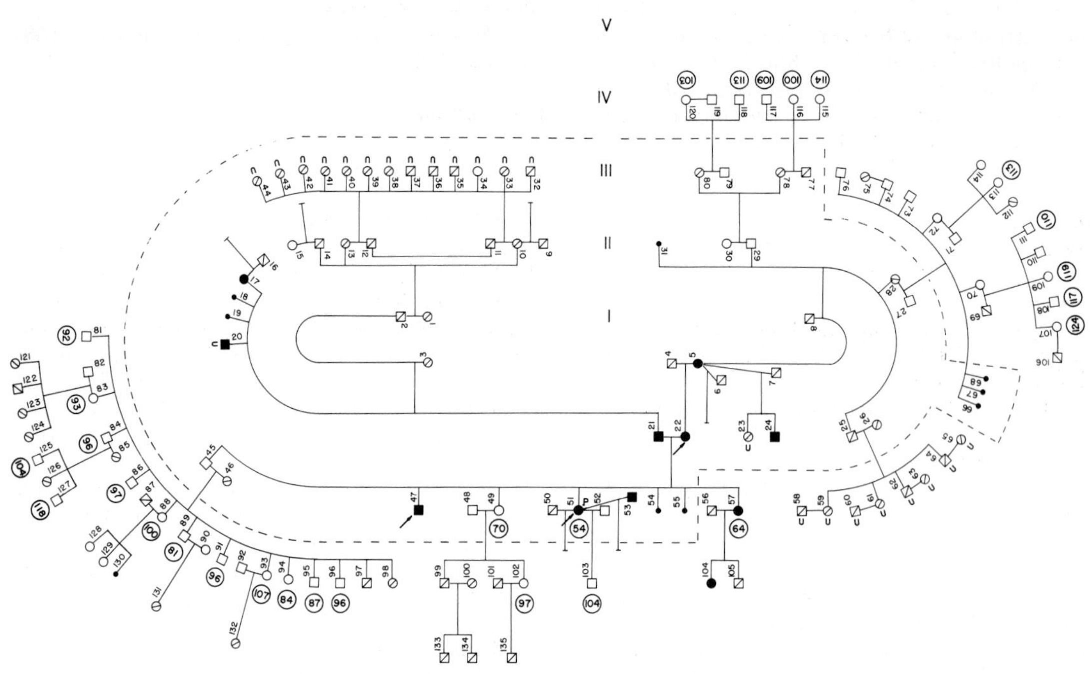

KMD 91

KMD 91

The Proband

The proband (51) was born in 1898, institutionalized at age 3 years, was discharged to her parents in 1914 and has been married three times, once to a retarded man. She had a small head with a receding forehead. She had one child. IQ 54. *Diagnosis:* undifferentiated mental retardation.

Grandparents

Maternal grandmother divorced proband's grandfather and married three more times. She was retarded.

Parents

Father (21) was classified as retarded in the old records. He made a living for his family on a rented farm. He committed suicide.

Mother (22) was institutionalized in 1900 and discharged in 1909. She was retarded.

Their marriage was a forced one.

Aunts and Uncles

(24), proband's mother's half brother, was in and out of mental hospitals for 32 years, finally dying in one in 1944. He was unmarried and childless. He was retarded and also psychotic.

(28), proband's mother's half sister, was epileptic.

Paternal aunt (17) was married but childless. Retarded.

Paternal uncle (20) was single at age 38. Retarded.

Siblings

Brother (45) was classified as retarded by the early workers but he reared a family of 13 children without public assistance, and looked after the welfare of his retarded siblings. Normal intelligence.

Brother (47) was institutionalized in 1900 and discharged in 1910. He was single and childless, and died in 1945 of coronary thrombosis. He was a high-grade retardate.

Sister (49) married a normal man. She has an IQ of 70.

Two siblings (54) and (55) died in infancy.

Sister (57) was considered for institutionalization at one time but no hearing was held. She married a man of unknown intelligence who had a dilapidated farm and a reputation of always being in trouble.

Child

Son (103) has scored IQ's of 98, 100 and 104. He lives with his mother.

Nieces and Nephews

(99) and (102) both have adjustment problems. (99) has been in court with marital problems and (102) became illegitimately pregnant. Their mother (49) has an IQ of 70.

One niece (104) is retarded, degree unknown.

First Cousins

Not of interest.

More Distant Relatives

Not of interest.

Family Summary

The proband, her mother, her mother's half brother, her maternal grandmother, a paternal aunt and uncle, three siblings and a niece were all retarded with an IQ range of 50 to 70. The proband's son by a normal man was normal. The proband's normal brother had 13 children, 11 of whom are known to have low-normal or normal intelligence and no social problems. The proband's parents had seven children and 18 grandchildren, 13 of whom belong to the proband's one normal sibling.

Retardation of proband of probably genetic origin.

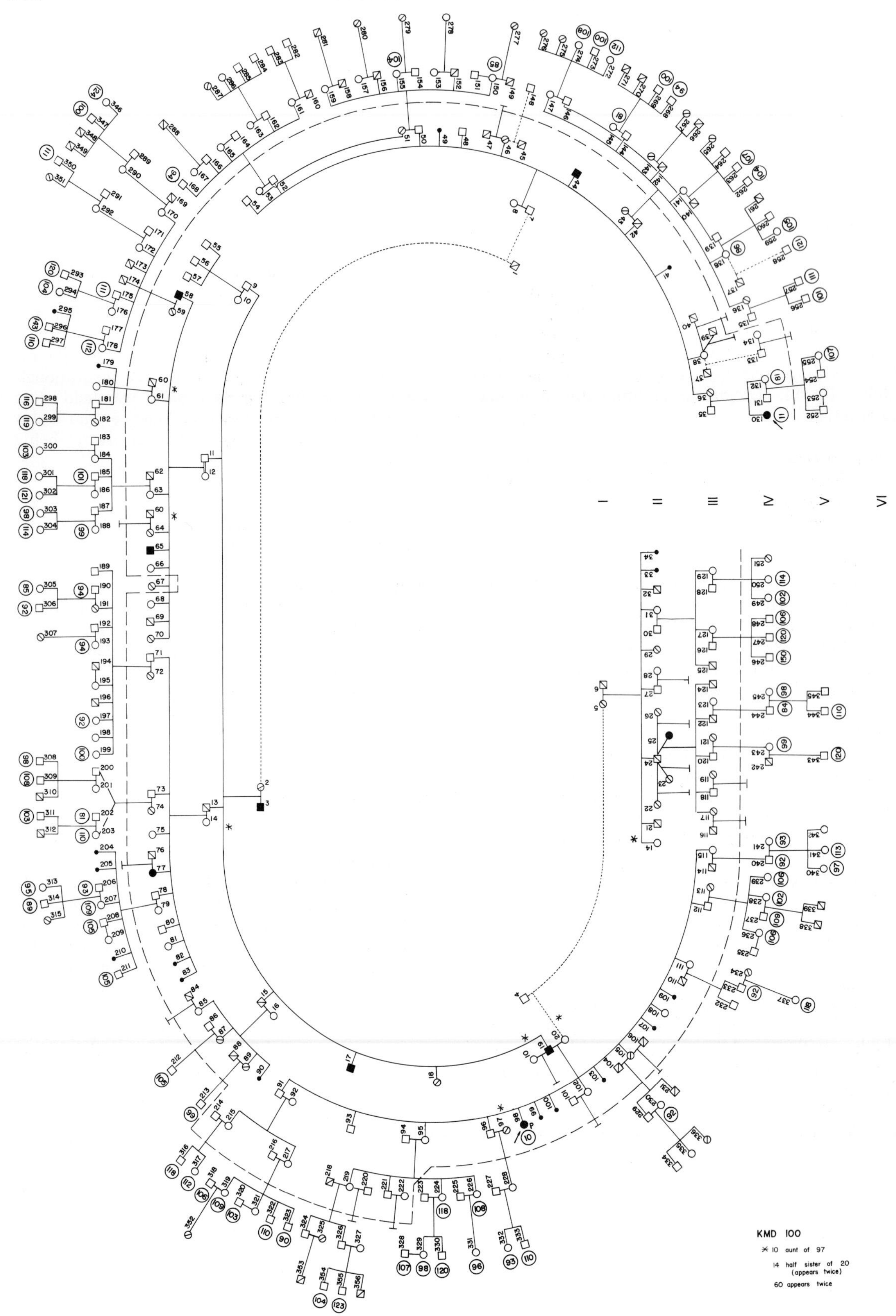
I
II
III
IV
V
VI
KMD 100
✳ 10 aunt of 97
14 half sister of 20 (appears twice)
60 appears twice

KMD 100

The Proband

The proband (98) was born in 1886, institutionalized at age 12 years and died of influenza in the institution in 1918. According to her parents, she had "brain fever" at the age of 6 years. She had no stigmata but did have a long history of cuts and bruises because she had little sense of pain. IQ 10. *Diagnosis:* undifferentiated mental retardation.

Grandparents

Both grandmothers had illegitimate children.

Paternal grandfather was an alcoholic, lazy and retarded. He never attempted to support his family.

Parents

Father (19) was an alcoholic, cruel and abusive to his wife, and retarded.

Mother (20) was a bright, industrious woman.

Aunts and Uncles

Paternal uncle (11) married his first cousin. Two of their ten children were retarded.

Paternal uncle (15) had epileptiform fainting spells.

Paternal uncle (17) was an unmarried, childless farm laborer and was retarded.

Maternal uncle (24) had four wives, one retarded.

Siblings

Brothers (91), (93), (96) and (112) all had normal intelligence.

Sisters (95), (102), (108), (111) and (115) all had normal intelligence.

Sisters (99) and (100) died of respiratory disease at 1 year.

(103) and (109) were miscarriages.

Sister (105) has unknown intelligence.

Brother (107) died of "brain fever" at 1 year.

Nieces and Nephews

Not of interest.

First Cousins

(44) is an unmarried, childless farm laborer and is retarded.

(58) and (65), two brothers, were retarded.

(77) is married but childless and retarded.

More Distant Relatives

First cousin (36) had a retarded child, IQ 11, who died in the institution in 1917.

Family Summary

The proband, IQ 10, her paternal grandfather, father, paternal uncle and four first cousins were retarded. With the exception of the proband the others were high-grade retardates. The proband's parents had 16 children and 15 grandchildren.

Retardation of proband of probably genetic origin.

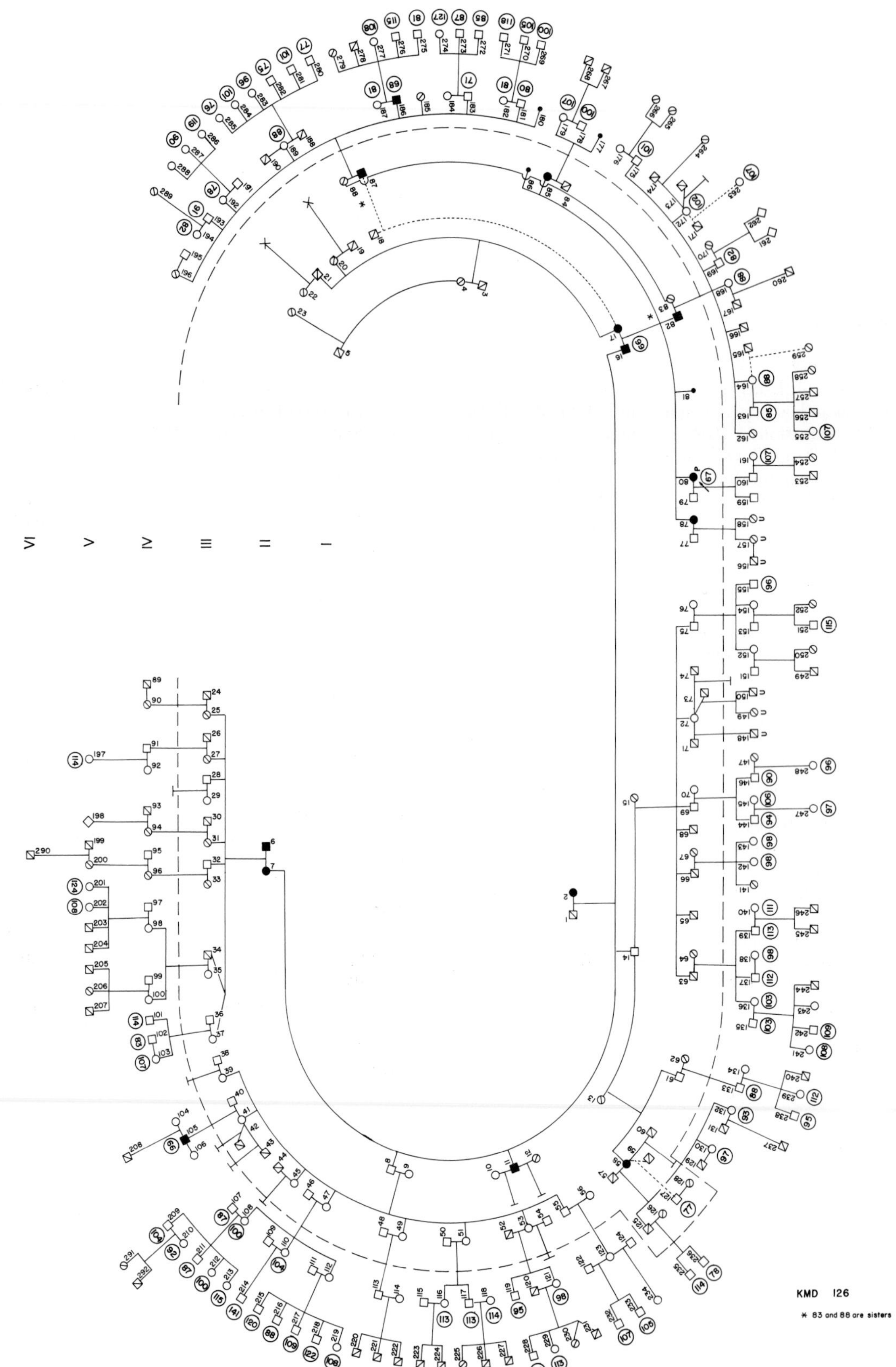

KMD 126

* 83 and 88 are sisters

KMD 126

The Proband

The proband (80) was born in 1895, institutionalized at age 17 years and discharged eight years later. She had no history of early trauma and no stigmata. She married a foreign born man of normal intelligence, and they operated a restaurant in 1961. The proband attended school until age 14 when she was still in the third grade. IQ 67. *Diagnosis:* undifferentiated mental retardation.

Grandparents

Paternal grandfather committed suicide.

Paternal grandmother was retarded.

Parents

Father (16) was a cobbler, IQ 66.

Mother (17) died following a criminal abortion. She could not learn in school and was unable to keep house.

Aunts and Uncles

Paternal uncle (8) had normal intelligence but tried to commit suicide by hitting his head with a hammer.

Paternal aunt (7) and paternal uncle (11) were retarded. (11) was married twice but was childless.

Maternal relatives unknown except proband's mother and a half sister (23) who was a bedridden invalid.

Siblings

Sister (78) married a normal man but is retarded.

Brother (81) died at birth.

Brother (82) was most uncooperative. He lives in a poor section but keeps an unlisted telephone. He is a welder and retarded.

Sister (85) refused to cooperate, claiming that an organization was persecuting her and that our interviewer was their representative. Old records classify her as retarded. She, her brother (82) and her half brother (87) married siblings—(83) who refused to cooperate, (84) who "hasn't worked for years," and (88) who had an illegitimate daughter and illegitimate granddaughter.

Half Sibling

Half brother (87) had been in trouble with the police and was retarded.

Children

Son (159) graduated from high school with poor grades and is in the Army.

Son (160) graduated from high school and works in an office. He scored at his proper grade level on achievement tests. Wife's IQ is 107.

Nieces and Nephews

Child (186) of half brother has an IQ of 68.

There are eight borderline and low-normal IQ scores in the tests given to 12 nieces and nephews. Only two were above 100.

First Cousins

(58) is retarded. While married to (57), she had an illegitimate child (127), IQ 77, by (59).

More Distant Relatives

First cousin (41) has a son (105), IQ 66, who has been married to two normal women, but has only one child.

Family Summary

The proband, her parents, paternal grandmother, paternal aunt and uncle, three siblings, one half sibling, a half nephew, first cousin and second cousin once removed were retarded. The proband married a normal man and has two normal children. Most of her nieces and nephews have below average IQ scores. The proband's parents had six children and 13 grandchildren.

Retardation of proband of probably genetic origin.

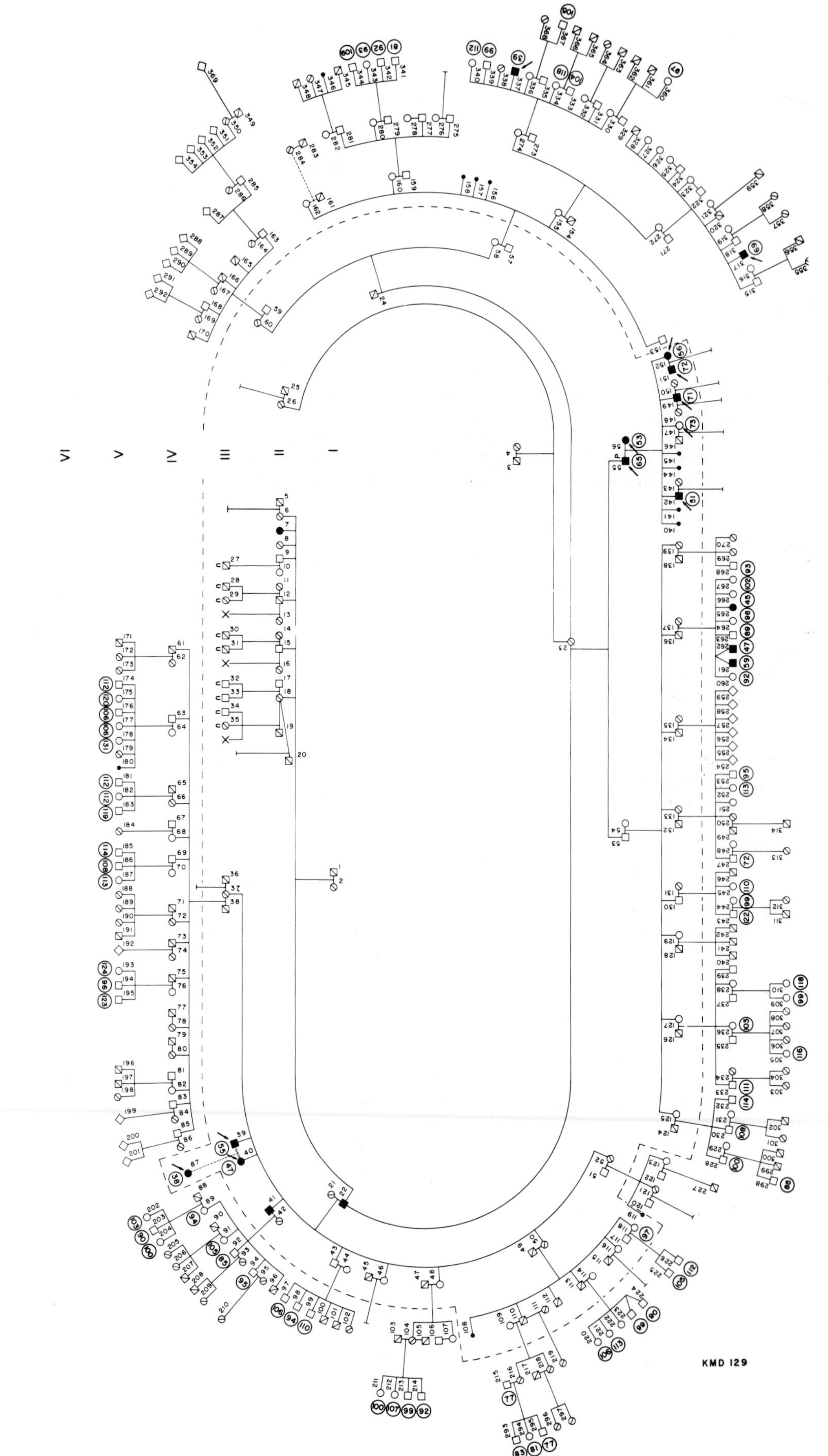

KMD 129

KMD 129

The Proband

The proband (55) was born in 1871, institutionalized, together with his wife and four children, at age 41 years. He was discharged in 1914 and died of cerebral hemorrhage and Pott's Disease in a "Home" in 1925. He had no stigmata and no history of early trauma. His family lived in great poverty and squalor. He was nearly illiterate. Before his institutionalization for mental deficiency he was adjudged mentally ill after a complaint by his wife, and was sent to a mental hospital for three months for attempted suicide. The proband "worked all the time" but could not provide for his family. IQ 65. *Diagnosis:* undifferentiated mental retardation.

Grandparents

Not of interest except that the maternal grandmother was epileptic.

Parents

Father (22) was a retarded laborer.

Aunts and Uncles

Paternal aunt (7) was a low-grade retardate who could not walk or talk and died at age 15 years.

Siblings

Brother (53) had normal intelligence.

Half Siblings

Half sister (37) has unknown intelligence.

Half brother (39), IQ 55, was born in 1883, institutionalized in 1929 and placed under outside supervision in 1944. He is on the waiting list for readmission. He and his sister (40) had a child (87).

Half sister (40) was institutionalized in 1929 and has remained in the institution ever since. She had an illegitimate child by her brother. She received a physical and neurological examination from J. A. Böök, M.D., and John Schut, M.D., in 1950. IQ 47. *Diagnosis:* retardation with progressive schizophrenia.

Half brother (41) was classified as retarded by the original workers.

Half brother (43) had normal intelligence but was imprisoned for four years for assault and attempted rape of his employer's daughter. He became an itinerant preacher after his release. His wife wrote us a long letter about the "communist menace," and other irrelevant matters.

Half sister (46) is crippled from a fall. She is a clerk with normal intelligence.

Half sister (48) is normal.

Half sisters (50) and (52) have unknown intelligence.

Half sister (58) was normal. Her husband, her husband's mother, two of her four adult children (three children died in infancy) and two of her four grandchildren from a blind daughter are all blind.

Half sister (60) had unknown intelligence. Her children refused to cooperate.

Spouse

Proband's wife (56) was institutionalized at the same time as her husband and their children. She was discharged in 1915, married a second time after the proband's death (second husband was the father of a family with similar social history), and was on the waiting list for reinstitutionalization when she died of mammary carcinoma in 1931. Her parents and all three of her adult siblings were retarded. IQ 53.

Children

Sons (140) and (141) died in infancy, one of cholera infantum, one of "spasms."

Son (142) was institutionalized at age 10 years, left seven years later in 1917, was readmitted in 1927, sterilized in 1930 and paroled to live with his sister in 1945. He married and works as a dishwasher. IQ 51.

(144) and (145) were miscarriages.

Daughter (147) was institutionalized at age 9 years in 1912, discharged in 1924. She had a voluntary sterilization operation in 1928 and works in a department store. IQ 73.

Son (149) was institutionalized at age 6 years in 1912 and returned to outside supervision in 1916. He served a three year term in a reformatory (1920 to 1923) and another term in 1928. He was readmitted in 1929, sterilized in 1930 and discharged in 1931. He was imprisoned for breaking and entering in 1931. Since that time he has been married twice and when last heard of in 1944 was in prison again. IQ 71.

Daughter (152) was institutionalized at age 4 years in 1912, sterilized in 1938 and placed under outside supervision in 1943. She married a retarded man who had been in and out of the institution several times and had been sterilized. (His mother also had been institutionalized.) IQ 72.

Grandchildren

None.

Nieces and Nephews

Child (87) of proband's half brother and half sister was born in 1909 and institutionalized at age 20 years. She died of cancer in the institution in 1954. She received a physical and neurological examination by Dr. Böök and Dr. Schut in 1950. IQ 38. Their diagnosis: retardation with catatonic schizophrenia.

Continued on page 298

KMD 129 – *Continued*

First Cousins

Not of interest.

More Distant Relatives

Brother (53) has three grandchildren (261), (262) and (265) with IQ's of 59, 47 and 45, respectively.

Half sister (58) has two great-grandchildren (317) and (337) who are institutionalized, IQ's 69 and 39, respectively. (317) has a diagnosis of "high grade moron, unstable, post traumatic natal, psychopathic personality."

Family Summary

The proband, his father, his wife, four children, paternal aunt, three half siblings, a half niece and five more distant relatives were retarded. The entire family of the proband (wife and four children) was institutionalized together with five other relatives. The family lived in "the utmost squalor and poverty." There was no history of syphilis. Institutionalization and sterilization prevented further reproduction. The proband had no grandchildren; the proband's parents had two children and eight grandchildren. These latter all belonged to the proband's normal brother who, however, has three retarded grandchildren. There are six generations of retarded persons in the proband's immediate family (including half siblings).

Retardation of proband of probably genetic origin.

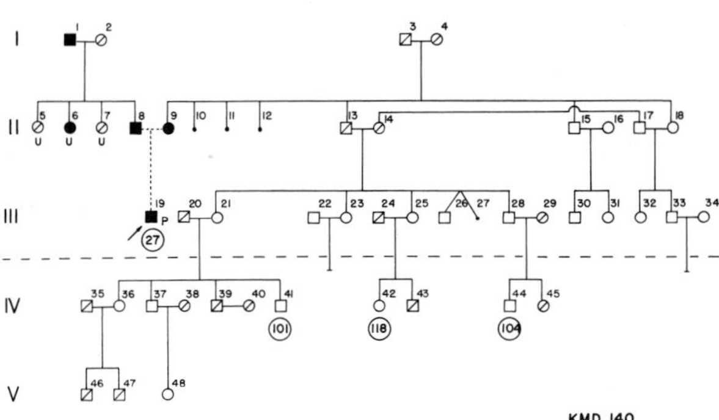

KMD 140

The Proband

The proband (19) was born in 1884, institutionalized at age 14 years and died of pulmonary tuberculosis and diabetes in the institution in 1952. He was an illegitimate child who lived with his maternal aunt in a fine home. He had no stigmata and no history of early trauma. IQ 27. *Diagnosis:* undifferentiated mental retardation.

Grandparents

Paternal grandfather was retarded.

Parents

Father (8) was retarded.

Mother (9) learned little in school and was retarded.

Aunts and Uncles

Paternal aunt (6) was retarded.

Siblings

None.

Nieces and Nephews

None.

First Cousins

Not of interest. Paternal ones remained in Germany. Maternal ones have normal intelligence.

More Distant Relatives

Not of interest.

Family Summary

The proband, IQ 27, his parents, his paternal grandfather and a paternal aunt were retarded. The proband lived in a good home with his maternal aunt. He was an illegitimate child, the only one born to his parents.

Retardation of proband of probably genetic origin.

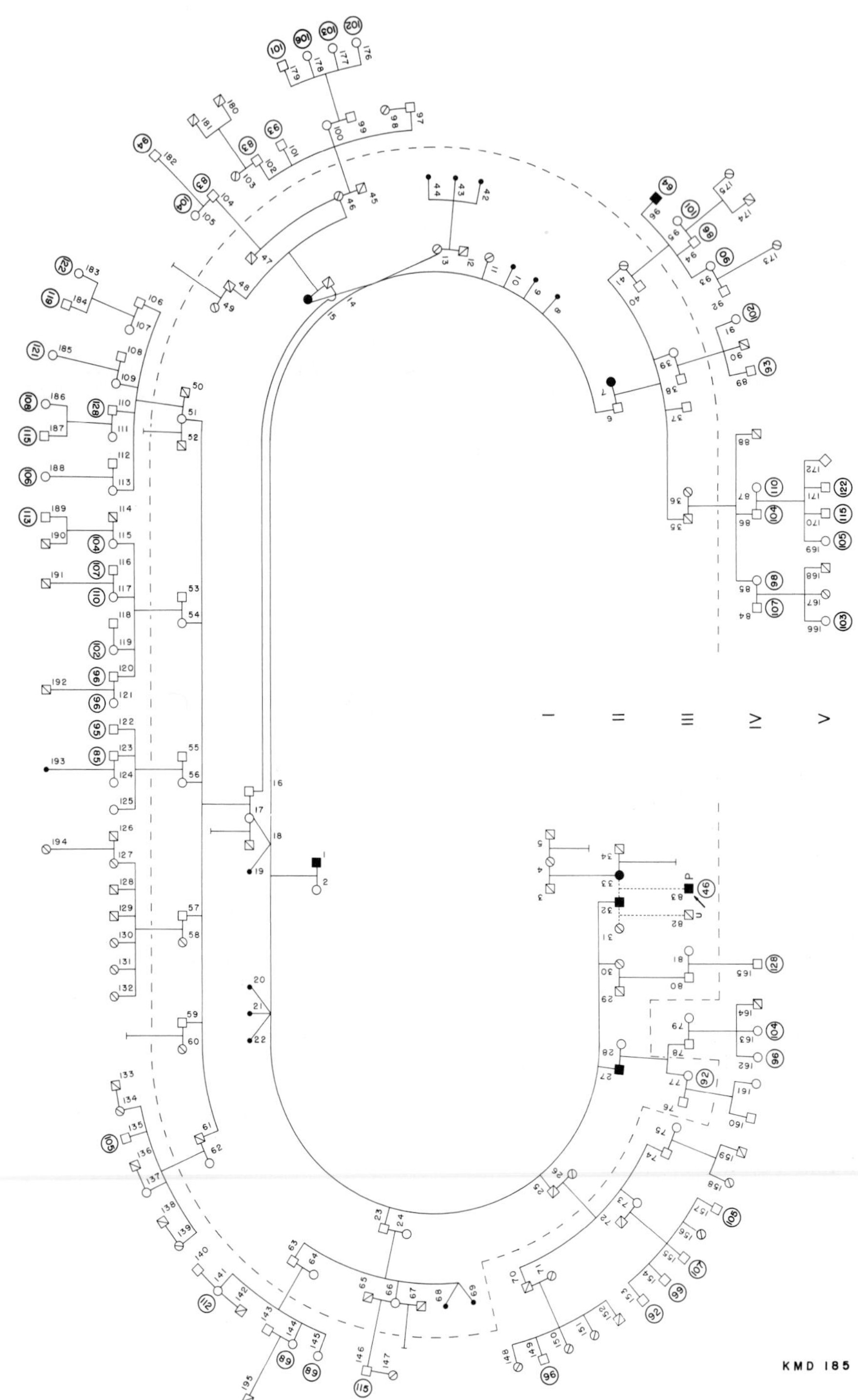

KMD 185

KMD 185

The Proband

The proband (83) was born in 1901, institutionalized at age 5 years and remained in the institution. He was illegitimate and his home environment was bad physically but he was treated kindly. His birth followed a difficult labor but there was no history of trauma. IQ 46. *Diagnosis:* undifferentiated mental retardation.

Grandparents

Paternal grandfather was retarded.

Maternal grandfather deserted his family.

Parents

Father (32) had another illegitimate child by another woman. He was an alcoholic and retarded.

Mother (33) was retarded.

Aunts and Uncles

Paternal aunt (15) was retarded and had tumors on her face and body.

Paternal uncle (27) was retarded but married a normal wife.

Siblings

Only an unknown half brother.

Nieces and Nephews

None.

First Cousins

(41) knew little about her three children, said they had not lived with her. She gave the impression of a mentally ill person. One of her three children, (96), has an IQ of 64.

More Distant Relatives

First cousin's child (96) has an IQ of 64.

Family Summary

The proband, IQ 46, his parents, his paternal grandfather, a paternal aunt and a paternal uncle were retarded. The proband was two months premature but there was no history of trauma. The proband's parents had one child, no grandchildren.

Retardation of proband of probably genetic origin.

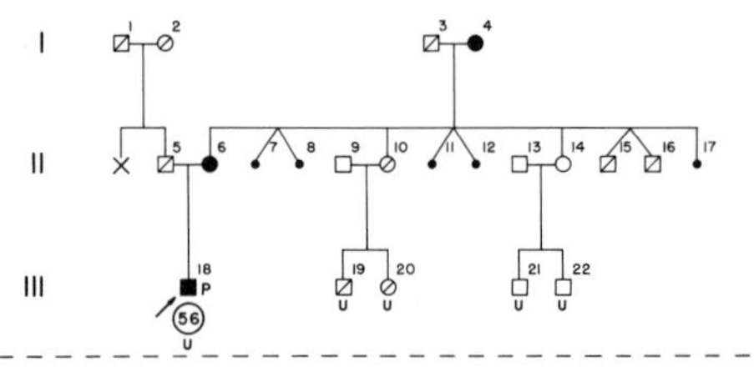

KMD 186

KMD 186

The Proband

The proband (18) was born in 1904, institutionalized at age 7 years, discharged and readmitted twice within the next seven years. He has not been heard of since 1922 when he was in a reformatory in Montana. His father deserted his mother seven months before his birth and the proband and his mother lived with the maternal grandparents in great poverty and squalor. His birth was uneventful and there was no history of perinatal trauma. He had pneumonia at age 4 years with "cerebral complications." Stigmata included a high arched palate and short, thick hands. IQ 56. *Diagnosis:* undifferentiated mental retardation.

Grandparents

Maternal grandmother was retarded.

Parents

Father (5) was an alcoholic laborer of unknown intelligence.

Mother (6) was retarded.

Aunts and Uncles

Not of interest.

Siblings

None.

Nieces and Nephews

None.

First Cousins

Not of interest.

More Distant Relatives

Unknown.

Family Summary

The proband, IQ 56, his mother and his maternal grandmother were retarded. The proband's father deserted his pregnant wife. The proband and his mother lived in a poor environment. The proband has not been heard of since his discharge from the institution in 1919 and imprisonment in a reformatory in 1922. The proband's parents had no other children, grandchildren unknown.

Retardation of proband of probably genetic origin.

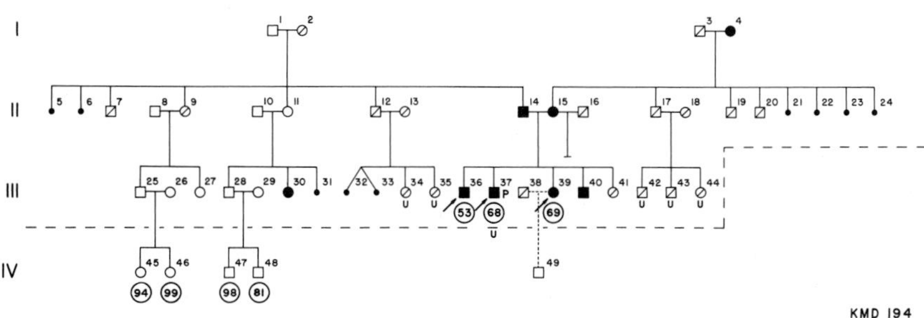

KMD 194

The Proband

The proband (37) was born in 1896, institutionalized at age 12 years, discharged in 1919 and has not been heard of since that time. He attended school for seven years but could not do fourth grade work. His birth and early development seemed normal, although he always stammered. The home environment was poor. IQ 68. *Diagnosis:* undifferentiated mental retardation.

Grandparents

Maternal grandmother was retarded. She could not keep house.

Parents

Father (14) was a retarded alcoholic who was frequently imprisoned for non-support.

Mother (15) stammered, was an alcoholic and retarded. She could not keep house.

Aunts and Uncles

Paternal aunt (9) was epileptic.

Maternal uncles (17), (19) and (20) all stammered, as did their father.

Siblings

Brother (36) was first sent to a school for deaf mutes in 1903 at age 8 years. He was then transferred to the institution for the retarded in 1915, discharged in 1923 but readmitted in 1924 and died of a heart attack in the institution in 1943. He walked at age 4 years. IQ 53. His deafness was attributed to the effects of typhoid fever (age at time of illness unknown).

Sister (39) was institutionalized in 1936 at age 37 years after the birth of an illegitimate child (49). She escaped and was returned three times. In 1937 a sterilization operation was performed. She was in and out of the institution several times. She also served several workhouse sentences for sex offenses, drunkenness and profane language. She was murdered in 1963 by a drunken thief. She was a well known character in a slum area. IQ 69.

Brother (40) died of diphtheria at age 10 years. He stammered and was retarded.

Sister (41) died of diphtheria at age 8 years. She was a year retarded in school.

Nieces and Nephews

Only one, (49), the illegitimate child of (39). He was adopted, completed the tenth grade and is a farmer.

First Cousins

(30) could not talk and was uneducable.

More Distant Relatives

Not of interest.

Family Summary

The proband, IQ 68, both his parents, three siblings, his maternal grandmother and a first cousin were retarded. Two of the proband's siblings were institutionalized. They had IQ's of 53 and 69. The sibling with IQ 69 had an illegitimate child who has normal intelligence. The sibling with IQ 53 was a deaf mute. Since the proband's parents were alcoholics, in addition to their retardation, the home environment was poor. The proband's parents had five children and one grandchild.

Retardation of proband of probably genetic origin.

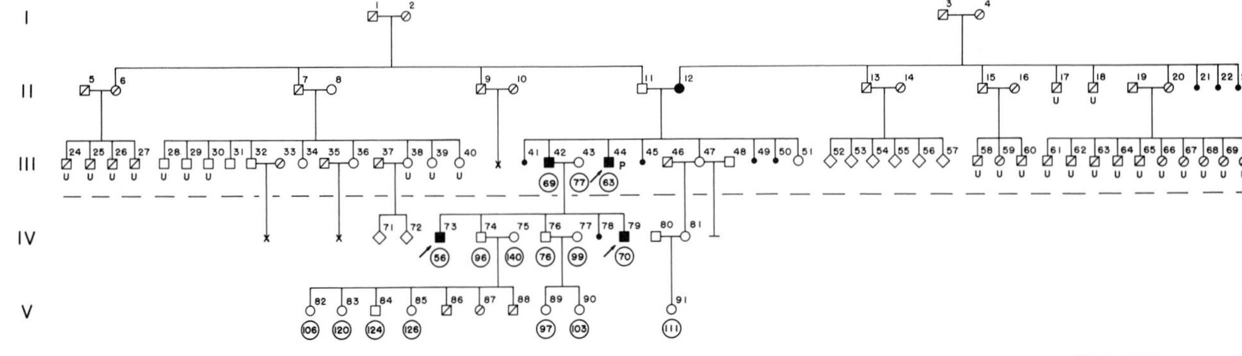

KMD 202

The Proband

The proband (44) was born in 1897, institutionalized at age 16 years and was still in the institution in 1961. Institutional diagnosis was moron, familial. He was a healthy baby who had no stigmata. He was committed to the institution from the Juvenile Court. The home was poor and the treatment of the children was abusive. The proband attended school for ten years but could not complete the fourth grade. IQ 63. *Diagnosis:* undifferentiated mental retardation.

Grandparents

Not of interest.

Parents

Father (11) had normal intelligence but was an alcoholic. He was cruel and abusive to his family.

Mother (12) was retarded.

Aunts and Uncles

Paternal uncle (7) was hospitalized for mental illness.

The paternal and maternal siblings were not well known to the early workers.

Siblings

Brother (41) died at age 2 days, cause of death unknown.

Brother (42) was an alcoholic laborer with IQ 69. His divorced wife has an IQ of 77 and has been hospitalized for mental illness.

Brothers (45), (49) and (50) all died in infancy of "summer complaint."

Sister (47) left home at age 14 years because of abusive treatment. She was deserted by her first husband. She has normal intelligence.

Sister (51) had normal intelligence but according to the old records was epileptic. A niece reported she had cerebral palsy. She died at age 8 years.

Nieces and Nephews

Nephew (73) was institutionalized in 1925 at age 4 years and escaped in 1942. His present status is unknown. His diagnosis was moron, cause undiagnosed. IQ 56 and epileptic.

Nephew (79), brother to (73), had been in and out of institutions for the retarded and mental hospitals, and died in the institution in 1961. Three diagnoses were made: in 1939, of moron, familial with eunuchoidism; in 1950, of dementia praecox; in 1956, of moron, familial with dementia praecox simple. His twelve IQ scores range from 43 to 84 over a period of 21 years. At age 13 on an individual Kuhlmann test he obtained a score of 70, the one used on the chart.

First Cousins

Nearly all are unknown.

More Distant Relatives

Not of interest.

Family Summary

The proband, IQ 63, his mother, his brother and two nephews were retarded. In addition, one sister was epileptic and one brother had an IQ of 70 and a psychotic wife with IQ 77. The proband had no history of injury or infection. The home environment was poor but, despite the poverty and ill treatment, two of the proband's siblings evinced normal intelligence. The proband's parents had eight children and seven grandchildren.

Retardation of proband of probably genetic origin.

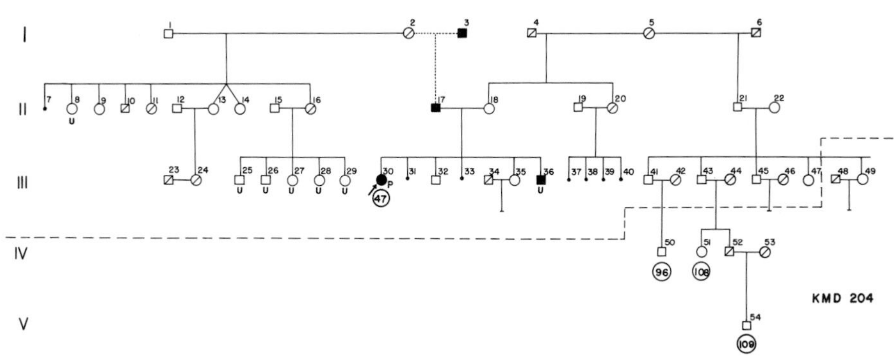

KMD 204

The Proband

The proband (30) was born in 1891, institutionalized at age 16 years, discharged to friends six years later and is unmarried and childless. Her birth was uneventful, she had no stigmata and no history of perinatal infection. IQ 47. *Diagnosis:* undifferentiated mental retardation.

Grandparents

Paternal grandfather was retarded.

Parents

Father (17) was an illegitimate child. He was retarded.

Mother (18) had normal intelligence but was hospitalized for mental illness.

Aunts and Uncles

Not of interest.

Siblings

Brother (31) died at age 2 weeks.

Brother (32) was put in an orphanage at age 7 years, then placed in a foster home five years later. He is a carpenter and has normal intelligence.

Sister (33) died at age 3 days.

Sister (35) was put in an orphanage at age 5 years and later sent to a foster home. She has normal intelligence.

Brother (36) was placed in an excellent foster home at preschool age but despite every effort to educate him, he proved to be retarded. The foster parents attempted to have him institutionalized but no action was taken and his present status is unknown.

Nieces and Nephews

Probably none. The only possibility is children of the unknown retarded brother (36).

First Cousins

Not of interest.

More Distant Relatives

Not of interest.

Family Summary

The proband, IQ 47, his brother, his father and paternal grandfather were all retarded. The home environment was poor. When the proband's mother was institutionalized for mental illness, the children were placed in the state orphanage and later in foster homes. Despite the unfavorable home environment, two of the proband's siblings had normal intelligence and were successful. Unfortunately, the present status of the retarded brother could not be ascertained. The proband's parents had six children. There were probably no grandchildren.

Retardation of proband of probably genetic origin.

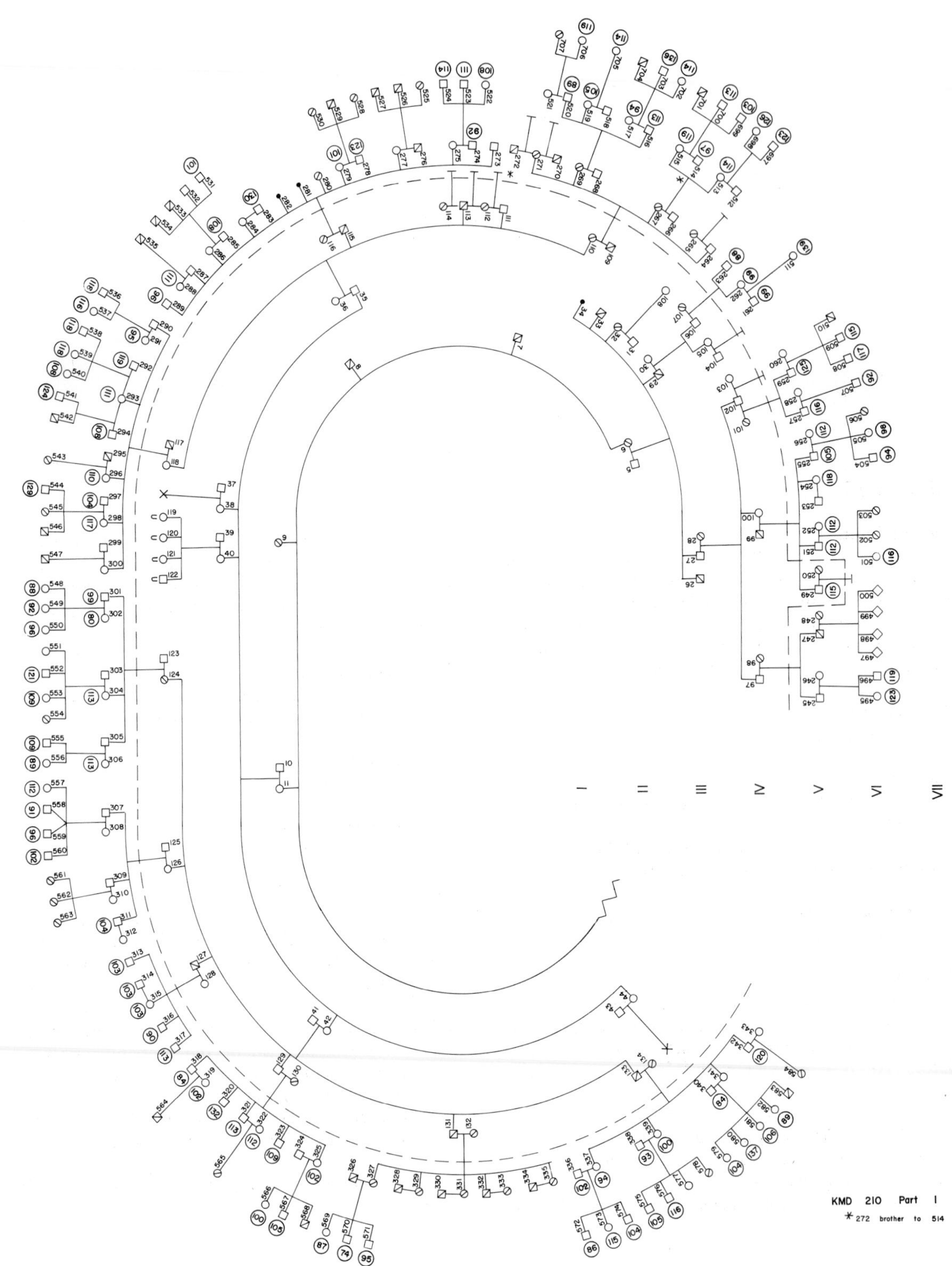

KMD 210 Part I

* 272 brother to 514

KMD 210

The Proband

The proband (86) was born in 1878, institutionalized at age 34 years and transferred to a mental hospital three years later where she died of pulmonary tuberculosis in 1941. Mental hospital records state that she was transferred there because she had tuberculosis and could receive appropriate treatment. She was not recorded as having been mentally ill. There was no history of difficult delivery or of perinatal infection. IQ 27. *Diagnosis:* undifferentiated mental retardation.

Grandparents

Maternal grandmother (4) was retarded.

Parents

Father (18) had normal intelligence but had poor health. He was an alcoholic, "queer" and a religious fanatic.

Mother (19) was retarded.

Aunts and Uncles

Paternal aunt (13) was retarded.

Maternal aunt (21) was retarded.

Siblings

Brother (75) died unmarried and childless. He was retarded.

Sisters (77), (79), (81) and (84) all had normal intelligence. (79) married a retarded man and (81) committed suicide.

Brother (82) committed suicide at age 25. He was retarded.

Brother (85) died unmarried and childless. He had normal intelligence but was crippled from tuberculosis of the hip.

Nieces and Nephews

Not of interest.

First Cousins

(71) was retarded. His wife was normal but one (198) of his nine children was retarded.

More Distant Relatives

(178), the only person who grew to adulthood in a sibship of six, died unmarried and childless at age 27 years. He was retarded. His parents were first cousins.

(393) died in an institution. IQ 11.

(198) died unmarried and childless at age 22 years. He was retarded.

(456), nephew to (198), was institutionalized for mental retardation (idiot level) and died of bronchopneumonia and epilepsy in the institution.

(638) has an IQ of 54, husband's IQ 88.

Family Summary

The proband, IQ 27, her mother, her maternal grandmother, a maternal and a paternal aunt, two brothers, one first cousin and five more distant relatives were retarded. In addition, two of the proband's siblings committed suicide. One sister married a retarded man, one married a religious fanatic and one married a man who later deserted her. The proband's parents had eight children and 19 grandchildren.

Retardation of proband of probably genetic origin.

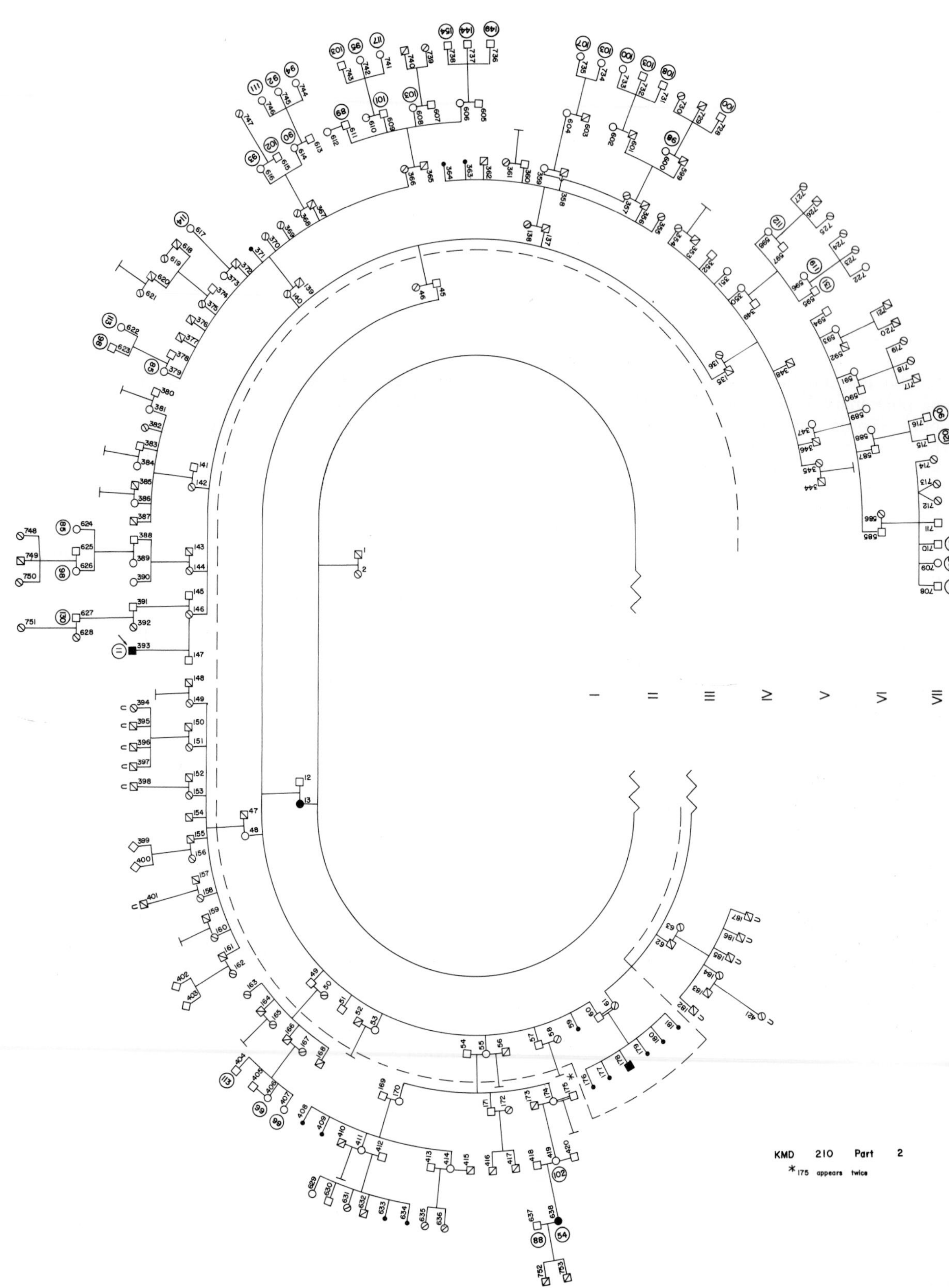
I
II
III
IV
V
VI
VII
KMD 210 Part 2
* 175 appears twice

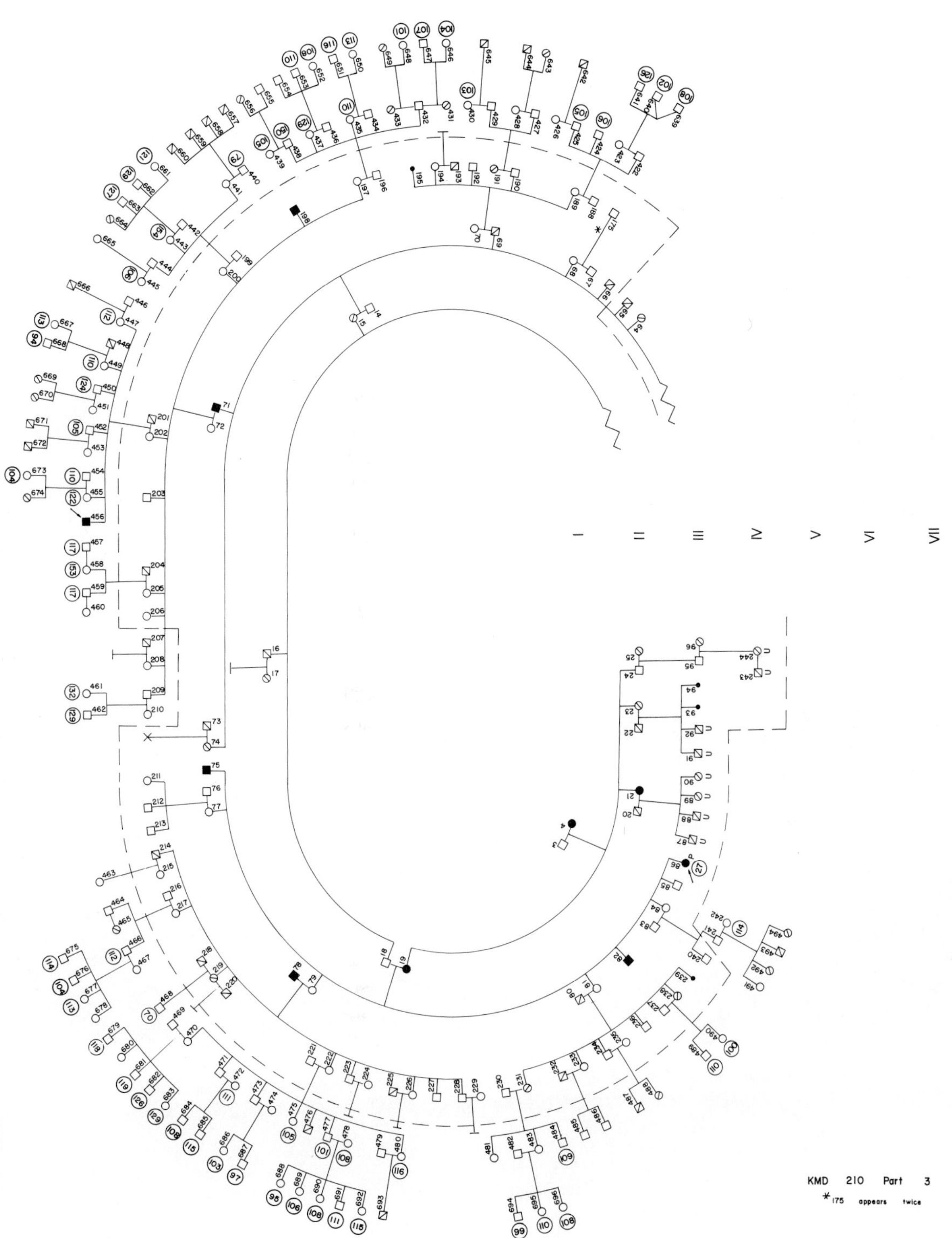
I
II
III
IV
V
VI
VII
KMD 210 Part 3
*175 appears twice

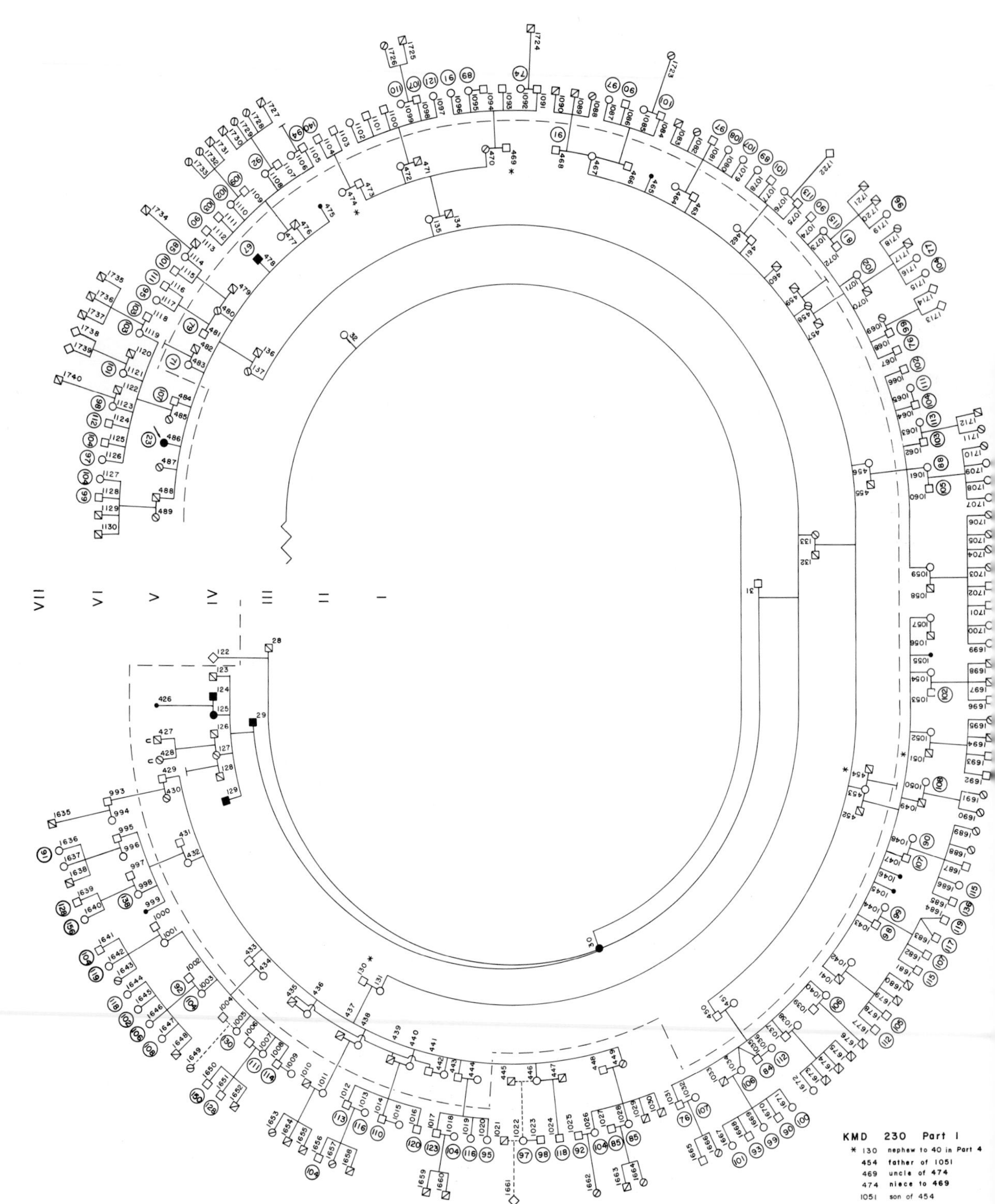

KMD 230 Part I

* 130	nephew to 40 in Part 4
454	father of 1051
469	uncle of 474
474	niece to 469
1051	son of 454

KMD 230

The Proband

The proband (39) was born in 1857, institutionalized at age 53 years, became "somewhat disturbed mentally" nine years later and was transferred to a mental hospital where she died six months after admission, cause of death unknown. She was a small baby who was crippled and defective from birth. She was round shouldered and flat chested. Her reflexes were normal. She had no history of birth injury or perinatal disease. Her home environment was poor because of the alcoholism and retardation in the family. IQ 33. *Diagnosis:* undifferentiated mental retardation.

Grandparents

Not of interest.

Parents

Father (9) was an alcoholic and retarded.

Mother (10) was retarded and had an "insane temper."

Aunts and Uncles

Paternal relatives were unknown to the original workers.

Maternal relatives were unknown to the original workers but the proband's mother's half siblings were found in the follow-up. They are not of interest.

Siblings

Sister (30) was retarded, as was one of her husbands and two of their four children.

Sister (32) died at age 11 years. She had normal intelligence.

Sister (34) had normal intelligence.

Brother (35) was retarded, wife normal. One of their 12 children was retarded.

Brother (37) was "mentally slow."

Sister (41) had normal intelligence.

Brother (42) died at age 3 months, cause of death unknown.

Brother (43) had normal intelligence.

Brother (45) died in an accident at age 6 years.

Nieces and Nephews

Niece (125) was retarded, as was her husband. Their only child died at birth.

Nephew (129) was classified as an imbecile. He died unmarried and childless.

Nephew (150) is retarded.

Niece (172) was retarded. She was forced to marry her first cousin (171), of unknown intelligence, after she had a child by him. Three of their four children are retarded, but these three retardates all had normal children.

Niece (174) is retarded, husband and two children of unknown intelligence, one normal.

Niece (183) and her husband, whom she was forced to marry, are both retarded, as is one of their six children.

Nephew (184) is retarded, wife and two children of unknown intelligence, three children normal.

Niece (203) knew little about her eight children and seemed dull, but the interviewer did not feel justified in classifying her as retarded. Her children were all placed in the state orphanage.

First Cousins

No paternal or maternal first cousins are known.

The children of the proband's mother's half siblings are not of interest.

More Distant Relatives

(478) has been committed as mentally retarded but not institutionalized. He served a prison term for first degree grand larceny. IQ 67.

(486), sister to (478), was institutionalized in 1932 at age 9 years for mental retardation. IQ 23.

(540) spent two years in the seventh grade, receiving lower grades the second year and left school in the seventh grade at age 16 years. He is a milk hauler.

(571) repeated the eighth grade four times and is probably retarded. Her husband and three children are normal.

(572) repeated the eighth grade for three years and is probably retarded. His wife and five of their six children are known to have normal intelligence; one is too young to be tested.

(574), sibling to (571) and (572)—all the children of a consanguineous marriage—repeated the third grade once, the eighth grade twice and left school at age 16 years without passing. He is probably retarded. Wife's intelligence unknown. All three children normal.

(603) was committed as retarded and institutionalized in 1938 at age 13 years with a diagnosis of moron, endocrine disorder. In 1942 he was transferred to a mental hospital with a diagnosis of schizophrenia. IQ 47.

(638) has an IQ of 41. Husband's intelligence unknown. Children normal.

(662) was institutionalized in 1936 at age 36 years, sterilized and placed under outside supervision. She has been married six times, divorced four times (one husband died) and had seven children, two of whom are retarded and have been institutionalized.

The above are all great-nieces and great-nephews of the proband.

(727) completed the third grade.

(784) is a mechanic's helper with IQ 59.

Continued on page 312

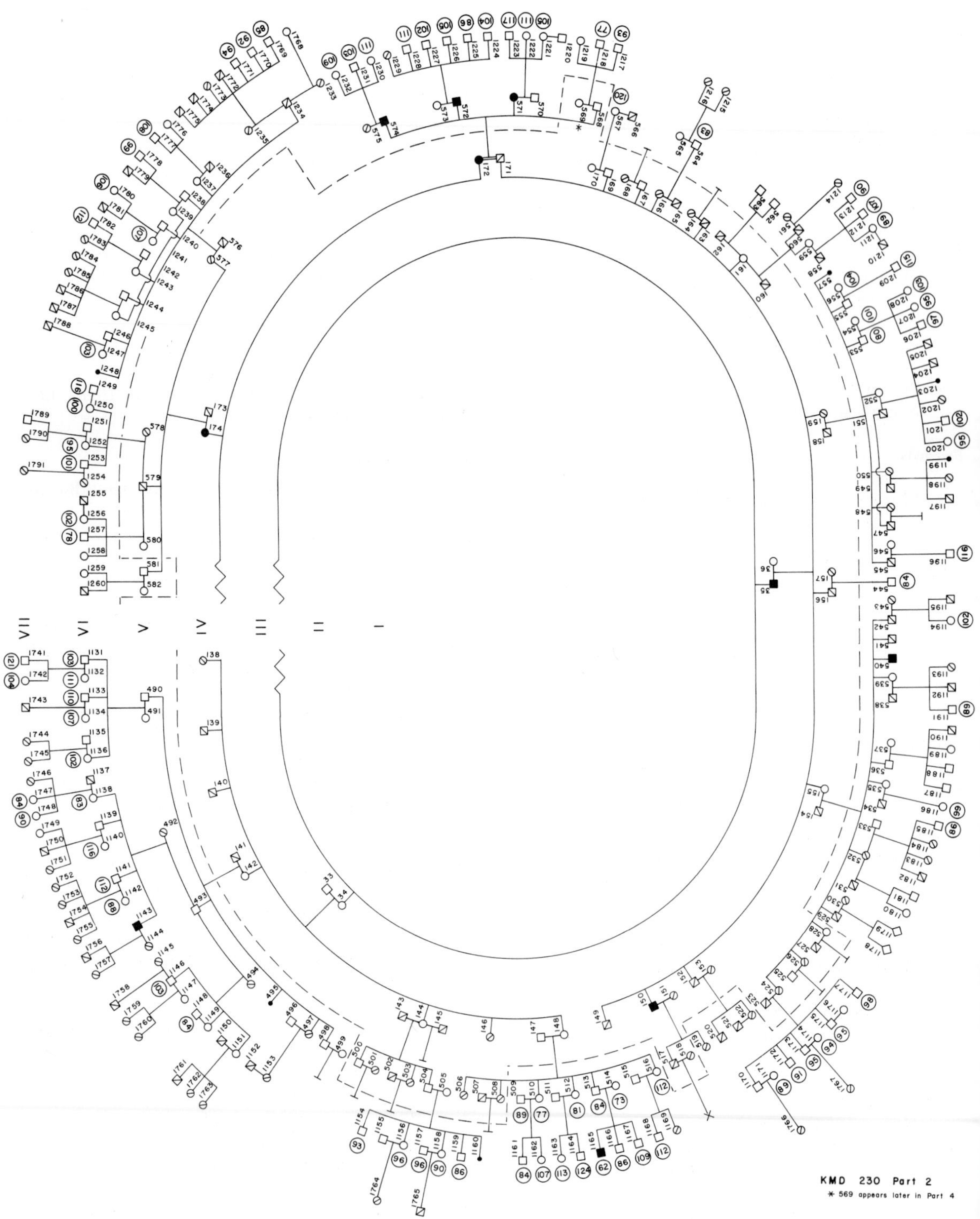

KMD 230 Part 2
* 569 appears later in Part 4

KMD 230 – *Continued*

(1143) completed the sixth grade in special classes.

(1165) has an IQ of 62, parent's IQ's 84 and 73, siblings IQ's 86 and 109.

(1278) has an IQ of 67.

(1340) completed the sixth grade at age 16 years.

(1379) was institutionalized in 1930 at age 11 years and died in the institution. IQ 19.

(1384), sister to (1379), was institutionalized in 1939 at age 16 years. IQ 54.

(1808) has an IQ of 64.

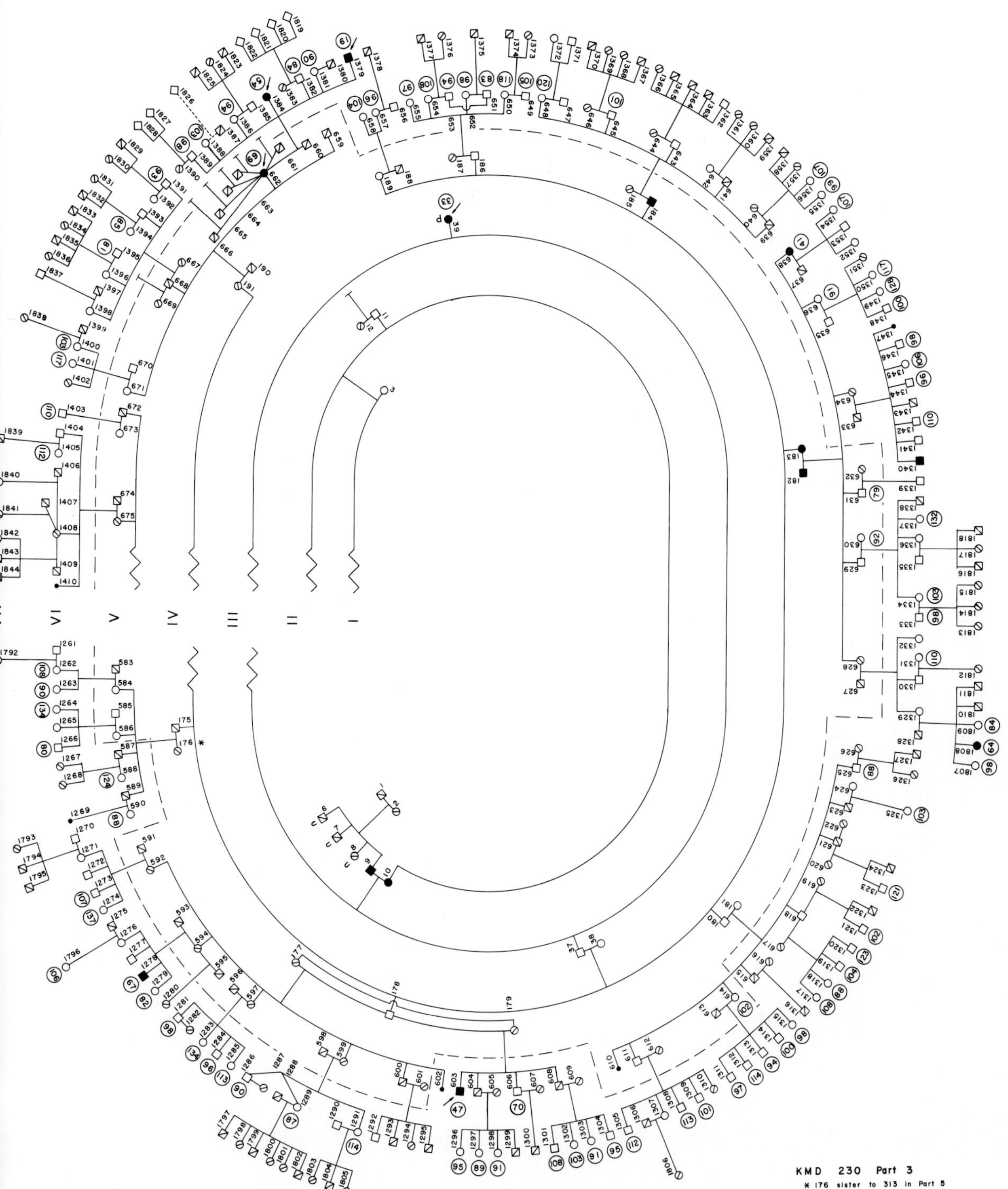

Family Summary

The proband, IQ 33, her parents, two siblings, seven nieces and nephews and 18 more distant relatives were retarded, all of middle to high grade with one exception. The proband's aunts, uncles and first cousins were unknown to the original workers. The proband was reared in a poor home but had no history of injury or disease. Her parents had ten children and 54 grandchildren.

Retardation of proband of probably genetic origin.

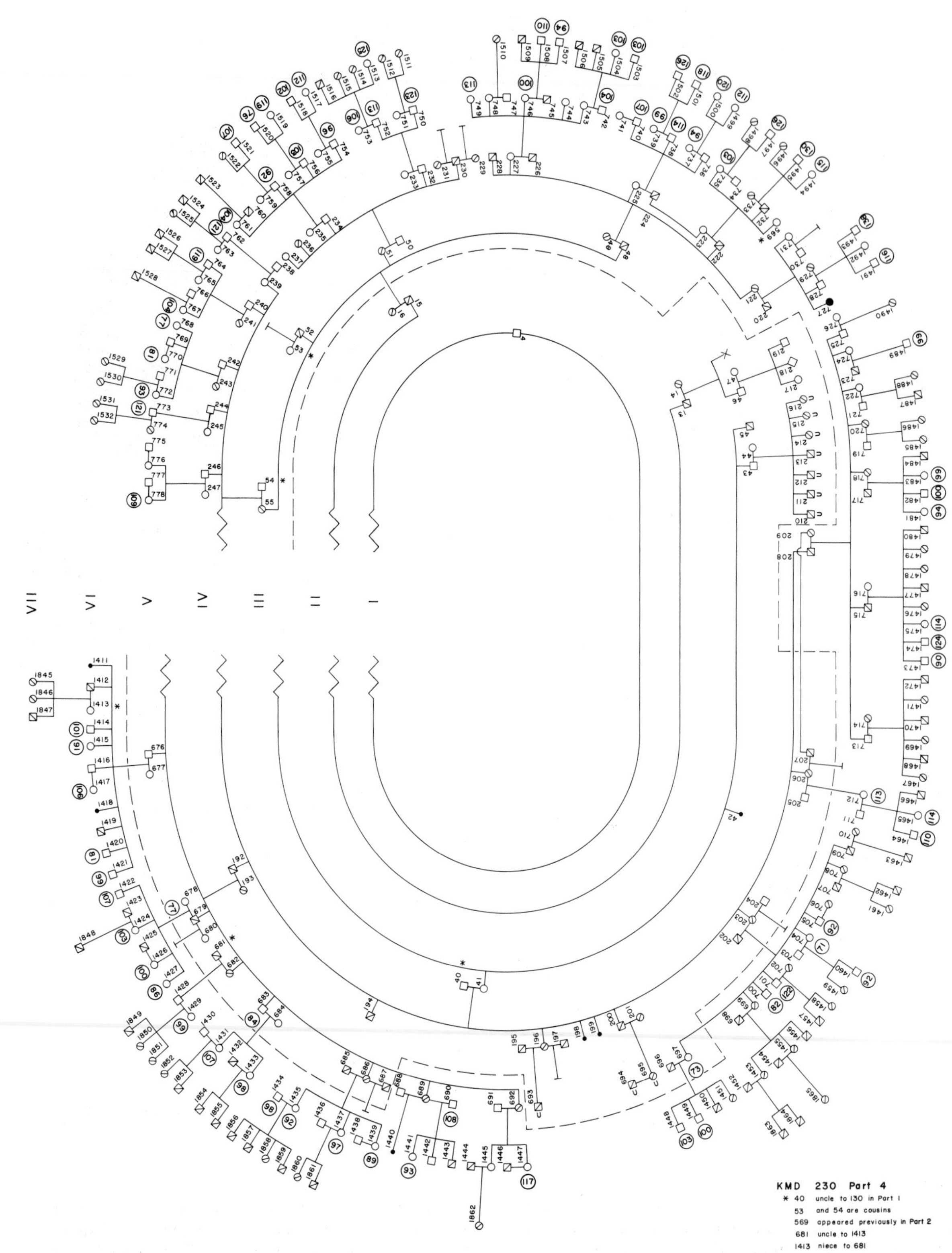

KMD 230 Part 4

* 40 uncle to 130 in Part I
53 and 54 are cousins
569 appeared previously in Part 2
681 uncle to 1413
1413 niece to 681

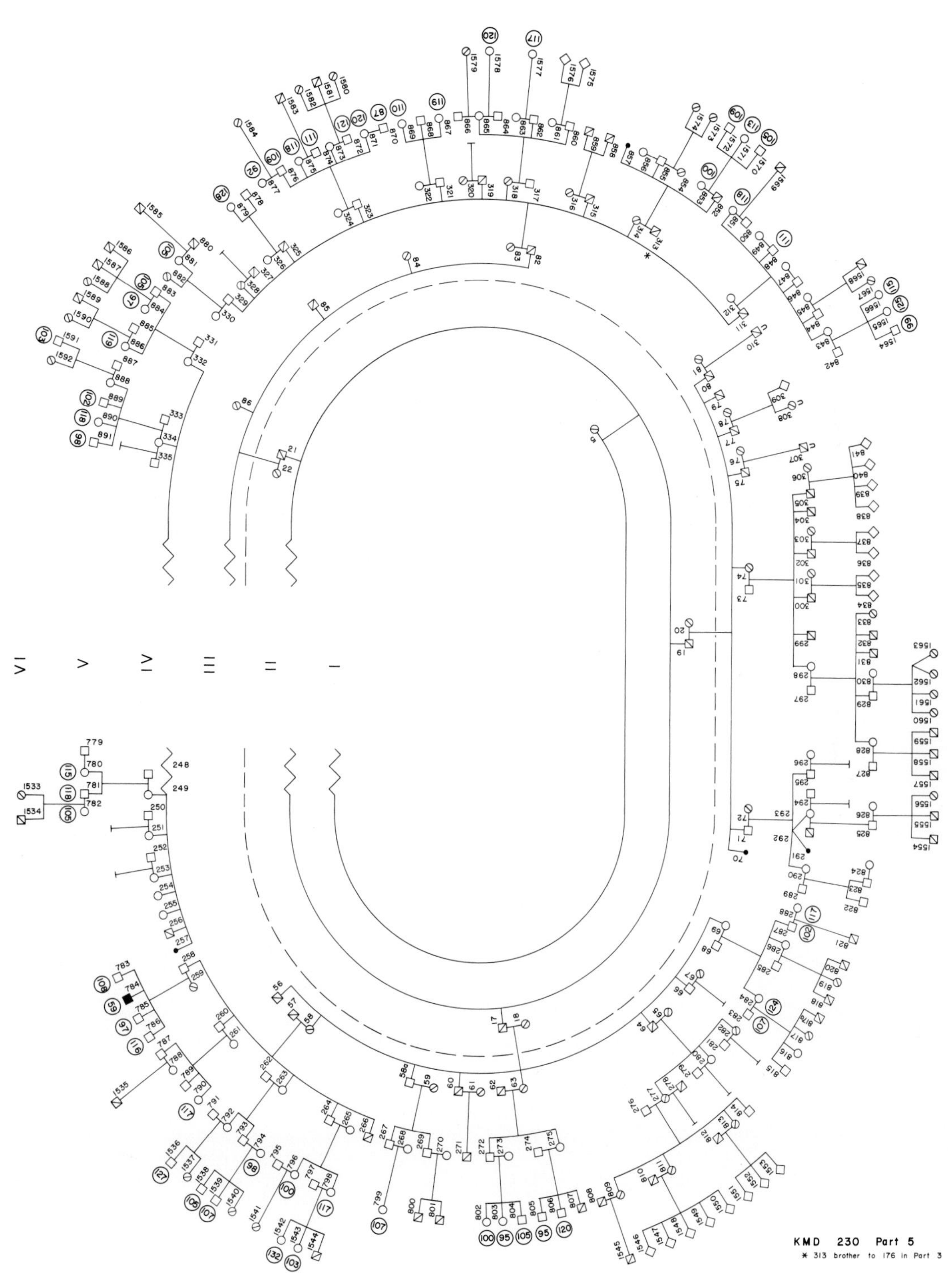

KMD 230 Part 5
* 313 brother to 176 in Part 3

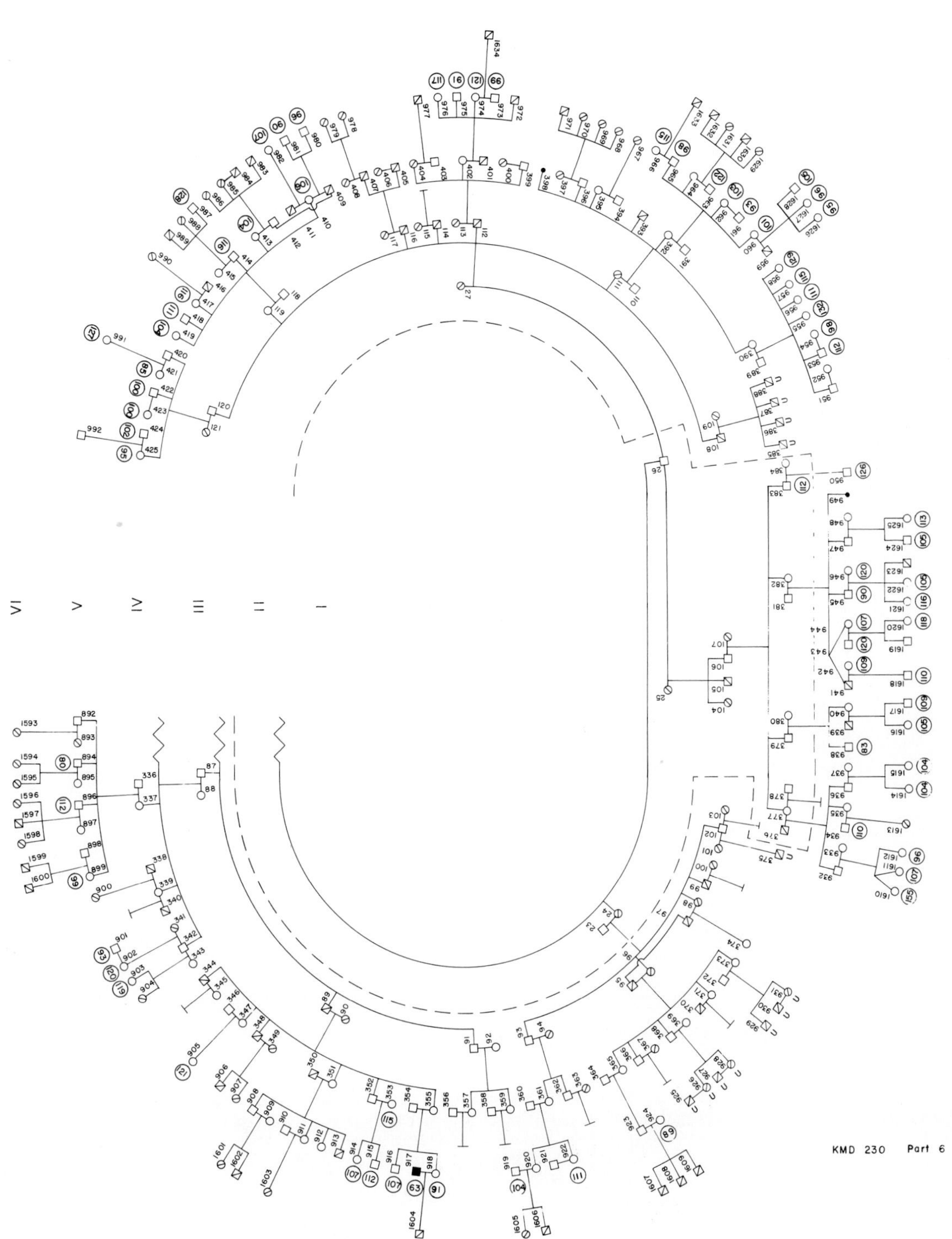

KMD 230 Part 6

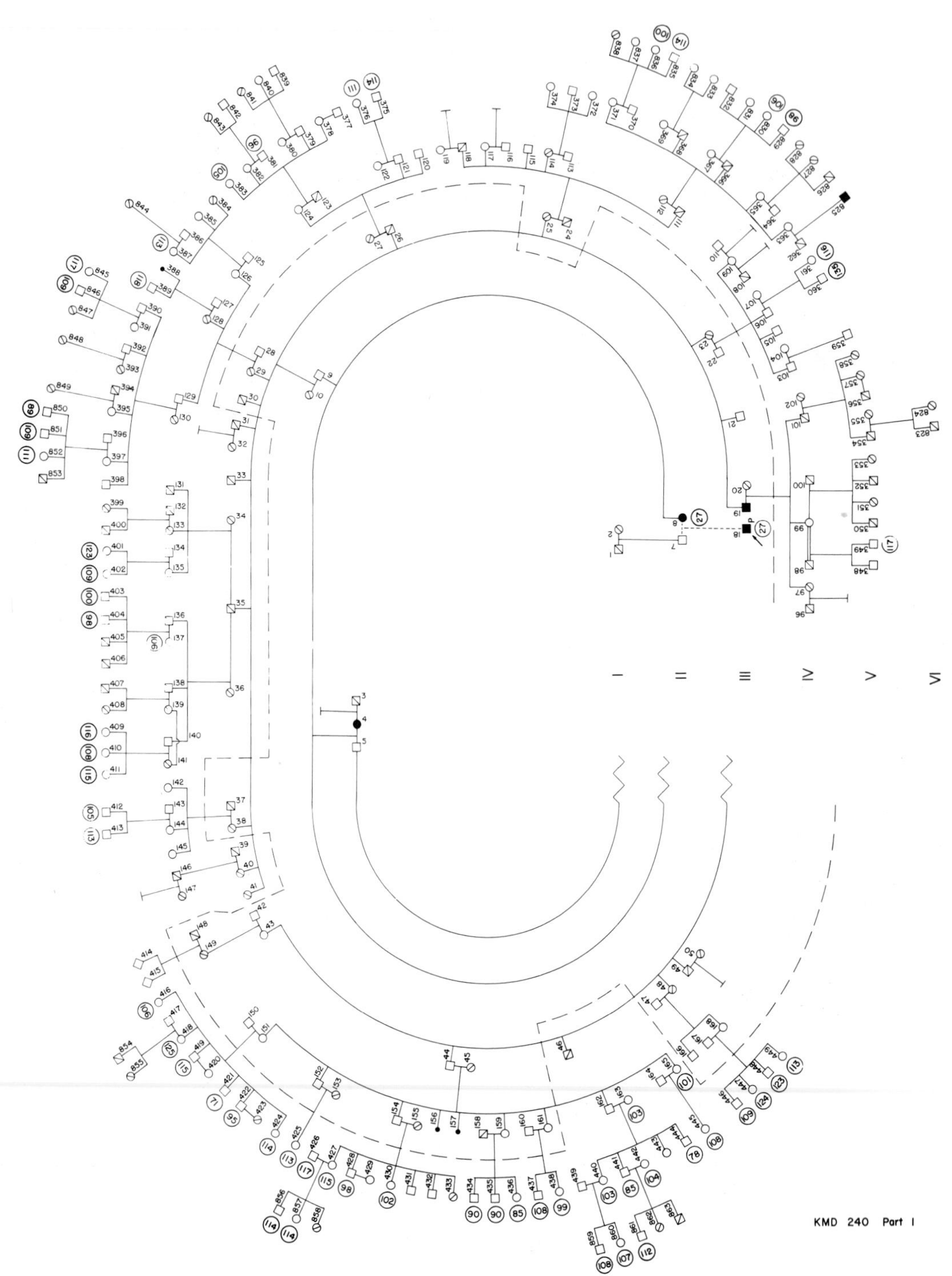

KMD 240 Part I

KMD 240

The Proband

The proband (18) was born in 1879, institutionalized at age 15 years and died of a cerebral hemorrhage in the institution in 1944. He was an illegitimate child who was slow to develop. His right eye was lower than the left and he had scoliosis and clubbed fingers. He lived with his aunt in a good environment. IQ 27. *Diagnosis:* undifferentiated mental retardation.

Grandparents

Maternal grandmother was retarded.

Parents

Father (7) was an alcoholic but had normal intelligence.

Mother (8) was retarded with IQ 27.

Aunts and Uncles

Proband's mother's half brother (16) had senile dementia.

Siblings

None.

Nieces and Nephews

None.

First Cousins

(19) was retarded.

More Distant Relatives

First cousin (73) has a child (260) with IQ 30 and poor vision.

(554) is hydrocephalic.

(825) is at the fourth grade level at age 15 years. He received "social promotions" in school.

(994) has an IQ of 69.

(1012) has an IQ of 65.

(1066) attended an ungraded elementary school and is retarded.

Family Summary

The proband, IQ 27, and his mother were similar in mental ability. The maternal grandmother was also retarded, as was a first cousin and six more distant relatives. This was a large kindred of 1130 persons. The proband's parents had only one child, an illegitimate one, and no grandchildren. The proband's mother's two normal brothers and two normal half brothers produced all the rest of the offspring. The family of (577) and (578) is of interest because their four children, (915), (916), (917) and (918) have IQ's of 136, 149, 138 and 131, respectively.

Retardation of proband of probably genetic origin.

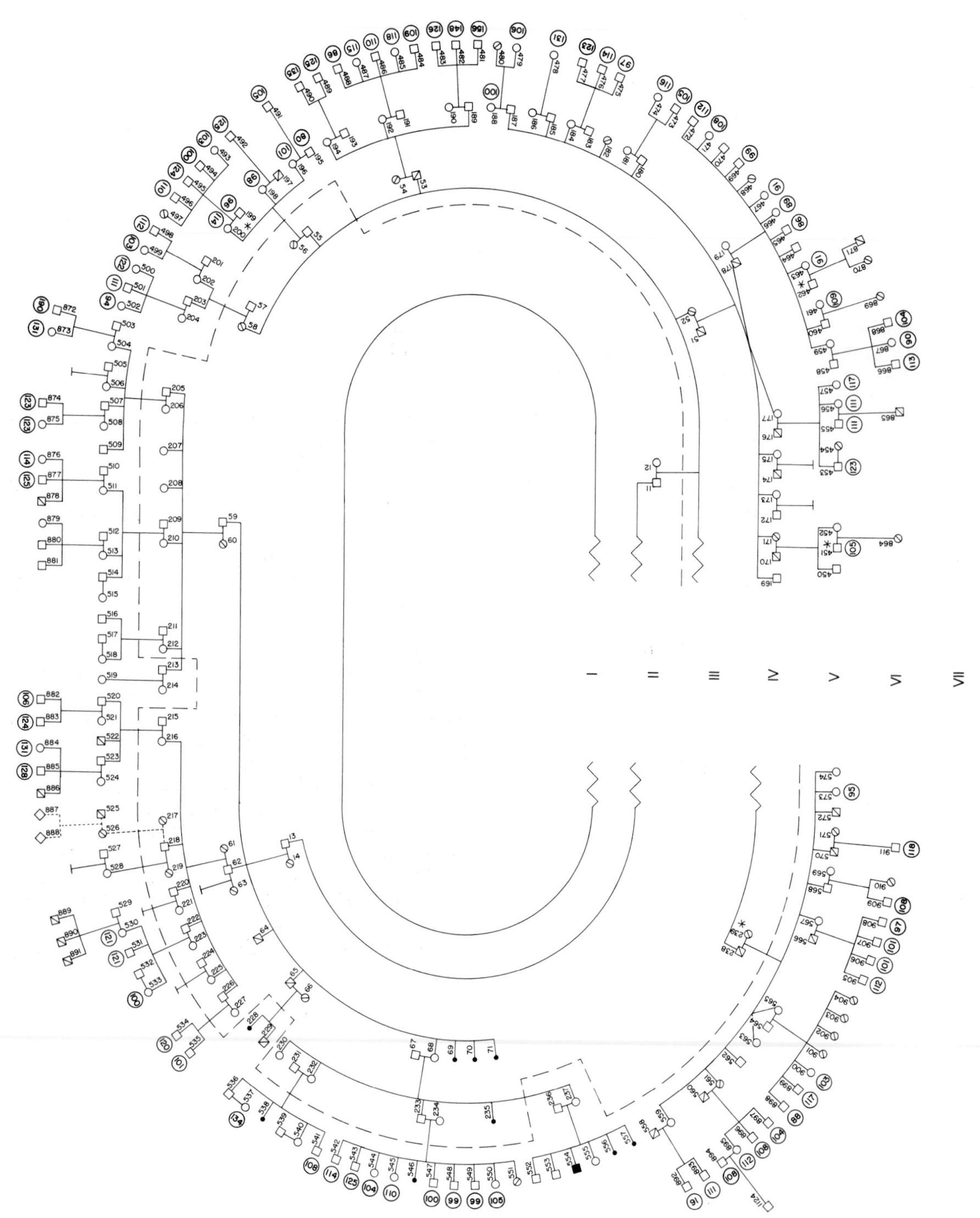

KMD 240 Part 2

* 199 son of 274, cousin to 664, 668 in Part 3

239 sister of 88, 89, 94 in Part 4, 258 in Part 3

451 brother of 462

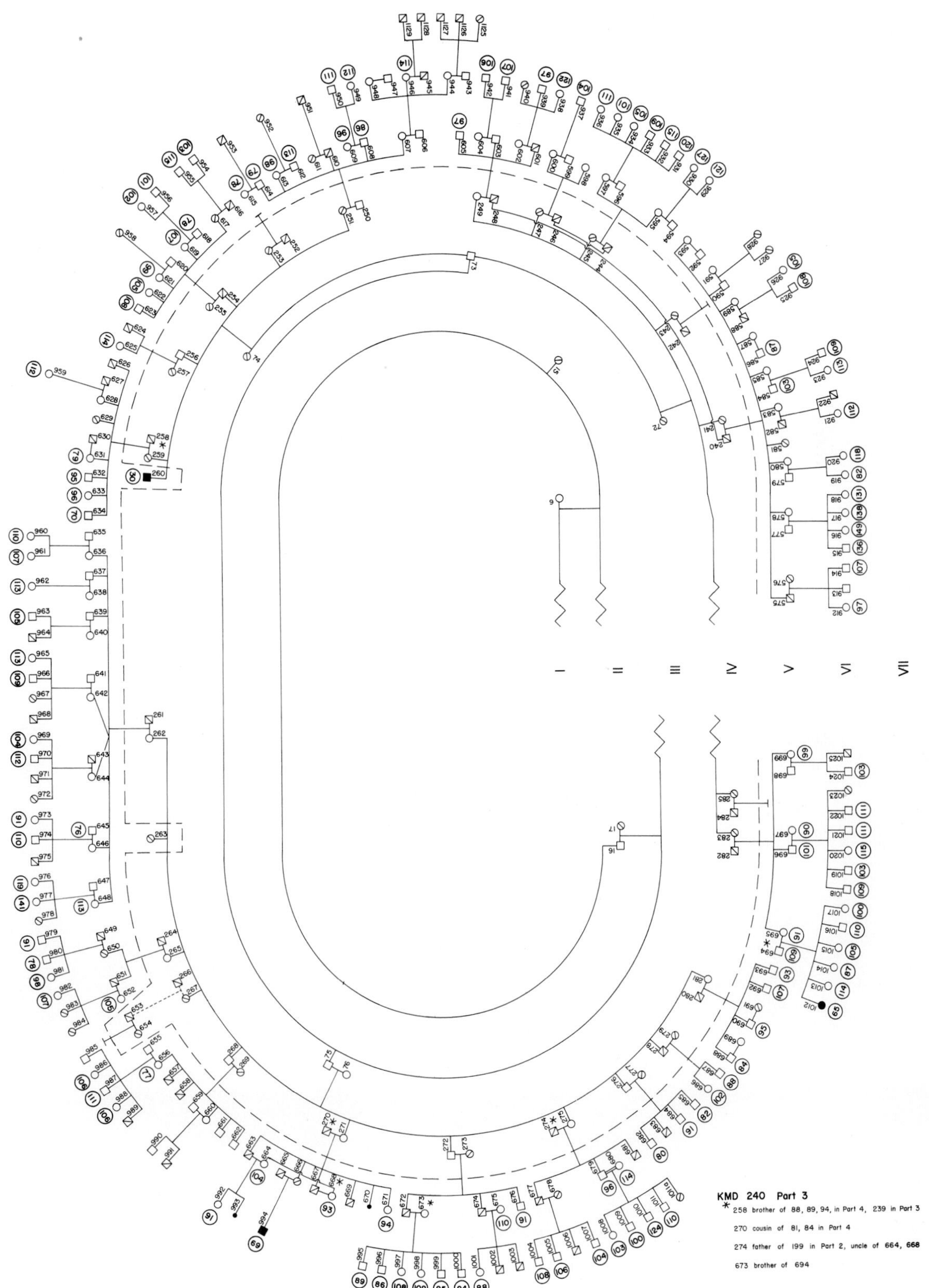
KMD 240 Part 3
* 258 brother of 88, 89, 94, in Part 4, 239 in Part 3
270 cousin of 81, 84 in Part 4
274 father of 199 in Part 2, uncle of 664, 668
673 brother of 694

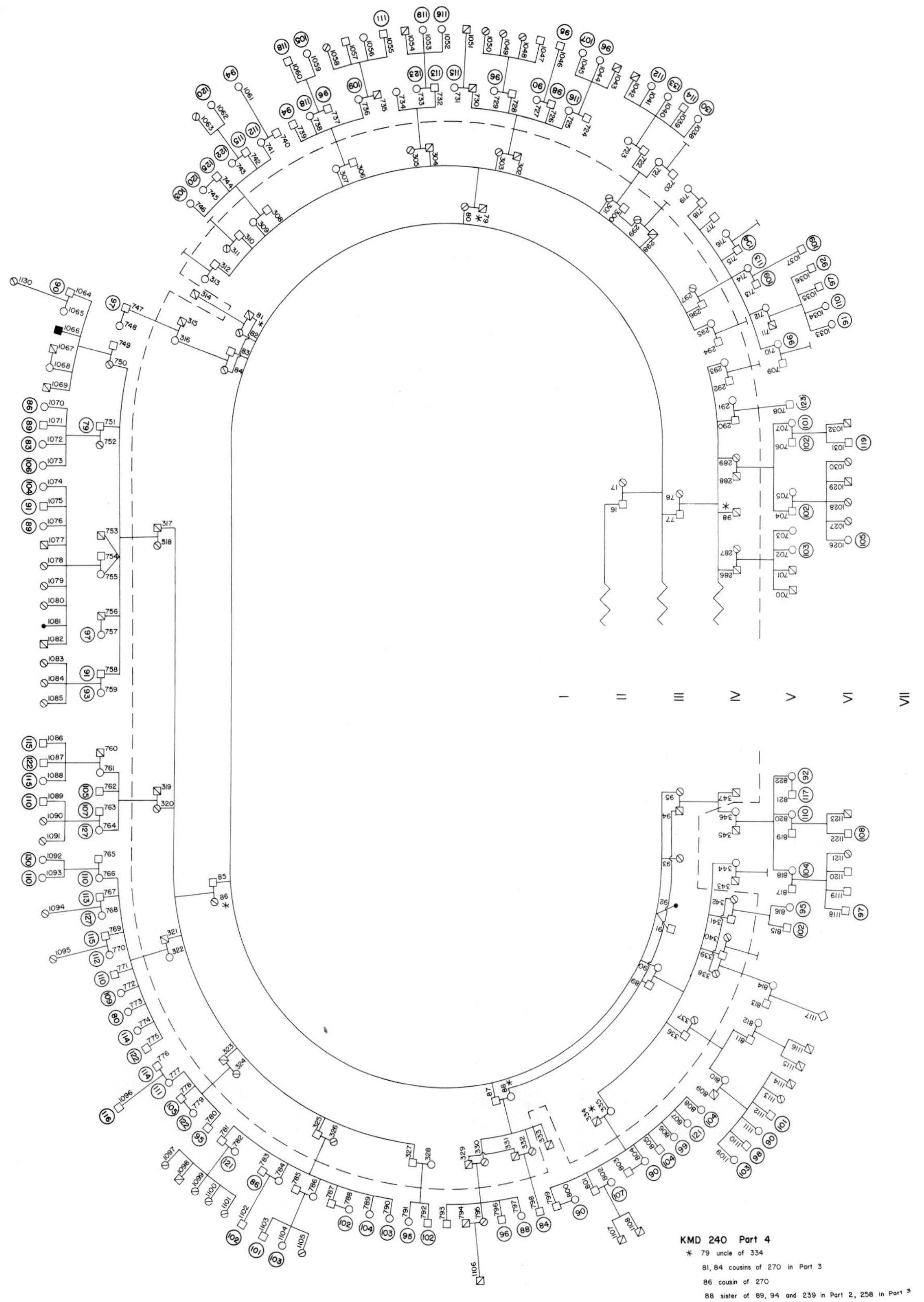
I
II
III
IV
V
VI
VII
KMD 240 Part 4
* 79 uncle of 334
81, 84 cousins of 270 in Part 3
86 cousin of 270
88 sister of 89, 94 and 239 in Part 2, 258 in Part 3

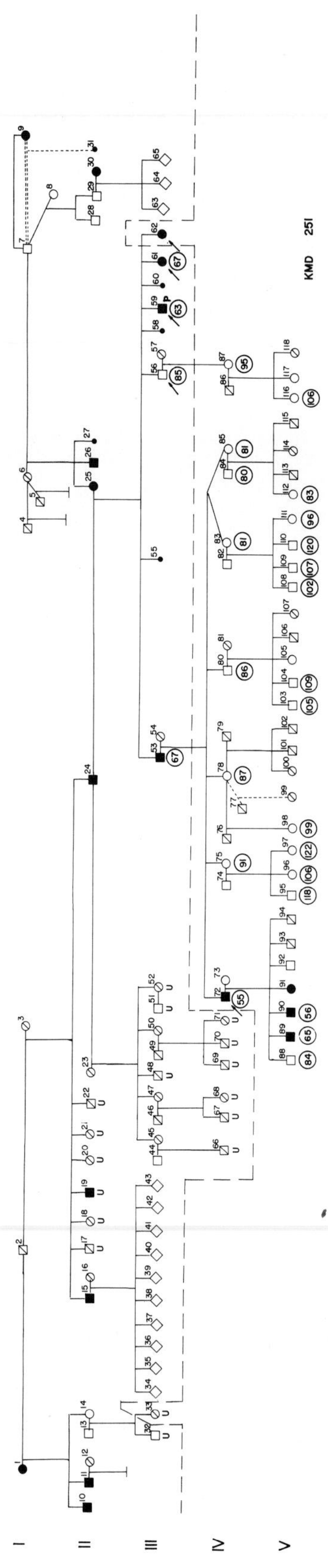
KMD 251

KMD 251

The Proband

The proband (59) was born in 1904, transferred from the state orphanage to the institution at the age of 8 years and died of bronchopneumonia in the institution four years later. His home environment was poor. The parents neglected the children and finally abandoned them. He had no history of difficult delivery or perinatal infection. He did have webbed fingers. IQ 63. *Diagnosis:* undifferentiated mental retardation.

Grandparents

Paternal grandfather was "dull and slow, a poor manager."

Maternal grandmother was an alcoholic, promiscuous and mentally ill.

Maternal grandfather lived for some years with his sister and had a child by her.

Parents

Father (24) was an alcoholic, retarded and cruel to his family.

Mother (25) was promiscuous, an alcoholic and retarded. She was hospitalized at one time for mental illness. She would "go to sleep while talking and on awakening have delusions."

Aunts and Uncles

Paternal uncle (15) was an alcoholic and retarded.

Paternal uncle (19) was retarded.

Proband's father's half brothers (10) and (11) were retarded.

Maternal uncle (26) died at age 8 years. He was a blind, low-grade retardate.

Siblings

Brother (53) completed the fifth grade and is a carpenter's helper. He was in Minnesota State Prison at one time for child abandonment. IQ 67.

(55) and (58) were miscarriages.

Brother (56) was institutionalized at age 12 years and discharged to relatives three years later. He worked on a road construction crew and died following an operation in 1927. IQ 85.

Sister (60) died of "spasm glottis" at 18 days. She was "not right."

Sister (61) was institutionalized at age 4 years, died of bronchopneumonia in the institution the next year. She had a cleft lip and cleft palate, IQ 67 (at age 3 years).

Sister (62) was born in 1916, institutionalized at age 4 years and died in the institution in 1927. She was a low-grade retardate.

Half Siblings

All of unknown intelligence.

Nieces and Nephews

Nephew (72) was institutionalized at age 17 years in 1935, discharged in 1950 and is a laborer. His wife finished high school at age 20 years with a report that indicated her IQ was above 70. Of his seven children, three are retarded, two normal and two not tested yet. One (88), with IQ 84, was thought to have tested too high by the school. He is a poor student and a social problem.

Niece (78) had an illegitimate child. Her IQ is 87.

First Cousins

Unknown.

More Distant Relatives

Nephew's (72) children (89) and (90) have IQ's of 65 and 56, respectively. Their brother (88) has an IQ of 84, but the teacher reported he thought this was "too high."

Family Summary

The proband, IQ 63, both his parents, two paternal uncles, two siblings, a nephew, two grandnephews and one grandniece were high-grade retardates. One maternal uncle and one sibling were low-grade retardates. This family presents a picture of alcoholism, illegitimacy and law breaking. Despite the four generations of retardation and poor environment, most of the individuals in the last two generations have normal intelligence. The proband's parents had eight children and seven grandchildren.

Retardation of proband of probably genetic origin.

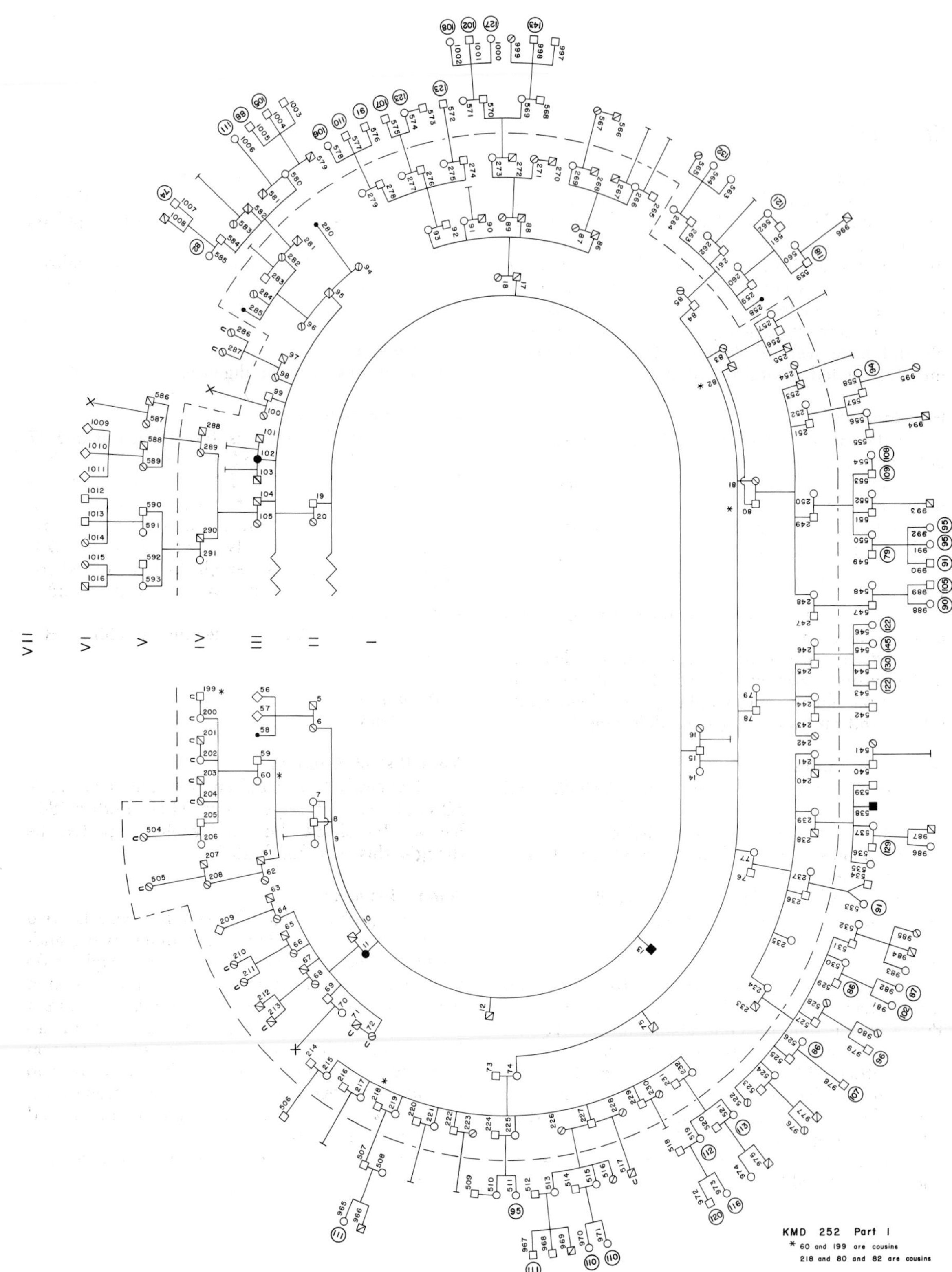

KMD 252 Part I

* 60 and 199 are cousins
218 and 80 and 82 are cousins

KMD 252

The Proband

The proband (132) was born in 1880, institutionalized at age 21 years and died of scirrhus carcinoma in the institution in 1941. She had no history of birth injury or perinatal infection and had no stigmata. She had an illegitimate child by either her father or her brother. IQ 34. *Diagnosis:* undifferentiated mental retardation.

Grandparents

Paternal grandmother was "periodically insane." The early workers thought she had a manic depressive psychosis.

Maternal grandfather died of epilepsy.

Parents

Father (29) and mother (30) were both retarded. The proband's home environment was poor.

Aunts and Uncles

Paternal aunt (11) was retarded.

Paternal uncle (13) died in a mental hospital. He was both retarded and mentally ill.

Paternal uncle (17) was mentally ill, although he was never institutionalized.

Paternal uncle (19) died of epilepsy.

Paternal uncle (27) was both retarded and mentally ill. He was married but childless.

Maternal aunt (36) was retarded. Husband's intelligence is unknown and one of her six children is a known retardate.

Maternal uncle (37) was "erratic and peculiar" and his wife (38) was hospitalized for many years for mental illness.

Maternal aunt (48) was retarded. She was married twice but childless.

Siblings

Sister (120) was retarded. Intelligence of husband unknown. One of her five surviving children (338) was retarded.

Brother (121) died at age 5 years.

Brother (122) died of "dropsy on the brain," probably hydrocephalus, at 3 years. He did not walk or talk and had a large head.

Brother (123) died of diphtheria at age 1 year.

Brother (124) was a retarded laborer who died single and childless.

Brother (125) was retarded, wife (126) normal, three surviving children apparently not retarded. See (339) under "Nieces and Nephews." (125) was the "best of the bunch."

Sister (128), retarded, married the normal brother of (126) and had six children, four normal, one of unknown intelligence, one retarded (349).

Sister (129) was institutionalized in 1901 at age 23 years and died in the institution in 1946, IQ 27 and a deaf mute. She had two illegitimate children by either her father or her brother. One (354) died shortly after birth. The other (356) has normal intelligence.

Brother (130), a retarded laborer, married (131) a retarded woman and had eight surviving children, two of whom (363) and (365) are known to be retarded.

Child

Son (377) died shortly after birth.

Nieces and Nephews

Niece (338) died at age 11 years. She never went to school.

Niece (339) was in the fifth grade at age 15 years. She had "chorea" and was reported to be "very slow mentally." She took a handicapped child from the state orphanage to keep because she was lonely. He was blind in one eye, crippled and "not in his right mind." She refused to allow the state to give him an intelligence test.

Nephew (349) is epileptic and retarded.

Nephew (363) is a retarded married but childless laborer.

First Cousins

(102), retarded, was married twice but had no children.

(148), retarded, had two children by a normal husband, one retarded (413), one of unknown intelligence (415). (413) had a retarded, illegitimate child.

More Distant Relatives

(379) is an odd job man with IQ 65 and four children, one retarded, two borderline and one low-normal child, (799), (801), (803) and (796).

(413) was an alcoholic and retarded. His illegitimate child (858) is also retarded.

(431) is a farm laborer with IQ 53.

(538) was deaf, blind and a high-grade retardate. Perhaps the retardation was the result of his other handicaps, since he completed the fifth grade and was in the sixth when he left school at age 15 years.

(660) was retarded; "very much below average" on school report.

(765) is a farm laborer with IQ 52.

(768), sister to (765), has an IQ of 63. She also has three siblings (760), (764) and (767) with borderline IQ's of 72, 78 and 77, respectively.

(799) had an IQ of 66. She was married twice but died childless. Two of her three siblings (801) and (803) have borderline IQ's of 75 and 74, one (796) has an IQ of 82.

(858) had micropthalmus and an IQ of 26.

Continued on page 329

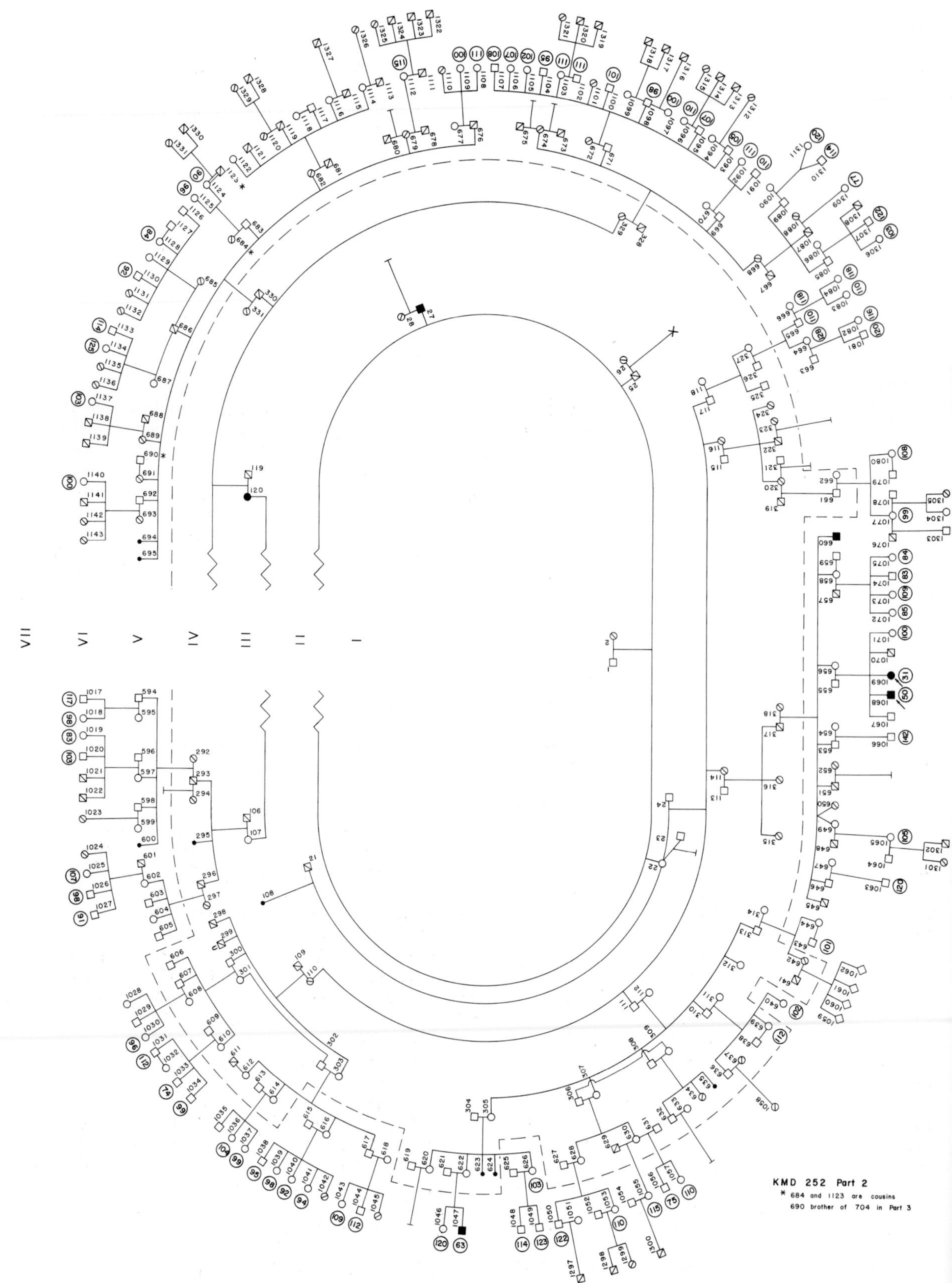

KMD 252 Part 2
* 684 and 1123 are cousins
690 brother of 704 in Part 3

KMD 252 – *Continued*

She was institutionalized and is the proband for KMD 22.

(919) is institutionalized with IQ 28.

(1047) was in a special school with IQ 63.

(1068) was committed as a ward at one time but never institutionalized. IQ 50.

(1069), sister to (1068), was institutionalized. She had limited speech, poor coordination and convulsions. One diagnosis was myxedema, absolute absence of thyroid function. IQ 31.

(1242) was institutionalized at age 4 years. IQ 48 at age 3 years.

Family Summary

The proband, IQ 34, both her parents, four paternal aunts and uncles, two maternal aunts, all seven of her adult siblings, three nephews and one niece, two first cousins and 14 more distant relatives were retarded. The proband had an illegitimate child who died shortly after birth. Her home environment was poor. However, retardation is appearing among the grandchildren of the proband's parents, so it would seem that more than poor environment is effective here. The proband's parents had ten children and 30 grandchildren (seven of whom died in infancy).

Retardation of proband of probably genetic origin.

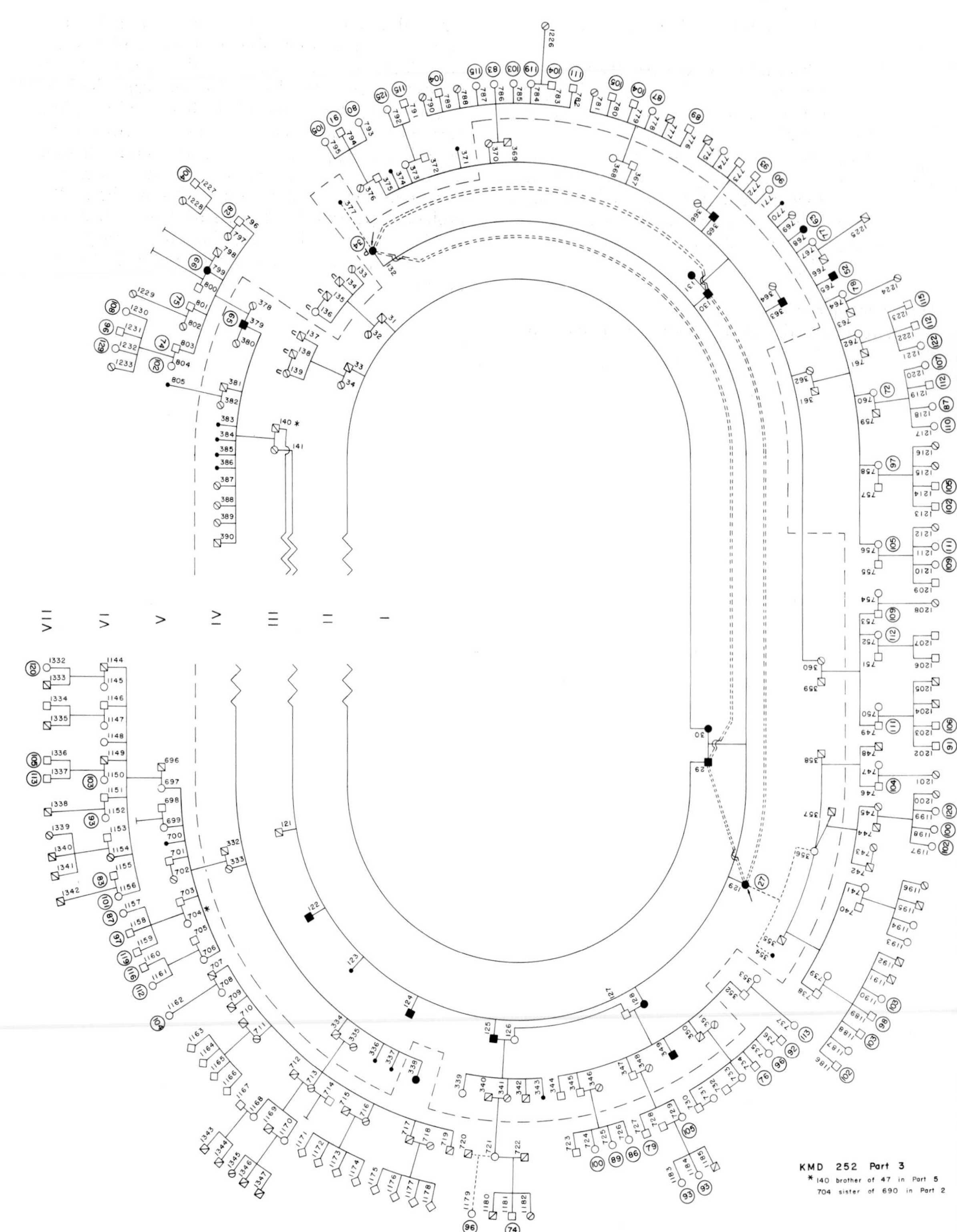

KMD 252 Part 3
* 140 brother of 47 in Part 5
704 sister of 690 in Part 2

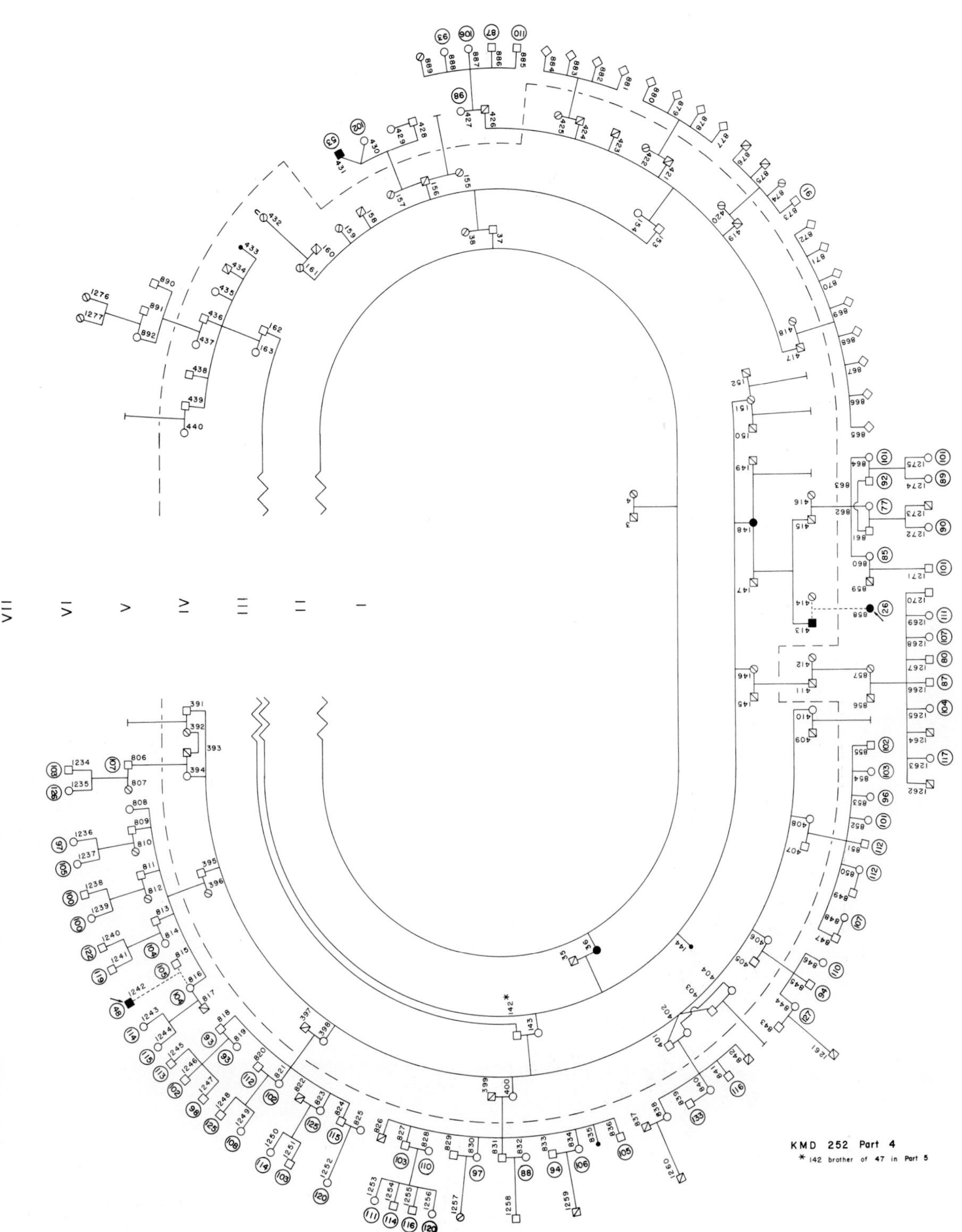

KMD 252 Part 4

* 142 brother of 47 in Part 5

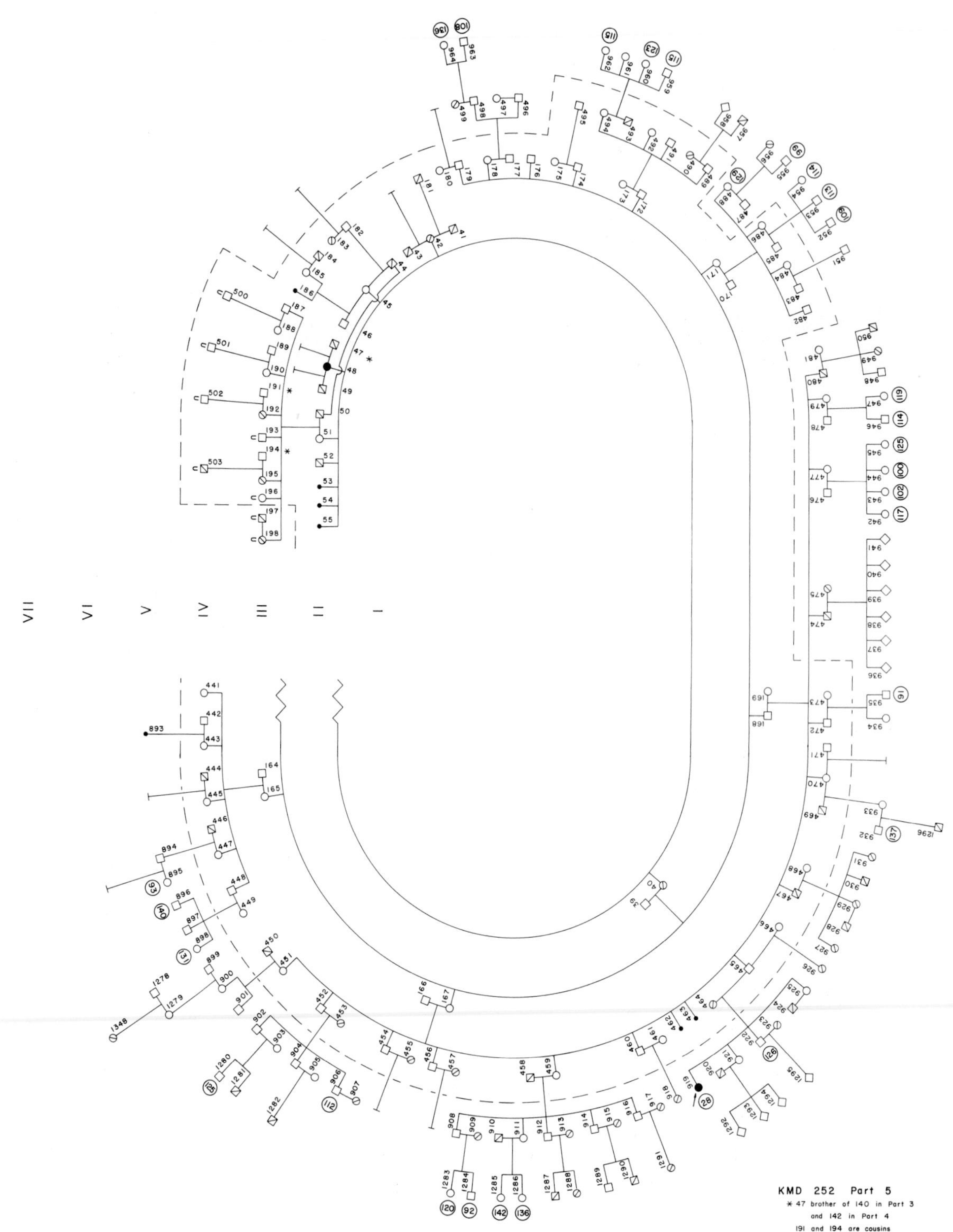

KMD 252 Part 5

* 47 brother of 140 in Part 3 and 142 in Part 4

191 and 194 are cousins

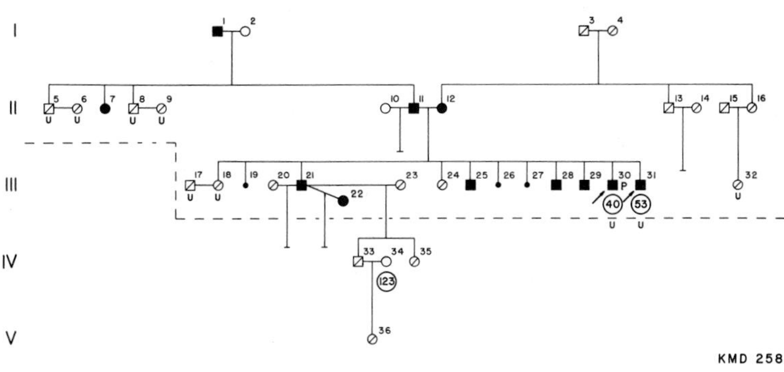

KMD 258

The Proband

The proband (30) was born in 1893, placed in an orphanage upon the death of his mother and transferred to the institution at the age of 4 years. He had no history of difficult birth or perinatal infection. He ran away in 1918 and has not been heard of since, except that he was in jail in 1925. IQ 40. *Diagnosis:* undifferentiated mental retardation.

Grandparents

Paternal grandfather was retarded—"could learn nothing."

Parents

Proband's father (11) had dwarfish stature and was afflicted with a chronic eye disease that made him blind in one eye. He went to school until the age of 15 or 16 years, but never learned to write his name. He worked steadily, but never could manage his affairs.

Probands' mother (12) could not learn to keep house.

Aunts and Uncles

Paternal aunt (7) died at age 10 years. She was a helpless cripple who could "walk a little" and was epileptic and retarded.

All the maternal and paternal relatives remained in Holland.

Siblings

Sister (18) remained in Holland.

Sister (19) died at age 1 month.

Brother (21) was retarded. He was married three times but had only two children, both of unknown intelligence.

Sister (24) died of diphtheria at age 9 years.

Brother (25) is unmarried, childless and retarded.

Brother and sister (26) and (27) both died of "spasms" in infancy.

Brother (28) is unmarried, childless and retarded.

Brother (29) was accidently shot in a hunting accident at age 22 years. He was retarded.

Brother (31) was institutionalized at age 1 year. He ran away in 1917 and has not been heard of since. IQ 53.

Nieces and Nephews

Not of interest.

First Cousins

Unknown.

More Distant Relatives

Unknown.

Family Summary

The proband, IQ 40, his paternal grandfather, a paternal aunt, both parents, and five siblings were retarded. One retarded brother had two children of unknown intelligence. The proband and his institutionalized brother both ran away from the institution as young men and have not been heard of since. The proband's parents had 11 children and two known grandchildren.

Retardation of proband of probably genetic origin.

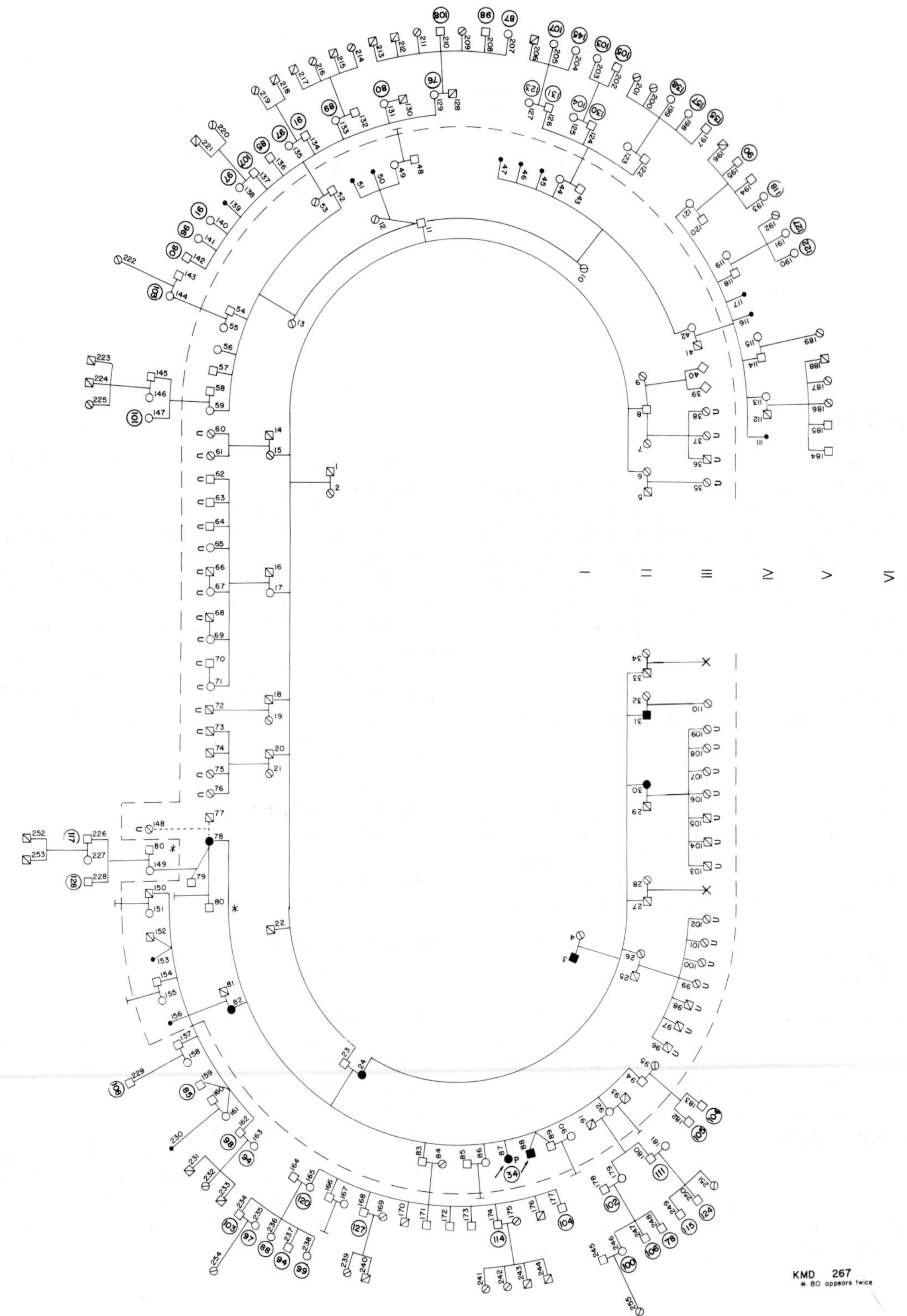

KMD 267
* 80 appears twice

KMD 267

The Proband

The proband (87) was born in 1894, institutionalized at age 9 years and died of carcinoma of the uterus in the institution in 1950. She walked at 18 months, talked at 3 years. She was reared in a good home and had no history of early trauma or infection. As a child she was always "very nervous and would shake all over." IQ 34. *Diagnosis:* undifferentiated mental retardation.

Grandparents

Maternal grandfather was retarded and had "spells."

Parents

Father (23) had normal intelligence but was subject to epileptoid attacks.

Mother (24) was retarded and was hospitalized for mental illness a year before her death, at age 52.

Aunts and Uncles

Maternal aunt (30) and uncle (31) were retarded.

Siblings

Sister (78) had an illegitimate child. She was a high-grade retardate.

Sister (82) was a high-grade retardate with five normal children and two children of unknown intelligence.

Brothers (83), (89) and (94) have normal intelligence. (83) has epileptoid attacks.

Sisters (86) and (92) have normal intelligence.

Brother (88) was institutionalized at age 8 years and died of myocarditis and enteritis in the institution in 1910 at the age of 14 years. He was a low-grade retardate.

Nieces and Nephews

Not of interest.

First Cousins

Unknown. The paternal and maternal relatives all remained in Denmark, except for one family (11).

More Distant Relatives

Not of interest.

Family Summary

The proband, IQ 34, and her institutionalized brother were rather low-grade retardates. The proband's maternal grandfather, mother, a maternal aunt and uncle and two sisters were high-grade retardates. The home environment was good. The proband's parents had nine children and 25 grandchildren.

Retardation of proband of probably genetic origin.

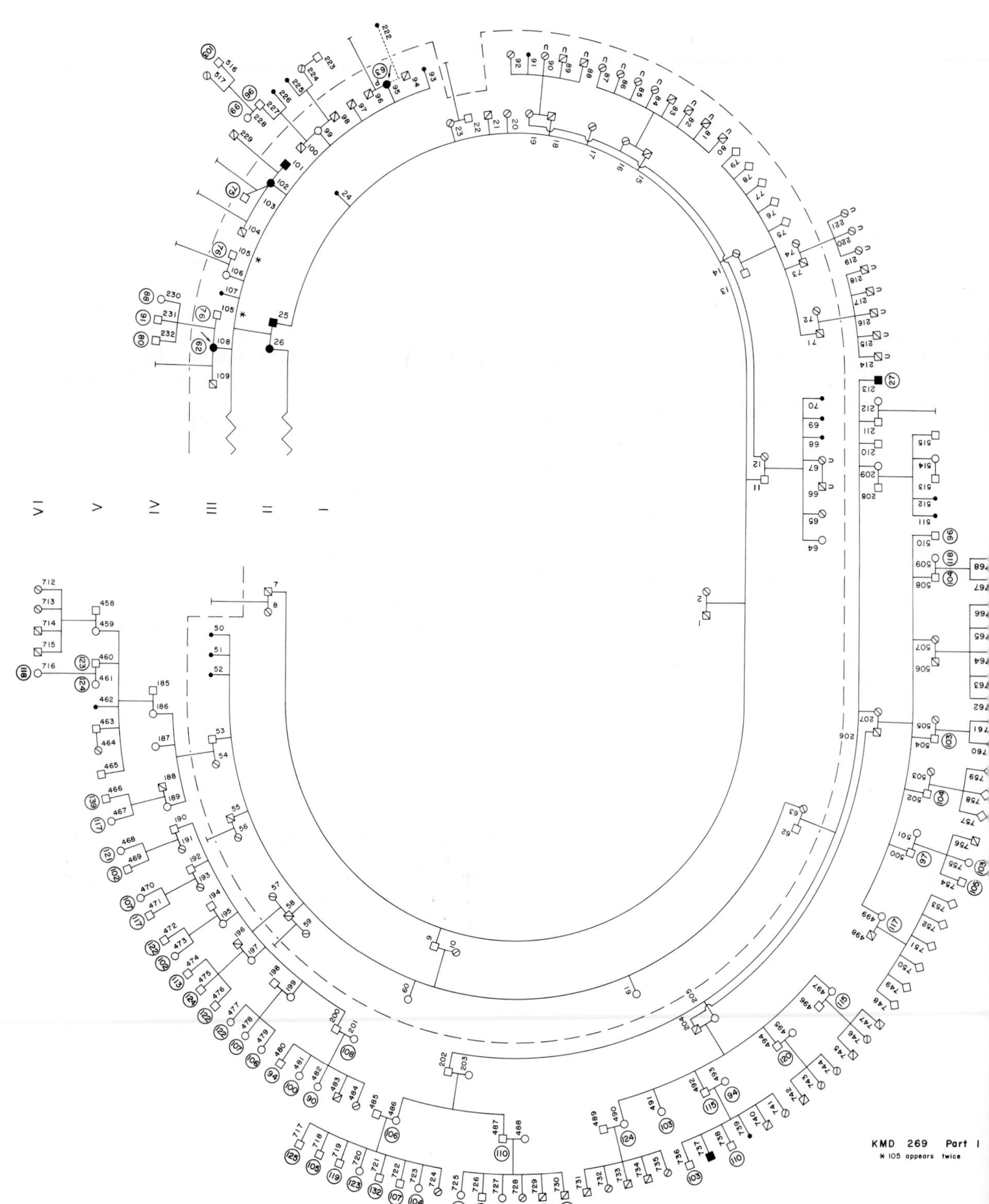

KMD 269 Part I
* 105 appears twice

KMD 269

The Proband

The proband (95) was born in 1893, institutionalized from the state orphanage at age 18 years and was discharged to her parents five years later. She was reinstitutionalized in 1920 after the birth of an illegitimate child in 1917. She was sterilized after her readmission and placed under outside supervision. After a second, two-year readmission she married and in 1947 was discharged from guardianship because she had made a good adjustment. She had no history of birth injury or perinatal infection and no stigmata. The home environment was so poor that the proband and her siblings were removed to the state orphanage. IQ 63. *Diagnosis:* undifferentiated mental retardation.

Grandparents

Maternal grandfather was retarded.

Parents

Father (25) was an alcoholic, retarded. He was blind for the last 25 years of his life.

Mother (26) was promiscuous and retarded.

Aunts and Uncles

Paternal relatives not of interest.

Maternal uncle (28) was a retarded laborer. One of his nine children, by two wives of unknown intelligence, had an IQ of 41.

Maternal uncle (36) was a retarded laborer. His wife and child are of unknown intelligence.

Maternal uncle (38) was a retarded laborer. His wife and two children are of unknown intelligence.

Proband's mother's half brother (43) was a retarded farm laborer who was married but childless.

Siblings

Brother (93) died of a hemorrhage at 4 weeks.

Brother (97) died of spinal meningitis at age 3 years.

Sister (99) was originally described as retarded but she finished the ninth grade. She refused to cooperate.

Sister (102) was in the second grade at age 15 years. She is retarded and has a bad reputation. Her first husband (101) was divorced from her. Her second husband (103) had a prison record and an IQ of 75. Her third husband (104) was killed in a brawl. She had only one child (229) whose intelligence is unknown.

Sister (106) had normal intelligence.

(107) was a miscarriage.

Sister (108) was institutionalized in 1932 at age 31 years, sterilized and was placed under outside supervision. She first married (105), the husband of her deceased sister (106). His IQ is 76. Their three children were committed as dependent, neglected and unsuitable for adoption. One is retarded. Her second husband, (109) with unknown intelligence, had himself had six children, two of whom have been committed as retarded. IQ of (108) is 62.

Brother (113) has been accused of incest. He was once a communist and also at one time was an "Apostolic" preacher. He will not cooperate. He has been married four times, once to a retarded woman (111) with IQ 56, once to an Indian, and twice to unknown women. His children are not retarded.

Brother (115) is an unmarried and childless freight handler with IQ 75.

Sister (117) was institutionalized in 1924 at age 18 years. Her illegitimate child was born in the institution. Consent was not obtained for a sterilization operation. She was placed under outside supervision in 1930 and was discharged in 1935 because she was out of the state. She had no stigmata. IQ 66.

Child

Son (222) died at age 1 month, cause of death unknown.

Nieces and Nephews

Nephew (231) has been in a reformatory and as a child was considered unsuitable for adoption. IQ 91.

Nephew (232) was considered as unsuitable for adoption and has an IQ of 80. He was in a mental hospital for a short time.

Nieces (243) and (244) have both been in tuberculosis hospitals. No school record could be obtained for either of them. They may be deceased.

First Cousins

Some of the paternal cousins are unknown.

(134) has been diagnosed as a "typical imbecile." IQ 41.

(149) died in a mental hospital.

(169) married her first cousin. They both had unknown intelligence although both completed the eighth grade. Their seven tested children have IQ's ranging from 73 to 106.

More Distant Relatives

(213) has an IQ of 27.

(245) married his first cousin (246), both with unknown intelligence and had two children: (518) who is deaf and has IQ 74 and (519) with IQ 111.

(260) with IQ 78 married (259) with IQ 65.

(264) is institutionalized with IQ 42.

(265) is institutionalized with IQ 42 and a diagnosis of "imbecile, familial."

Continued on page 339

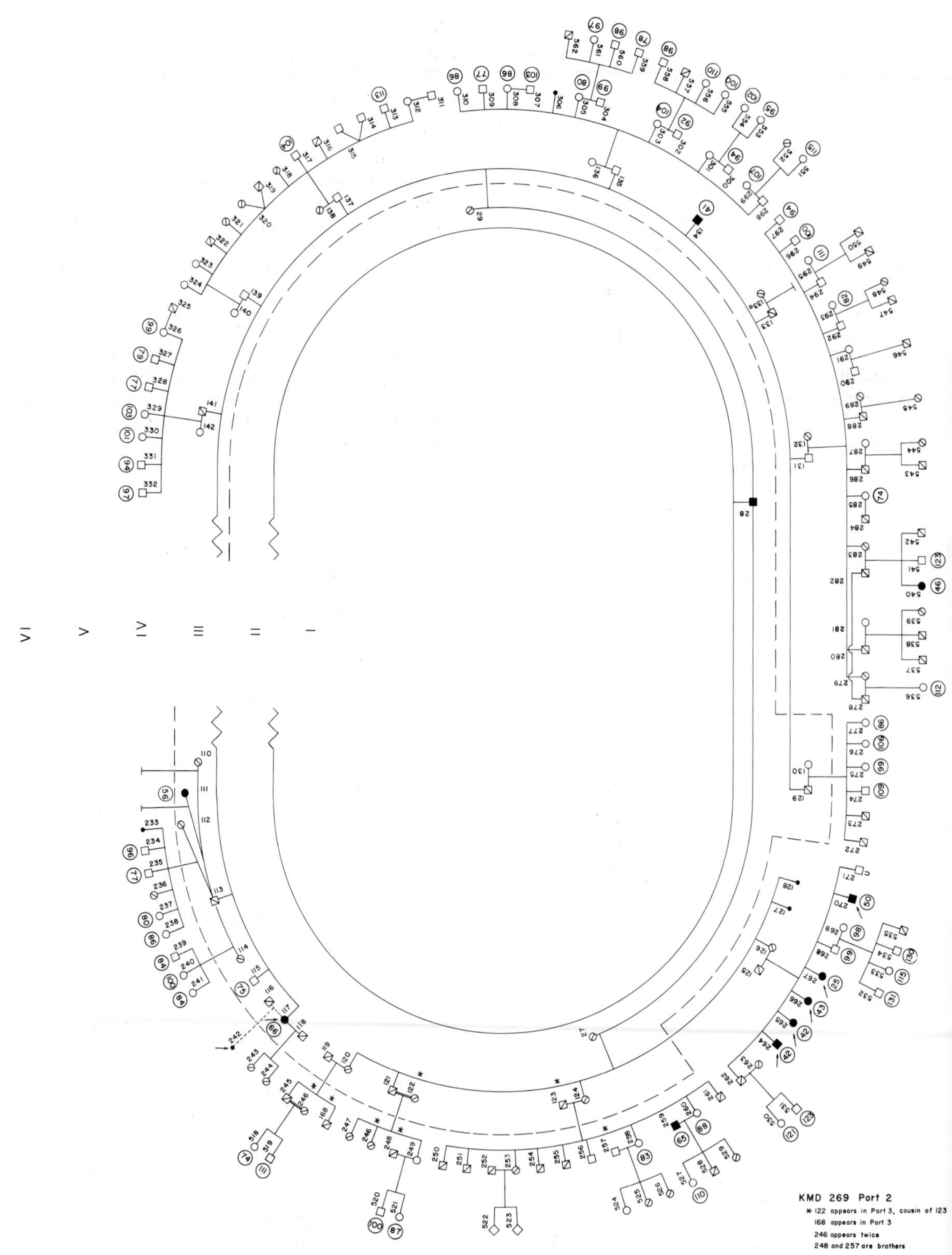
VI
V
IV
III
II
I
KMD 269 Part 2
* 122 appears in Part 3, cousin of 123
168 appears in Part 3
246 appears twice
248 and 257 are brothers

KMD 269 – *Continued*

(266) is institutionalized with IQ 43 and a diagnosis of "imbecile, familial."

(270), sibling to (264), (265) and (266), was institutionalized at age 34, sterilized and is now under outside supervision. IQ 50.

(268), a normal brother to the above, with IQ 99 (wife's IQ 98) has three children who have IQ's of 131, 115 and 130, respectively.

(397) has IQ 63.

(540) has IQ 46.

(570) has IQ 69.

(648) repeated the second, fourth and fifth grades and completed the seventh at age 16 years.

(651) with IQ 80 married (650) who was in the sixth grade at age 16 years.

(655), sibling to (648) and (651), is institutionalized with IQ 28. Two other siblings have borderline intelligence.

(737) does not go to school. The school reports he is retarded.

(804) has IQ 65.

Family Summary

The proband, IQ 63, her maternal grandfather, both parents, three maternal uncles and the proband's mother's half brother, three sisters, one first cousin and 12 more distant relatives were retarded. In the proband's immediate family all the retardates were high grade. One brother, with unknown intelligence, has exhibited erratic social behavior. The home environment was poor. The proband and a sister each had an illegitimate child, and the seven married persons in this sibship have had a total of 16 spouses (including the two fathers of the illegitimate children). The brother referred to above has had four wives. Despite the overall picture of retardation, mental instability and poor environment, two sisters had normal intelligence and no record of social difficulties. The proband's parents had 11 children and 21 grandchildren, including five who died in infancy.

Retardation of proband of probably genetic origin.

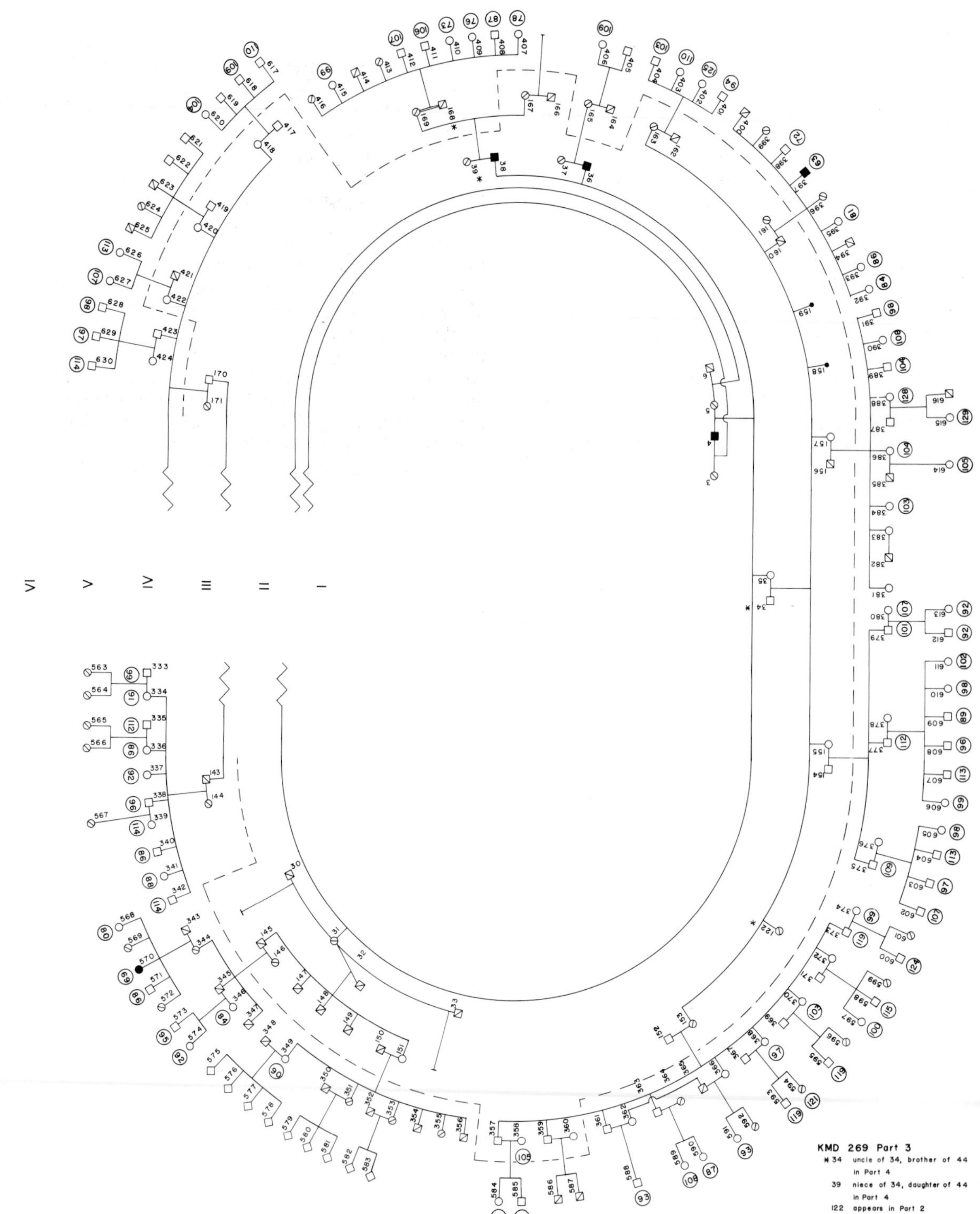

KMD 269 Part 3

* 34 uncle of 34, brother of 44 in Part 4

39 niece of 34, daughter of 44 in Part 4

122 appears in Part 2

168 appears in Part 2

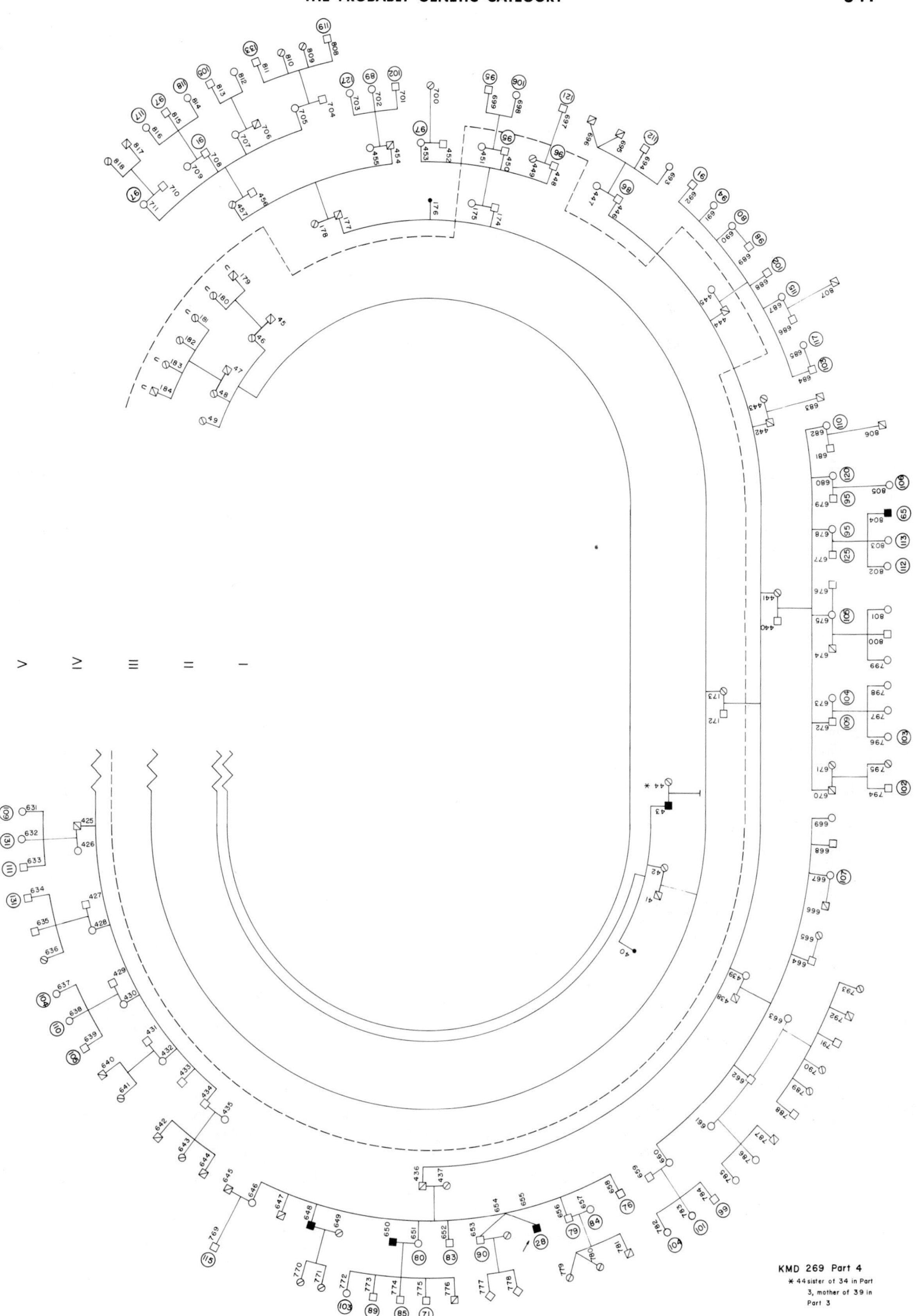

KMD 269 Part 4

* 44 sister of 34 in Part 3, mother of 39 in Part 3

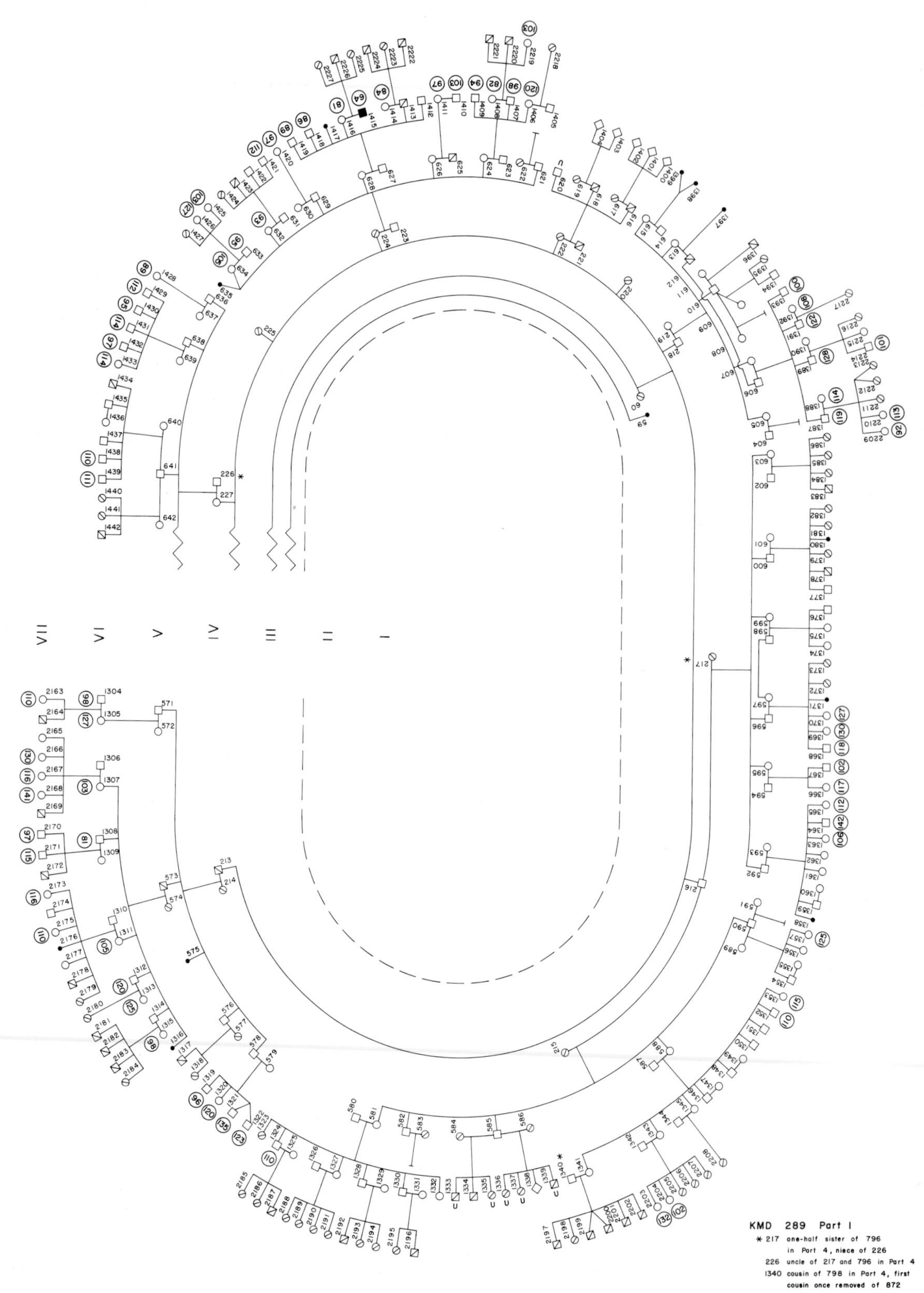

KMD 289 Part I

* 217 one-half sister of 796 in Part 4, niece of 226
226 uncle of 217 and 796 in Part 4
1340 cousin of 798 in Part 4, first cousin once removed of 872 in Part 5

KMD 289

The Proband

The proband (195) was born in 1895, institutionalized at age 16 years and discharged four years later to his family. He was admitted to a mental hospital in 1918 where he died of influenza and pneumonia two months later. Apparently he was not hospitalized because of mental illness. He had no history of birth injury or perinatal infection. IQ 53. *Diagnosis:* undifferentiated mental retardation.

Grandparents

Maternal grandparents were both retarded. The maternal grandfather was in a mental hospital for a short time. He was so retarded that the court appointed a "conservator" for him.

Parents

Father (39) was retarded. He did not support his family and was divorced by the proband's mother (40), also retarded. She was in a mental hospital for a short period.

Aunts and Uncles

Paternal uncle (26) was retarded. He was married but childless.

Maternal aunt (43) was retarded. Her children's intelligence is unknown.

Maternal uncle (48) was hospitalized for mental illness at one time. There is some doubt as to whether he was mentally ill. He was a middle-grade retardate, however.

Maternal aunt (52) was institutionalized twice for mental retardation. She was also epileptic. She had a normal son by a normal man.

Siblings

Brother (191) died in a mental hospital after he had been hospitalized at age 20 years.

Sister (192) died from lack of care at age 7 months.

Brother (193) died in a mental hospital. His diagnosis was psychosis with mental deficiency.

Brother (194) was a retarded laborer who died single and childless.

Sister (197) was a high-grade retardate who married twice and had four children, all normal.

Sister (200) was a high-grade retardate. Her husband and four children all had normal intelligence.

(201) was a stillbirth.

Nieces and Nephews

Eight, all with normal intelligence.

First Cousins

(206) was retarded.

More Distant Relatives

(360) was retarded.

(1021) completed the eighth grade at the age of 21. Her husband has normal intelligence.

(1030) and (1032), siblings to (1021), are both retarded. (1030) left school in her teens when she completed the sixth grade. (1032) completed the fifth grade with "social promotions." He is deaf but could not learn to use a hearing aid and his parents refused to send him to the school for the deaf.

(1940) has an IQ of 64.

(1954) has an IQ of 70 and a long welfare record. His wife completed the ninth grade.

(1966) is retarded with possible cerebral palsy.

(1968) died of bronchopneumonia and Schilder's disease. The pediatrician reported he was mentally retarded. He was a brother to (1966).

(2299) is institutionalized with an IQ of 45 and his brother (2300) is also institutionalized with an IQ of 56.

(1416), (1453), (1628) and (2259) are interesting because all four had normal intelligence but married retarded spouses.

Family Summary

The proband, IQ 53, his maternal grandparents, both his parents, one paternal uncle, two maternal aunts and one maternal uncle, four siblings, one first cousin and nine more distant relatives were retarded. In addition, one retarded sibling and one of unknown intelligence were mentally ill, as was a maternal uncle. Aside from the proband's own family, six of the nine more distantly related retardates appear among the descendants of (91), a normal cousin. The rest of the paternal side of this large family is composed almost entirely of healthy, normal, well balanced individuals, with few social problems. They are descendants of pioneer Mormons who emigrated west and south to Utah and Mexico.

The maternal relatives were completely different. They present a picture of three generations of retardation, epilepsy, mental illness, alcoholism and promiscuity. While the proband's maternal grandparents had 12 children, including a miscarriage, a stillbirth, an infant death, two drownings (46) and (47) and two institutionalizations, they had only 19 grandchildren of whom four died in infancy and four who were known to have been childless. This left only 11 as possible parents. Unfortunately, several of these persons could not be found for follow-up. The proband's own parents had eight children and eight grandchildren.

Retardation of proband of probably genetic origin.

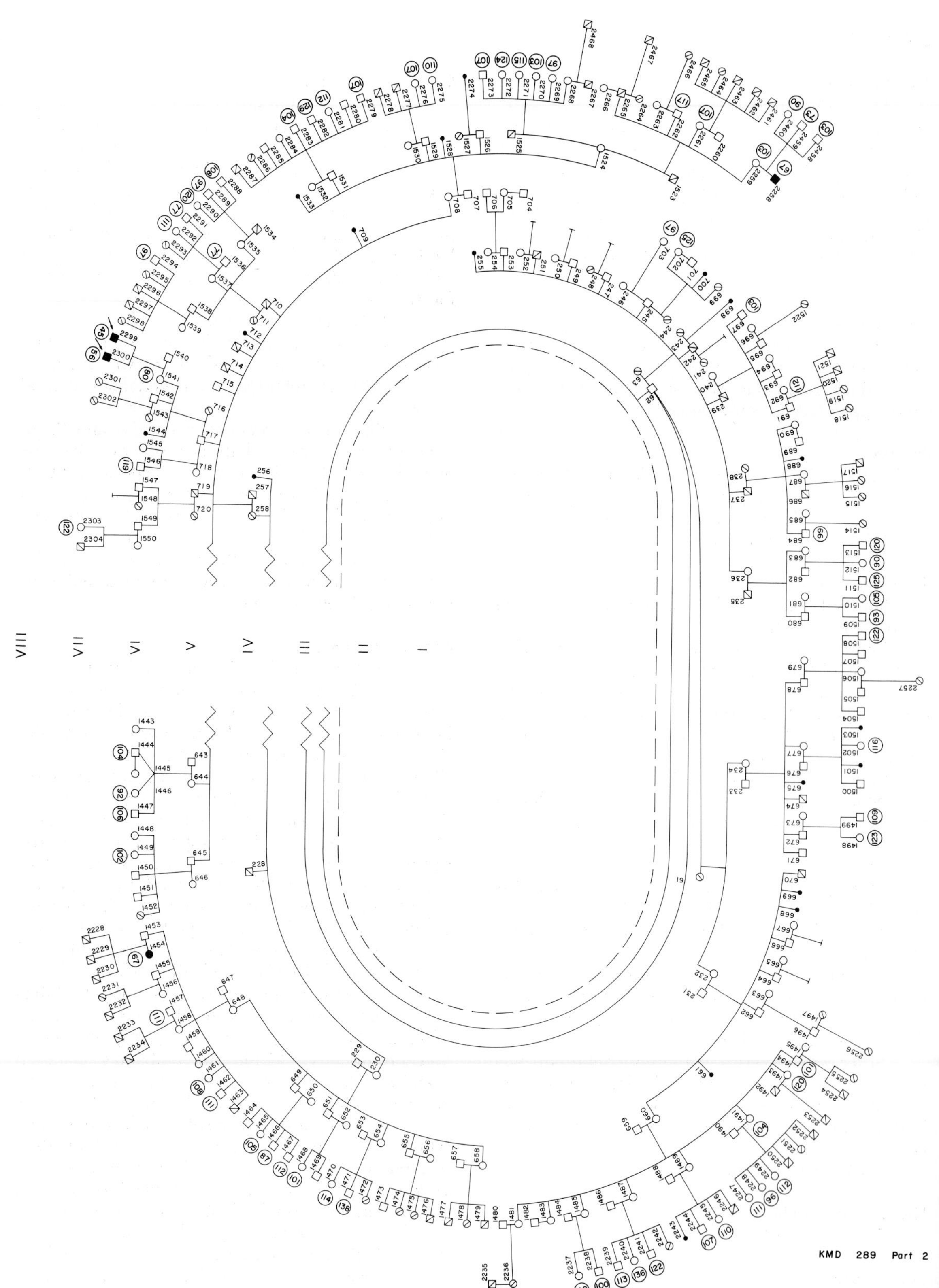

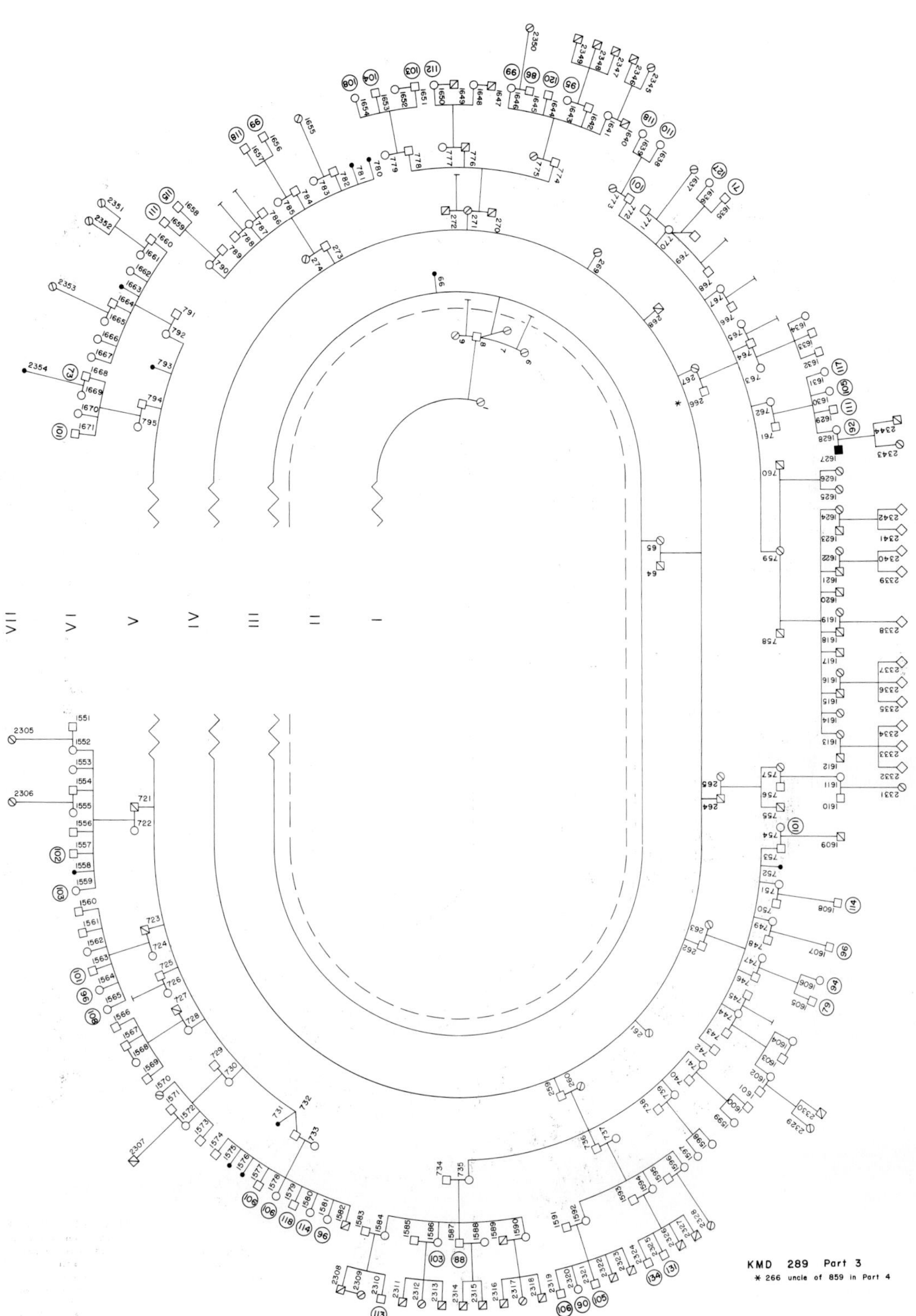

KMD 289 Part 3

* 266 uncle of 859 in Part 4

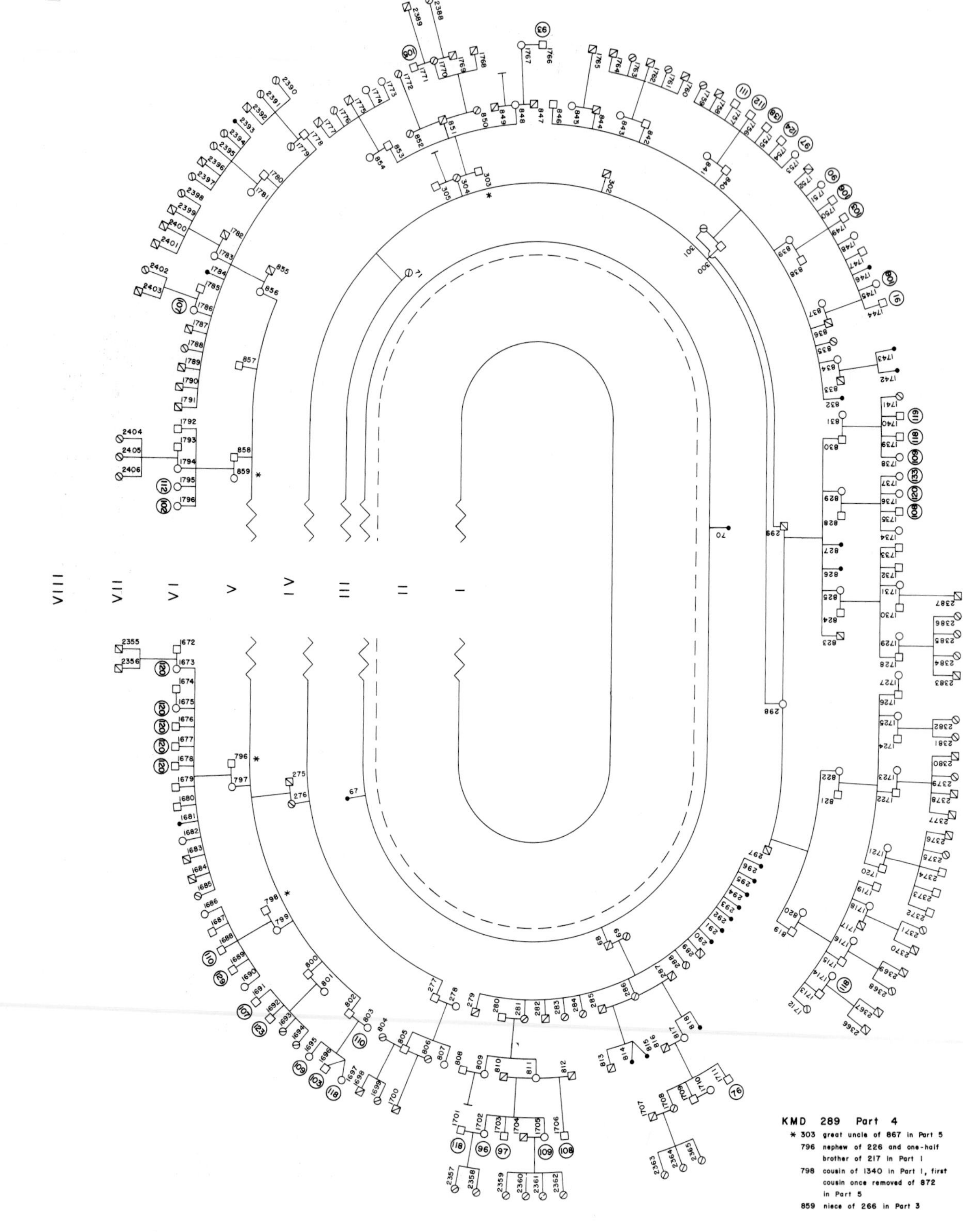

KMD 289 Part 4

* 303 great uncle of 867 in Part 5

796 nephew of 226 and one-half brother of 217 in Part I

798 cousin of 1340 in Part I, first cousin once removed of 872 in Part 5

859 niece of 266 in Part 3

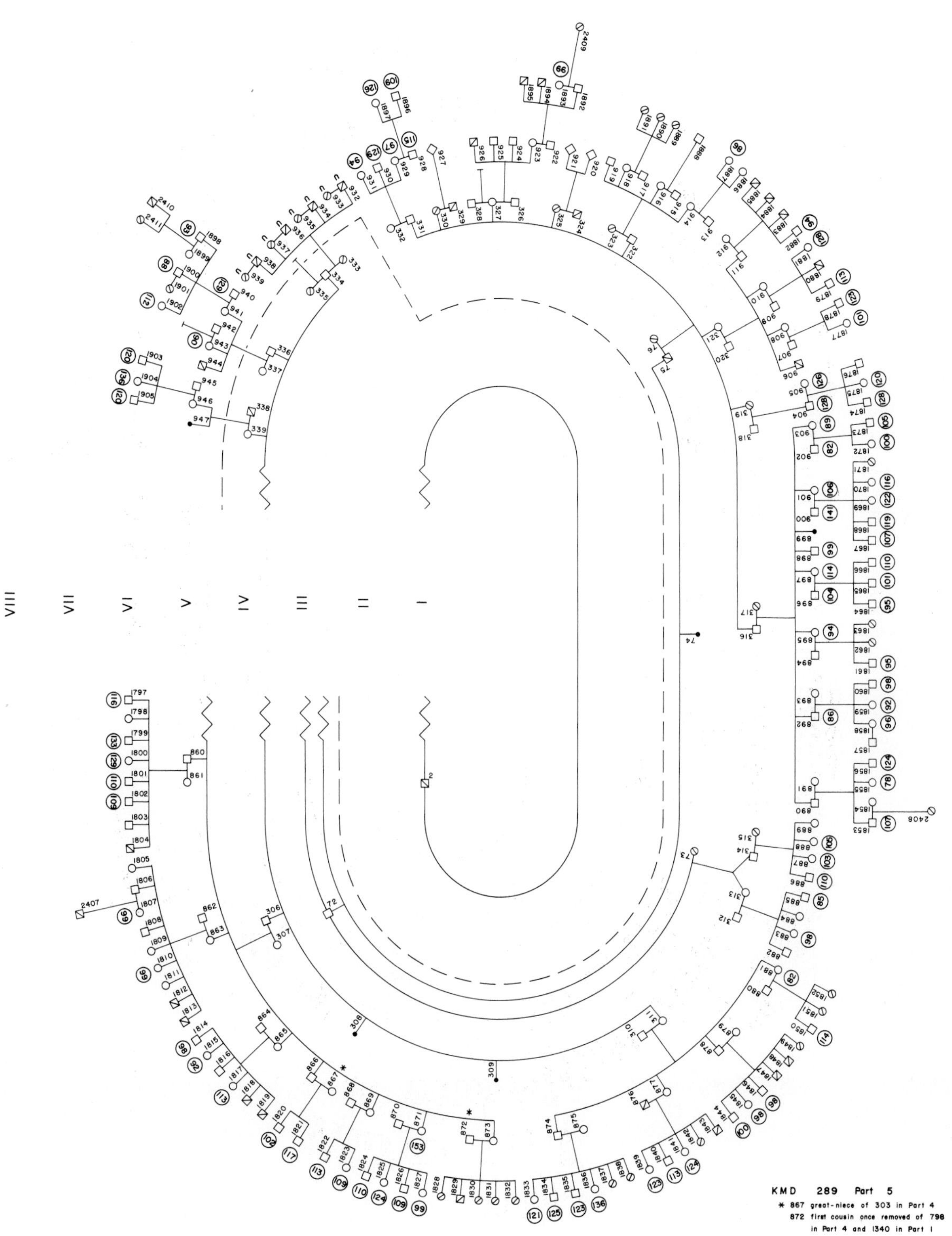

KMD 289 Part 5

* 867 great-niece of 303 in Part 4

872 first cousin once removed of 798 in Part 4 and 1340 in Part 1

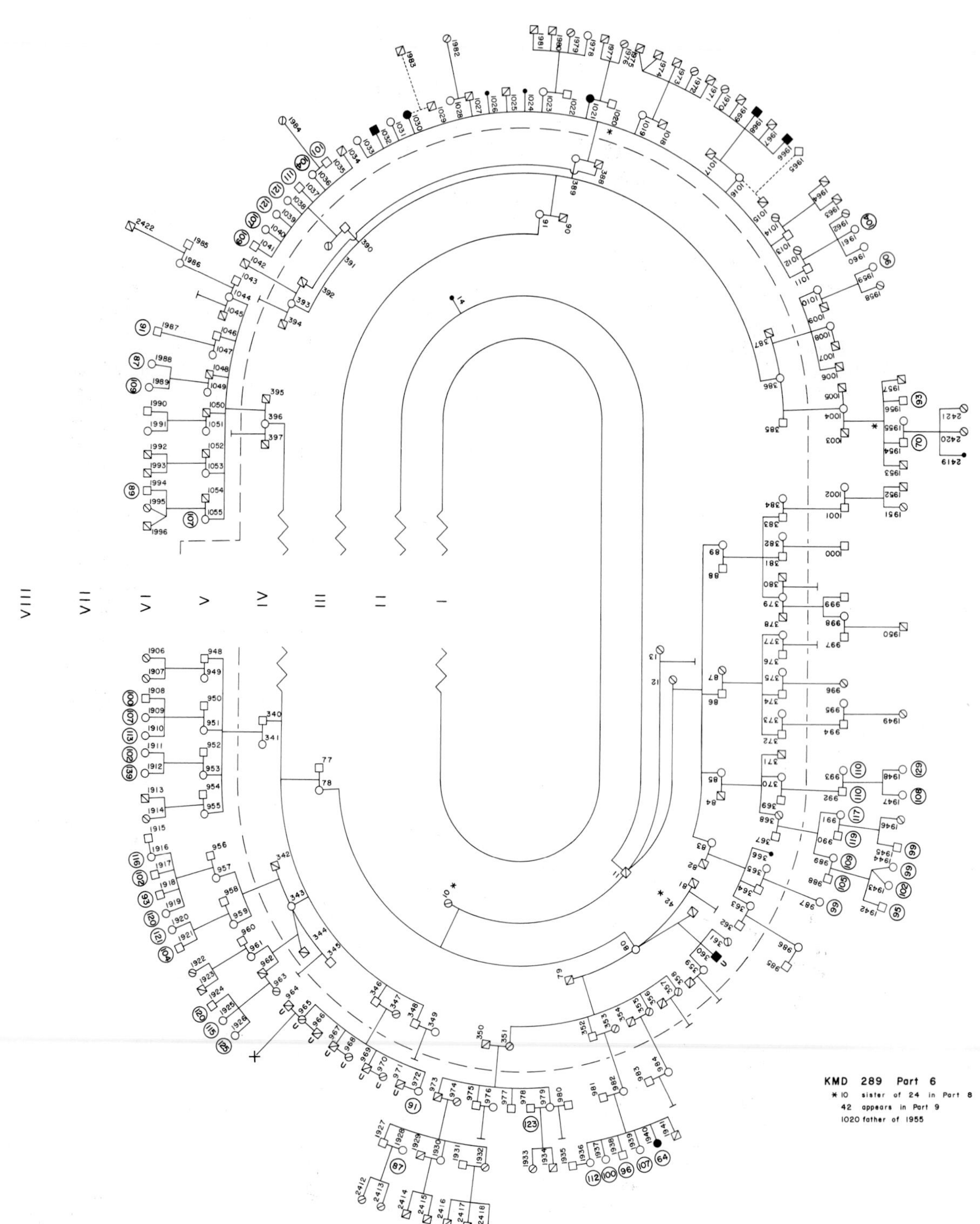

KMD 289 Part 6
✱ 10 sister of 24 in Part 8
42 appears in Part 9
1020 father of 1955

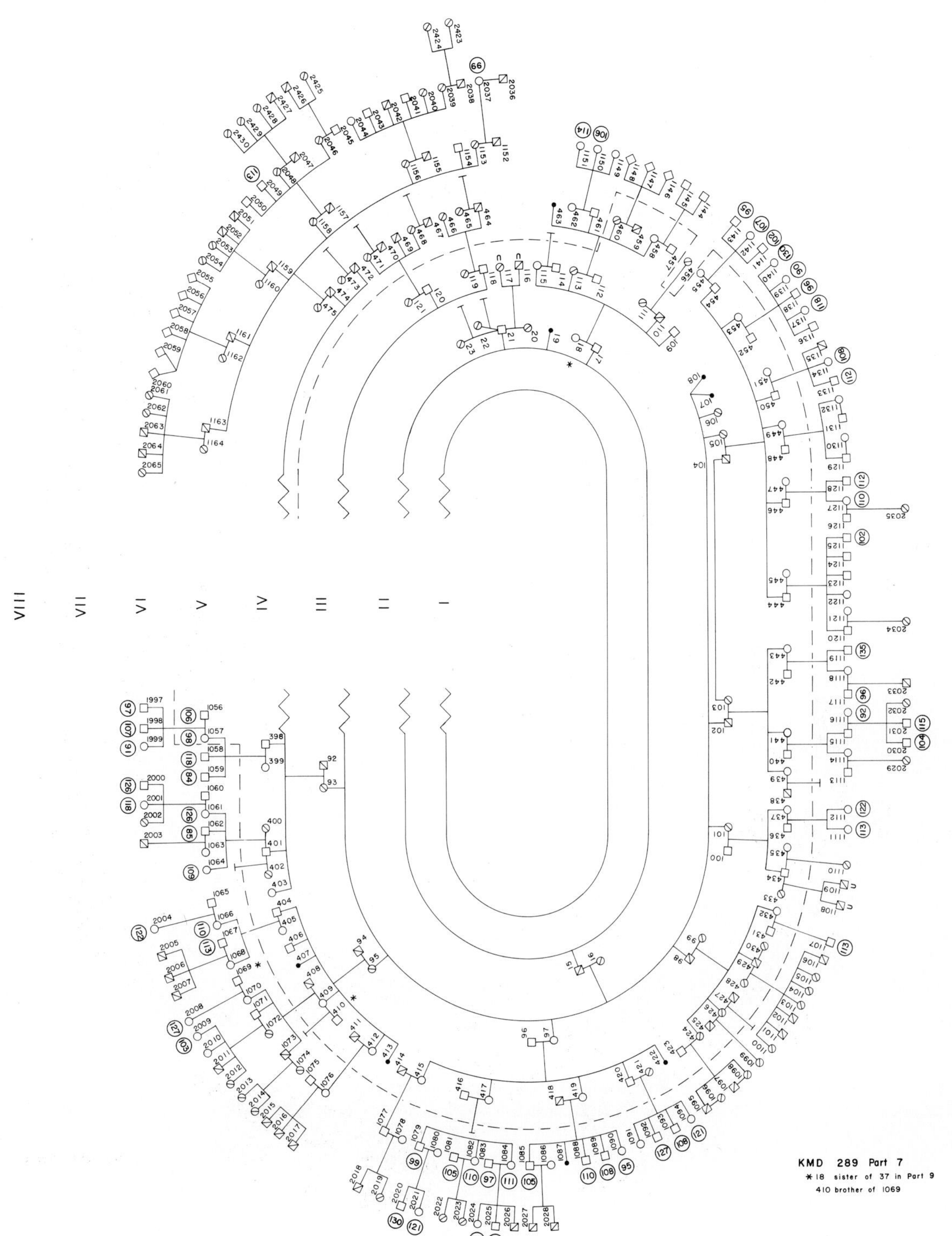

KMD 289 Part 7

✱18 sister of 37 in Part 9

410 brother of 1069

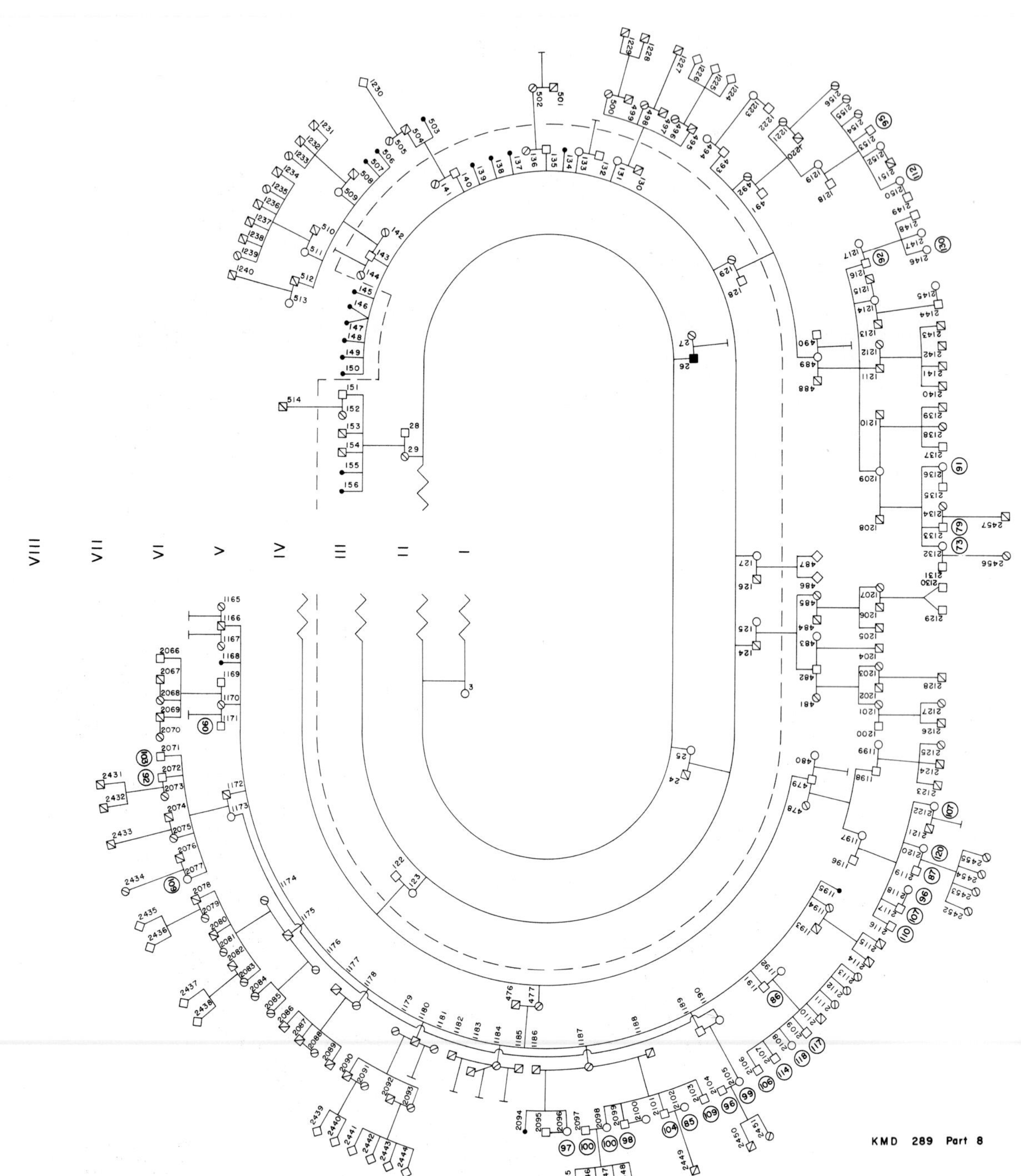

KMD 289 Part 8

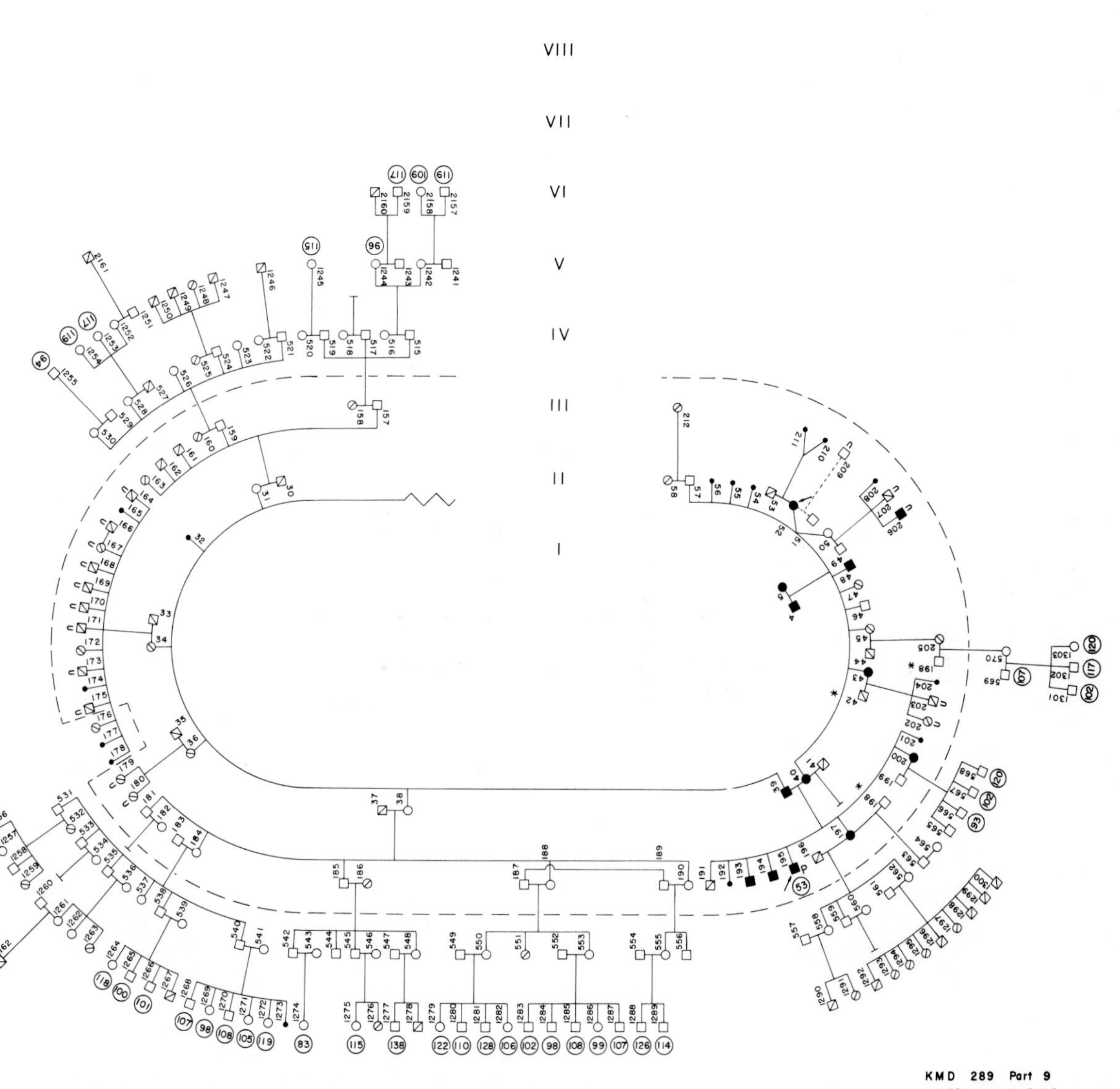

KMD 289 Part 9
* 42 appears in Part 6
198 appears twice

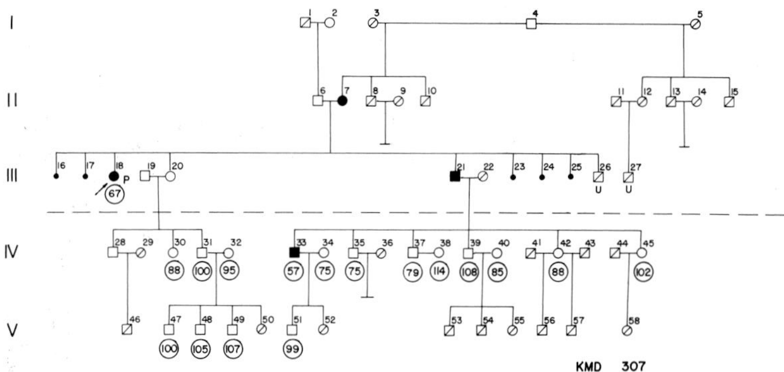

KMD 307

The Proband

The proband (18) was born in 1894, institutionalized at age 13 years, and died of chronic glomerulonephritis, anemia and mental deficiency in the institution in 1951. She was delivered by instruments, had poor eyesight and did not walk or talk for several years. She was first placed in an orphanage because of the poor home conditions. Medical records state "cretinoid appearance," but institution diagnosis is moron. IQ 67. *Diagnosis:* undifferentiated mental retardation.

Grandparents

Maternal grandparents were both alcoholics.

Parents

Father (6) was promiscuous and an alcoholic, but had normal intelligence.

Mother (7) was an alcoholic, a prostitute and retarded.

Aunts and Uncles

No paternal relatives. The proband's father was an only child.

Maternal relatives only: Two uncles, full siblings to (7), both alcoholic, both childless. Three half siblings to (7) had only one child among them.

Siblings

Brother (16) died of "summer complaint" at 7 months.

(17) was a miscarriage.

Sister (20) has normal intelligence.

Brother (21) was a problem in foster homes, refusing to work and running away. He was in the seventh grade at age 17 years and is now a garbage man. He is retarded, as is one of his six children.

Sister (23) died two days after birth.

(24) was a stillbirth.

Sister (25) died of neglect at age 3 weeks. The mother abandoned her.

Brother (26) is unknown to relatives.

Nieces and Nephews

Nephew (33) works in a brewery. He has an IQ of 57, his wife has an IQ of 75.

Nephew (35) was in several schools with special classes for children with IQ's of 75 to 80.

Nephew (37) had two IQ's, one of 52 and one of 79. Since he is a mail clerk who went to high school, the IQ of 79 was chosen as the more representative. His wife has an IQ of 114.

First Cousins

Unknown.

More Distant Relatives

Not of interest.

Family Summary

The proband, IQ 67, her mother, one brother and one nephew were retarded. In addition, two nieces have IQ's of 88 and two nephews have borderline IQ's of 75 and 79, respectively. The retarded nephew, IQ 57, has a child with an IQ of 99 at age 6 years. The proband's parents had nine children and nine known grandchildren. (The present status of one brother of the proband is unknown).

Retardation of proband of probably genetic origin.

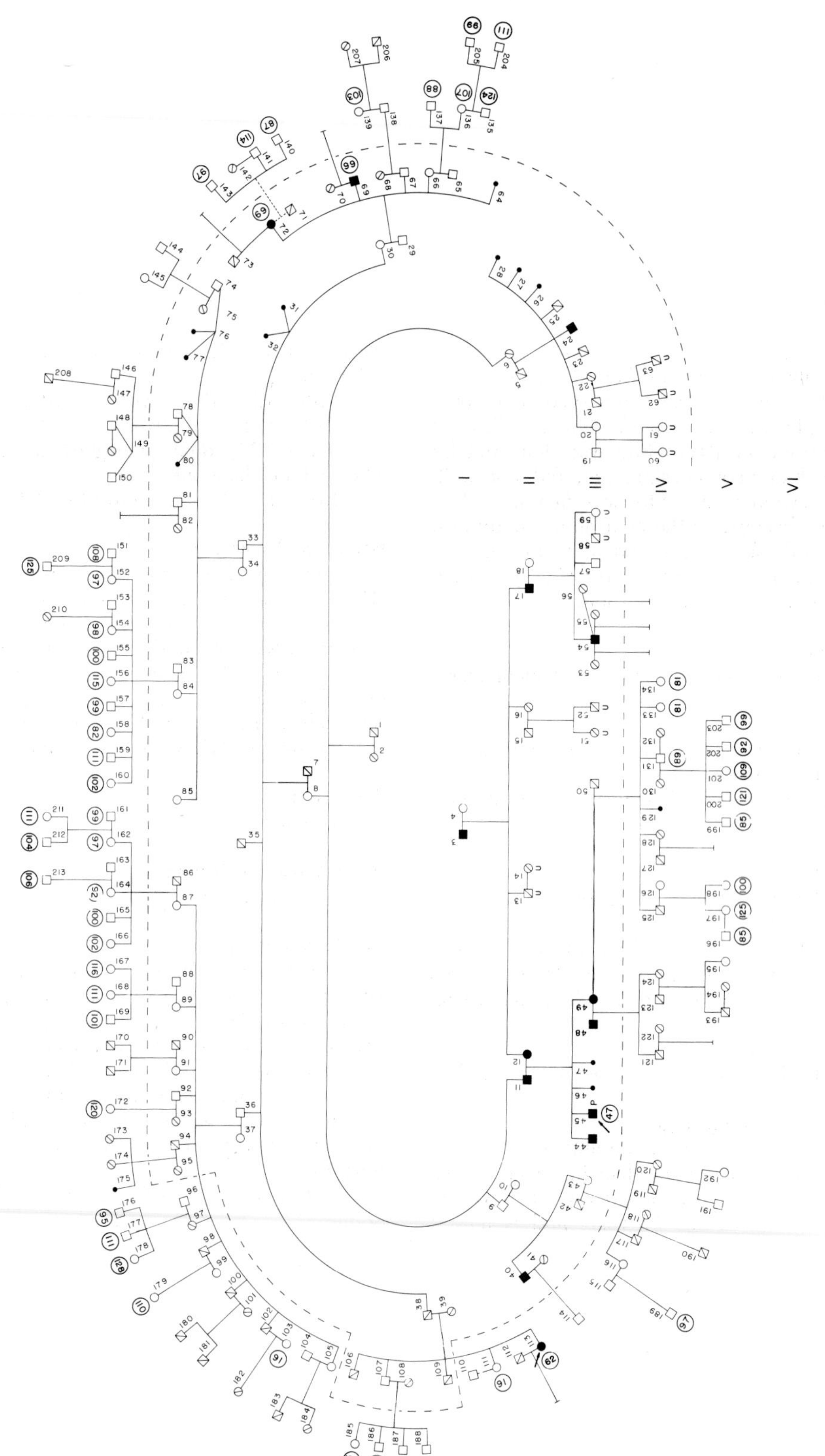

KMD 320

KMD 320

The Proband

The proband (45) was born in 1887, institutionalized at age 8 years, escaped in 1920 and was under outside supervision until he was placed in a county work home in 1947. He died in 1950. He was reared in a poor home and was removed to the state orphanage, together with his brother, when his mother was hospitalized for mental illness. There was no history of difficult birth or perinatal infection and he had no stigmata. IQ 47. *Diagnosis:* undifferentiated mental retardation.

Grandparents

Maternal grandfather was so retarded he was "the laughing stock of the town," and was the object of many practical jokes.

Parents

Father (11) was retarded and a county charge for many years.

Mother (12) was both retarded and schizophrenic.

Aunts and Uncles

Maternal uncle (17) was retarded but married a woman with normal intelligence. He had a retarded child (54).

Siblings

Brother (44) was a retarded laborer who died unmarried and childless.

Brothers (46) and (47) died in infancy.

Sister (49) was adopted at the age of 6 months. She was retarded (learned very little in school) and was also hospitalized for mental illness with a diagnoses of "psychosis with cerebral arteriosclerosis, pre-senile psychosis, Dick's Disease." Her first husband (48) was a retarded, alcoholic thief. Their children were taken by the paternal grandparents. Her second husband (50) was a laborer of unknown intelligence. (49) died in 1953.

Nieces and Nephews

Nephew (121) is a "transient wanderer." He is married but childless and has unknown intelligence.

Niece (124) was hostile and uncooperative. She completed the sixth grade. Her intelligence is unknown.

First Cousins

(24) was a retarded, unmarried and childless farm laborer.

(40) is a retarded farmer with one normal child.

(54) was retarded. He was arrested for stealing the rings from his mother's body after her death. He was married and divorced three times, but had no children.

More Distant Relatives

First cousin (30) with normal intelligence has two retarded children (69) and (72). (69) is married but childless. He is in the navy, IQ 66. (72), with IQ 69, had three illegitimate children with IQ's of 87, 114 and 97, respectively.

First cousin (38) has an institutionalized daughter (113) with an IQ of 62. She was first sent to the Girl's Reformatory, later was institutionalized and sterilized. She is now married and under outside supervision.

Family Summary

The proband, IQ 47, his maternal grandfather, both his parents, a maternal uncle, two siblings, three first cousins and three more distant relatives were retardates, all of about the same level. In addition, the proband's mother and sister had complications of mental illness. The proband's parents had five children and eight grandchildren. Two grandchildren have personality problems, three grandchildren have low-normal IQ scores of 89, 81, and 81 and one great-grandchild has an IQ of 80.

Retardation of proband of probably genetic origin.

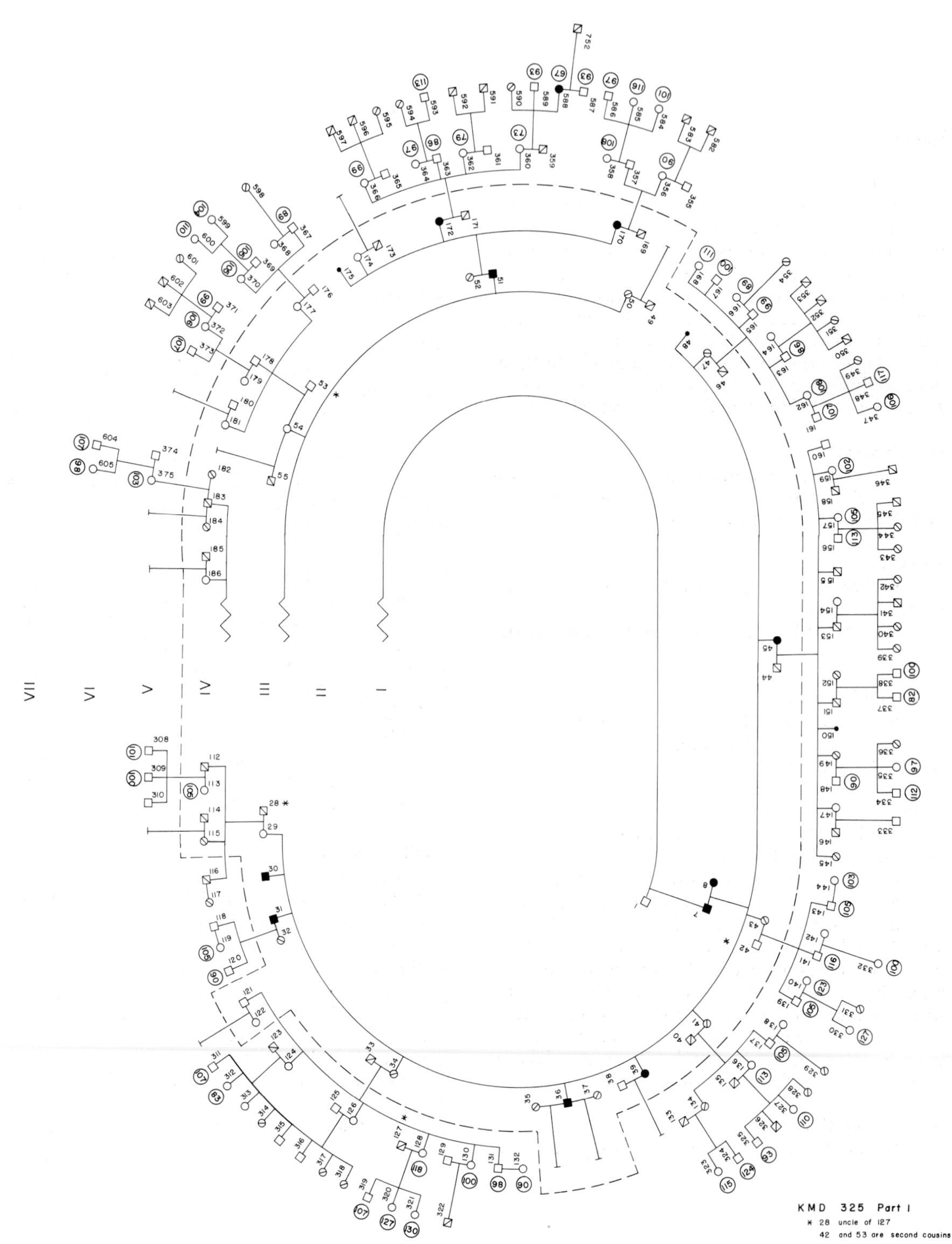

KMD 325 Part I

* 28 uncle of 127

42 and 53 are second cousins

KMD 325

The Proband

The proband (106) was born in 1896, institutionalized at age 6 years and was still in the institution in 1961 with a diagnosis of imbecile, familial. Her diagnosis in 1937 was dementia praecox but it was changed in 1940. Her birth and early development were uneventful and she had no stigmata. Her parents died when their children were young so the proband and her siblings were institutionalized. A sister (108) upon reevaluation was found to have normal intelligence. IQ of proband is 47. *Diagnosis:* undifferentiated mental retardation.

Grandparents

Paternal grandmother was epileptic.

Maternal grandmother was retarded. Maternal grandfather deserted her.

Parents

Father (21) was a retarded, alcoholic laborer.

Mother (22) was illiterate and retarded. Her first husband (23) was epileptic and died in a mental hospital. Two of his sisters were also epileptic and were hospitalized for mental illness.

Aunts and Uncles

Paternal aunt (14) was retarded. Her husband was normal and three of her seven children were retarded.

The proband's father's half brother (7) was retarded, as was his wife (8) and six of their ten surviving children.

The proband's father's half brother (11) was retarded. He had nine children by a normal wife, three of whom were retarded.

Maternal aunt (27) was a married but childless retardate.

Siblings

Brother (105) was institutionalized in 1901 at age 8 years. He ran away from the institution at age 18 years and is an unmarried, childless laborer. He is a middle-grade retardate.

Sister (108) was institutionalized in 1903 at age 6 years and was taken out of the institution in 1915 by her first cousin once removed, who married her. (108) has had three admissions to mental hospitals. Her original diagnosis was psychosis with mental deficiency and her IQ's were 57 in 1911 and 60 in 1938. In 1954 upon reevaluation she scored an IQ of 99 on a Wechsler-Bellevue test, was interviewed and the diagnosis revised to psychosis with normal intelligence. Her husband (107) was her first cousin once removed and an invalid for years with multiple sclerosis. He was classified as retarded by the first workers.

Half Siblings

Half sister (109) died of typhoid fever at age 3 years.

Half brother (110) died at age 1 year. He "was poisoned," no other details.

Half brother (111) was institutionalized in 1901 at age 12 years and left the institution eight years later. He died unmarried and childless in 1930. He was a rather low-grade retardate who was also epileptic. His father (23) was mentally ill and epileptic.

Nieces and Nephews

They are of particular interest because they are all the children of the proband's mentally ill sister (108) by her retarded first cousin once removed (107).

Niece (300) completed the eleventh grade with a D minus average. Her four children, (572), (573), (574) and (575) have normal intelligence, but (572) is a delinquent.

Nephew (301) has a borderline IQ of 76. His wife is also borderline. Two children, one (576) is known to be normal.

Niece (304) also has a borderline IQ of 78. Her husband is a mechanic of unknown intelligence. A child (578) has an IQ of 137.

Niece (306) has an IQ of 94. Her husband's IQ is 105. Two children, (580) has an IQ of 82 and (581) has an IQ of 99.

First Cousins

Only one maternal uncle could have reproduced although he was not known to have had any children.

The children of the proband's father's half siblings:

(30) is an unmarried, childless retarded farm laborer.

(31) is a retarded laborer, wife unknown, with two children, both normal.

(36) was married and divorced twice but was childless and retarded.

(39) was retarded and married but childless.

(45), sister to the four above, is retarded, husband and five children of unknown intelligence, four children with normal intelligence.

(51) was retarded, wife unknown, two of three surviving children retarded.

(64) was a retarded, divorced laborer. Intelligence of wife and one child unknown, one child with IQ 85.

(67), brother to (51) and (64), completed the fourth grade, is divorced and has four children by two marriages, two retarded and two normal. He is retarded, wives' intelligence unknown.

(70), retarded, married a retarded wife and had two retarded children by her. By a wife of unknown intelligence he had one retarded, one unknown and one normal child.

(76) was retarded, wife and four children normal.

(79), sister to (70) and (76), has been

Continued on page 359

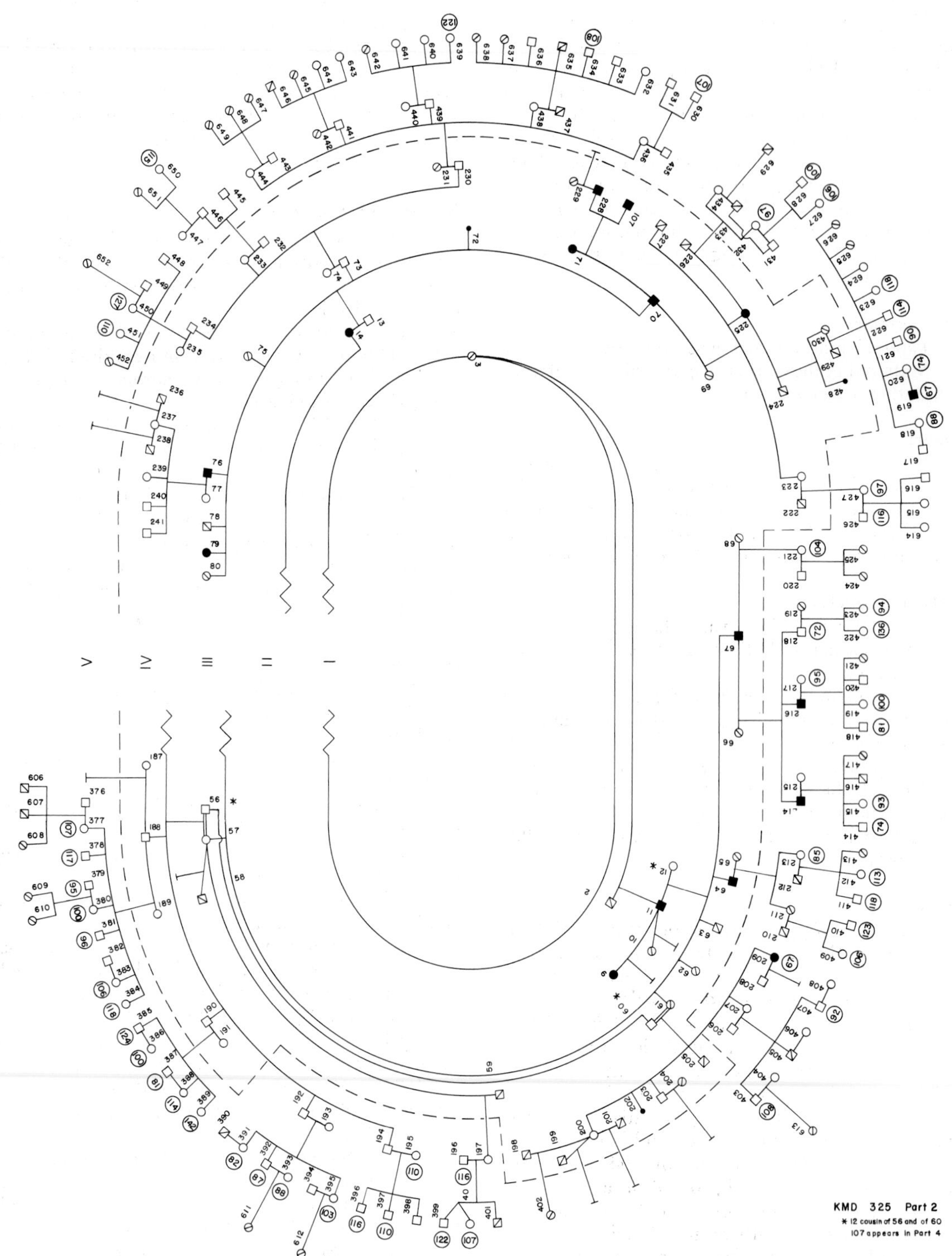

KMD 325 Part 2

* 12 cousin of 56 and of 60

107 appears in Part 4

KMD 325 – *Continued*

hospitalized for mental illness and was considered to have been both retarded and mentally ill.

(84) and (89) both have been mentally ill. (84) committed suicide after admission to a mental hospital. (89) was hospitalized for a time.

(102) was retarded and had an illegitimate child (288).

More Distant Relatives

(170) is a high-grade retardate.

(172) is a high-grade retardate. She is a sister to (170) and both women have normal children.

(209) was first sent to a girls' reformatory for immorality, then committed as retarded but never institutionalized. She has been married and divorced and is childless.

(214) left the eighth grade at age 18 years and is a laborer.

(216), brother to (214), was in the seventh grade at age 18 years. Their brother (218) has a borderline IQ of 72. The children of these three brothers have an IQ range of 74 to 136.

(225) was retarded. She committed suicide.

(228) is a married but childless retardate who also has a speech defect. His brother, (107), who appeared as the proband's sister's husband, was also retarded.

(280) was considered for commitment at one time but the judge refused to commit him because he played cribbage with him. IQ 55. His divorced wife (281) was institutionalized but refused sterilization. She had one illegitimate, retarded child. Of their 11 children, five are known to be retarded. Three of the retardates have been institutionalized and one has been in a reformatory twice. One (551) tested 67 at age 9 years but scored 100 at age 17. (552) was born in the institution. Prompt institutionalization of (280) could have prevented the production of this large and expensive family of retardates and delinquents.

(497) has an IQ of 70, husband's IQ 103, one child with IQ 103, one with IQ 70.

(540) was committed as retarded but never institutionalized. He was in a reformatory twice. IQ 59. His wife has an IQ of 120. One child has IQ 81.

(544) is under outside supervision, IQ 61.

(545) is under outside supervision, IQ 62.

(547) was under outside supervision but has been restored to capacity. IQ 55. (544), (545) and (547) all were sent to the state school for educable retardates.

(549) has an IQ of 66 and is under outside supervision.

(571), the proband's great-nephew, came from a broken home and has been in court for shoplifting, window breaking, stealing and finally was sent to a reformatory for attempted rape. IQ 89.

(588) has an IQ of 67.

Family Summary

The proband, IQ 47, her maternal grandmother, both parents, a paternal aunt and maternal aunt, two half brothers of the proband's father, one brother and one half brother, four first cousins, eight children of the proband's father's half brothers, and 15 more distant relatives were retarded, all of the undifferentiated middle- to high-grade type. In addition, the paternal side of the family included several cases of mental illness and the proband's sister is hospitalized for a psychosis. She married a retarded relative and has four children, three with borderline intelligence, one with IQ 94. This family also includes social problems of divorce and delinquency. The proband's parents had three children and four grandchildren.

Retardation of proband of probably genetic origin.

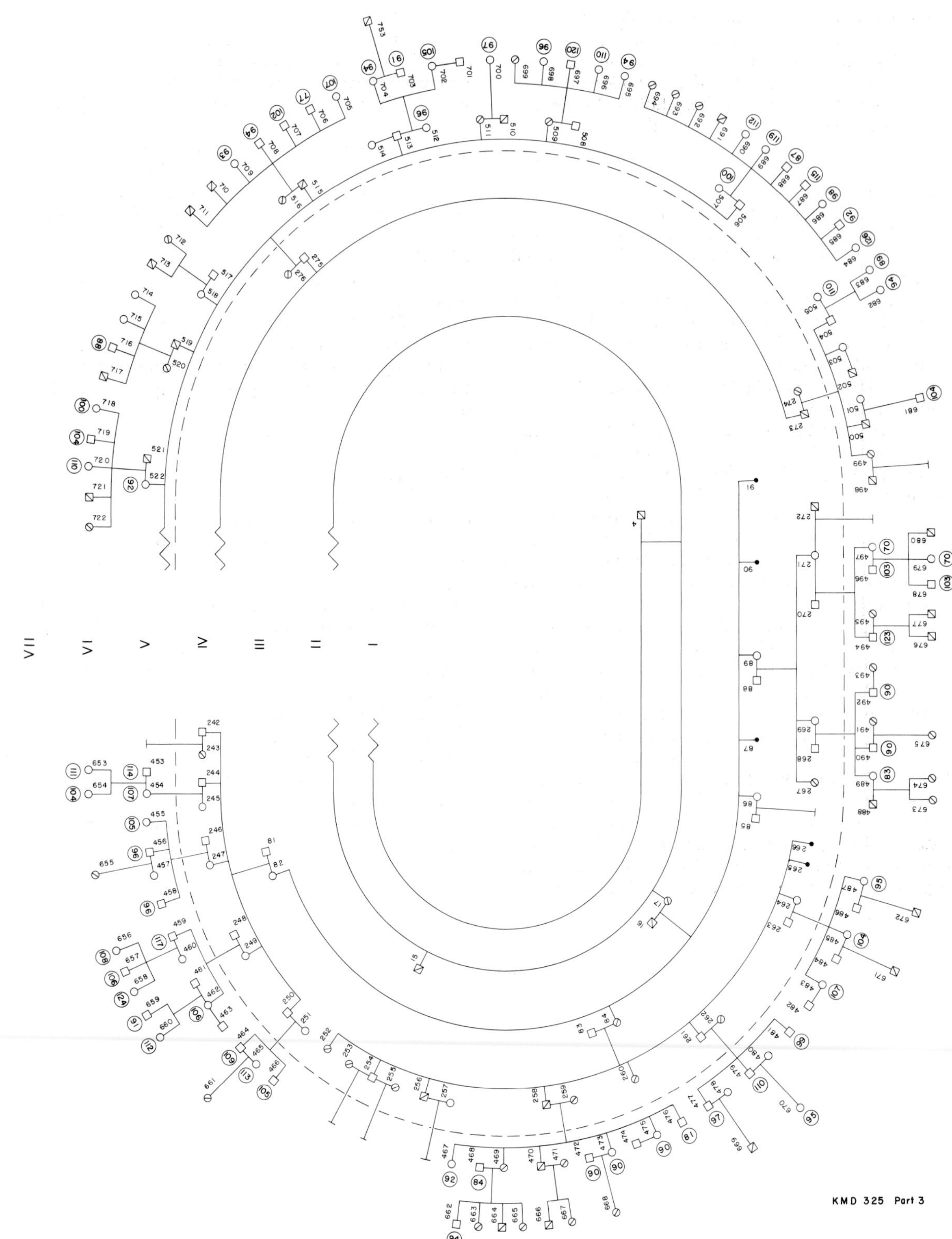

KMD 325 Part 3

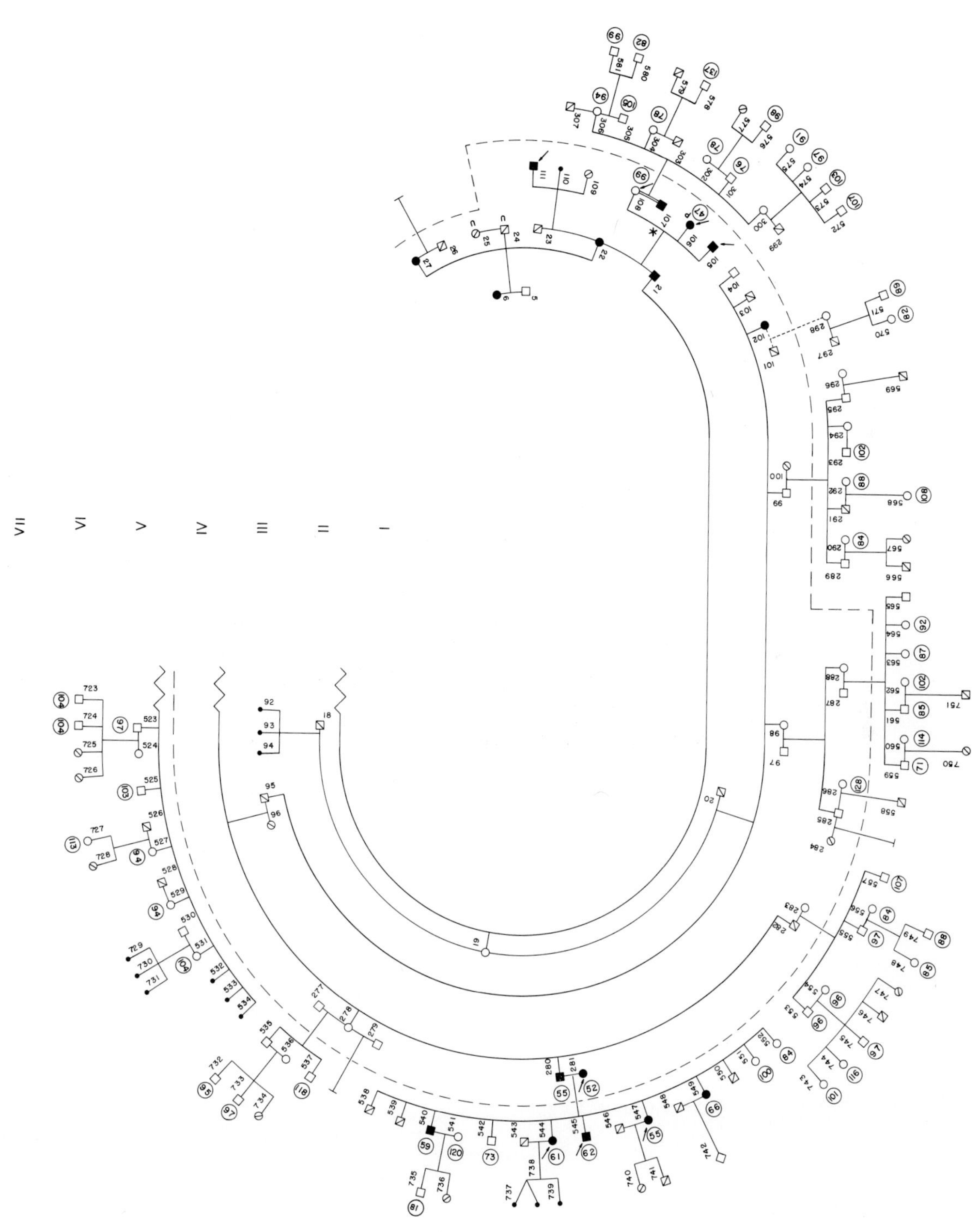

KMD 325 Part 4

* 107 appears in Part 2

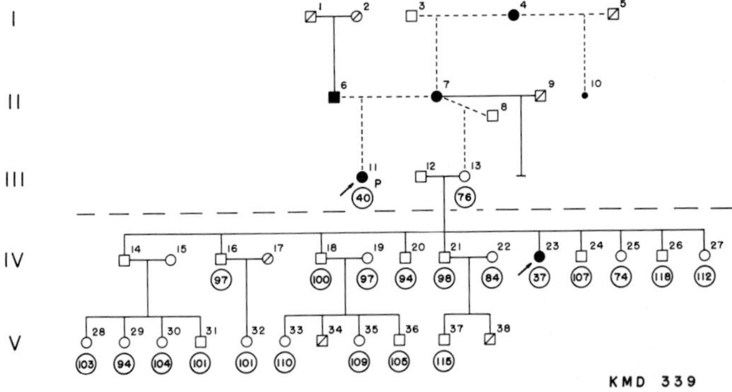
I
II
III
IV
V
KMD 339

KMD 339

The Proband

The proband (11) was born in 1892, institutionalized at age 16 years and died of a cerebral hemorrhage in the institution in 1953. She was a lethargic baby, never talked well, and attended school for eight years with poor results. She was an illegitimate child reared in a poor home environment, but had no history of difficult birth or perinatal infection, and had no stigmata. IQ 40. *Diagnosis:* undifferentiated mental retardation.

Grandparents

Maternal grandmother had two illegitimate children and was retarded.

Parents

Father (6) was a retarded alcoholic laborer.

Mother (7) was an illiterate retarded housemaid.

Aunts and Uncles

Only one, a half sibling to the proband's mother, who died in infancy.

Siblings

One illegitimate half sister (13), IQ 76.

Nieces and Nephews

The children of proband's half sister:

(14) is deaf and was at one time thought to be retarded. However, he made fair progress in school and has supported a wife and four children despite his handicap. All four of his children and his wife are deaf, but have normal intelligence.

(16) was committed as retarded at one time because of behavior problems, but was never institutionalized. He completed the sixth grade and has IQ scores of 76, 68, 73 and 97.

(23) is an institutionalized, deaf retardate, IQ 37.

(25) was educated in special classes, IQ 74.

First Cousins

None.

More Distant Relatives

Not of interest.

Family Summary

The proband, IQ 40, her mother, maternal grandmother and one niece are retarded. The proband, her mother and her niece were all middle-grade retardates. The proband's parents had one child, no grandchildren. The deafness in the children of the proband's half sister does not seem to be associated with the retardation. One deaf person has normal intelligence and four deaf children with normal intelligence, while his sibling (IQ 37) is also deaf.

Retardation of proband of probably genetic origin.

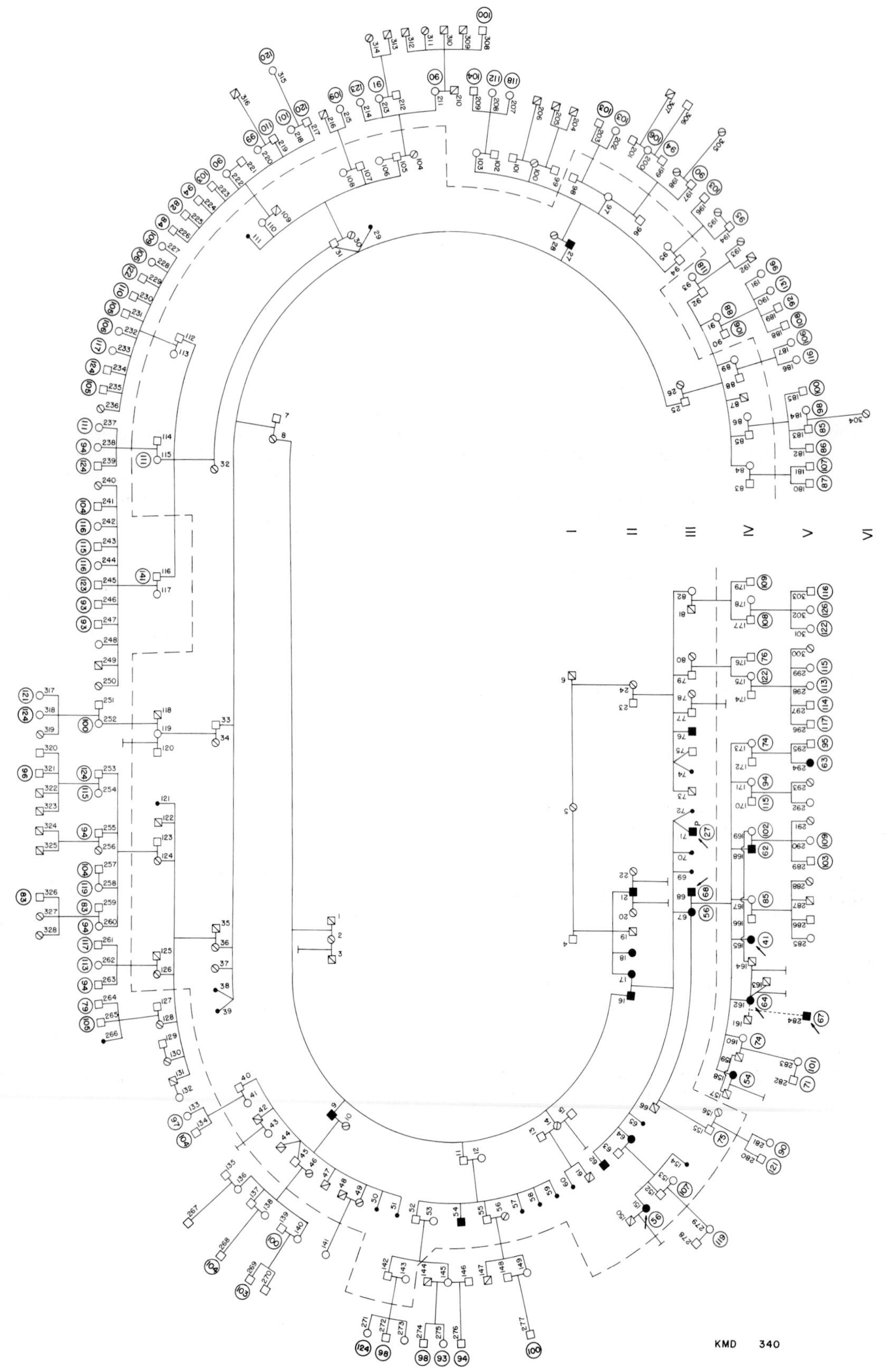

KMD 340

KMD 340

The Proband

The proband (71) was born in 1899, institutionalized at age 13 years and was still in the institution in 1961. He was a twin whose birth was uneventful. His eyes were deformed, but he was not blind. He walked at 18 months and talked at two years. He was reared in a poor home environment. IQ 27. *Diagnosis:* undifferentiated mental retardation.

Grandparents

Both maternal grandparents were epileptic.

Parents

Father (16) was retarded and brought food home to his family from garbage dumps.

Mother (17) was retarded and epileptic. The epilepsy was supposed to have followed an attack of scarlet fever at age 6 years.

Aunts and Uncles

Paternal uncle (9) was retarded and had epileptiform attacks.

Maternal aunt (18) died of hydrocephalus at age 2 years.

Maternal uncle (21) had a guardian. He was married twice, once to a prostitute whom he divorced, and a second time to a woman who died in a mental hospital. He had no children. He was retarded and epileptic.

Siblings

Brother (62) is an unmarried, childless retardate.

Sister (64) is retarded, but married a man with normal intelligence. She has one retarded and one normal child.

(65) was a miscarriage.

Sister (67) divorced her first husband (66) following a forced marriage. She married a second husband (68) who had been arrested 16 times for drunkenness and non-support and was finally institutionalized and sterilized. His IQ was 68, her IQ was 56. (67) was never institutionalized. Four of their eight children are retarded.

Sister (69) died of "spasms" at age 3 weeks.

(70) was a miscarriage.

(72) was a twin who died of "lung fever" at 5 months.

Nieces and Nephews

Niece (151) was institutionalized in 1932 at age 22 years, sterilized at age 26 years and placed under outside supervision in 1949. She married a disabled man of unknown intelligence. Her IQ is 56 and she is also epileptic.

Niece (158) had an IQ of 54. She was married, but died childless at age 20 years.

Nieces (160) and (173) have borderline IQ's of 74. (160) has a child with IQ 101 and (173) has one child with IQ 63 and one with IQ 95.

Niece (162) was institutionalized in 1937 at age 20 years when illegitimately pregnant. After the birth of her child she was sterilized and placed under outside supervision. She married and divorced her child's father, and has had two more husbands since that time. Her child (284) has an IQ of 67 and was educated in special classes.

Niece (165) was institutionalized in 1941, sterilized and placed under outside supervision, but is on the waiting list for readmission. IQ 41.

Nephew (168) has an IQ of 62. His wife has an IQ of 89 and their two tested children have IQ's of 103 and 109.

Niece (171) deserves mention because she went to high school and has a normal IQ of 94. Her husband is a machinist with IQ 115.

First Cousins

(27) according to old records was retarded. Her children all have normal intelligence.

(54) died unmarried and childless. He was retarded.

(76) died unmarried and childless. He had spinal meningitis at age 2 years and was retarded.

More Distant Relatives

Great-nephew (284), IQ 67, and great-niece (294), IQ 63.

Family Summary

The proband, IQ 27, both parents, a paternal uncle, a maternal aunt and uncle, three siblings (all the siblings who grew to adulthood), four nieces and a nephew, two first cousins and a great-niece and nephew were all retarded. The retarded maternal aunt was hydrocephalic, and one retarded first cousin had a childhood history of spinal meningitis. The other retardates were high-grade except for the proband and one sister with IQ 41. The proband had no siblings with normal intelligence, but six of his 12 nieces and nephews have IQ's ranging from 74 to 94. One retarded sister of the proband had two children, one with IQ 56, the other with IQ 107. Another retarded sister had nine children (by two husbands), four of whom were retarded and five who had IQ's of 75, 74, 85, 94 and 74, respectively. In this sibship of nine, one retarded woman had a retarded child, one retarded man had two children with normal IQ's of 103 and 109, one borderline girl had a retarded child and a normal one, the other two borderlines had three children with IQ's of 121, 90 and 101. This family presents a history of serious epilepsy in several generations and a bad social history of promiscuity, divorce, indigence and delinquency. Despite the social record, normal individuals are appearing among the descendants. Institutionalization and sterilization considerably reduced the reproductive rate of this inadequate family. The proband's parents had eight children and 12 grandchildren.

Retardation of proband of probably genetic origin.

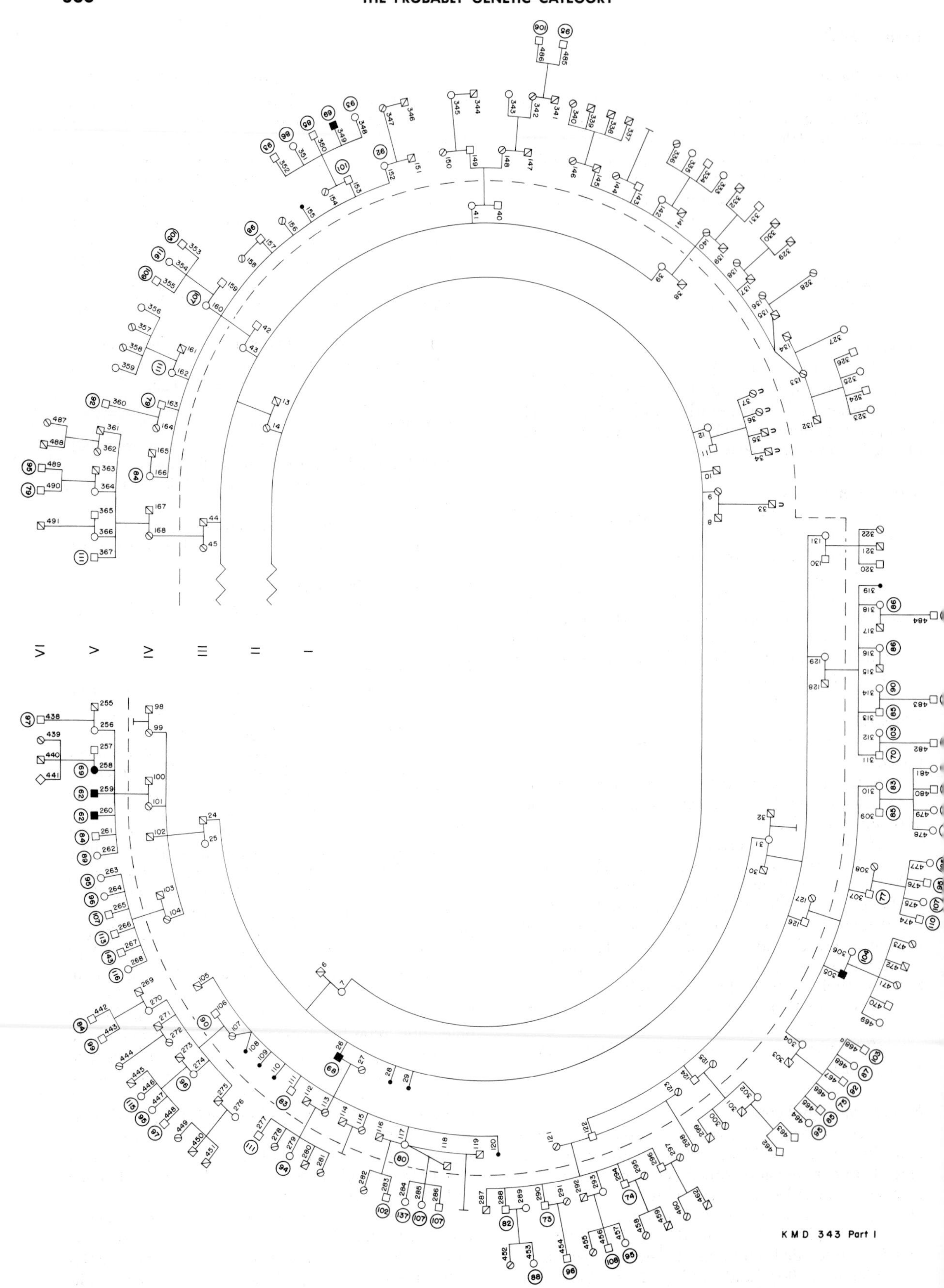

KMD 343 Part I

KMD 343

The Proband

The proband (79) was born in 1899 and institutionalized at age 12 years. She became pregnant during a vacation and her illegitimate child was born in the institution in 1921. In 1927 a sterilization operation was performed. After five years away from the institution under outside supervision she returned and was there in 1961. A physical and neurological examination was given to her in 1950 by J. A. Böök, M.D., and John Schut, M.D. She has hysterical seizures which were not considered epileptic attacks by the examiners. No stigmata were found, and there was no history of early trauma. IQ scores of 60, 53, 53, 57, 57 and 60 were taken over a period of 16 years. *Diagnosis:* undifferentiated mental retardation with convulsive disorder (nonepileptic).

Grandparents

Maternal grandfather deserted his family.

Parents

Father (18) was a degenerate alcoholic laborer who had incestuous relationships with his daughter and stepdaughter. He was retarded.

Mother (19) died in childbirth in 1907. She was retarded and epileptic.

Aunts and Uncles

Paternal aunt (7) was mentally ill at one time but had normal intelligence.

Paternal uncle (16) was much like proband's father (18). His first wife (15) divorced him, taking their children with her. His second wife (17) was epileptic but had normal intelligence. (16) was murdered by his daughter's rejected suitor. He was a retarded laborer.

Siblings

Sister (75) was promiscuous. She had two illegitimate children, later married and had eight more children, four of whom are retarded. The old records classified her as retarded, but more recent workers claimed she had normal intelligence. She died in 1935.

Brother (77) left school at 16 when he was in the third grade. He died of carcinoma of the hip, unmarried and childless, at 19 years. Mentally retarded.

Sister (82) had one child by her father, a second illegitimate child and one legitimate child. Her first husband was an exconvict with an IQ of 64. Her second husband was a convicted murderer. She divorced both these men. Her third husband died. She lives with her fourth husband who is a laborer, intelligence unknown. (82) was described as retarded in the old records, but recent workers report she has normal intelligence.

Sister (86) was institutionalized at age 9 and has been in and out of the institution ever since. She is still institutionalized with a diagnosis of convulsive disorder, periods of psychosis. She was also examined by Dr. Böök and Dr. Schut in 1950. No stigmata were found. IQ 64.

(87) was a stillbirth.

Sister (88) was institutionalized at age 5 years and has remained in the institution ever since. Her examination by Dr. Böök and Dr. Schut revealed no stigmata. The institution diagnosis is familial mental deficiency with paranoid schizophrenia. IQ 52.

Illegitimate half sister (91) had two illegitimate children, then married "an ignorant" farmer and had five more children. She died in 1927. Two of her children are retarded, and two others have been in prison. She was in the fifth grade at 18 years and was considered mentally retarded.

Child

(239) was born in the institution in 1921 and has remained institutionalized ever since. Her physical and neurological examination by Dr. Böök and Dr. Schut in 1950 revealed no stigmata. IQ 61.

Nieces and Nephews

Nephew (233) is a retarded handyman who was retained for two years in the fifth grade and two years in the sixth grade. He has one child of unknown intelligence.

Niece (235) left school after spending two years in the fourth grade. She is unmarried and keeps house for her father. Retarded.

Nephew (236) lives with his father, is a handyman, and spent two years in each of the first, second and fourth grades. He then left school. Retarded.

Nephew (237) spent two years in both the fifth and sixth grades. He clerked in a store. He abandoned his wife and child and joined the army. Retarded.

Children of Proband's Half Sister

(247) is single, works for the highway department, and has an IQ of 64.

(248) is married, wife and child's intelligence unknown. IQ 68.

(250) is in prison for robbery with assault. IQ 96.

(251) has a prison record. IQ's 59, 58 and 72.

First Cousins

(26) is deceased, IQ 68. There are no known retardates among his descendants.

(58) completed the fourth grade at 15 years and is a farmer. He is retarded and one of his ten surviving children (174) has an IQ of 50.

(60) completed the fourth grade at 15 years and is a farmer. He is retarded, but no retardation has appeared among his descendants.

Continued on page 369

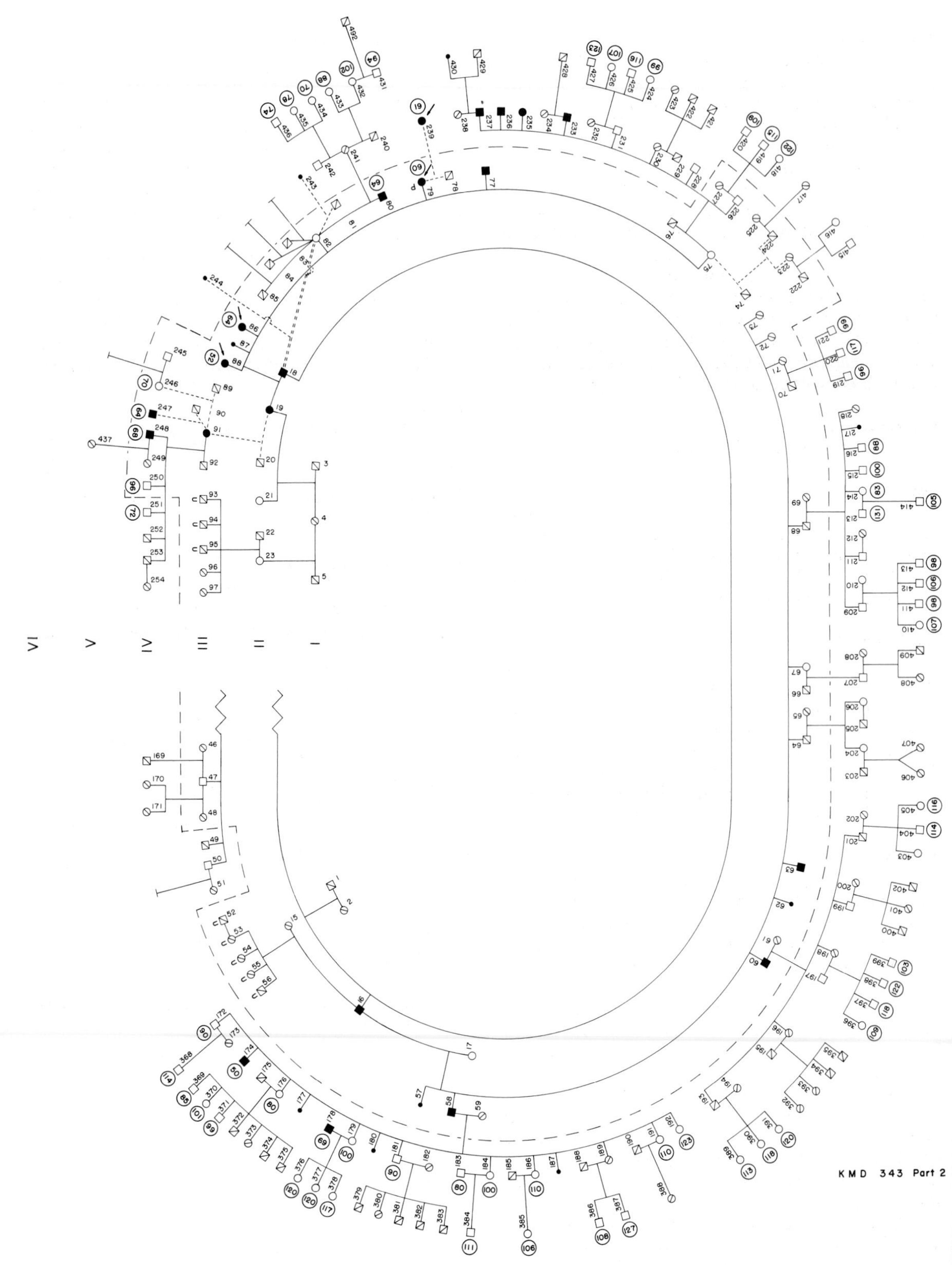

KMD 343 Part 2

KMD 343 – *Continued*

(63) died of pneumonia and blood poisoning at age 13. He was in the third grade at the time. Retarded.

More Distant Relatives

(174) works in a factory, IQ 50.

(258) has an IQ of 69.

(259) has an IQ of 62.

(260), brother to (258) and (259), has an IQ of 62.

(305) is a retarded dairy worker, wife and children normal.

(349) has an IQ of 69.

Family Summary

The proband, IQ 60, her parents, three siblings and a half sister were retarded, as were the proband's child, seven nieces and nephews (two of these latter belonged to the half sister), one paternal uncle, four first cousins and six other relatives. In addition to the low intelligence, the social history of this family includes death by murder, prison records, incest and eight illegitimate births. There are four generations of retardates in the proband's immediate family. The proband's parents had seven children and 14 grandchildren. One of the grandchildren is institutionalized, one died in infancy and three are unmarried adults in their thirties. The IQ scores for all the retardates fall within the range 50 to 70. While the family environment was almost the worst possible, two children with normal intelligence did appear, although both were delinquents. One has four retarded children, the other has a retarded grandchild.

Retardation of proband of probably genetic origin.

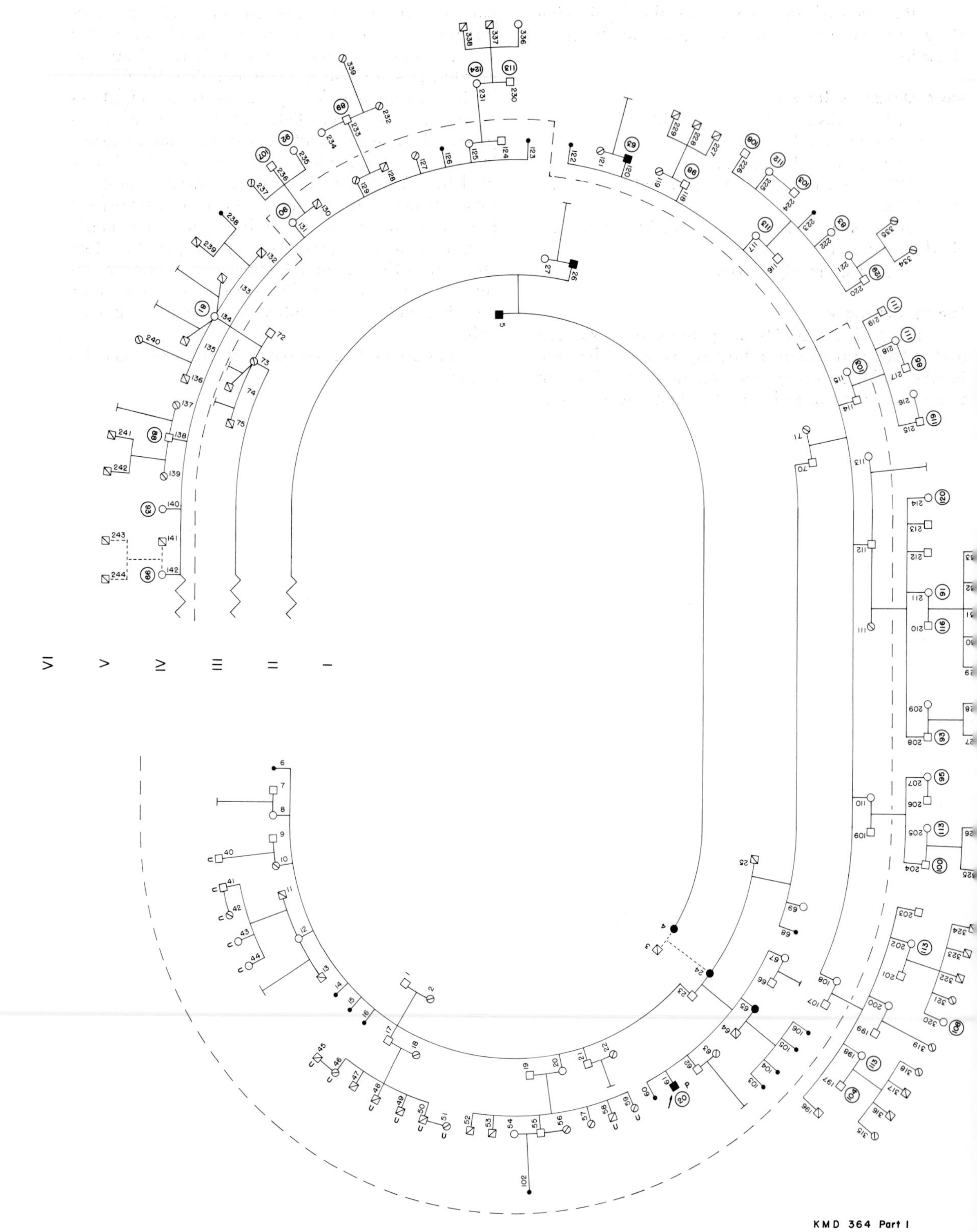

KMD 364 Part I

KMD 364

The Proband

The proband (61) was born in 1869, institutionalized at age 13 years and died of coronary thrombosis in the institution in 1933. According to relatives, his mother had severe convulsions before and at the time of his birth, but he was apparently not injured and his early development was uneventful although he was "sickly." He had no stigmata. IQ 20. *Diagnosis:* undifferentiated mental retardation.

Grandparents

Maternal grandmother was retarded. The proband's mother was her illegitimate child.

Parents

Father (23) was a sailor and farmer of normal intelligence.

Mother (24) was retarded and had epileptoid attacks. She became a "medium" for a traveling spiritualist.

Aunts and Uncles

Paternal relatives all had normal intelligence.

The proband's mother had no full siblings, only half siblings by two stepfathers.

Maternal uncle (26) was a married but childless retardate.

Maternal uncle (28) was retarded. Wife's intelligence was unknown and one of his eight children is known to be retarded.

Maternal uncle (32) was an alcoholic and retarded. He was married four times but had only one child (91), a normal girl.

The father (5) of (26), (28) and (32) was retarded.

Siblings

(60) was a stillbirth.

Brother (62) completed the tenth grade and was a farmer.

Sister (65) was retarded.

Sister (67) had normal or above normal intelligence.

Nieces and Nephews

Only four, all of whom were miscarriages or infant deaths.

First Cousins

Little could be found out about the paternal side of the children of the proband's mother's half siblings.

(82) had a prison record but normal intelligence.

(85) was retarded. Her husband was normal and she had no known retarded children.

(99), (100) and (101), siblings, were retarded.

More Distant Relatives

(120) had an IQ of 63.

(159) with IQ 99 married a man with IQ 69.

Family Summary

The proband, IQ 20, his mother, his maternal grandmother, one sibling, four first cousins and one more distant relative were retarded. The proband's mother had severe convulsions before and during the birth of the proband and was subject to epileptoid attacks in addition to her retardation. All the known retardation occurs on the maternal side of the family. The proband's retarded sister had four conceptions but no surviving children and the proband's two normal siblings were married but childless. The proband's parents had five children and no surviving grandchildren (only four miscarriages and infant deaths).

Retardation of proband of probably genetic origin.

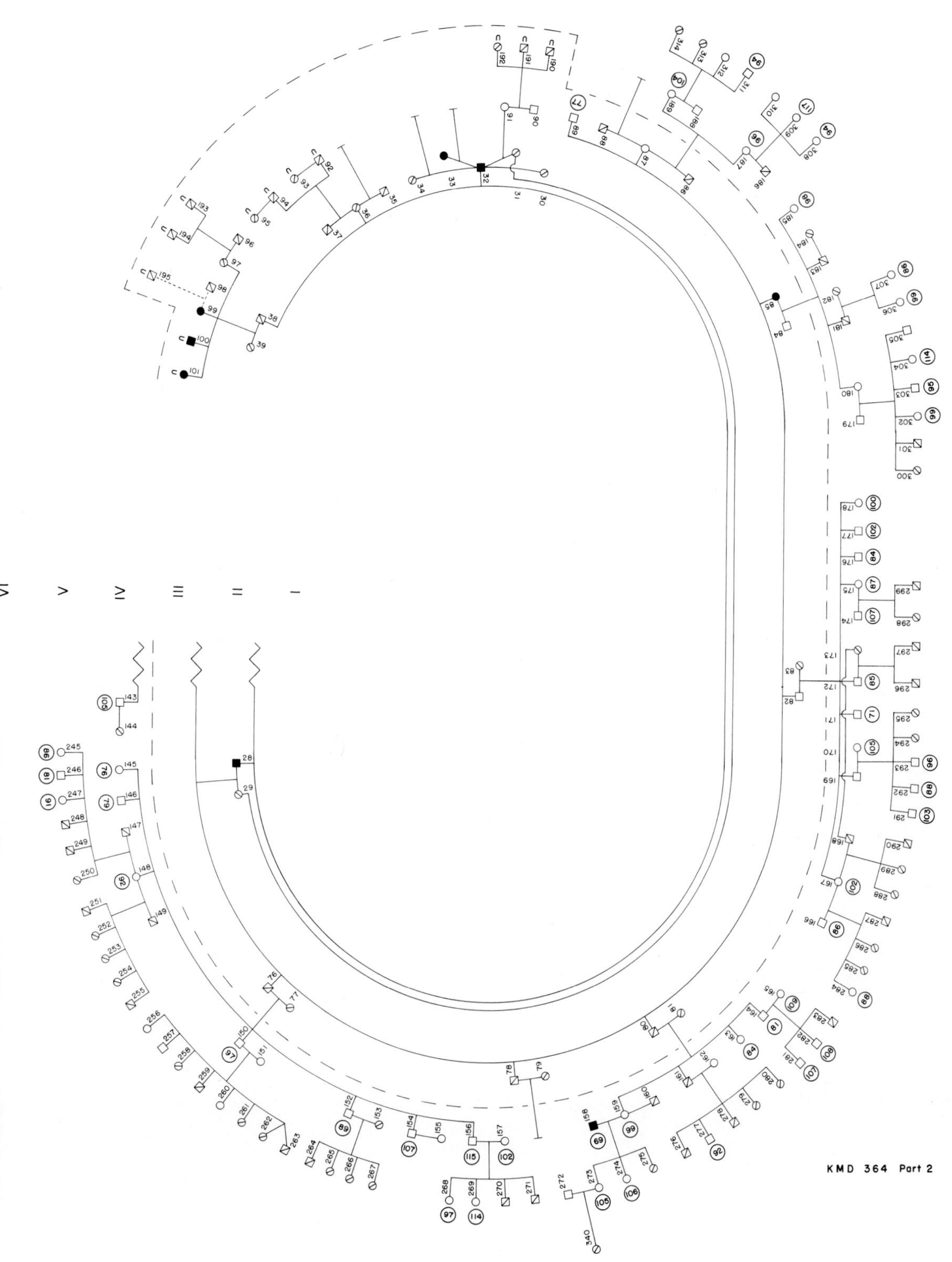

KMD 364 Part 2

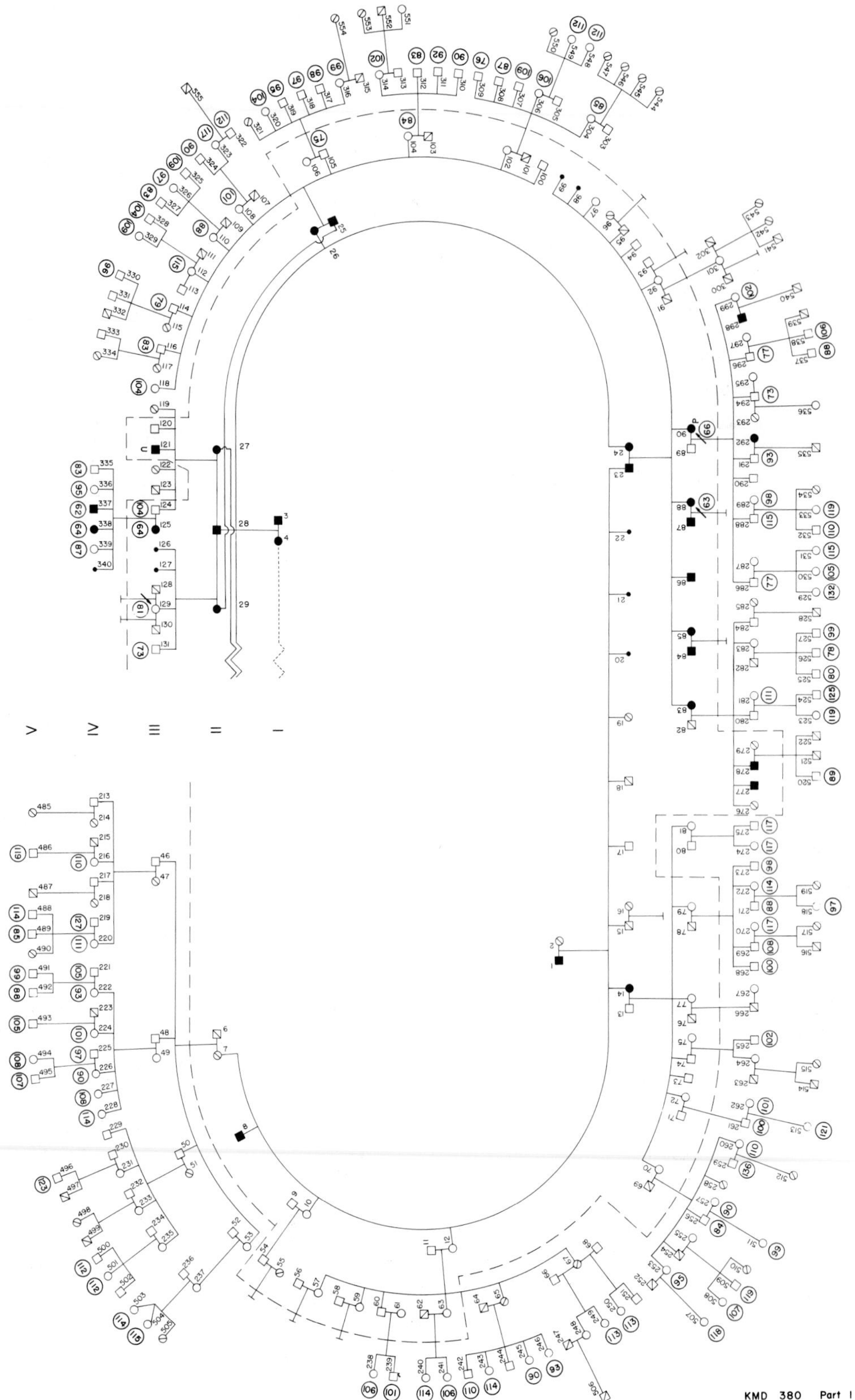

KMD 380 Part I

KMD 380

The Proband

The proband (90) was born in 1899, institutionalized at age 15 years and discharged to relatives in 1915. She grew up in a poor home, but had no history of difficult birth or perinatal infection. She married (89), a foreign born man with normal intelligence and has seven children. She was working as a cleaning woman in a restaurant in 1961. (For a detailed study of her immediate family, see Reed and Phillips, 1959). IQ 66. *Diagnosis:* undifferentiated mental retardation.

Grandparents

Paternal grandfather and both maternal grandparents were retarded. Maternal grandfather was also epileptic.

Parents

Father (23) was an alcoholic and never supported his family. He was retarded.

Mother (24) was epileptic and retarded.

Aunts and Uncles

Paternal uncle (8) was an alcoholic, retarded and died single and childless.

Paternal aunt (14) was retarded. Her husband was normal but a thief. Their children were normal.

Maternal aunt (26) could not keep house or take care of her children. Husband is retarded and ten children have borderline to normal IQ's.

Maternal uncle (28) was an alcoholic, epileptic and retarded. Both his wives were retarded. One of his seven children and two of his five surviving grandchildren were also retarded.

Maternal uncle (36) was retarded. His wife and two of their eight surviving children are also retarded.

Maternal uncle (41) was retarded. His children of two marriages all have normal intelligence.

Proband's mother's half sister (44) was retarded. Her husband and three of her four surviving children were normal. One child was retarded.

Siblings

Sister (83) completed the seventh grade. She knew little about her children's birthdates or her grandchildren's names and was classified as retarded as were two of her six children.

Sister (85) is retarded as is her husband. They are childless.

Brother (86) died of tuberculosis unmarried and childless. He was retarded.

Sister (88) was institutionalized at age 15 years in 1912, and discharged three years later. She deserted her husband and died of pulmonary tuberculosis. She was childless.

Sister (92) was adopted from the state orphanage and is a clerk with a normal child.

Brother (94) was adopted from the state orphanage. He has normal intelligence.

Brother (95) was reared in a foster home. He completed the eighth grade and is a painter. His intelligence is unknown.

Sister (97) died of pulmonary tuberculosis when young. She had normal intelligence.

Sister (98) died of neglect at 18 months of age.

Brother (99) died at 6 weeks of age—"sickly from birth."

Children

Son (286) is a truck driver with IQ 77. His wife and children are of normal intelligence.

Son (288) is a salesman with IQ 115. His wife has an IQ of 98. The children are normal.

Son (290) was an average student. He was killed by a hit and run driver at age 11 years.

Son (291) graduated from high school and is a laborer, IQ 93. His wife has "an IQ lower than her sister" who has an IQ of 64.

Son (294) is a painter with IQ 73. He has been married twice and has one child who is normal.

Son (296) is on probation for selling mortgaged property. He is a laborer with IQ 77. His wife and children are of normal intelligence.

Daughter (299) graduated from high school and has an IQ of 102. She married an illiterate retarded man who only completed the fourth grade.

Grandchildren

The IQ's of 11 are known. They range from 78 to 132.

Nieces and Nephews

Nephew (277) is an unmarried, childless and retarded farm laborer.

Nephew (278) is retarded, according to his teacher.

First Cousins

(121) was retarded.

(124), brother to (121), has an IQ of 104 but married a woman with IQ 64.

(129) was removed from the home as a baby because of parental neglect and paregoric poisoning. She was institutionalized for a time, also was hospitalized for mental illness and later was sent to a reformatory for incorrigibility and sex relations with her stepbrother. The community refused to have her on a parole status. She was sterilized while under commitment and has a diagnosis of psychopathic personality without psychosis. IQ 81.

(131) was committed as an epileptic and died in a state hospital. IQ 73.

Continued on page 377

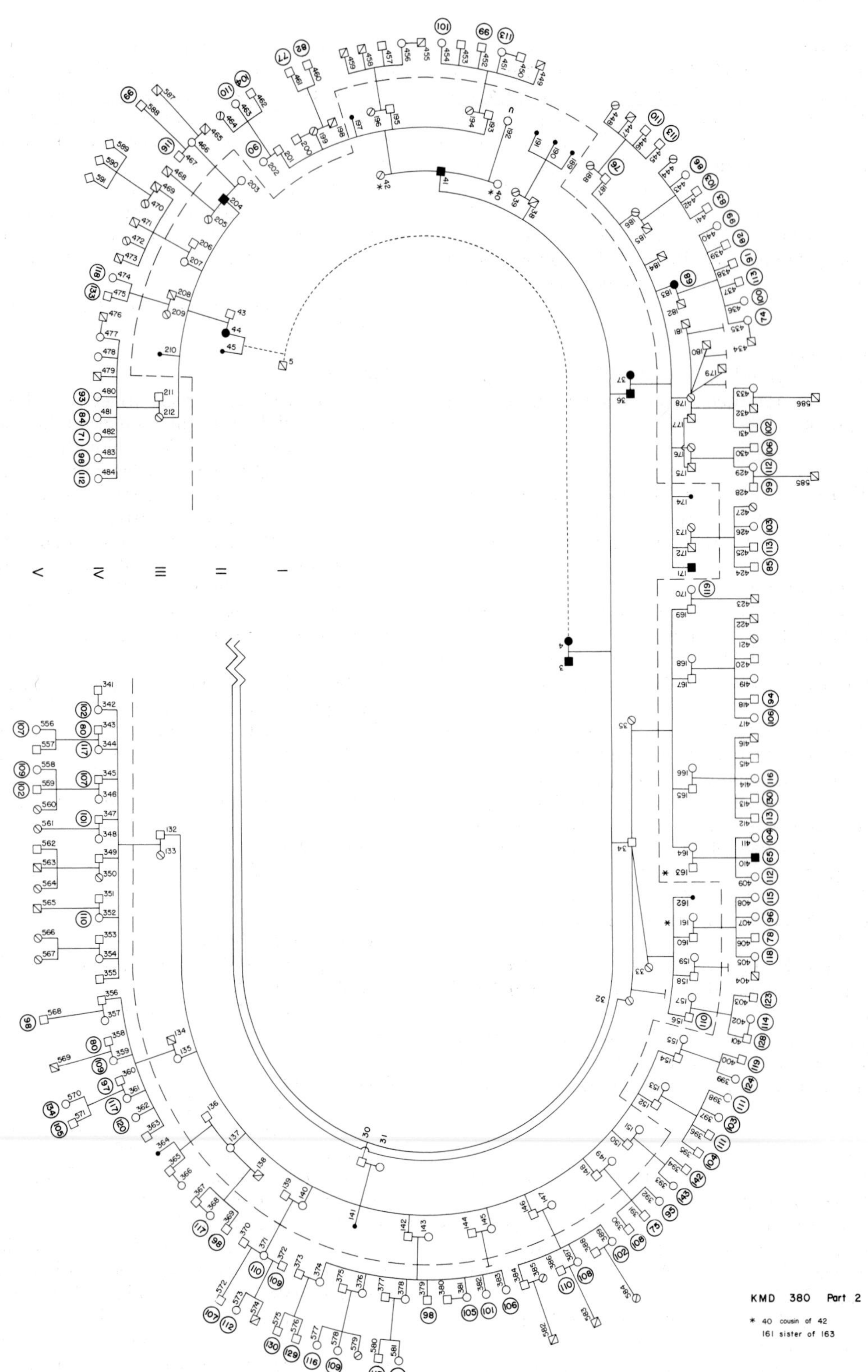

KMD 380 Part 2

* 40 cousin of 42
161 sister of 163

KMD 380 – *Continued*

(171) is a crippled, middle-grade retardate.
(183) has an IQ of 68.
(204) is retarded.

More Distant Relatives

First cousin (124) with IQ 104 has five living children. Two of them (337) and (338), have IQ's of 62 and 64, respectively. The others have IQ's of 83, 95 and 87. The father's IQ is 64.

First cousin (163) has a retarded child (410) with IQ 65.

Family Summary

The proband, IQ 66, came from a large family that had a varied record of alcoholism, crime, retardation and mental instability. Her immediate family was described in some detail in 1959 (Reed and Phillips). Her paternal grandfather, both maternal grandparents, both parents, a paternal aunt and uncle, three maternal uncles, a maternal aunt and the proband's mother's half sister, four siblings, two nephews, four first cousins and three more distant relatives were all high-grade retardates with the exception of one imbecile. In addition, three persons of normal intelligence married retarded spouses, one first cousin was a diagnosed psychopathic personality and her brother was committed for epilepsy. The proband married a man of normal or above normal intelligence. Her six children have an IQ range of 73 to 102. Two of these children married retarded spouses and one child has a prison record. The grandchildren show an IQ range of 78 to 132. The proband's parents had 11 children and 14 grandchildren.

Retardation of proband of probably genetic origin.

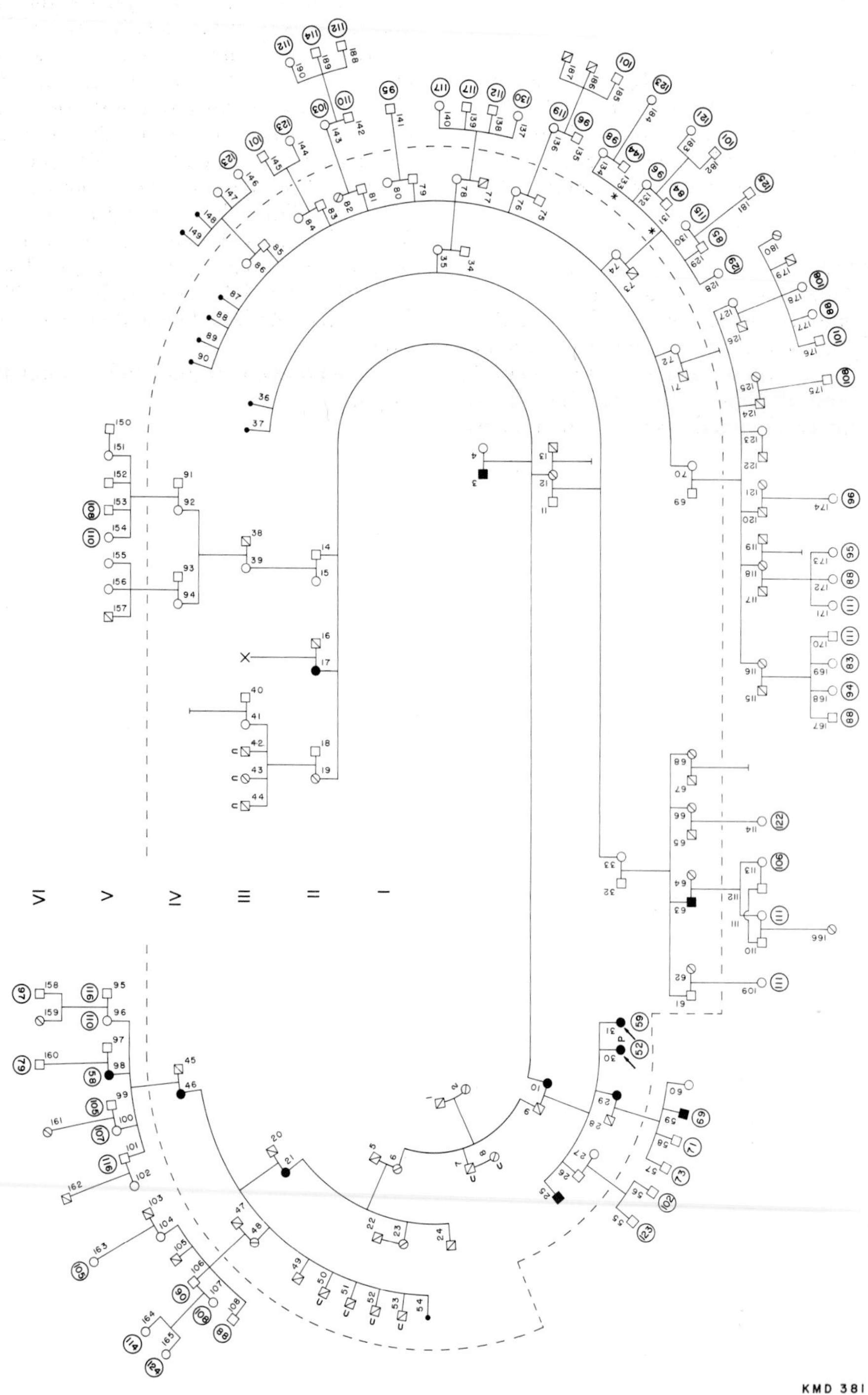

KMD 381

* 131 nephew of 133

KMD 381

The Proband

The proband (30) was born in 1901, institutionalized at age 15 years and died of pulmonary tuberculosis in the institution in 1929. No details are known of her birth or early development since her retarded mother could not recall them. IQ 52. *Diagnosis:* undifferentiated mental retardation.

Grandparents

Paternal grandparents unknown.

Maternal grandfather was an industrious laborer but was "foolish," "like the children" (proband and her siblings).

Parents

Father (9) was a crippled alcoholic laborer of unknown intelligence.

Mother (10) was an alcoholic and "very deficient mentally."

Aunts and Uncles

Paternal aunt (6) died of alcoholism. Her husband committed suicide.

Maternal aunt (17) was retarded.

Siblings

Brother (25) died unmarried and childless at age 21 years. He was retarded.

Brother (26) completed the eighth grade and works for a meat packing company. He was helpful and informative.

Sister (29) is now a patient in a mental hospital with a diagnosis of neuropsychiatric disorder with mental deficiency. Her tested children have IQ's of 123, 102, 73, 71 and 69.

Sister (31) was institutionalized in 1902 at age 12 years and is still in the institution. In 1950 she was given a physical and neurological examination by J. A. Böök, M.D., and John Schut, M.D. They found no stigmata and reported that she was "neurologically entirely negative." An EEG administered at this time showed normal reaction in both waking and sleeping. IQ 59 and epileptic.

Nieces and Nephews

Nephew (59) has an IQ of 69. He has two brothers with borderline IQ's of 73 and 71. All three were in special classes, and (58) with IQ 71 has a speech defect.

First Cousins

(21) was an alcoholic and retarded.

More Distant Relatives

(46) is retarded, as is her daughter (98) who has an IQ of 58. Her other three children have normal intelligence.

(61) hired an attorney to write us that our letter "upset him." His brother (63) is hospitalized with a diagnosis of psychosis with mental deficiency. The old records classified him as normal mentally.

Family Summary

The proband, IQ 52, her maternal grandfather, mother, one paternal aunt, one maternal aunt, three siblings, a nephew, one first cousin and three more distant relatives were all middle- or high-grade retardates, two with a psychosis also (one the proband's sister). The proband's parents had five children and six grandchildren, three of the latter with IQ's of 69, 71 and 73, respectively.

Retardation of proband of probably genetic origin.

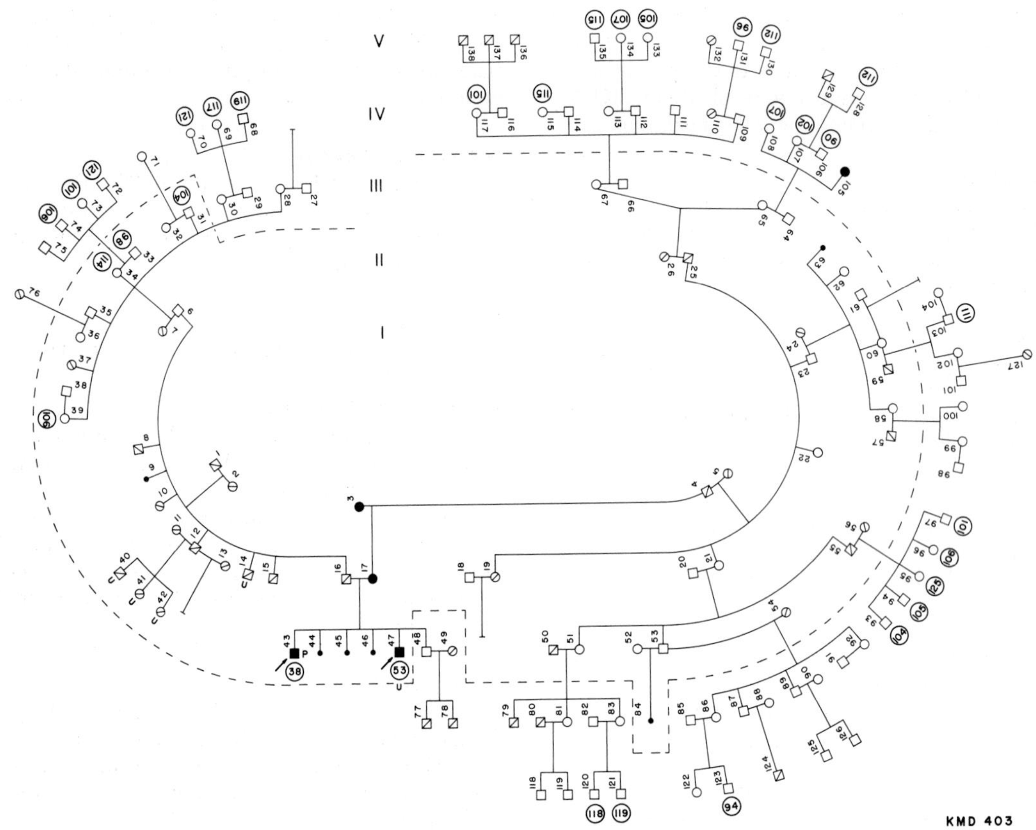

KMD 403

KMD 403

The Proband

The proband (43) was born in 1907, institutionalized at age 5 years and died of perforation of the small bowel in the institution in 1951. His birth was uneventful and there is no record of serious infection. The home surroundings were poor. IQ 38. *Diagnosis:* undifferentiated mental retardation.

Grandparents

Maternal grandmother was retarded. The relatives attributed her condition to a bad fall at age 35 years.

Parents

Father (16) was a laborer of unknown intelligence. He was telephoned by a field worker but it was almost impossible to understand him—a neighbor interpreted for him but little information could be obtained. Some of his difficulty may have been the result of age.

Mother (17) was hospitalized for mental illness three times and died in a mental hospital with a diagnosis of depressive reaction. She did not talk until the age of 5 years and left school at age 17 years when in the fourth grade. She was both retarded and mentally ill.

Aunts and Uncles

Not of interest.

Siblings

Brother (44) died at age 2 months from "over feeding and stomach trouble."

Sister (45) died of suffocation at age 2½ months—"neighbor's child sat on the cradle."

Brother (46) died at age 2 months from "careless feeding."

Brother (47) was born in a mental hospital. He was institutionalized at age 15 years, escaped a year later and has not been heard from since 1939. IQ 53.

Brother (48) was adopted as a child. He completed the eighth grade and a farm course. He has normal intelligence.

Nieces and Nephews

Not of interest.

First Cousins

Not of interest.

More Distant Relatives

First cousin (65) has a daughter (105) who completed the fifth grade, has a speech defect and is retarded. The mother says the retardation is the result of a birth injury. This girl has two normal brothers.

Family Summary

The proband, IQ 38, his brother, maternal grandmother, mother and one more distant relative were retarded. The proband's mother was also mentally ill and died in a mental hospital. Three of the proband's siblings died of lack of care and neglect in infancy. The proband's parents had six children and two grandchildren.

Retardation of proband of probably genetic origin.

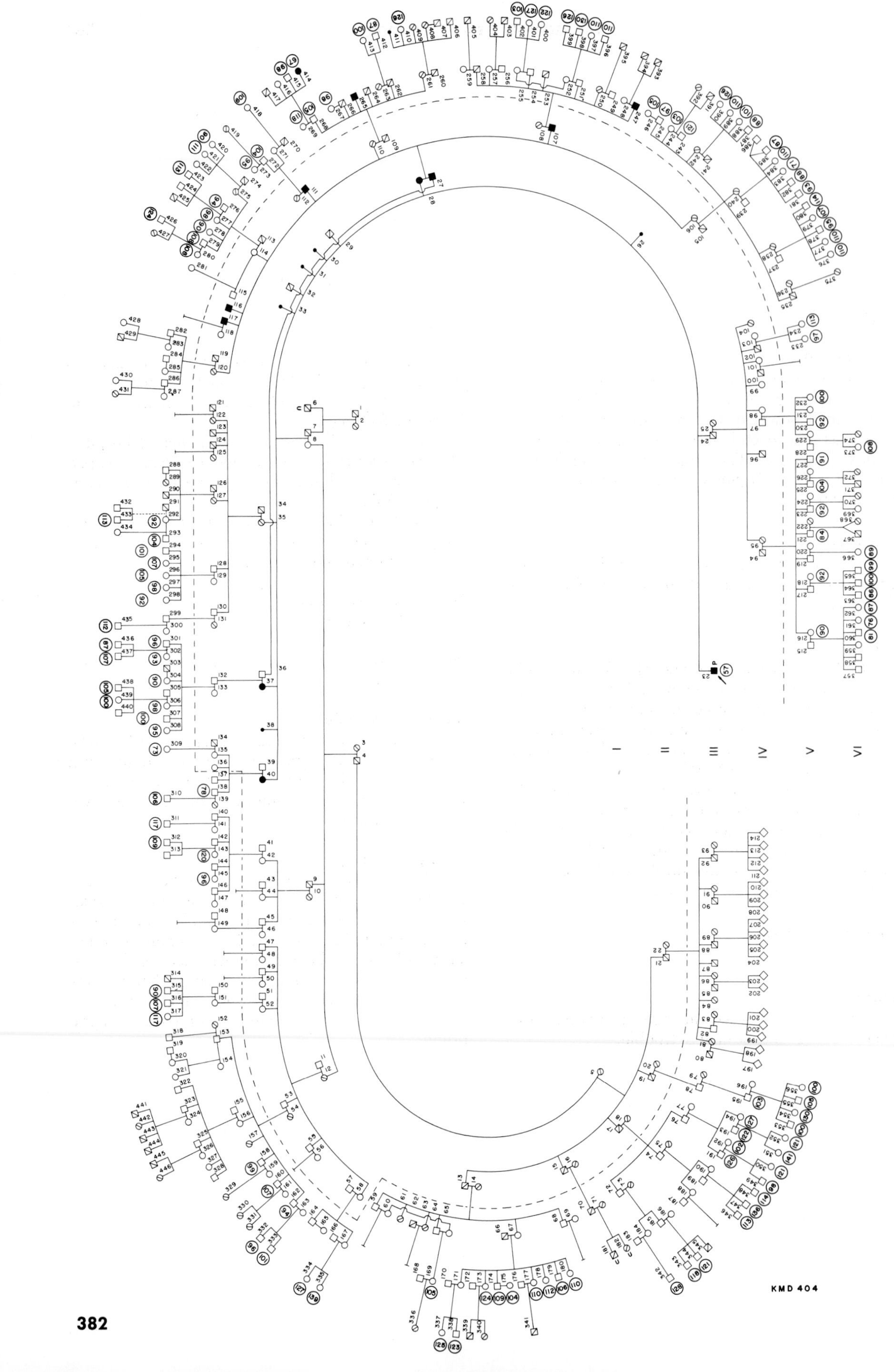
KMD 404

KMD 404

The Proband

The proband (23) was born in 1862, institutionalized at age 48 years, ran away to his relatives in 1917 and died in 1936 of heat prostration. He was reared in a good home and attended school with poor results until age 14 years. He deteriorated considerably after a stroke at age 35 years. IQ 57. *Diagnosis:* undifferentiated mental retardation.

Grandparents

Not of interest.

Parents

Father (7) had unknown intelligence.

Mother (8) had normal intelligence.

Aunts and Uncles

Paternal relatives were unknown.

Maternal relatives not of interest.

Siblings

Brothers (24), (29), (32) and sister (35) had unknown intelligence.

Brother (26) died a few days after birth.

Sister (28) was promiscuous and retarded. Her husband (29) and four of her eight children were also retarded.

(30), (31) and (33)–two brothers, one sister–died in infancy.

Sister (37) was a high-grade retardate with a normal husband and child.

Brother (38) died at birth because of a craniotomy. The doctor said he had "rickets."

Sister (40) was a high-grade retardate. Her husband and four children were normal.

Nieces and Nephews

Nephew (107) completed the fifth grade and is a high-grade retardate.

Nephew (111) completed the seventh grade at age 15 years and is retarded.

Nephew (116) died unmarried and childless at age 31 years. He was retarded.

Nephew (117) was in the third grade at age 12 years and is retarded. He was married but childless.

First Cousins

Not of interest.

More Distant Relatives

Great-nephew (247) failed the fourth grade for the second time at age 14 years.

Great-nephew (265) completed the fourth grade. He is now a paraplegic as the result of an auto accident.

(414) grandson to niece (110) has an IQ of 67.

Family Summary

The proband, IQ 57, three siblings, four nephews and three more distant relatives were all high-grade retardates. There was no record of syphilitic infections, epilepsy, mental illness or serious social problems. All the retardates appear in the descendants of the proband's parents. The proband's parents had 13 children and 26 grandchildren.

Retardation of proband of probably genetic origin.

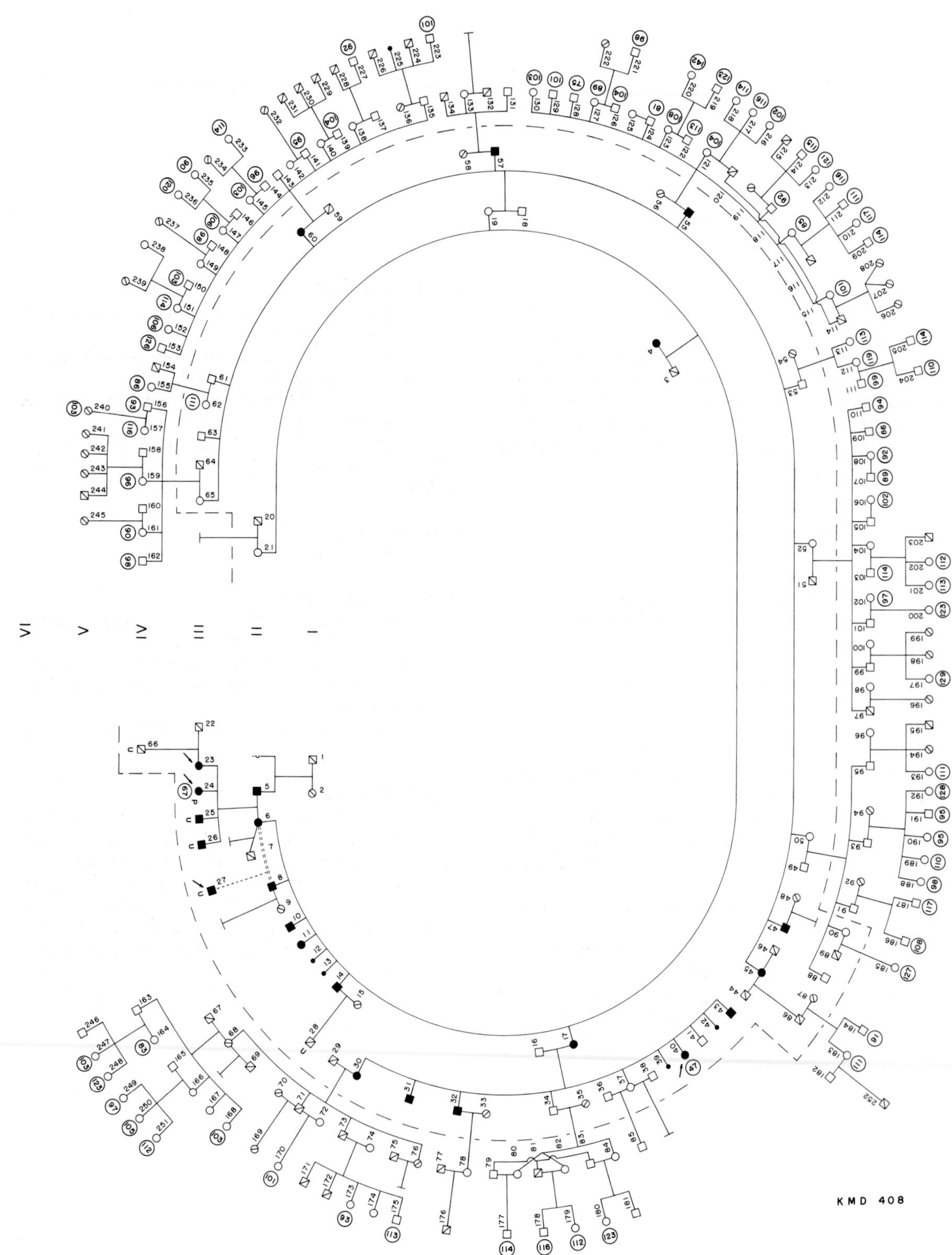

KMD 408

KMD 408

The Proband

The proband (24) was born in 1892, institutionalized at age 14 years and discharged to her mother in 1911. The family later moved to the west coast with the result that the present status of the proband is unknown. She had no history of injury or infection and no stigmata. The home environment was impoverished. IQ 67. *Diagnosis:* undifferentiated mental retardation.

Grandparents

Paternal grandparents are unknown.

Maternal grandmother was unable to keep house or to take care of her family.

Parents

Father (5) was retarded.

Mother (6) was retarded. She had a child (27) by her brother (8) before her marriage.

Aunts and Uncles

Paternal relatives unknown.

Maternal uncle (8) was imprisoned for incest with the proband's mother. He was retarded, as was his child.

Maternal uncle (10) was a childless, retarded laborer.

Maternal aunt (11) was retarded. She died at age 8 years.

Maternal uncle (14) was a retarded logger who had one child.

Maternal aunt (17) was both mentally ill and retarded. Her husband was normal but an alcoholic and a thief. Five of their eight surviving children were retarded.

Siblings

Sister (23) was institutionalized in 1902 at age 12 years and discharged in 1911. She married and went to the west coast. She could not be found for the follow-up. She was a high-grade retardate; intelligence of husband and child unknown.

Brothers (25) and (26) were both retarded. Neither one could be found for the follow-up.

Half Siblings

Half brother (27) was institutionalized in 1900 at age 15 years but was taken out by relatives two years later and could not be found for the follow-up. He was a low- to middle-grade retardate classified as uneducable. He had a rather large head and a continuous motion of the face and limbs. His parents were brother and sister.

Nieces and Nephews

Unknown.

First Cousins

(30) was a high-grade retardate. No retarded persons have appeared among her descendants.

(31) was a high-grade retardate who died unmarried and childless.

(32) was retarded. Wife's intelligence is unknown. His daughter was normal.

(40) was institutionalized for a time and later died unmarried and childless. IQ 47.

(43), brother to all the above, is an unmarried, childless retardate.

(45) was retarded. Intelligence of husband and child is unknown.

(47) is married but a childless retardate.

(55) was retarded. Intelligence of wife is unknown. Ten children have IQ's from 75 to 108.

(57) was retarded. Intelligence of wife is unknown. There were two normal children and one of unknown intelligence.

(60), sister to (45), (47), (55) and (57), was retarded. Intelligence of husband is unknown. Her 11 children are all normal.

More Distant Relatives

Not of interest.

Family Summary

The proband, IQ 67, her parents, her maternal grandmother, three siblings, one half brother, three maternal uncles, two maternal aunts and ten first cousins were retarded, all but the half brother being of high grade. The home environment was poor for nearly all the persons in the older generations. Of the 17 retarded whose status is known, eight had no children. This fact, plus the probable occurrence of some of the retardation as a result of the bad environment, can account for the disappearance of the retardation in the more recent generations. It is very disappointing that the proband's immediate family could not be traced. The child of the incest was of lower grade than his parents and probably demonstrates a genetically influenced type of retardation. The nieces and nephews of the proband would be of great interest. The proband's parents had four children and at least one grandchild.

Retardation of proband of probably genetic origin.

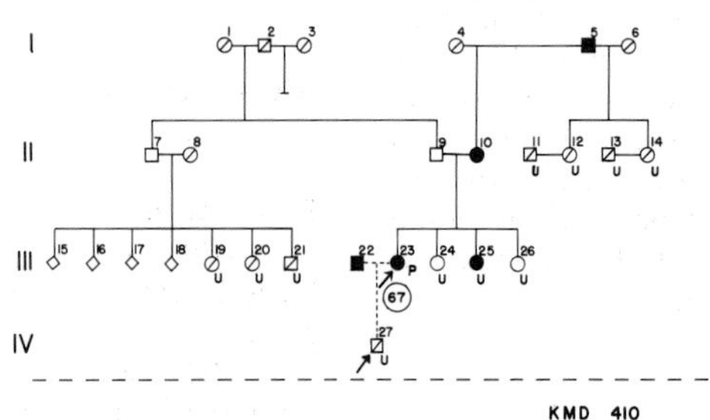

KMD 410

The Proband

The proband (23) was born in 1895, institutionalized at age 17 years when she became pregnant and was discharged to her parents in 1913. Her present status is unknown. There was no history of birth injury or perinatal infection. She attended school until age 14 years when she was in the fifth grade. The teacher reported she was incapable of doing fourth grade work. She became incorrigible from lack of supervision and finally became illegitimately pregnant. IQ 67. *Diagnosis:* undifferentiated mental retardation.

Grandparents

Maternal grandfather was retarded.

Parents

Father (9) was epileptic but had normal intelligence.

Mother (10) was promiscuous and retarded.

Aunts and Uncles

Only one paternal relative, a normal man.

The proband's mother had no full siblings and only two half sisters of unknown intelligence.

Siblings

Sister (24) was "better than" the proband in school.

Sister (25) was repeating the third grade for the third time at age 14 years.

Sister (26) was "bright."

Child

Son (27) was born in the institution. His intelligence and present status are unknown. Institution records stated he was walking and could say few words when discharged at age 15 months. He was described as "a beautiful boy."

Nieces and Nephews

Unknown. No one of this family could be found for the follow-up.

First Cousins

Unknown.

More Distant Relatives

Unknown.

Family Summary

The proband, IQ 67, her maternal grandfather, mother and one sister were high-grade retardates. The proband had an illegitimate son of unknown intelligence, but who was apparently normal at age 15 months. This family could not be found for the follow-up, partly because they had a frequently occurring Scandinavian name and partly because the proband's siblings were all girls who may have married and changed their names. The proband's parents had four children, grandchildren unknown.

Retardation of proband of probably genetic origin.

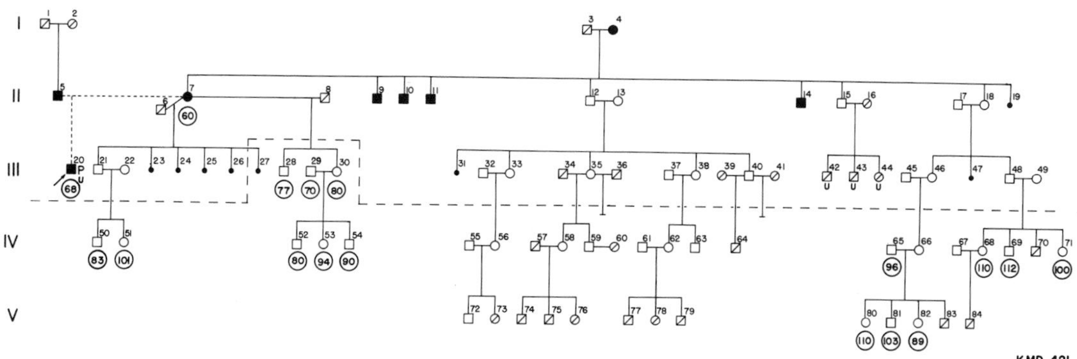

KMD 421

The Proband

The proband (20) was born in 1907, institutionalized at age 7 years, escaped several times, was reinstitutionalized after being found in jail and was finally discharged from guardianship in 1948 because he had left the state. He was a three pound baby delivered after a prolonged labor of three days, but without the use of instruments. He walked at age 2 years, talked at age 3 years. At age 3 years he fell 14 feet and was in a hospital for three months. After this episode he had to learn to walk again. His home environment was poor. IQ 68. *Diagnosis:* undifferentiated mental retardation.

Grandparents

Maternal grandfather was an alcoholic and cruel and abusive to his family.

Maternal grandmother was retarded.

Parents

Father (5) did not talk until age 7 years. He was an alcoholic and retarded.

Mother (7) was a poor housekeeper who neglected her children. She was up for commitment as retarded at one time, but the petition was withdrawn. IQ 60. The proband was illegitimate and later (7) had two legal husbands, (6) and (8). (6) served jail terms for assault and drunkenness.

Aunts and Uncles

Maternal uncles (9), (10), (11) and (14) were retarded. (9) was an alcoholic laborer who "spent all his money on women." All were single, childless laborers.

(10) and (11) were illiterate.

Siblings

No full siblings.

Half Siblings

Half brother (21) completed the eighth grade and is an electroplater with normal intelligence and a normal family.

(23), (24), (25) and (26) were miscarriages.

Half brother (28) completed the fifth grade and died at age 14 years. IQ 77.

Half sister (30) completed the seventh grade. Her IQ is 80. She married a man with IQ 70. Their children's IQ's are 80, 94 and 90.

Nieces and Nephews

All five are the children of half siblings. Two have low-normal IQ's of 83 and 80, three have normal ones of 101, 94 and 90.

First Cousins

Not of interest.

More Distant Relatives

Not of interest.

Family Summary

The proband, IQ 68, maternal grandmother, both parents (mother with IQ 60) and four maternal uncles were all high-grade retardates. The proband was premature and was hospitalized at age 3 years for three months following a fall. Two of the proband's half siblings have borderline and low-normal IQ's of 77 and 80. The proband's parents had one child, no grandchildren. Despite the history of possibly early trauma, the family pattern indicates a genetic component in this three generation history of retardation.

Retardation of proband of probably genetic origin.

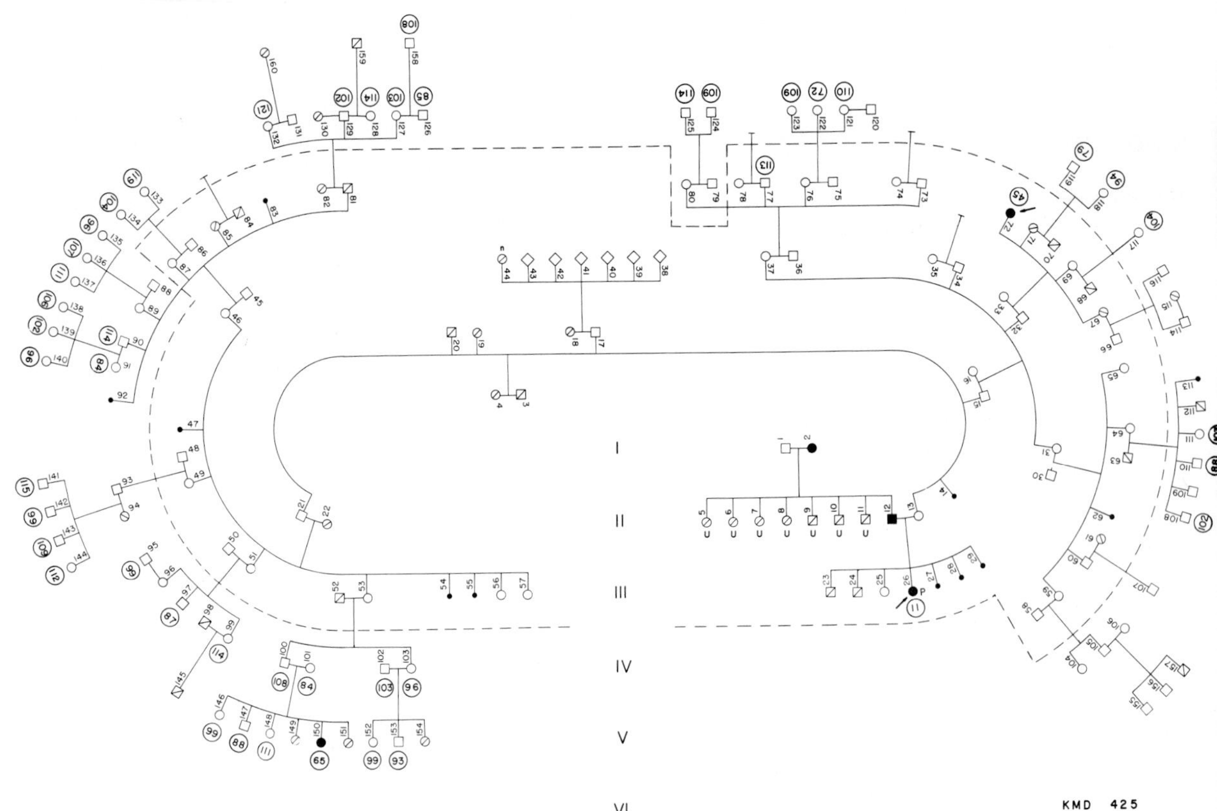

KMD 425

KMD 425

The Proband

The proband (26) was born in 1891, institutionalized at age 22 years and died of pernicious anemia in the institution in 1946. She had "brain fever" at age 3 months. She walked at age 4 years. She had a long, narrow head but no other stigmata. IQ 11. *Diagnosis:* undifferentiated mental retardation.

Grandparents

Paternal grandmother was retarded.

Parents

Father (12) was retarded. He assisted in a greenhouse but was never allowed to work unsupervised.

Mother (13) had normal intelligence.

Aunts and Uncles

All paternal relatives were said to have been retarded but they were never seen by the early workers because the proband's father was the only one who came to this country.

Maternal uncle (20) was mentally ill and died single at age 25 years.

Siblings

Brother (23) of unknown intelligence, died unmarried and childless at age 68 years.

Brother (24) of unknown intelligence, died unmarried and childless at age 30 years.

Sister (25) with normal intelligence works in a box factory. She is unmarried and childless.

Brothers (27), (28) and (29) died in infancy; (29) died of "spasms," the other two of intestinal infections.

Nieces and Nephews

None.

First Cousins

Not of interest.

More Distant Relatives

First cousin (32) has an institutionalized child (72) with IQ 45 and a diagnosis of "cerebral palsy of childhood."

(150) has an IQ of 65 at age 7 years.

Family Summary

The proband, IQ 11, her paternal grandmother, her father and two more distant relatives were retarded. Only the proband was a low-grade retardate. She was supposed to have had "brain fever" at age 3 months.

Retardation of proband of probably genetic origin.

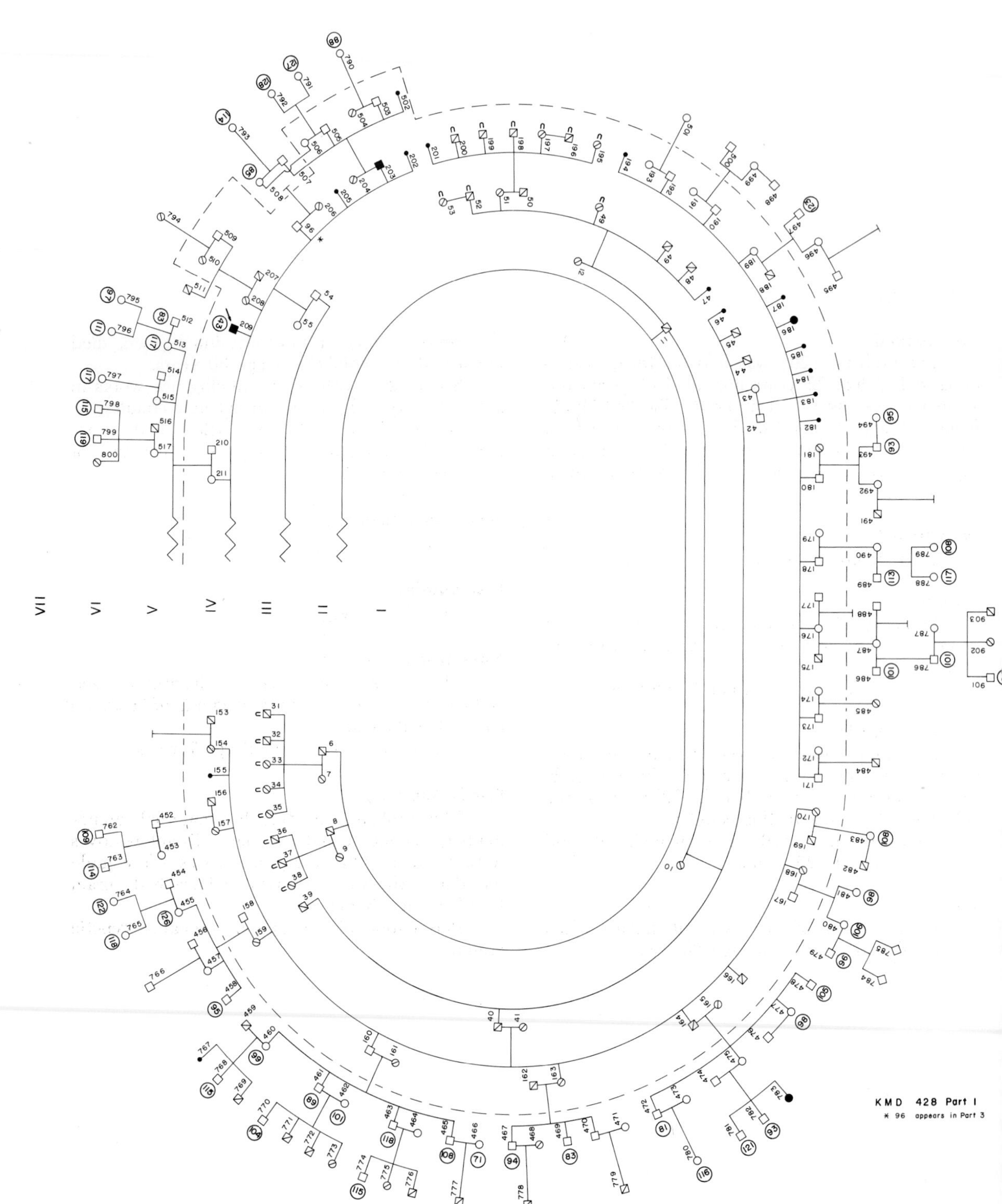

KMD 428 Part I
* 96 appears in Part 3

KMD 428

The Proband

The proband (22) was born in 1868, institutionalized at age 46 years and died of carcinoma of the liver, pancreas and mesenterium in the institution in 1950. She had no history of birth injury or perinatal infection and she had no stigmata. Her parents ascribed her condition to a fall at age 3 years. The institution diagnosis was imbecile, cause undiagnosed. She attended school for two years with poor results. Her home treatment was unkind. When she was 17 she had a child by her mother's half brother (23), an epileptic of unknown intelligence. This child died at age 14 months. The proband had a second illegitimate child by the illegitimate son (59) of her brother's first wife (56). This child was institutionalized in 1902 at age 13 years with a diagnosis of "idiot-familial" and died of an intestinal obstruction in the institution in 1937. His IQ was 19. The proband's IQ was 28. *Diagnosis:* undifferentiated mental retardation.

Grandparents

Not of interest.

Parents

Father (13) was a farmer and cattle dealer.

Mother (14) died of a brain tumor at age 64 years. This may have been the cause of the mental illness and epilepsy she suffered from during the last six years of her life. Her intelligence was unknown.

Aunts and Uncles

Paternal side not of interest.

Proband's mother's only sibling (15) died at age 16 years of unknown causes.

Proband's mother's half brother (23) was the father of the proband's first illegitimate child. He was epileptic, intelligence unknown. He had two children by (24) of unknown intelligence, a normal daughter and a son of unknown intelligence.

Proband's mother's half sister (26) died in a mental hospital. She was epileptic and psychotic. She had eight children who died in infancy of unknown causes and three daughters who were adopted.

Proband's mother's half sister (30) was hospitalized for mental illness and epilepsy.

Siblings

Brother (54) was a successful businessman with a normal wife but two of his seven surviving children are retarded.

Brother (57) had normal intelligence as did his wife and children.

Brother (60) died at age 6 months, cause unknown.

Sister (61) died at age 6 months, cause unknown.

Brother (62) was a foreman in a factory. He married his normal "half" cousin (63). Their two surviving children (of eight born) have normal intelligence.

Brother (64) committed suicide.

Brother (66) was a retarded truck driver. His wife was also retarded, as were four of their 12 children.

Sister (69) had normal intelligence and normal children.

(70) and (71), twin girls, one of whom died shortly after birth, the other at age 2 years of "lung trouble."

Children

Son (116) died at age 14 months, cause unknown.

Son (225) was institutionalized at age 14 years and died in the institution, IQ 19. Both fathers had unknown intelligence but the father of (116) was a half brother of the proband's mother and was epileptic.

Nieces and Nephews

Nephew (203) was retarded, wife's intelligence unknown, three surviving children all with normal intelligence.

Nephew (96) married his first cousin once removed. The IQ's of their seven surviving children range from 78 to 134.

Nephew (209) was institutionalized in 1913 at age 21 years and died of epilepsy in the institution in 1917. IQ 43.

Niece (222) had normal intelligence but developed epilepsy after a fall at age 25 years.

(226), (227), (228), (231), (234) and (235) siblings and the children of a consanguineous marriage, all died in infancy of unknown causes. Two siblings survived, (229) with a Ph.D. and (233) who graduated from college.

Nephew (247) is an unmarried, retarded laborer.

Niece (250) is a retarded waitress. Her three children have normal intelligence (intelligence of divorced husband is unknown). One daughter (562) has had two illegitimate children and three children by a husband who deserted her.

Nephew (251) is a retarded laborer, wife's IQ 102, daughter's IQ 110.

Niece (254) completed the fifth grade, is retarded, and has epileptoid attacks; husband's intelligence unknown. Four children (570), (572), (573) and (575) have IQ's of 79, 123, 101 and 98, respectively.

First Cousins

(106) and his sister (108) were shot to death in Chicago. The only sibling who would

Continued on page 393

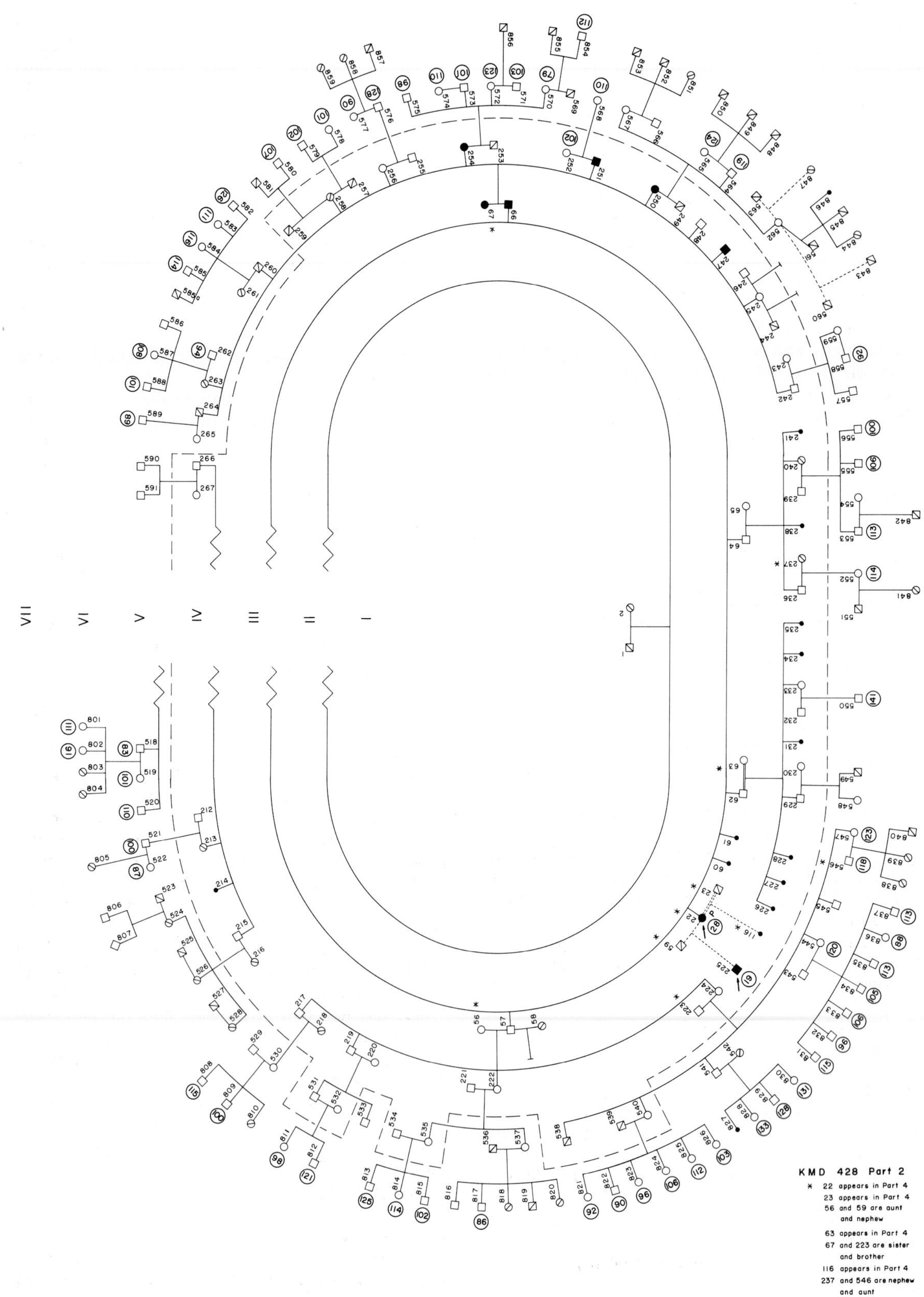

KMD 428 Part 2

* 22 appears in Part 4
23 appears in Part 4
56 and 59 are aunt and nephew
63 appears in Part 4
67 and 223 are sister and brother
116 appears in Part 4
237 and 546 are nephew and aunt

KMD 428 – *Continued*

cooperate (115) refused to give any details about the rest of her family.

More Distant Relatives

(186) is a high-grade retardate.

(783) is in a special education room for children with IQ's 50 to 80. She has cerebral palsy and is deaf.

Family Summary

The proband, IQ 28, and her son, IQ 19, were the only low- and middle-grade retardates known in this family. The proband's mother developed epilepsy and mental illness during the last six years of her life but these conditions may have been the result of a brain tumor which ultimately caused her death. However, the proband's mother had an epileptic half brother and two half sisters who were both epileptic and psychotic. One of the proband's brothers committed suicide. One brother, six nieces and nephews and two more distant relatives were high-grade retardates. In addition, a niece and a nephew developed epilepsy. Several sibships had poor social histories and a great number of relatives refused to cooperate. The proband's parents had nine children and 42 grandchildren of whom 11 died in infancy.

Retardation of proband of probably genetic origin (mother and child of similar low grade).

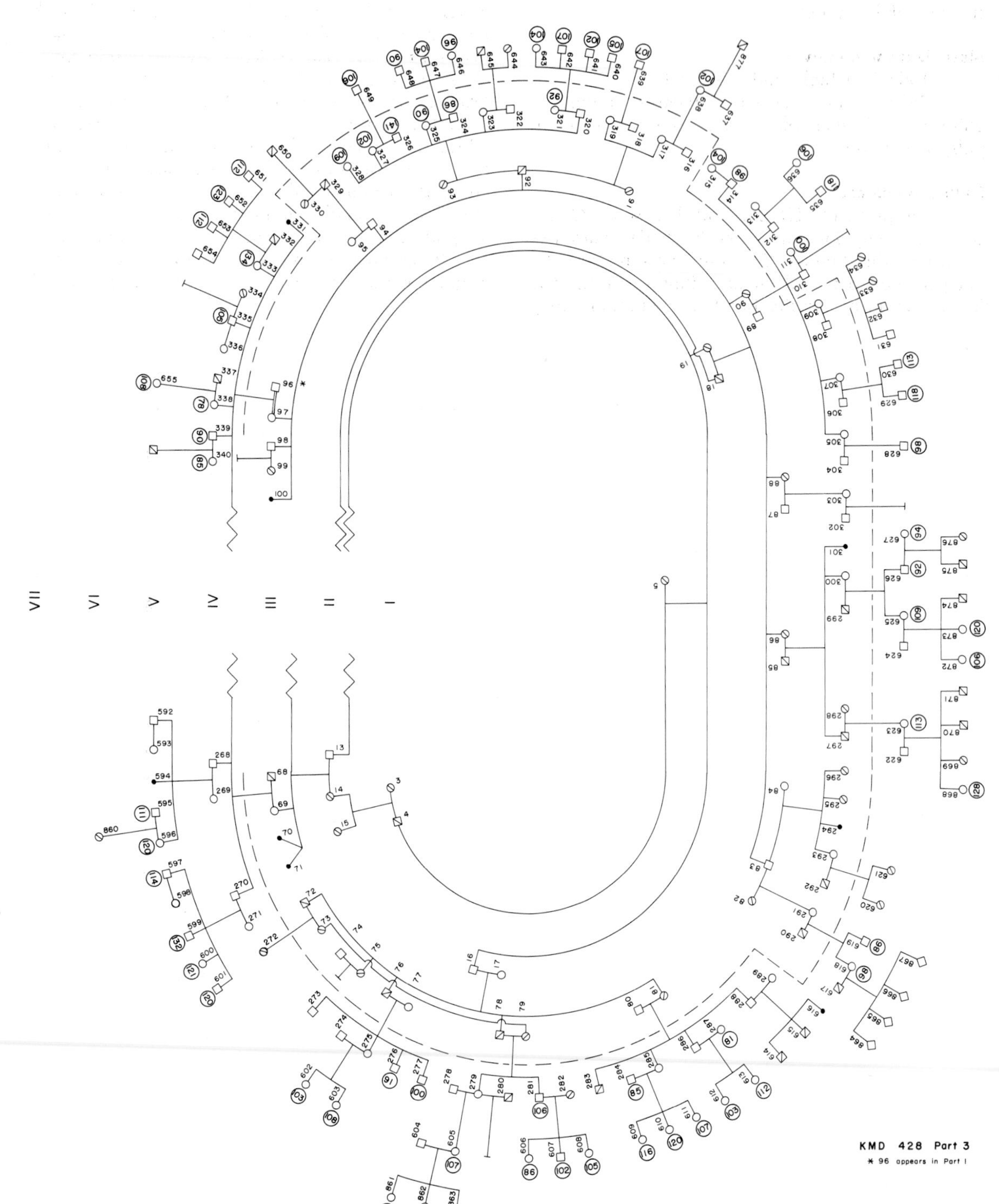

KMD 428 Part 3
* 96 appears in Part I

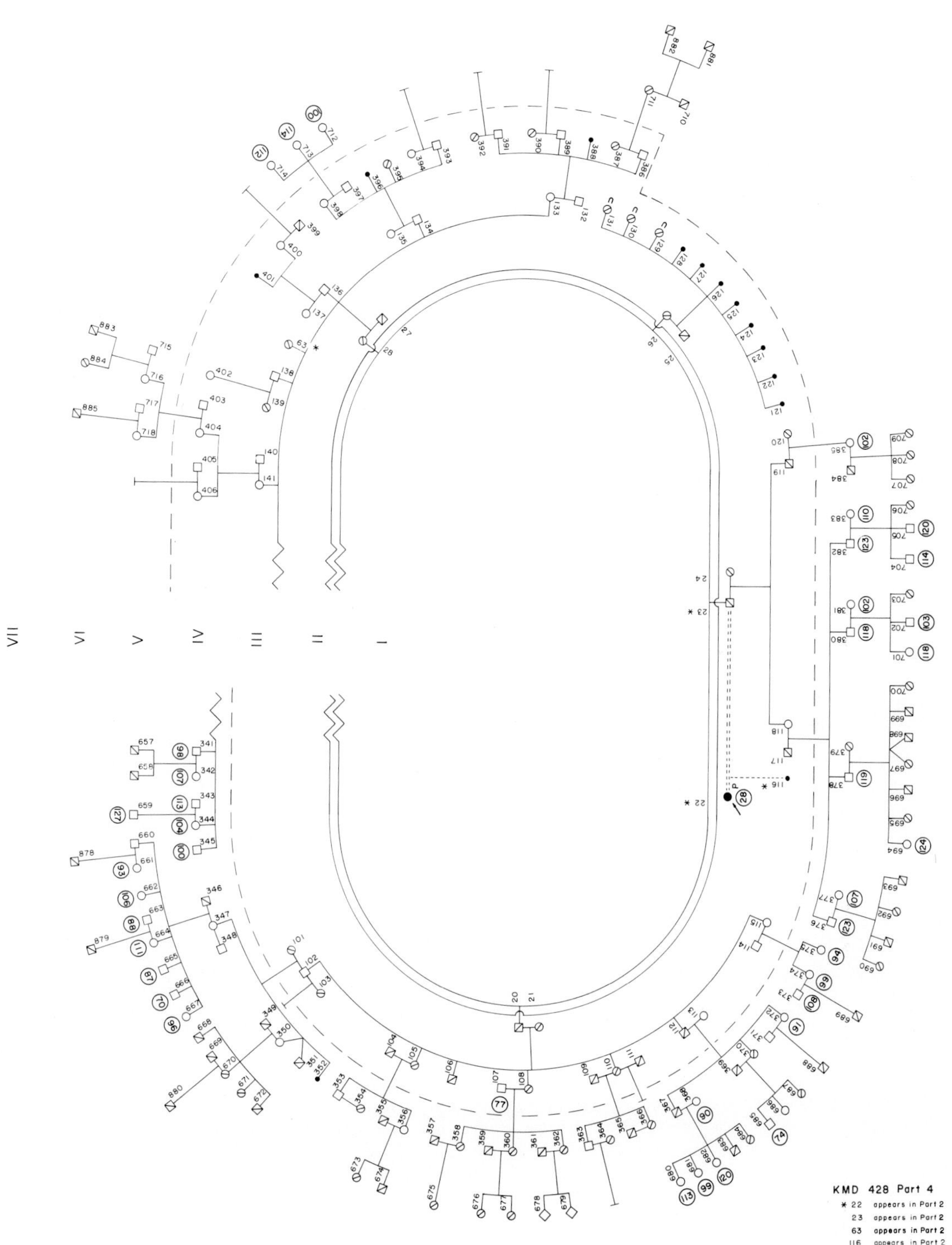

KMD 428 Part 4

* 22 appears in Part 2
23 appears in Part 2
63 appears in Part 2
116 appears in Part 2

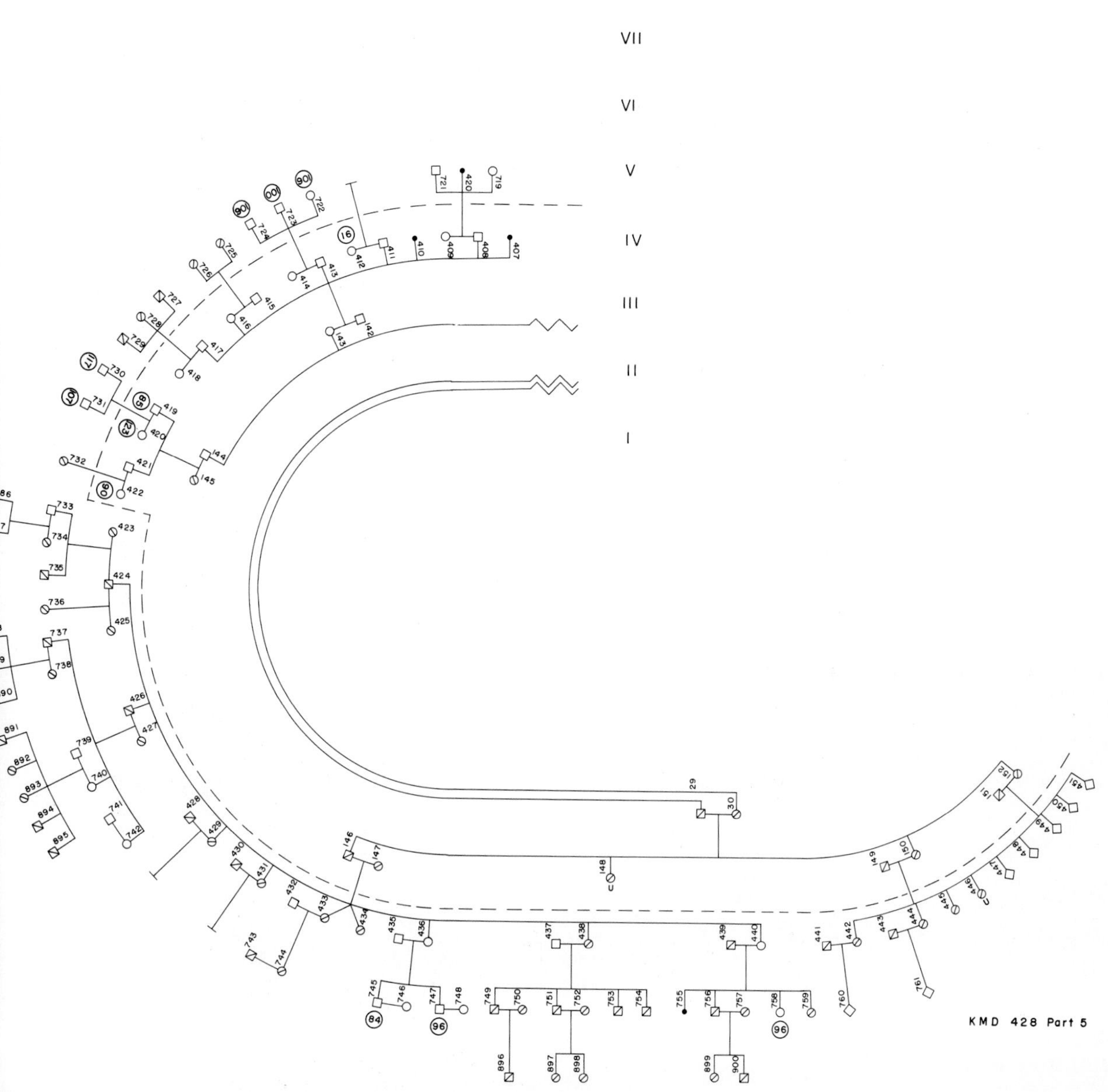
VII
VI
V
IV
III
II
I
KMD 428 Part 5

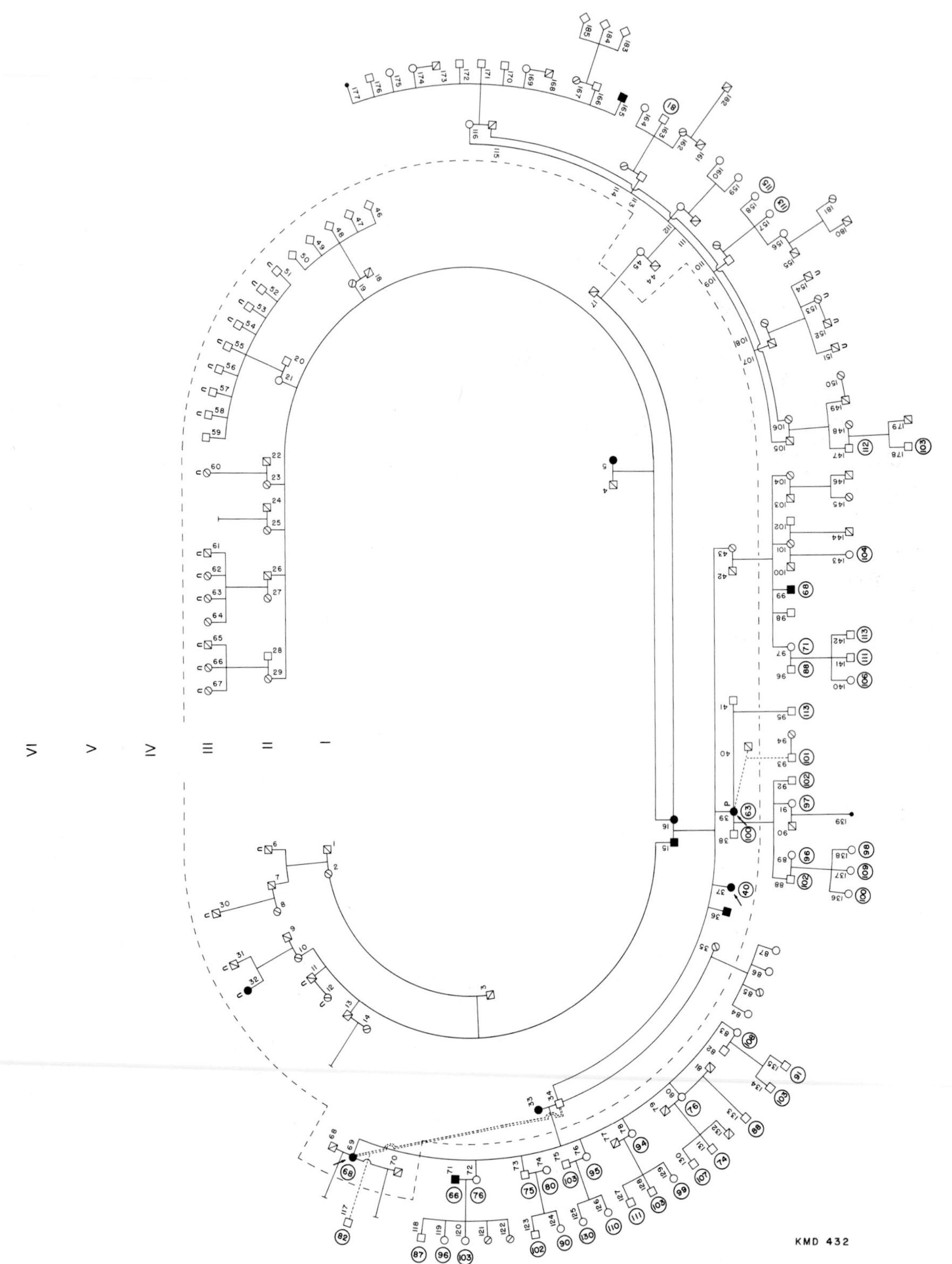

KMD 432

KMD 432

The Proband

The proband (39) was born in 1893, institutionalized at age 21 years and discharged two years later. Her birth and early development were uneventful. She married (38) in 1917 and divorced him in 1924. He had an IQ of 100. She was committed as retarded after the illegitimate birth of (93) in 1927, but was not institutionalized. In 1935 she married a second husband (41), a foreman, and was living under outside supervision in 1961. She has five children, one of whom is illegitimate. IQ 63. *Diagnosis:* undifferentiated mental retardation.

Grandparents

Paternal grandparents unknown.

Maternal grandmother was retarded.

Parents

Father (15) was an alcoholic and retarded. He served a prison term for incest with his daughter and later was hospitalized for a time in a mental hospital. He was also epileptic.

Mother (16) was retarded.

Aunts and Uncles

Not of interest.

Siblings

Brother (34) served a term in the state reformatory for "carnal knowledge." He had a child by his daughter (69). According to the prison records he has normal intelligence. His divorced first wife (33) was retarded. His eight children have IQ's ranging from 68 to 108. His tested grandchildren show an IQ range from 74 to 130.

Brother (36), retarded, died unmarried and childless. He served a prison term for assaulting a young girl.

Sister (37) was institutionalized in 1900 at age 15 years and died of serial epilepsy in the institution in 1914. IQ 40.

Sister (43) completed the eighth grade. Her intelligence is unknown, as is that of her husband. One of her five children is retarded.

Half Siblings

Half sister (45) had normal intelligence, but has a retarded grandchild.

Children

Son (88) completed the eleventh grade and is a salesman, IQ 102. His wife and children are normal.

Daughter (91) has an IQ of 97.

Son (92) completed the ninth grade and is an orderly. IQ 102.

Son (93) completed the tenth grade and is a laborer. IQ 101.

Son (95) has an IQ of 113.

Nieces and Nephews

Niece (69) was sent to a girls' reformatory for delinquency (illegitimate child by father) at age 17 years. She was institutionalized in 1934 at age 20 years, sterilized two years later and placed under outside supervision. She has divorced two husbands and is a beauty operator. She was discharged from guardianship in 1948 because she is out of the state. IQ 68. Her son (117) has an IQ of 82.

Niece (72) was in a girls' reformatory for delinquency. She has a borderline IQ of 76 and married (71) who is a window washer with IQ 66. Her children are not retarded.

Niece (97) with IQ 71, and spouse with IQ 88, has three children with IQ's of 106, 111 and 113, respectively.

Nephew (99) is a laborer with IQ 68.

First Cousins

Unknown except that (32) was known to have been retarded.

More Distant Relatives

(165) was failing the seventh grade at age 16 years.

Family Summary

The proband, IQ 63, her maternal grandmother, both parents, two siblings, a niece and nephew, one first cousin, and one more distant relative were known to have been high-grade retardates. The proband's father and one sister were epileptic in addition to their retardation. The proband's father and two brothers, one normal, one retarded, served prison terms for sexual offenses. The proband and her retarded sister had illegitimate children. The proband's five children all have normal intelligence as do her three grandchildren. The fathers of four of the proband's children are known to have had normal intelligence, with one having an IQ score of 100. The fifth child, the one with the highest IQ was illegitimate, father unknown. The proband's normal brother (wife retarded) had eight children with IQ's ranging from 68 to 108 and 16 tested grandchildren with IQ's ranging from 74 to 130. The proband's parents had five children and 21 grandchildren. The regression of the IQ's toward the mean in the more recent generations is especially marked in this history.

Retardation of proband of probably genetic origin.

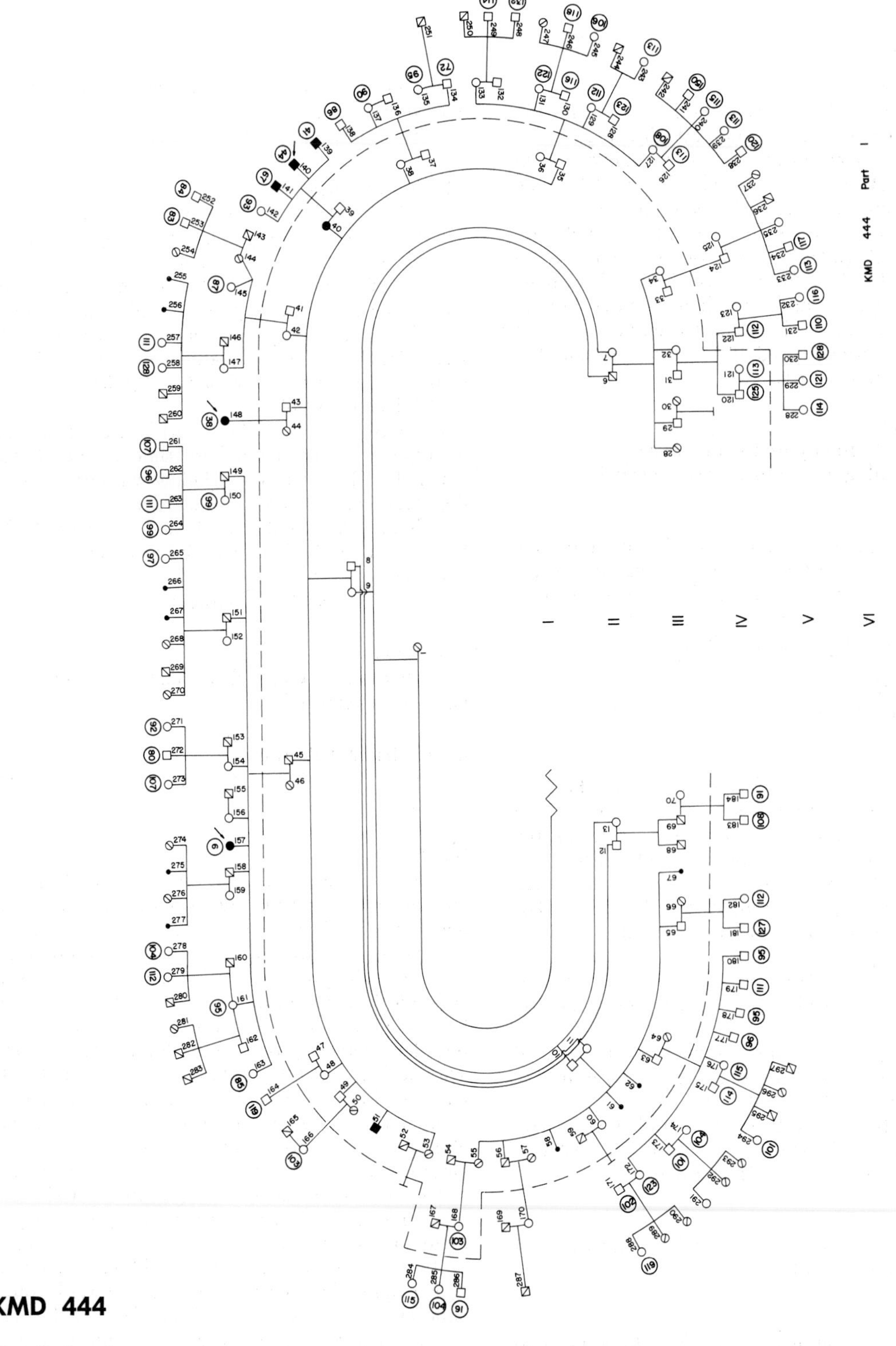

KMD 444

The Proband

The proband (111) was born in 1910, institutionalized at age 6 years and died of bronchopneumonia in the institution in 1939. His birth and early development were uneventful and he had no stigmata. IQ 33. *Diagnosis:* undifferentiated mental retardation.

Grandparents

Maternal grandmother was retarded.

Parents

Father (21) had normal intelligence.

Mother (22) was a high-grade retardate.

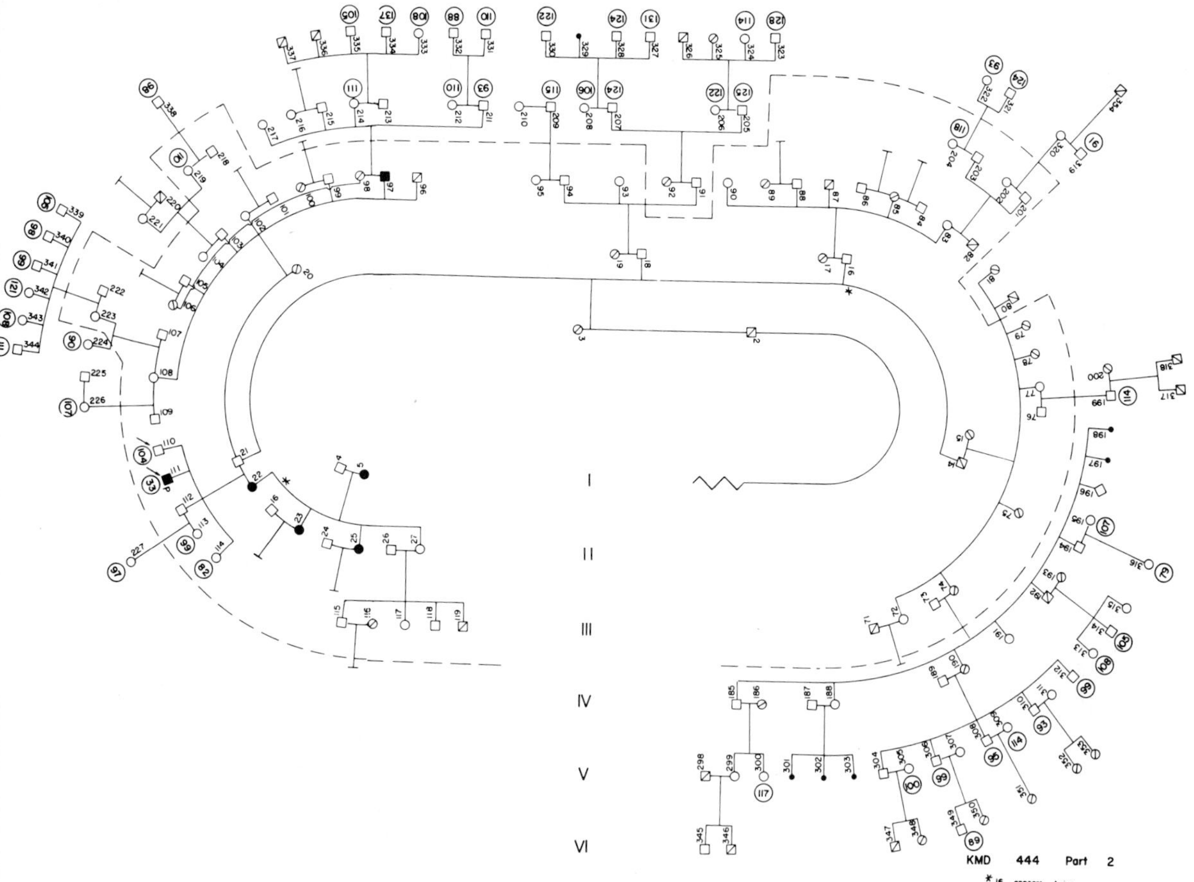

Aunts and Uncles

Maternal aunts (23) and (25) were retarded.

Siblings

Brother (110), the original patient, was institutionalized in 1914 at age 5 years. He was premature and had rickets so that his development was so slow he was considered retarded. He was discharged in 1918 to relatives and has IQ's of 87, 91 and 104 taken over a period of 26 years. He was in prison at one time. He is now an unmarried, childless laborer with a diagnosis of cerebellar ataxia.

Brother (112) completed the tenth grade and is a "set-up" man in a factory.

Sister (114) was considered for commitment at one time but the petition was denied. She is now in a mental hospital with a diagnosis of paranoid schizophrenia and IQ's of 68, 76, 80 and 82 taken over a period of six years.

Half Siblings

Half brother (96) was hospitalized twice for mental illness.

Half brother (97) was classified as retarded. He has four children with normal intelligence.

The other five half siblings (99), (102), (103), (105) and (108) have normal intelligence. The mother of these children had unknown intelligence.

Nieces and Nephews

Only one, a niece (227) with an IQ of 97. Children of half siblings not of interest.

First Cousins

Not of interest.

More Distant Relatives

(40), the daughter of the proband's father's half sister, is retarded and three of her four children (139), (140) and (141) are also retarded. The father (39) has normal intelligence.

(51) is in a mental hospital with a diagnosis of psychosis with mental deficiency.

(139) has an IQ of 41.

(140) is institutionalized with IQ 44. The diagnosis is mild mental deficiency, familial, with psychotic reaction.

(141) has an IQ of 67.

(148) is institutionalized with IQ 38 and a diagnosis of undifferentiated mental retardation.

(157) was institutionalized with IQ 6 and died of epilepsy at age 11 years. The diagnosis was mental deficiency with congenital cerebral spastic paraplegia.

Family Summary

The proband, IQ 33, his maternal grandmother, two maternal aunts, one half brother and seven more distant relatives were retarded. One of the retardates was also psychotic and one died of epilepsy. One sibling of the proband had cerebellar ataxia and another was a paranoid schizophrenic. One half brother had also been hospitalized for mental illness, diagnosis unknown. The proband's parents had four children and only one grandchild, a girl with IQ 97.

Retardation of proband of probably genetic origin.

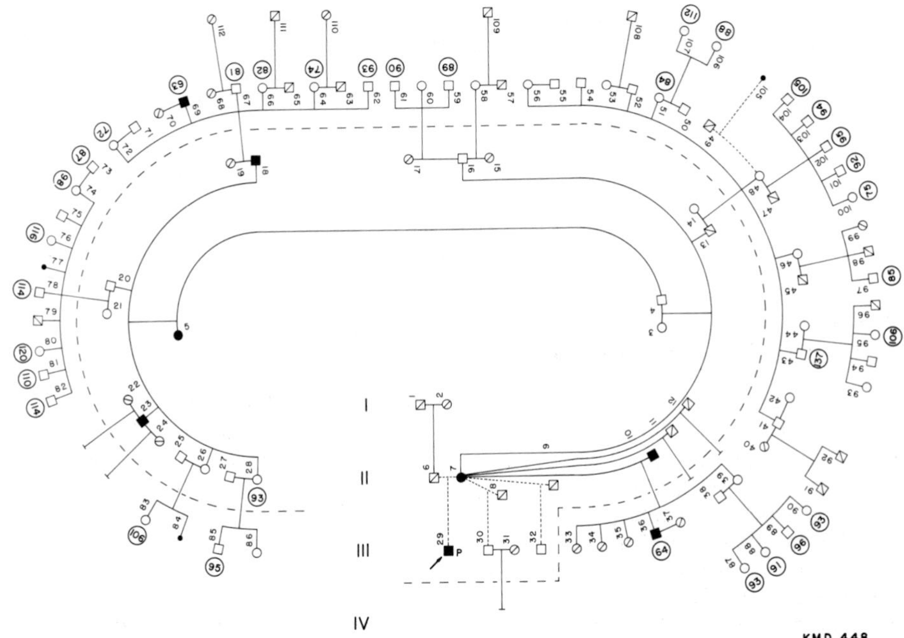

KMD 448

KMD 448

The Proband

The proband (29) was born in 1910, institutionalized at age 5 years and died of pulmonary tuberculosis in the institution in 1915. He was delivered by instruments but was a strong baby. At the time of institutionalization he was found to be neglected and undernourished. He never walked or talked and was a low-grade retardate, but had no stigmata. *Diagnosis:* undifferentiated mental retardation.

Grandparents

Maternal grandfather's second wife (5) was retarded.

Parents

Father (6) was forced to marry (7) after their child was born. (6) was an alcoholic laborer of unknown intelligence.

Mother (7) was considered for institutionalization at one time. She neglected her family and was promiscuous. She had three illegitimate children and five legitimate ones. The original workers estimated her IQ at about 60, although persons who knew the family well thought she was a much lower grade, possibly an imbecile.

Aunts and Uncles

No paternal relatives. The proband's father was an only child.

Maternal relatives not of interest except as below.

Half Siblings of Proband's Mother

(18) and (23) are retarded. (23) has been married and divorced twice, but is childless. (18) had six children, one (69) with IQ 63, two (64) and (72) with borderline IQ's of 74 and 72.

Siblings

No full siblings.

Half Siblings

Half brother (30) illegitimate, had normal intelligence, but committed suicide at age 38 years.

Half brother (32), illegitimate, died of influenza as a child. He had normal intelligence.

Half sisters (33), (34) and (35) all died of influenza in childhood.

Half brother (36) is a taxi driver with IQ 64.

Half sister (39) has normal intelligence. The father of (33), (34), (35), (36) and (39) was retarded and a mason's helper. He and the proband's mother lived in great poverty and squalor. Despite this, (39) completed the eighth grade, married a high school graduate and has four children (87), (88), (89) and (90) with IQ's of 93, 91, 96 and 93, respectively.

Nieces and Nephews

Only four, the children of a half sister, all with normal intelligence.

First Cousins

(69), son of proband's mother's half brother (18), has an IQ of 63. His siblings (62), (64), (66), (67) and (72) have IQ's of 93, 74, 82, 81 and 72, respectively.

More Distant Relatives

Not of interest.

Family Summary

The proband, a low-grade retardate, his mother, a half brother of the proband's mother and two of his children, and a half brother of the proband were all retarded, and all middle- to high-grade retardates except for the proband. The home conditions were poor. Nevertheless, three of the proband's half siblings had normal intelligence. The proband's parents had one child, no grandchildren.

Retardation of the proband of probably genetic origin. The proband's parentage was quite uncertain. There was some evidence his father may have been his mother's first cousin, but this could not be confirmed.

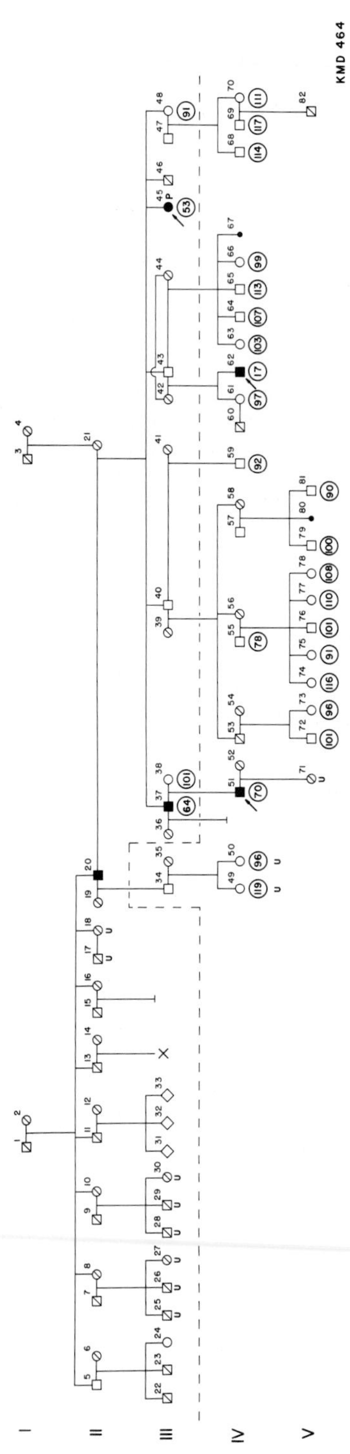
KMD 464

KMD 464

The Proband

The proband (45) was born in 1907, institutionalized at age 9 years and was still in the institution in 1961. Little is known of her early life except that she was greatly abused and neglected as a child. She had no stigmata. She attended school for two years but learned very little. IQ 53. *Diagnosis:* undifferentiated mental retardation.

Grandparents

Not of interest.

Parents

Father (20) was an alcoholic, retarded laborer.

Mother (21) was an alcoholic. Her intelligence was unknown.

Aunts and Uncles

Not of interest.

Siblings

Brother (37) was first sent to a reformatory at the age of 10 years. He then served four prison terms before he was put in a mental hospital in 1927 at the age of 31 years, for alcoholic psychosis. He was discharged as cured in 1931, was imprisoned in Arizona for "aggravated assault" for four years. After another offense in Minnesota in 1935, he was readmitted to the mental hospital and discharged in 1938. In 1939 he was sentenced to 10–80 years in the state prison for robbery. IQ 64. His wife has an IQ of 101 but has had three illegitimate children by three fathers and has been in a girls' reformatory. (37) and (38) have one child with IQ 70.

Brothers (40) and (43) were juvenile delinquents but have normal intelligence. (43) has a retarded child.

Brother (46) died of diphtheria at age 8 years.

Sister (48) has an IQ of 91. Her children have normal intelligence.

Half Siblings

Half brother (34) is a foreman for the railroad.

Nieces and Nephews

Nephew (51) was institutionalized in 1926 at age 6 years. He escaped twice but was reinstitutionalized until 1947 when he was placed under outside supervision. He is a laborer with IQ 70.

Nephew (62) was institutionalized in 1931 at age 4 years. He has a small head and cannot talk. The institution does not give a diagnosis of microcephaly, only "idiocy, cause undiagnosed." IQ 17.

First Cousins

Unknown.

More Distant Relatives

Not of interest.

Family Summary

The proband, IQ 53, her father, one brother and two nephews were retarded. All were high grade except one nephew with IQ 17. The family environment was poor. The proband's brothers were all delinquents but the two brothers with normal intelligence adjusted to society when they became adult. The retarded brother has served six prison terms and also has been hospitalized twice for alcoholic psychosis. The proband's parents had six children and 14 grandchildren.

Retardation of proband of probably genetic origin.

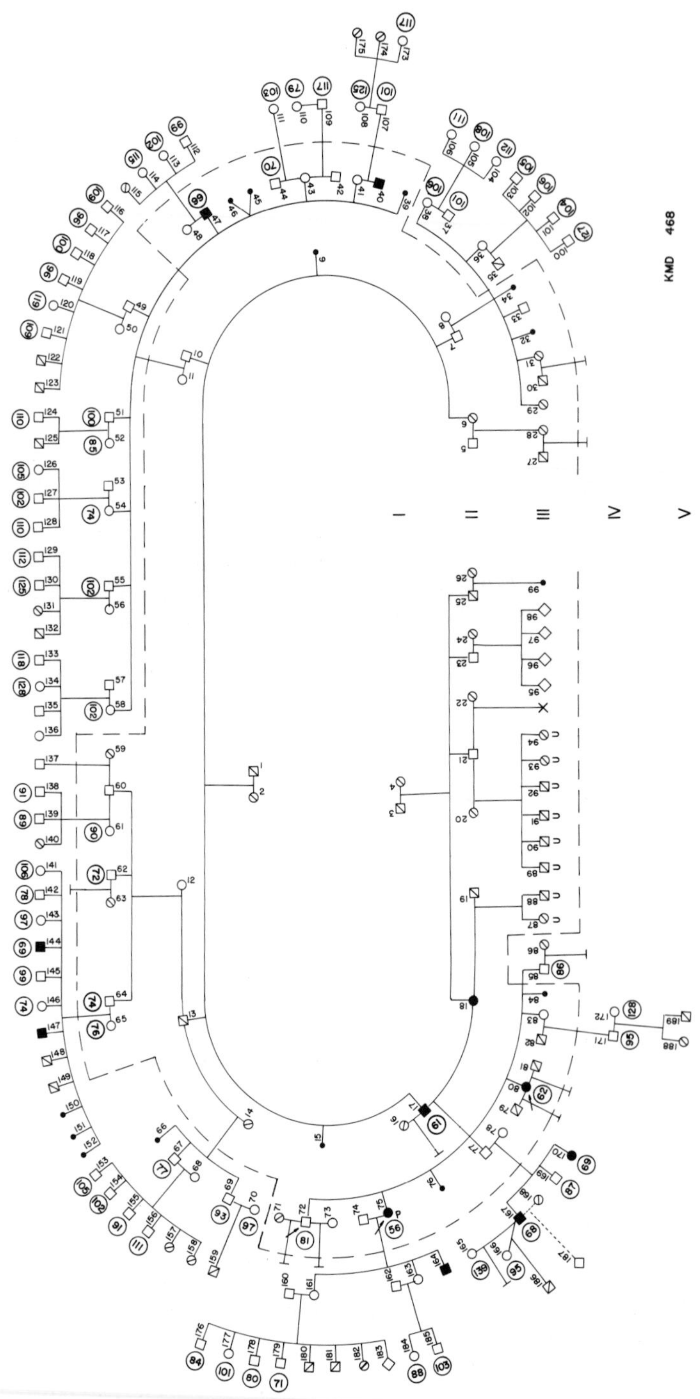

KMD 468

The Proband

The proband (75) was born in 1903, institutionalized at age 13 years, discharged in 1918, married in 1919, readmitted for one week in 1920 and paroled to her husband the same year. They moved out of the state so she was discharged from guardianship in 1928. Her husband later divorced her and she is now deceased. She attended special classes in school but learned little. Her home surroundings were poor but she had no history of birth injury or perinatal infection. She was obese. IQ 56. *Diagnosis:* undifferentiated mental retardation.

Grandparents

Not of interest.

Parents

Father (17) was a laborer who could not support his family. He was in the state prison at one time. IQ 61.

Mother (18) could not keep house and was retarded.

Aunts and Uncles

Not of interest.

Siblings

Brother (72) was a juvenile delinquent who had several court appearances for petit larceny, burglary and truancy and a term in a reformatory for breaking and entering before he was tested by a psychologist. He scored an IQ of 67 at age 13 years and was institutionalized in 1916 at age 15 years, but was discharged nine months later. He was imprisoned in 1937 for carnal knowledge and released in 1941. In 1942 he was restored to competency and is now a mechanic. He has been married and divorced and has married a second time. His second wife is a deaf-mute with normal intelligence. (72) scored an IQ of 81 in 1937. He is childless.

Brother (76) was born without an anus and died at age 3 days.

Brother (77) graduated from deaf school and is a laborer. His deafness is attributed to scarlet fever at age 3 years and diphtheria at age 4 years. He has normal intelligence. His wife has normal intelligence and is also deaf and they have three children, two of whom are retarded.

Sister (80) was institutionalized in 1920 at age 11 years, sterilized in 1934, married and was discharged from guardianship in 1948. She divorced her first husband and has married again. IQ 62 and obese.

Sister (83) was interviewed. She completed the eighth grade, does precision factory work and has normal intelligence as does her child.

Sister (84) died of diphtheria at age 1 year.

Brother (85) completed the eighth grade in an orphanage and was a master sergeant in the army. IQ 86.

Half Siblings

Two, (87) and (88), who never came to this country and are unknown.

Children

Daughter (161) had passing grades in the ninth grade at age 17 years, and probably has low-normal intelligence. Her husband completed two years of college. Their four tested children in a family of eight have IQ's of 84, 101, 80 and 71, respectively.

Daughter (163) was obese. She was in the fifth grade at age 13 years, but the school reported that she "could be an average student" if she attended school regularly. She has two children with IQ's of 88 and 103 and a husband of "average" intelligence.

Son (164) was in the second grade at age 11 years. He is an unmarried childless shipfitter (probably a "helper").

The father of these children (74) has normal intelligence.

Nieces and Nephews

Nephew (167) was married twice to normal women. His first wife (165) has been in court for robbery and is now in a mental hospital with a diagnosis of sociopathic personality, dyssocial reaction. Her IQ is 139. The second wife (166) was illegitimately pregnant by (167) at age 15 years. Her IQ is 95. There was a second illegitimate pregnancy involving (168). (167) has an IQ of 68. He and his brother (169), with IQ 87, have extensive records of delinquency and both are now in prison, (167) in the State Reformatory and (169) in a federal reformatory. Court records describe their father (77) as being demanding and undependable and having a persecution complex. (169) is diagnosed as a "neurotic delinquent with obsessive compulsive trends" and recommended that he be kept under close supervision.

Niece (170) was in a girls' reformatory at one time. IQ 69.

First Cousins

(41), a high school graduate, married a retarded man who was in special classes. Their only child (107) has an IQ of 101. (43) the sister to (41), also a high school graduate, married and divorced a normal man and then married a laborer with IQ 70. She has one child by each marriage, (109) with IQ 117 and (111) with IQ 103.

(47) was in the State Reformatory at one time. He has an IQ of 66 but married a normal woman and has four children (112), (113), (114) and (115) with IQ's of 99, 102 and 115. The other child is too young to test.

(62) was in the State Reformatory for burglary. IQ 72.

(64) is self-employed selling flowers. His IQ is 74, wife's IQ 76 and they had nine children and three miscarriages. Two of the nine children, (144) and (147), are retarded.

The maternal cousins are unknown.

More Distant Relatives

(144) has an IQ of 69.

(147) was adopted. The school reports he is unable to do first grade work and has no interest in learning words.

Family Summary

The proband, IQ 62, one child, her parents, one sibling, two nephews and a niece, one first cousin and two more distant relatives were retarded, all to about the same degree. The family environment was poor, and there are extensive records of delinquency and prison terms, especially for two nephews. Two normal cousins married retarded spouses. The proband had three children and ten grandchildren. Her parents had eight children and seven grandchildren; two of the children were retarded and three of the grandchildren were retarded.

Retardation of proband of probably genetic origin.

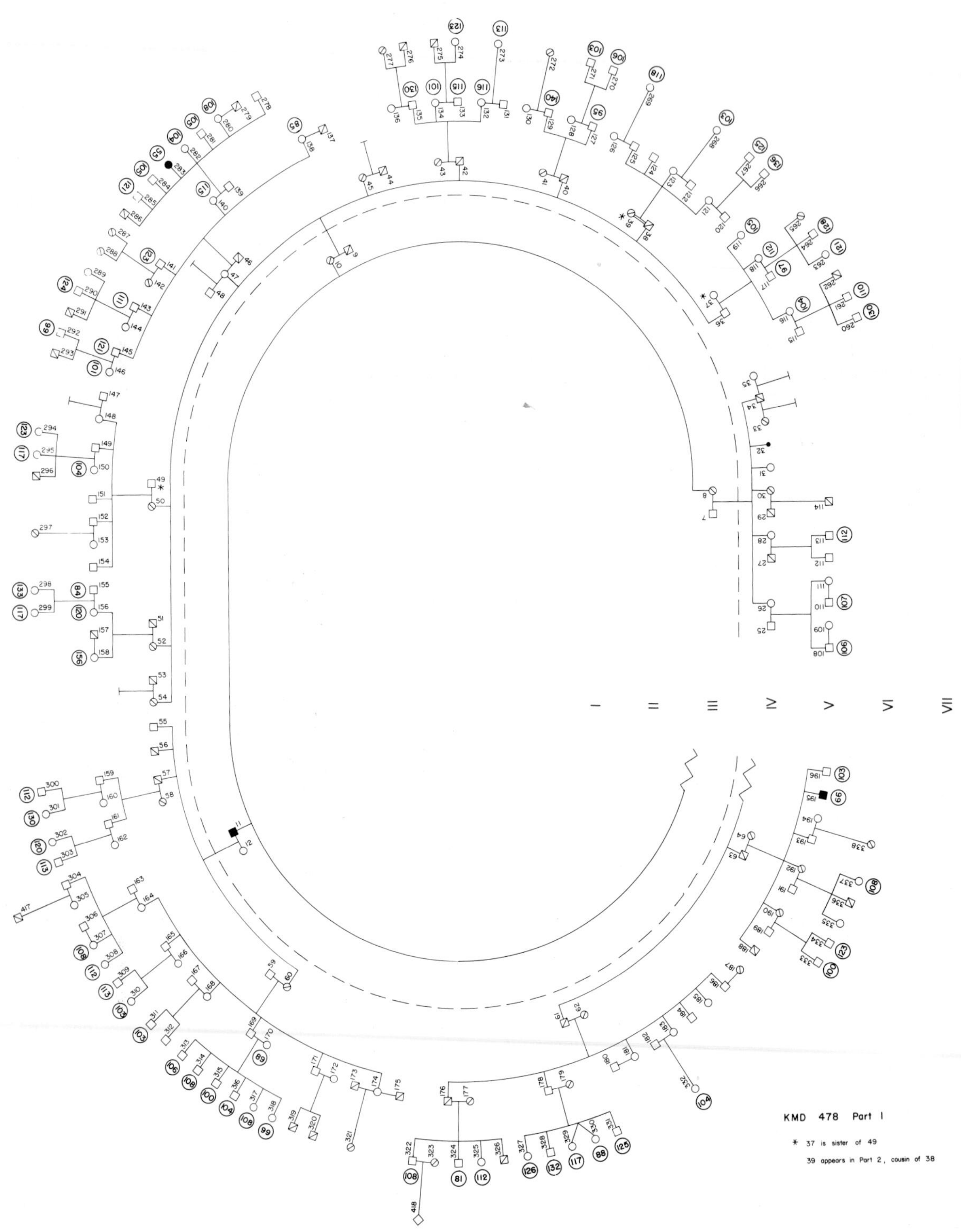

KMD 478 Part I

* 37 is sister of 49

39 appears in Part 2, cousin of 38

KMD 478

The Proband

The proband (24) was born in 1854, institutionalized at age 55 years and died of chronic mitral regurgitation and stenosis in the institution in 1929. No details are known about her birth and early development. She was promiscuous and was forced to marry a blind, retarded man (23) whom she divorced soon after marriage. Her child (107) was nearly blind and was retarded. IQ 40. *Diagnosis:* undifferentiated mental retardation.

Grandparents

Nothing is known about them.

Parents

Both father (5) and mother (6) had unknown intelligence.

Aunts and Uncles

None.

Siblings

Sisters (8), (10) and (14) and brothers (17) and (19) had unknown intelligence.

Brother (11) was retarded.

Brothers (15) and (21) had normal intelligence.

Child

Daughter (107) was a retarded, blind woman who was married twice. She divorced her first husband (106) by whom she had five children, two of unknown intelligence and three retarded. She had no children by her second husband (107a). The intelligence of neither man was known. (106) was 20 years older than his wife and (107a) was 27 years older than she.

Grandchildren

(256) has unknown intelligence. (259) is deaf in one ear, blind in one eye and losing the sight of the other but completed the eleventh grade. He was in prison at one time for carnal knowledge.

(257) is institutionalized for severe idiopathic mental deficiency, IQ 42.

(258) is a retarded, unemployed laborer who has been hospitalized for alcoholism. His wife (258a) is also retarded and his family is well known to welfare agencies since two of his children are retarded and one was an unmarried mother.

(259b) completed the third or fourth grade, spent some years in a Lutheran home and now is an unemployed laborer.

Nieces and Nephews

Not of interest.

First Cousins

None.

More Distant Relatives

Nephew (63) has a child (195) with IQ 66.

(283) has cerebral palsy quadriplegia with IQ 55.

(385) has an IQ of 64. Four other siblings (384), (386), (387) and (388) have borderline IQ's of 70, 74, 79 and 72, respectively. The mother (223) has an IQ of 117.

Family Summary

The proband, IQ 40, her brother, her daughter, three grandchildren and six more distant relatives were retarded, all of middle to high grade. The proband married a blind, retarded man and their child was partially blind in addition to being retarded. One cousin-marriage of a nephew and a niece of the proband resulted in four normal children. The proband's parents had nine children and 45 grandchildren. The proband herself had one child and five grandchildren.

Retardation of proband of probably genetic origin.

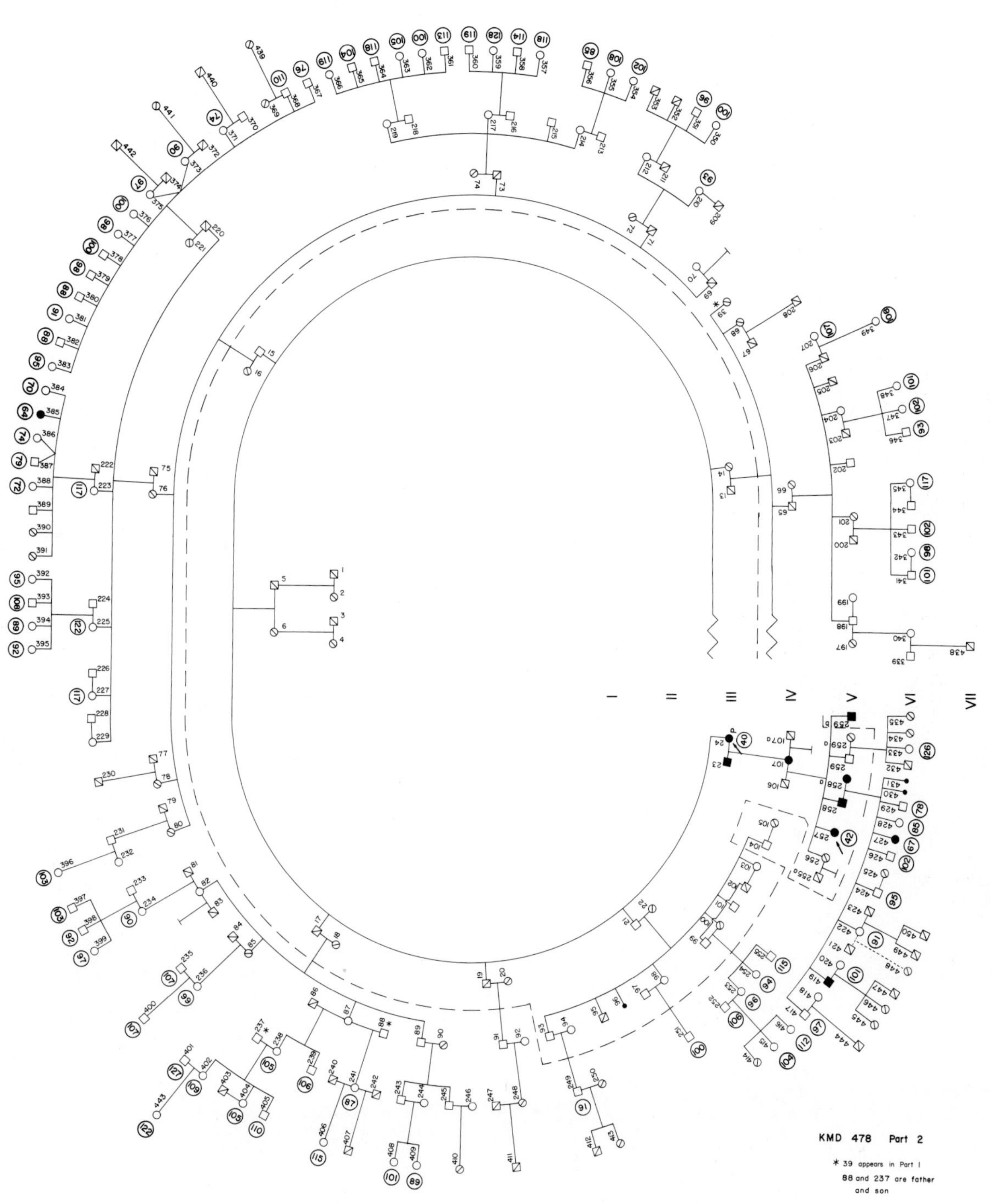

KMD 478 Part 2

* 39 appears in Part I
88 and 237 are father and son

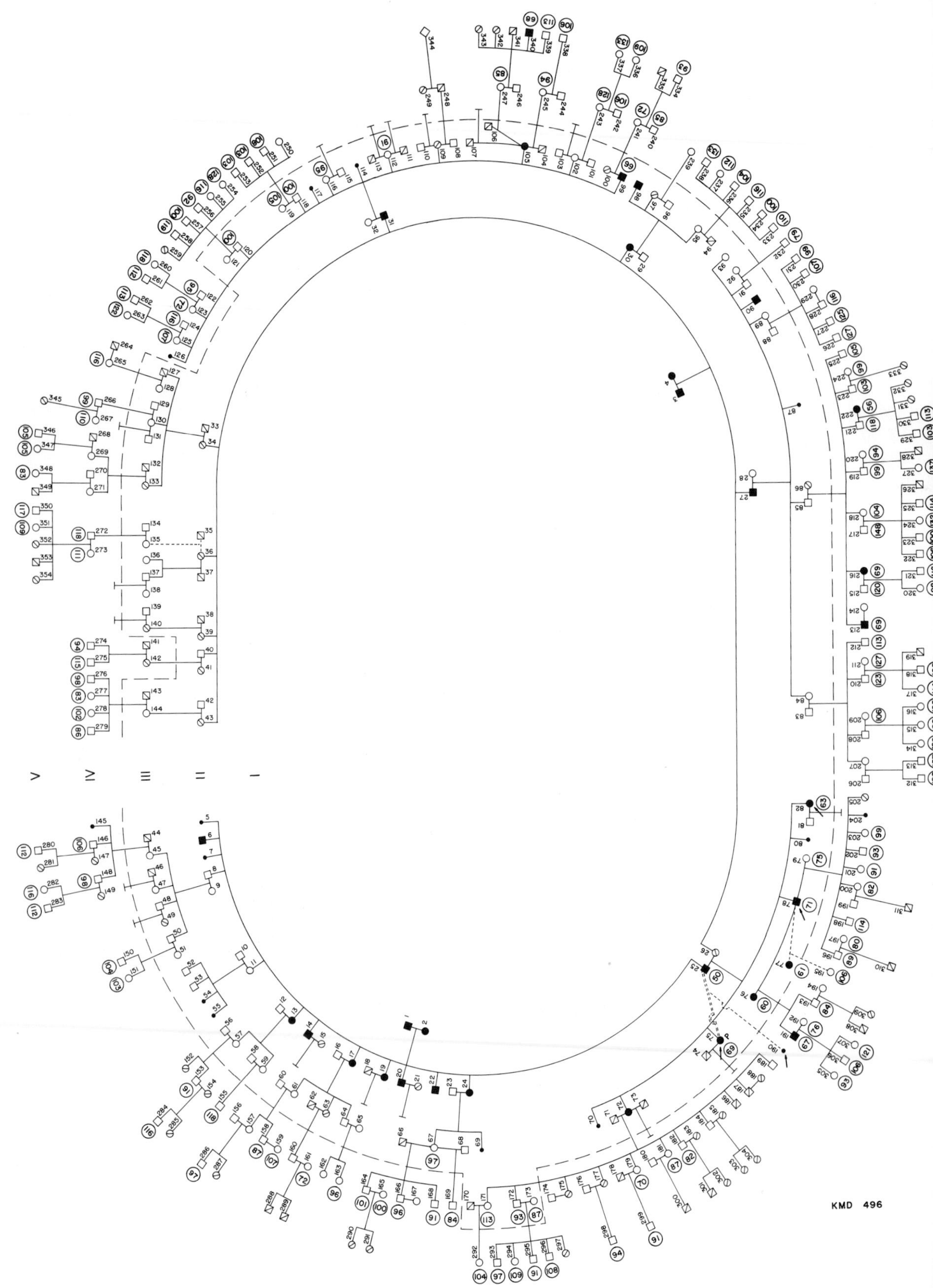

I
II
III
IV
V
KMD 496

KMD 496

The Proband

The proband (75) was born in 1896, institutionalized at age 19 years and placed under outside supervision in 1925. She was discharged from guardianship in 1948 because of a satisfactory home and marriage adjustment. She had a child by her father but no children by her husband since she married at age 49 years. The home conditions were poor and the proband became an alcoholic and promiscuous before her institutionalization. She had no history of difficult birth or perinatal infection and had no stigmata. IQ 69. *Diagnosis:* undifferentiated mental retardation.

Grandparents

Both the paternal and maternal grandparents were retarded. The paternal grandmother had a mental age of about 8 years.

Parents

Father (25) was an illiterate section hand with IQ 50.

Mother (26) was epileptic, intelligence unknown.

Aunts and Uncles

Paternal uncle (6) was retarded and never walked because his lower limbs did not develop.

Paternal uncle (8) was originally classified as retarded but he was head miller in a flour mill which indicates a higher IQ.

Paternal aunt (13) was retarded but married a normal man and her two children have normal intelligence.

Paternal uncle (14) retarded, was married but childless.

Paternal aunt (17) was retarded but married a normal man. Two of her three children are known to have normal intelligence, one has unknown intelligence.

Paternal aunt (19) was retarded. She was married but childless.

Paternal uncle (22) died unmarried and childless at age 29 years. He was retarded.

Paternal aunt (24) was retarded but married a normal man and had a daughter with IQ 97.

Maternal uncle (27) was retarded but married a normal woman. They have seven children, one retarded.

Maternal aunt (30) was retarded but married a prosperous farmer. They had three children, one retarded.

Maternal uncle (31) was retarded but married a normal woman and had 13 children, two retarded, one borderline.

Maternal aunt (34) was epileptic, intelligence unknown.

Siblings

(70) was a stillbirth.

Sister (72) is retarded. Her first husband (71) was an alcoholic and abusive man of unknown intelligence who deserted her. One of their 11 children has an IQ of 70, two others were juvenile delinquents. The second husband of (72) was in a state mental hospital at one time.

Brother (78) was institutionalized in 1943 at age 45 years, escaped a year later and was discharged from guardianship in 1948 since he was no longer in the state. He was a chronic alcoholic. His IQ was 71 at age 30 and 60 at age 39. His first wife (76) was retarded, IQ 60, his second wife (79) was considered for commitment as retarded at one time, IQ 75, and he had an illegitimate child, IQ 106, by (77), who had an IQ of 61. All of his 11 children were committed as dependent and neglected. One is retarded, one is blind from congenital optic atrophy, one was a juvenile delinquent and three were placed in boarding homes. Of these latter, the IQ of (203) rose from 67 to 99 over a period of nine years.

Sister (80) died of convulsions at age 6 weeks.

Sister (82) was institutionalized in 1915 at age 12 years, sterilized in 1929 and placed under outside supervision. She married (81), a man with normal intelligence, and was discharged from guardianship in 1949 because of a satisfactory adjustment to home and marriage. Her IQ is 63.

Child

Daughter (190) was born in 1915 in the institution and died of enteritis and syphilis at age 8 months. She had no congenital deformities.

Nieces and Nephews

Niece (179) has an IQ of 70 with a child with IQ 91.

Nephew (182) was delinquent and incorrigible and was sent to a training school. He was killed by a hit and run driver. IQ 82.

Nephew (184) was a truant and had been implicated in a burglary but has normal intelligence.

Nephew (191) was considered for commitment at one time but was found not mentally deficient by the court. He is a spot welder, IQ 67. His divorced wife's (192) IQ is 76 and his three children (305), (306) and (307) have IQ's of 93, 106 and 121, respectively.

Nephew (193) has been on probation, IQ 84. He is divorced from a normal wife.

Niece (195) was illegitimate. IQ 106.

Nephew (196) has congenital optic atrophy, IQ 89.

First Cousins

(90) is an unmarried, childless retardate.

(98) was in the third grade for four years and the teacher reported he was "impossible to teach." He is an unmarried and childless farm laborer.

(90) has an IQ of 66, wife's IQ unknown, daughter (241) has an IQ of 72.

(105) is retarded, her two children (245) and (247) have IQ's of 94 and 85, respectively.

Continued on page 414

More Distant Relatives

(213) has an IQ of 69.

(216) has an IQ of 69, [husband (215) has an IQ of 120], children have IQ's of 98 and 116.

(221) has an IQ of 118 but wife (222) is retarded with IQ 56, children with IQ's of 103 and 113.

(340) has an IQ of 68.

Family Summary

The proband, IQ 69, all four grandparents, her father, eight paternal aunts and uncles, three maternal aunts and uncles, two siblings, a niece and nephew, four first cousins and three more distant relatives were all high-grade retardates. The social history of the proband's family was one of incest, alcoholism, delinquency and indigence. The proband's only child died in infancy of enteritis and syphilis. The proband's mother was epileptic. There were 28 known retarded persons in the line of descent, or 31 counting retarded spouses, in this family of 354 individuals (8.8 per cent retardation). The proband's parents had six children and 23 grandchildren. The retardation is not as apparent in the later generations although the social problems are still numerous. Of the 28 retarded persons in the line of descent, ten are childless.

Retardation of proband of probably genetic origin.

KMD 498

The Proband

The proband (58) was born in 1892, institutionalized at age 22 years when she became illegitimately pregnant, and died of coronary thrombosis in the institution in 1960. Her child, a boy with IQ 85, was born in the institution. She left school at age 16 years when in the fourth grade. There was no history of birth injury or perinatal infection. She was deaf. IQ 54. *Diagnosis:* undifferentiated mental retardation with deafness.

Grandparents

Maternal grandfather was retarded.

Parents

Father (13) was an alcoholic and had a difficult time in school.

Mother (14) was retarded of about the same degree as the proband.

Aunts and Uncles

Maternal uncle (15) was institutionalized for many years as retarded.

Maternal aunt (19) was retarded of about the degree of the proband. Her husband had normal intelligence; their two children died in infancy.

Maternal aunt (20), retarded, died in the institution at age 45 years.

Maternal aunt (23) lived in a rest home. She was retarded of about the degree of the proband.

Siblings

Twin brothers (59) and (60) both died of diphtheria at age 8 years. They were "smart but never went to school." Their mental status was unknown.

Sister (61) died of pneumonia at age 6 years.

Brother (62) was retarded. He was killed in World War I. His wife left him after three weeks of marriage because he was so abusive.

Sister (64) is unmarried and childless. She was incorrigible and was once considered for institutionalization. IQ 60.

Half Siblings

Six half siblings (47), (48), (50), (52), (53) and (55) all of whom are known to have had normal intelligence, as do their children and grandchildren.

Child

Son (129) born in the institution in 1914, was committed as mentally deficient in 1919, discharged as not mentally deficient in 1921, then committed as dependent in 1924 and discharged as independent in 1932. IQ 85 at age 9 years. His present status is unknown.

Nieces and Nephews

No full nieces and nephews.

Children and grandchildren of half siblings all known to be normal except for (253) who has not been tested and is, therefore, of unknown intelligence.

First Cousins

Not of interest.

More Distant Relatives

Not of interest.

Family Summary

The proband, IQ 54 and deaf, her maternal grandfather, her mother, three maternal aunts and one maternal uncle, and two siblings were retarded, all of about the same degree. No deafness was reported for any of the proband's relatives. None of the paternal relatives was known to have been retarded. The proband had an illegitimate child of low-normal intelligence. Of the four retarded maternal aunts and uncles, two were institutionalized and only one was married. The two children of the latter died in infancy, so there were no descendants of any retarded persons except of the proband herself, her mother and her maternal grandfather. The proband's half siblings all had normal intelligence. The proband's parents had six children and one grandchild.

Retardation of proband of probably genetic origin.

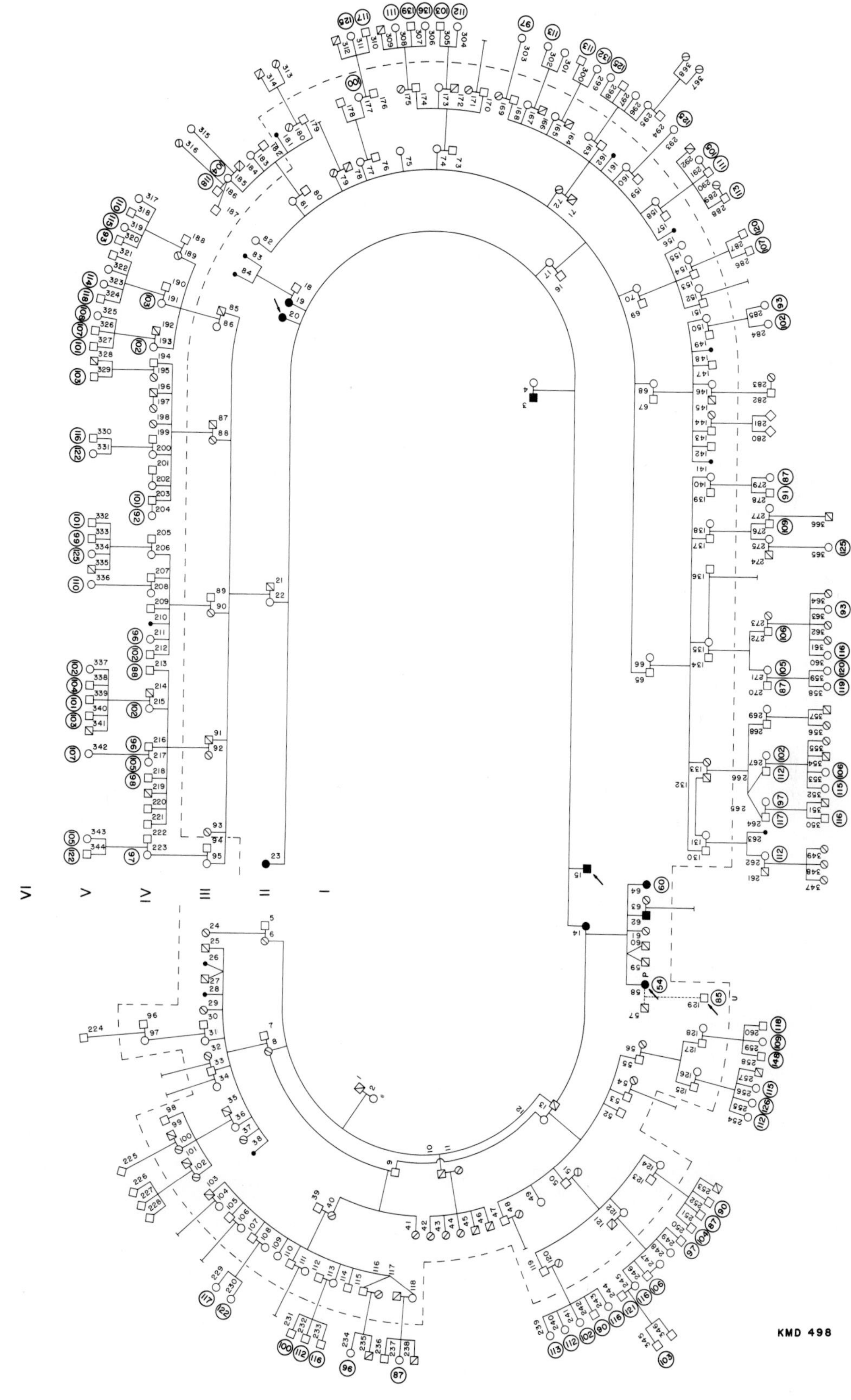

KMD 498

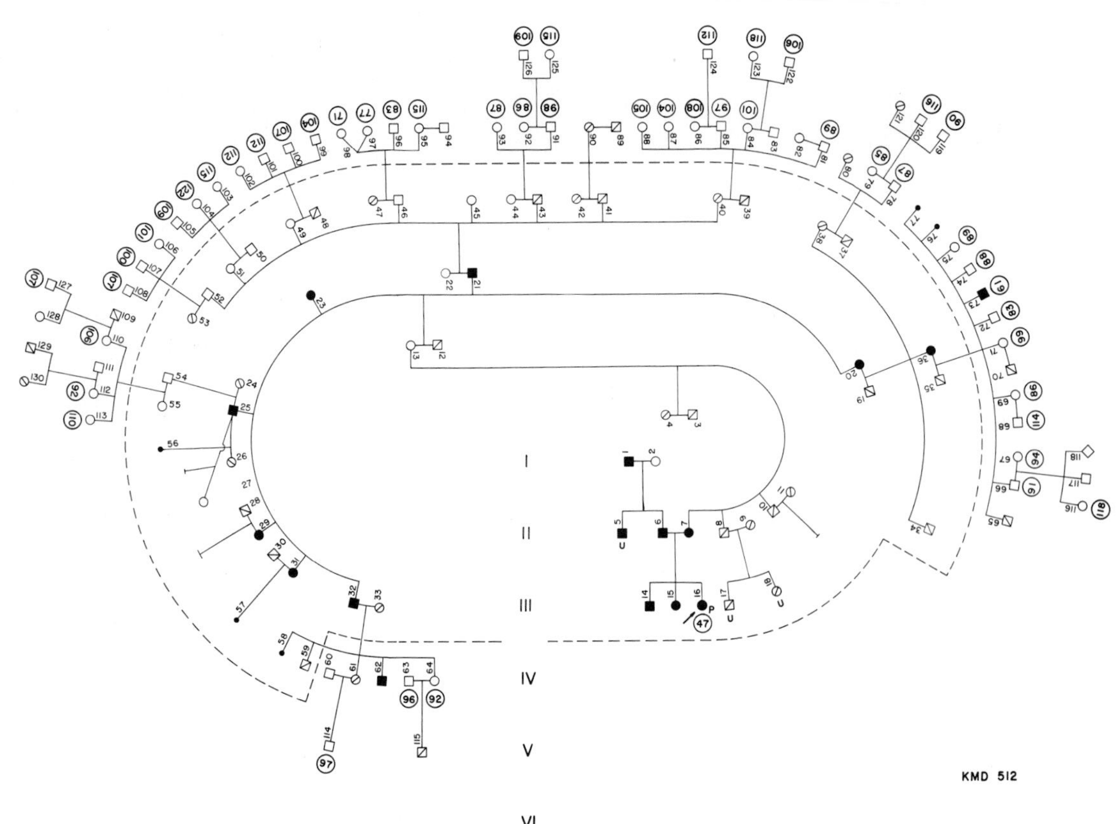

KMD 512

KMD 512

The Proband

The proband (16) was born in 1878, institutionalized at age 37 years and died of hypostatic pneumonia in the institution in 1942. After the proband's mother died when the proband was about age 20, the family lived in poverty and semi-starvation until after the father's death in 1911. The three children were placed in foster homes but two of the three had to be institutionalized (one was admitted to a mental hospital). The proband was promiscuous but never had a child. She was difficult to test because she spoke only German. Her IQ was about 47. *Diagnosis:* undifferentiated mental retardation.

Grandparents

Paternal grandfather was retarded.

Parents

Both the father (6) and the mother (7) were retarded.

Aunts and Uncles

Paternal uncle (5) was retarded.

Maternal uncle (8) committed suicide.

Siblings

Brother (14) died single and childless in a mental hospital with a diagnosis of psychosis with cerebral arteriosclerosis. He was also retarded.

Sister (15) died single and childless. She had a mental age of about 8 years and could do housework but not cook.

Nieces and Nephews

None.

First Cousins

(18) was deported by the immigration authorities, reason unknown.

(20) was retarded with a mental age of about 10 years. She had a retarded child and a retarded grandchild.

(21) was illiterate and retarded but his wife was a "healthy, energetic, capable woman" and the manager of the farm. No retardation has appeared among their children or grandchildren.

(23) was a cook who died childless. She was retarded.

(25) was retarded. Although he was married three times, he had only one child who survived to adulthood.

(29) was retarded and "too mean to have children."

(31) was retarded. She died in childbirth and her child died at age 2 years.

(32) was retarded, and one of his four adult children was retarded (62).

More Distant Relatives

First cousin's (20) child (36) was retarded. (34), brother to (36), died single and was reported to have been an "invalid." Their sister (38) was in the fourth grade at age 13 years.

First cousin's (32) child (62) left school when failing the seventh grade at age 16 years.

(73) has an IQ of 61.

Family Summary

The proband, IQ 47, her two siblings, both parents, the paternal grandfather, a paternal uncle, six first cousins and two more distant relatives were retarded, all of middle or high grade. The proband and her family lived in great poverty and squalor. The proband's parents had three children, no grandchildren. Two retarded cousins had one retarded child each, two retarded cousins had no retarded children in their families.

Retardation of proband of probably genetic origin.

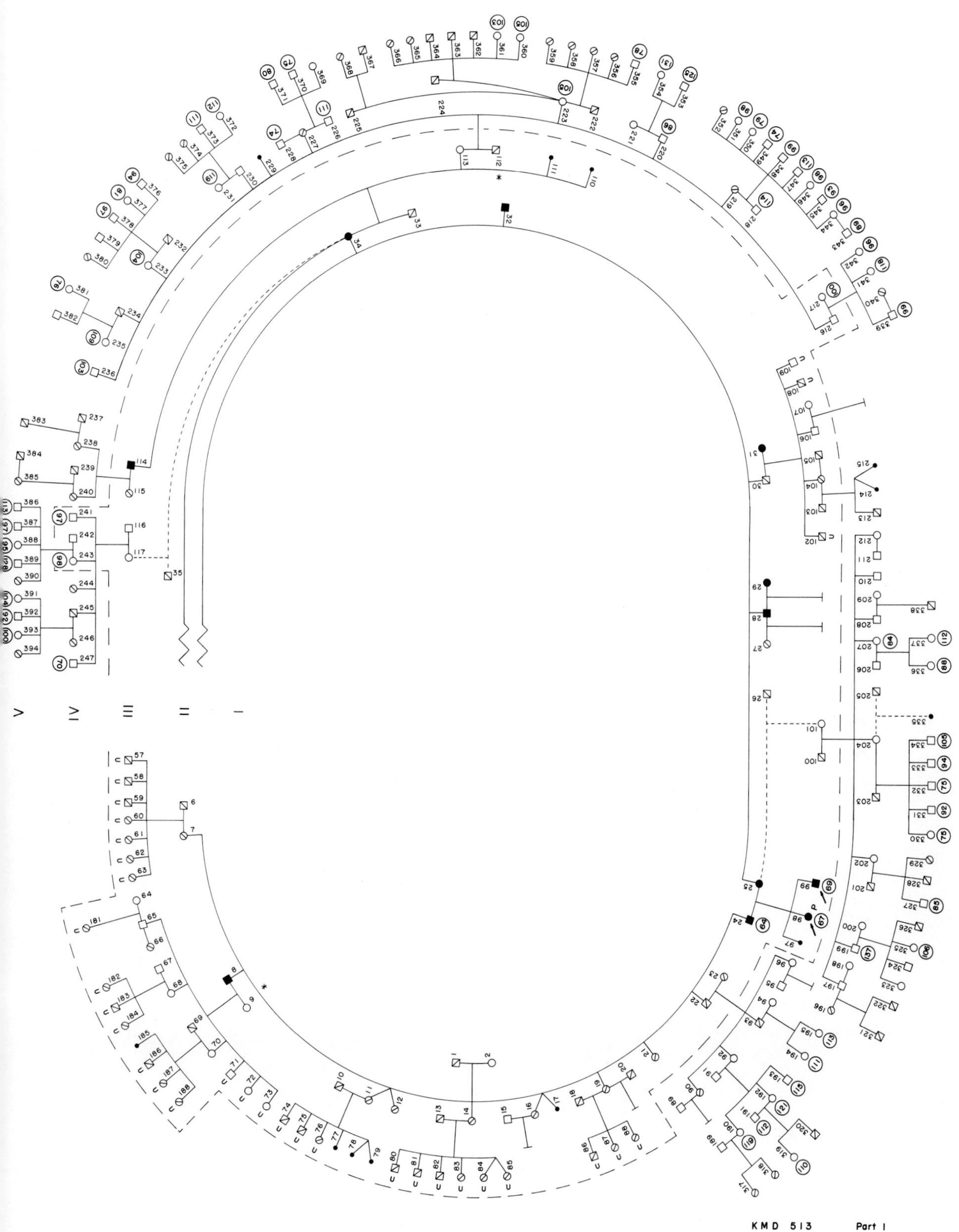

KMD 513 Part I

* 9 and 112 are sisters and are sisters to 50 in Part 2

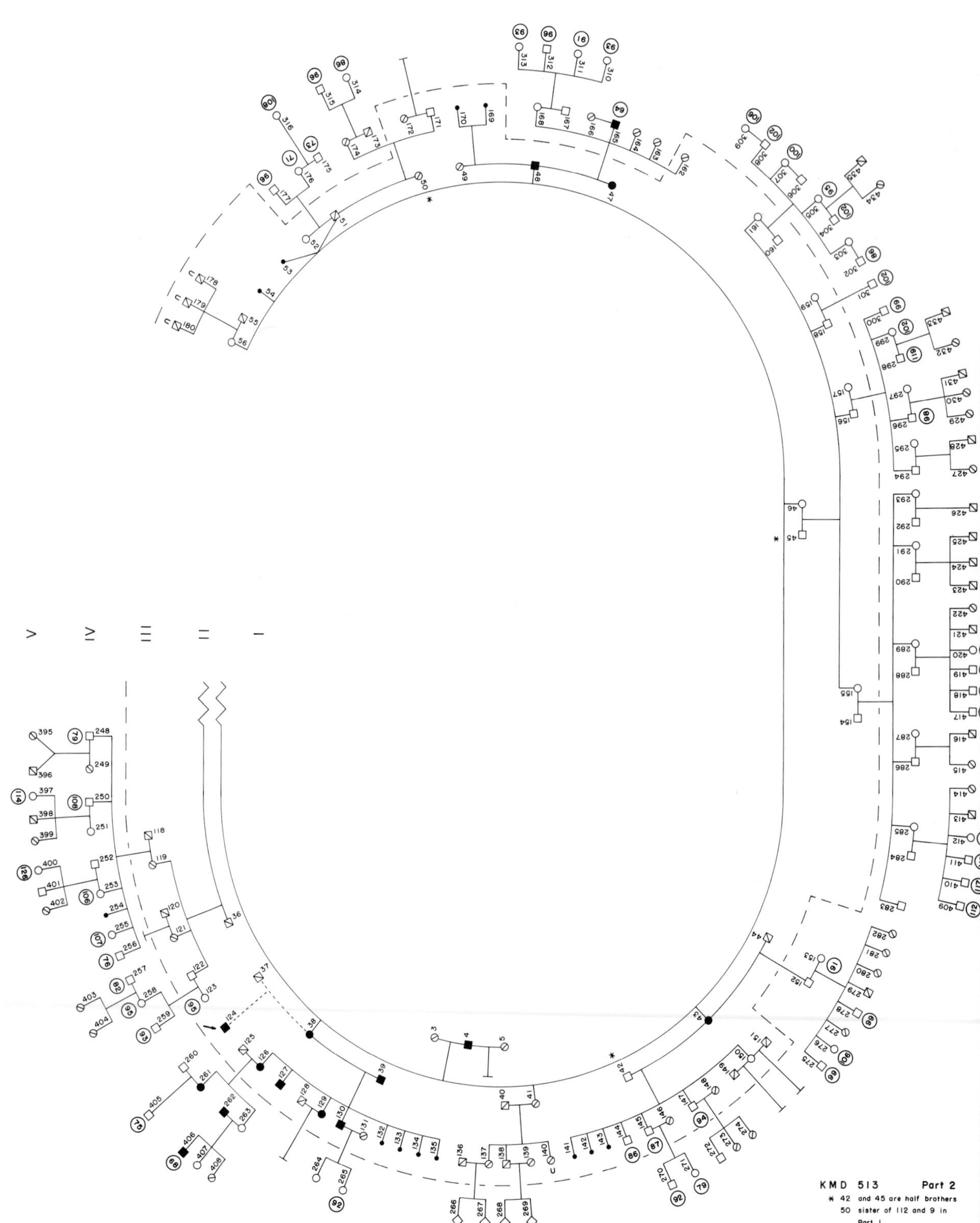

KMD 513 Part 2

* 42 and 45 are half brothers

50 sister of 112 and 9 in Part 1

KMD 513

The Proband

The proband (98) was born in 1900, institutionalized at age 15 years and died of pulmonary tuberculosis in the institution in 1917. She had no history of birth injury or perinatal infection. She had notched front teeth and right external strabismus. Her Wassermann test was negative and her reflexes were normal. The home environment was very poor. IQ 67. *Diagnosis:* undifferentiated mental retardation.

Grandparents

Paternal grandparents not of interest.

Maternal grandfather was retarded.

Maternal grandmother died of epilepsy.

Parents

Father (24) had an IQ of 64.

Mother (25) could not keep house or take care of her children.

Aunts and Uncles

Paternal uncle (8) was a retarded junk dealer, wife and six children normal.

Maternal uncle (28), retarded, was married twice but had no children.

Maternal uncle (30) of unknown intelligence, married a retarded woman. His five children were all given out for adoption. None is known to have been retarded.

Maternal uncle (32) was an unmarried, childless retardate.

Maternal aunt (34) was retarded, as was one of her six surviving children by three fathers.

Maternal aunt (38) was retarded as were all of her five surviving children. Several of the children had syphilis and gonorrhea. (38) was also epileptic. She and her sister (34) both had illegitimate children.

Maternal aunt (43) was epileptic and retarded. All five of her children have normal intelligence. The father (42) of four of them was also known to have had normal intelligence.

Maternal uncle (48) was retarded. His first wife (47) was retarded. His second wife (49) deserted him. He had a retarded child by (47).

Maternal aunt (53) died of convulsions at age 6 months.

Siblings

Brother (97) died a few hours after birth of a fractured skull.

Brother (99) was institutionalized in 1915 at age 14 years. He had normal reflexes and a negative Wassermann. He is an unmarried, childless laborer. IQ 69.

Nieces and Nephews

None.

First Cousins

Many paternal cousins are unknown.

Maternal cousins (102), (104), (106), (108) and (109) were adopted. Two of them, (104) and (109), were behavior problems.

(114) is a married, retarded laborer with two children of unknown intelligence.

(117) had normal intelligence but was a juvenile delinquent.

(124) was institutionalized in 1908 at age 16 years and stayed in the institution for three years. He is an unmarried, childless farm laborer.

(126) is epileptic and retarded. One of her two children is retarded, as is one of her four grandchildren.

(127) is an unmarried, childless retarded warehouseman.

(129) is retarded. She is married but childless.

(130) is a retarded warehouseman with two normal children. (130) and his siblings (126), (127) and (129) had syphilis and gonorrhea, so some of the retardation may be the result of infection. Their last four siblings (132), (133), (134) and (135) all died at birth.

(165) is a cab driver with IQ 64.

(169) died of "screaming spells" at age 1 month.

(176) has IQ 71, husband's IQ 73, child's IQ 108.

More Distant Relatives

(241) has an IQ of 97 but a diagnosis of schizophrenic reaction, paranoid type and has had a prefrontal lobotomy.

(261) was at the fourth grade achievement level at age 14 years. She was in special classes.

(263), the normal sister to (261), married (262) a warehouseman who only completed the third grade.

(406), son of (263), has an IQ of 68.

Family Summary

The proband, IQ 67, her maternal grandfather, both her parents, her brother, one paternal uncle, three maternal aunts and three maternal uncles, seven first cousins and two more distant relatives were retarded, all of middle to high grade. In addition, the maternal grandmother, two of the retarded maternal aunts and one retarded first cousin had epilepsy. The family as a whole (especially the maternal side) had a lot of social problems such as illegitimacy, venereal disease and delinquency. The proband's parents had three children and no grandchildren.

Retardation of proband of probably genetic origin.

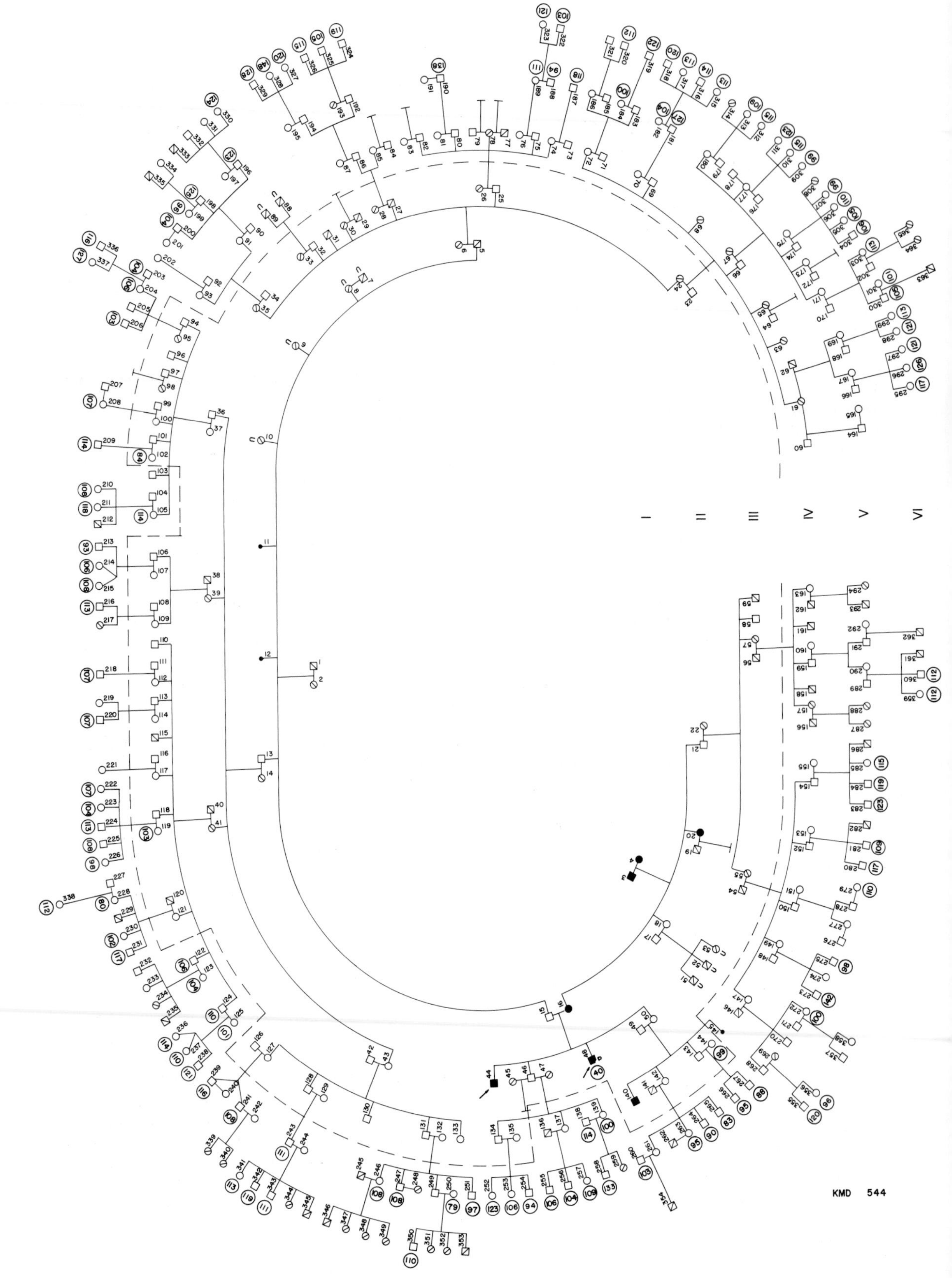

KMD 544

KMD 544

The Proband

The proband (48) was born in 1873, institutionalized at age 10 years and died of myocarditis and influenza in the institution in 1926. He walked and talked when past the age of 3 years and went to school for five or six years but learned little. His home environment was impoverished but kind. He had rickets but no history of birth injury or perinatal infection. He had a high palate. IQ 40. *Diagnosis:* undifferentiated mental retardation.

Grandparents

Maternal grandparents were both retarded.

Parents

Father (15) was a farmer, shoemaker, carpenter and farm owner.

Mother (16) was retarded.

Aunts and Uncles

Paternal uncle (5) committed suicide.

One maternal aunt was reported to have been retarded but there was no indication as to which one, so (20) was selected for purposes of the chart, since (18) had a farm and her husband took her name and went there to live. It does not seem likely that (18) was retarded.

Siblings

Brother (44) was institutionalized at one time. He died unmarried and childless. He talked indistinctly and had a short, thick tongue.

Brother (46) was an engineer and janitor in a furniture store and was "barely up to par." No retardation has appeared among his descendants.

Sister (50) has normal intelligence (husband also normal) but has a retarded child (140).

Nieces and Nephews

Nephew (140) is an unmarried and childless farm laborer. He completed the third grade.

First Cousins

Not of interest.

More Distant Relatives

Not of interest.

Family Summary

The proband, IQ 40, his maternal grandparents, mother, one maternal aunt, one brother and a nephew were retarded, all of middle or high grade. The collateral relatives were all normal, well adjusted people, as far as is known except for a paternal uncle who committed suicide. The proband's parents had four children (two retarded) and seven grandchildren, one retarded.

Retardation of proband of probably genetic origin.

THE PRIMARILY ENVIRONMENTAL CATEGORY

There were 27 probands whose retardation appeared to have been primarily the result of environmental trauma. Birth injuries and serious diseases in infancy predominated in this group.

Brief family summaries accompany the 35 pedigree charts in this group. These include the data for KMD's 25, 35, 48, 81, 101, 119, 153, 161, 172, 189, 191, 196, 205, 272, 284, 287, 305, 379, 386, 391, 392, 393, 395, 411, 475, 492 and 539.

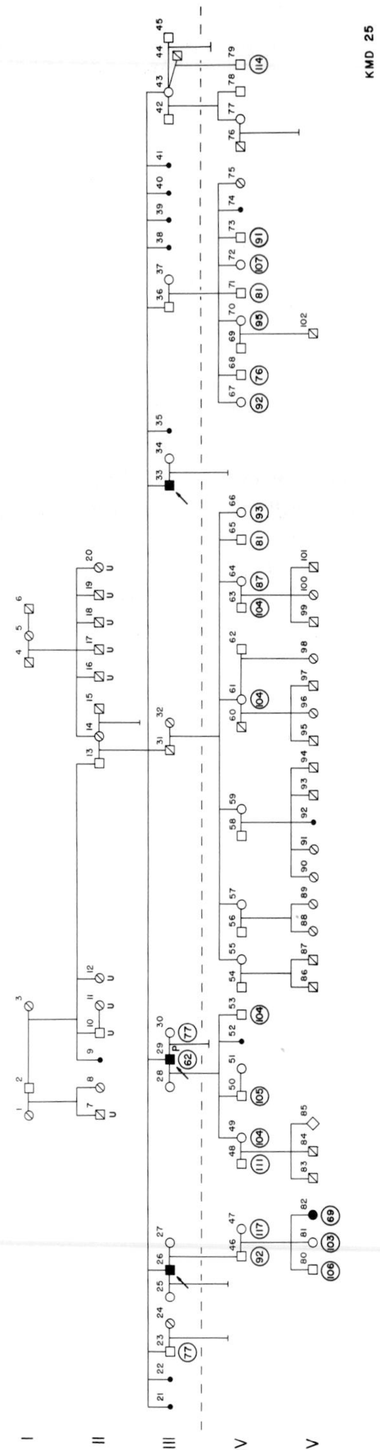
KMD 25
I
II
III
IV
V

KMD 25

The Proband

The proband (29) was born in 1898, institutionalized at age 11 years, escaped four times and was dropped from the records in 1916. He had eczema and "running ears" at birth and did not talk until age 7. He learned little in school. He married a normal woman who divorced him. He then married a woman from a family with an extensive welfare record and an IQ of 77. The proband was working in an iron foundry in 1961. IQ 62. *Diagnosis:* undifferentiated mental retardation.

Grandparents

Not of interest.

Parents

Father (13) was a good workman but was an alcoholic, improvident and cruel to his family. Normal intelligence.

Mother (14) was taken from her home in Cuba as a small child and trained to perform on the trapeze in a circus. The Humane Society of Chicago placed her in an orphanage when she was 12. She went to work at 14. She attempted suicide at one time, divorced her husband in 1916, remarried in 1919, and died in 1946. She was syphilitic and had defective sight as a result of the infection. Intelligence unknown.

Aunts and Uncles

Unknown.

Siblings

(21) died of pneumonia at 17 months.

(22) died of boils and erysipelas in infancy.

Brother (23) completed the tenth grade, was a printer and died in 1945. He had reformatory and prison records. IQ 77.

Brother (26) was institutionalized at age 10 for five years. Two years later he served a term in the reformatory. He is a laborer who changes jobs frequently. His first wife, a normal woman, divorced him. His second wife is also a normal woman. He is retarded.

Brother (31) was placed in the state orphanage and later served a term in the reformatory. He is a laborer of unknown intelligence.

Brother (33) was institutionalized at age 5 for a year or two, later he served time in the reformatory. He was three years retarded in school. He is a cook and is divorced from his wife, a normal woman. Retarded.

(35) died of convulsions at 9 months. He lay for hours without making a sound and may have been mentally retarded.

Brother (36) graduated from high school and is a laborer. He has normal intelligence as does his wife.

Four miscarriages (38), (39), (40) and (41).

Sister (43) has had three husbands. The two children of her first marriage were awarded to the father after the divorce. She divorced her second husband also, and now operates a restaurant with her third husband.

Children

Daughter (49) completed the 11th grade, IQ 104, married a normal man, a bus driver with an IQ of 111.

Son (50) graduated from a trade school, is a mechanic, IQ 105, and married a secretary.

Son (52) died in infancy.

Son (53) completed the 11th grade and is a buffer and polisher. IQ 104.

Nieces and Nephews

The twelve who were tested have IQ scores ranging from 76 to 114.

First Cousins

Unknown.

More Distant Relatives

One nephew (46) has a retarded child (82) with IQ 69.

Family Summary

The proband, two brothers and one great-niece are retarded. The proband and three of his six adult siblings have been divorced. Four of the proband's five brothers have served prison terms and the court took two of his sister's children away from her. This is a family with many social problems. Only one of the proband's siblings has led a law abiding, maritally sound existence. The proband's parents had 14 children and 23 grandchildren, including four children of the proband. The proband's own three surviving children have IQ scores above 100. The proband's mother had diagnosed syphilis and of her children there were three miscarriages, one infant death from "boils" and four born with skin lesions referred to as "eczema." Some of the sociological problems in the family may also have been related to brain damage from neurosyphilis.

Retardation of proband of primarily environmental origin (syphilis).

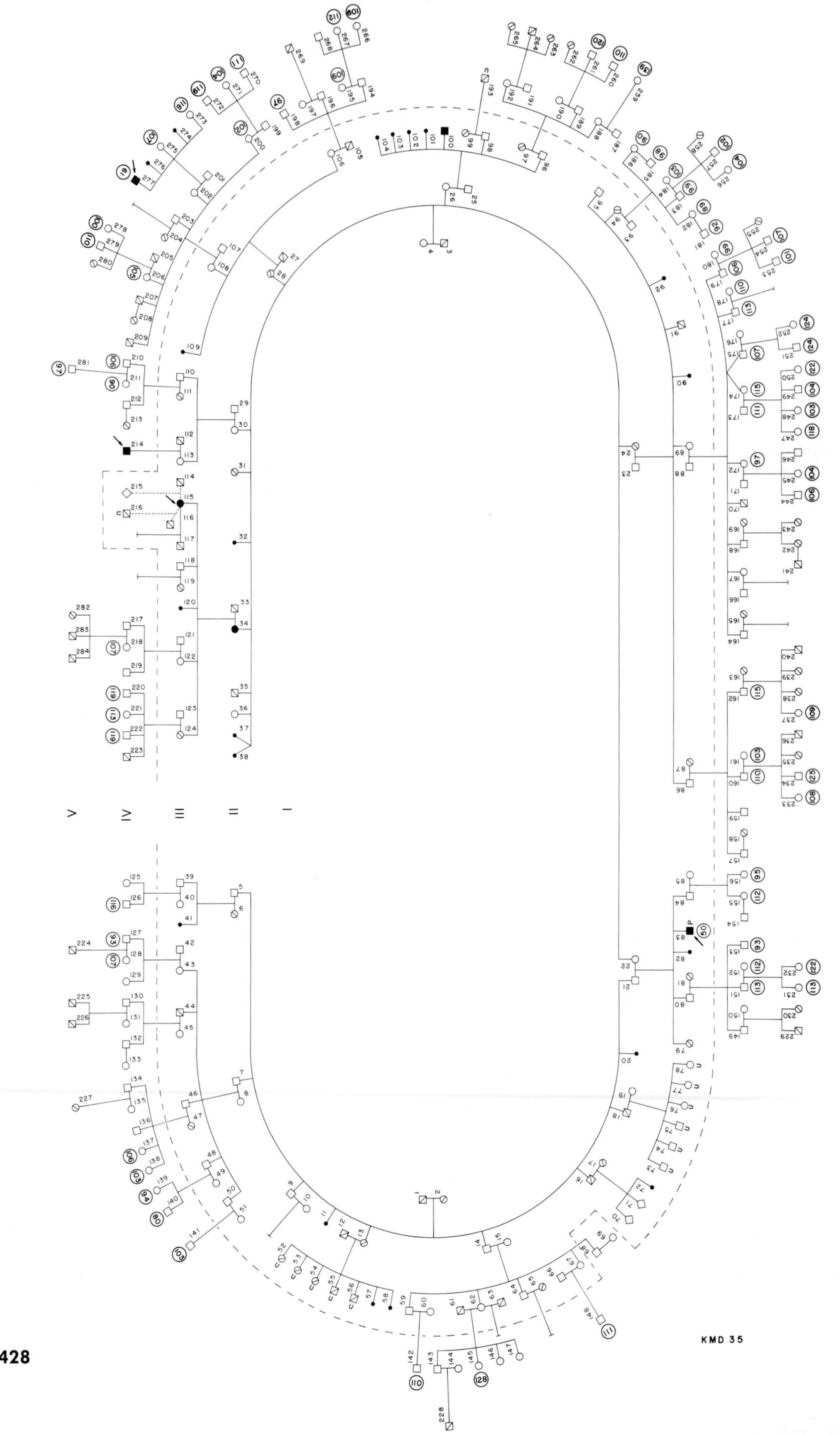
I
II
III
IV
V
KMD 35

KMD 35

The Proband

The proband (83) was born in 1897, institutionalized at 9 years and discharged to his mother in 1915. He was living with relatives in 1961. His birth was uneventful. He was a healthy baby who walked at 11 months. At 14 months he had pneumonia and spinal meningitis which resulted in a prolonged illness of 18 months. His head became enlarged so that it was a long time before he could raise it. IQ 50. *Diagnosis:* hydrocephalus resulting from infection.

Grandparents

Not of interest.

Parents

Father (21) was a stationary engineer. Both he and the mother (22) had normal intelligence.

Aunts and Uncles

Maternal aunt (34) was mentally retarded.

Siblings

Sister (79) died of typhoid fever at age 12.

Brother (80) is a city fireman; normal intelligence.

(82) was a miscarriage.

Brother (84) is a clerk; normal intelligence. Both brothers have children with normal intelligence.

Nieces and Nephews

All five have normal intelligence.

First Cousins

(100) never walked, talked very little, and died at 2 years of "dropsy."

(115) was institutionalized for two years. After the birth of two illegitimate children her case was brought up for permanent commitment as mentally retarded but it was dismissed by the court. She has married and lives with her mother. She is a middle-grade retardate who had two illegitimate children of unknown intelligence.

More Distant Relatives

A second cousin (202), supposedly deaf as the result of an infection (both her parents were deaf mutes), married a deaf man and had one child (274) who died in convulsions at 3 months, a stillbirth (276) and a retarded institutionalized child who was nearly three months premature, nearly blind and partly deaf with IQ 61, in addition to two normal children.

(214) is institutionalized for retardation, degree unknown.

Family Summary

The proband was the only retarded person in his immediate family. The parents had five children and five grandchildren. All the grandchildren and two of the great-grandchildren are known to have normal intelligence.

Retardation of proband of primarily environmental origin (infection).

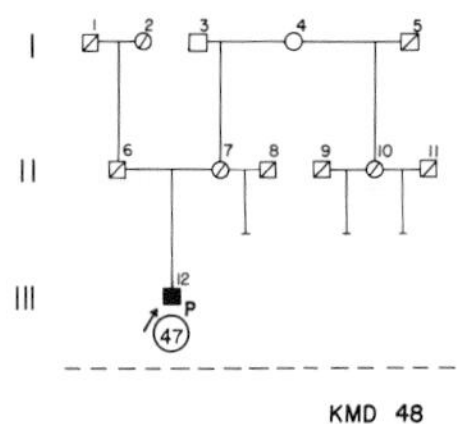

KMD 48

KMD 48

The Proband

The proband (12) was born in 1896, institutionalized at age 15 years and died of myocarditis in the institution in 1915. His head was "somewhat crushed" during an instrument delivery and it developed a ridge along the longitudinal suture. IQ 47. *Diagnosis:* undifferentiated mental retardation.

Grandparents

Paternal grandparents unknown. Proband's father was an adopted child.

Parents

Father (6) was a cook on a railway diner, intelligence unknown.

Mother (7) had unknown intelligence.

Aunts and Uncles

Proband's mother had a childless half sister, intelligence unknown.

Siblings

None.

Nieces and Nephews

None.

First Cousins

None.

More Distant Relatives

None.

Family Summary

The intelligence of the proband's parents is unknown. The proband was delivered by instruments, during which he sustained serious injury to his head. The proband had no close relatives other than his parents and his mother's half sister.

Retardation of proband of primarily environmental origin (head injury).

KMD 81

The Proband

The proband (55) was born in 1898, institutionalized at age 14 years and left the institution in 1913. He was still living at home in 1961. He was unmarried and childless. He was a seven-month child and was born after prolonged and difficult labor. IQ 63. *Diagnosis:* undifferentiated mental retardation.

Grandparents

Not of interest.

Parents

Father (14) was epileptic but had normal intelligence.

Mother (15) was normal.

Aunts and Uncles

Not of interest.

Siblings

None.

Half Siblings

Three half siblings, all normal.

Children of Half Siblings

Not of interest.

First Cousins

Not of interest.

More Distant Relatives

First cousin (39) has a retarded child (291), IQ 47.

Family Summary

The proband and one more distant relative were retarded. The proband's parents had only one child, no grandchildren.

Retardation of proband of primarily environmental origin (prematurity and difficult delivery).

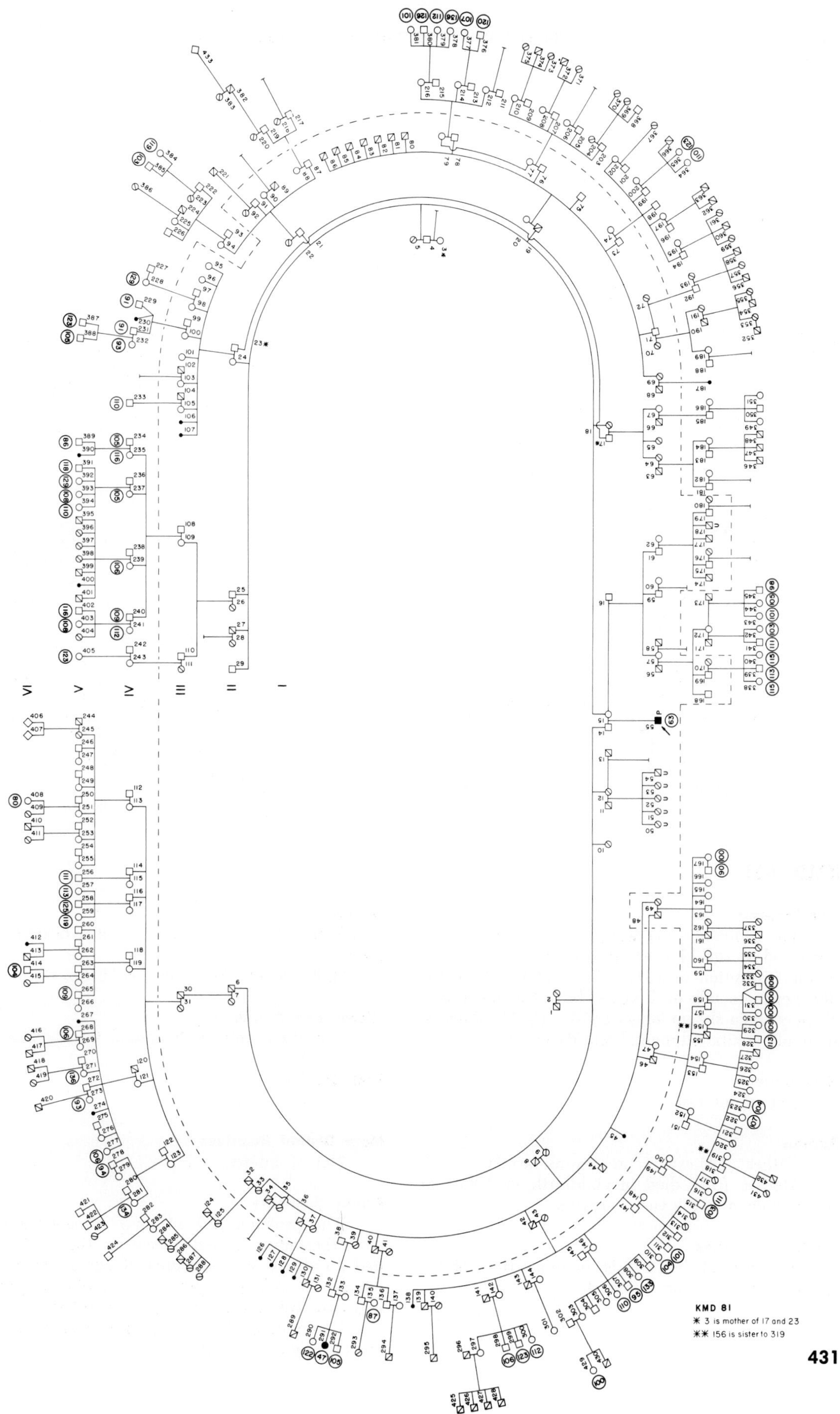

KMD 81

✱ 3 is mother of 17 and 23

✱✱ 156 is sister to 319

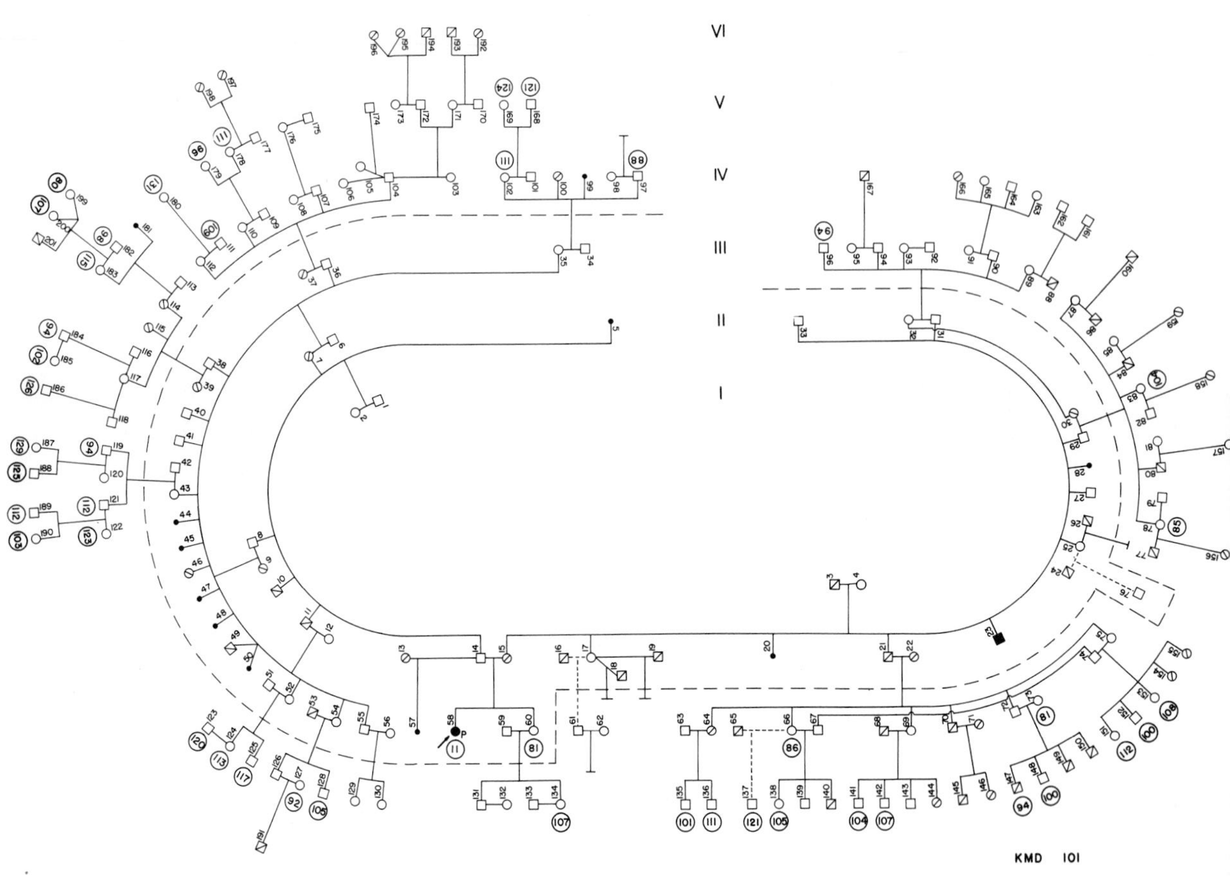

KMD 101

The Proband

The proband (58) was born in 1898, institutionalized at age 11 years and died of tuberculosis in the institution in 1917. She had no stigmata. She began to talk at 2 years, but after an attack of pneumonia she no longer spoke. IQ 11. *Diagnosis:* undifferentiated mental retardation.

Grandparents

Not of interest.

Parents

Father (14) was a prosperous farmer.

Mother (15) died in childbirth in 1900, so was unknown to the early workers.

Aunts and Uncles

Maternal uncle (23) is an unmarried, childless farm laborer and retarded.

Siblings

Sister (60) died at age 34 of a heart attack. IQ 81.

Half sibling (57) was a stillbirth.

Nieces and Nephews

Only two, both with normal intelligence.

First Cousins

Not of interest.

More Distant Relatives

Not of interest.

Family Summary

The proband, IQ 11, and a maternal uncle were the only retarded persons in the family. She had an attack of pneumonia at age 2 years, after which she no longer spoke. The proband's parents had two children and two grandchildren.

Retardation of proband of primarily environmental origin (infection).

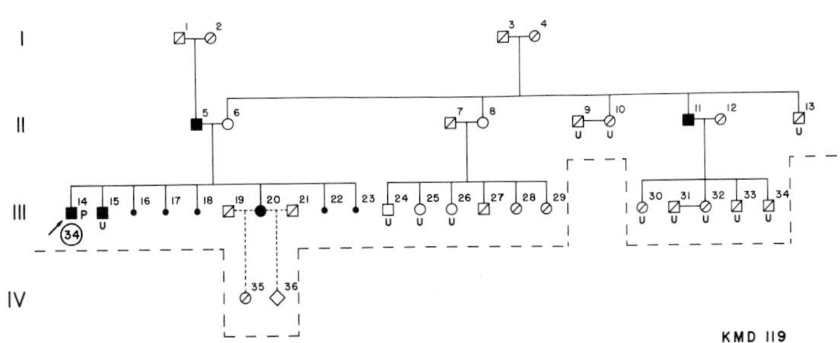

KMD 119

The Proband

The proband (14) was born in 1885, sent to a mental hospital at age 16 years, institutionalized at age 24 years and died of rheumatic valvulitis and mitral stenosis in the institution in 1953. He attended school for three years with little result. His birth was uneventful. He was syphilitic, as were his parents and siblings. IQ 34. *Diagnosis:* undifferentiated mental retardation.

Grandparents

Not of interest.

Parents

Father (5) was illiterate, an alcoholic, abusive to his family and syphilitic.

Mother (6) was illiterate but had normal intelligence. She supported the family but was often incapacitated by syphilitic ulcers. The home environment was poor.

Aunts and Uncles

No paternal relatives. Proband's father was an only child.

Maternal uncle (11) was retarded.

Siblings

Brother (15) was abusive, an alcoholic and promiscuous. He was syphilitic and retarded.

Siblings (16), (17), (18), (22) and (23) were full term babies who died at or shortly after birth, probably of syphilis according to the attending physician.

Sister (20) had two illegitimate children. She was syphilitic and retarded.

Nieces and Nephews

(35) had syphilis.

First Cousins

Unknown.

More Distant Relatives

Unknown.

Family Summary

The proband, his father and two of his siblings were retarded. Both parents of the proband, the proband, and all of his siblings were syphilitic. The syphilitic infection was especially serious in this family, with five of the proband's siblings dying in infancy of syphilis and the mother infected with chronic ulcers. No one in this family could be found by the present workers. The parents had eight children and two known grandchildren.

Retardation of proband of primarily environmental origin (syphilis).

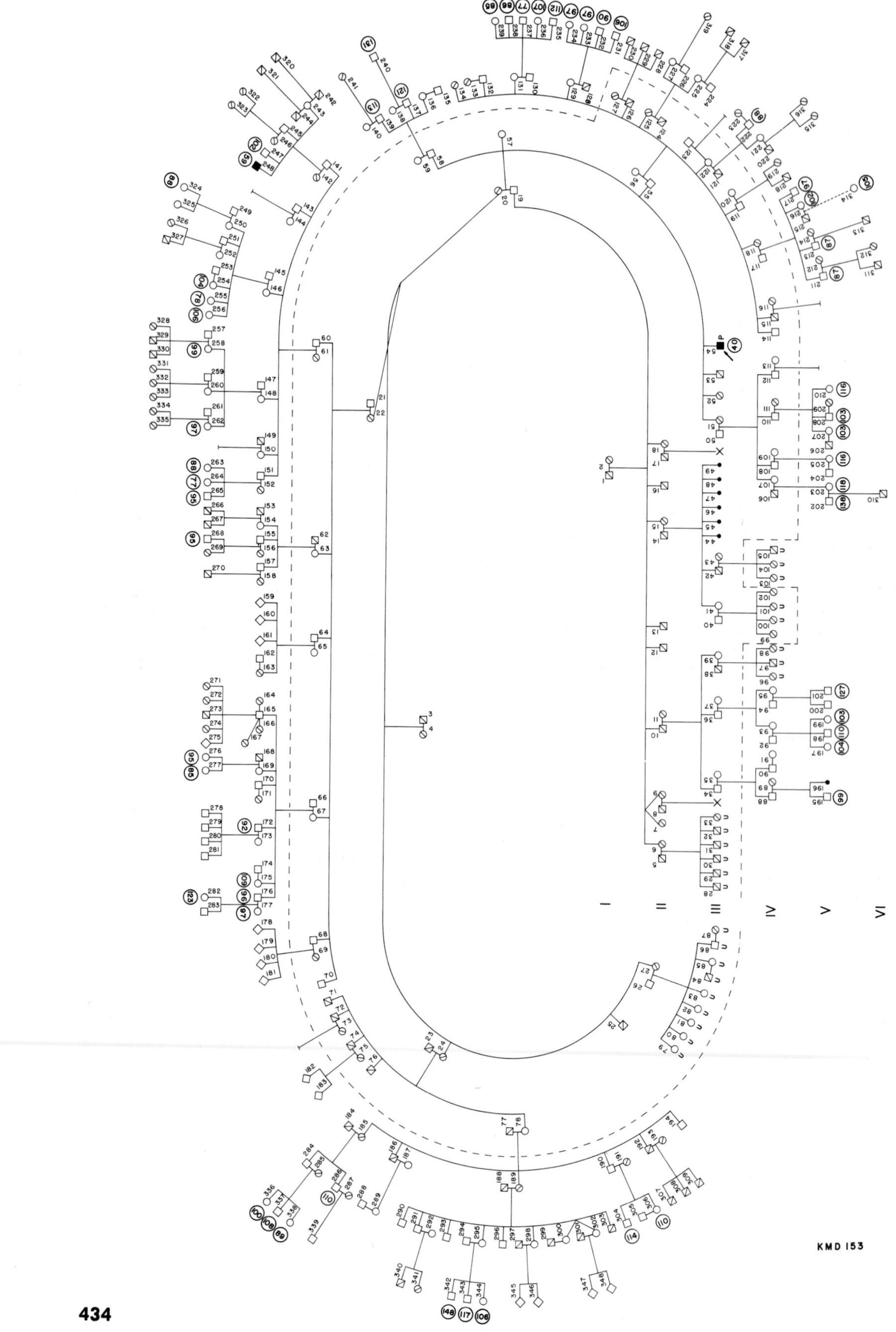
KMD 153

KMD 153

The Proband

The proband (54) was born in 1877, institutionalized at age 11 years and died of typhoid fever in the institution in 1914. He had diphtheria followed by erysipelas at the age of 2 years. He attended schools for several years but learned little. He was a fairly good farm helper. IQ 40. *Diagnosis:* undifferentiated mental retardation.

Grandparents

Not of interest.

Parents

Father (19) had normal intelligence.

Mother (20) died in 1887 of "creeping palsy" at age 34 years. She became completely helpless. Intelligence unknown.

Aunts and Uncles

Not of interest.

Siblings

Sisters (51) and (52) had unknown intelligence. (52) died of diphtheria at 6 years.

Brother (53) died of diphtheria at 4 years.

Brothers (55) and (58) and sister (57) all have normal intelligence.

Nieces and Nephews

Not of interest.

First Cousins

Not of interest.

More Distant Relatives

First cousin (60) has a retarded grandchild (248) with IQ 59.

Family Summary

The proband, IQ 40, was the only retarded person in this kindred with the exception of a first cousin's grandchild. The proband had diphtheria followed by erysipelas at the age of 2 years. After his illness he did not resume talking for a long time. The proband's parents had seven children and 18 grandchildren.

Retardation of proband of primarily environmental origin (infection).

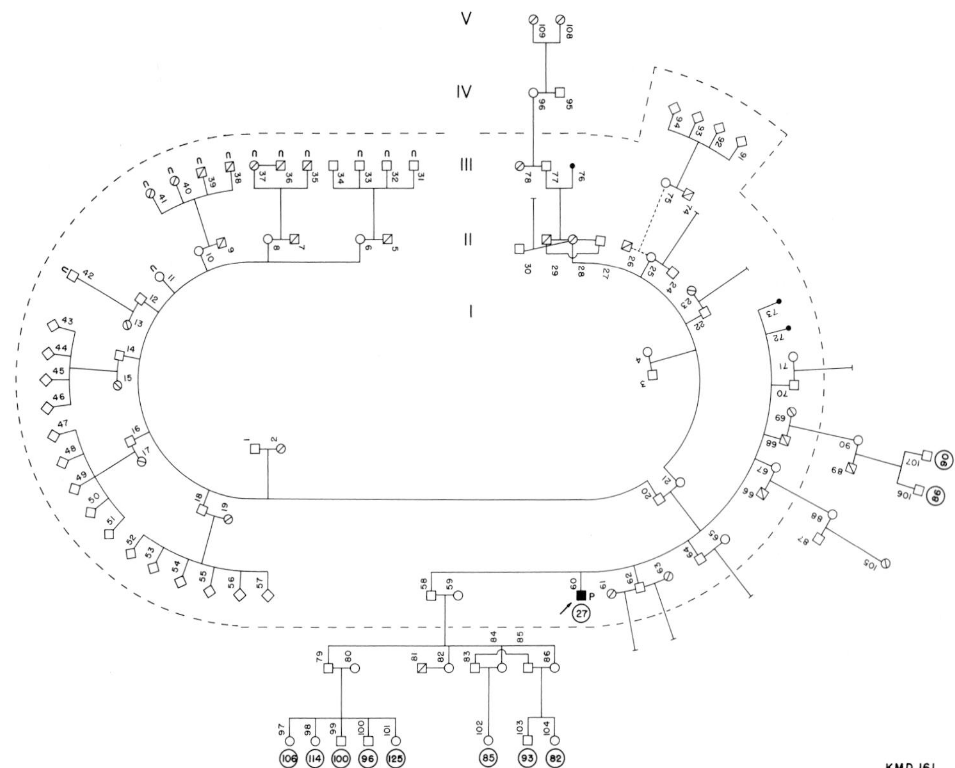
V
IV
III
II
I
P
KMD 161

KMD 161

The Proband

The proband (60) was born in 1891, institutionalized at age 13 years and was discharged to relatives in 1908. He was readmitted in 1911, transferred to a mental hospital in 1924 and to a second mental hospital in 1949 where he died of a cerebral hemorrhage in 1957. Mother and child both had measles at his birth. He walked at the usual time but did not talk until the age of 6 or 7 years. He was such a behavior problem at school that they would not keep him. The mental hospitals had no records of any diagnosis of mental illness. IQ 27. *Diagnosis:* undifferentiated mental retardation.

Grandparents

Maternal grandmother developed epilepsy at age 65 years and died of it a year later.

Parents

Father (20) and mother (21) both had normal intelligence. The father was a railroad yardmaster.

Aunts and Uncles

Not of interest.

Siblings

Brothers (58), (62), (64) and (70), and sister (67) all have normal intelligence.

Brother (68) has unknown intelligence.

Brother (72) died of a hemorrhage following circumcision.

Brother (73) died of cholera infantum at age 2 years. He "seemed normal."

Nieces and Nephews

Not of interest.

First Cousins

Nearly all unknown because they lived in other states.

More Distant Relatives

Not of interest.

Family Summary

The proband, IQ 27, was the only retarded person in his immediate family. He and his mother had measles at the time of his birth. The proband's parents had nine children but only six grandchildren, despite the fact that all their normal adult children (six in number) were married.

Retardation of proband of primarily environmental origin (infection).

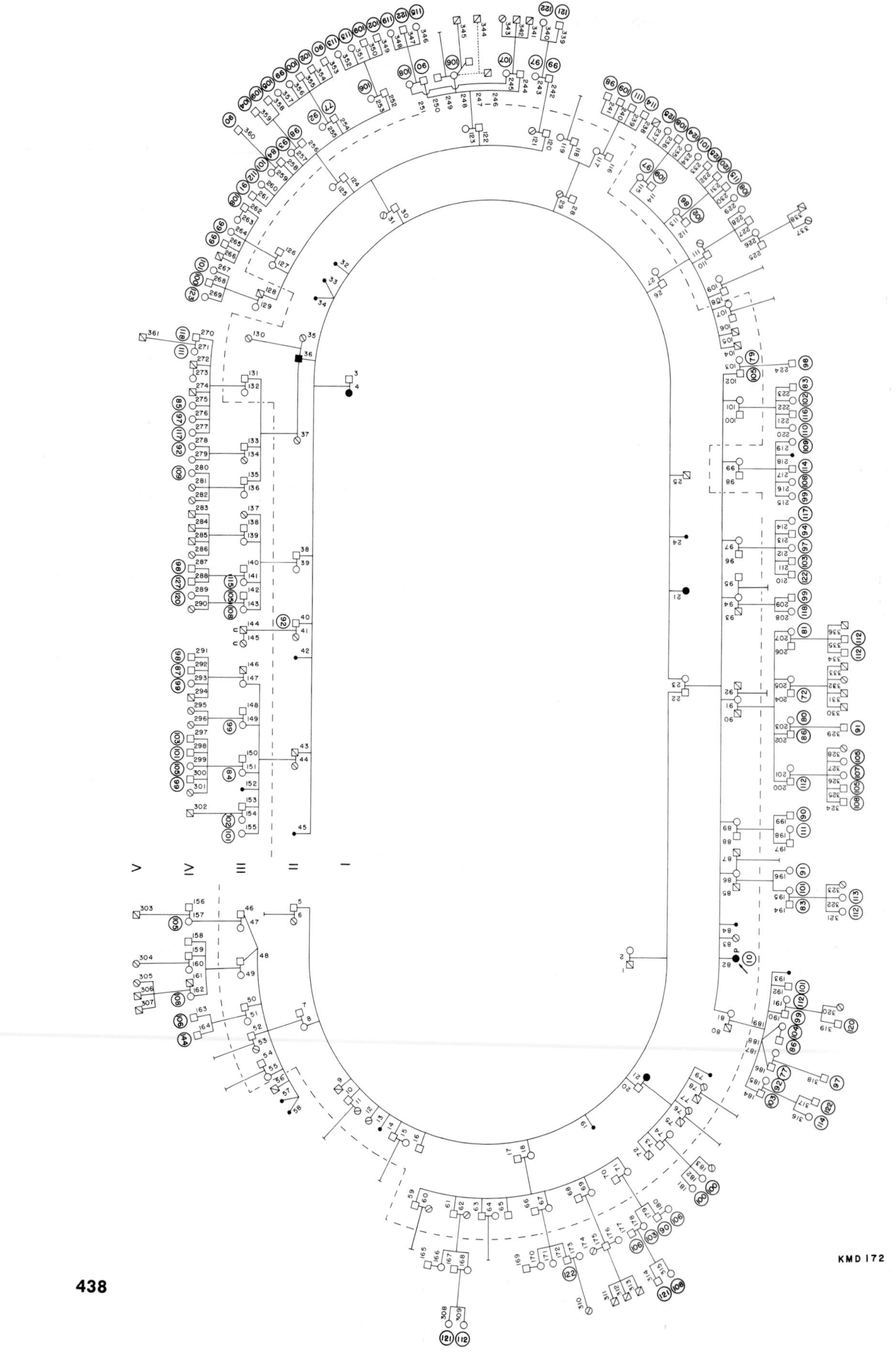

KMD 172

KMD 172

The Proband

The proband (82) was born in 1896, institutionalized at age 15 years and died of hypertensive cardiovascular disease in the institution in 1940. Her birth was uneventful but she was deficient in animation and was paralyzed immediately after birth. She had whooping cough at 6 months, pneumonia at 6 years. She walked a little at 5 years but had a left hemiplegia and was a deaf mute. IQ 10. *Diagnosis:* mental deficiency with hemiplegia and deaf mutism.

Grandparents

Paternal grandfather was syphilitic.

Maternal grandmother was retarded.

Parents

Father (22) was syphilitic and "of low order of mentality." Probably not retarded.

Mother (23) had normal intelligence.

Aunts and Uncles

All paternal uncles were syphilitic, alcoholic and promiscuous.

Maternal aunt (21) was retarded. She is the same person as the wife of paternal uncle (20).

Maternal uncle (26) died of carbon monoxide poisoning, probably suicide. His wife (27) had Huntington's chorea and committed suicide.

Maternal uncle (36) was retarded.

Maternal uncle (40) has been hospitalized in a mental hospital, diagnosis "without mental disorder" but committed for "habits and traits of character." IQ 92.

Siblings

Sister (81) had rheumatism, kidney trouble and convergent strabismus as a young woman. She has normal intelligence.

Sister (83) died of diphtheria at 4 years of age.

Sister (84) died of diphtheria at 18 months.

Sisters (86), (89), (91), (94), (97), (99) and (101) all have normal intelligence as does the brother (102) who has an IQ of 105. No retardation has appeared among their descendants.

Nieces and Nephews

All have normal intelligence.

First Cousins

Not of interest.

More Distant Relatives

Not of interest.

Family Summary

The proband had an IQ of 10 with a history of severe whooping cough. She was paralyzed at birth, had left hemiplegia and was a deaf mute. The paternal side was notorious for alcoholism, promiscuity and syphilitic infection. The maternal grandmother, one maternal aunt and a maternal uncle were high-grade retardates. The proband's parents had 12 children and 31 grandchildren, all with normal intelligence except the proband. The institution diagnosis was posttraumatic natal idiocy.

Retardation of proband of primarily environmental origin.

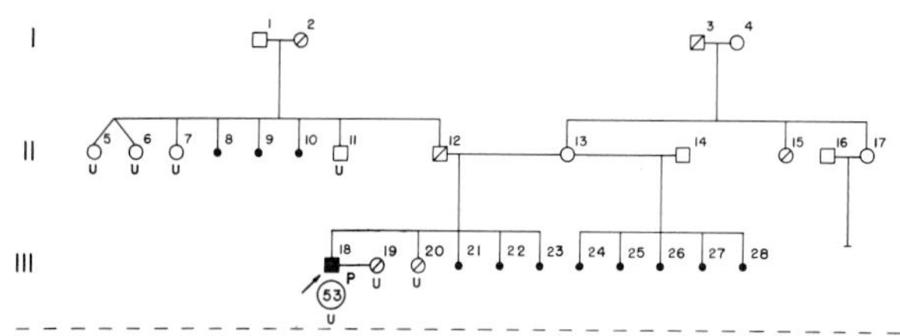

KMD 189

KMD 189

The Proband

The proband (18) was born in 1898, institutionalized at age 15 years, discharged in 1914 and sent to a reformatory in 1915. There was no history of difficult birth but the proband had congenital syphilis. He could not be found for the follow-up. A record from the reformatory states he enlisted in the Polish Army in 1918 and returned to Poland and married. He attended school for seven years, completing the second grade. He was a truant and thief. IQ 53. *Diagnosis:* undifferentiated mental retardation.

Grandparents

Not of interest.

Parents

Father (12) was a cook in the army. He was syphilitic, intelligence unknown.

Mother (13) had normal intelligence but was syphilitic.

Aunts and Uncles

Paternal relatives remained in Austria.

Maternal relatives not of interest.

Siblings

Sister (19) remained with her maternal grandmother in Austria.

Brother (20) died of "spasms" at age 2 months.

Sister (21) died of whooping cough and "spasms" at age 8 months.

Sister (22) died at 3 days, cause unknown.

Half Siblings

(23) died at 15 days, cause unknown.

(24) was a stillbirth.

(25) died from "effects of heat" at age 4 months. He was hydrocephalic.

(26) was delivered by instruments, died at age 3 days, "turned blue."

(27) died of pneumonia at age 7 days.

Nieces and Nephews

Unknown.

First Cousins

Unknown.

More Distant Relatives

Unknown.

Family Summary

The proband, IQ 53, and one sister were the only survivors of ten pregnancies of their mother by two spouses. Both the proband's parents had syphilis, as did the proband himself. The proband's parents had five children, grandchildren unknown.

Retardation of proband of primarily environmental origin (syphilis).

KMD 191

The Proband

The proband (49) was born in 1858, institutionalized at age 31 years and died of pulmonary tuberculosis and mitral and myocardial insufficiency in the institution in 1923. She had spinal meningitis at age 6 months and scarlet fever at 3 years. She had a residual muscular weakness from the meningitis. She attended school for several years with poor results. IQ 53. *Diagnosis:* undifferentiated mental retardation.

Grandparents

Not of interest.

Parents

Father (14) and mother (15) had normal intelligence.

Aunts and Uncles

Not of interest.

Siblings

Sister (39) had senile dementia for ten years before she died. Her intelligence was unknown.

Brother (41) had unknown intelligence. He was considered peculiar.

Sister (44) had normal intelligence.

Brothers (45), (47) and (52) all had normal intelligence. (47) had "nervous prostration" for a year but recovered.

Brother (50) drowned at age 34 years, single and childless. He was an alcoholic and retarded.

Nieces and Nephews

Not of interest.

First Cousins

(37) died in an institution. She was epileptic and retarded.

More Distant Relatives

Proband's nephew (192) has two retarded grandsons, (774) and (777).

(576), a great-niece, is retarded.

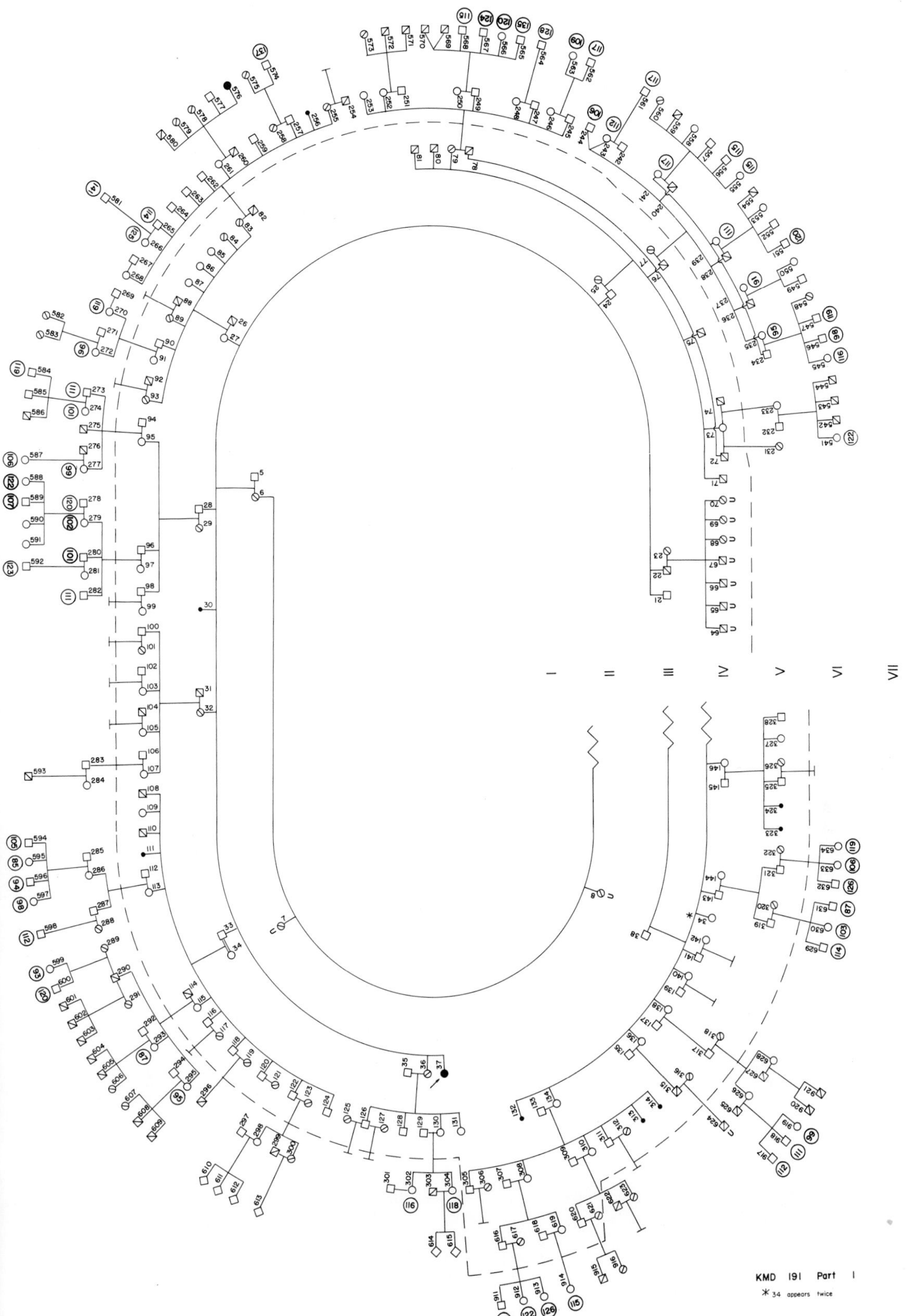

Family Summary

The proband and one brother were retarded. One first cousin and three more distant relatives in this large family were also retarded. The proband had meningitis at age 6 months with subsequent muscle weakness, and scarlet fever at 3 years. The proband's parents had seven children and 56 grandchildren.

Retardation of proband of primarily environmental origin (infection).

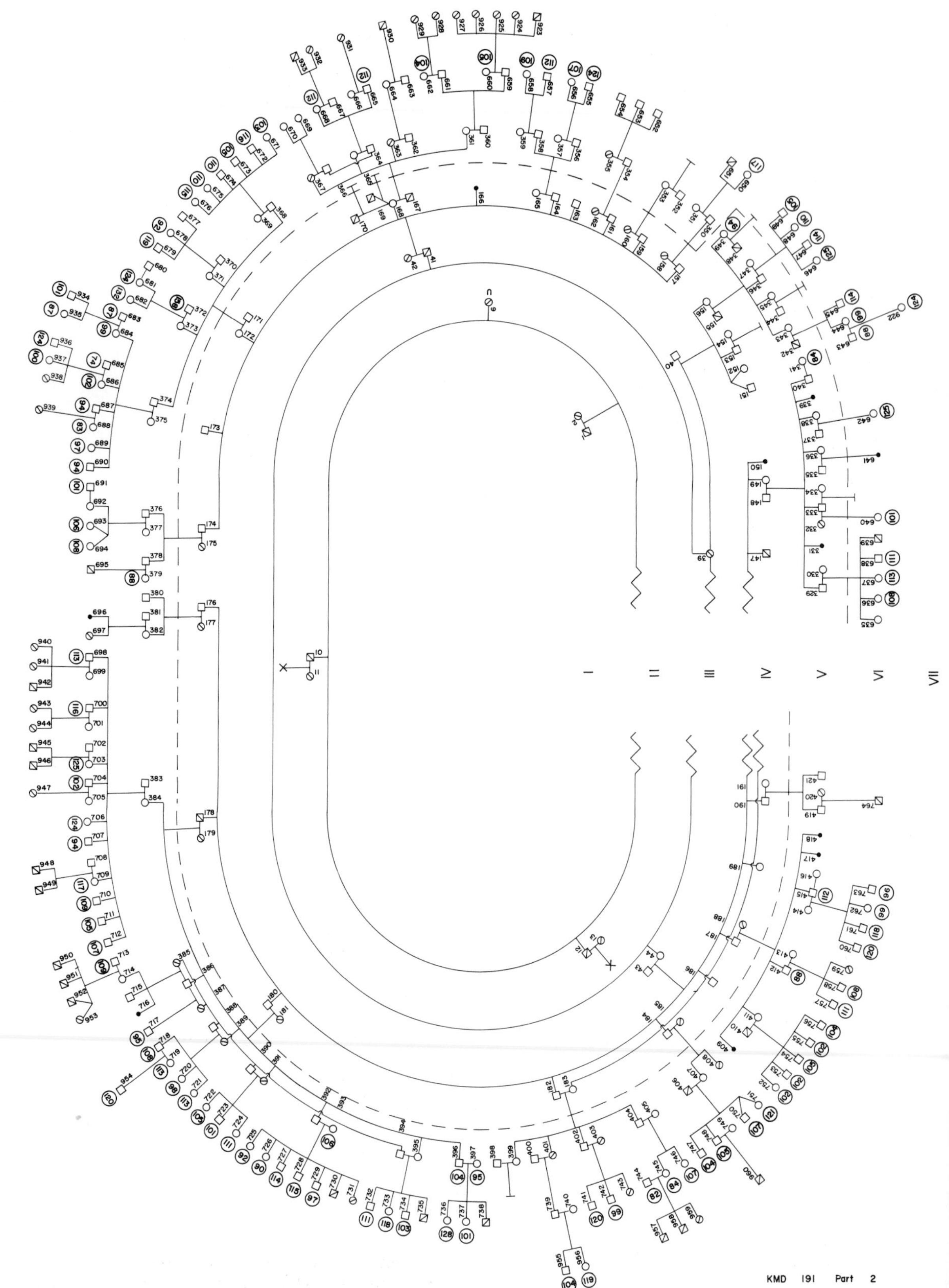

KMD 191 Part 2

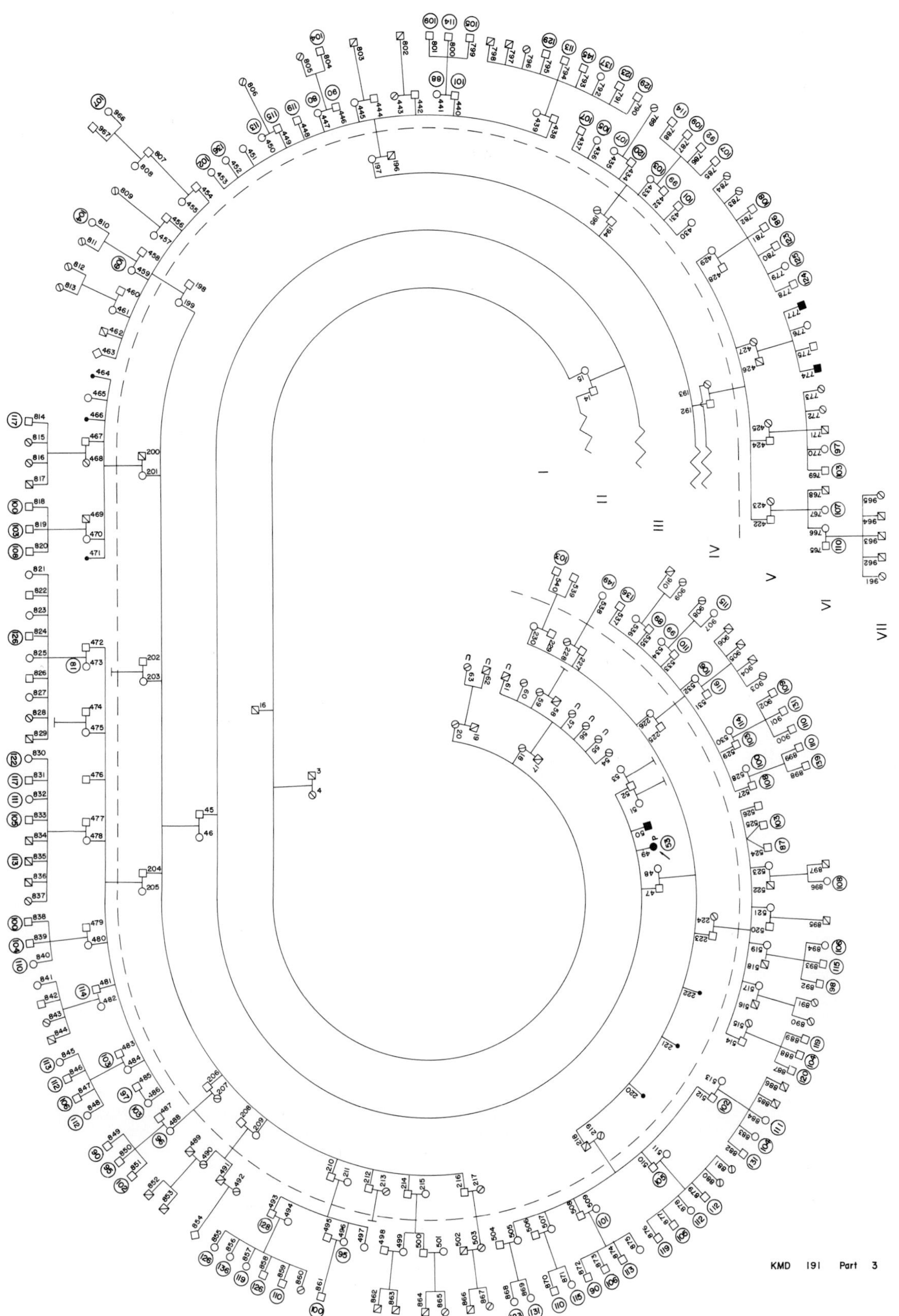

KMD 191 Part 3

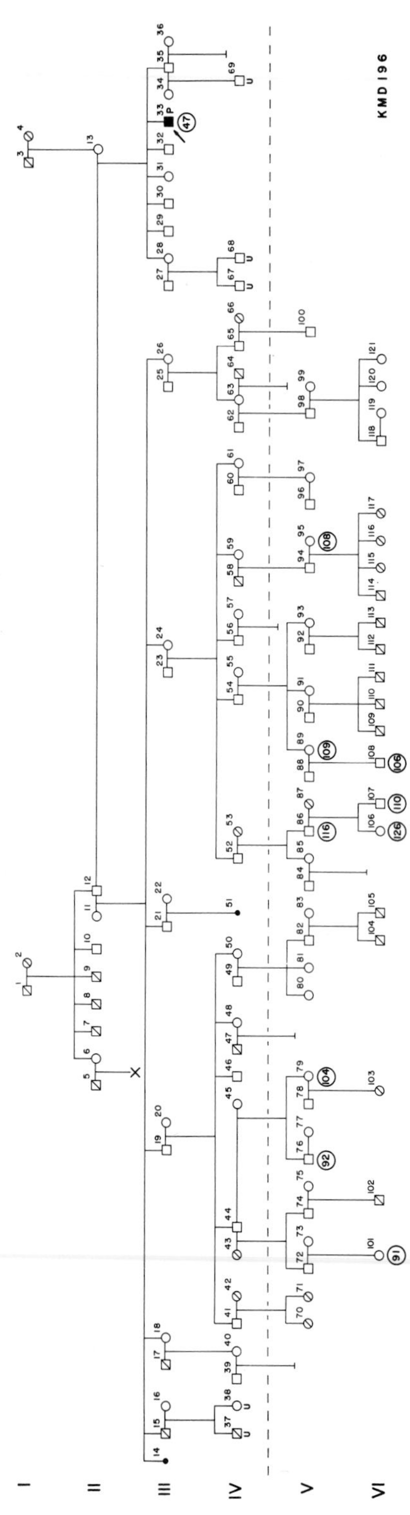

KMD 196

The Proband

The proband (33) was born in 1847, institutionalized at age 54 years and died of chronic interstitial nephritis in the institution in 1914. He left school at age 12 years, apparently normal, and worked as a clerk for some years. He became an alcoholic and at about age 20 fell from a wagon injuring his head, and was left for some time without medical attention. After this accident he became retarded. His family refused to take him in so he became a public charge until his institutionalization. IQ 47. *Diagnosis:* unknown.

Grandparents

Not of interest.

Parents

Father (12) was a prosperous contractor.
Mother (13) had normal intelligence.

Aunts and Uncles

Not of interest.

Siblings

All, including half siblings, were known to have had normal intelligence except for half brother (15) whose intelligence was unknown. He was incorrigible and had served time in a reformatory.

Nieces and Nephews

All had normal intelligence, as did all the children of the half siblings, with the exception of (37) whose intelligence is unknown.

First Cousins

Unknown.

More Distant Relatives

Unknown.

Family Summary

The proband, IQ 47, was the only retarded person in this family. He was apparently normal until the age of 18 or 20 when he became an alcoholic. At this time, while intoxicated, he fell from a wagon and injured his head. After this episode his mental ability deteriorated to the retarded level. His family refused to keep him, so for many years he was dependent on local charity for his existence. The proband's parents had seven children and three grandchildren. Two of the proband's unmarried siblings died of tuberculosis. One, also single, was killed in the Civil War. The other unmarried sibling died at age 9 years.

Retardation of proband of primarily environmental origin (injury).

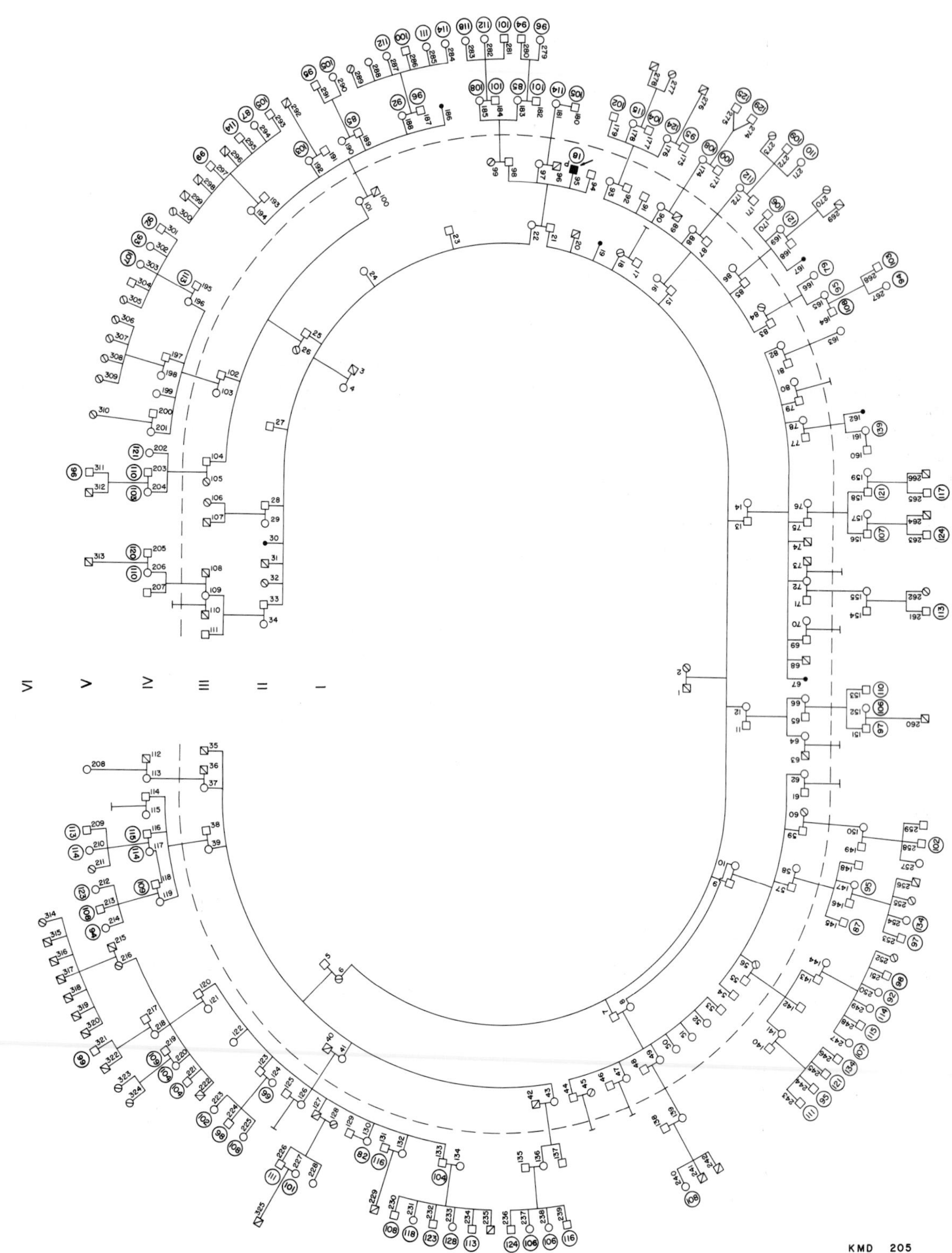

KMD 205

KMD 205

The Proband

The proband (95) was born in 1898, institutionalized at age 7 years and died of acute indigestion and paralytic idiocy in the institution in 1925. His birth was not attended by a doctor. It was reported that he was born "with spine twisted." He had right-sided hemiplegia and could never sit up. He also had a history of a serious disease in infancy, either meningitis or poliomyelitis. IQ 18. *Diagnosis:* mental retardation with cerebral palsy.

Grandparents

Not of interest.

Parents

Father (21) was a prosperous farmer.

Mother (22) had normal intelligence.

Aunts and Uncles

Paternal aunt (18) was epileptic.

Siblings

Brother (94) is a polio invalid who completed one year of high school. He attempted suicide at age 16 years.

Sister (97) and brother (98) are normal.

Nieces and Nephews

Only three, all of normal intelligence.

First Cousins

Not of interest.

More Distant Relatives

Not of interest.

Family Summary

The proband was severely retarded, IQ 18, and spastic. He was thought to have been injured at birth and also to have had either meningitis or poliomyelitis in infancy. He was the only retarded person in this kindred. The proband's parents had four children and three grandchildren.

Retardation of proband of primarily environmental origin (either birth injury or infection, or both).

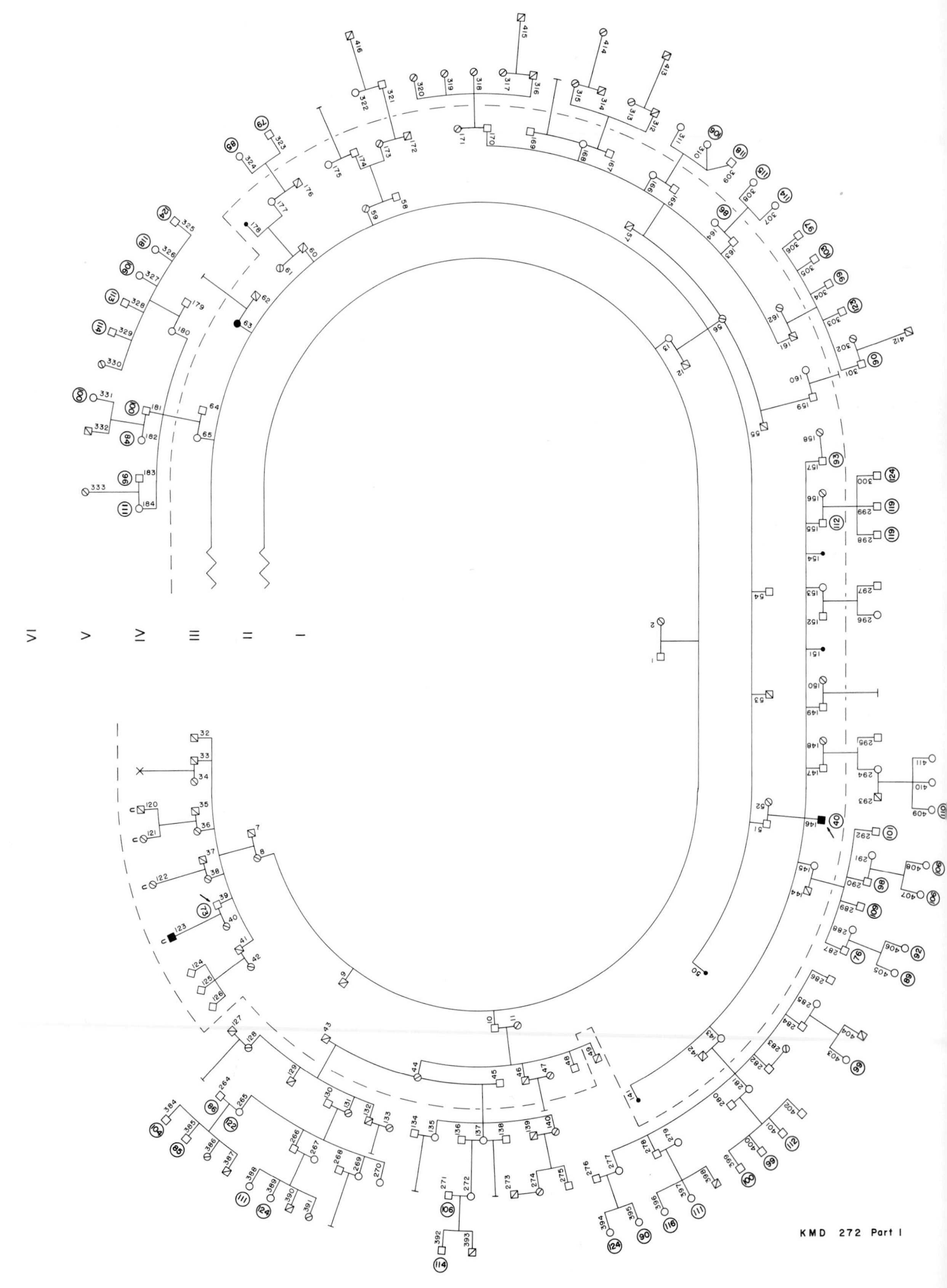

KMD 272 Part I

KMD 272

The Proband

The proband (75) was born in 1886, institutionalized at age 9 years and died of bronchopneumonia in the institution in 1912. His was an instrument delivery after a prolonged labor. He was deficient in animation and had a poorly shaped head with injuries which did not heal for six months. He was crippled and could not walk. The home environment was poor. IQ 6. *Diagnosis:* undifferentiated mental retardation.

Grandparents

Paternal grandfather died in an epileptic seizure.

Maternal grandfather had epileptoid attacks, "sinking fits."

Parents

Father (15) and mother (16) were both retarded and the mother was also epileptic.

Aunts and Uncles

Paternal uncle (14) was an unmarried, childless retardate.

The proband's mother had only half siblings, of whom (18) was promiscuous, syphilitic and blind (her children were taken away from her), and (26) took poison "accidentally" and died.

Siblings

Brother (76) was a married but childless retardate.

Nieces and Nephews

None.

First Cousins

(39) was institutionalized in 1915 at age 40 years when he developed epilepsy following an accident and died of epilepsy in 1918. His family received a great deal of help because (39) was an alcoholic and refused to work. IQ 73 at age 40 years.

(63) was a married but childless retardate.

The proband had no full maternal cousins, only the children of his mother's half siblings.

(79) was placed in the state orphanage and then tried in six boarding homes. He was returned from all of these homes for dishonesty, cruelty and incorrigibility. He was finally returned to the county authorities as being unsuitable for the state orphanage and at age 21 years was imprisoned for grand larceny. Later he was imprisoned for traveling about the state with his sister and posing as her husband. He died in the state prison in 1958 to which he had been sentenced in 1916 for first degree murder.

(83) was also tried in boarding homes with no success because he was "deceitful and unmanageable." Some persons thought he was mentally ill.

(86), sister to (79) and (83), led an unfortunate early life as a victim of incest with her father and brother. She was thought at one time to have been retarded. However, once she was freed of her family she improved greatly, although she had a complicated marital history which included at least three husbands.

More Distant Relatives

(123) was a retarded juvenile delinquent.

(146) was institutionalized for Down's syndrome with IQ 40.

(208) was in the fourth grade at age 12 years with a "D" average.

(347) "cannot pass" at age 8 years, according to the school.

(355), with IQ 83, married a retarded woman (356) with IQ 69.

(370) has an IQ of 65.

(371), sister to (370), is "like her brother" according to the school. They also report poor home conditions, but two siblings (369) and (372) have normal intelligence.

Family Summary

The proband, IQ 6, both his parents, his brother, a paternal uncle, one first cousin and six more distant relatives were retarded. Of these last, one was diagnosed as having Down's syndrome. All the other retardates were of high grade except the proband, who had a history of difficult birth and poor care. In addition, the proband's paternal grandfather, his mother and a first cousin were epileptic, and one of the mother's half siblings and three of her children evinced antisocial behavior. The proband's parents had two children and no grandchildren.

Retardation of proband of primarily environmental origin (birth injury). (It is possible that the proband would have been retarded in any circumstance because of the general pattern in this family, but the medically reported birth injuries were enough to have played a major part in the retardation.)

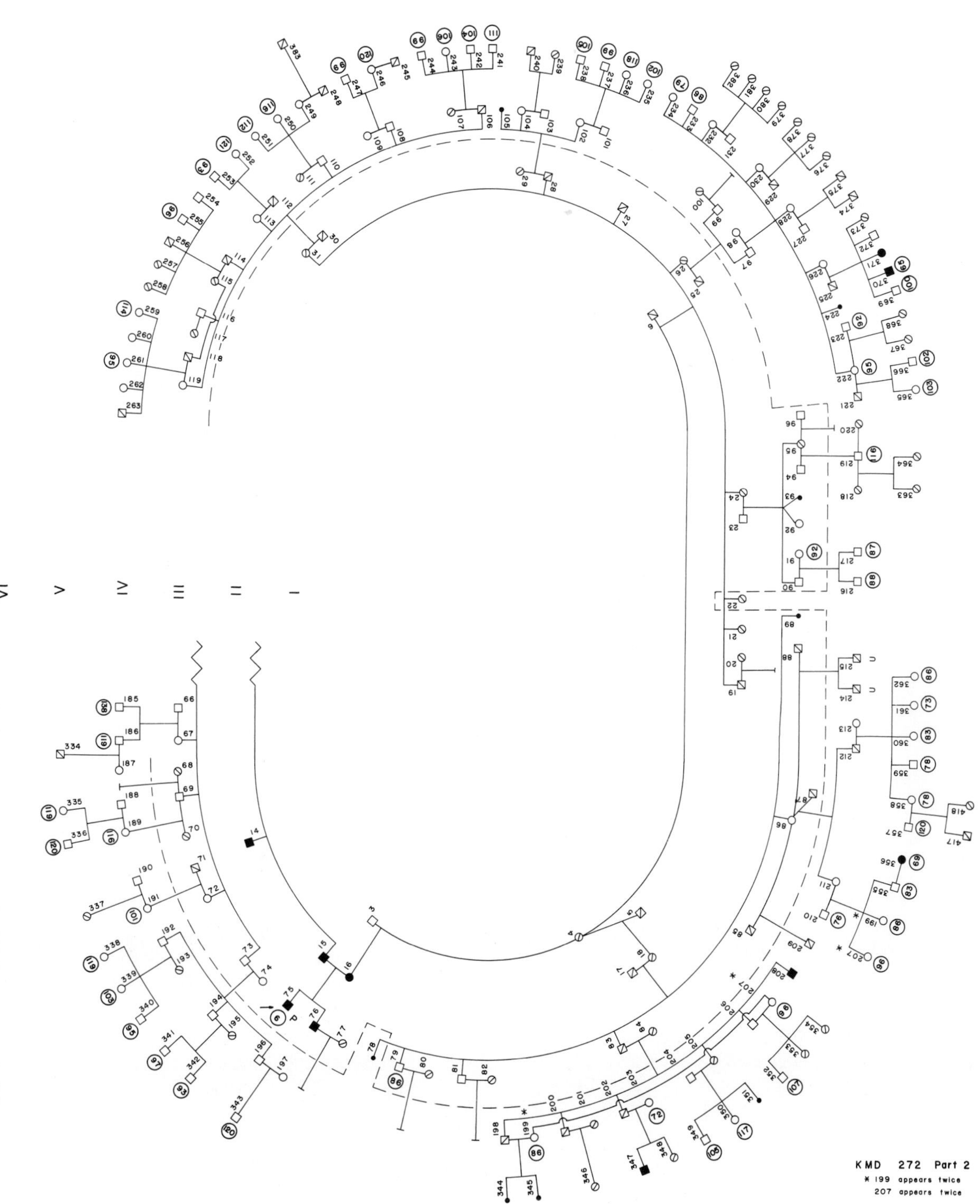

KMD 272 Part 2
* 199 appears twice
207 appears twice

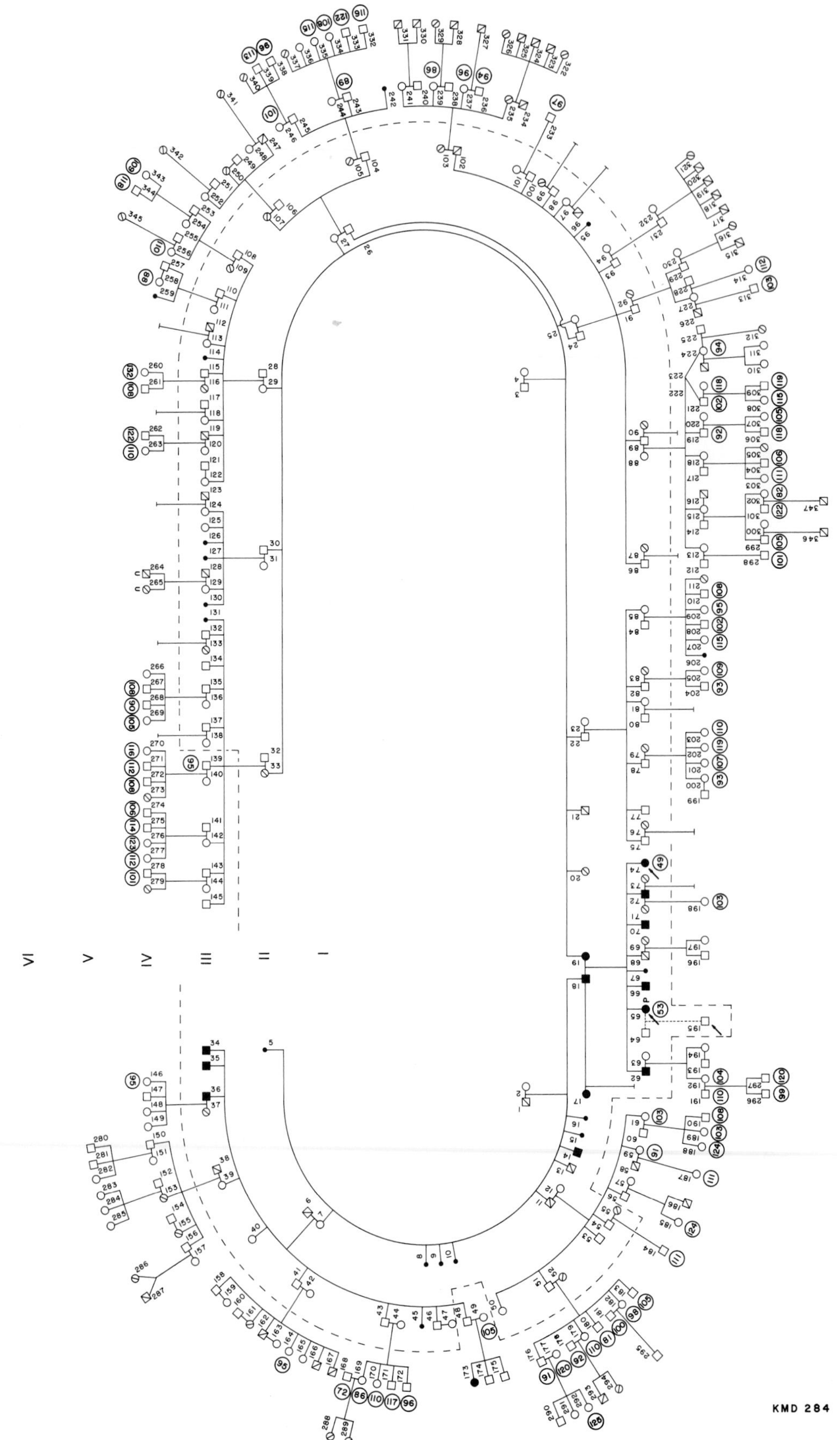
KMD 284

KMD 284

The Proband

The proband (65) was born in 1893, institutionalized at age 19 years when pregnant and died of lobar pneumonia in the institution in 1913. She was the victim of incest with her father and brother and was much abused by her father and stepmother. She had no history of birth injury or perinatal infection and had no stigmata. Her home environment was described as "the worst possible." IQ 53. *Diagnosis:* undifferentiated mental retardation.

Grandparents

Not of interest.

Parents

Father (18) was promiscuous, an alcoholic and retarded.

Mother (19) was promiscuous and retarded.

Aunts and Uncles

Paternal uncle (14) was retarded.

Three paternal uncles died of "spasms" in infancy.

Siblings

Brother (62) completed the third grade at age 14 years. He was an alcoholic, incestuous and retarded. His wife graduated from high school and is a typist. They have two children, both with normal intelligence.

Brother (66) was an unmarried and childless retardate who was killed in World War I.

Brother (67) died at age 4 months.

Brother (68) is a machinist (according to his son) although the old records classify him as retarded. His intelligence is unknown.

Brother (70) completed the fourth grade and is an unmarried, childless retardate.

Brother (72) completed the third grade. He was married twice, but had only one child, a girl with normal intelligence.

Sister (74) was institutionalized at age 21 years in 1923, sterilized three years later and transferred to a second institution, where she has remained ever since. She is epileptic and retarded. IQ 49.

Child

Son (195) was born in the institution. He was adopted, served in the army and was killed in an accident in 1947. He was unmarried, childless and had normal intelligence.

Nieces and Nephews

Only five, all with normal intelligence.

First Cousins

(34) left school at age 16 years when in the fourth grade. He died single and childless in World War I.

(35) left school at age 15 years when in the third grade. He was killed by a tornado. He was unmarried and childless.

(36) completed the sixth grade and is a farmer. He was considered retarded by the early workers. He had four children all with normal intelligence.

More Distant Relatives

First cousin (48) has a child (173) who tests at the second grade level at the age of 12 years.

Family Summary

The proband, IQ 53, and her sister, IQ 49 and epileptic, were institutionalized. In addition, the proband's parents, a paternal uncle, three first cousins and one first cousin's child were retarded. The home environment was the "worst possible"; the proband was assaulted by her father and brother, and beaten by her stepmother until she finally ran away from home. She had an illegitimate child of normal intelligence. Two of her retarded brothers had a total of three children, all with normal intelligence. The proband's parents had eight children and six grandchildren. Of the proband's seven siblings, five were known to have been retarded, but none of the proband's five nieces and nephews is retarded.

Retardation of proband of primarily environmental origin (abuse and deprivation).

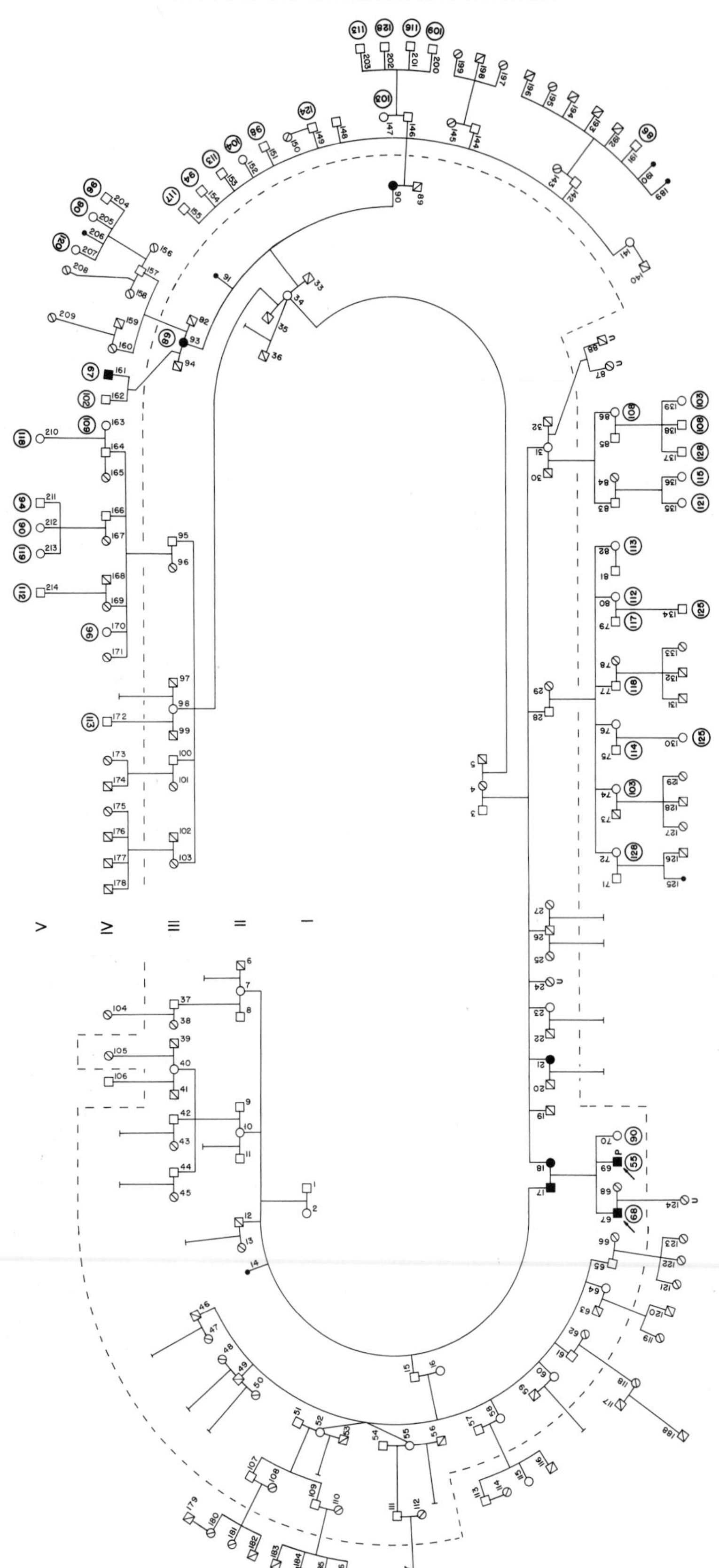

KMD 287

KMD 287

The Proband

The proband (69) was born in 1900, institutionalized at age 9 years and was still in the institution in 1961. He was a sickly baby who began to walk and talk at age 2 years. The mother reported that he was beaten by his alcoholic father, after which time he was unable to walk without help. He had a positive Wassermann at age 15 years. He was given a physical and neurological examination in 1950 by J. A. Böök, M.D., and John Schut, M.D. Their diagnosis was imbecility with spastic diplegia. (They also found dilated unequal pupils, slight ptosis and some optic atrophy—possible signs of congenital syphilis.) IQ 55. *Diagnosis:* mental retardation with spastic diplegia.

Grandparents

Maternal grandfather had incestuous relations with his daughters until they were forced to leave home. He had normal intelligence.

Parents

Father (17) was an alcoholic, promiscuous and retarded. He ran away from home and spent nine years in the navy. He was a porter in a saloon. He had been imprisoned several times for drunkenness, disorderly conduct and contempt of court.

Mother (18) divorced (17) who did not support her. She was also promiscuous, and after her divorce she went to live with her former husband's brother. She left school at age 15 years when she was in the fourth grade.

Aunts and Uncles

Both sides of the proband's family are referred to by the early worker as "one of the most, if not the most, degenerate I have ever dealt with—past reformation." Of the paternal aunts and uncles, both aunts divorced their husbands for alcoholism, and both uncles were promiscuous, alcoholics and married to women of the same type; they divorced them later, and lived with other women. (12) was a shoe clerk but had "no judgment." He committed suicide.

The maternal aunts were all subjected to incest with their father and (31) was sent to the girls' reformatory for immorality. The proband's father induced her to live with him for some time. Maternal aunt (21) was promiscuous, an alcoholic, syphilitic, crippled and retarded. Maternal aunt (24) was promiscuous. She went to California 30 years ago and has not been heard from since that time. Maternal uncle (26) was sent to reform school at the age of 7 years and stayed there until he became of age. Maternal uncle (28) was a delinquent and recorded as retarded in the old records. However, he has been very active in the labor movement and was elected to Congress at one time.

The proband's mother's half sister (34) was promiscuous and lived with three men, two of whom were alcoholics who refused to support her and were "worthless good-for-nothings." Her second "husband" spent most of his time avoiding arrest for larceny. Despite her record of poor social behavior and a classification of retarded in the old records, she proved a very accurate and helpful informant. Her marital status was never clarified.

Siblings

Brother (67) was sent to a boy's reformatory at the age of 10 years for running away from school and staying out all night, cruelty to animals and children and incorrigibility. After his parole he was transferred to the institution in 1915 at the age of 17 years. Institution records state he was "one of the most difficult boys in the institution to manage." He had a negative Wassermann and no stigmata. He ran away from the institution and joined the army in 1917 but deserted. He was sentenced to prison for seven to 30 years for attempted rape and prior conviction. He disappeared after his release and when last heard of was in Florida. He married a crippled woman and has one child of unknown intelligence. IQ 68.

Sister (70) died at age 14 years. IQ 90.

Nieces and Nephews

Only one, a niece whose intelligence is unknown.

First Cousins

Two children (90) and (93) of the proband's mother's half sister (34) are retarded. (90) could not do fifth grade work when she left at age 16 years. Her 11 children all have normal intelligence.

(93) had an IQ of 68. She had a retarded child (161) who is a construction worker with a long police record of vagrancy, traffic violations and drunkenness and an IQ of 67. His brother (162), IQ 102, also has police records for auto burglary and larceny.

More Distant Relatives

(161) see above.

Family Summary

The proband, IQ 55, and his brother, IQ 68, were institutionalized. The proband was a sickly baby who was injured by a beating at age 2 years and who probably had syphilis. In view of the sociological problems in this family, the authors are in some doubt as to the mental capacity of the proband's parents. Both were seen and interviewed by the original workers and classified as retarded. A maternal aunt, two half cousins and one more distant relative were all high-grade retardates. This whole family had an extraordinary number of divorces, police problems and welfare contacts. The proband's mother and her siblings were left motherless when the youngest child was 2 and grew up unsupervised except for stays in reformatories and orphanages. Only two of the proband's mother's seven full siblings had any children but they had six and four, respectively. Despite the many marriages, the four paternal aunts and uncles have only 13 children and 13 grandchildren among them. The proband's parents had three children and only one grandchild.

Retardation of proband of primarily environmental origin (injury and, perhaps, syphilis).

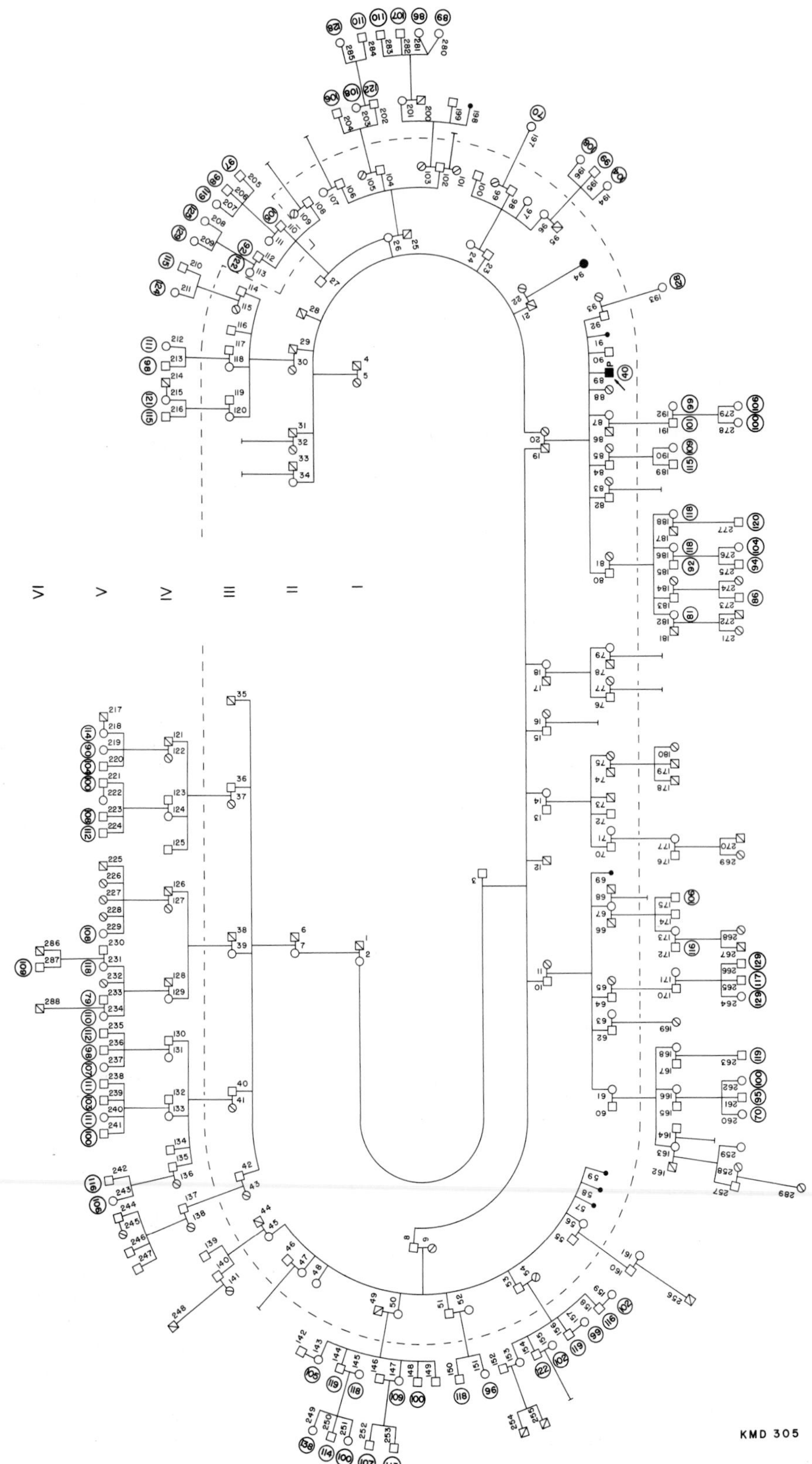

KMD 305

KMD 305

The Proband

The proband (89) was born in 1900, institutionalized at age 10 years and was still in the institution in 1961. He had no history of difficult birth and no stigmata. According to his father he had meningitis at age 6 years and was badly treated by the housekeeper. He was once found locked in an attic, almost naked and numb with cold. IQ 40. *Diagnosis:* undifferentiated mental retardation.

Grandparents

Not of interest except that the maternal grandfather was an illiterate, alcoholic teamster.

Parents

Father (19) had unknown intelligence. He was abusive to his wife and did not support his family. After his wife's death his housekeeper refused to take care of more than one child, so he sent the others to orphanages and to work.

Mother (20) had unknown intelligence. She had "spells" during which she had to be restrained and given sedatives.

Aunts and Uncles

Not of interest.

Siblings

Brothers (80), (82), (84), (90) and (92) have normal intelligence.

Sister (87) has normal intelligence.

Sister (88) died of diphtheria at age 3 years.

(91) was a miscarriage.

Nieces and Nephews

All have normal intelligence.

First Cousins

(94) is an unmarried, childless retarded woman.

More Distant Relatives

Not of interest.

Family Summary

The proband, IQ 40, was the only retarded person in this family with the exception of a first cousin. He had spinal meningitis at age 6 years and was severely abused and neglected. The proband's parents had nine children and eight grandchildren.

Retardation of proband of primarily environmental origin (infection and deprivation).

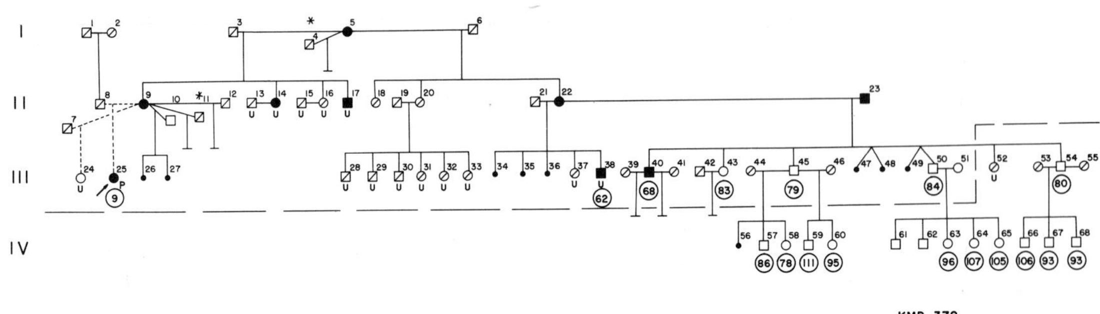

KMD 379
*11 is son of 4

KMD 379

The Proband

The proband (25) was born in 1908, institutionalized at age 6 years and died of bronchopneumonia in the institution in 1931. She was a three pound baby who was delivered by instruments and was congenitally infected with syphilitic ulcers and had a crippled right leg. Her mother had a severe case of active syphilis during her pregnancy. IQ 9. *Diagnosis:* undifferentiated mental retardation.

Grandparents

Maternal grandfather deserted his wife. He was hospitalized for alcoholism and drug addiction.

Maternal grandmother was promiscuous and retarded.

Parents

Father (8) was a baggage man of unknown intelligence.

Mother (9) was a promiscuous, syphilitic retardate.

Aunts and Uncles

Paternal relatives were unknown since the proband was illegitimate.

Maternal aunt (14) was retarded and a thief.

Maternal uncle (17) served numerous jail sentences for fighting, drunkenness and theft. He was retarded.

Proband's mother's half sister (22) was a promiscuous retardate whose first husband abandoned her and was later imprisoned, and whose second husband was a retarded Negro.

Siblings

No full siblings.

Half Siblings

Half sister (24) was a normal girl who was reared by a great-aunt.

(26) was a miscarriage.

Half sister (27) died of syphilis at age 1 week.

Nieces and Nephews

None known.

First Cousins

Two children (38) and (40) of proband's mother's half sister (22) were retarded. (38) has an IQ of 62. (40) has an IQ of 68 and has been in three prisons for theft.

More Distant Relatives

Not of interest.

Family Summary

The proband, IQ 9, was an illegitimate child who was born with a severe case of congenital syphilis and a crippled right leg. The proband's family presented a picture of promiscuity, alcoholism, lawlessness and venereal disease. The proband's maternal grandmother, mother, maternal aunt and uncle, mother's half sister and two of her children were high-grade retardates. The proband's mother's half sister (22) had two retarded children by two husbands. Her family line shows a probably genetic type of inheritance. The proband's parents had one child and no grandchildren.

Retardation of proband of primarily environmental origin (birth injury and syphilis).

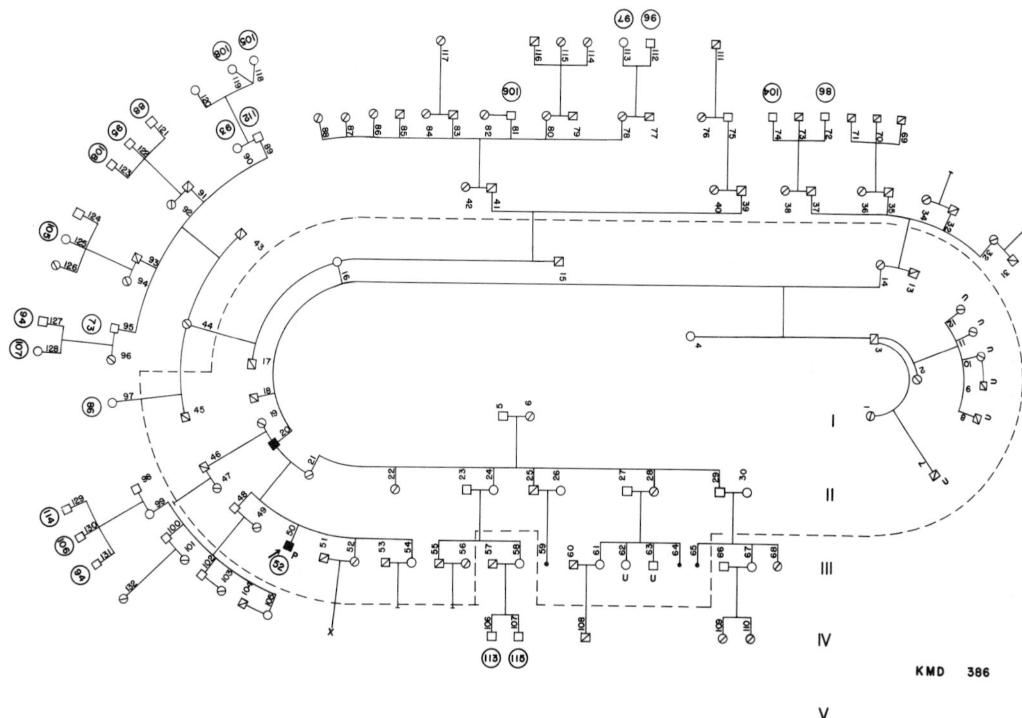

KMD 386

The Proband

The proband (50) was born in 1900, institutionalized at age 12 years and was still in the institution in 1961. He had whooping cough at the age of 2 years and "after that he was not right." He had no stigmata. IQ 52. Psychologist's diagnosis in 1959 was "moderate retardation via psychosis as a result of brain damage." *Diagnosis:* mental retardation with psychosis.

Grandparents

Maternal grandmother was mentally ill.

Parents

Father (20) "could never manage." He was illiterate and retarded.

Mother (21) died at age 36 years of acute mania.

Aunts and Uncles

Proband's father's half brother (8) and half sister (11) were mentally ill. (11) was hospitalized.

Paternal uncle (18) was hospitalized for mental illness.

Maternal aunt (28) became unbalanced after she was struck by lightning.

Siblings

Brother (48) was described as retarded in the old records but he has always been self supporting, first as a pattern maker and now as a trucker. He has been a helpful and informative correspondent, and apparently has normal intelligence.

Sister (52) is unknown to relatives.

Sister (54) was adopted as a child. She has normal intelligence.

Half Sibling

Half brother (46) works for the railroad. His intelligence is unknown.

Nieces and Nephews

Not of interest.

First Cousins

(68) is hospitalized with a diagnosis of "psychoses with organic brain disease (congenital anomalies of the brain)."

More Distant Relatives

Not of interest.

Family Summary

The proband, IQ 52, and his father were retarded. There was also a history of mental illness on both sides of the family, including the proband's mother. The proband had whooping cough at age of 2 years after which he regressed mentally. The proband's parents had four children and seven or eight grandchildren (one of the proband's sisters was known to have "three or four" children).

Retardation of proband of primarily environmental origin (infection).

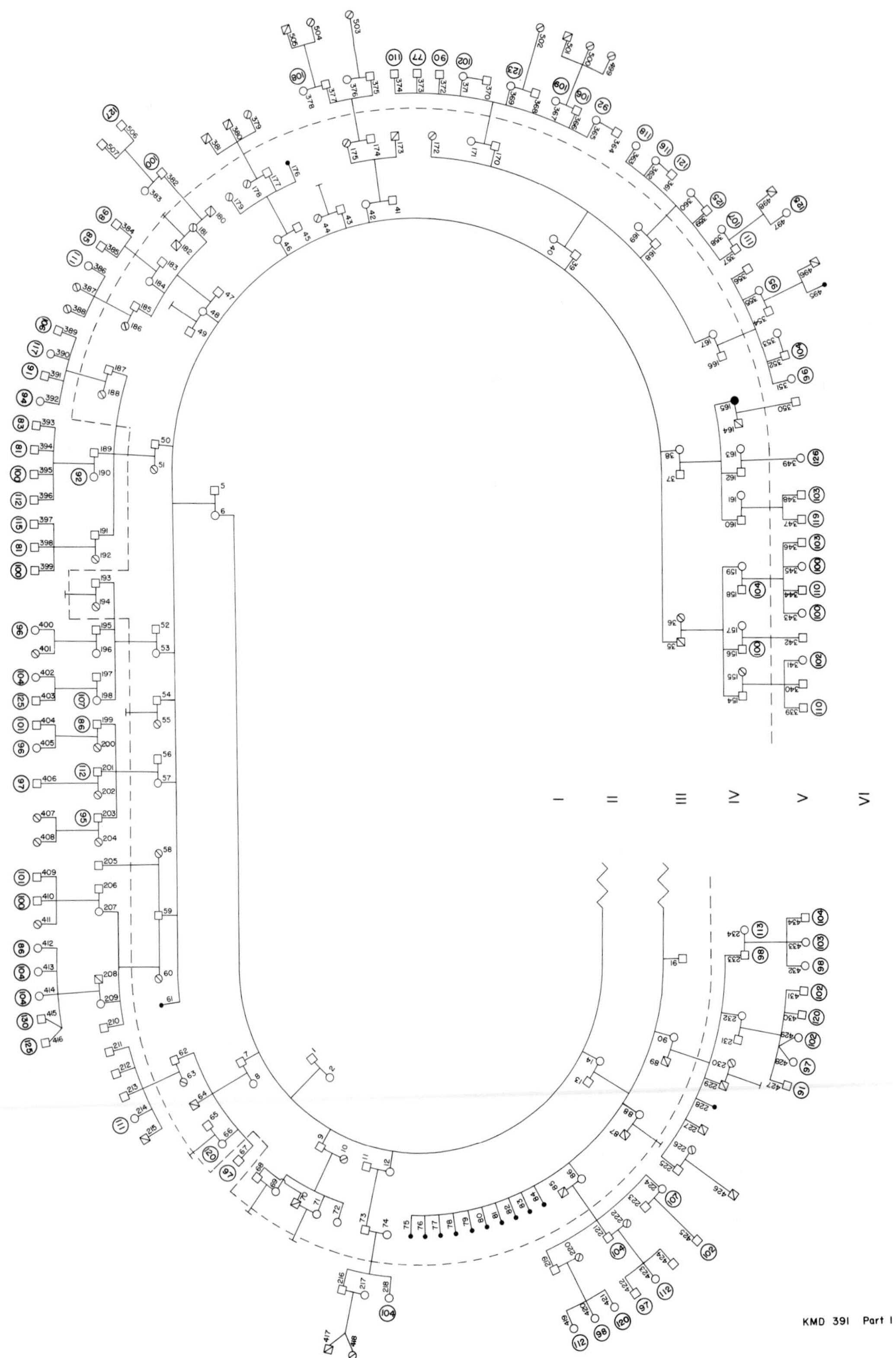

KMD 391 Part I

KMD 391

The Proband

The proband (135) was born in 1901, institutionalized at age 8 years and died of acute infectious hepatitis due to influenza in the institution in 1946. He was born with a large head and at age 4 months had spinal meningitis. His lower limbs did not develop well. The home environment lacked adequate shelter and food. IQ 38. *Diagnosis:* undifferentiated mental retardation.

Grandparents

Not of interest.

Parents

Father (27) was irresponsible and shiftless. He was a "worthless drunkard" and was retarded.

Mother (28) died following childbirth from infection, lack of care and nourishment. She was "a bright woman and a splendid housekeeper."

Aunts and Uncles

Paternal uncle (21) married a retarded woman and two of his three children were retarded.

Siblings

Brother (132) is an unmarried, childless, retarded laborer.

Sister (134) has normal intelligence.

Nieces and Nephews

None.

First Cousins

(111) could not do sixth grade work at age 16 years. (He operates a drill press and is considered retarded, as was his mother, his sister and his son.)

(115) left school at age 16 years when she was in the fourth grade. Her husband (114) had epileptoid attacks.

More Distant Relatives

First cousin (38) had a child (165) who was "never right" after an attack of scarlet fever in childhood. She is in a rest home.

First cousin (111), see above, has a son (264) with IQ 70 who was institutionalized and sterilized and is now a maintenance man under outside supervision. His diagnosis from the institution was moron—meningitis—postinfectional.

Family Summary

The proband, IQ 38, his father, brother, two first cousins and three more distant relatives were high-grade retardates. The proband was born with a large head and at the age of 4 months had spinal meningitis. His lower limbs did not develop properly. The proband's first cousin, a man with normal intelligence but with a retarded wife, had two known retarded children out of three (the third one died at age 6 years of spinal meningitis) and one retarded grandchild. The proband's father was an alcoholic and irresponsible man who never provided for his family. The proband's parents had three children and no grandchildren.

Retardation of proband of primarily environmental origin (meningitis). (The institution had no diagnosis of hydrocephalus but did have a medical record of diagnosed meningitis.)

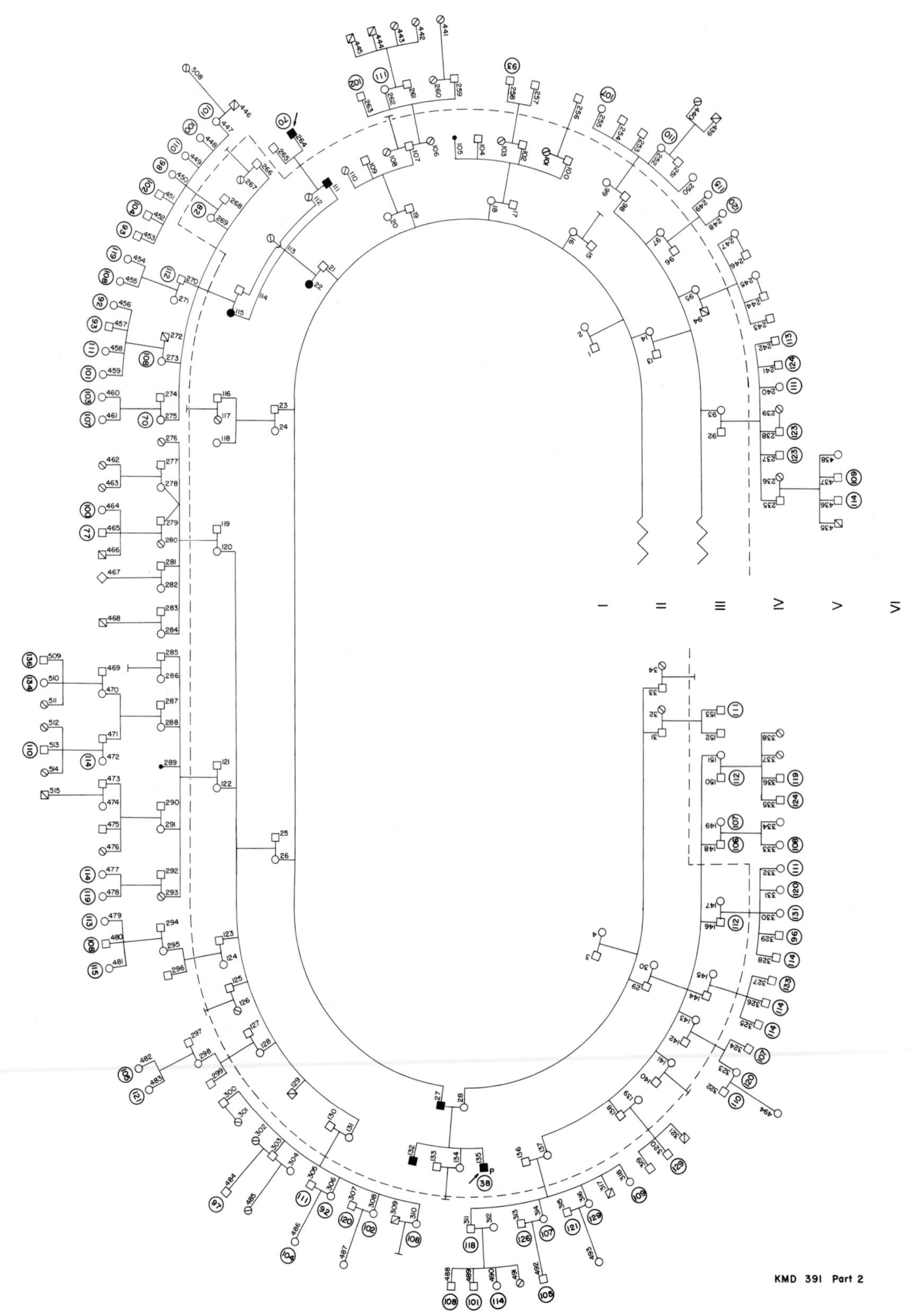

KMD 391 Part 2

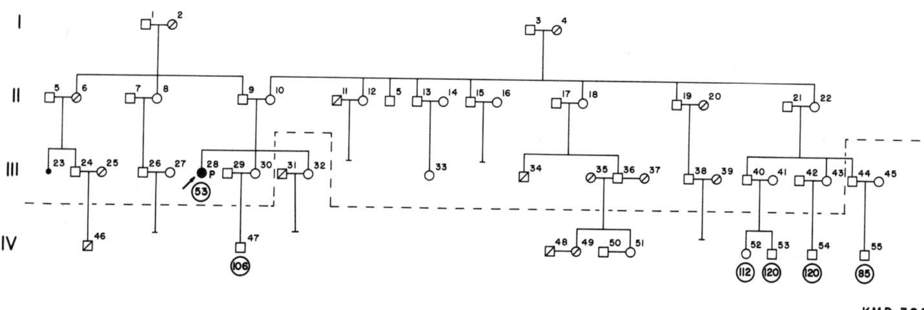

KMD 392

KMD 392

The Proband

The proband (28) was born in 1904, institutionalized at age 9 years and was still in the institution in 1961. She was seriously injured during her instrument delivery which resulted in a misshaped head, facial disfigurement and some impairment of the right side. She was nearly blind from birth. IQ 53. *Diagnosis:* undifferentiated mental retardation.

Grandparents

Not of interest.

Parents

Father (9) and mother (10) both had normal intelligence. The mother had "very weak" eyes.

Aunts and Uncles

Not of interest.

Siblings

Sister (30) graduated from high school and is a secretary.

Sister (32) graduated from high school and was an assistant buyer for a department store.

Nieces and Nephews

Only one, a nephew (47) with IQ 106.

First Cousins

Not of interest.

More Distant Relatives

Not of interest.

Family Summary

The proband, IQ 53, was the only retarded person known in this family. She was nearly blind from birth and was injured about the head and face during a difficult instrument delivery. The proband's parents had three children and one grandchild. The entire family had a very low rate of reproduction despite their normal intelligence and good mental health. The maternal and paternal siblings of the parents totaled nine persons. These nine persons had ten children and only seven grandchildren.

Retardation of proband of primarily environmental origin (birth injury).

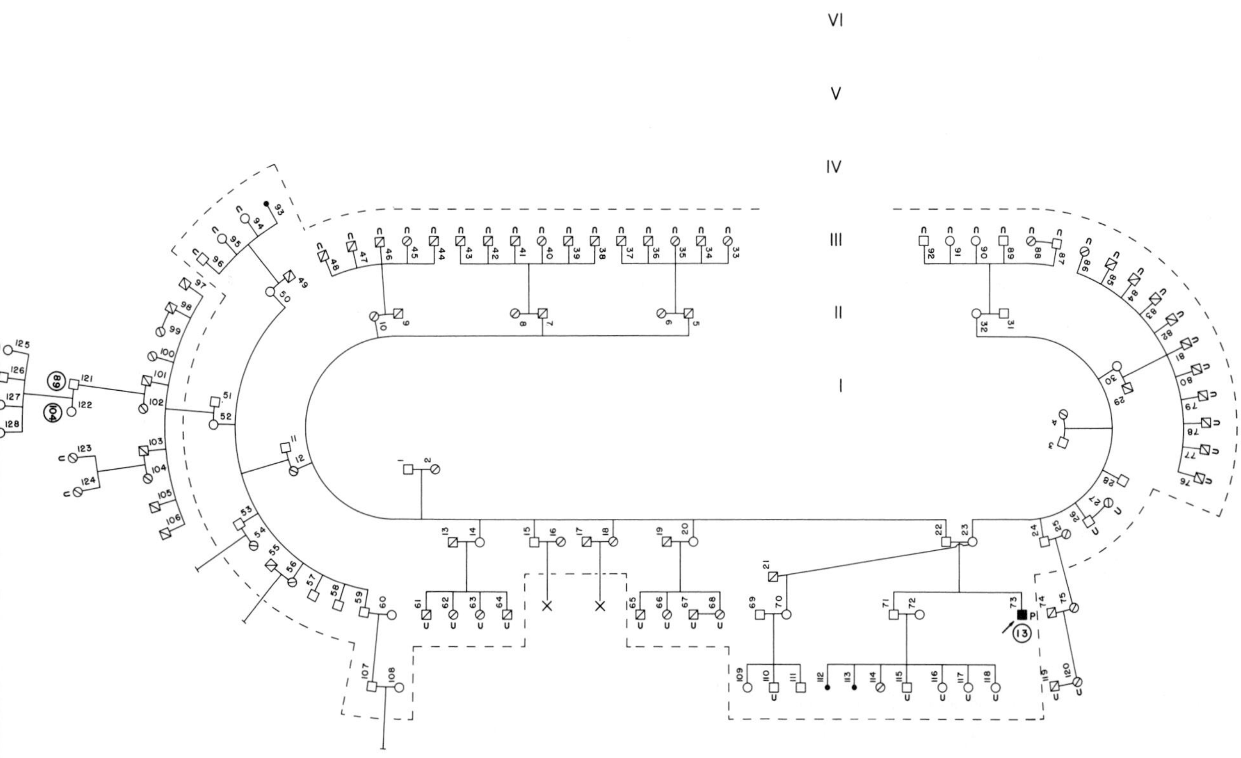

KMD 393

The Proband

The proband (73) was born in 1852, institutionalized at age 55 years and died of influenza in the institution in 1918. He fell down stairs at age 9 months and had scarlet fever at age 2 years, after which he regressed and became retarded. He had no stigmata and was reared in a good home. IQ 13. *Diagnosis:* undifferentiated mental retardation.

Grandparents

Not of interest.

Parents

Father (22) and mother (23) both had normal intelligence.

Aunts and Uncles

Not of interest.

Siblings

Brother (71) was a prosperous farmer.

Half Siblings

Half sister (70) had normal intelligence.

Nieces and Nephews

Not of interest except that two of the seven children of (71) were "blue babies" and one more died in convulsions at 9 months, apparently from an infection.

First Cousins

Not of interest.

More Distant Relatives

Nearly all are unknown because this family is so scattered.

Family Summary

The proband, IQ 13, was the only retarded person known in this family. Nearly all the more recent generations are unknown because the proband was so old in 1915 that many family contacts had been lost. The proband had a history of injury and illness in early childhood. He fell down stairs at age 9 months (followed by unconsciousness) and had a diagnosed case of scarlet fever at age 2 years. The proband's parents had two children and seven grandchildren.

Retardation of proband of primarily environmental origin (injury or infection, or both).

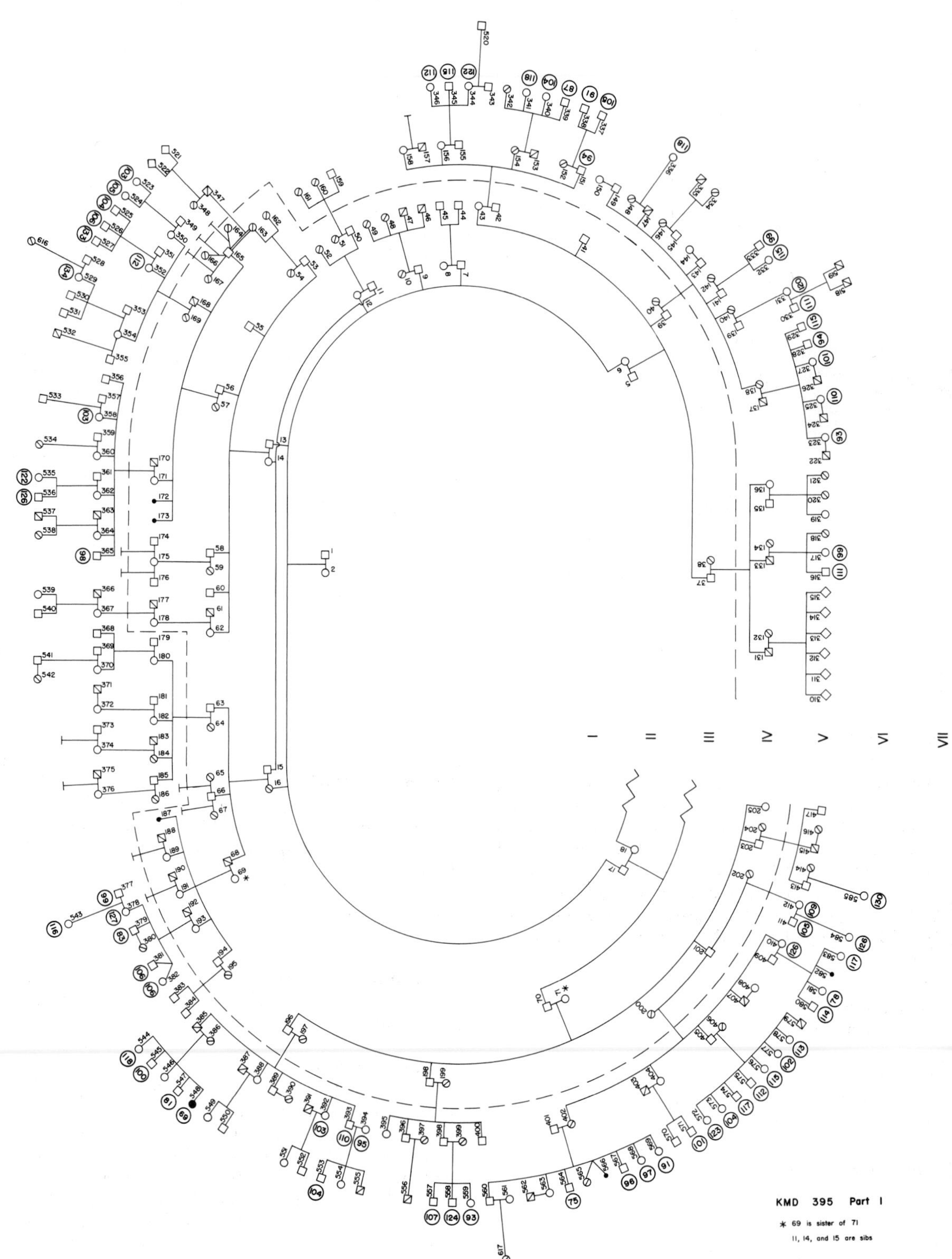
I
II
III
IV
V
VI
VII
KMD 395 Part I
* 69 is sister of 71
11, 14, and 15 are sibs

KMD 395

The Proband

The proband (79) was born in 1878, institutionalized at age 27 years and died of an intestinal obstruction in the institution in 1920. His birth and infancy were uneventful and he talked and walked at the usual time. At age 2 years he was injured in a fall from a wagon and shortly afterward he nearly died of cholera infantum and a subsequent attack of scarlet fever. He attended school for several years with poor results. IQ 40. *Diagnosis:* undifferentiated mental retardation.

Grandparents

Not of interest.

Parents

Father (17) and mother (18) both had normal intelligence.

Aunts and Uncles

Maternal uncle (31) abandoned his wife.

Siblings

All four siblings had normal intelligence.

Nieces and Nephews

Not of interest.

First Cousins

Not of interest.

More Distant Relatives

First cousin (101) had an institutionalized daughter (248) who was classified as an "idio-imbecile," and who died of marasmus in the institution in 1911. She is the proband for KMD 396.

First cousin (107), a brother to (101), has a daughter who failed the fourth, sixth and eighth grades and never completed grade school. She is unmarried and lives at home.

Nephew (196) has a retarded grandchild (548) with an IQ of 69.

Family Summary

The proband, IQ 40, was the only retarded person known in his immediate family. Three distant relatives were retarded, one a low to middle grade, the other two high grade. The proband had a history of injury and severe illness at about the age of 2 years. The proband's parents had five children and 17 grandchildren.

Retardation of proband of primarily environmental origin (infection).

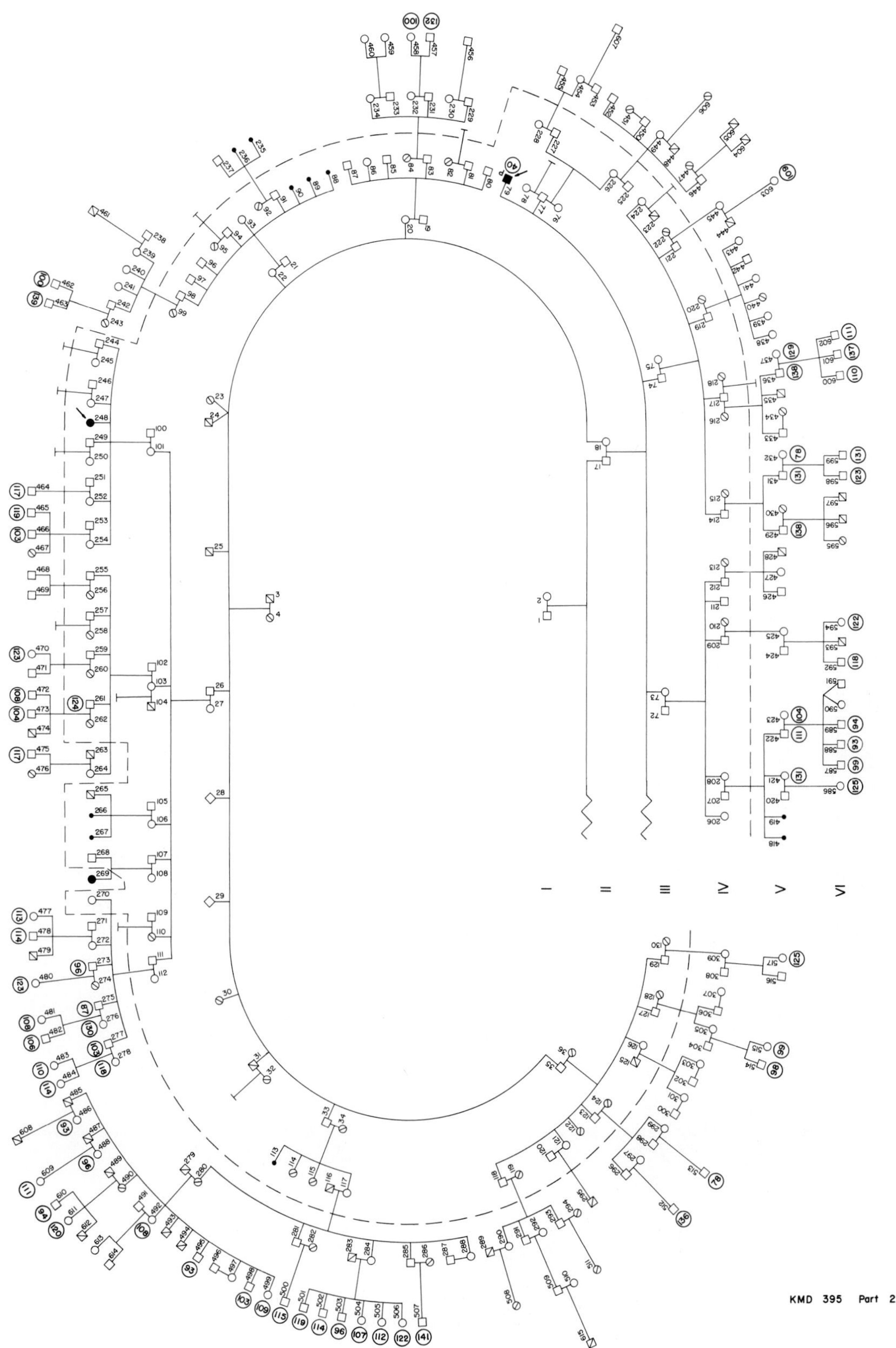

KMD 395 Part 2

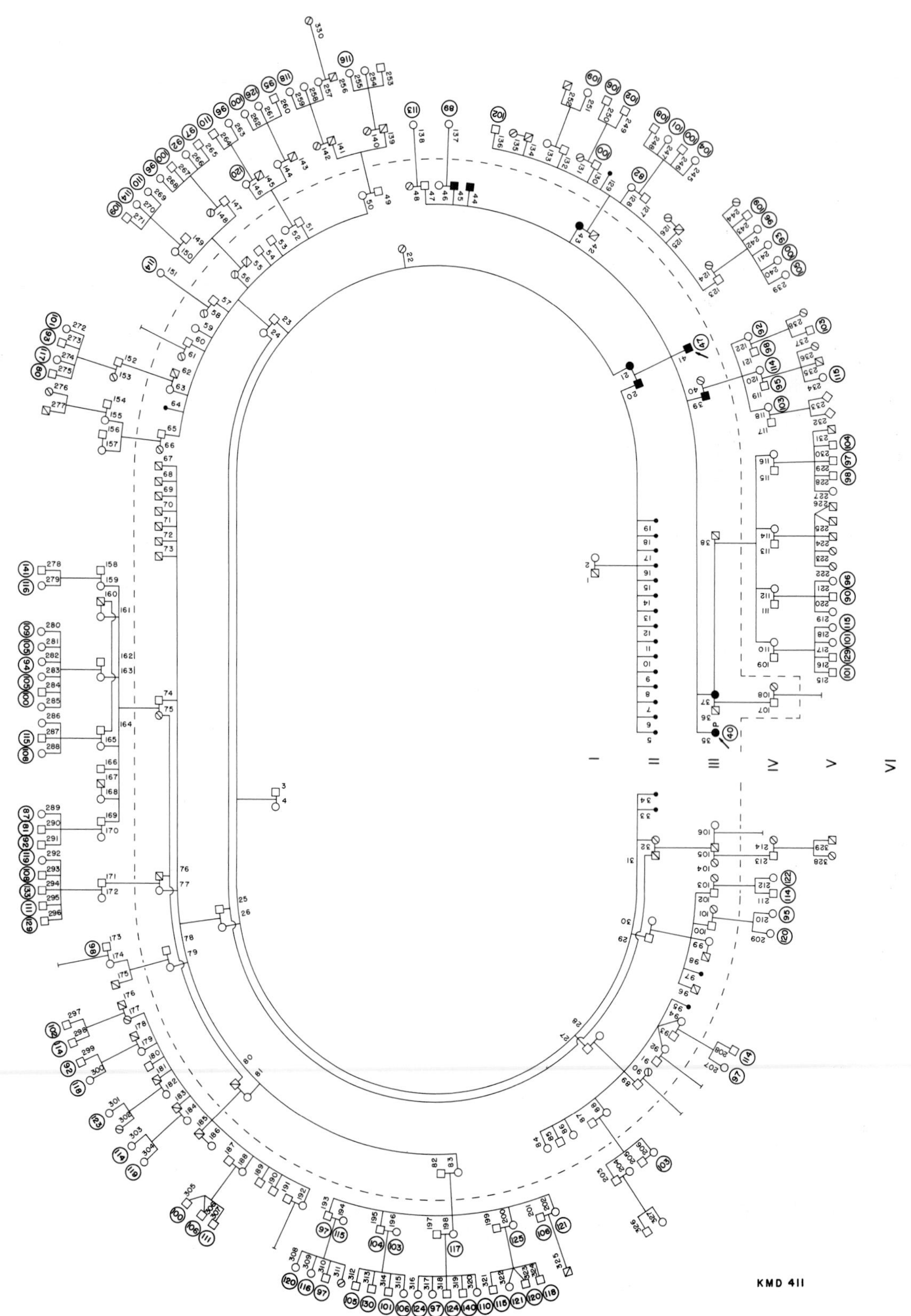

KMD 411

KMD 411

The Proband

The proband (35) was born in 1889, institutionalized at age 15 years and died of pressure on the recurrent laryngeal nerve by goiter in the institution in 1912. There was no history of birth injury. She walked and talked at age 3 years. She was reared in a poor environment. Both parents were syphilitic and all their children (including the proband) had Hutchinson's teeth, although they had no other signs of congenital syphilis. IQ 40. *Diagnosis:* undifferentiated mental retardation.

Grandparents

Paternal grandfather died of syphilis.

Maternal grandmother was mentally ill at one time, but had normal intelligence.

Parents

Father (20) was retarded and syphilitic.

Mother (21) was a "real bright nice girl" according to her family, but became illegitimately pregnant and was forced to marry (20) from whom she contracted syphilis. At the time of the first study she was classified as retarded when she was interviewed. Both parents had unusually severe, longstanding cases of frank syphilis.

Aunts and Uncles

Paternal aunts and uncles, 15 in number, all died in infancy of syphilis. The proband's father was the only survivor.

Maternal relatives not of interest.

Siblings

Sister (37) was a high-grade retardate who was deserted by her first husband. She had Hutchinson's teeth. Her five children have normal intelligence.

Brother (39) left school at age 15 when in the fifth grade. He is a high-grade retardate but has three children with normal intelligence. He had Hutchinson's teeth.

Brother (41) was institutionalized in 1905 at age 10 years, discharged to his parents in 1911 and died of epilepsy in a mental hospital in 1927. He had Hutchinson's teeth. IQ 47.

Sister (43) is a high-grade retardate who left school at age 15 years when in the fifth grade. She was forced to marry (42) who was "a drunkard and absolutely no good." She had Hutchinson's teeth. Five of her seven surviving children are known to have normal intelligence; the other two are unknown.

Brother (44) is an unmarried, childless retardate. He had Hutchinson's teeth.

Brother (45) is retarded with a normal wife and one child with IQ 89. He had Hutchinson's teeth.

Brother (46) was originally classified as retarded, but is an acetylene torch operator, which is a skilled occupation. He had Hutchinson's teeth. He has one child with IQ 113.

Nieces and Nephews

Despite the retardation in the proband's siblings, there is no retardation known among their children or grandchildren.

First Cousins

Not of interest.

More Distant Relatives

Not of interest.

Family Summary

The proband, IQ 40, both parents and six siblings were retarded. The entire family suffered from a severe syphilitic infection. The paternal grandfather died of syphilis as did 15 of his infant children. The proband's father, the sole survivor, was also infected. He gave the infection to his wife, and all of their children had Hutchinson's teeth. The proband's home was poor and her mother had to do all managing of the home and a small farm. The proband's parents had eight children (seven retarded) and 18 grandchildren, of whom 15 are known to have normal intelligence, one died in infancy and two are unknown. In view of the fact that medical evidence indicates a severe form of syphilis in this family with the proband the first born when the mother first became infected, and in consideration of the complete lack of retarded persons in the offspring of the proband's retarded siblings, it seems most appropriate to classify the retardation of the proband in this family as of primarily environmental origin even though she and a sibling had similar IQ's of 40 and 47.

Retardation of proband of primarily environmental origin (syphilis).

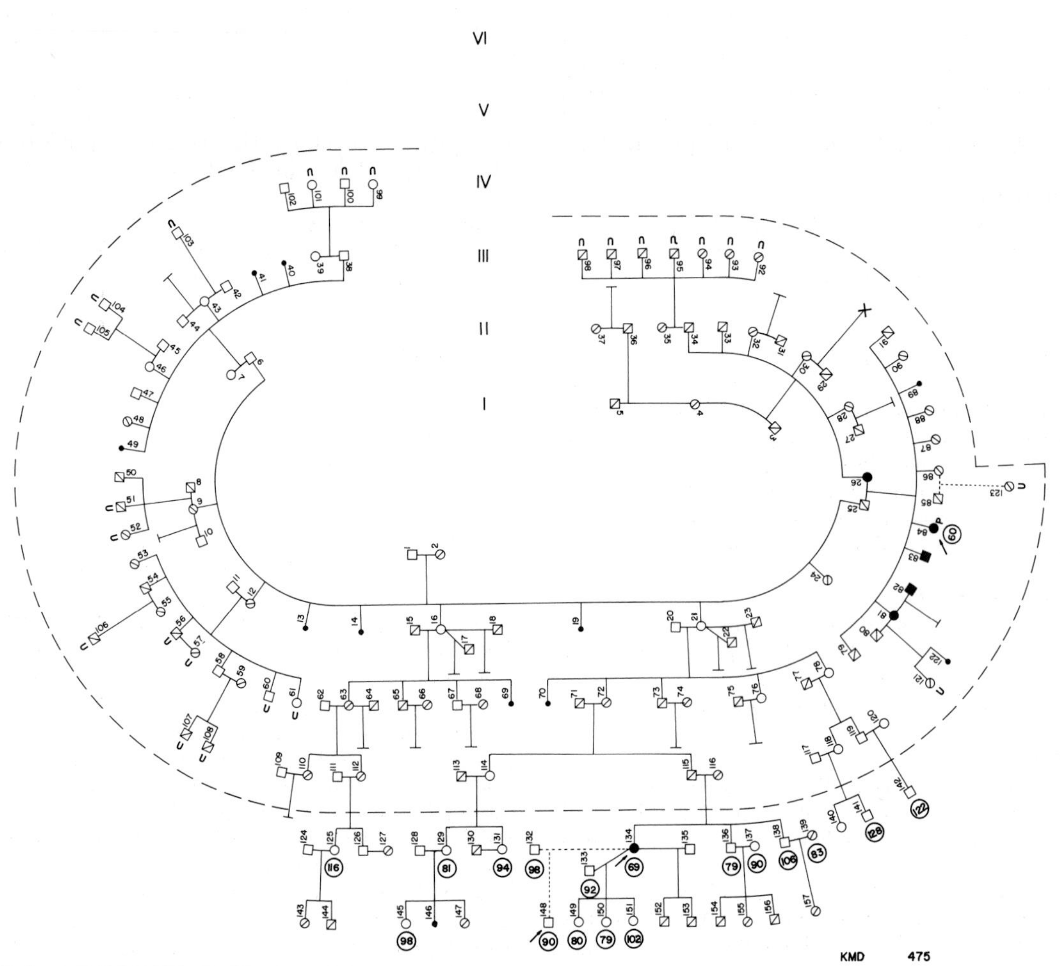

VI
V
IV
III
II
I
KMD 475

KMD 475

The Proband

The proband (84) was born in 1877, institutionalized at age 17 years and was still in the institution in 1961. She had no history of birth injury or perinatal infection. Her mouth was irregular, her toes turned inward and she was choreic upon admission. Both parents were alcoholics. The children were abused and the home environment was so bad that the authorities removed them from the home. The home was described as the "worst possible" by the early workers who also reported that the proband's aunt said that the proband was thrown down a flight of stairs by her father when an infant. The present institution diagnosis is moron, cause undiagnosed. IQ 60. *Diagnosis:* undifferentiated mental retardation.

Grandparents

Not of interest.

Father (25) was a boatman and odd job man who was an alcoholic. He was cruel and abusive to his family and had a chronic syphilitic infection.

Mother (26) was retarded and also developed a psychosis before her death at age 50 years.

Aunts and Uncles

Not of interest.

Siblings

Brother (79) was deaf, blind in one eye from an accident and served a prison term for theft. He was unmarried and childless.

Sister (81) could not learn much in school, was an alcoholic, promiscuous and retarded. Both she and her second husband (82), also retarded, were arrested frequently for drunkenness and disorderly conduct.

Brother (83) was a retarded, unmarried and childless laborer.

Sister (86) died shortly after the birth of her illegitimate child.

Sister (87) was a cripple from birth, alleged to be the result of the father kicking the pregnant mother.

Sister (88) died as a small child.

(89) was a stillbirth.

Sister (90) died at age 12 or 14 years.

Brother (91) died of neglect at age 6 years.

Nieces and Nephews

Only two (121) and (123) who survived and are unknown. They went to live with other relatives. (122) was a stillbirth.

First Cousins

Nearly all are unknown.

More Distant Relatives

(134) was institutionalized in 1947 at age 19 years and her illegitimate child (148) was born in the institution. (134) has a long history in social welfare files. She now has had six children by three normal men. Her tested children have IQ's of 90, 80, 79 and 102, respectively. Sterlization was refused on religious grounds. She has been divorced from one husband and the children are separated. Some are under county custody and live with relatives. Here is a problem family in the making.

Family Summary

The proband, IQ 60, her mother, two siblings and one more distant relative were all high-grade retardates. The home environment was bad, with alcoholism in both parents, a syphilitic and abusive father and a retarded mother. Many of the collateral relatives were not known, but the ones reported in the old records did not appear to have been retarded although many were alcoholics. At least one paternal uncle and one maternal uncle were suspected suicides, and several other relatives were notoriously promiscuous. Of the proband's 12 adult aunts and uncles, only seven had any children although ten were married. The proband's parents had ten children and three grandchildren, two of whom survived.

Retardation of proband of primarily environmental origin (injury or syphilis, or both).

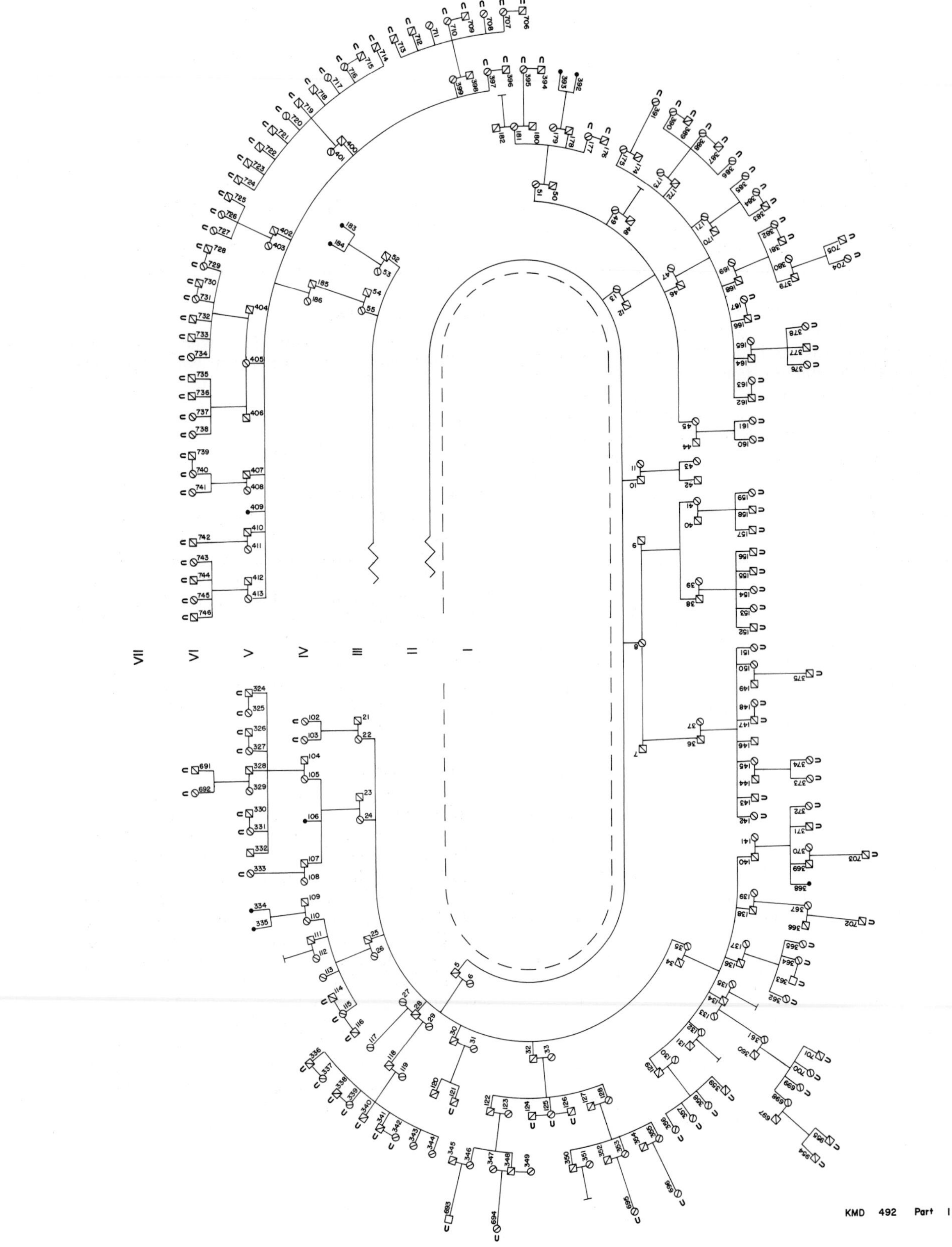

KMD 492 Part I

KMD 492

The Proband

The proband (92) was born in 1846, institutionalized at age 68 years but was discharged to his brother the same year and died of valvular heart disease at home in 1921. He was reported as having been a bright baby until the age of 2 years when he had a bad fall. He jumped from the top of the stairs to his sister's arms but went over her head onto the first floor landing and was unconscious for 48 hours. He walked and talked well before the accident but could do neither well for a long time after the accident. He reached the fourth grade at age 16 years and supported himself as a farm laborer. IQ 66. *Diagnosis:* undifferentiated mental retardation.

Grandparents

Nothing is known about them.

Parents

Both the father (19) and the mother (20) had normal intelligence. The entire family on both sides had a history of excellent physical and mental health.

Aunts and Uncles

No maternal relatives. The proband's mother was an only child.

Paternal relatives not of interest.

Siblings

Sister (79) died in infancy.

Sisters (81), (83), (87) and (96) all had normal intelligence. Three of these sisters (81), (83) and (96), together with one brother (89), all had "rheumatism deformans."

Brothers (84), (85), (89), (93) and (98) all had normal intelligence.

Brother (88) died of "summer complaint" at age 3 years.

Brother (91) died in infancy.

Siblings (sex unknown) (100) and (101) died in infancy.

Nieces and Nephews

Niece (280) was a low-grade retardate who developed little mentally or physically. She died at age 13 years.

First Cousins

Not of interest.

More Distant Relatives

(840) has an IQ of 63 and the school reports he is postencephalitic.

This family had extensive records for the older generations which went back for hundreds of years, but no one had kept up the records for a large proportion of the more recent generations.

Family Summary

The proband, IQ 66, one low-grade retardate niece and one more distant relative who is a postencephalitic retardate were the only retarded persons known in this large family of 1008 persons. The proband had a serious fall at age 2 years following which he was unconscious for 48 hours and then regressed so that he did not again talk well until age 10 years. He supported himself as a farm laborer for many years. His whole family had a reputation in the community for good mental and physical health. The proband's parents had 15 children and 25 grandchildren.

Retardation of proband of primarily environmental origin (injury).

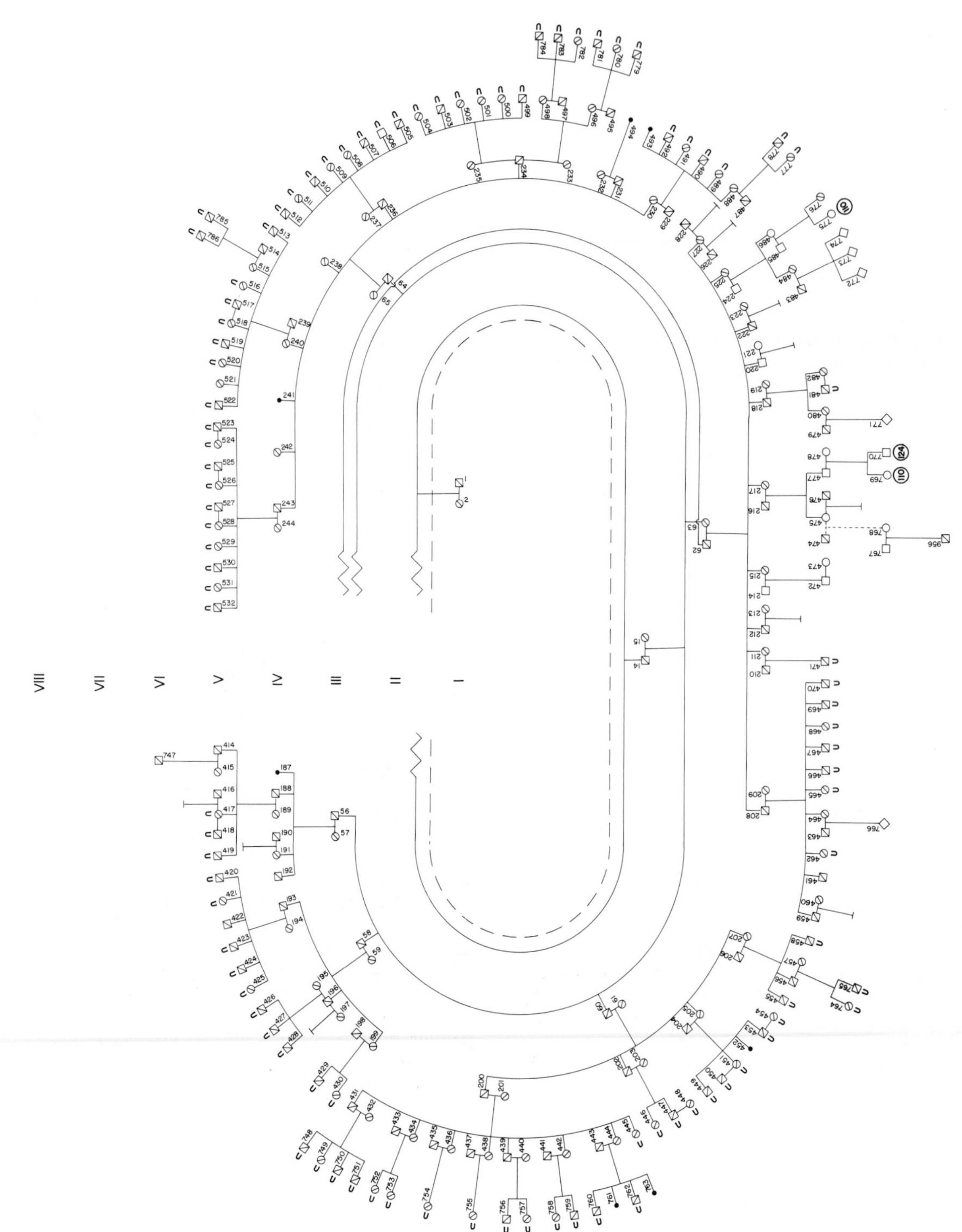

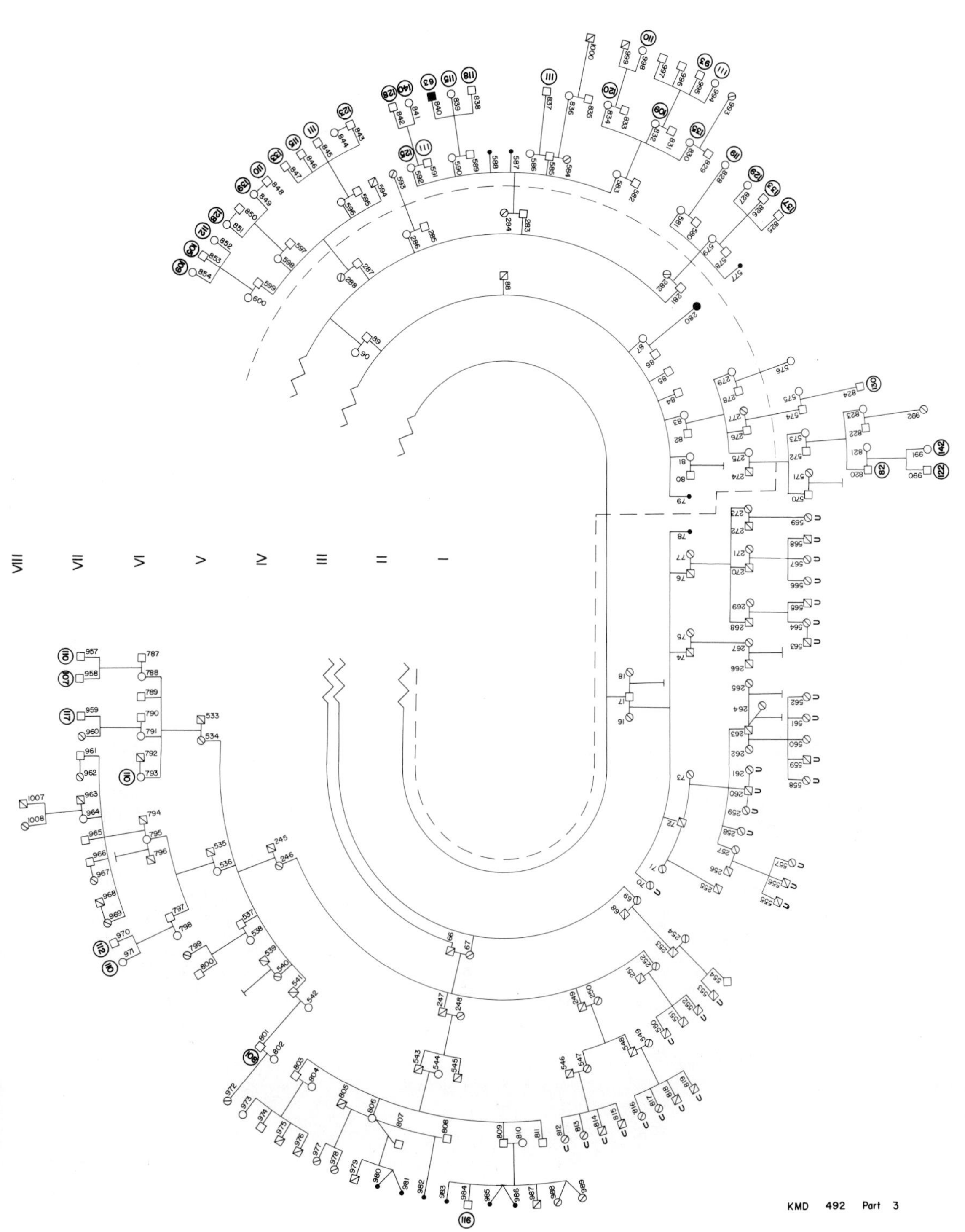

KMD 492 Part 3

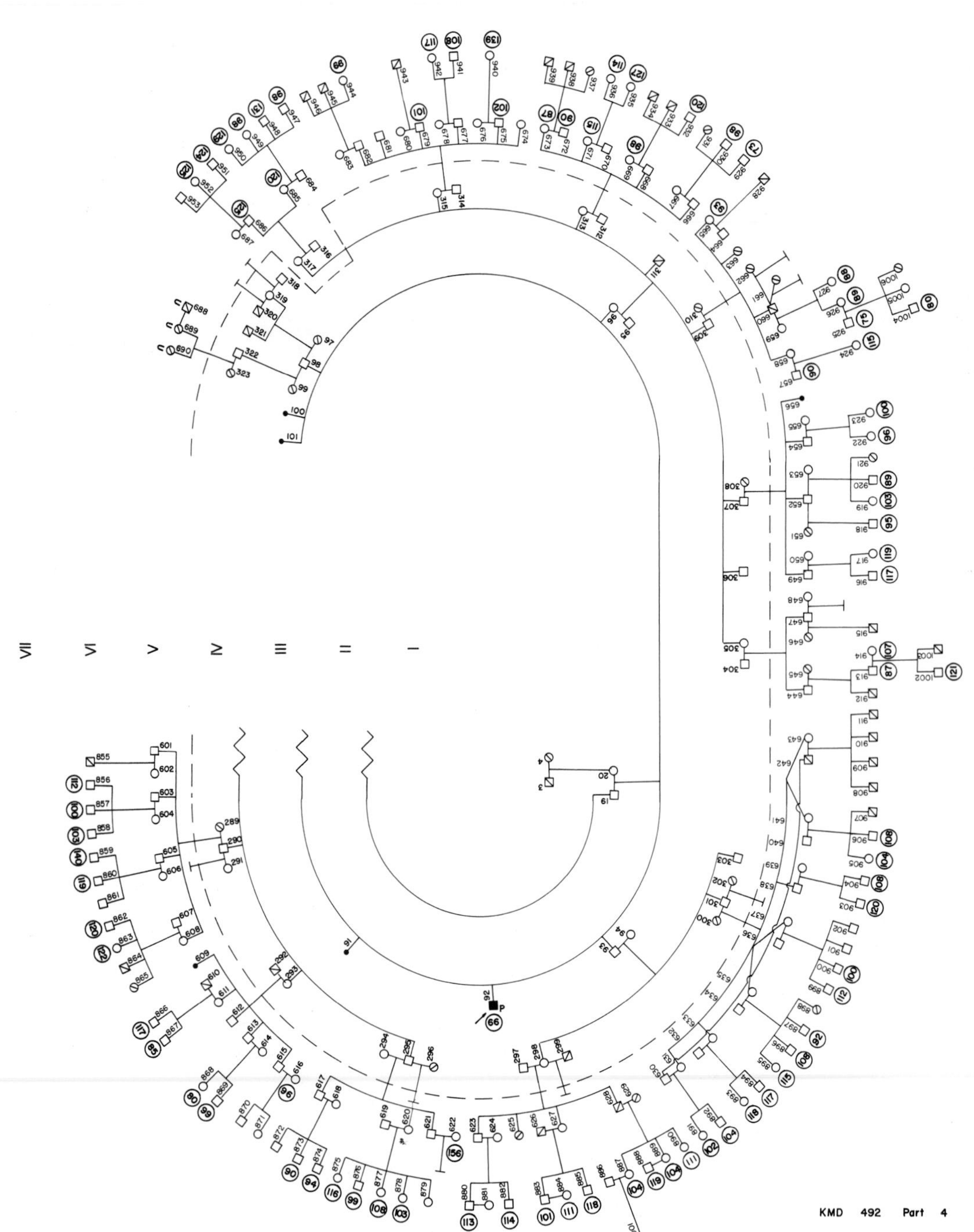

KMD 492 Part 4

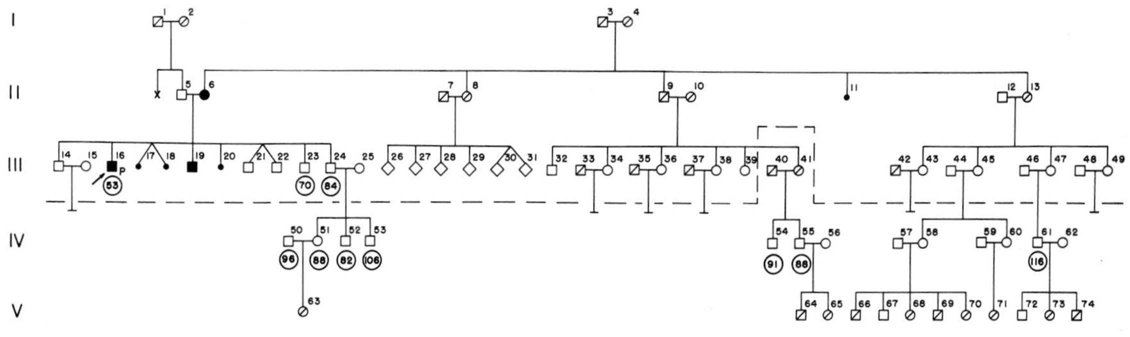

KMD 539

KMD 539

The Proband

The proband (16) was born in 1895, was first sent to the State School for the Blind, then institutionalized at age 16 years and discharged in 1918 to his mother. Since his discharge he has worked as a janitor and supported his mother and psychotic brother. The mother is now deceased and the brother has been hospitalized for mental illness. The proband had a difficult birth, is knock kneed, drags his feet, has Hutchinson's teeth, a speech defect and poor eyesight. IQ 53. *Diagnosis:* undifferentiated mental retardation.

Grandparents

Not of interest.

Parents

Father (5) was a cabinet maker.

Mother (6) was retarded and was "most unreasonable."

Aunts and Uncles

None of the paternal relatives came to this country.

Maternal relatives not of interest.

Siblings

Brother (14) works for a retail delivery service. He had to leave school in the sixth grade to support his parents and siblings. He has poor eyesight, but has normal intelligence and married a normal woman.

(17) was a stillbirth.

(18) was a twin to (17) who died at age 4 days. The twins were premature. Brother (19) died of influenzal pneumonia at age 20 years. He was blind (became blind at age 8 or 9) and also retarded. He was sent to the State School for the Blind for several years.

(20) was a stillbirth.

Brother (21) is department manager for a publishing company.

Brother (22), a twin to (21), has been hospitalized for mental illness diagnosed as "psychosis with syphilitic encephalitis." He is a pinsetter in a bowling alley. He was described as "mentally slow."

Brother (23) worked for a laundry. He became difficult to employ and is described in welfare records as "psychophrenic" and "wavers between extreme excitability and good nature" and is a "chronic loafer." IQ 70.

Brother (24) was a laundry supervisor with an IQ of 84. He was the only sibling who reproduced. His wife (25) has normal intelligence, and his three children (51), (52) and (53) have IQ's of 88, 82 and 106, respectively.

Nieces and Nephews

Only three, see above.

First Cousins

Not of interest.

More Distant Relatives

Not of interest.

Family Summary

The proband, IQ 53, was lame, partly blind and had a speech defect, but despite these handicaps has supported himself (and also his mother until her death) working as a janitor. The proband's mother was retarded, as was one brother who also became blind in childhood. The sighted, borderline brother is psychotic (diagnosed as "psychosis with syphilitic encephalitis") and another one with low-normal intelligence is described as "psychophrenic." One normal brother has poor eyesight. Only one sibling reproduced. He had an IQ of 84 with no psychological or physical problems and produced three children with IQ's of 88, 82 and 106, respectively. The proband's parents had ten children and three grandchildren. The history of prematurity, stillbirths, blindness and syphilitic encephalitis indicates a serious syphilitic infection in this family. The proband had Hutchinson's teeth and two positive Wassermann tests.

Retardation of proband of primarily environmental origin (syphilis).

THE CATEGORY OF UNKNOWN CAUSES

There were 123 probands who had no history of environmental insult, had only undifferentiated kinds of retardation and had no known family background of several generations of retardation. Some of these 123 persons are in this group because their families could not be traced completely enough to enable us to determine the mental status of the more recent generations. It is quite likely that with more information available some of the probands would have been included in one of the preceding three categories.

Brief family summaries accompany the 164 pedigree charts. These summaries include

KMD's 1, 6, 7, 8, 9, 11, 19, 20, 28, 30, 37, 38, 39, 46, 47, 56, 60, 70, 80, 84, 85, 86, 87, 88, 93, 94, 122, 125, 130, 131, 134, 139, 143, 146, 149, 154, 156, 165, 168, 177, 180, 195, 198, 199, 200, 206, 207, 219, 222, 223, 226, 234, 235, 246, 249, 253, 259, 266, 276, 282, 283, 300, 310, 312, 313, 315, 316, 318, 321, 322, 324, 326, 329, 334, 341, 346, 355, 361, 367, 368, 382, 396, 401, 405, 409, 413, 418, 429, 430, 433, 434, 436, 437, 438, 439, 441, 442, 443, 450, 453, 463, 466, 467, 473, 474, 479, 480, 481, 486, 489, 494, 495, 515, 516, 517, 519, 521, 524, 535, 536, 537, 542 and 545.

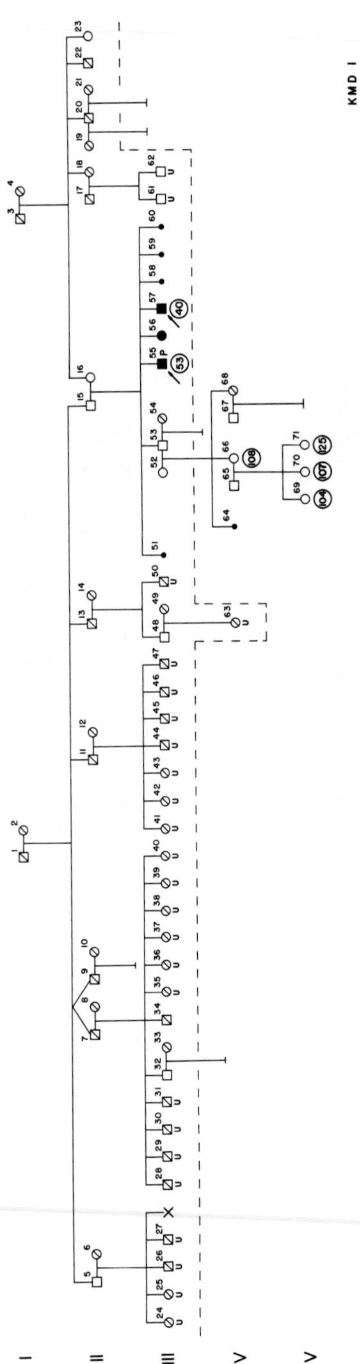
KMD I
I
II
III
IV
V

KMD 1

The Proband

The proband (55) was born in 1888, institutionalized at age 12 and has spent all his life in the institution. His birth was uneventful and he had no stigmata. At age 20 he became disturbed, slept little and had delusions for an unknown period of time. He attended school for six years but completed only the second grade. IQ 53. *Diagnosis:* undifferentiated mental retardation.

Grandparents

Maternal grandfather (3) was an alcoholic, a gambler and cruel to his family. He deserted them several times.

Maternal grandmother (4) supported the family.

Parents

Father (15) was a builder who had normal intelligence but was subject to epileptoid symptoms from the age of 33 to 48.

Mother (16) had numerous self-induced abortions, was mentally ill and died of exhaustion in senile dementia in a mental hospital. She was a good housekeeper and had normal intelligence.

Aunts and Uncles

All the paternal uncles, with the exception of (9) remained in Scotland. The maternal aunts and uncles lived in the United States, but not in Minnesota. No new information could be collected for these relatives. As far as is known, they are not of interest.

Siblings

Several self-induced abortions.

One normal brother (53) is a real estate dealer.

Sister (56) was in three mental hospitals, finally died in one at age 63. She left school at age 12 when in the fourth grade and was unmarried and childless. *Diagnosis:* schizophrenic reaction with mental deficiency.

Brother (57) was institutionalized at age 13 and discharged to his father two years later. He died single and childless of carcinoma in 1941. He had mild epileptiform attacks until age 14. IQ 40.

Nieces and Nephews

Not of interest except that one child was too large to be delivered normally and died at birth.

First Cousins

Unknown.

More Distant Relatives

Unknown.

Family Summary

The proband's mother attributed the retardation of the children to her husband's supposed syphilis. The father attributed the retardation to his wife's attempted abortions. There is no confirmation of either statement in the old records except that the proband had a positive Wassermann at one time. The proband had two retarded siblings (one of whom was also schizophrenic) and one normal one. The present mental condition of the other relatives is unknown. The proband's parents had only two surviving grandchildren, both apparently normal.

Retardation of proband of unknown origin.

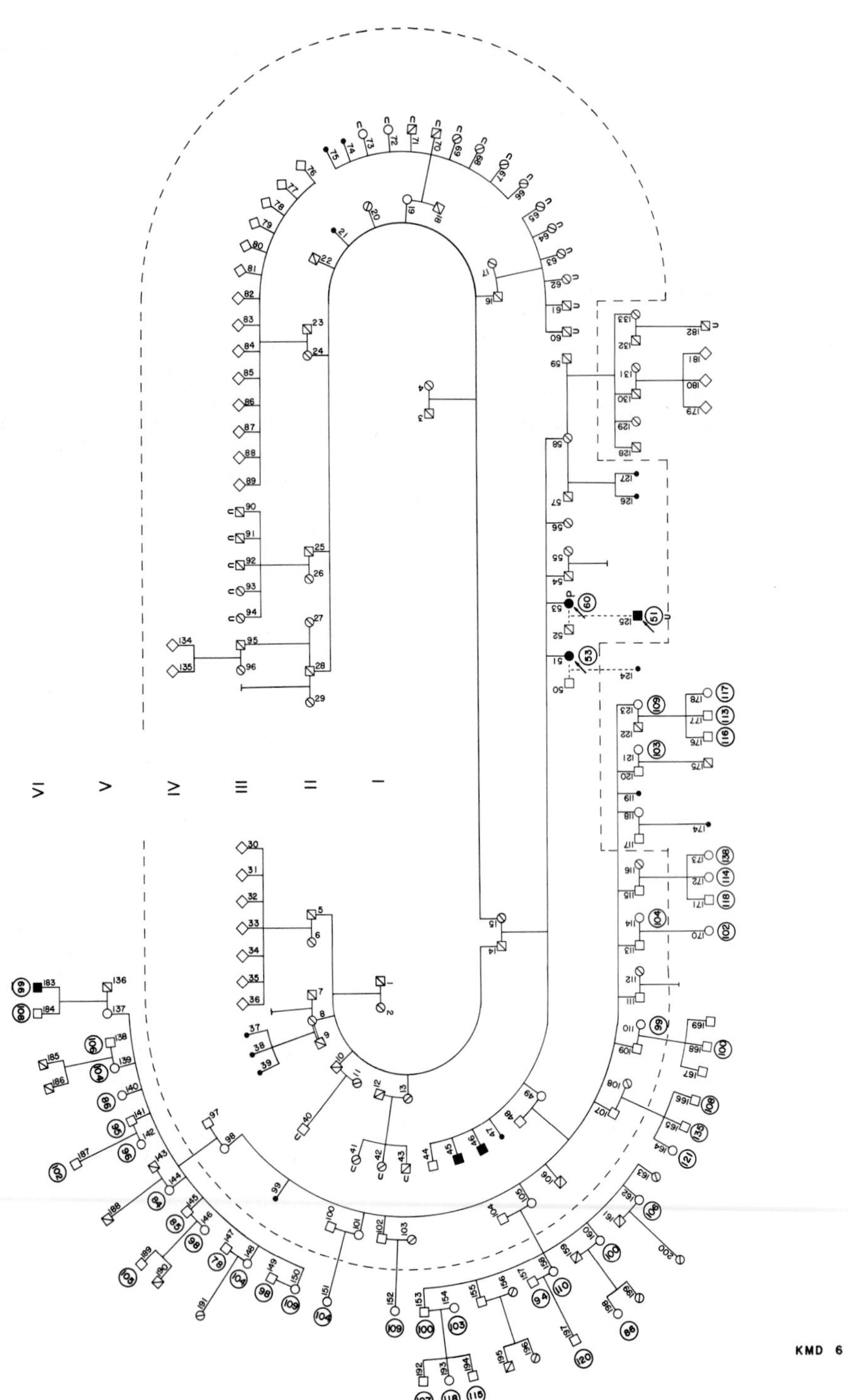

KMD 6

KMD 6

The Proband

The proband (53) was born in 1875, institutionalized at age 29 years and transferred to a county home for the aged in 1944 where she died of jaundice and gallstones in the same year. She had no stigmata and no history of disease in early life. She went to school until the age of 15 but learned only to read and write a little. She became incorrigible and her sexual promiscuity resulted in an illegitimate pregnancy. IQ 60. *Diagnosis:* undifferentiated mental retardation.

Grandparents

Both maternal and paternal grandmothers became mentally ill in old age.

Parents

Intelligence of proband's father (14) was unknown. He was a flagman on the railroad. Proband's mother (15) is reported as having had "small intelligence, due to her lifelong environment probably."

Aunts and Uncles

A paternal uncle (10) died in a mental hospital. Another paternal uncle (5) died of alcoholism.

Siblings

Brother (44) was a successful farmer who died single and childless.

Brother (45) died single and childless. He was a freight handler and was mentally retarded.

Brother (46) is unmarried and childless. He is a freight handler and is mentally retarded.

Sister (49) married a normal man and has normal intelligence. Children are also normal.

Sister (51) had an illegitimate child who died in infancy. The father was a normal man. She was institutionalized at age 27 and is now in a county home for the aged. IQ 53.

Two childless siblings (54) and (56) died young. They had unknown intelligence.

One sister (58) lives in Canada. Her intelligence is unknown.

Child

Proband's illegitimate son was born in 1904 and reared by his grandmother (15). He was institutionalized at age 14 but escaped four years later. His present status is unknown. IQ 51.

Nieces and Nephews

Not of interest.

More Distant Relatives

Proband's paternal aunt (8) married her first cousin and had three children, all of whom died between the ages of 2 and 6 years.

(183) has an IQ of 66.

Family Summary

Two brothers and one sister of the proband, and her child, were mentally retarded. There were only two offspring from the four retarded siblings, one of whom died shortly after birth, and the other was a retarded boy. The three known IQ's of these retardates are similar. The proband's parents had ten offspring who produced 23 children, five of whom died in infancy.

Retardation of proband of unknown origin.

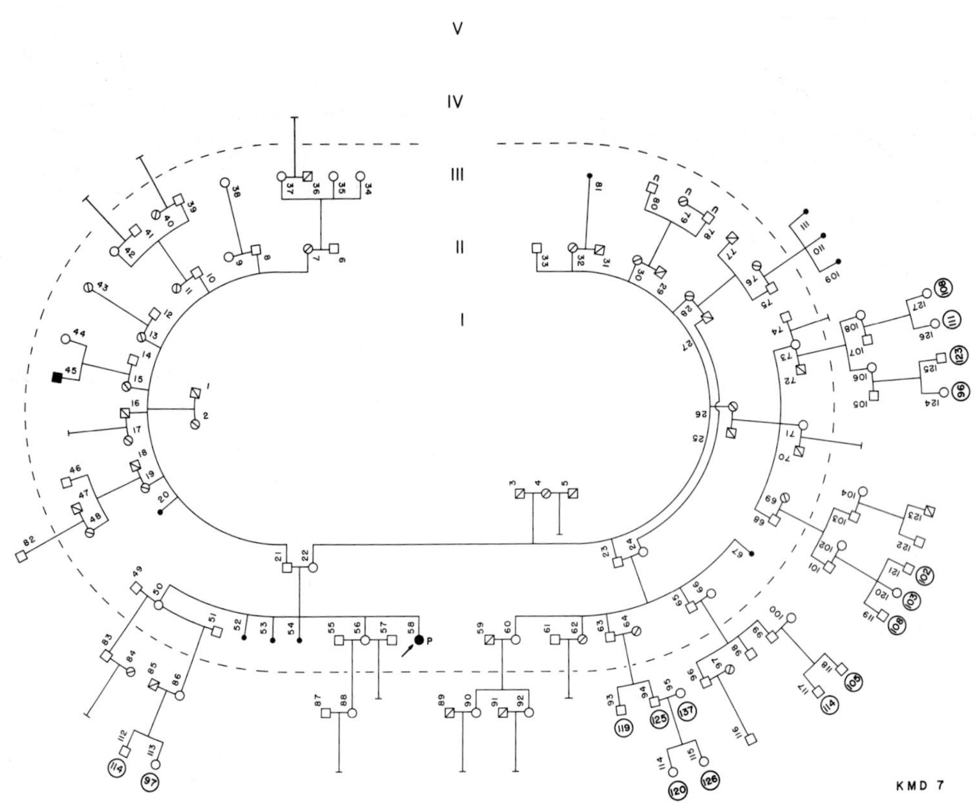
V
IV
III
II
I
P
KMD 7

KMD 7

The Proband

The proband (58) was born in 1881, institutionalized at age 5 years and died of tuberculosis in the institution in 1916. She was delivered by instruments. She did not talk and never attended school. She was noisy and excitable and at some time after admission developed convulsive attacks. No IQ score was available for her. *Diagnosis:* undifferentiated mental retardation.

Grandparents

Not of interest.

Parents

Both parents (21) and (22) had normal intelligence. The father operated a printing business.

Aunts and Uncles

Not of interest.

Siblings

Two normal sisters (50) and (56) had normal husbands and children.

Three miscarriages.

Nieces and Nephews

Not of interest.

First Cousins

One cousin (45) was mentally retarded. He died of heart trouble single and childless at age 18 years.

More Distant Relatives

Not of interest.

Family Summary

Only the proband (58) and one cousin (45) were mentally retarded. The parents, both normal, had six children, including the three miscarriages. The two normal children had three offspring.

Retardation of proband of unknown origin.

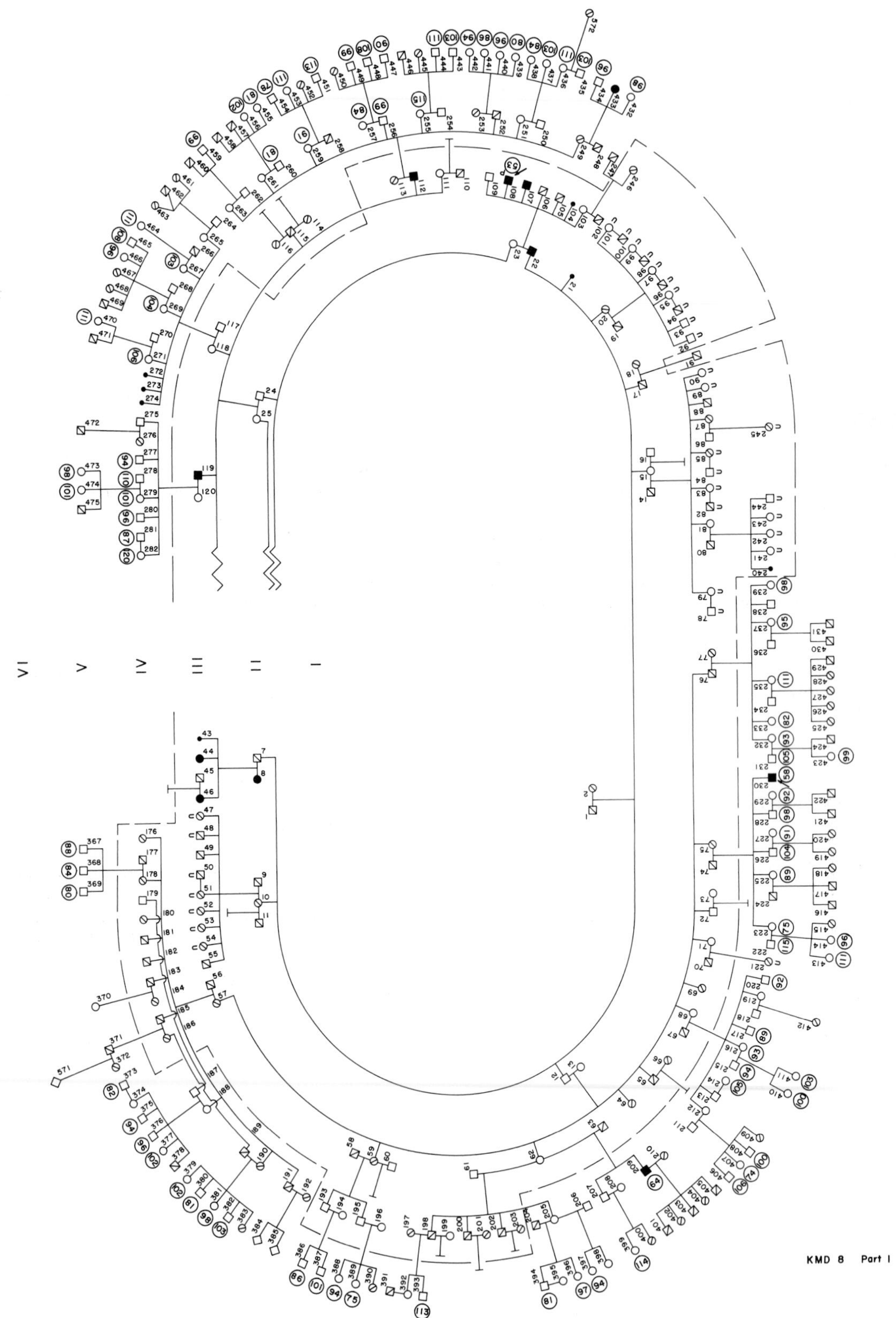

KMD 8 Part I

KMD 8

The Proband

The proband (108) was born in 1895, institutionalized at age 16 and died of tuberculosis in the institution in 1912. He walked and talked at the usual time but had not completed the second grade by age 15. He was troublesome in school. There was no record of perinatal infection or congenital stigmata. IQ 53. *Diagnosis:* undifferentiated mental retardation.

Grandparents

Not of interest.

Parents

Father (22) was retarded and worked as a fireman's helper in a mill.

Mother (23) grew up in a deprived environment, never went to school and was illiterate. She was classified by the early workers as having normal intelligence.

Aunts and Uncles

Paternal uncle (7) of unknown intelligence, married a retarded woman and had three children, two retarded, one miscarriage.

Maternal uncle (24) died of alcoholism.

Siblings

Sister (103) and brother (109) had normal intelligence.

Sister (104) died in infancy.

Brothers (105) and (106) both died young, and both were unknown as to intelligence.

Brother (107) left school at age 15 in the fourth grade and was retarded. He died unmarried and childless.

Nieces and Nephews

Only two, (246) and (247) of unknown intelligence, both of whom died childless and single.

First Cousins

(44) and (46), sisters who were retarded as was their mother (8).

(112) was a belligerent, quarrelsome high-grade retardate.

(119), brother to (112), was suspended from school for striking the teacher. He was 17 years old and in the fifth grade at the time, and was considered retarded.

(166) and (168), siblings, were high-grade retardates.

More Distant Relatives

(209) is a mechanic with IQ 64.

(230) is institutionalized with an IQ of 58 and a diagnosis of idiopathic mental deficiency.

(310) left school after she was unable to complete the fourth grade.

(433) has no IQ score but school reports state that it is "very low."

(520) was at the fourth grade level in school at age 15 years.

Family Summary

The proband, his father, one sibling, six cousins and five more distant relatives were retarded, all, with the exception of one low-grade, were middle- or high-grade retardates. Many of the cases appear sporadically throughout the kindred which consisted largely of families of poor social class in the older generations. Poor school records, alcoholism and delinquency were part of the family pattern and are among many of the environmental factors which may be of importance in some of these cases of retardation. It was impossible in some cases to distinguish between retarded and normal intelligence. The proband's parents had seven children and only two grandchildren, both of whom died childless.

Retardation of proband of unknown origin.

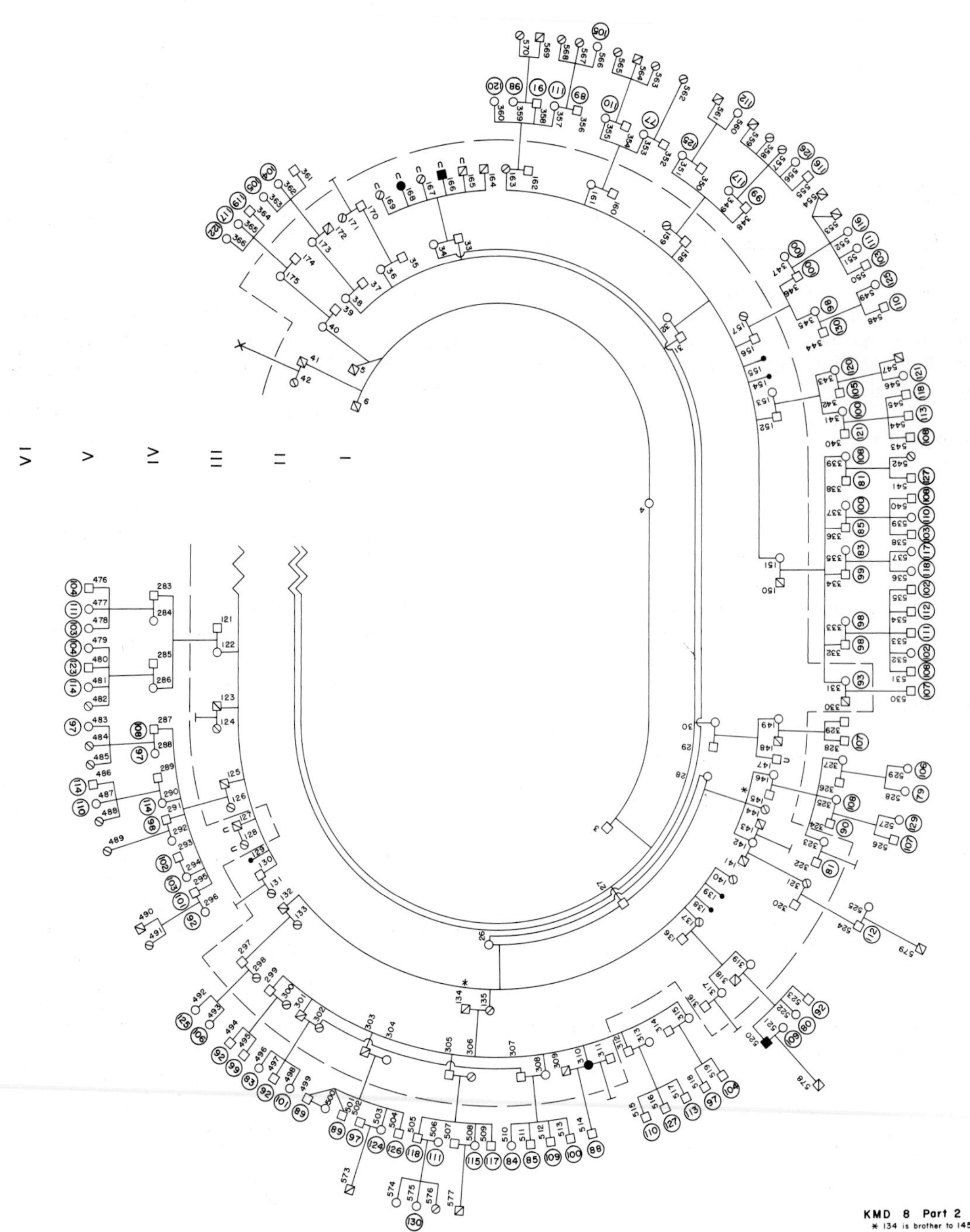

KMD 8 Part 2
* 134 is brother to 145

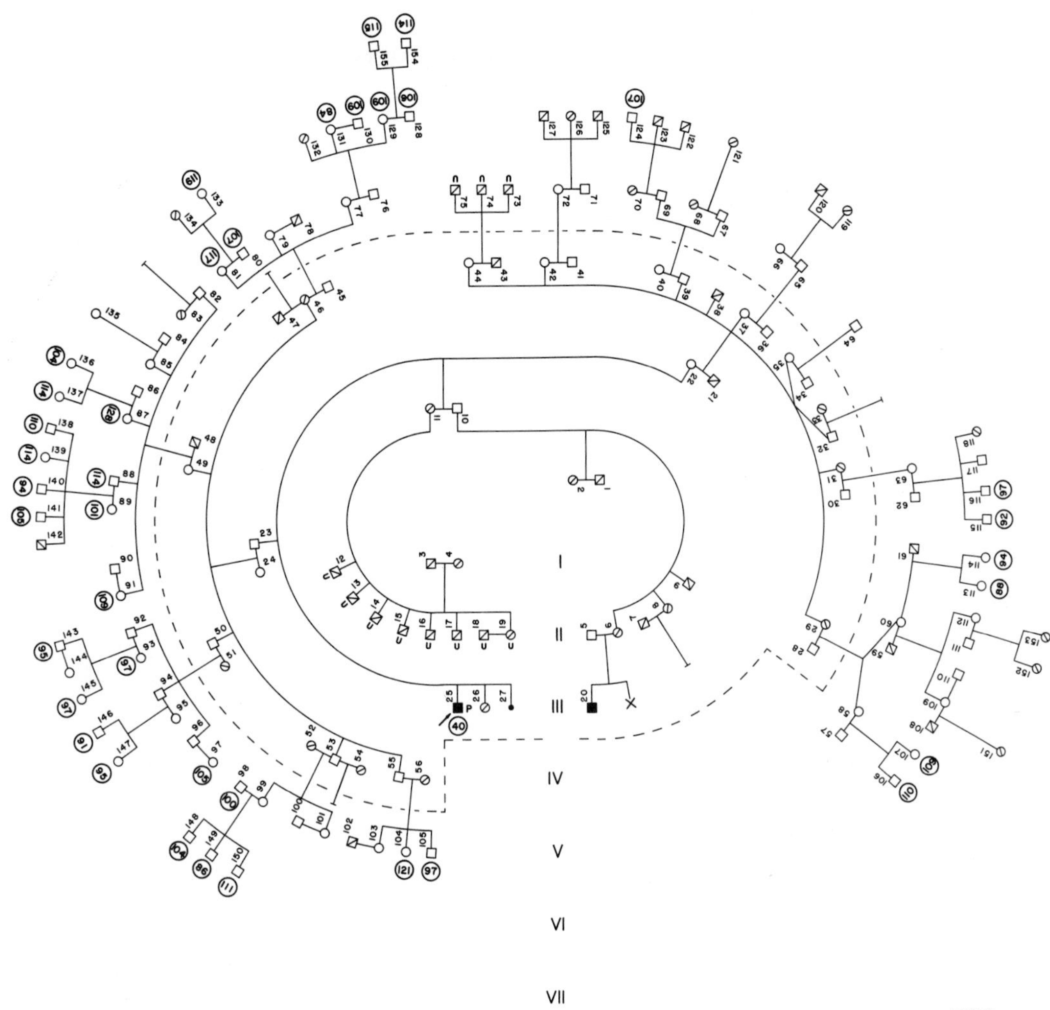

KMD 9

The Proband

The proband (25) was born in 1863, institutionalized at 29 years and died of apoplexy in 1932 single and childless. His birth was uncomplicated. He had no stigmata and he attended school but learned little. He was a good helper at the institution. IQ 40. *Diagnosis:* undifferentiated mental retardation.

Grandparents

Paternal grandfather was epileptic.

Parents

Father (10) was epileptic, but had normal intelligence. He was a fruit seller.

Mother (11) had unknown intelligence.

Aunts and Uncles

All remained in England. Their present status is unknown.

Siblings

One sister (22) and one brother (23) had normal intelligence as did their children.

Sister (26) died at 16 years. She was epileptic (ascribed to a fall at age 4 years), intelligence unknown.

One stillbirth (27).

Nieces and Nephews

Not of interest.

First Cousins

All unknown except for (20) who was mentally retarded.

More Distant Relatives

Not of interest except for (146) who has an IQ of 91 but a diagnosis of "emotionally submerged and apathetic." "Has developed withdrawal symptoms as well as symptoms of the compulsive-obsessive type."

Family Summary

One retarded cousin (20) was found in addition to the proband. No retardation appeared in the proband's nephews and nieces. The proband's parents had five children, including a stillbirth. The two normal siblings (22) and (23) had 14 offspring. No retardation has appeared among the children, grandchildren or great-grandchildren of the proband's two normal siblings.

Retardation of proband of unknown origin.

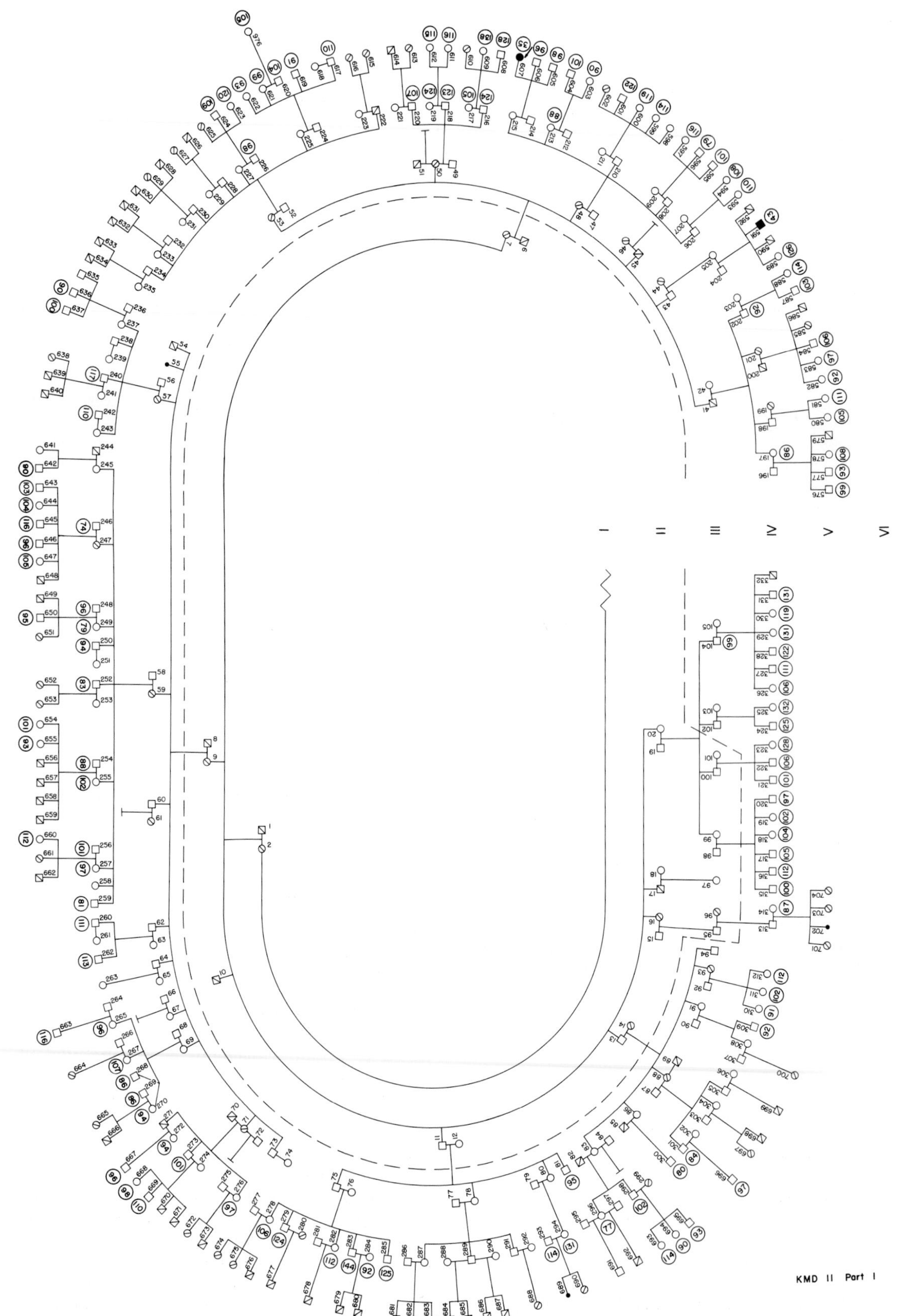

KMD 11

The Proband

The proband (151) was born in 1897, institutionalized at age 10 and died of coronary disease in the institution in 1955. He had a peculiarly shaped head, but his birth was uneventful and he had no history of perinatal infection. His speech was limited. IQ 30. *Diagnosis:* undifferentiated mental retardation.

Grandparents

Not of interest.

Parents

Father (25) and mother (26) both had normal intelligence. The father was a prosperous farmer who was separated from his wife.

Aunts and Uncles

Not of interest.

Siblings

One brother (143) was listed as a probable suicide on his death record.

Intelligence of the other five siblings was known to have been normal except for (145) whose intelligence is unknown. No retardation has appeared in their descendants.

Nieces and Nephews

Not of interest.

First Cousins

(176), a college student and teacher, married a retarded man (175) with an IQ of 69.

More Distant Relatives

First cousin's child (376) is institutionalized, IQ 46 and epileptic.

Two great-grandchildren (591) and (607) of the proband's father's half sister (7) have IQ's of 43 and 35, respectively. The diagnosis for (607) is posttraumatic retardation, prenatal anoxia.

Family Summary

No further retardation has occurred in the proband's immediate family. The parents had seven children and 16 grandchildren, all apparently normal except the proband.

Retardation of proband of unknown origin.

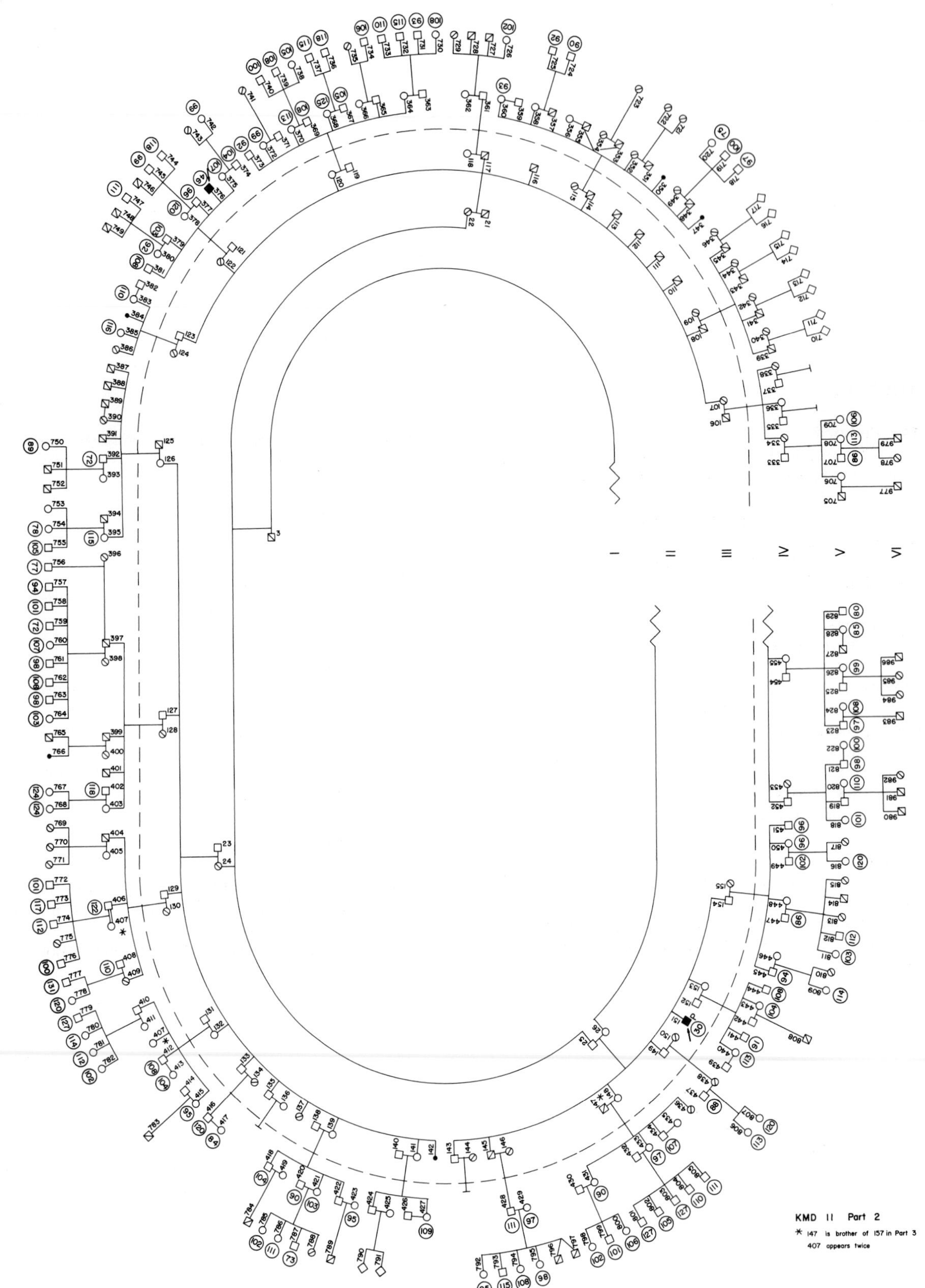

KMD II Part 2

* 147 is brother of 157 in Part 3

407 appears twice

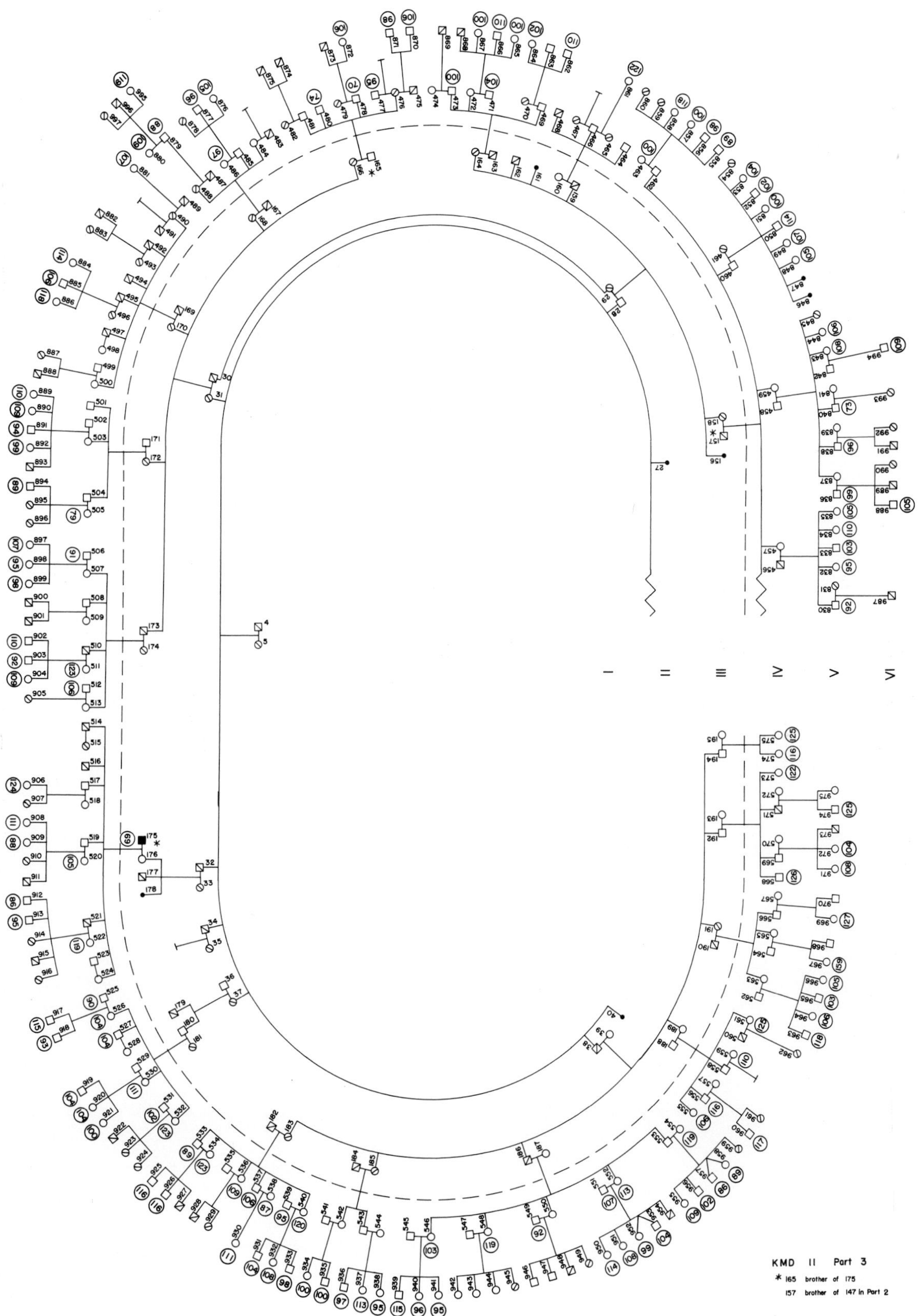

KMD II Part 3

* 165 brother of 175

157 brother of 147 in Part 2

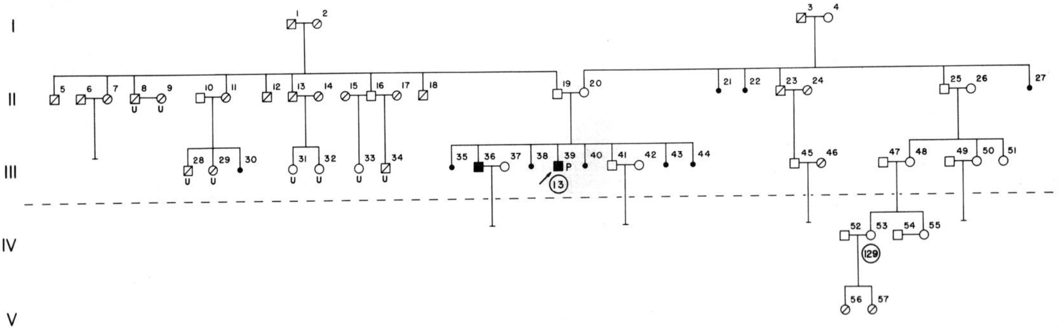
I
II
III
IV
V
KMD 19

KMD 19

The Proband

The proband (39) was born in 1885, institutionalized at age 14 years and died of valvular heart disease, tuberculosis and peritonitis in the institution in 1931. The proband was always quiet, "no trouble as a baby." He attended school for seven years where he evinced a talent for drawing. About age 12 he stopped drawing and would sit for hours in the same position. He was "quite a bright boy" until age 12 or 13 years. He then regressed until he could no longer even dress himself. IQ 13. *Diagnosis:* unknown.

Grandparents

Not of interest except that the maternal grandmother was mentally ill.

Parents

Both parents (19) and (20) had normal intelligence.

Father (19) was a bookkeeper.

Aunts and Uncles

Paternal uncle (18) was a suspected suicide.

(21) and (22) died of convulsions before the age of 2 years.

(27) died of inanition at 12 days.

Siblings

(35) died in infancy of cholera infantum and "congestion of brain."

Brother (36) had very poor health, could not support himself and was considered retarded by the early workers. He was married but childless.

(38), (40) and (43) were miscarriages.

Brother (41) was an accountant.

(44) died of marasmus at 9 months.

Nieces and Nephews

None.

First Cousins

Not of interest.

More Distant Relatives

Not of interest.

Family Summary

The proband was the only low-grade retarded person in his immediate family. He was apparently normal until the age of 12 or 13 years when he began to regress. The parents had eight children, no grandchildren. The entire maternal side of the proband's family has only two descendants of reproductive age, (53) and (55). The family pattern suggests possible schizophrenia.

Retardation of proband of unknown origin.

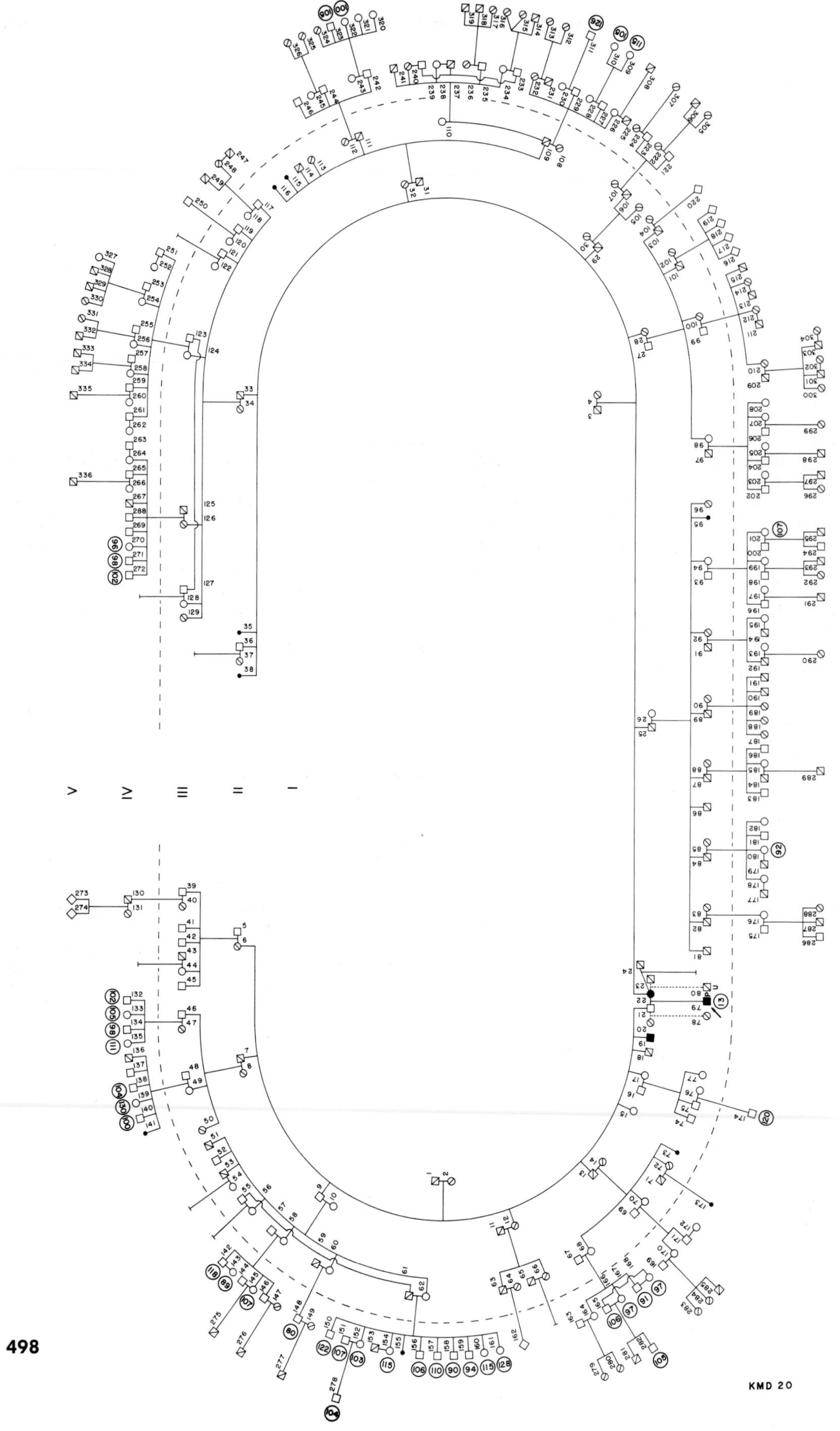

KMD 20

KMD 20

The Proband

The proband (79) was born in 1888, institutionalized at age 9 years and died of tuberculosis in the institution in 1931. His birth was uneventful and there was no record of perinatal infection. He did not talk until the age of 5. He attended school one year but learned little. He regressed after age 18 years until he stopped speaking and "just sat." IQ 13. *Diagnosis:* undifferentiated mental retardation with subsequent psychosis.

Grandparents

Not of interest.

Parents

Father (21) had an illegitimate child before his marriage to the proband's mother. He had normal intelligence.

Mother (22) also had an illegitimate child before her marriage. Her second husband (24) was a bigamist. She was retarded and had a case of arrested syphilis before the birth of the proband. The proband had no signs of congenital syphilis.

Aunts and Uncles

Paternal aunt (15) was hospitalized for mental illness. She was a teacher.

Paternal uncle (19) died at 13 years of "brain fever." He was retarded.

Maternal uncles (29) and (36) were epileptic but had normal intelligence.

Half Siblings

(78), illegitimate half sister thought to have died in childhood.

(80) illegitimate half brother who was adopted. He ran away from his adoptive home some time before 1912 and has never been heard from since that time.

Proband had no full siblings.

Nieces and Nephews

None.

First Cousins

(129) was deaf from the age of 2 years. She completed three and one half grades in five years of schooling and developed schizophrenia at age 33. She had a prefrontal lobotomy in 1954 and is hospitalized.

More Distant Relatives

Not of interest.

Family Summary

The proband, IQ 13, became quite withdrawn after age 18 years, "never spoke and just sat." The proband's parents both evinced poor social behavior. Each had an illegitimate child before marriage. The father was "enterprising" and apparently had normal intelligence. The mother was much lower grade in intelligence, did not take proper care of her child and lived in filth and squalor. The proband's aunt, a teacher, was hospitalized for mental illness, as was one first cousin. The proband's parents had one child, no grandchildren.

Retardation of proband of unknown origin.

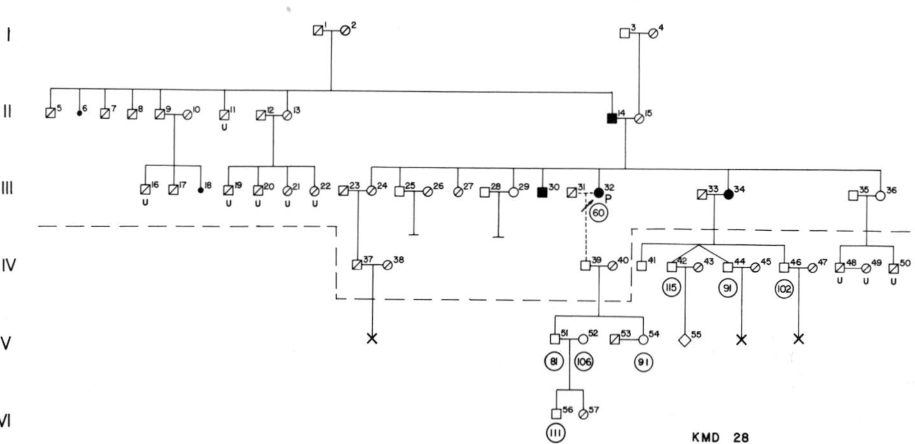

KMD 28

The Proband

The proband (32) was born in 1890, institutionalized at age 20 years, transferred a year later (when she became hallucinated and excitable) to a mental hospital, sent eight years later to another mental hospital where she died of a gastric hemorrhage in 1921. The diagnosis from the mental hospital was mental retardation. The proband's birth and early life were uneventful. She had an illegitimate child at age 17. IQ 60. *Diagnosis:* undifferentiated mental retardation.

Grandparents

Not of interest.

Parents

Father (14) was a mentally retarded laborer.

Mother (15) was mentally ill. Her intelligence was unknown.

Aunts and Uncles

Paternal aunt (13) was mentally ill.

Siblings

Sister (24) had unknown intelligence.

Brother (25) and sisters (28) and (36) all had normal intelligence.

Sister (27) died at age 15 years of tuberculosis.

Brother (30) was an unmarried, retarded laborer who died when he fell from a window while feeding pigeons.

Sister (34) is mentally retarded and also mentally unbalanced, but her four children have normal intelligence.

Child

Proband's illegitimate child (39) was reared by her mother as her own. He thinks his mother is his sister. He completed two years of high school and is a storehouse clerk with normal intelligence. His father is unknown.

Grandchildren

Two grandchildren, (51) and (54). IQ's 81 and 91, respectively.

Great-Grandchildren

Two, one (56) has an IQ of 111.

Nieces and Nephews

Not of interest.

First Cousins

Unknown.

More Distant Relatives

Unknown.

Family Summary

The proband, IQ 60, her father and two of her siblings were retarded. The proband's mother, an aunt and one of the retarded siblings were mentally ill. The proband's parents had eight children and eight grandchildren.

Retardation of proband of unknown origin.

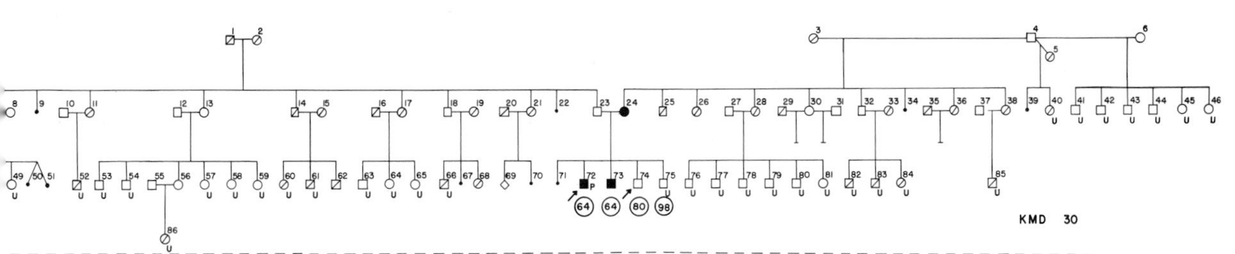

KMD 30

The Proband

The proband (72) was born in 1901, institutionalized at age 7 years and discharged to his parents in 1917. He enlisted in the army in 1918. In 1925 he was put under state guardianship and institutionalized. He was transferred to a mental hospital in 1938, then to two veterans' hospitals, and was discharged from guardianship and restored to competency in 1945. IQ 64. *Diagnosis:* mental retardation with subsequent psychosis.

Grandparents

Paternal grandfather committed suicide at age 50 years.

Parents

Father (23) was a cabinet maker and had normal intelligence.

Mother (24) was mentally retarded.

Aunts and Uncles

Maternal aunt (36) was epileptic.

Siblings

Stillbirth (71).

Brother (73) had an IQ of 64. He lived in a county "home."

Brother (74) was institutionalized at age 5 years and died of status epilepticus in the institution a year later. IQ 80 at age 6 years.

Brother (75) was adopted in 1912 and could not be found. IQ 98 at age 5 years.

Nieces and Nephews

Unknown.

First Cousins

Not of interest.

More Distant Relatives

Unknown.

Family Summary

The proband, IQ 64, his mother and one of his siblings were retarded. Two siblings had normal intelligence, but one was institutionalized and died of epilepsy. His IQ was 80 at age 6 years. The parents had five children; it is not known if their normal child had any children, since he was adopted in 1912 and is unknown at the present time. It was impossible to follow up this family because it had one of the most frequently occurring Scandinavian family names.

Retardation of proband of unknown origin.

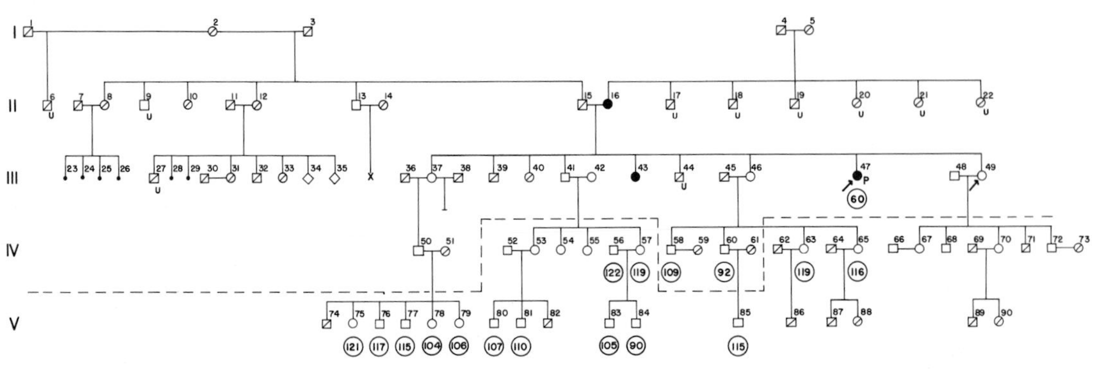

KMD 37

The Proband

The proband (47) was born in 1876 and institutionalized at 19 years. She remained in the institution until she was transferred to a county home for the aged in 1950. The alleged cause of the retardation was a severe fall of the mother during pregnancy. IQ 60. *Diagnosis:* undifferentiated mental retardation.

Grandparents

Not of interest.

Parents

Father (15) was a laborer, intelligence unknown.

Mother (16) died at age 44 years in a mental hospital. She was also mentally retarded.

Aunts and Uncles

Not of interest. Most of the family remained in Europe.

Siblings

Sisters (37), (46) and (49) and brother (41) had normal intelligence with no retardates in their families.

Brothers (39), (44) and sister (40) had unknown intelligence. (39) and (40) died young.

Sister (49) was put in an orphanage when she was a baby, then transferred to the institution for the retarded at age 6. She remained there for 13 years until her discharge to her sister (37). She has since made a good adjustment, reared a family of five children and has normal intelligence.

Sister (43) is unmarried, works as a chambermaid and is retarded.

Nieces and Nephews

Not of interest.

First Cousins

Not of interest.

More Distant Relatives

Not of interest.

Family Summary

The proband, her mother and one sister were retarded. The mother died in a mental hospital, leaving a motherless family of nine children. One sister of normal intelligence was institutionalized along with her retarded sibling. The parents had nine children and 14 grandchildren. No retardation has appeared among the descendants.

Retardation of proband of unknown origin.

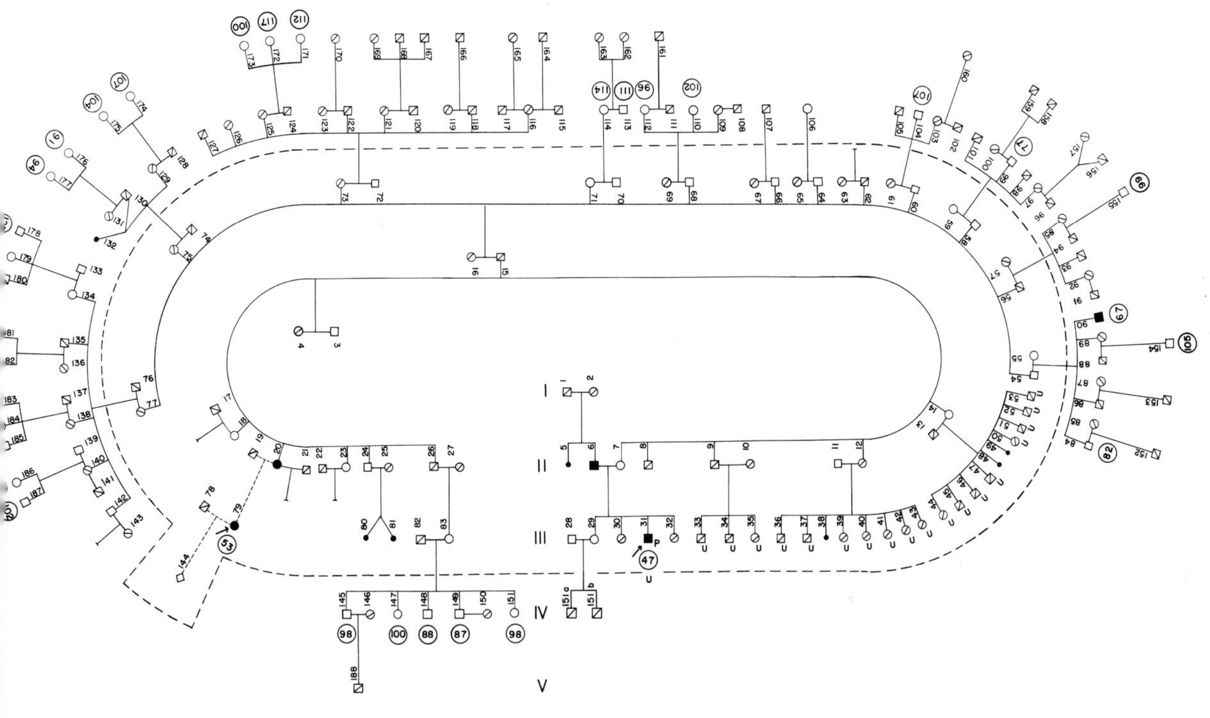

KMD 38

KMD 38

The Proband

The proband (31) was born in 1889, institutionalized at age 22 and remained in the institution for two years. His birth was uneventful and he was a healthy baby. He had been arrested for sexual delinquency and was transferred from the reformatory to the institution. After his discharge he worked in the iron mines for a time. His relatives do not know what his present status is. IQ 47. *Diagnosis:* undifferentiated mental retardation.

Grandparents

Not of interest.

Parents

Father (6) was mentally retarded. He was a miner.

Mother (7) had normal intelligence.

Aunts and Uncles

Maternal aunt (18) died in a mental hospital after becoming mentally ill in middle age.

Maternal aunt (20) had an institutionalized illegitimate child (79) with IQ 53. The aunt is also retarded.

Siblings

One normal sister (29); one sister (30) who died of diphtheria at age 3 years; one sister (32) who died of "St. Vitus fits" at age 3 years.

Nieces and Nephews

Two, (151a) and (151b) who are unknown to relatives.

First Cousins

(79) was first sent to a reformatory, then hospitalized at a home for girls for the birth of her illegitimate child (144). She was institutionalized in 1912, discharged in 1925, readmitted in 1927 and sterilized in 1928. She remained in the institution, however, where she developed a psychosis due to tertiary syphilis and died there in 1937 of syphilis. IQ 53.

More Distant Relatives

First cousin (54) had a retarded child who was in special classes. IQ 67.

Family Summary

The proband, IQ 47, his father, a maternal aunt, one first cousin and one more distant relative were retarded. The parents had four children and two grandchildren.

Retardation of proband of unknown origin.

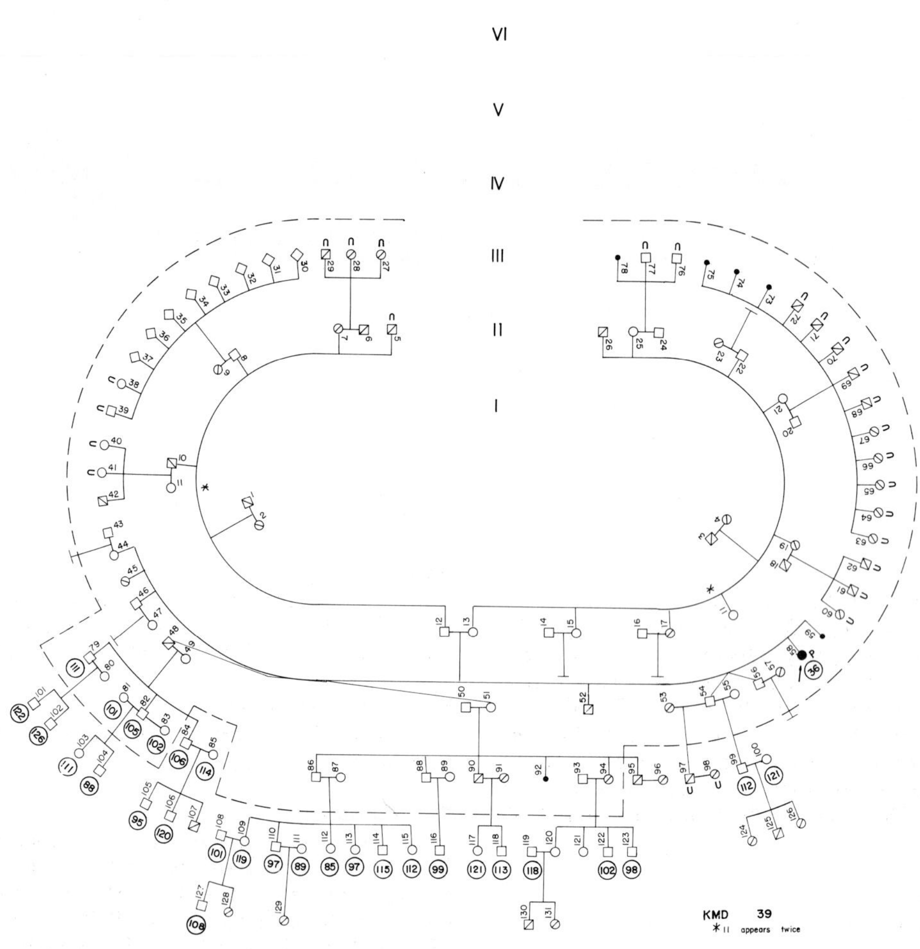

VI
V
IV
III
II
I
KMD 39
*11 appears twice

KMD 39

The Proband

The proband (58) was born in 1895, institutionalized at age 15 years and was in the institution in 1961. There was no history of difficult birth or perinatal disease. She attended school for several years but learned very little. IQ 36. *Diagnosis:* undifferentiated mental retardation.

Grandparents

Not of interest.

Parents

Father (12) was a lithographer. He was very alcoholic but had normal intelligence.

Mother (13) was an excellent business woman. She had to support the family because of the father's alcoholism.

Aunts and Uncles

Not of interest.

Siblings

Two had unknown intelligence. (45) died of diphtheria at 5 years and (52) was a plumber and died unmarried at age 27. All the rest had normal intelligence and normal children. (59) was a miscarriage.

Nieces and Nephews

Not of interest.

First Cousins

Unknown. They lived in other states and could not be found.

More Distant Relatives

Not of interest.

Family Summary

The proband was the only retarded person in this family group which includes six generations. Her parents had ten children including two sets of twins, and 11 grandchildren.

Retardation of proband of unknown origin.

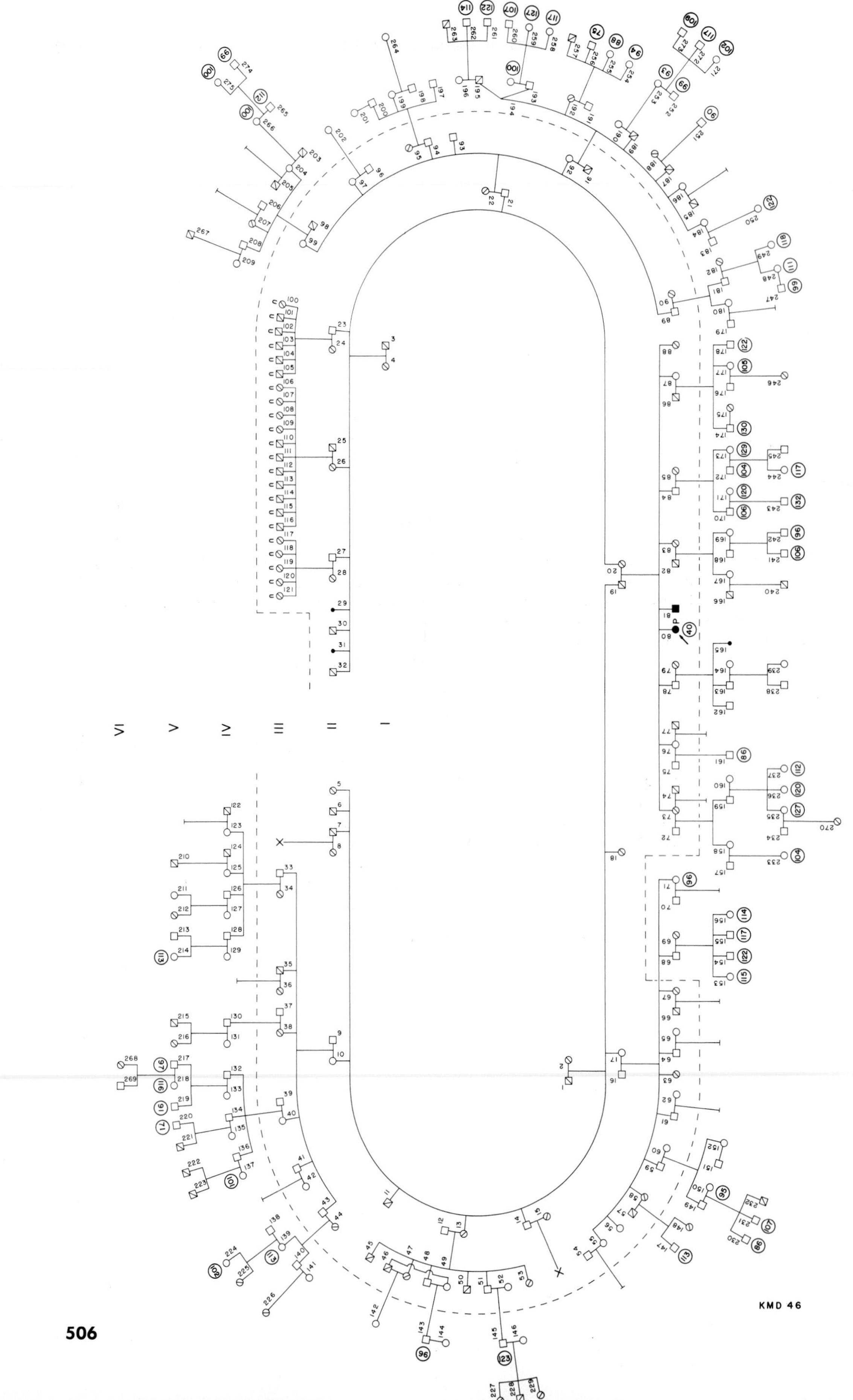

KMD 46

KMD 46

The Proband

The proband (80) was born in 1893, institutionalized at age 18 years and was discharged to her parents three years later. She had no stigmata or childhood history of disease. In 1927 she was placed in a mental hospital where she died in 1956. The hospital diagnosis was dementia praecox (hebephrenic type) and mental retardation. She went to school for five years but learned little and was unmarried and childless. IQ 40. *Diagnosis:* undifferentiated mental retardation.

Grandparents

Not of interest.

Parents

Father (19) was a laborer of unknown intelligence.

Mother (20) had unknown intelligence.

Aunts and Uncles

Paternal aunt (5) died of epilepsy at age 30 years.

Siblings

Three sisters (73), (83) and (88) of unknown intelligence.

Two sisters (76) and (87), and two brothers (78) and (84), all with normal intelligence.

All the siblings who reproduced had normal children.

One brother (81) is a single laborer, spent three years in the eighth grade and is "incapable of learning but reliable at mechanical work." He was retarded.

Nieces and Nephews

Not of interest.

First Cousins

Not of interest.

More Distant Relatives

Not of interest.

Family Summary

The only retarded persons known in this history are the proband and one brother. The proband had schizophrenia in addition to her retardation. The parents had nine children and 13 grandchildren. The grandchildren, with the possible exception of one who died at birth as a result of eclampsia in the mother, all have normal intelligence.

Retardation of proband of unknown origin.

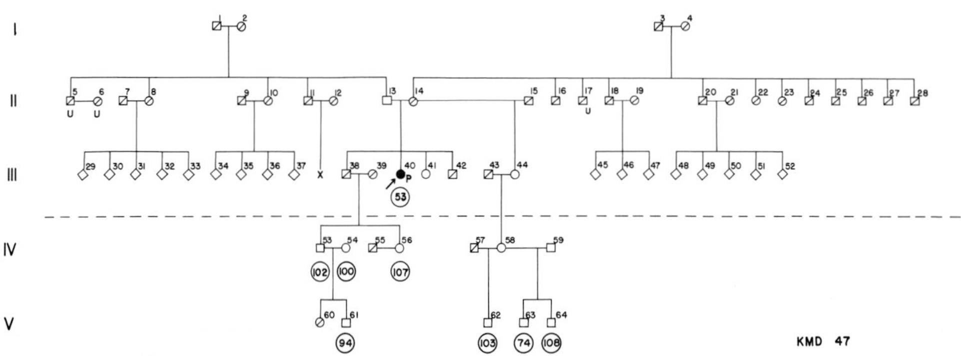

KMD 47

The Proband

The proband (40) was born in 1898 and institutionalized at age 15 years. She was transferred to a mental hospital in 1913 as psychotic when she became alternately excited and withdrawn. She died of cardiac failure and tuberculosis in the institution in 1932. She attended school until age 15, learned to read and write but could not learn arithmetic. The mental hospital diagnosis was mental retardation only. There was no history of early trauma. IQ 53. *Diagnosis:* undifferentiated mental retardation.

Grandparents

Not of interest.

Parents

Father (13) was "powder boss" in a mine. Normal intelligence.

Mother (14) had unknown intelligence.

Aunts and Uncles

Both the paternal and maternal relatives remained in Finland.

Siblings

Brother (38) left school in the fifth grade at age 14 years to work in the mines. He is now a janitor, intelligence unknown, children normal.

Sister (41) unmarried, has normal intelligence.

Brother (42) drowned as a young man. Intelligence unknown.

Half sister (44) had normal intelligence.

Nieces and Nephews

Not of interest.

First Cousins

Unknown.

More Distant Relatives

Unknown.

Family Summary

The proband is the only known retardate in this family. The parents had four children and two grandchildren. The grandchildren have IQ scores of 102 and 107. The proband's mother had a daughter by a previous marriage. This woman has normal intelligence, as does her daughter.

Retardation of proband of unknown origin.

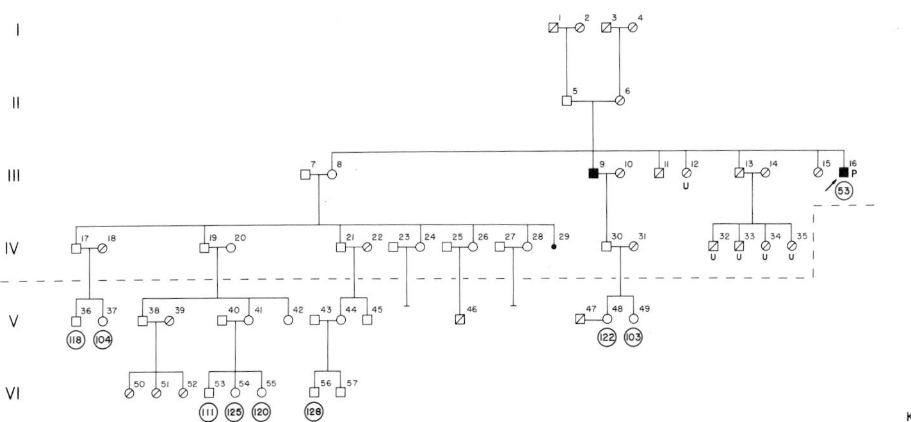

KMD 56

The Proband

The proband (16) was born in 1881, institutionalized at age 19 years and died of apoplexy in the institution in 1933. The family attributed his condition to a fall at 6 months. He was dropped from a stair landing and injured his head which was abnormally shaped from birth. He went to school but learned little. He was a good helper in the institution. IQ 53. *Diagnosis:* undifferentiated mental retardation.

Grandparents

Not of interest.

Parents

Father (5) was a mechanical engineer. He had a violent temper, abused his family and was arrested when he threatened them with a gun. He later committed suicide.

Mother (6) had unknown intelligence.

Aunts and Uncles

None.

Siblings

Sister (8) had normal intelligence, as did her husband and children.

Brother (9) was an elevator operator and was retarded. He had a normal son.

Brother (11) died of convulsions at 3 years, intelligence unknown.

Sister (12) ran away from home before 1912. She is unknown to relatives, intelligence unknown.

Brother (13) moved out of the state and could not be located. Intelligence unknown.

Sister (15) died unmarried of tuberculosis at age 20, intelligence unknown.

Nieces and Nephews

Not of interest.

First Cousins

None.

More Distant Relatives

Not of interest.

Family Summary

The proband and one brother were retarded. The proband's retardation was ascribed to a fall at age 6 months, but there is no medical confirmation of this. The proband's parents had seven children and 12 known grandchildren. The proband's normal sister had seven normal children, his retarded brother had only one child, also normal.

Retardation of proband of unknown origin.

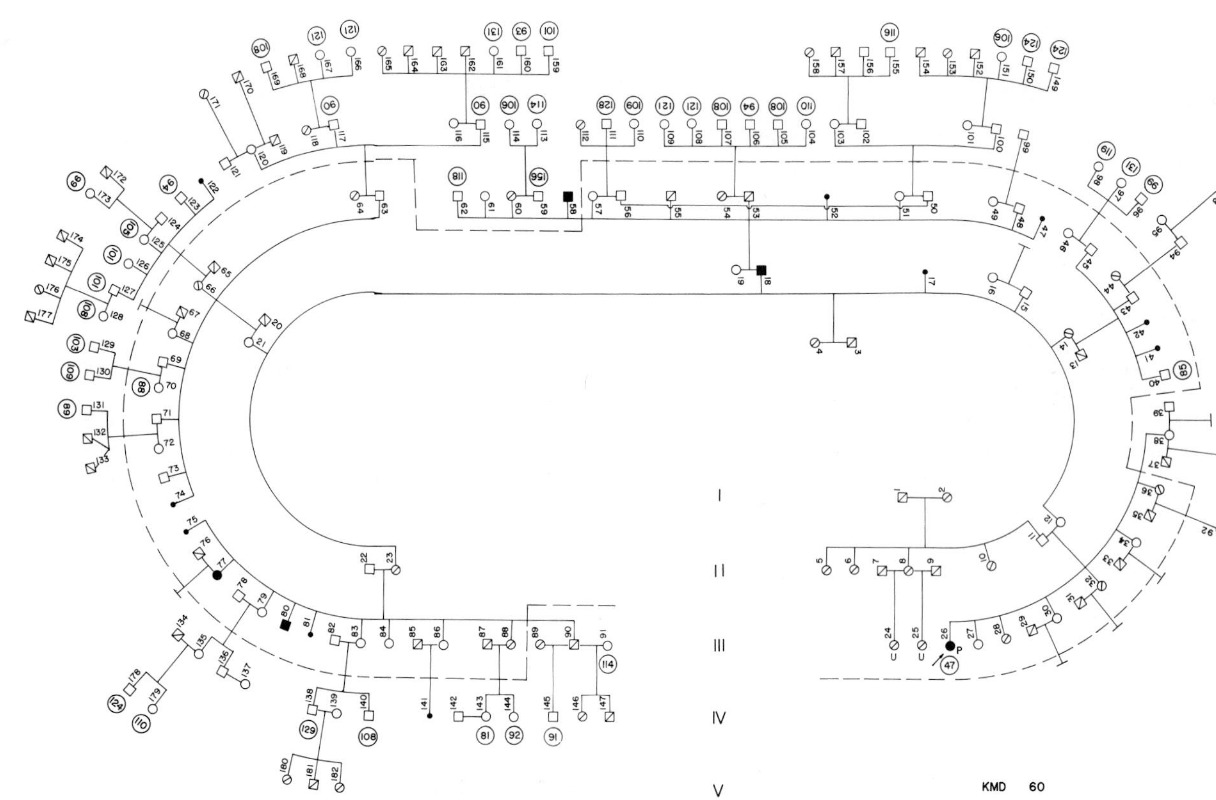
I
II
III
IV
V
KMD 60

KMD 60

The Proband

The proband (26) was born in 1897, institutionalized at age 12 years and discharged to relatives in 1911. There was no history of difficult birth or perinatal infection. She was placed in a mental hospital in 1913 when she became confused, violent and destructive. She died of influenza and pneumonia in the institution in 1957. The mental hospital reported a diagnosis of idiopathic mental retardation. She went to school for six or seven years but learned little. IQ 47. *Diagnosis:* undifferentiated mental retardation.

Grandparents

Not of interest.

Parents

Both parents (11) and (12) had normal intelligence.

Aunts and Uncles

Maternal uncle (18) was a peddler and was always in trouble with the police. He was retarded.

Siblings

Sister (27), unmarried, works in an office. Normal intelligence.

Sister (28) is unemployed and lives at home. (28), (32) and (36) all have unknown intelligence. Only (36) reproduced.

Sisters (30), (34) and (38) have normal intelligence.

Sister (38) was the only one in this sibship who would give us any information. She married twice and has one child. Her sisters refused her own request as well as those of the investigators.

Nieces and Nephews

Only two, of unknown intelligence.

First Cousins

(40) is hospitalized for schizophrenia. IQ 85.

(58) is an unmarried warehouseman who was in special classes at school. Mentally retarded.

(77) is retarded. She is married but childless.

(80) died in an accident at age 18. Retarded.

More Distant Relatives

Not of interest.

Family Summary

The proband, IQ 47, an uncle and two first cousins were retarded. The proband's parents had eight children and two grandchildren. The proband's parents were immigrants of poor social class. Some relatives had trouble with the police. The proband's mother and sisters were very hostile and uncooperative. One cousin has been hospitalized for schizophrenia.

Retardation of proband of unknown origin.

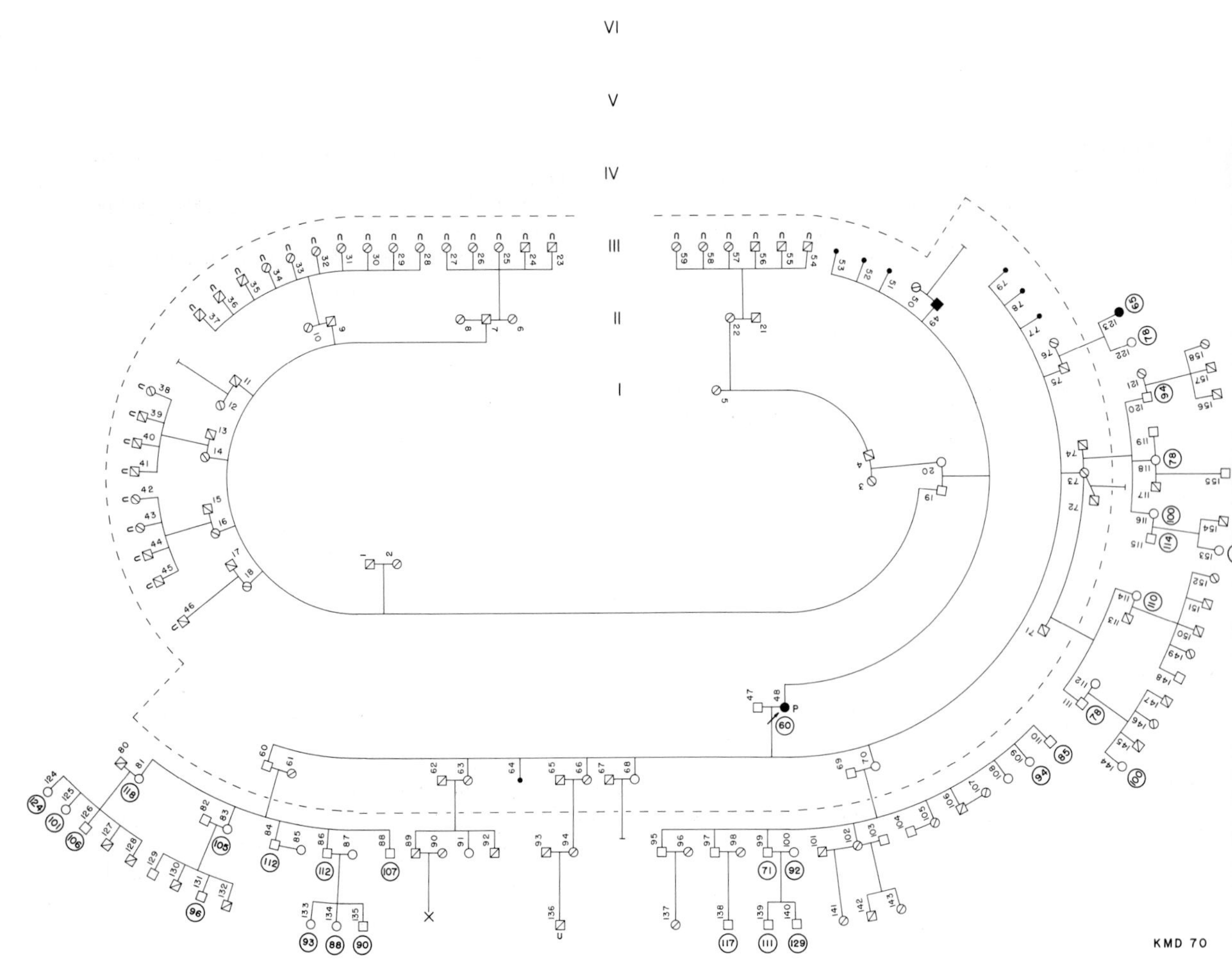
VI
V
IV
III
II
I
P
KMD 70

KMD 70

The Proband

The proband (48) was born in 1870, institutionalized at age 42 and discharged in 1920. She had no medical history of difficult birth or perinatal infection. In 1931 she was imprisoned, then transferred to a mental hospital where she died in 1943. The diagnosis was mental deficiency without psychosis. She attended school and was literate. At age 18 she married a man of normal intelligence but sexually promiscuous. She was incapable of caring for her family (at least one child died for lack of care) and finally became a prostitute. IQ 60. *Diagnosis:* undifferentiated mental retardation.

Grandparents

Not of interest.

Parents

Both parents (19) and (20) had normal intelligence.

Aunts and Uncles

Not of interest.

Siblings

Brother (49) was an alcoholic, a trouble maker and retarded. His wife (50) ran away with the proband's father.

(51) died of "summer complaint" at 6 months.

(52) died of inanition at 1 month.

(53) stillbirth.

Children

Son (60) died at 51 years. He was frequently jailed for alcoholism. He was a painter and paperhanger with normal intelligence and his children are normal.

Daughter (63) was also an alcoholic. She eloped with a barber who deserted his legal wife. Intelligence unknown.

Son (64) died of cholera infantum at 5 months.

Daughter (66) died, date unknown. She did very poor work in school. Intelligence unknown.

Daughter (68) went to high school and has an adopted child.

Daughter (70) has normal intelligence and married a normal man 15 years older than she. Her children are apparently normal.

Daughter (73) has been married three times. She refused to give information saying she was "too nervous" and telling about her six operations. Her intelligence is unknown but she has normal children.

Son (75) completed seven grades in school and is a laborer. His intelligence is unknown. He has one retarded child and one child with IQ 78.

(77), (78) and (79) proband's children who died in infancy; (77) of cholera infantum, (78) of birth injuries and (79) of neglect.

Grandchildren

(123) has an IQ of 65.

Four, (99), (111), (118) and (122), with borderline IQ's of 71, 78, 78 and 78, respectively. (99) is also epileptic.

Nieces and Nephews

None.

First Cousins

Unknown.

More Distant Relatives

Not of interest.

Family Summary

The proband, IQ 60, her brother and one granddaughter were high-grade retardates. The family also had problems of alcoholism, imprisonment and sexual misbehavior. The proband's parents had five children and 11 grandchildren (all belonging to the proband). Only one retarded person has appeared among the proband's known 71 offspring (11 children, 25 grandchildren and 35 great-grandchildren).

Retardation of proband of unknown origin.

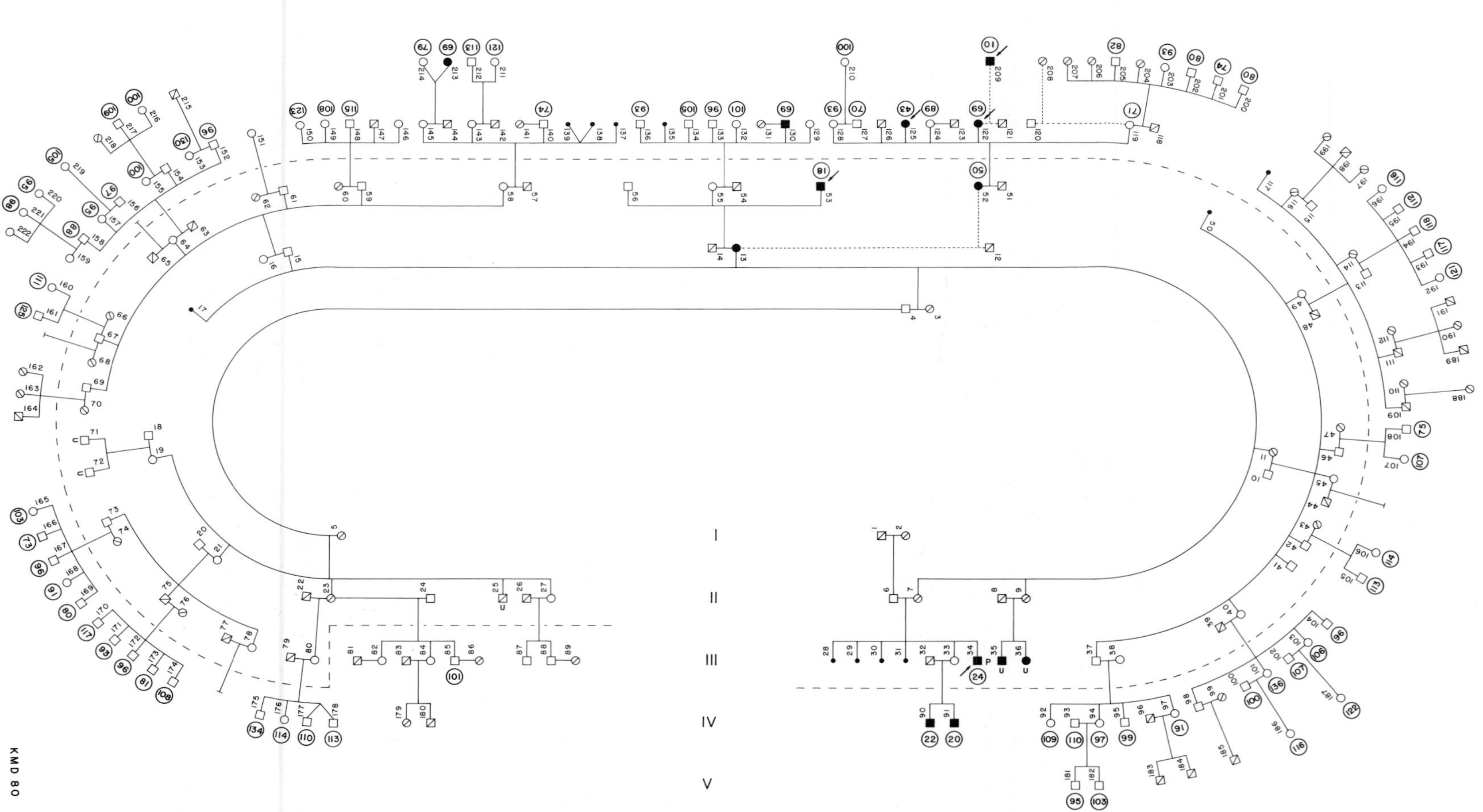

KMD 80

KMD 80

The Proband

The proband (34) was born in 1905, institutionalized at age 7 years and died of general septicemia in the institution in 1925. He walked at 5 years, talked at 6. There was no record of difficult delivery or perinatal infection and he had no stigmata. IQ 24. *Diagnosis:* undifferentiated mental retardation.

Grandparents

Not of interest.

Parents

Father (6) was a farmer of normal intelligence.

Mother (7) was of unknown intelligence.

Aunts and Uncles

No paternal relatives (father was an only child).

Maternal aunt (13) had an illegitimate child (52) before her marriage to (14). She is retarded.

Siblings

Four, (28), (29), (30) and (31), died in infancy. Two died of digestive disorders, one of "teething" and one of unknown cause (very wrinkled and ugly).

Sister (33) is normal but has two retarded children.

Nieces and Nephews

Only two, (90), IQ 22, and (91), IQ 20. Neither is institutionalized.

First Cousins

(35) and (36) remained in Sweden, present status unknown. Both are retarded and one was described as an idiot.

(52) has a family with an extensive social welfare record. IQ 50.

(53) was institutionalized at age 10 years. He is epileptic. IQ 18.

More Distant Relatives

First cousin (52), IQ 50, has two retarded children. (122) was institutionalized for a few months at age 15 years, had an illegitimate child 11 years later and has been under outside supervision ever since. Her illegitimate child (209) was institutionalized. His institution diagnosis is cultural familial retardation, profound, with behavioral reaction. IQ 10. Another child of (52), (125), was institutionalized at age 7 years, IQ 43, epileptic and with a catatonic schizophrenic reaction. The other children of (52) are under the supervision of social agencies. A daughter (119), IQ 71, has one illegitimate child and eight legitimate children (one a juvenile delinquent with IQ 74). A second daughter (128), IQ 93, married a man with IQ 70, and has a child with IQ 100.

The half sibling to (52), who is (55) and normal, has a retarded son (130) with IQ 69.

First cousin (58) has a retarded grandchild (213) with IQ 69.

Family Summary

The proband, IQ 24, two nephews, two first cousins and one more distant relative are low-grade retardates with no stigmata. A maternal aunt, her daughter and three of her grandchildren are high-grade retardates. One great-grandchild is low grade with IQ 10. The family of this aunt has always been a social problem with records of illegitimacy, delinquency and retardation. The retardation in three generations of family of (13), the proband's aunt, is of probably genetic origin. Unfortunately, this family is continuing to reproduce itself. (13) had four children and 13 grandchildren, six from the retarded daughter (52), and seven from the normal one (55). The retarded daughter (52) is the grandmother of 11, including one large family of nine which constitutes a continuing social welfare problem for the county. The mother of the nine (119) has an IQ of 71. The proband's parents had six children and two grandchildren (both retarded). This sibship will probably become extinct.

Retardation of proband of unknown origin.

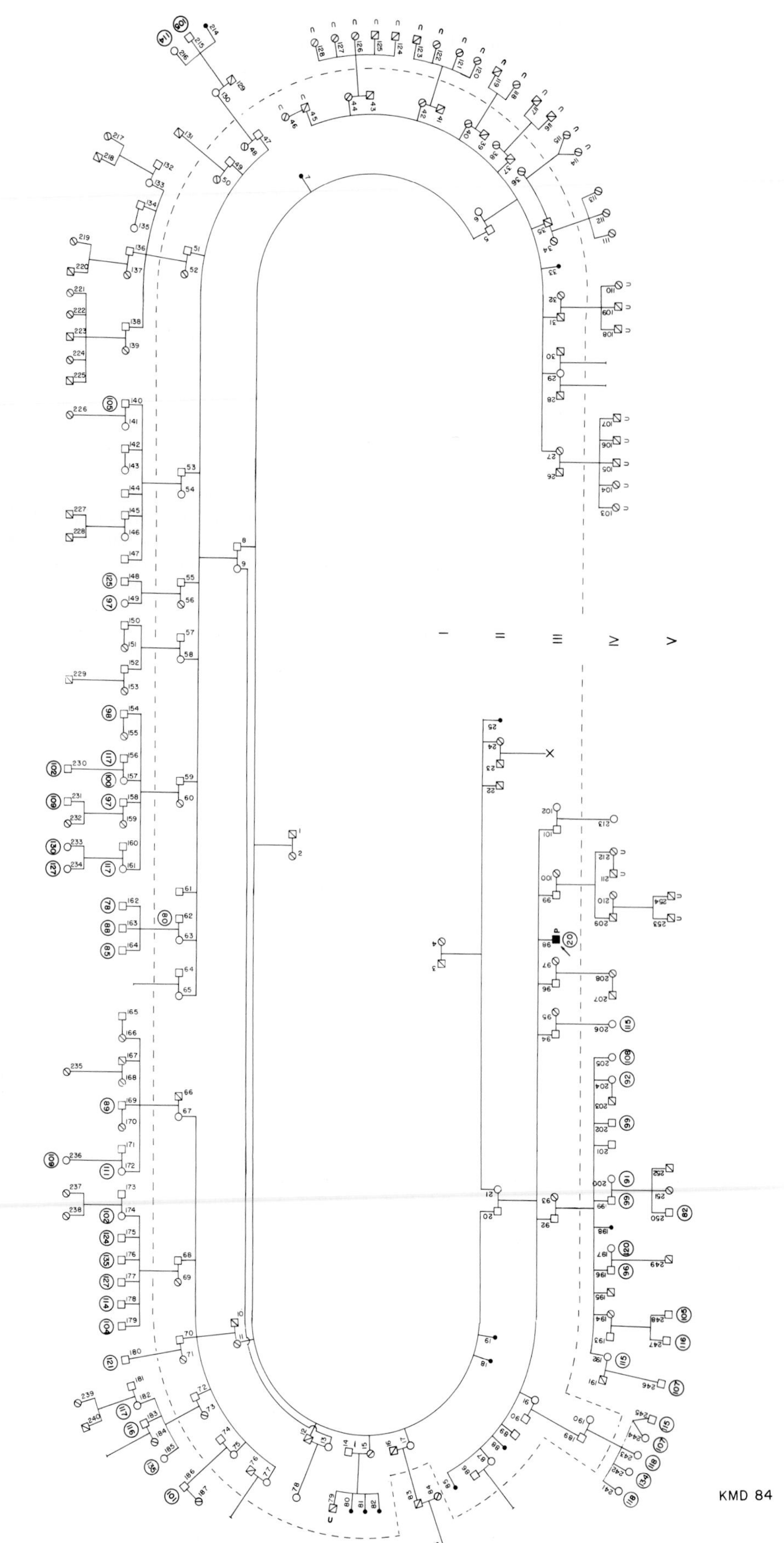

KMD 84

KMD 84

The Proband

The proband (98) was born in 1894, institutionalized at age 12 years and died of acute enteritis in the institution in 1934. He had difficulty in walking and talked at 6 years. His birth and early life were uneventful. He was an excitable idiot with very active reflexes and a box-shaped head. IQ 20. *Diagnosis:* undifferentiated mental retardation.

Grandparents

Not of interest.

Parents

Both parents (20) and (21) had normal intelligence. The father was a machinist.

Aunts and Uncles

Paternal uncle (8) was psychotic at times but had normal intelligence.

Paternal aunt (15) died in a mental hospital.

Siblings

Brother (85) died of diphtheria at 14 months.

Sisters (87) and (91), brothers (92), (94), (96), (99) and (101) had normal intelligence and there is no retardation among their descendants.

Brother (88) died at 14 months—"caught cold."

Brother (89) died of sunstroke at 4 years.

Nieces and Nephews

Not of interest.

First Cousins

Not of interest.

More Distant Relatives

Not of interest.

Family Summary

The proband was the only retarded person in this family. His birth was uneventful and there was no record of perinatal infection. The parents had 11 children and 16 grandchildren.

Retardation of proband of unknown origin.

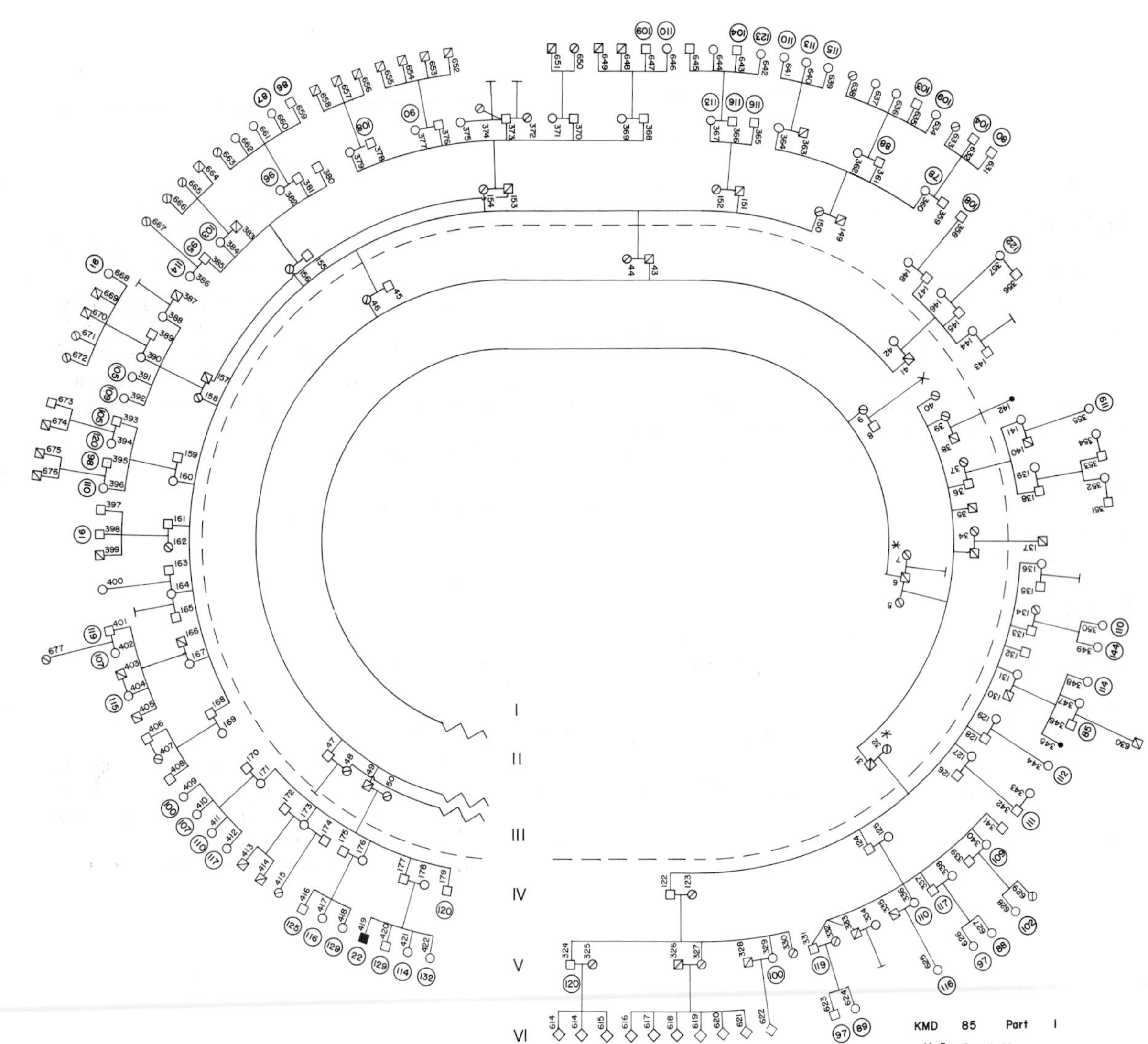

I
II
III
IV
V
VI
KMD 85 Part I
* 7 mother of 32

KMD 85

The Proband

The proband (112) was born in 1901, institutionalized at age 9 years and died of tuberculosis in the institution in 1928. He walked at 3 years and learned to talk a little. He had genu valgum, winged scapulae and flat feet. IQ 34. *Diagnosis:* undifferentiated mental retardation.

Grandparents

Not of interest.

Parents

Father (23) abused his family. He was an alcoholic and retarded.

Mother (24) had normal intelligence.

Aunts and Uncles

Paternal uncle (12) married his first cousin. No retardation was apparent in their children.

Maternal relatives remained in Scotland.

Siblings

Sisters (102), (108) and (111) all had normal intelligence. (108) had an illegitimate child. There is no retardation among their descendants.

Sister (104) died of "spasms" after a fall at 3½ years.

Brother (105) is unknown.

Brother (106) died of diphtheria at age 7 years.

Nieces and Nephews

Not of interest.

First Cousins

(77) is unmarried, childless and retarded.

More Distant Relatives

First cousin (49) has a retarded grandchild (419), IQ 22.

First cousin (73) has a retarded son (220). He has never gone to school.

Family Summary

The proband, IQ 34, and his father were the only retarded persons in the immediate family. Two distant relatives were low-grade retardates. The proband's parents had seven children and at least 28 grandchildren.

Retardation of proband of unknown origin.

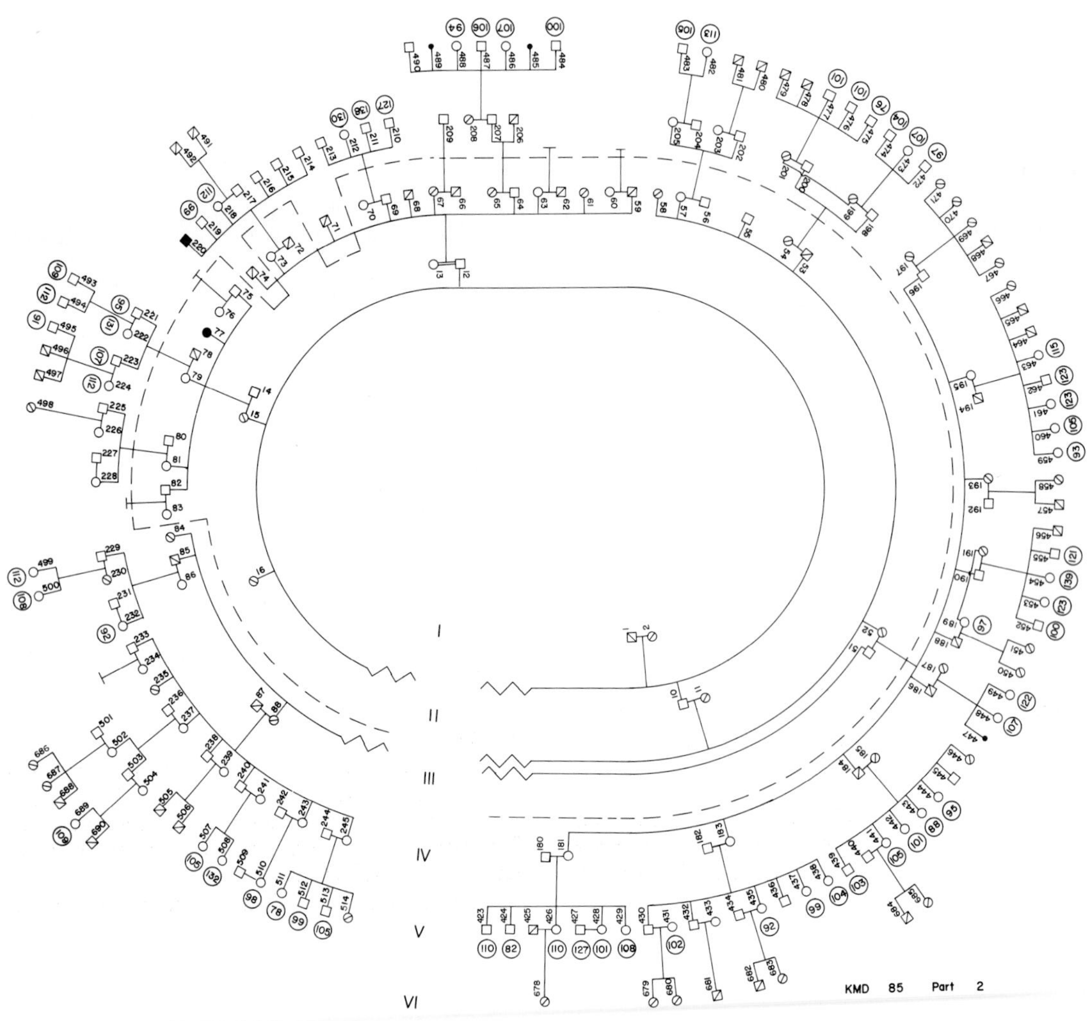
I
II
III
IV
V
VI
KMD 85 Part 2

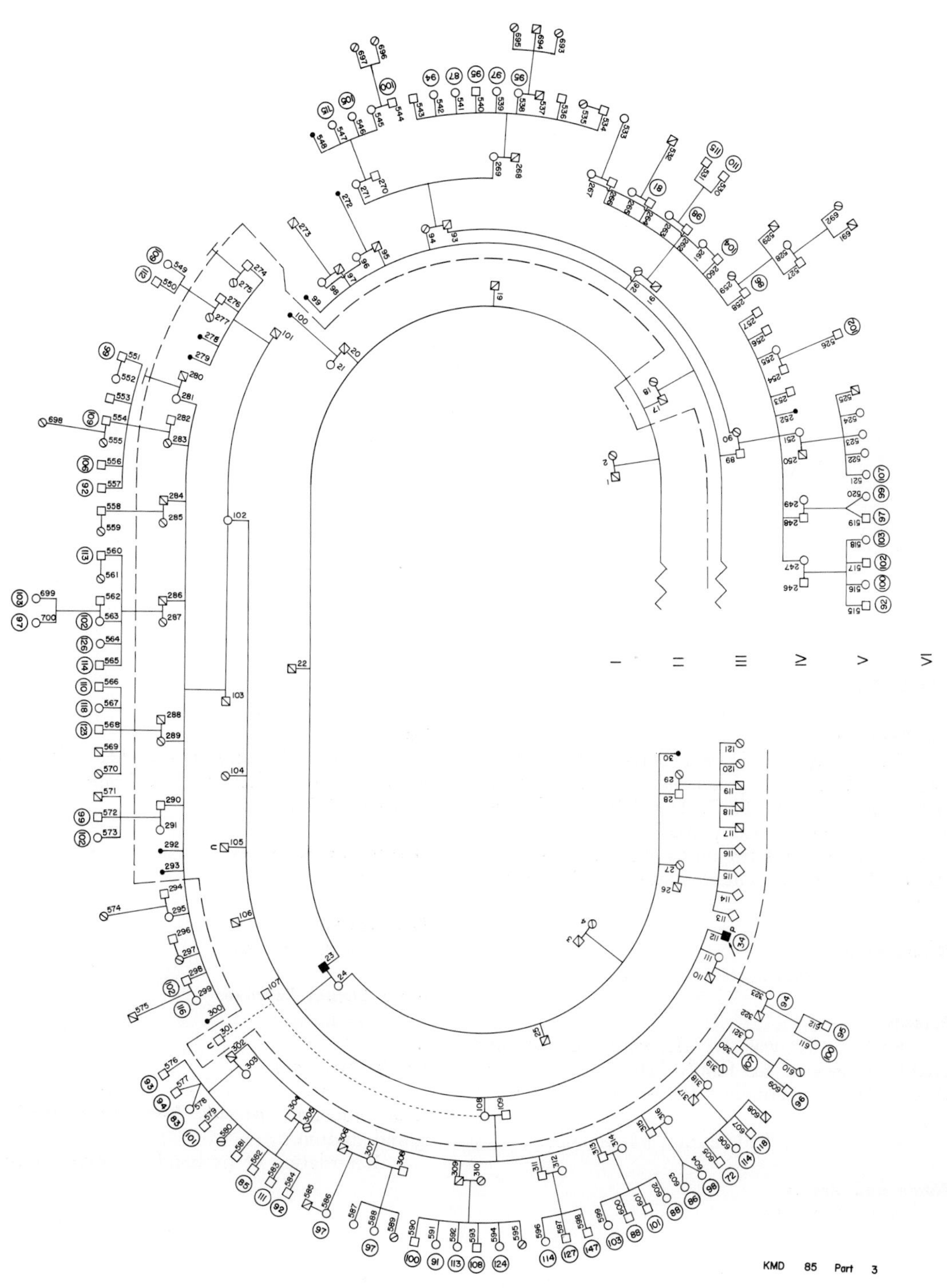

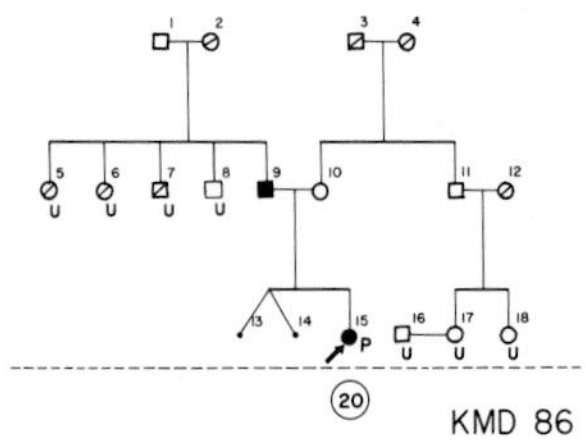

KMD 86

The Proband

The proband (15) was born in 1892, institutionalized at age 17 years and died of septicemia in the institution in 1917. Her left foot dragged and her right hand was partially paralyzed. There was no record of birth injury or brain infection. IQ 20. *Diagnosis:* undifferentiated mental retardation.

Grandparents

Not of interest.

Parents

Father (9) was an alcoholic, abusive and unable to support his family. He finally deserted them. He was mentally retarded of "a rather low degree."

Mother (10) had normal intelligence.

Aunts and Uncles

Not of interest.

Siblings

Twins (13) and (14). (13) died at two weeks, cause unknown. (14) died of "gastric trouble" at 1 month.

Nieces and Nephews

None.

First Cousins

Not of interest.

More Distant Relatives

Unknown.

Family Summary

The proband and her father were retarded. The proband's parents had three children, no grandchildren.

Retardation of proband of unknown origin.

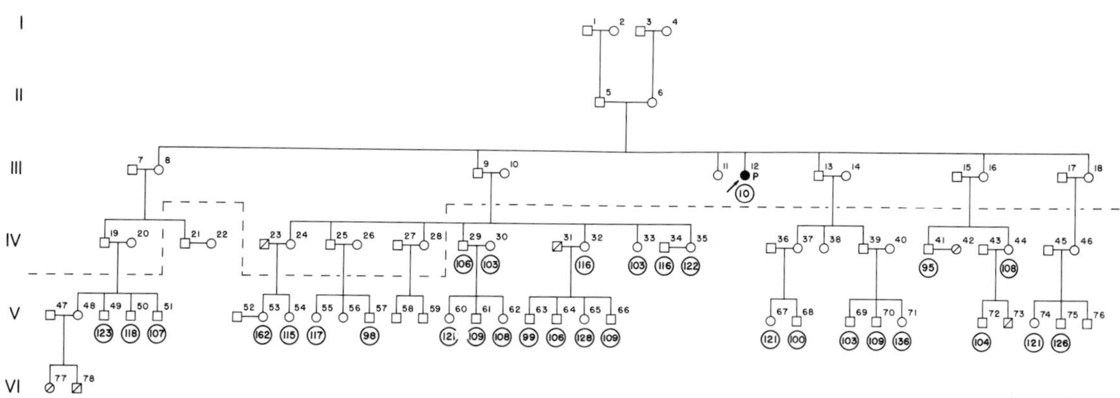

KMD 87

The Proband

The proband (12) was born in 1882, institutionalized at age 27 years and died of pulmonary tuberculosis in the institution in 1913. She was born "terribly deformed" from the hips down and was helpless. *Diagnosis:* double talipes equinovarus, double genu valgus, coxa vara plus undifferentiated mental retardation. IQ 10.

Grandparents

All normal.

Parents

Father (5) was a Lutheran minister.

Mother (6) was a semi-invalid of normal intelligence.

Aunts and Uncles

None, both parents were only children.

Siblings

All had normal intelligence and normal children except (11) who was a helpless cripple from rheumatisim as was her maternal grandfather, and (18) who was born with a "lobster claw" foot.

Nieces and Nephews

All had normal intelligence but nephew (25) has a "lobster claw" foot, and niece (28) married a man with the same affliction.

First Cousins

None.

More Distant Relatives

Not of interest.

Family Summary

The proband was a helpless cripple with IQ 10. All her immediate family are normal in intelligence, but a sister and a nephew have deformed feet ("lobster claw"). The proband's parents had seven children and 15 grandchildren.

Retardation of proband of unknown origin.

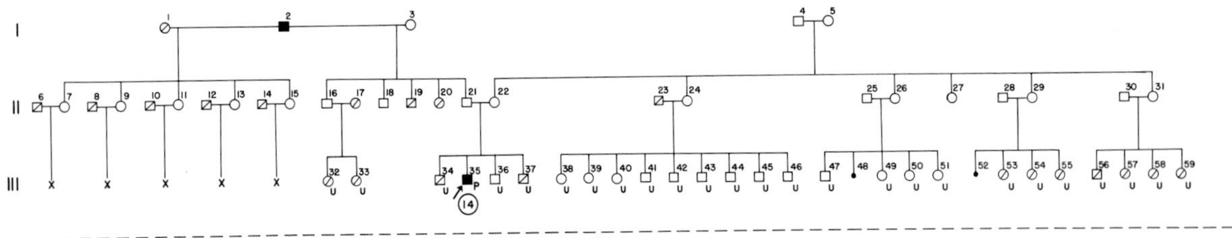
I
1 2 3 4 5
II
6 7 8 9 10 11 12 13 14 15 16 17 18 19 20 21 22 23 24 25 26 27 28 29 30 31
III
X X X X X
32 33 34 35 36 37 38 39 40 41 42 43 44 45 46 47 48 49 50 51 52 53 54 55 56 57 58 59
P
14

KMD 88

KMD 88

The Proband

The proband (35) was born in 1901, institutionalized at age 6 years and died of tuberculosis in the institution in 1919. His birth was uneventful and he had no history of perinatal disease. By age 2 he had trembling and crying spells and would run away. IQ 14. *Diagnosis:* undifferentiated mental retardation.

Grandparents

Paternal grandfather was an alcoholic, poverty stricken and retarded.

Other grandparents all normal.

Parents

Father (21) was a farmer of fair financial status and normal intelligence.

Mother (22) was unusually robust and an excellent manager.

Aunts and Uncles

Maternal aunt (27) was epileptic and died of paralysis. She had normal intelligence.

Siblings

Brothers (34) and (37) could not be found. Intelligence unknown.

Brother (36) could not be found but from the old records is known to have normal intelligence.

Nieces and Nephews

Unknown.

First Cousins

Not of interest.

More Distant Relatives

Unknown.

Family Summary

The proband, IQ 14, and his maternal grandfather, a middle- or high-grade retardate, were the only retarded persons known in this family. The proband's parents had four children. It is not known whether or not they had grandchildren. The family could not be found for the follow-up because their family name is a frequently occurring Scandinavian name.

Retardation of proband of unknown origin.

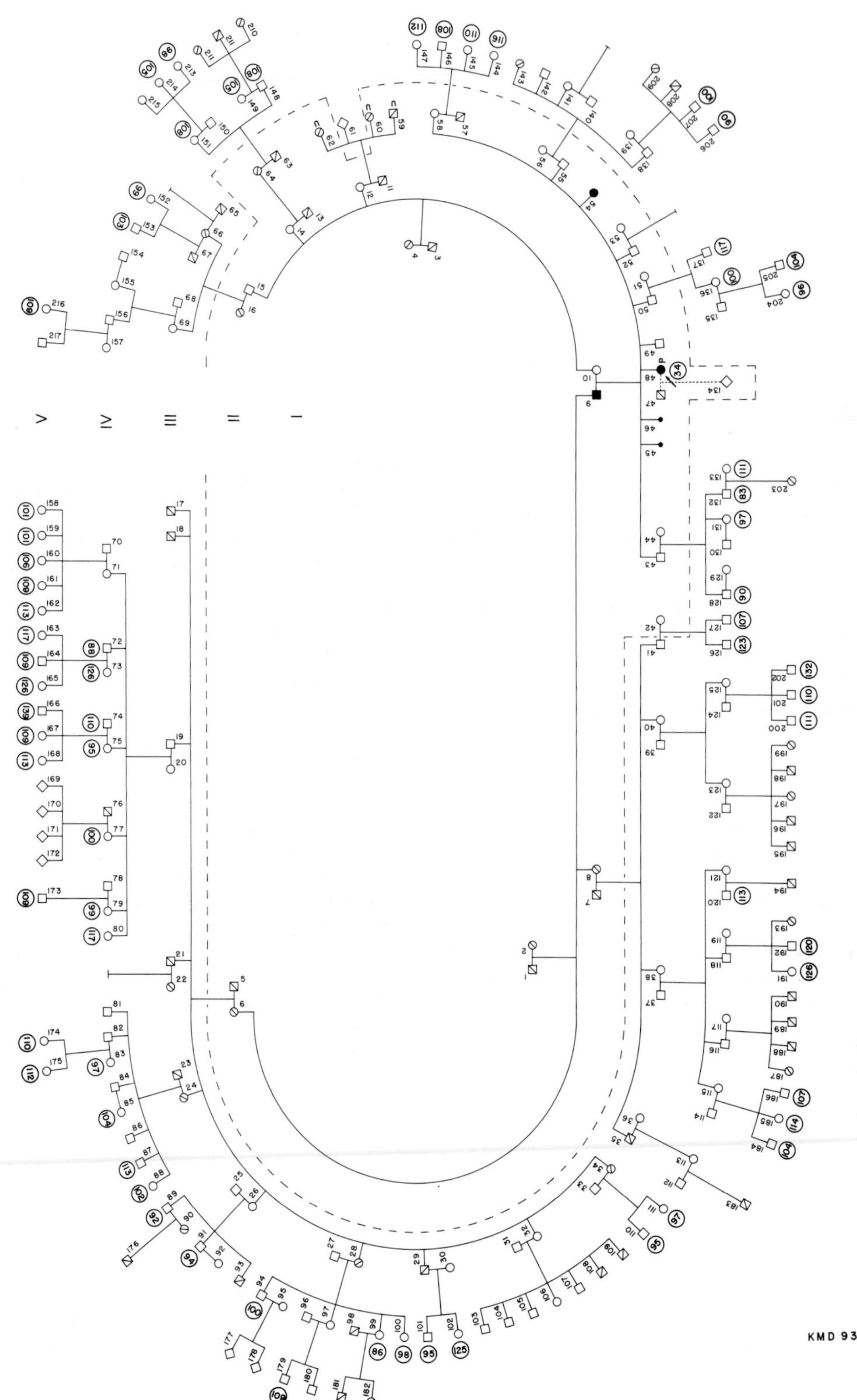

KMD 93

KMD 93

The Proband

The proband (48) was born in 1892, institutionalized at age 19 years and died of acute abdominal tuberculosis in the institution in 1925. She was late in walking and talking, learned little at school and became quite unmanageable as she grew older. She had no history of early trauma. She had an illegitimate child before her admission to the institution. IQ 34. *Diagnosis:* undifferentiated mental retardation.

Grandparents

Not of interest.

Parents

Father (9) could do only the simplest work and could not support his family. Twelve persons lived in a two room cabin in a swamp.

Mother (10) worked very hard to support the family. She had normal intelligence.

Aunts and Uncles

Not of interest.

Siblings

Brother (43) completed two years of college and owns a music store. His wife and children are normal.

Sister (45) died at birth. She was born prematurely.

Brother (46) died of pneumonia at 7 months.

Brother (49) was an electrician who died single and childless.

Brothers (50), (52) and (55) are skilled workmen and have normal intelligence, as do their wives and children.

Sister (54) completed the sixth grade and died single and childless. She was crippled by paralysis and was retarded.

Sister (58) completed the eleventh grade in school. She had normal intelligence.

Child

The proband's child is unknown as to age, sex or present status.

Nieces and Nephews

Not of interest.

First Cousins

Not of interest.

More Distant Relatives

Not of interest.

Family Summary

The proband, her sister and her father were retarded. The family lived in great poverty and squalor because of the incompetent father. In spite of this, six of the proband's siblings have normal intelligence. The proband's parents had ten children and 14 grandchildren.

Retardation of proband of unknown origin.

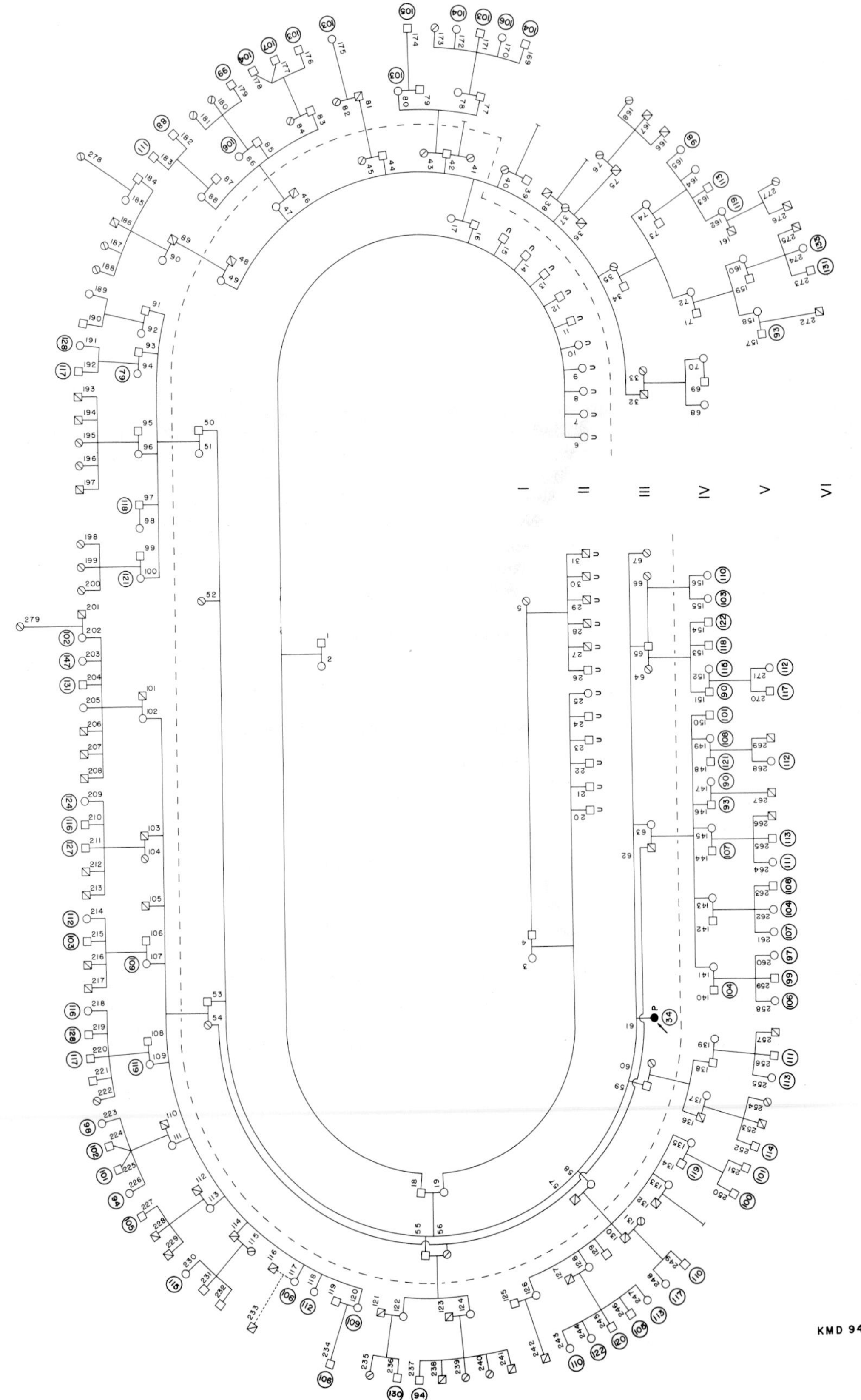
I
II
III
IV
V
VI
P
KMD 94

KMD 94

The Proband

The proband (61) was born in 1897, institutionalized at age 15 years and was discharged four years later. She was readmitted in 1924 and died of influenza and pneumonia in the institution in 1928. She was very backward in walking and talking, never went to school and became difficult to manage as she grew older. She had a malformed palate and jaw, a "moderate Hutchinson's nose" and a negative Wassermann. IQ 34. *Diagnosis:* undifferentiated mental retardation.

Grandparents

Not of interest.

Parents

Father (18) was a good workman and farmer.
Mother (19) had normal intelligence.

Aunts and Uncles

Father's five siblings remained in Sweden. One brother came to this country.

Mother's siblings all remained in Sweden.

Siblings

Brothers (50), (53), (59) and (65) are all prosperous farmers of normal intelligence with normal children.

Sister (52) was killed by a train at the age of 4 years.

Sisters (58) and (63) have normal intelligence, as do their children.

Sister (67) died of heart trouble at 3 years.

Nieces and Nephews

Niece (117) had an illegitimate child. She left school in the seventh grade with failing grades but scored an IQ of 106.

First Cousins

Not of interest.

More Distant Relatives

Not of interest.

Family Summary

The proband was the only retarded person in this family of prosperous normal farmers. The proband's parents had ten children and 37 grandchildren.

Retardation of proband of unknown origin.

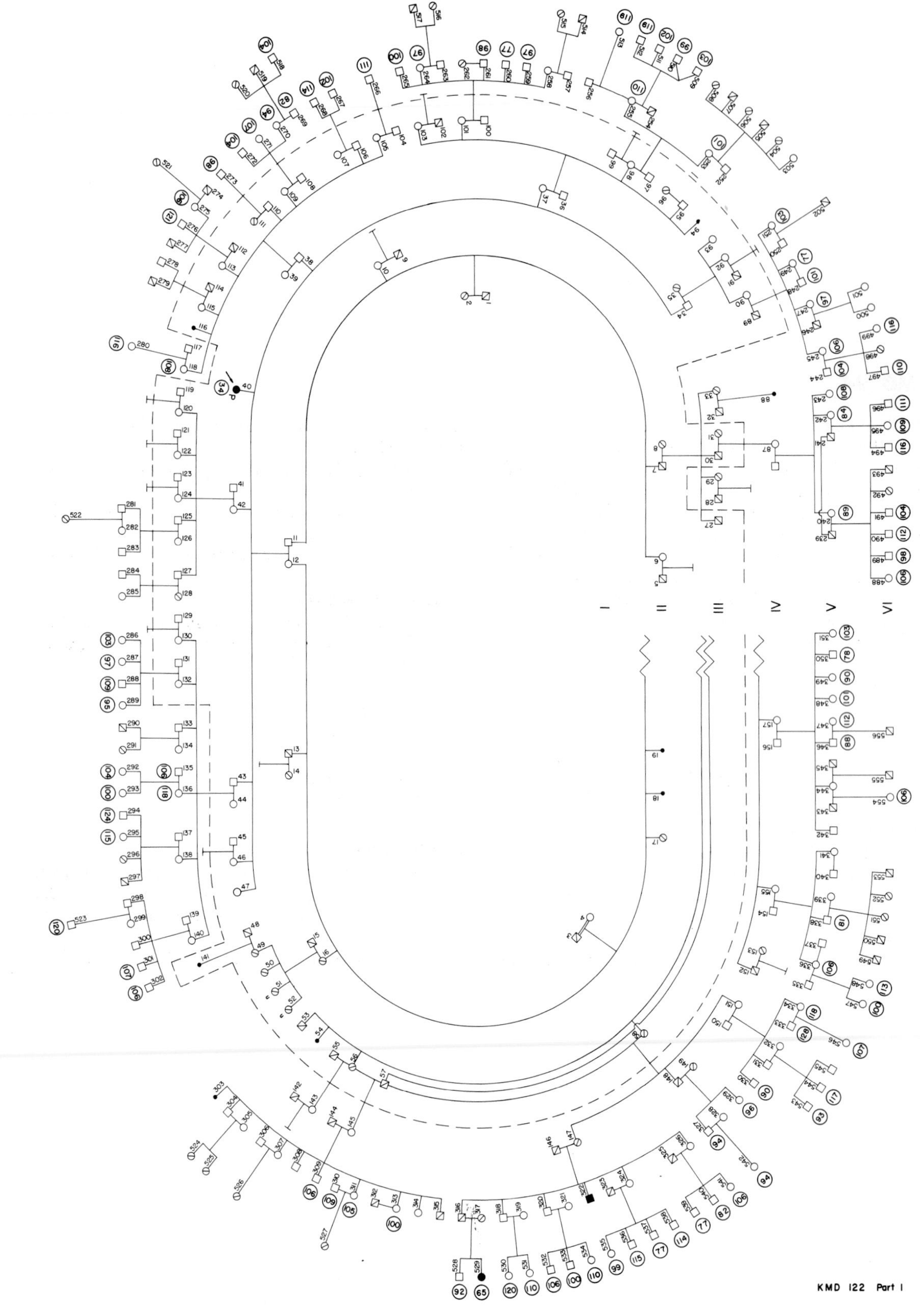

KMD 122 Part I

KMD 122

The Proband

The proband (40) was born in 1878, institutionalized at age 14 years and died in a mental hospital in 1926, cause unknown. She became "more and more demented" and began having hallucinations three years before her death. She was unmarried and childless. She walked at 4 years, talked at 5. She went to school for seven years but learned little. There was no history of early trauma and she had no stigmata. Institution records describe her only as retarded. IQ 34. *Diagnosis:* Undifferentiated mental retardation.

Grandparents

Maternal grandparents were first cousins.

Parents

The parents owned and operated a prosperous farm. Both parents (11) and (12) had normal intelligence.

Aunts and Uncles

Not of interest, except that maternal uncle (20) committed suicide.

Siblings

One sister (47) hospitalized for mental illness at age 13. She died in 1931 of bronchial pneumonia and acute maniacal excitement.

All the other siblings (34), (37), (38), (42), (43) and (46) were normal as are their descendants.

Nieces and Nephews

Not of interest.

First Cousins

Not of interest.

More Distant Relatives

Proband's cousin's daughter (147) has a son (322) who completed three years of school and is a single, farm laborer. He is mentally retarded. The brother of (322) has a daughter (529) with an IQ of 65.

Proband's cousin's daughter (172) has an institutionalized child (373) who is a polydactylous cretin, IQ 20. Her brother (176) has two children (385) and (386) with IQ's of 50 and 66.

Proband's cousin's daughter (203) has an institutionalized child (434) who is epileptic, IQ 19. Psychologist's report states there is evidence of severe brain damage.

Proband's cousin's daughter (210) has one mentally retarded daughter (445), no IQ, but who tested at the fifth grade level on achievement tests at 15 years.

Family Summary

The proband's parents were healthy normal persons who operated a prosperous farm. Their family of eight produced 27 offspring. All the normal siblings except (46) had children—27 in all. No mental retardation has appeared among any of their children or grandchildren. There are sporadic cases of retardation among the more distant relatives, including an epileptic, a polydactylous cretin and five high-grade retardates. There is no apparent environmental or genetic cause for the proband's retardation.

Retardation of proband of unknown origin.

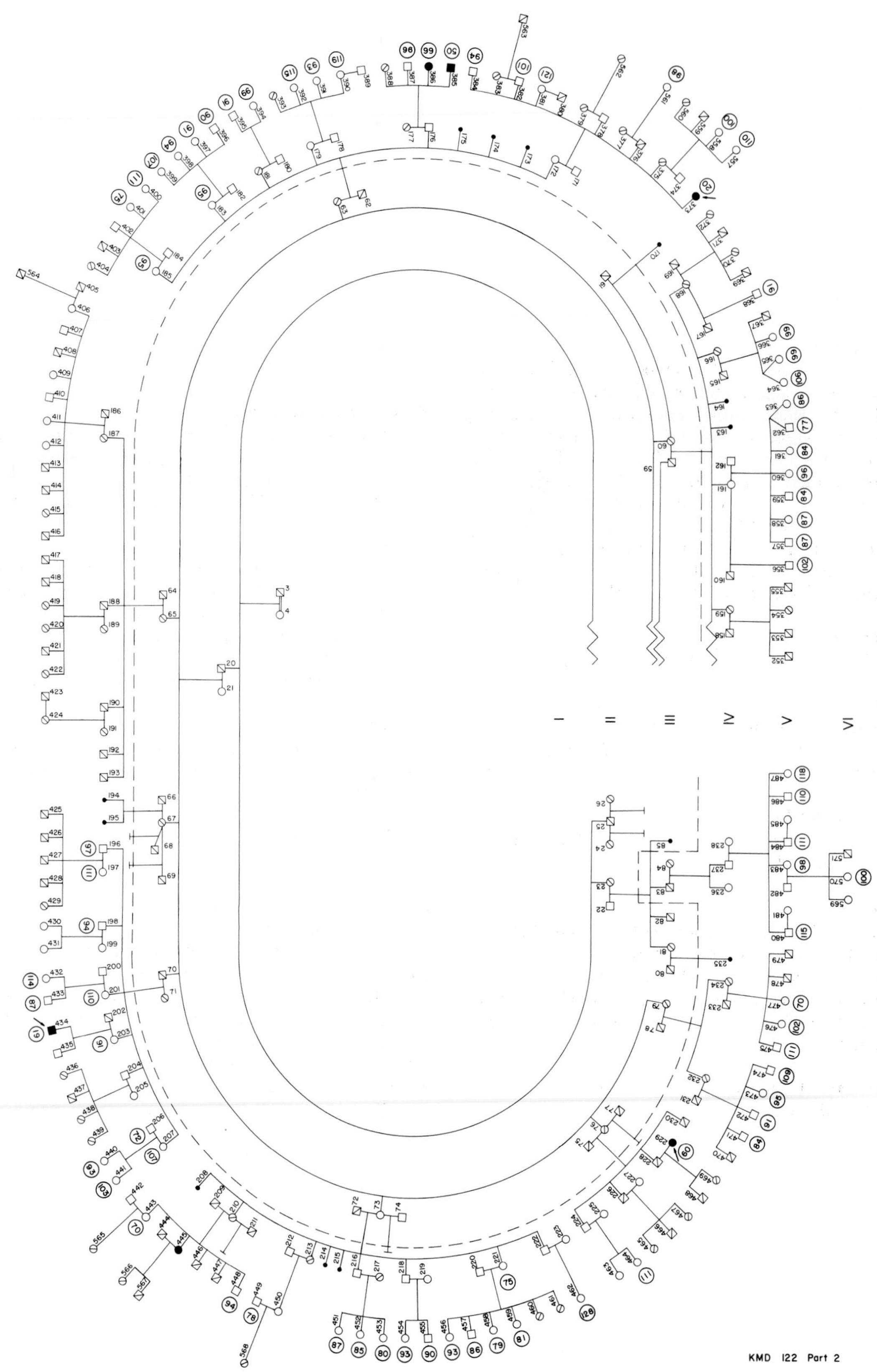

KMD 122 Part 2

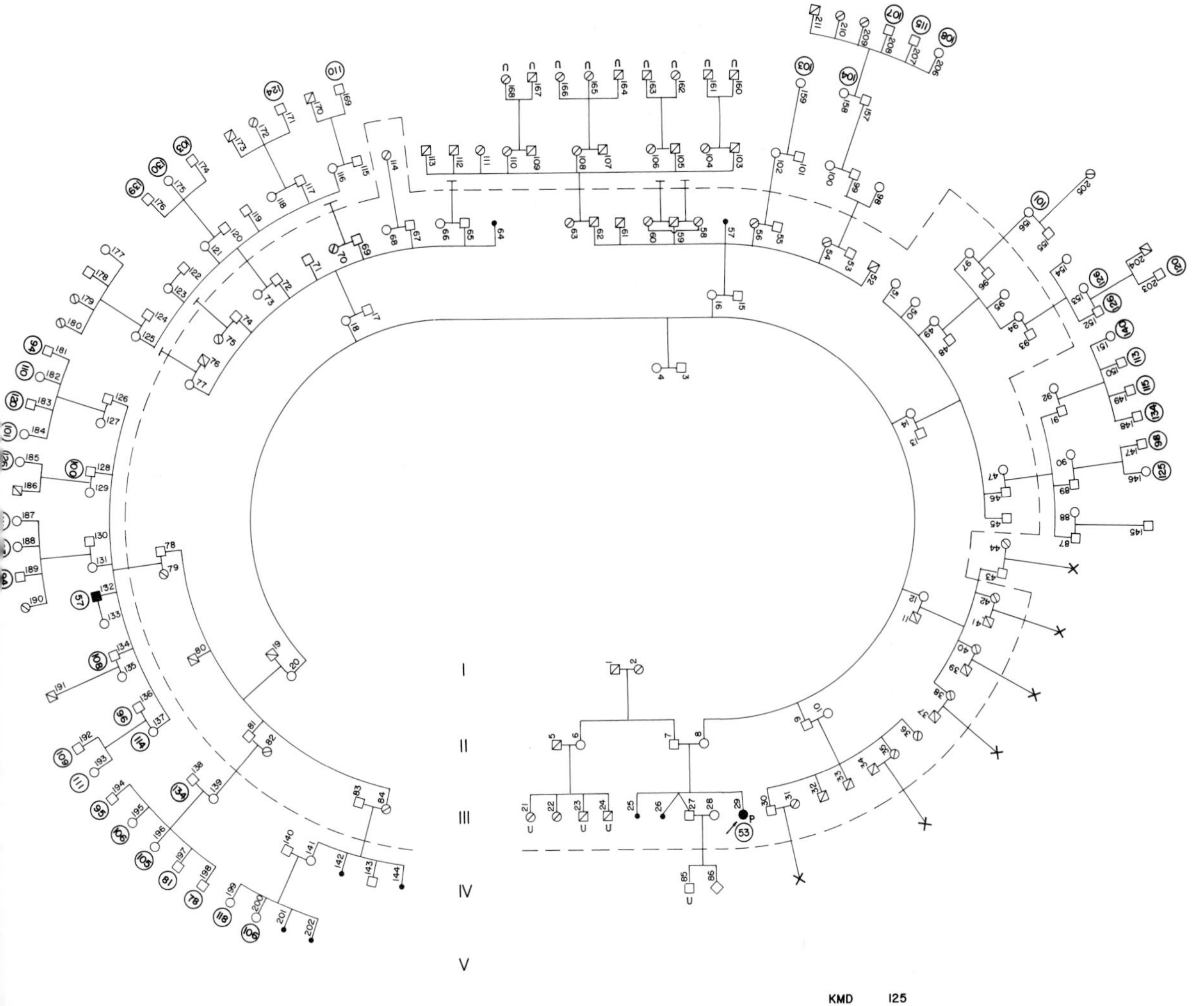

KMD 125

The Proband

The proband (29) was born in 1883, institutionalized at age 16 years, transferred to a state hospital in 1924 and discharged to a home for the aged in 1948. The state hospital diagnosis was mental deficiency without psychosis. She made little progress in school and was institutionalized after her mother's death, when her aunt feared she might become illegitimately pregnant. There was no evidence of early trauma. IQ 53. *Diagnosis:* undifferentiated mental retardation.

Grandparents

Not of interest.

Parents

Father (7) had normal intelligence but was an alcoholic, promiscuous and syphilitic.

Mother (8) had normal intelligence but was syphilitic.

Aunts and Uncles

Not of interest.

Siblings

Brother (25) was a miscarriage.

Brother (26), a twin, died shortly after birth and was "deformed."

Brother (27), twin to (26), was a bookkeeper.

Nieces and Nephews

Only two, (85) and (86), one of normal intelligence, one unknown.

First Cousins

Not of interest.

More Distant Relatives

First cousin (78) has a retarded son (132) who works in a foundry, IQ 57. He is married but childless at age 42 years.

Family Summary

The proband and one second cousin were the only retarded persons in the family. The probond's parents were both syphilitic. The proband had a negative Wassermann and no recorded stigmata of congenital syphilis. They had four children and two grandchildren.

Retardation of proband of unknown origin.

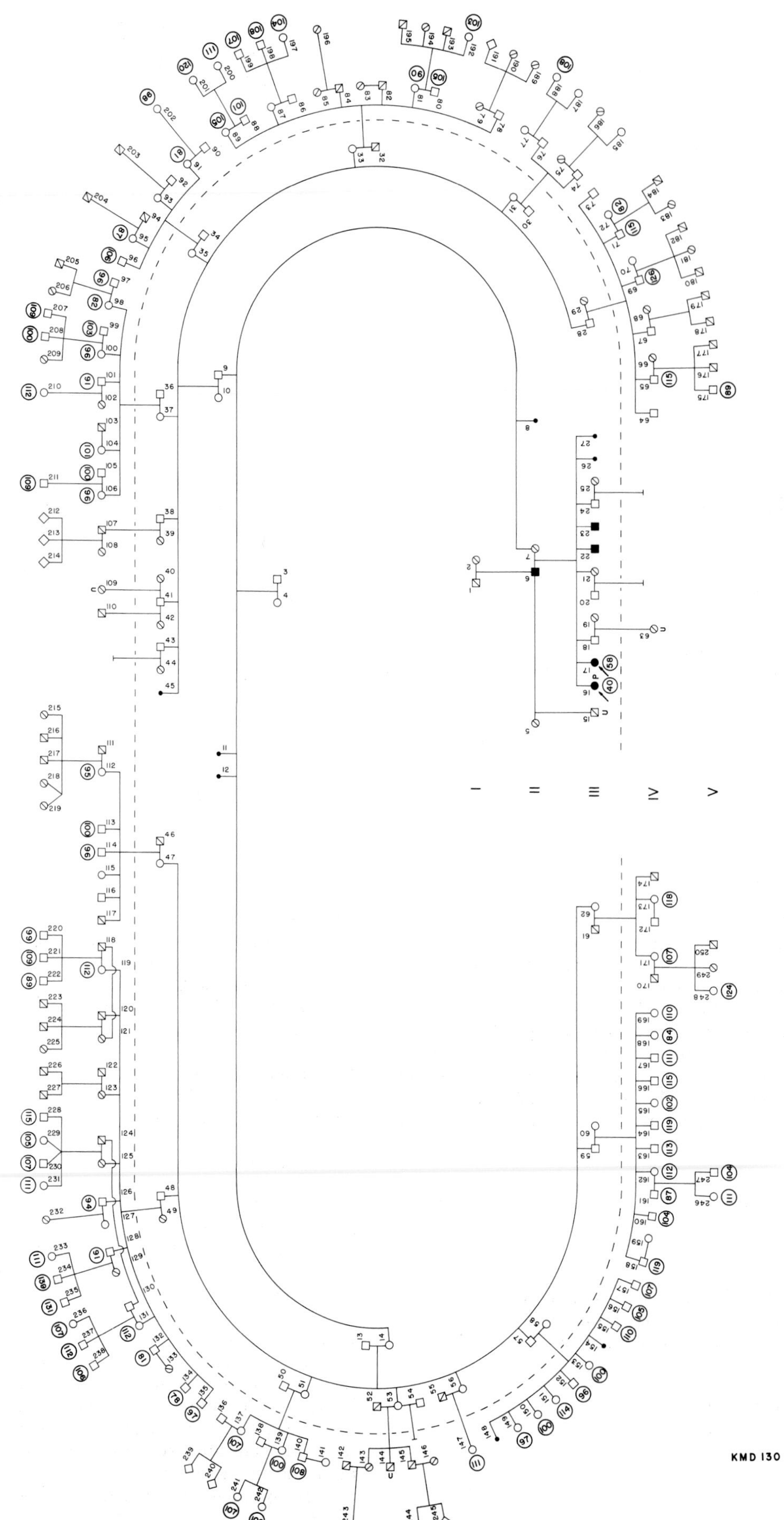

KMD 130

KMD 130

The Proband

The proband (16) was born in 1889, institutionalized at age 21 years and died of an intestinal obstruction in the institution in 1950. Her home was "hardly more than a shelter." She had no stigmata and no history of early trauma. IQ 40. *Diagnosis:* undifferentiated mental retardation.

Grandparents

Not of interest.

Parents

Father (6) was an alcoholic, retarded farm laborer.

Mother (7) was "mentally slow."

Aunts and Uncles

No paternal relatives. Her father was an only child.

Maternal relatives all had normal intelligence.

Siblings

Sister (17) was institutionalized at age 19 years and has remained in the institution ever since. She was given a physical and neurological examination by J. A. Böök, M.D., and John Schut, M.D., in 1950. She is extremely obese but no stigmata were found. IQ 58. *Diagnosis:* undifferentiated mental retardation.

Brothers (18) and (24) are normal.

Sister (21) is a waitress of unknown intelligence.

Brother (22) drowned as a young man. He could not work without supervision and was retarded.

Brother (23) is a single, childless farm laborer and is retarded.

(26) and (27) were stillbirths.

Half Siblings

Half brother (15) is unknown.

Nieces and Nephews

Only one, (63), who is unknown to relatives.

First Cousins

Not of interest.

More Distant Relatives

Not of interest.

Family Summary

The proband, her father and three siblings were retarded. The proband and her siblings were all of about the same degree of retardation. The proband's parents had nine children and one grandchild.

Retardation of proband of unknown origin.

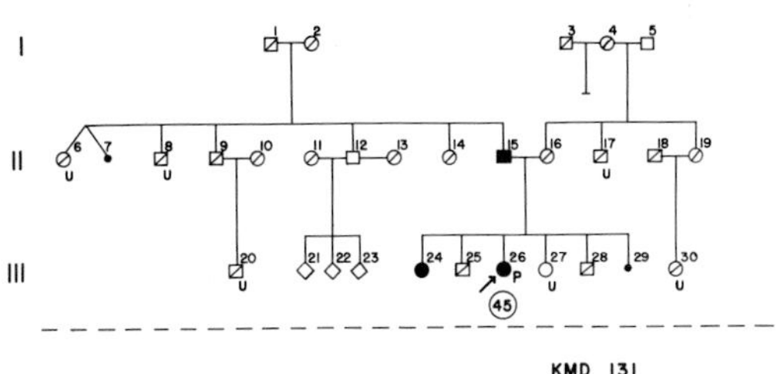

KMD 131

KMD 131

The Proband

The proband (26) was born in 1894, institutionalized at age 19 years and died of tuberculosis in the institution in 1913. She lived in great squalor but there is no record of birth injury or perinatal infection. She and her sisters were placed in the state orphanage when the proband was 6 years old. The proband was transferred to a foster home from which the father removed her, and she was then institutionalized. She had a lateral curvature of the spine and lordosis of the lumbar vertebrae. IQ 45. *Diagnosis:* undifferentiated mental retardation.

Grandparents

Not of interest.

Parents

Father (15) was an odd job man who was retarded and an alcoholic.

Mother (16) had unknown intelligence.

Aunts and Uncles

Not of interest.

Siblings

Sister (24) died in the state orphanage at age 15 years. Retarded.

Brother (25) drowned at 9 years.

Sister (27) was sent to a reformatory for incorrigibility. After her release she left the state and is unknown at the present time. She had normal intelligence.

Brother (28) died of whooping cough at age 4 years.

Sister (29) died of "brain fever" at 9 months.

Nieces and Nephews

Unknown.

First Cousins

Unknown.

More Distant Relatives

Unknown.

Family Summary

The proband, her sister and her father were retarded. The family lived in great squalor and poverty. The proband's parents had six children. It is not known if there were grandchildren; if so, they would be the descendants of the only normal adult sibling of the proband.

Retardation of proband of unknown origin.

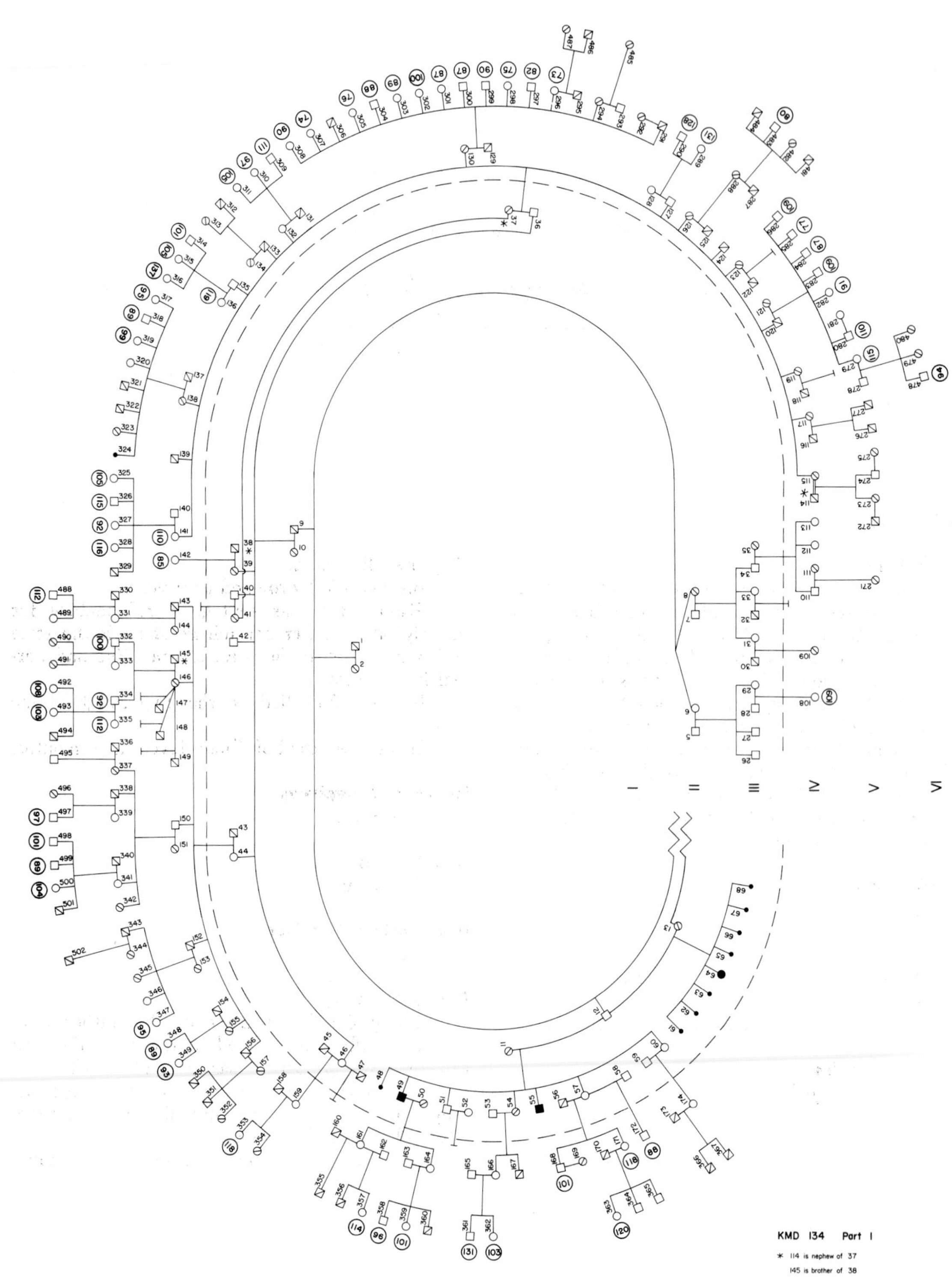

KMD 134 Part I

* 114 is nephew of 37
145 is brother of 38

KMD 134

The Proband

The proband (100) was born in 1880, institutionalized at age 20 years and was still in the institution in 1961. She was a twin and was reared in a well kept, kindly home. Her birth was uneventful, but she was deficient in animation and her early nutrition was far below par. She never walked and could not be tested because "she said 'no' to 'practically everything,'" according to the psychologist. She was a low-grade retardate who could not walk because of the shortness of the muscles on the posterior aspect of the legs. *Diagnosis:* undifferentiated mental retardation.

Grandparents

Not of interest.

Parents

Father (21) had unknown intelligence.
Mother (22) had normal intelligence.

Aunts and Uncles

Not of interest.

Siblings

(96) was a stillbirth.

(97), (98) and (99) were miscarriages.

(101), twin to proband, died of "lung fever" at 3 months.

Sister (103) had normal intelligence, as did her husband and her six children.

Nieces and Nephews

Not of interest.

First Cousins

(49) is retarded but has two normal children. His wife's intelligence is unknown.

(55), brother to (49), is a single, childless handyman and is retarded.

(64), the only one to reach adulthood in a sibship of six miscarriages and one infant death, died of appendicitis at age 24 years, single and childless. She was retarded. Her mother (13) spent many years in a mental hospital. (64) never talked and would stand and stare for hours.

More Distant Relatives

First cousin (83) has a retarded grandchild (423) who completed the fifth grade and lives at home.

Four of the 15 children of (130) have borderline IQ's, four have low-normal IQ's while three of their cousins, (289) (290) and (316), have IQ's of 131, 128 and 137.

Family Summary

The proband, three first cousins and one more distant relative were retarded. The proband was a low-grade retardate, a twin and a member of a sibship which included one stillbirth, three miscarriages and only one surviving normal child. There was no history of difficult delivery or of perinatal infection. She was deficient in animation at birth and her early nutrition was far below par.

Retardation of proband of unknown origin.

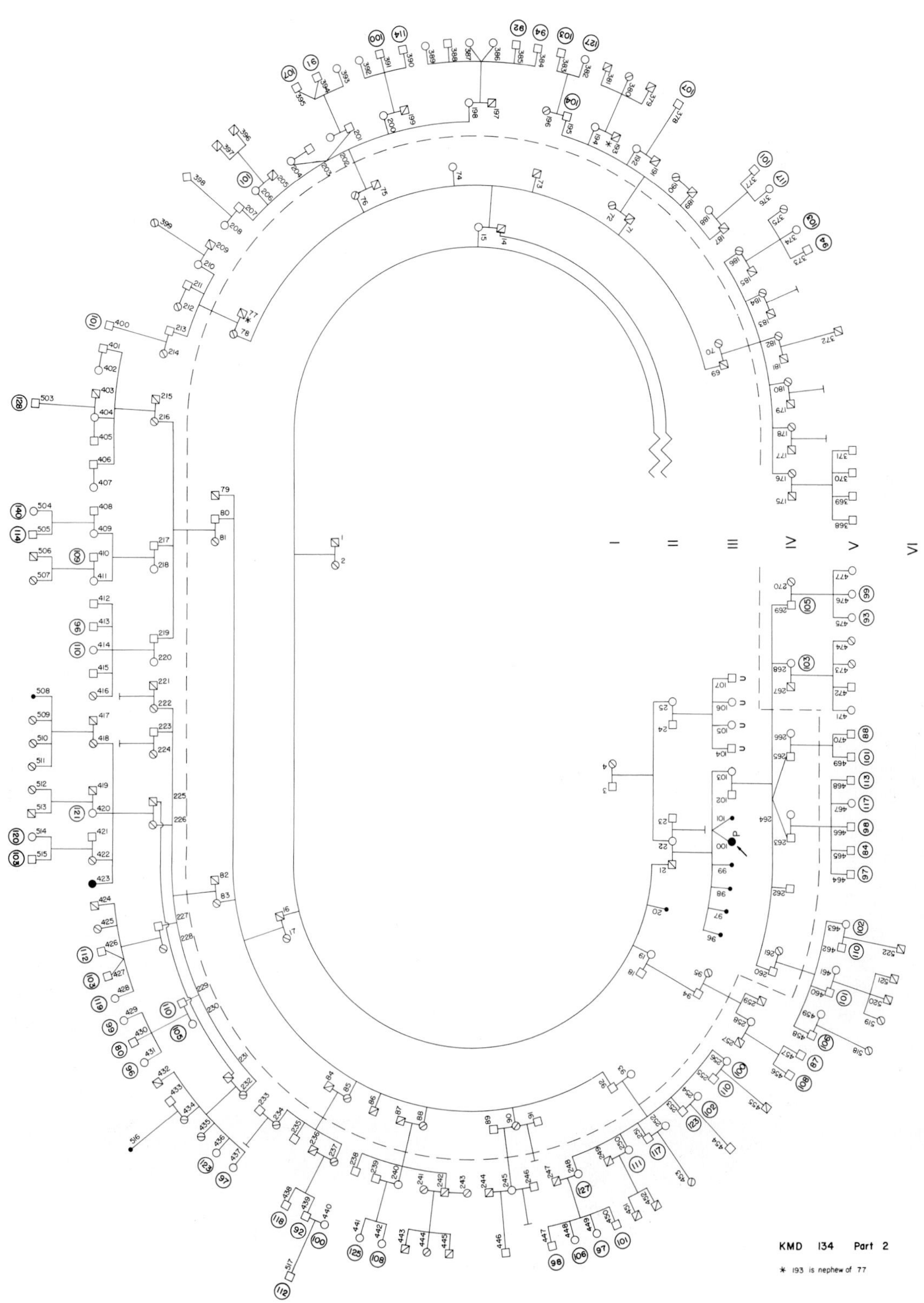

KMD 134 Part 2

* 193 is nephew of 77

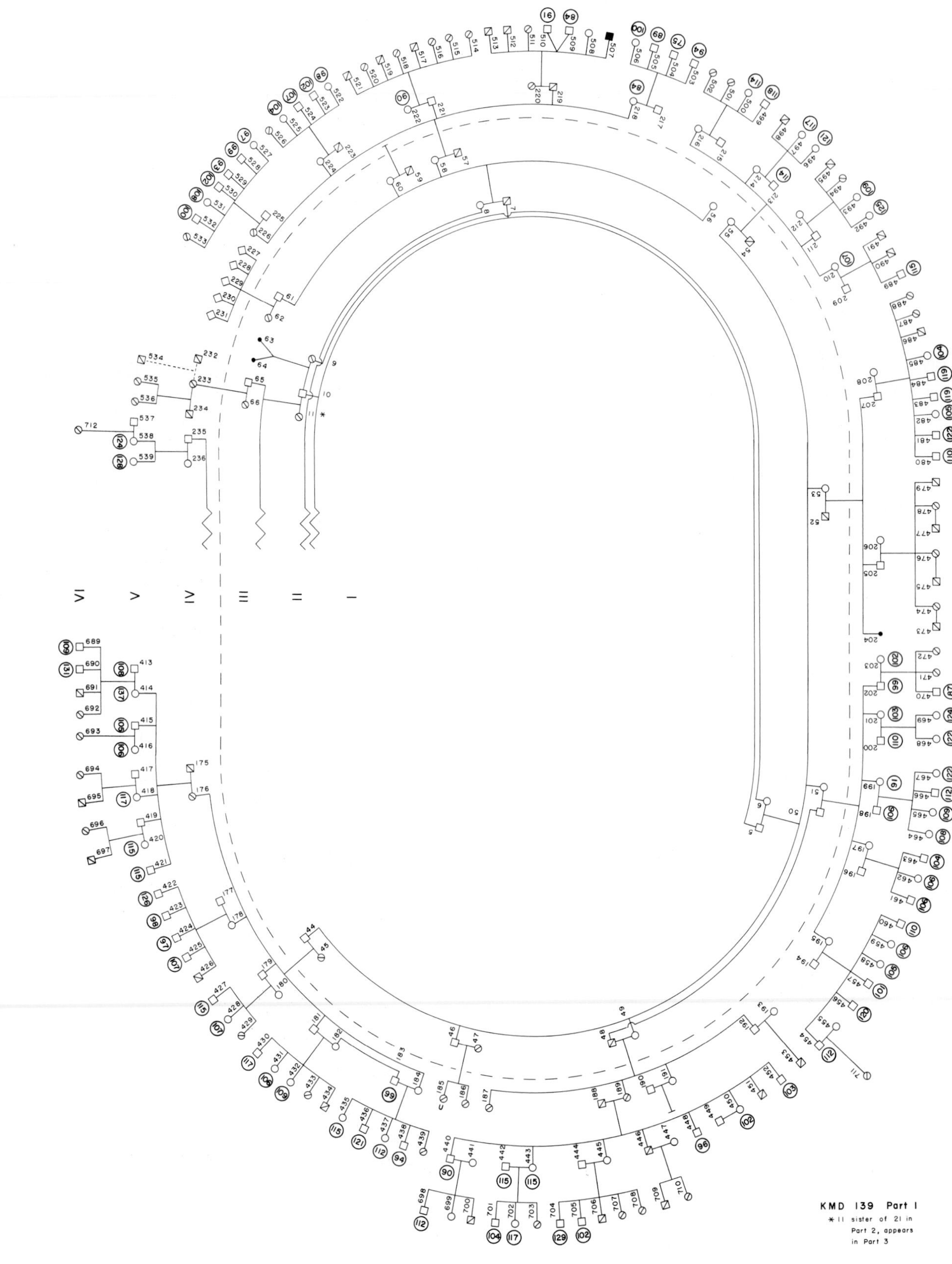
KMD 139 Part I
* 11 sister of 21 in Part 2, appears in Part 3

KMD 139

The Proband

The proband (103) was born in 1889, institutionalized at age 14 years and died of pulmonary tuberculosis in the institution in 1912. He had no history of birth injury or perinatal disease and no stigmata. He walked, but talked very little and was destructive. His home environment was very good. IQ 10. *Diagnosis:* undifferentiated mental retardation.

Grandparents

Not of interest.

Parents

Father (20) had normal intelligence.

Mother (21) had normal intelligence but was epileptic.

Aunts and Uncles

Not of interest except for the first cousin marriage of maternal uncle (27) and his wife (28), both of unknown intelligence. No retardation has been found among their descendants.

Siblings

Sister (102) has normal intelligence.
(104) and (105) were miscarriages.
Sister (106) is a teacher.
(107), (108) and (109) were miscarriages.
(110) was a registered nurse.
(111) and (112) were miscarriages.
(114) was a teacher with a normal child.

Nieces and Nephews

Only one, (310), a nephew with IQ 100, wife (311) and four children (623), (624), (625) and (626) with IQ's of 114, 102, 101, 116 and 91, respectively.

First Cousins

(46) had normal intelligence but was hospitalized for "simple" schizophrenia.

More Distant Relatives

(507) is a retarded farm laborer.

(601) has an IQ of 63. His father (287) was also retarded, IQ 67, but his mother (288) had an IQ of 118. His three siblings have IQ scores of 108, 111 and 126.

Family Summary

The proband, IQ 10, was the only known retardate in this family with the exception of two distant relatives who were high-grade retardates. His mother was epileptic but had normal intelligence. One first cousin was hospitalized for schizophrenia. The proband had no history of birth injury, early infection or environmental deprivation. His parents had 12 conceptions of which seven were miscarriages. The remaining four normal children were all girls only one of whom married, so that the proband's parents have only one grandchild. The high proportion of miscarriages in the proband's sibship suggests a genetic abnormality of some sort, but it cannot be identified.

Retardation of proband of unknown origin.

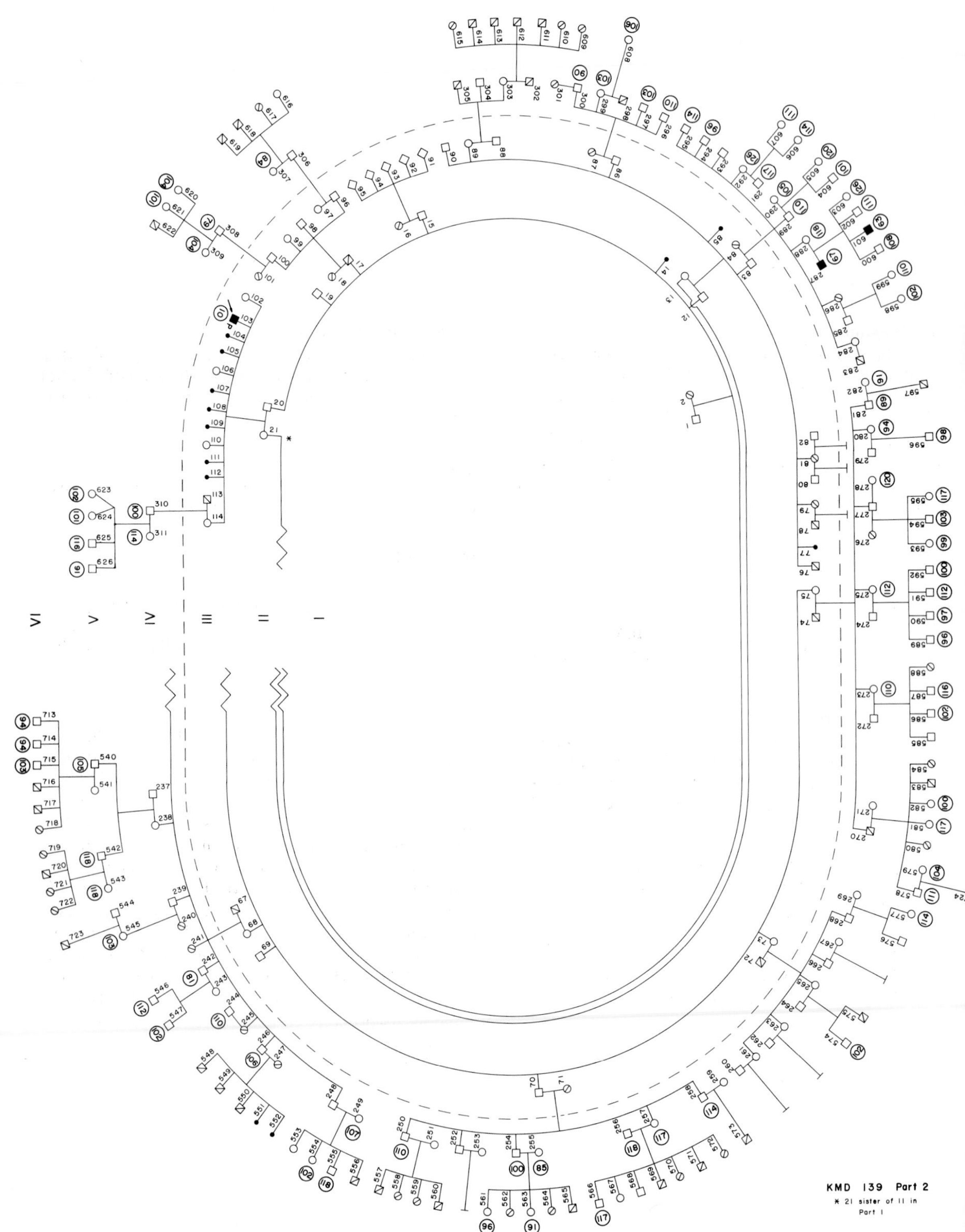

KMD 139 Part 2

* 21 sister of 11 in Part 1

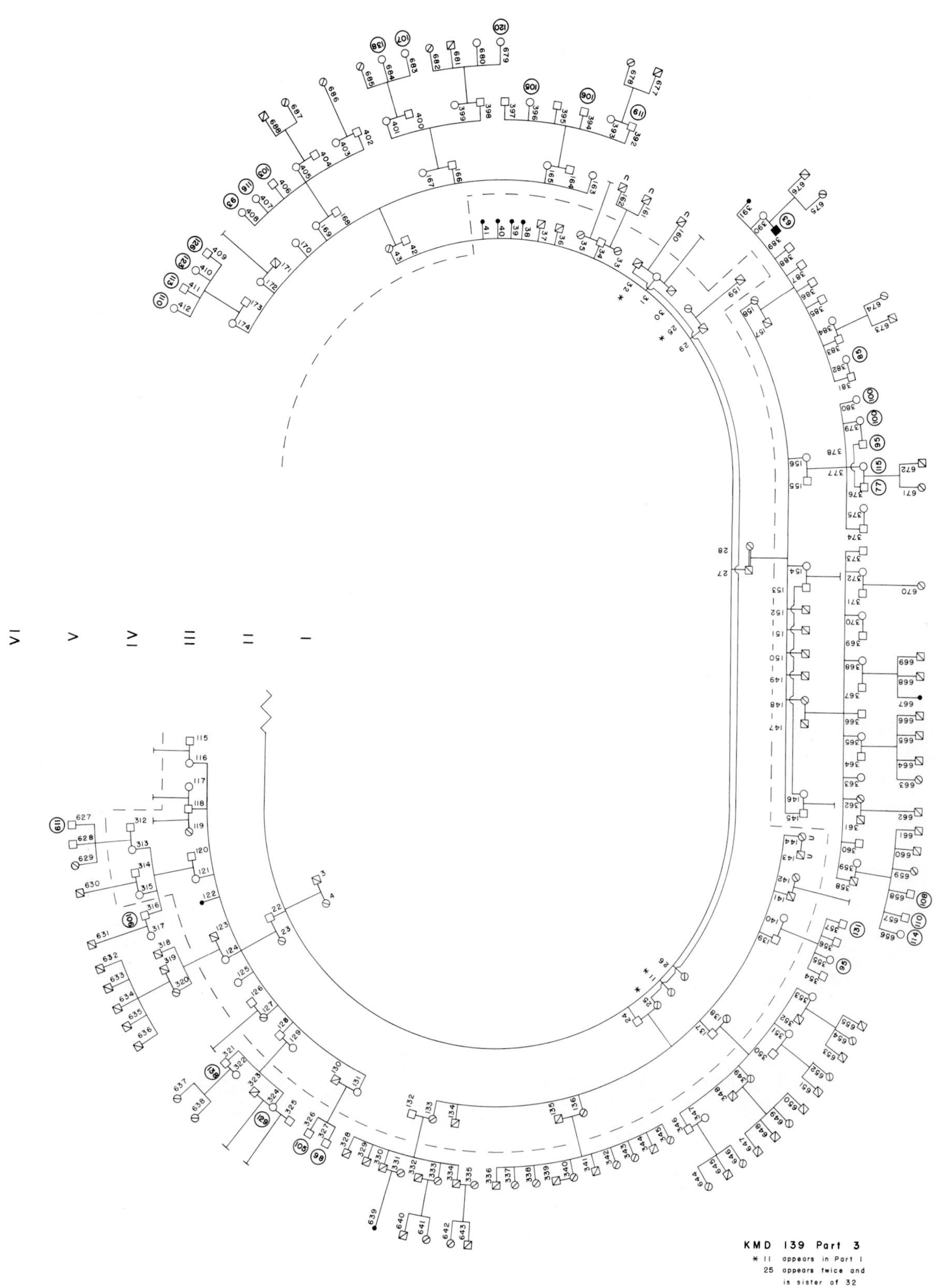

KMD 139 Part 3

* 11 appears in Part 1
25 appears twice and is sister of 32

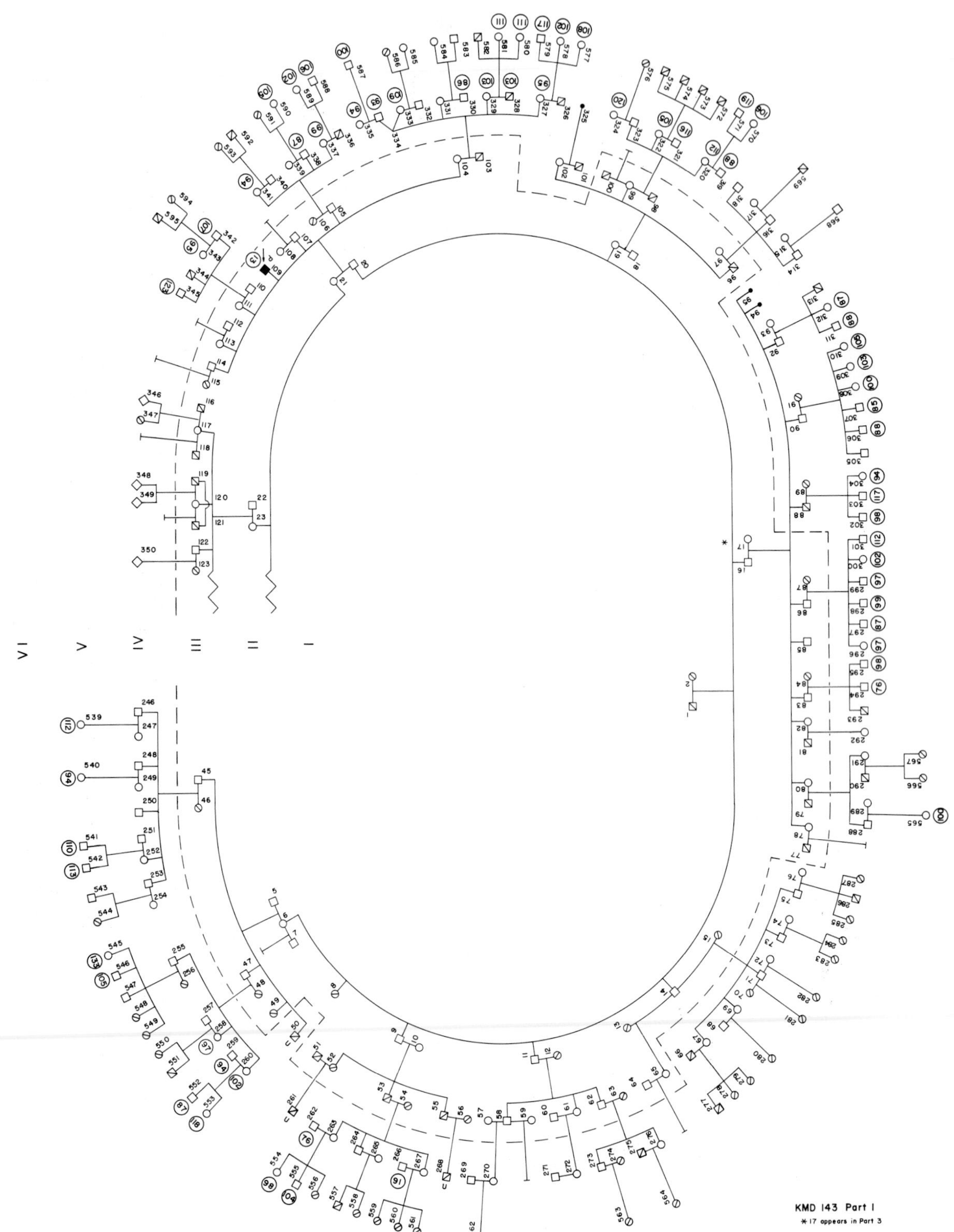

KMD 143 Part I

* 17 appears in Part 3

KMD 143

The Proband

The proband (109) was born in 1899, institutionalized at age 6 years and after one discharge of two years and readmission, died of mitral insufficiency in the institution in 1918. He was born after a prolonged labor but there was no history of birth injury or perinatal infection and he had no stigmata. The home environment was very good. IQ 13. *Diagnosis:* undifferentiated mental retardation.

Grandparents

Not of interest.

Parents

Both the father (20) and the mother (21) had normal intelligence.

Aunts and Uncles

All had normal intelligence.

Siblings

All had normal intelligence. No retardates have appeared among their children or grandchildren.

Nieces and Nephews

Not of interest.

First Cousins

Not of interest.

More Distant Relatives

(367) is a filling station attendant with IQ 67.

Family Summary

The proband, IQ 13, was the only retarded person in this family with the exception of one distantly related, high-grade retardate. He had no history of serious injury or infection, no stigmata and was reared in a good home. The proband's parents had seven children and only 11 grandchildren despite the fact that all their six normal children married. Three of these marriages were childless.

Retardation of proband of unknown origin.

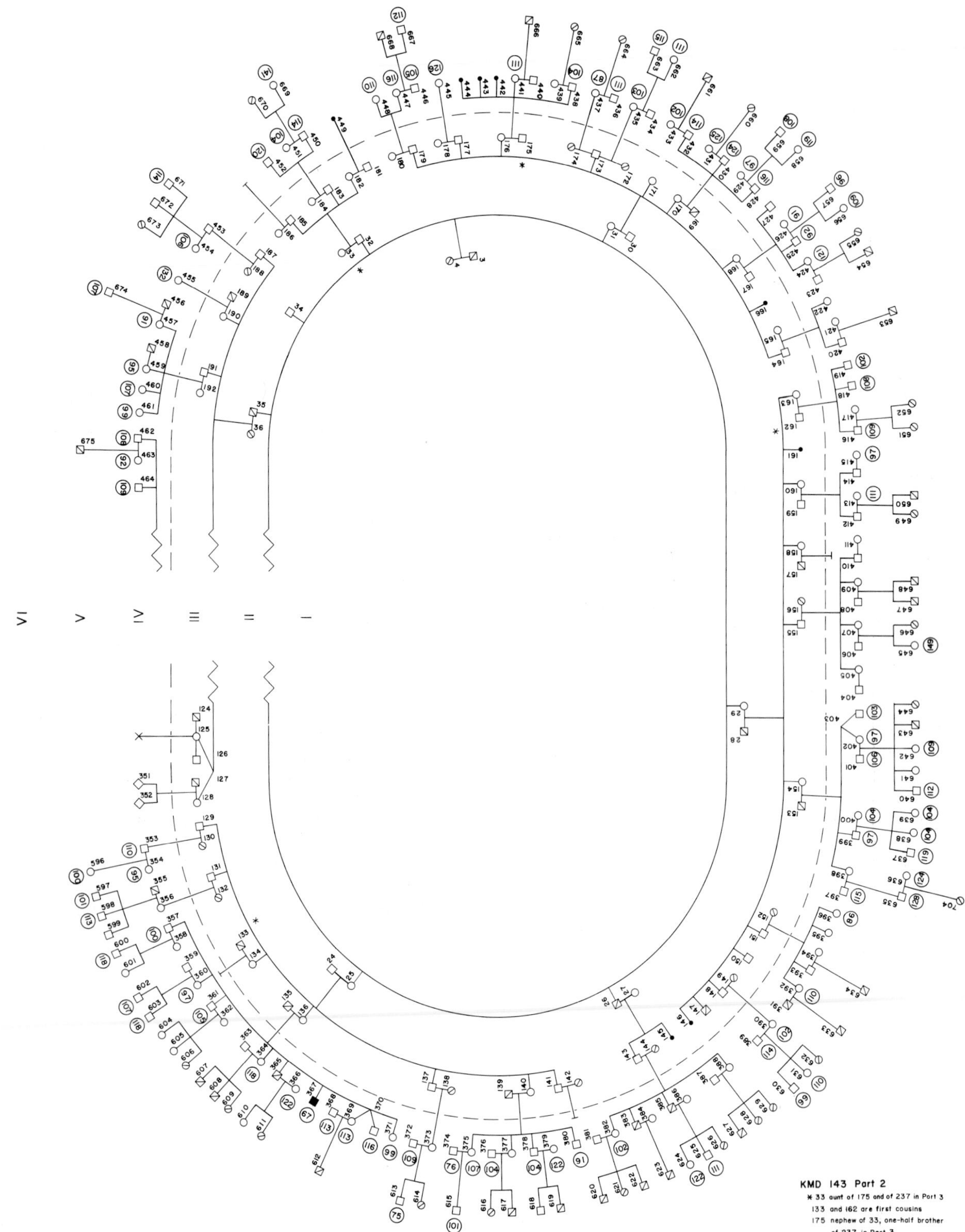
VI
V
IV
III
II
I
KMD 143 Part 2
* 33 aunt of 175 and of 237 in Part 3
133 and 162 are first cousins
175 nephew of 33, one-half brother of 237 in Part 3

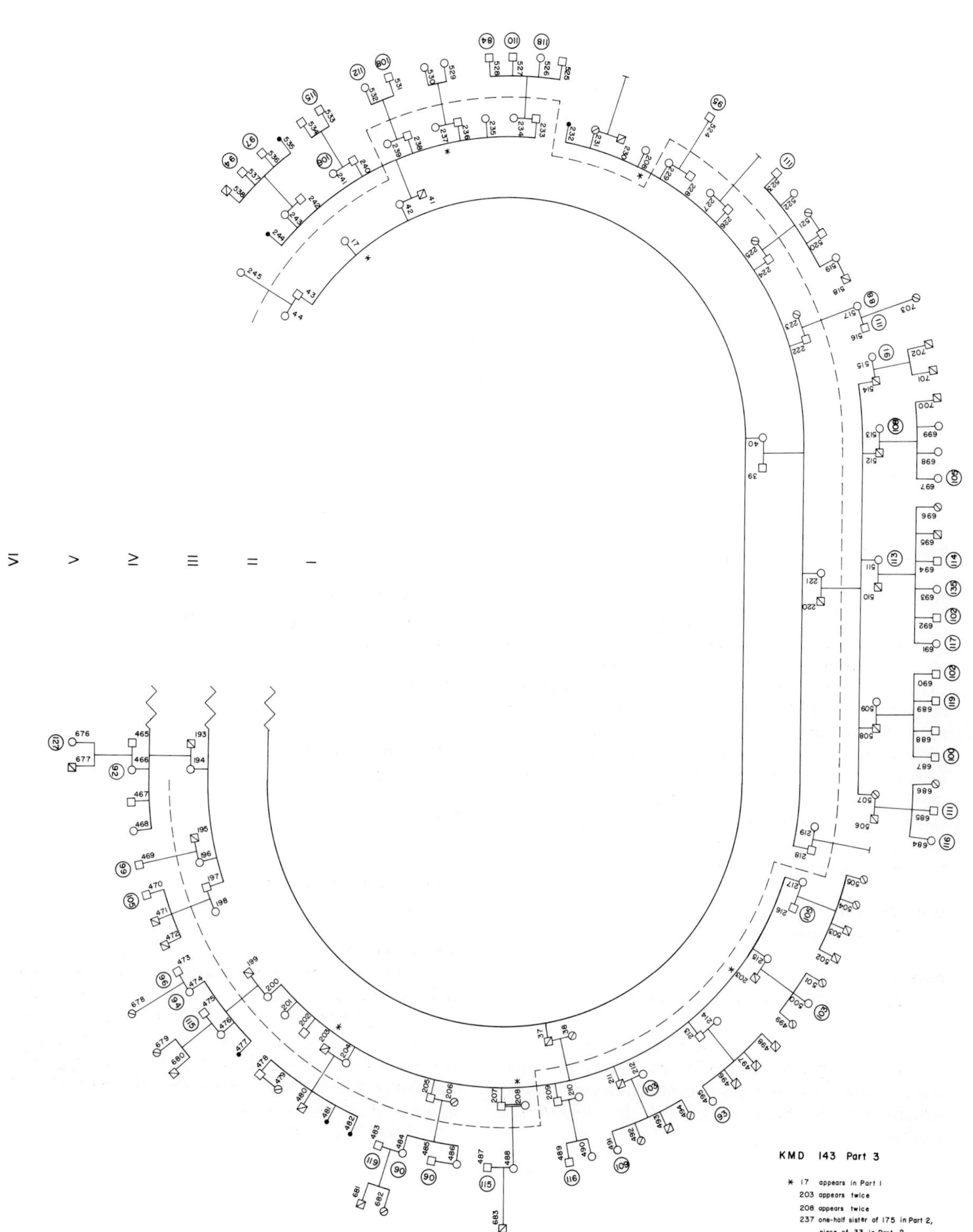

KMD 143 Part 3

* 17 appears in Part I
203 appears twice
208 appears twice
237 one-half sister of 175 in Part 2, niece of 33 in Part 2

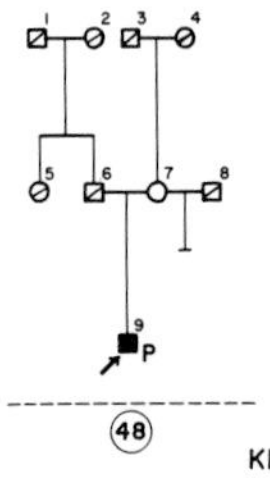

KMD 146

KMD 146

The Proband

The proband (9) was born in 1899 and institutionalized at age 13 years. After several years of being in and out of the institution, he was placed in a mental hospital in 1918, transferred to two others in the course of 11 years, the last time to the "Annex for the Dangerously Insane" after a three month prison sentence. He died in a mental hospital in 1935. He never talked well, went to school for seven years but completed only the first grade. He became quite incorrigible. IQ 48. *Diagnosis:* undifferentiated mental retardation with subsequent psychosis.

Grandparents

Not of interest.

Parents

Father (5) was a stonemason, intelligence unknown.

Mother (6) was a scrubwoman of apparently normal intelligence, but with some kind of personality disorder. She used several different names, usually the surnames of persons for whom she worked.

Aunts and Uncles

Only one, a paternal aunt who died at 16 years of age.

Siblings

None.

Nieces and Nephews

None.

First Cousins

None.

More Distant Relatives

None.

Family Summary

The proband was retarded in development and in school. In addition, he became mentally ill to the point that he was institutionalized in the "Annex for the Dangerously Insane" in a mental hospital. He had no close relatives since his only paternal relative died at 16 years. His mother was an only child, as was the proband.

Retardation of proband of unknown origin.

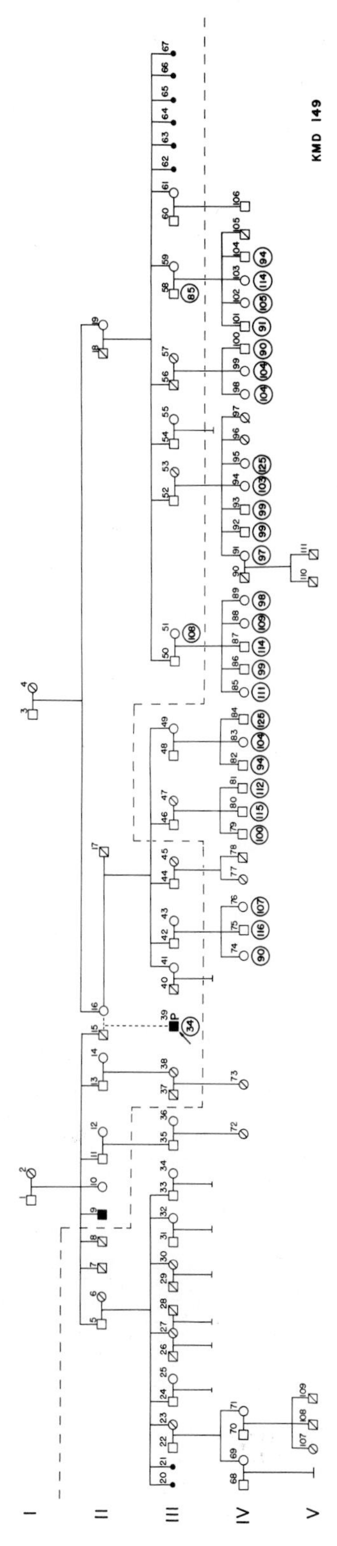

KMD 149

The Proband

The proband (39), an illegitimate child, was born in 1907, institutionalized at age 6 years and died in the institution in 1918 when he was accidently strangled by another patient. He was apparently normal until the age of 4 years when he developed a large appetite which could not be satisfied. He had no stigmata and no record of early trauma. He lost the power of speech at age 4. IQ 34. *Diagnosis:* unknown.

Grandparents

Maternal grandmother died in a mental hospital. She was epileptic and manic depressive and had as least seven siblings who were also hospitalized for mental illness.

Parents

Father (15) was a laborer "always ragged and dirty and seldom sober." Intelligence unknown.

Mother (16) went to high school, had normal intelligence but was syphilitic and mentally ill.

Aunts and Uncles

Paternal uncle (9) was retarded and was under bond at one time for incendiarism. He died unmarried and childless.

Maternal aunt was epileptic.

Siblings

No full siblings.

Half Siblings

All normal.

Nieces and Nephews

No full nieces and nephews.

Children of half siblings not of interest.

First Cousins

Cousin (50) has been arrested for drinking, abandonment and non-support. He had normal intelligence. On the Minnesota Multiphasic test his wife (51) scored as a psychopathic deviate, paranoid with amoral tendencies. IQ 108.

More Distant Relatives

Not of interest.

Family Summary

The proband and a paternal uncle were retarded. The proband's mother came from a family with an extensive history of mental illness. She was epileptic and syphilitic. The proband, however, showed no signs of congenital syphilis. The paternal side had a remarkably low reproductive rate; ten paternal cousins produced only four children. The proband's parents had one child, no grandchildren.

Retardation of proband of unknown origin.

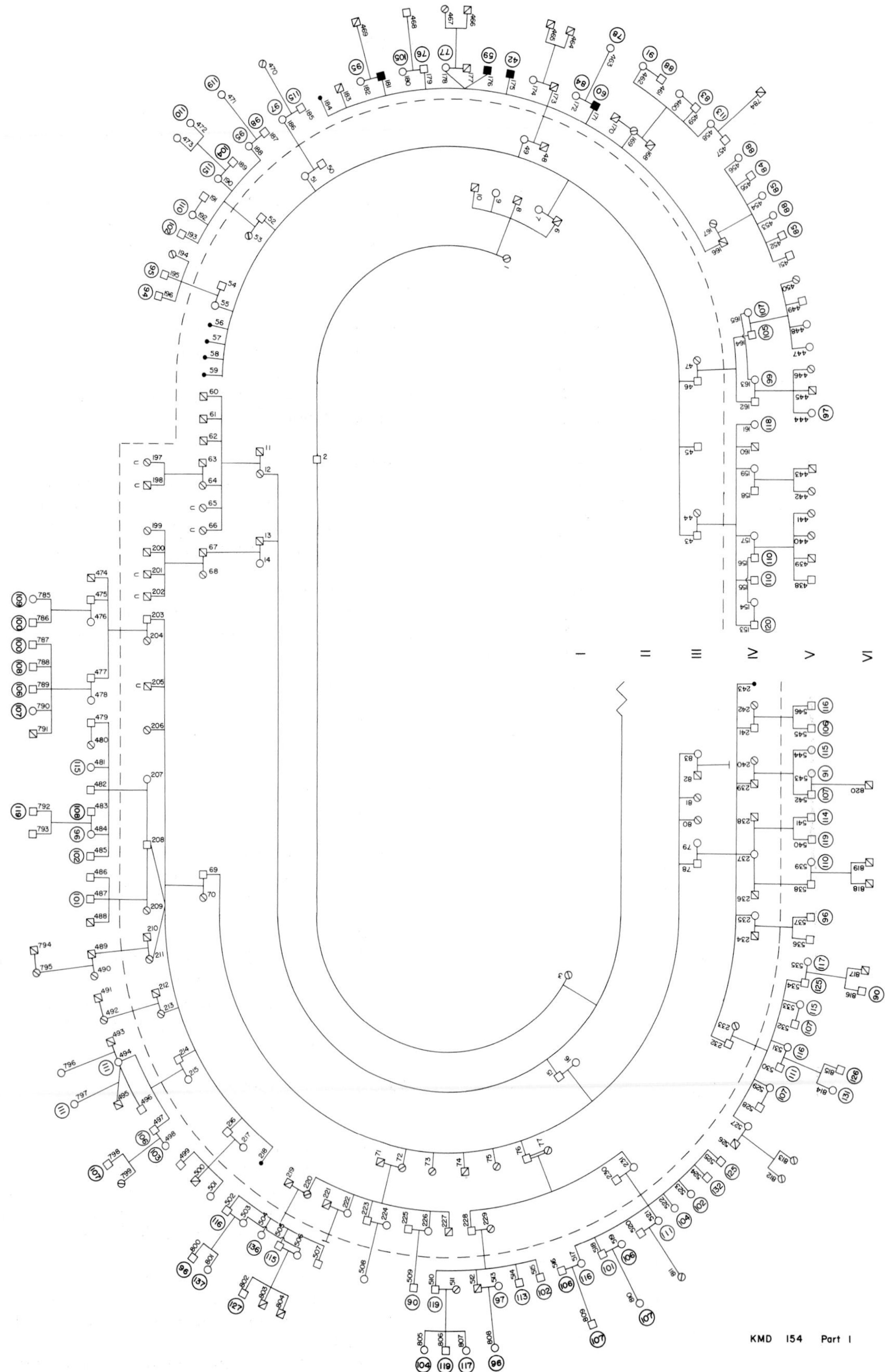

KMD 154

The Proband

The proband (97) was born in 1885, institutionalized at 25 years and died of pulmonary tuberculosis in the institution in 1912. She was unmarried and childless. There was no history of birth injury or perinatal infection but she was "different from other children from the beginning." She attended school, could read and write but "at about 11 years began to go backwards." Her IQ was 13 at age 26 years. *Diagnosis:* unknown.

Grandparents

Not of interest.

Parents

Proband's father (22) was a teacher in a religious school, was odd for many years and "overly" religious. Intelligence unknown.

The mother (23) had normal intelligence.

Aunts and Uncles

Paternal uncle (15) was hospitalized for mental illness.

Paternal uncle (21) died of alcoholism.

Maternal aunt (38) was epileptic but had normal intelligence.

Siblings

Brother (88) was hospitalized for mental illness and was also mentally retarded.

Sister (89) was hospitalized three times for mental illness. She died in a mental hospital. *Diagnosis:* imbecility but possibly deteriorated schizophrenia.

Sisters (90) and (96) died in infancy, causes unknown.

Sisters (92) and (94) had unknown intelligence. Both were married but childless.

Sister (95) was mentally retarded. She died at age 18 years.

Nieces and Nephews

None.

First Cousins

Proband's cousin (106) became mentally retarded, paralyzed and helpless, after a severe illness at the age of 3 years.

Proband's cousin (107), brother to (106), is mentally retarded, high grade.

The first cousin marriage of the normal brother (109) of the above persons resulted in the birth of three children, all normal (one died of mumps at 2 years).

More Distant Relatives

Proband's cousin (49) and her husband (48) both became physically and mentally incompetent because of syphilis, and had four retarded children (171), (175), (176) and (181).

(171) completed the sixth grade and is a farmer, IQ 60, wife's IQ 84, child's IQ 78.

(175) completed the third grade, is unmarried and unemployed, IQ 42.

(176) completed the sixth grade, is unmarried and works in a filling station, IQ 59.

(181) completed the third grade and is a farm laborer. No IQ score was available for him.

Family Summary

There is some doubt whether the retardation of the proband and her three siblings was congenital or might have been the result of schizophrenic deterioration. It seems unlikely, though, that four schizophrenics would appear in a sibship of six. There were two retarded cousins. The retardation of one cousin was ascribed to illness at age 3 years. Other relatives were retarded, possibly due to syphilitic infections. There were no descendants of the eight children in the proband's sibship.

Retardation of proband of unknown origin.

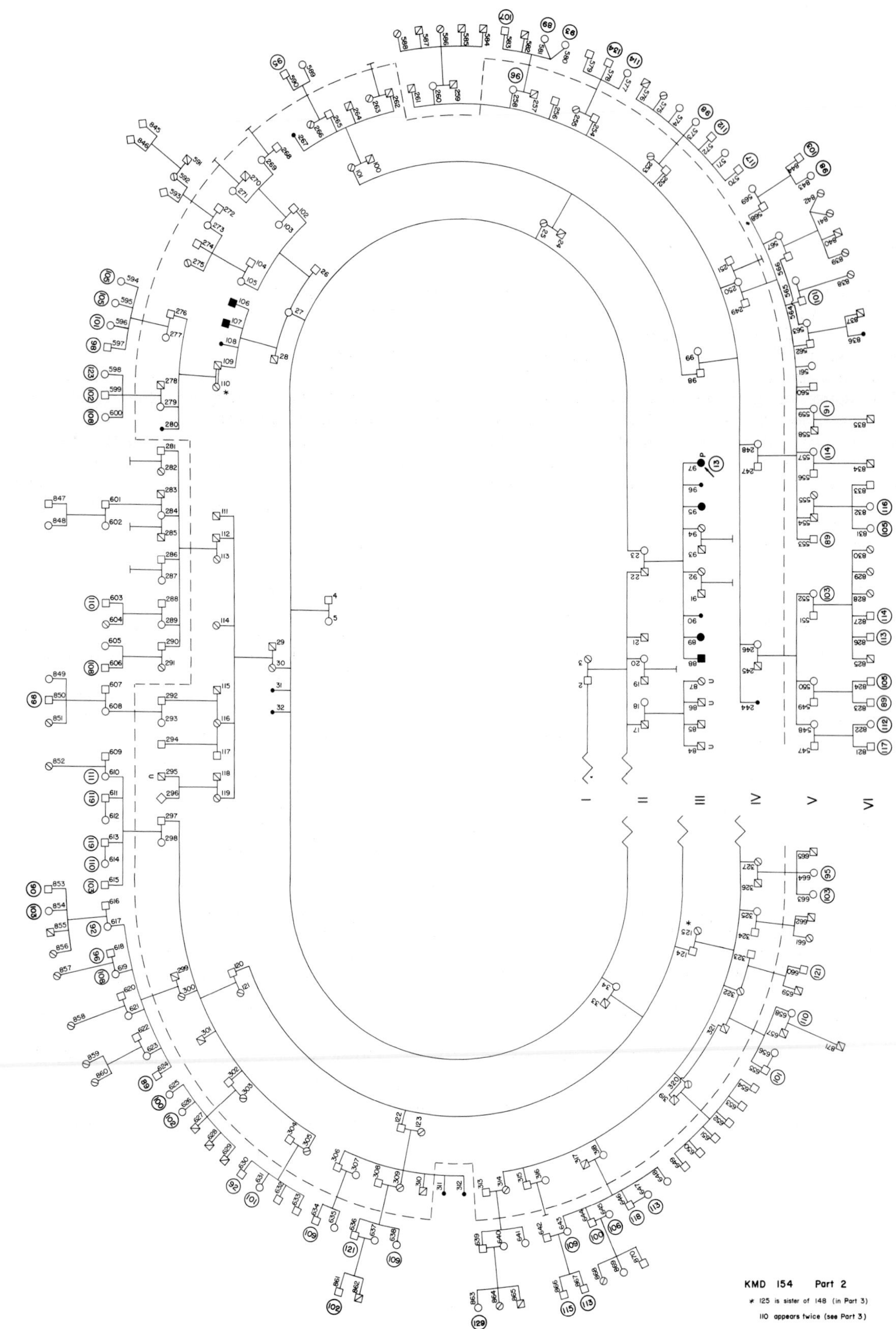

KMD 154 Part 2

* 125 is sister of 148 (in Part 3)

110 appears twice (see Part 3)

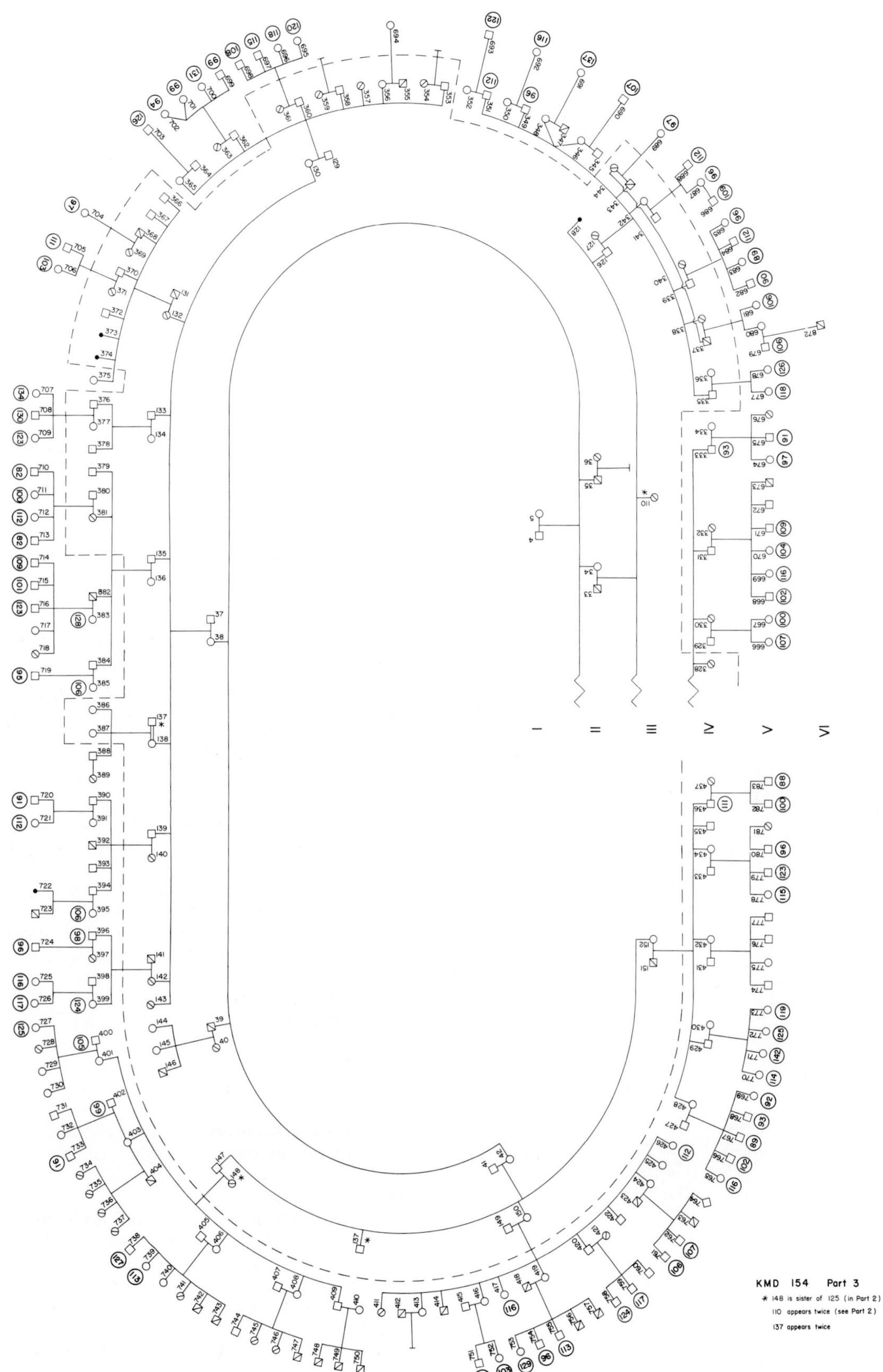

KMD 154 Part 3

* 148 is sister of 125 (in Part 2)

110 appears twice (see Part 2)

137 appears twice

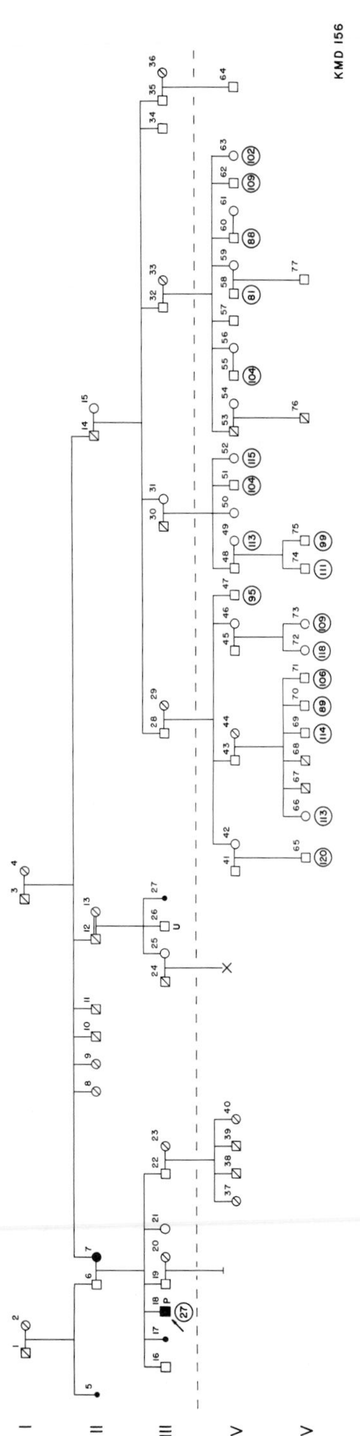

KMD 156

The Proband

The proband (18) was born in 1904, institutionalized at age 5 years and died of tuberculosis in the institution in 1925. He had no stigmata and no history of early trauma. He had rickets. He began to walk at 2½ years but never talked. IQ 27. *Diagnosis:* undifferentiated mental retardation.

Grandparents

Not of interest.

Parents

Father (6) was epileptic but had normal intelligence. He was a farmer.

Mother (7) was a very poor housekeeper but told workers she did well in school. The original investigator reported that she thought the mother was retarded.

Aunts and Uncles

Not of interest.

Siblings

Brother (16) was classified as retarded in the early records. He was a behavior problem in school. However, he completed the eighth grade and some extra manual training work in high school, so probably is not retarded. He is a laborer.

Brother (17) died of spina bifida at 3 months. (There is no record of spina bifida or hydrocephalus for the proband.)

Brother (19) completed the tenth grade and is a married, but childless, farmer with normal intelligence.

Sister (21) is an unmarried licensed practical nurse and has normal intelligence.

Brother (22) completed the ninth grade and is a farmer with normal intelligence.

Nieces and Nephews

Not of interest.

First Cousins

(27) died of epilepsy at 4 months.

More Distant Relatives

Not of interest.

Family Summary

The proband, IQ 27, and his mother were retarded. He had a brother who died of spina bifida. There is no evidence that the proband had either spina bifida or hydrocephalus. The proband's parents had six children and four grandchildren.

Retardation of proband of unknown origin.

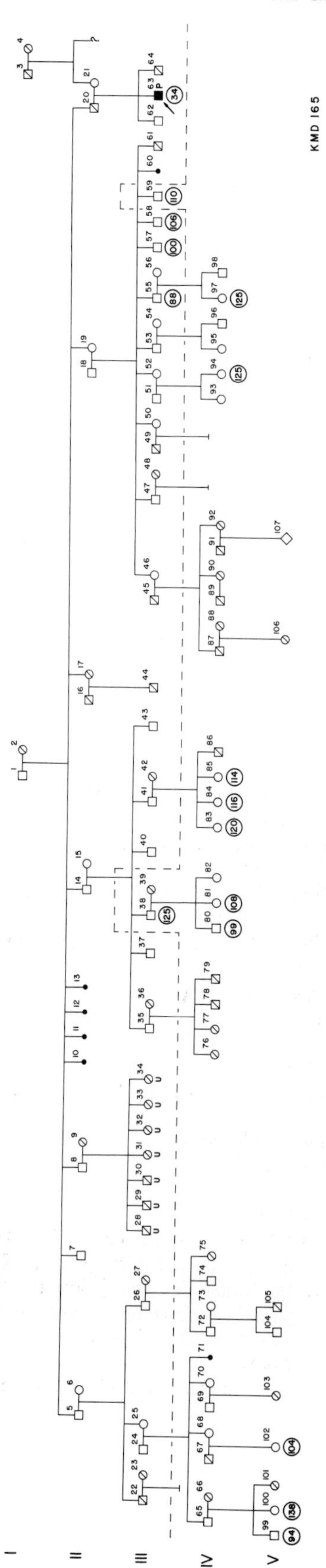

KMD 165

The Proband

The proband (63) was born in 1893 and institutionalized at age 6 years. He was transferred to a second institution as tubercular in 1938 and died there of tuberculosis in 1940. His mother was ill with tuberculosis at the time of his birth. He had no stigmata. IQ 34. *Diagnosis:* undifferentiated mental retardation.

Grandparents

Not of interest.

Parents

Father (20) was always in ill health and died of "tuberculosis of the bowels" at 36 years of age. He may have been syphilitic. Intelligence unknown.

Mother (21) had normal intelligence. She died of tuberculosis.

Aunts and Uncles

Not of interest.

Siblings

Brother (62) died of tuberculosis single and childless. He had normal intelligence.

Brother (64) died of tuberculosis single and childless. His intelligence was unknown. He was adopted at age 3 years and at that time "seemed normal."

Nieces and Nephews

None.

First Cousins

Not of interest.

More Distant Relatives

Not of interest.

Family Summary

The proband, IQ 34, was the only retarded person in the family. Both of the proband's parents, the proband and his two siblings all died of tuberculosis. The proband's parents had three children, no grandchildren.

Retardation of proband of unknown origin.

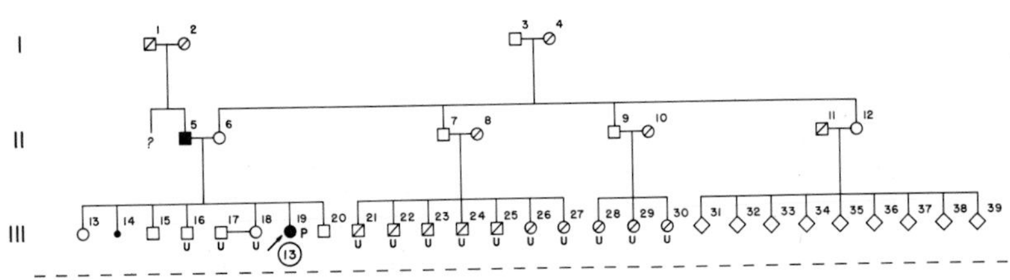

KMD 168

KMD 168

The Proband

The proband (19) was born in 1889, institutionalized at age 14 years and died of pneumonia in the institution in 1918. She was "never right" and used to sit and sing all the time. She had left lateral scoliosis and a large head that tapered toward the top. There was no history of early trauma. IQ 13. *Diagnosis:* undifferentiated mental retardation.

Grandparents

Not of interest.

Parents

Father (5) was an alcoholic, retarded and a "wanderer." He abandoned his family when the children were small.

Mother (6) was illiterate but had normal intelligence.

Aunts and Uncles

Paternal side unknown.

Maternal side had normal intelligence.

Siblings

Sister (13) died of measles at 3 years. She had normal intelligence.

Brother (14) died of measles at 1 year. He "seemed" normal.

Brother (15) was normal. He was killed by a train at age 18 years.

Brother (16) and sister (18) had normal intelligence.

Brother (20) had normal intelligence. He was killed by a train at age 15 years.

First Cousins

Unknown. All remained in Sweden.

More Distant Relatives

Unknown.

Family Summary

The proband had an IQ of 13. Her father was retarded but of a higher grade. The family could not be found for the follow-up because it had a frequently occurring Scandinavian name. The proband's parents had seven children, grandchildren unknown.

Retardation of proband of unknown origin.

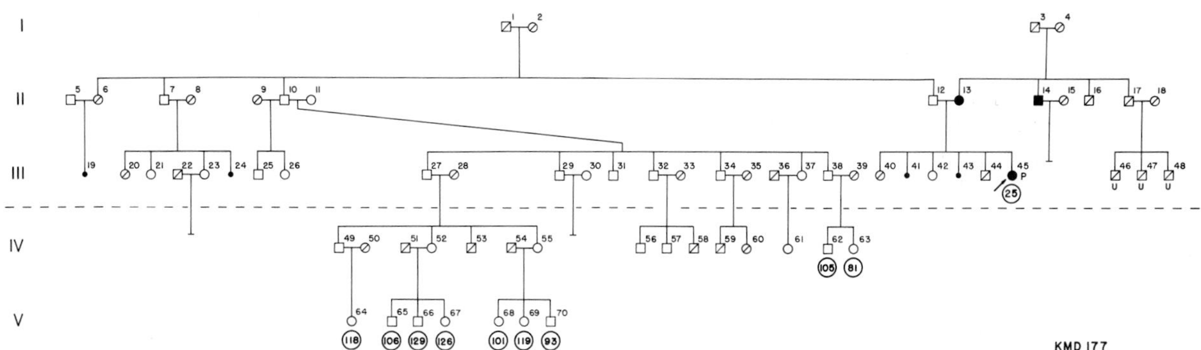

KMD 177

The Proband

The proband (45) was born in 1898, institutionalized at age 14 years, discharged in 1916 and placed in a boarding home in 1936, where she was living in 1961. There was no record of difficult birth or perinatal infection. She did not talk until the age of 8 years. She had rickets at 1 year and had defective hearing and a high arched palate. IQ 25. *Diagnosis:* undifferentiated mental retardation.

Grandparents

Not of interest.

Parents

Father (12) had normal intelligence but became blind and nearly helpless in middle age. The blindness resulted from degeneration of the optic nerve.

Mother (13) was considered to be retarded although she took excellent care of her invalid husband. "Mental age not more than eight years."

Aunts and Uncles

Maternal uncle was a laborer, married but childless and retarded.

Siblings

Sister (40) died of diphtheria at 2½ years.

Sisters (41) and (43) died of convulsions at 8 months.

Sister (42) died of diphtheria at 5 years. She had normal intelligence.

Brother (44) died of diphtheria and convulsions at 2½ years.

Nieces and Nephews

None.

First Cousins

(21) had normal intelligence but began to hear voices and was institutionalized in a mental hospital for a time.

There were only three maternal cousins, all of whom remained in Sweden.

More Distant Relatives

Unknown.

Family Summary

The proband had an IQ of 25. All of her five siblings died in childhood, three of convulsions. Her mother and a maternal uncle were high-grade retardates. The home environment was very good. The proband's parents had six children, no grandchildren.

Retardation of proband of unknown origin.

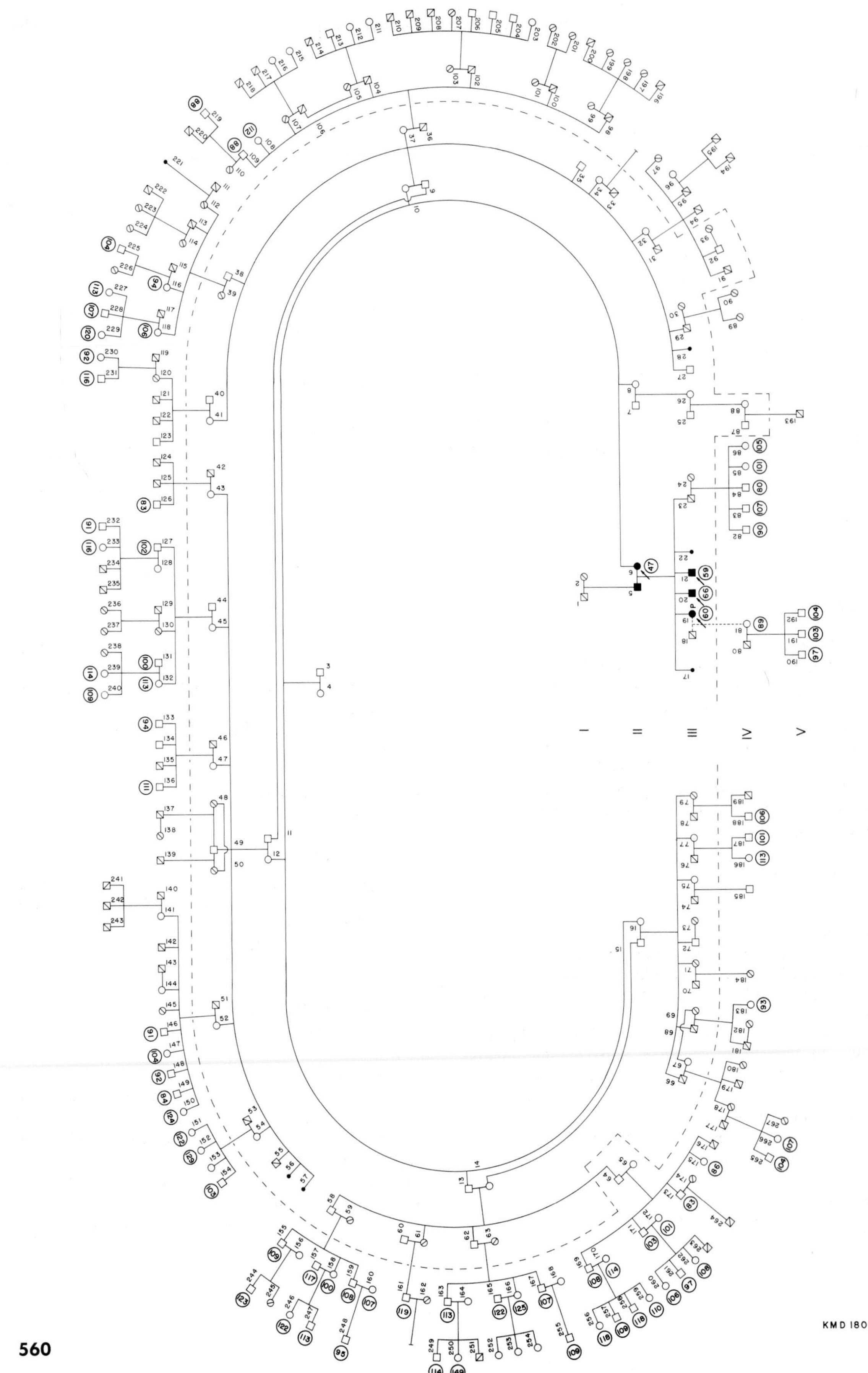

KMD 180

KMD 180

The Proband

The proband (19) was born in 1902 and institutionalized at age 11. She was discharged to her parents a year later, readmitted in 1925 and was living in a church home in 1961. She has been confined to a wheelchair with arthritis for several years. She was a seven months baby and in five years of schooling reached the second grade. She had an illegitimate child in 1923. IQ 60. *Diagnosis:* undifferentiated mental retardation.

Grandparents

Not of interest.

Parents

Father (5) was tuberculous and retarded. He and his family were town charges.

Mother (6) was retarded, IQ 47. She was institutionalized in 1925 at age 53 years and transferred a year later to a church home where she died in 1930.

Aunts and Uncles

All had normal intelligence.

Siblings

Sister (17) died of "spasms" at 3 months.

Brother (20) was institutionalized in 1913 at age 8 years. He was discharged in 1914 and died of tuberculosis in 1915. IQ 66.

Brother (21) was institutionalized in 1913 at age 5 years. He was discharged a year later and placed in a church home in 1926 where he has since remained. He had deteriorating muscular control and is now confined to a wheelchair. (The report did not state whether (21) has the same crippling affliction as the proband.) IQ 59.

(22) was a miscarriage.

Brother (23) completed the seventh grade and is a laborer. His intelligence is unknown.

Child

Proband's illegitimate daughter (81) graduated from high school. IQ 89.

Grandchildren

Three, all with normal intelligence.

Nieces and Nephews

Five, all with normal intelligence.

First Cousins

Not of interest.

More Distant Relatives

Not of interest.

Family Summary

The proband, her mother and two of her brothers were institutionalized. The proband's father was also retarded. All were fairly high-grade retardates. The proband was a premature baby. The entire family were town charges because the father was incapable of supporting the family and the mother could not keep house. The proband's illegitimate child had an IQ of 89 and her three grandchildren have normal intelligence. The proband's parents had six children and six grandchildren.

Retardation of proband of unknown origin.

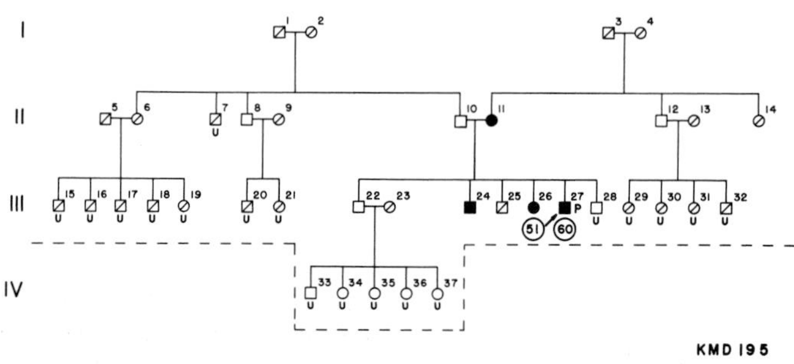

KMD 195

The Proband

The proband (27) was born in 1890, institutionalized at age 20 years and discharged in 1920. He was hospitalized at a mental hospital for observation in 1943 but was found not to be mentally ill. He was then committed as retarded and readmitted to the institution in 1945 where he was living in 1961. He had "brain fever" at age 4 years and had talked "some" before that time. He attended school for eight years with little result. The home environment was bad. His speech, hearing and vision are defective. He could not be tested upon his readmission to the institution in 1945 because he would not answer questions. His original IQ of 60 was taken in 1912. *Diagnosis:* undifferentiated mental retardation.

Grandparents

Not of interest.

Parents

According to the old records father (10) was a junk dealer and peddler and was retarded but commitment papers state he was a lumber dealer of fair financial status and that he left some inheritance to his daughter (26). It seems more likely that he was not retarded.

Mother (11) was retarded. She could not keep house.

Aunts and Uncles

Paternal uncle (8) was epileptic.

Siblings

Brother (22) was a cabinet maker and fur and hide dealer. His children are normal.

Brother (24) died single and childless at age 66. He was retarded.

Brother (25) died of tuberculosis at age 16 years. His intelligence was unknown.

Sister (26) has a long welfare record. She inherited property from her deceased parents but sold it and spent the money on bingo games. She is single and childless. IQ 51.

Brother (28) left home at age 20 years and has not been heard from since. He completed the eighth grade and was a printer.

Nieces and Nephews

Five are known, all with normal intelligence.

First Cousins

Unknown. Paternal relatives lived in other states and could not be found.

Maternal relatives lived in Russia.

More Distant Relatives

Unknown.

Family Summary

The proband, IQ 60, two siblings and the mother were retarded. The home environment was very poor but two of the proband's siblings had normal intelligence. The proband's parents had six children and five known grandchildren. The relatives could not be found for the follow-up since our only contact was the sister with IQ 51.

Retardation of proband of unknown origin.

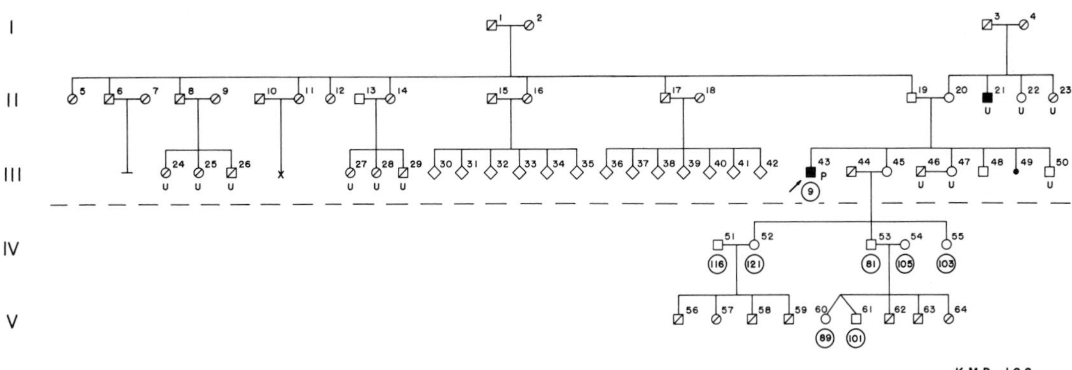

KMD 198

The Proband

The proband (43) was born in 1900, institutionalized at age 10 years and died of bronchopneumonia in the institution in 1920. He walked at age 18 months but never talked. There was no history of birth injury and no stigmata. IQ 9. *Diagnosis:* undifferentiated mental retardation.

Grandparents

Not of interest.

Parents

Father (19) was a poor farmer "of a low order of mentality" but was not classified as retarded. He was seen by the early workers.

Mother (20) was "very bright and capable" but died of epilepsy in a mental hospital.

Aunts and Uncles

Maternal uncle (21) was a retarded, alcoholic farm laborer. Nearly all the proband's aunts and uncles on both sides of the family remained in Sweden.

Siblings

Sister (45) grew up in boarding homes. She has normal intelligence.

Sister (47) could not be located for the follow-up. She was a normal child who grew up in a boarding home.

Brother (48) was adopted from the state orphanage. He had normal intelligence but died of diabetes at age 16 years.

Brother (49) died of whooping cough and convulsions at age 5 months.

Brother (50) was born in a state mental hospital and was adopted. He had normal intelligence. He also could not be found for the follow-up.

Nieces and Nephews

The three (52), (53) and (55) who are known have normal intelligence.

First Cousins

All remained in Sweden.

More Distant Relatives

Not of interest.

Family Summary

The proband, IQ 9, and a maternal uncle of higher grade are the only retardates in the family. When the proband's mother died of epilepsy her children were placed in boarding homes and two of them could not be found for the follow-up. The proband had no history of injury or disease in early childhood. He was reported to have had pneumonia at age 3 years but the retardation had become apparent before that time. The proband's parents had six children and at least three grandchildren.

Retardation of proband of unknown origin.

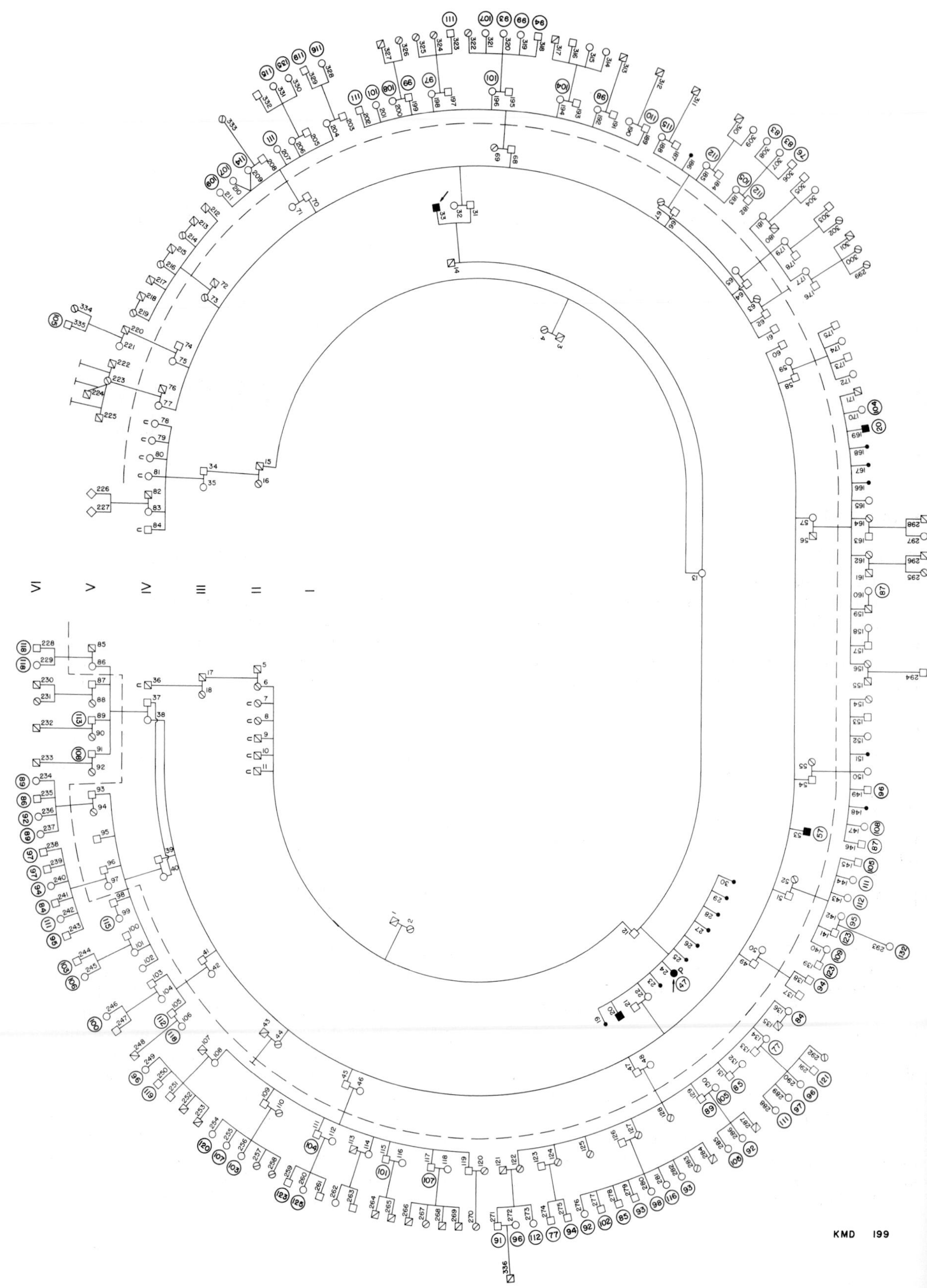

KMD 199

KMD 199

The Proband

The proband (24) was born in 1870 and institutionalized at age 19 years. She was transferred to a mental hospital in 1918 where she died of acute nephritis in 1928. She was very ill with measles at age 3 years. Her home environment was good. She was transferred to a mental hospital when she became delusional and wanted to kill herself. The mental hospital diagnosis was "imbecile." IQ 47. *Diagnosis:* undifferentiated mental retardation.

Grandparents

Not of interest.

Parents

Father (12) was a prosperous farmer.

Mother (13) had normal intelligence but was subject to epileptiform attacks.

Aunts and Uncles

Paternal relatives remained in Ireland.

One maternal uncle (15), intelligence unknown.

Siblings

Brother (19) died at 3 weeks.

Brother (20) died at age 14 years. He was epileptic and retarded.

Sister (22) had normal intelligence, as did her husband. One of her 13 children was retarded.

Sister (23) died shortly after birth.

Brother (25) died of "cold" at 9 months.

Sister (26) died of "cold" at 3 months.

(27), (28), (29) and (30) were stillbirths.

Half Siblings

Half brother (31) had normal intelligence.

Half brother (33) was institutionalized for mental retardation, mental illness and epilepsy. He died at age 22 years.

Nieces and Nephews

Nephew (53) is unmarried and childless. His IQ is 57.

First Cousins

Not of interest.

More Distant Relatives

Nephew (54) had a child (148) who died of convulsions following influenza. Another child (151) was a stillbirth.

Niece (57) had three stillbirths (166), (167) and (168), and a retarded child (169), IQ 20.

Family Summary

The proband, IQ 47, her brother, a half brother, a nephew and a great-nephew were retarded. There were also four infant deaths and four stillbirths in the proband's sibship. Both parents had normal intelligence. They owned and operated a prosperous farm. The proband's parents had 11 children and 13 grandchildren. The grandchildren all belonged to their normal daughter.

Retardation of proband of unknown origin.

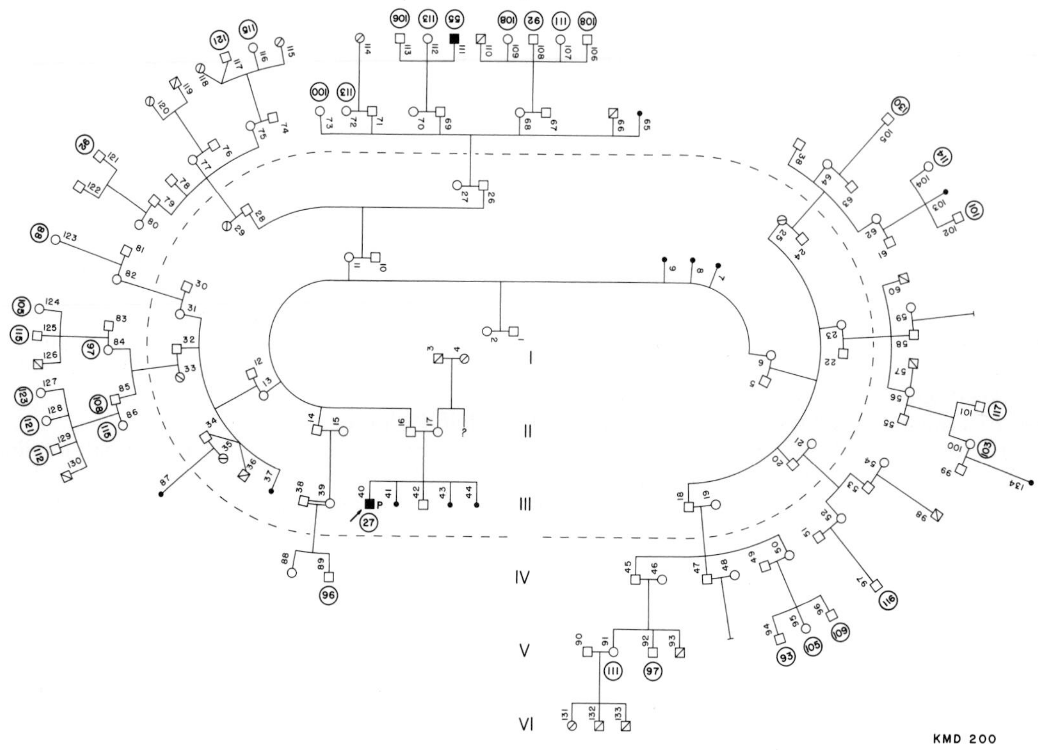

KMD 200

The Proband

The proband (40) was born in 1886 and institutionalized at age 11 years. He was discharged for a short time several years later, readmitted in 1905 and died of tuberculosis in the institution in 1927. His birth was uneventful and he had no stigmata nor any evidence of perinatal infection. He could not sit alone until the age of 3 years. IQ 27. *Diagnosis:* undifferentiated mental retardation.

Grandparents

Not of interest.

Parents

Father (16) had normal intelligence but was so alcoholic that his wife finally left him.

Mother (17) had normal intelligence.

Aunts and Uncles

Paternal relatives all had normal intelligence. Maternal relatives are unknown.

Siblings

Sister (41) died of "spasms" at 8 months.

Brother (42) died single and childless at age 40 years. He had normal intelligence.

(43) and (44) were miscarriages.

Nieces and Nephews

None.

First Cousins

Not of interest.

More Distant Relatives

First cousin (26) has a retarded grandchild (111), IQ 55.

Family Summary

The proband, IQ 27, was the only retarded person in this family with the exception of one first cousin's grandchild. The proband appeared retarded from the time of his birth, which was uneventful. The proband's parents had five children, no grandchildren.

Retardation of proband of unknown origin.

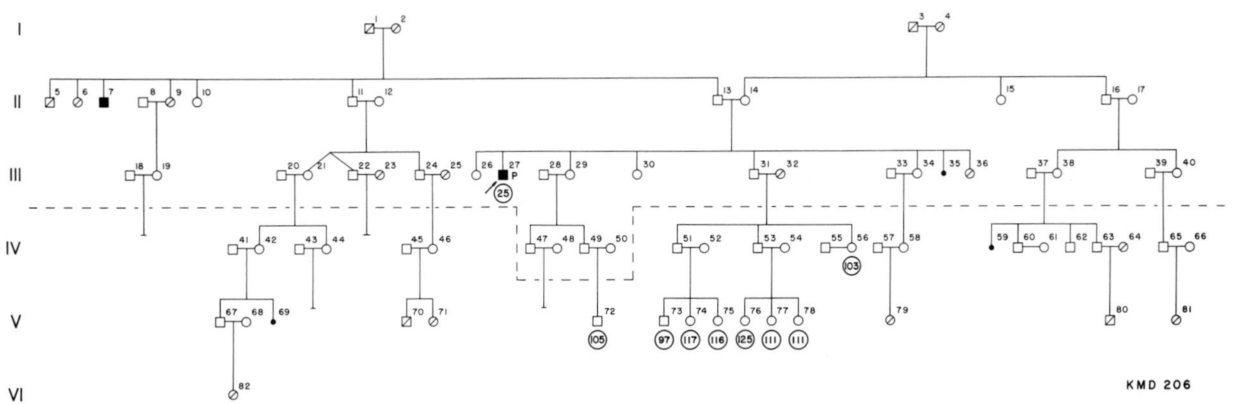

KMD 206

The Proband

The proband (27) was born in 1885 and institutionalized at age 25 years. He was discharged the same year to his parents, but was institutionalized again in 1936 after his mother's death. He had no history of difficult birth or perinatal infection. He died of tuberculosis in the institution in 1937. He had a cleft palate and never developed any front or lower teeth. IQ 25. *Diagnosis:* undifferentiated mental retardation.

Grandparents

Not of interest.

Parents

Father (13) was a successful businessman but was fanatically religious and withdrawn. He would go for long periods of time without speaking.

Mother (14) had normal intelligence.

Aunts and Uncles

Paternal uncle (7) died single and childless at age 52 years. He was retarded.

Siblings

Sister (26) died of "rheumatism" at age 12 years. She had normal intelligence.

Sisters (29), (30), (34) and brother (31) have normal intelligence. All had normal children except (30) who was unmarried and childless.

Sister (35) was born prematurely and died at birth.

Sister (36) died of diphtheria and convulsions at 3 years. Her intelligence was unknown.

Nieces and Nephews

Six, all of normal intelligence.

First Cousins

Not of interest.

More Distant Relatives

Not of interest.

Family Summary

The proband, IQ 25, was the only retarded person in this kindred. He had a cleft palate and did not develop any front or lower teeth. This entire family exhibits a very low rate of reproduction. The proband's generation, III, included 14 individuals. Generation V also has only 14 individuals, one of whom died in infancy. The proband's parents had eight children and six grandchildren.

Retardation of proband of unknown origin.

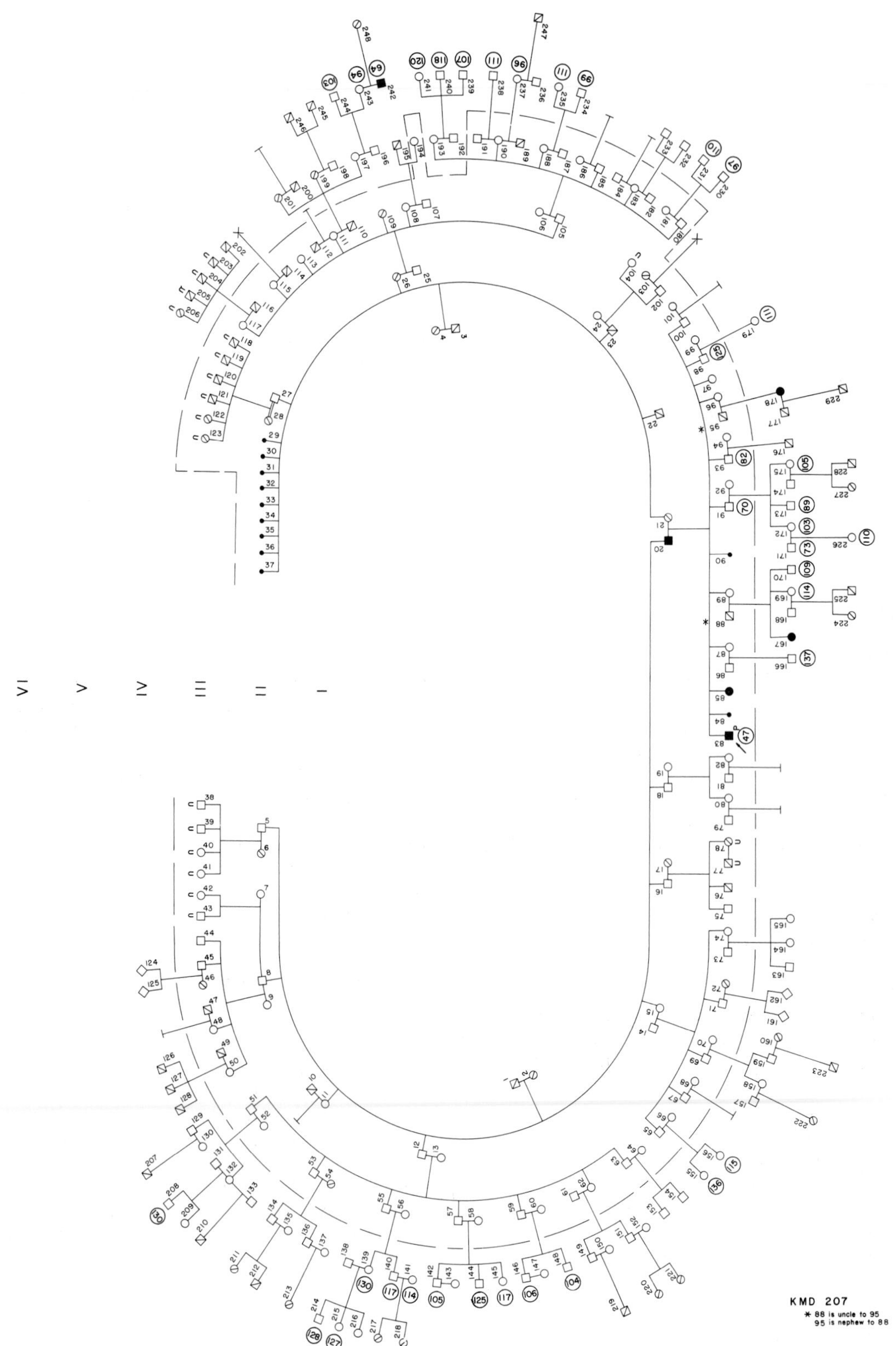
I
II
III
IV
V
VI
KMD 207
* 88 is uncle to 95
95 is nephew to 88

KMD 207

The Proband

The proband (83) was born in 1892, institutionalized at age 9 years and died of tuberculosis in the institution in 1925. He had a large lump "like a potato" on the crown of his head at birth but this gradually disappeared. He had no stigmata or any record of trauma. He walked and talked at about 19 months but did not grow well. He attended school for a year but learned very little. He was very poorly adjusted and was tried in every department of the institution. IQ 47. *Diagnosis:* undifferentiated mental retardation.

Grandparents

Maternal grandfather was mentally ill.

Parents

Father (20) was physically weak and mentally retarded. He was a peddler.

Mother (21) was "of a low order of mentality."

Aunts and Uncles

Not of interest.

Siblings

Sister (84) died of "spasms" at 6 months.

Sister (85) was hospitalized for schizophrenia. Old records classified her as retarded at age 20 years.

Sisters (87) and (89) had normal intelligence and good mental health. (89) had a retarded child.

Brother (90) died of "summer complaint and spasms" at 13 months.

Brother (91) has fits of crying but has no diagnosis of persecution complex or schizophrenia. IQ 70. His wife and three children have normal intelligence.

Brother (93) has had shock treatments. IQ 82. His child is in a mental hospital.

Sister (96) has been hospitalized twice for mental illness. Her only child is retarded.

Sister (97) was schizophrenic and committed suicide.

Brother (98) is a dentist. IQ 125.

Brother (100) is a bookkeeper.

Nieces and Nephews

(167) was hydrocephalic.

(172), IQ 103, married a man who had been in special classes, IQ 73.

(173) was born with no opening in the esophagus.

(176) is hospitalized for mental illness, probably schizophrenia.

(178) was in the fifth grade with a D— average at the age of 12.

First Cousins

Not of interest.

More Distant Relatives

First cousin (111) had a granddaughter (243), IQ 94, who married a retarded laborer with IQ 64.

Family Summary

The proband, IQ 47, his father, one of his siblings and two nieces were retarded. One of the nieces was hydrocephalic. In addition, five of the proband's siblings evinced symptoms of schizophrenia. Three of these persons were hospitalized, one is included among the retardates and one committed suicide. The proband's parents had 12 children and ten grandchildren.

Retardation of proband of unknown origin.

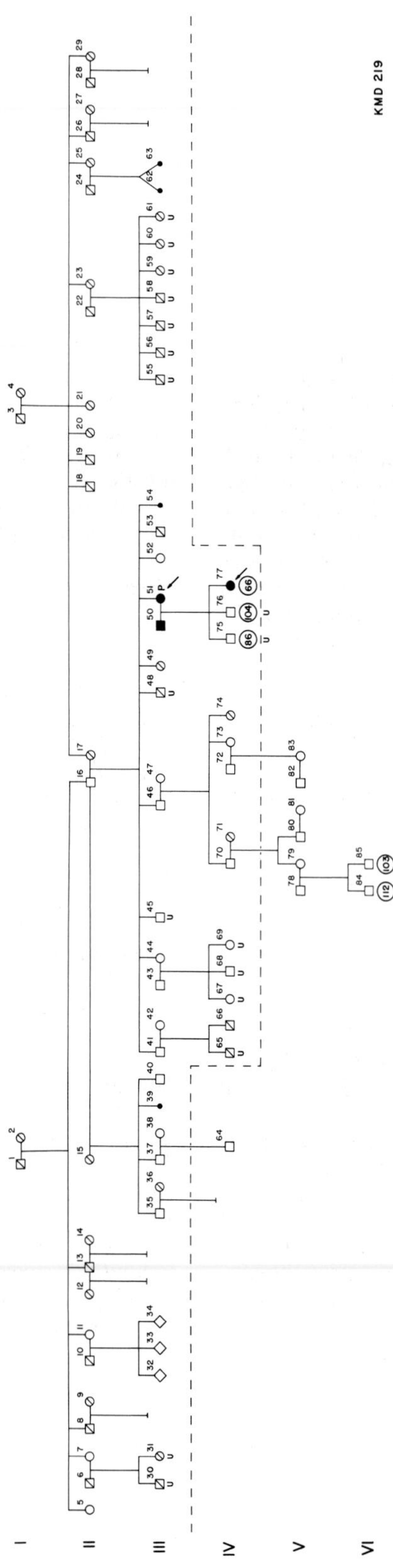
KMD 219

KMD 219

The Proband

The proband (51) was born in 1881, institutionalized at age 24 years and died of nephritis in the institution in 1931. There was no record of early trauma or infection. She was married and had two children before she was institutionalized. A third child was born in the institution. The proband went to school until age 14 years and could read and write. Shortly after her institutionalization she began to fail mentally and in 1915 was reported as "just sits in a heap on the floor—does nothing." The institution record listed her as a high-grade retardate upon admission. *Diagnosis:* unknown.

Grandparents

Not of interest.

Parents

Father (16) died of alcoholism. He was a contractor and builder.

Mother (17) had unknown intelligence. She was "always sick" and never took care of her home or her children.

Aunts and Uncles

Not of interest.

Siblings

Brothers (41), (45), (46) and sisters (44) and (52) had normal intelligence.

The intelligence of (48), (49) and (53) was unknown.

Brother (54) died of diphtheria in infancy.

Half Siblings

Four, three with normal intelligence, one who died of prematurity.

Spouse

(50) was a part time janitor who was retarded.

Children

Son (75) with IQ 86 at 11 years.

Son (76) with IQ 104 at 9 years.

Daughter (77) was born in the institution. She was considered for institutionalization in 1917 when her chronological age was 12 years and her mental age 8 years. IQ 66. The two oldest of the proband's children were reared in the utmost squalor and neglect; yet, they had normal intelligence at school age. Unfortunately, the children could not be found for the follow-up.

Nieces and Nephews

Not of interest.

First Cousins

Unknown.

More Distant Relatives

Not of interest.

Family Summary

The proband and her daughter were the only retarded persons in her family. The proband married a retarded man. Of her three children, two had IQ's of 86 and 104 and the other child was considered for institutionalization at one time. The proband grew up in a very poor home environment with an alcoholic father and a hypochondriacal mother. The proband's own home after marriage was of the utmost squalor. Some years after the proband's institutionalization she deteriorated from high-grade to low-grade retardation. The proband's parents had ten children and 11 grandchildren.

Retardation of proband of unknown origin.

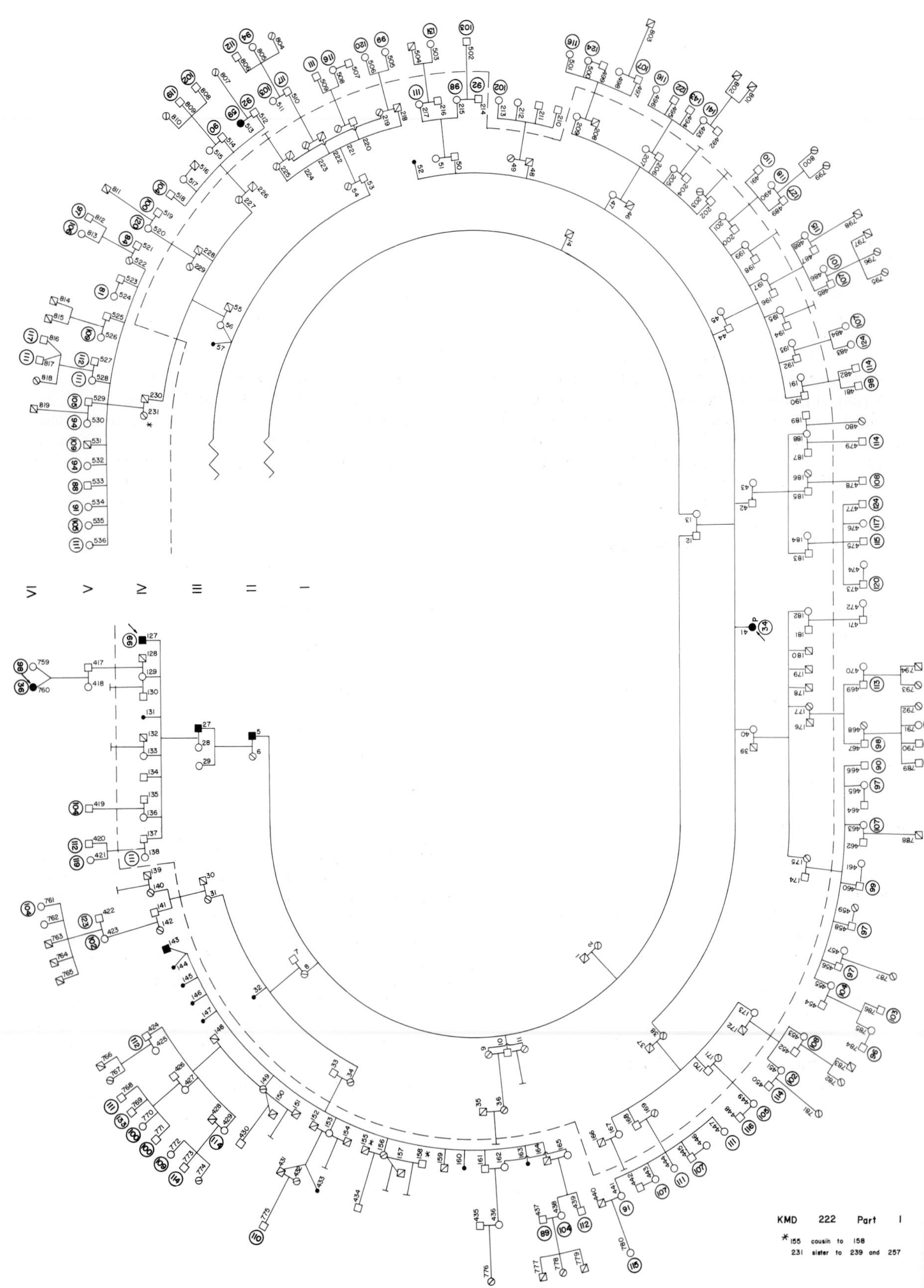
KMD 222 Part I
* 155 cousin to 158
231 sister to 239 and 257

KMD 222

The Proband

The proband (41) was born in 1868, institutionalized at age 24 years and died of chronic interstitial nephritis and fracture of femur in the institution in 1915. She walked and talked at age 2 years, went to school until the age of 9 but learned little. Her home environment was very good. There was no history of early trauma or infection. She was unmarried and childless. IQ 34. *Diagnosis:* undifferentiated mental retardation.

Grandparents

Maternal grandfather died of alcoholism.

Parents

Father (12) was a prosperous farmer.

Mother (13) had normal intelligence.

Aunts and Uncles

Paternal uncle (5) was retarded. His wife was mentally ill.

Maternal uncle (17) committed suicide, "became insane from drinking."

Siblings

Sister (38) and brother (48) had unknown intelligence.

Sisters (40) and (47) and brothers (42), (44) and (50) had normal intelligence. There are no known retardates among the descendants of the siblings.

(52) was a stillbirth.

Nieces and Nephews

Not of interest.

First Cousins

(27) was retarded.

(80) died unmarried and childless. He was epileptic and mentally ill.

More Distant Relatives

(127) is institutionalized for mental retardation. He is a deaf mute, IQ 66. He is the proband in KMD 141.

(143) completed the second grade and is an unmarried janitor. There were five infant deaths and one miscarriage in his sibship of 13 persons.

(383) went to special classes and is a lathe operater, IQ 69. His wife has an IQ of 109.

(547) and (549), brother and sister, have IQ's of 69 and 11, respectively. (549) is diagnosed as having cerebral palsy.

(553), cousin to (547) and (549), has an IQ of 68.

(594) has an IQ of 101 but married a retarded man. Their children have normal intelligence.

(711) has an IQ of 68. His father is retarded, IQ 69. His mother has normal intelligence, IQ 109.

(760) is institutionalized with a diagnosis of "defective fetal development, abnormal metabolism." IQ 36.

Family Summary

The proband, IQ 34, was the only retarded person in her immediate family. Her environment was very good and there was no history of birth injury or infectious disease. The proband's parents had nine children and 29 grandchildren. The proband's paternal uncle's family constitutes another family history of retardation, (KMD 141), in which the proband is a genetic deaf mute. There were four marriages of normal persons to high-grade retardates which produced a total of 16 normal children, three of unknown intelligence and two retardates. One marriage of normal persons produced three normal children, one retardate. A marriage of persons of unknown intelligence produced two retarded children and two with normal intelligence. These last two families were related, the father of one being a brother to the mother of the other.

Retardation of the proband of unknown origin.

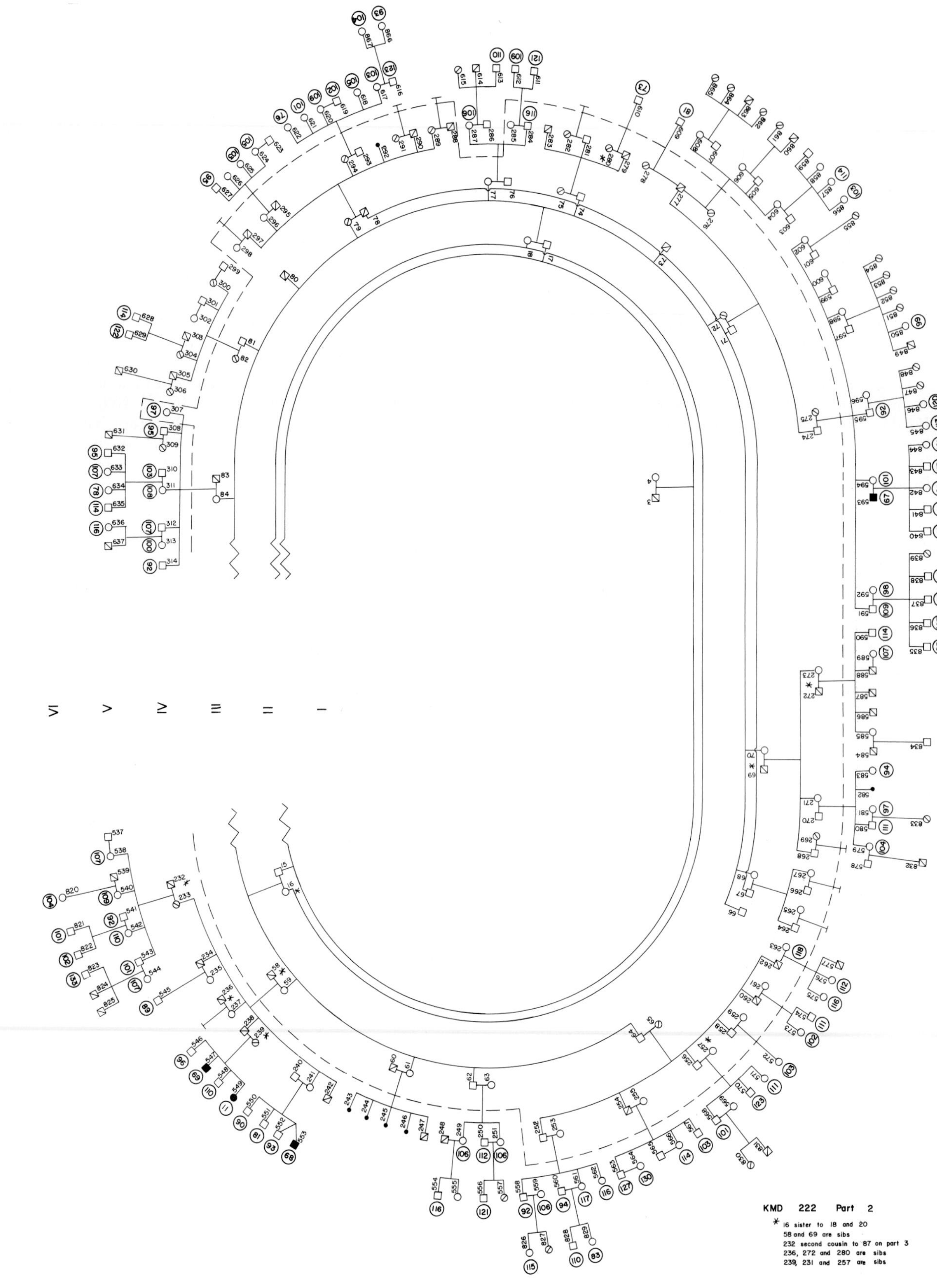

VI
V
IV
III
II
I
KMD 222 Part 2
* 16 sister to 18 and 20
58 and 69 are sibs
232 second cousin to 87 on part 3
236, 272 and 280 are sibs
239, 231 and 257 are sibs

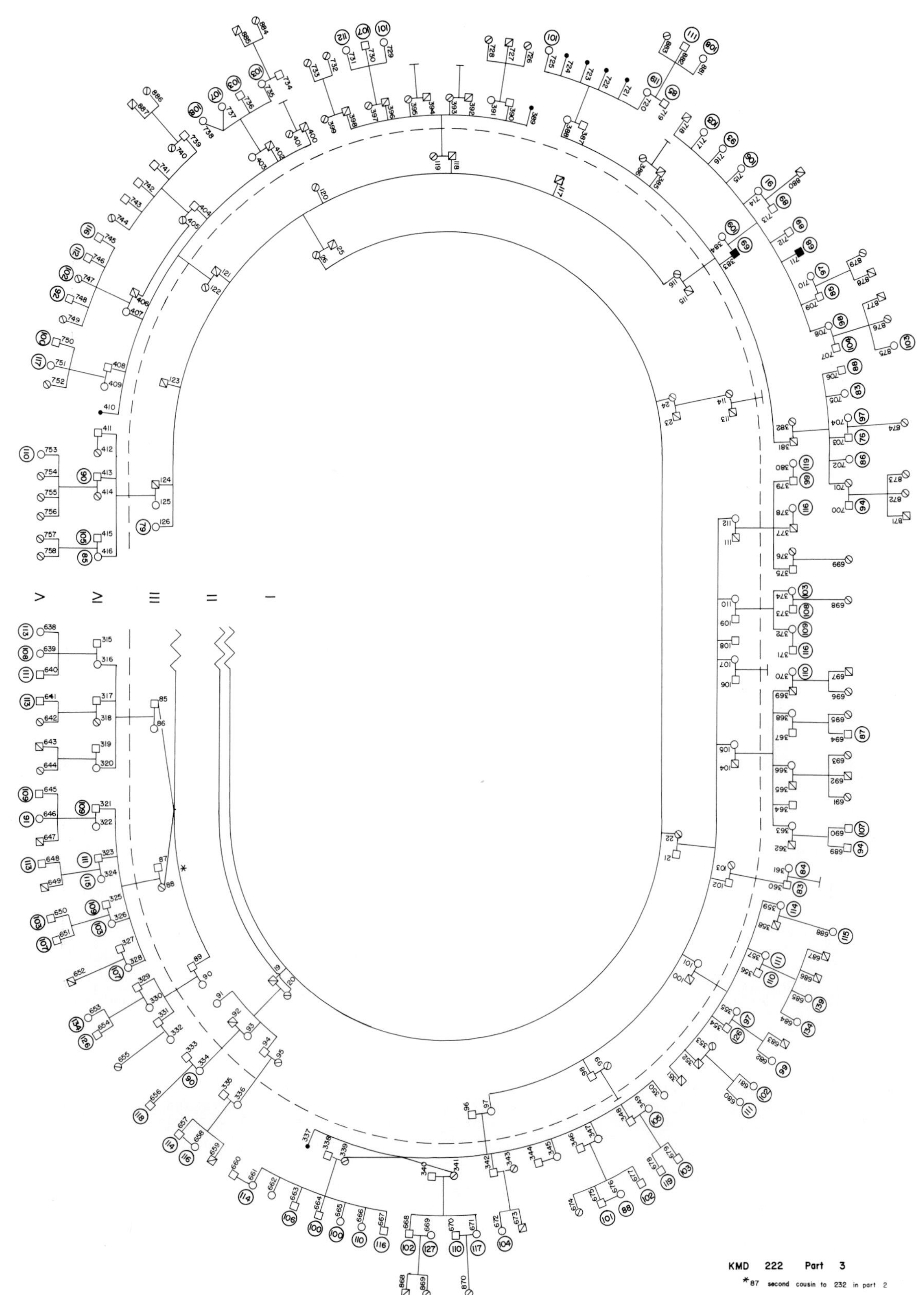

KMD 222 Part 3

*87 second cousin to 232 in part 2

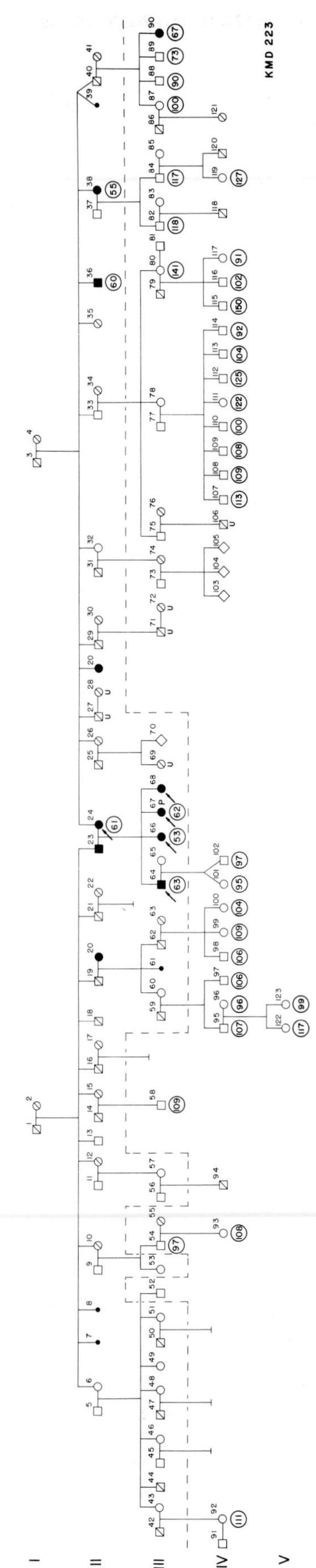
KMD 223

KMD 223

The Proband

The proband (67) was born in 1909, institutionalized at age 5 years and was still in the institution in 1961. Her home environment was very poor. She had a gonorrheal infection at the time of admission, but physical examination records of 1920 do not indicate congenital syphilis. IQ 62. *Diagnosis:* undifferentiated mental retardation.

Grandparents

Maternal grandmother was hospitalized twice for mental illness.

Parents

Father (23) was employed as a puddler's helper in a foundry. He was an alcoholic, promiscuous, syphilitic and retarded. He was cruel to his family and never supported them.

Mother (24) was institutionalized in 1913 at age 26 years. She was transferred to a second institution in 1927 and died there of pulmonary tuberculosis in 1935. She was epileptic, infected with gonorrhea and retarded. IQ 61.

Aunts and Uncles

Paternal uncle (19) was sent to a reformatory at one time. He married (20) a retarded woman who was also the proband's maternal aunt.

Maternal uncle (33) was hospitalized for mental illness.

Maternal uncle (36) died single and childless, IQ 60.

Maternal aunt (38) has an IQ of 55.

Maternal uncles (29) and (33) were juvenile delinquents.

Siblings

Brother (64) was institutionalized at age 15 years, paroled to an uncle six years later and was in the army from 1942 to 1945. He married a woman with normal intelligence and had two normal children. He died in 1948. He was epileptic and syphilitic, IQ 63.

Sister (66) was institutionalized in 1914 at age 7 years, transferred to a second institution in 1927 and died there of pneumonia in 1942. She had syphilis and gonorrhea. IQ 53.

Sister (68) was institutionalized at the age of 1 year in 1913 and died a year later of acute enteritis and pulmonary tuberculosis. She was seen by the early workers and was thought to be retarded and possibly epileptic. The lower limbs were poorly developed and the baby "noticed very little." She had bronchitis, eczema and "sore eyes."

Nieces and Nephews

Only two, IQ's 95 and 97.

First Cousins

(90) has an IQ of 67.

More Distant Relatives

Not of interest.

Family Summary

The proband, IQ 63, three siblings, and her mother were all institutionalized. In addition, the proband's father, a maternal aunt and uncle and one first cousin were high-grade retardates. The proband's home environment was very bad, with both parents retarded, both infected with venereal disease, the mother epileptic and the father cruel and abusive. The proband's parents had four children, all retarded, and two grandchildren, both with normal intelligence. In this family with such a constellation of mental and physical difficulties it is impossible to ascertain the underlying basis for the retardation. The two normal grandchildren may be so because they have been reared in a more favorable environment or because they have inherited a better genetic constitution.

Retardation of proband of unknown origin.

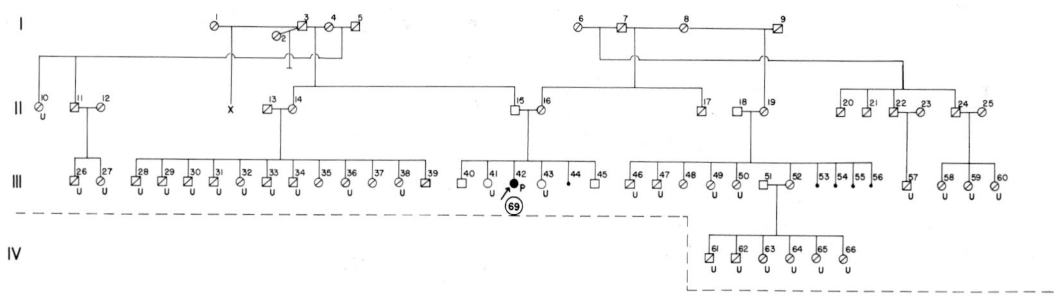

KMD 226

KMD 226

The Proband

The proband (42) was born in 1897, institutionalized at age 15 years and died of bronchopneumonia in the institution in 1931. She was a healthy child who walked at 16 months and talked at 3 years. She attended school for eight years and attained the sixth grade. Her IQ was 69 upon admission. By 1918 she "acted very low grade." Her IQ in 1925 was 39 and in 1930 she developed epilepsy. *Diagnosis:* unknown.

Grandparents

Not of interest.

Parents

Father (15) was a stone mason and teamster with "barely average" mentality.

Mother (16) had unknown intelligence.

Aunts and Uncles

Not of interest.

Siblings

Brother (40) died in a runaway at age 22 years. He was "very slow mentally."

Sister (41) could not be found for the follow-up. She had normal intelligence.

Sister (43) could not be found for the follow-up. She was "mentally slow."

Brother (44) died of pneumonia at age 2 years.

Brother (45) died of septicemia following a compound fracture at age 7 years. He had normal intelligence.

Nieces and Nephews

Unknown.

First Cousins

Not of interest.

More Distant Relatives

Unknown.

Family Summary

The proband, IQ 69, was the only retarded person in a sibship of six. She deteriorated to a lower level during institutionalization—her IQ dropped to 39 and she developed epilepsy. This family could not be found for the follow-up. Since the proband's surviving siblings were sisters, it is likely they have married and changed their names. The proband's relatives who came to this country had a very frequently occurring Scandinavian name so that they could not be traced. The proband's parents had six children, grandchildren unknown.

Retardation of proband of unknown origin.

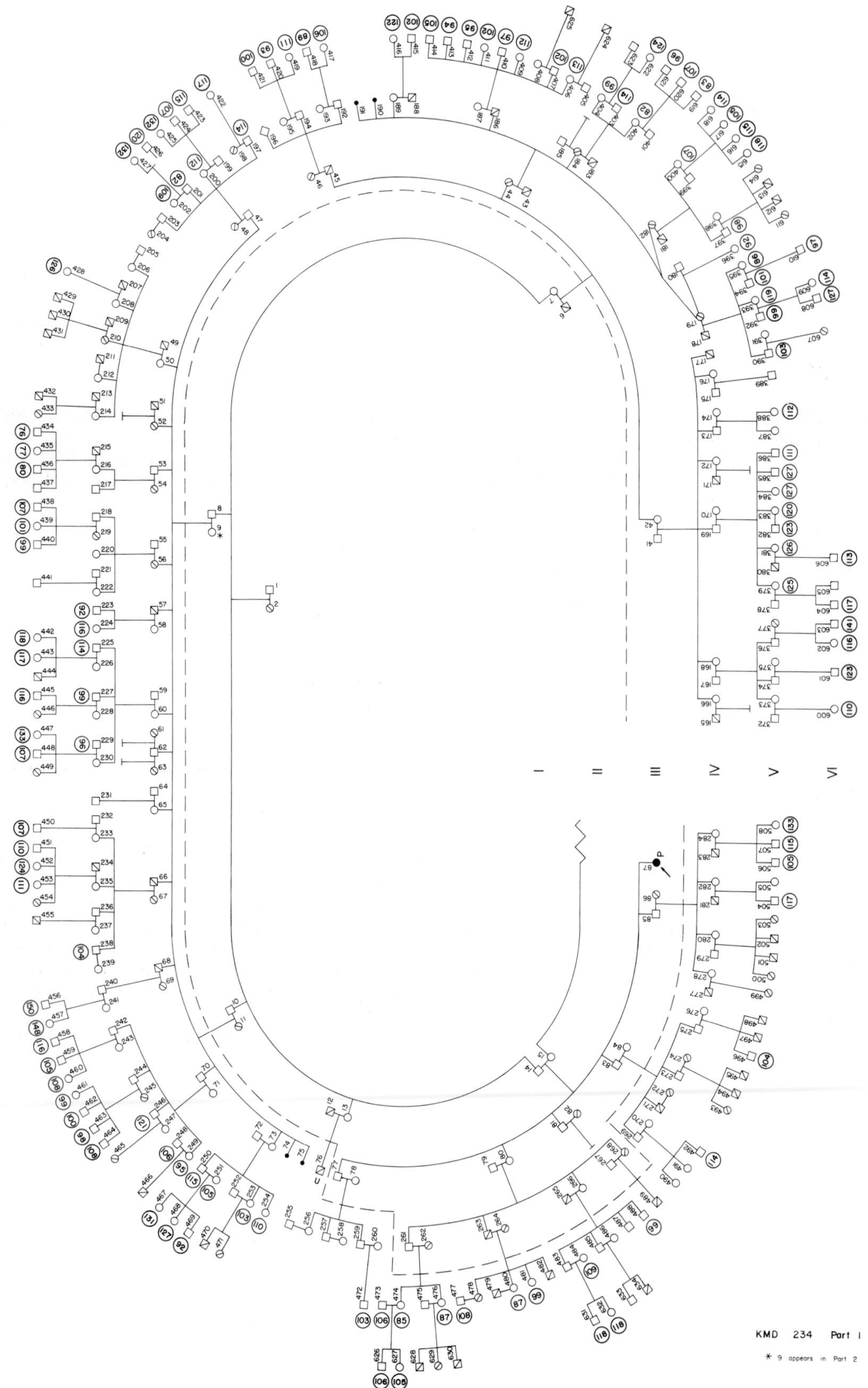

KMD 234 Part I

* 9 appears in Part 2

KMD 234

The Proband

The proband (87) was born in 1895, institutionalized at age 6 years and died of tuberculosis in the institution in 1913. Delivery was normal but the child did not walk until the age of 3 years. She was a low-grade retardate with no speech. *Diagnosis:* undifferentiated mental retardation.

Grandparents

Not of interest.

Parents

Father (14) was a prosperous farmer.
Mother (15) had normal intelligence.

Aunts and Uncles

Maternal aunt (23) was epileptic.

Siblings

All had normal intelligence, as do their descendants.

Nieces and Nephews

Not of interest.

First Cousins

Not of interest.

More Distant Relatives

First cousin (97) has a retarded daughter with an IQ of 63.

First cousin (88) has a retarded grandchild (519) who does not go to school and is mentally retarded.

Family Summary

The proband, a low-grade retardate, was the only retarded person in this family with the exception of two distant cousins. Her birth was uneventful and her environment good. The proband's parents had six children and 15 grandchildren.

Retardation of proband of unknown origin.

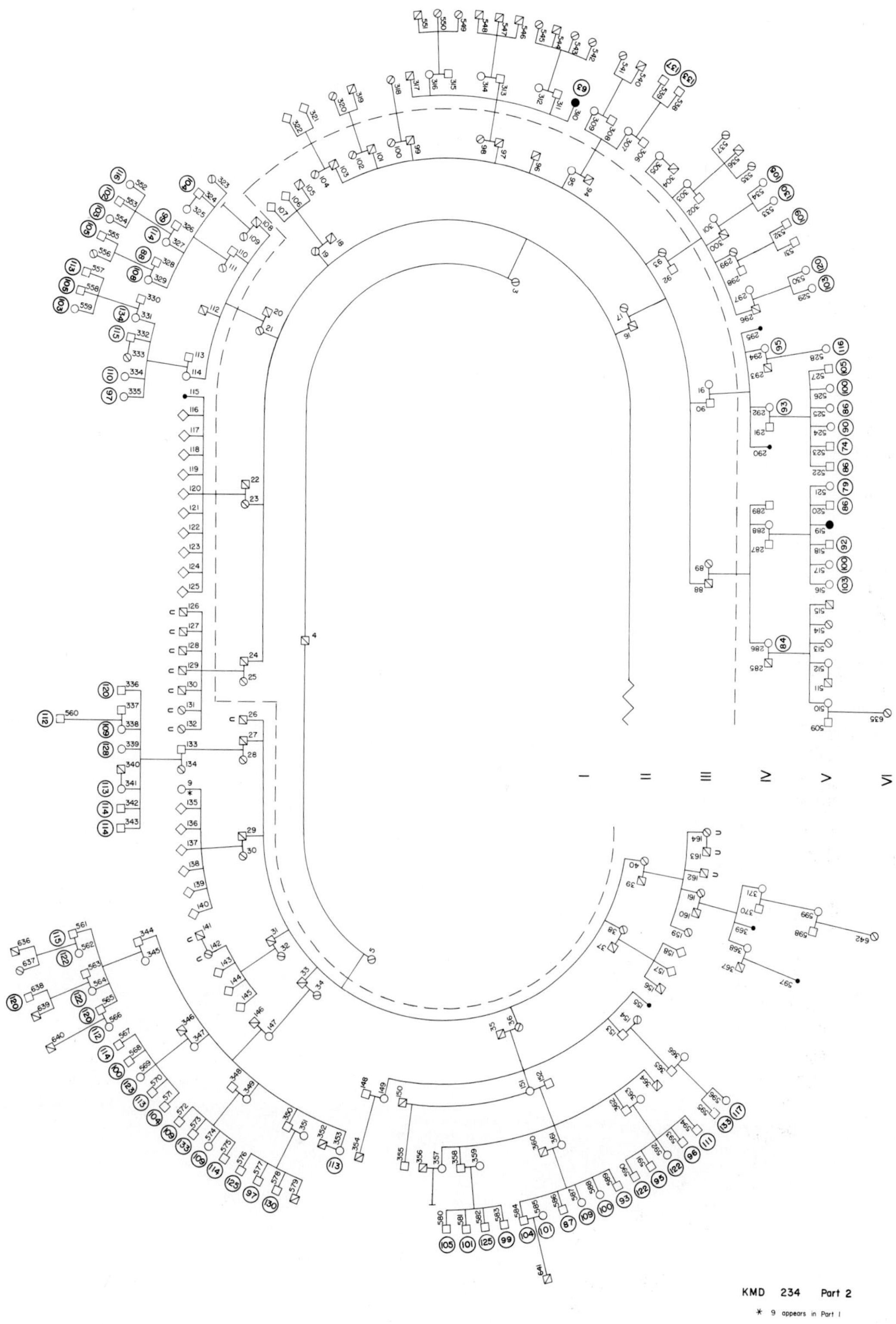

KMD 234 Part 2

* 9 appears in Part I

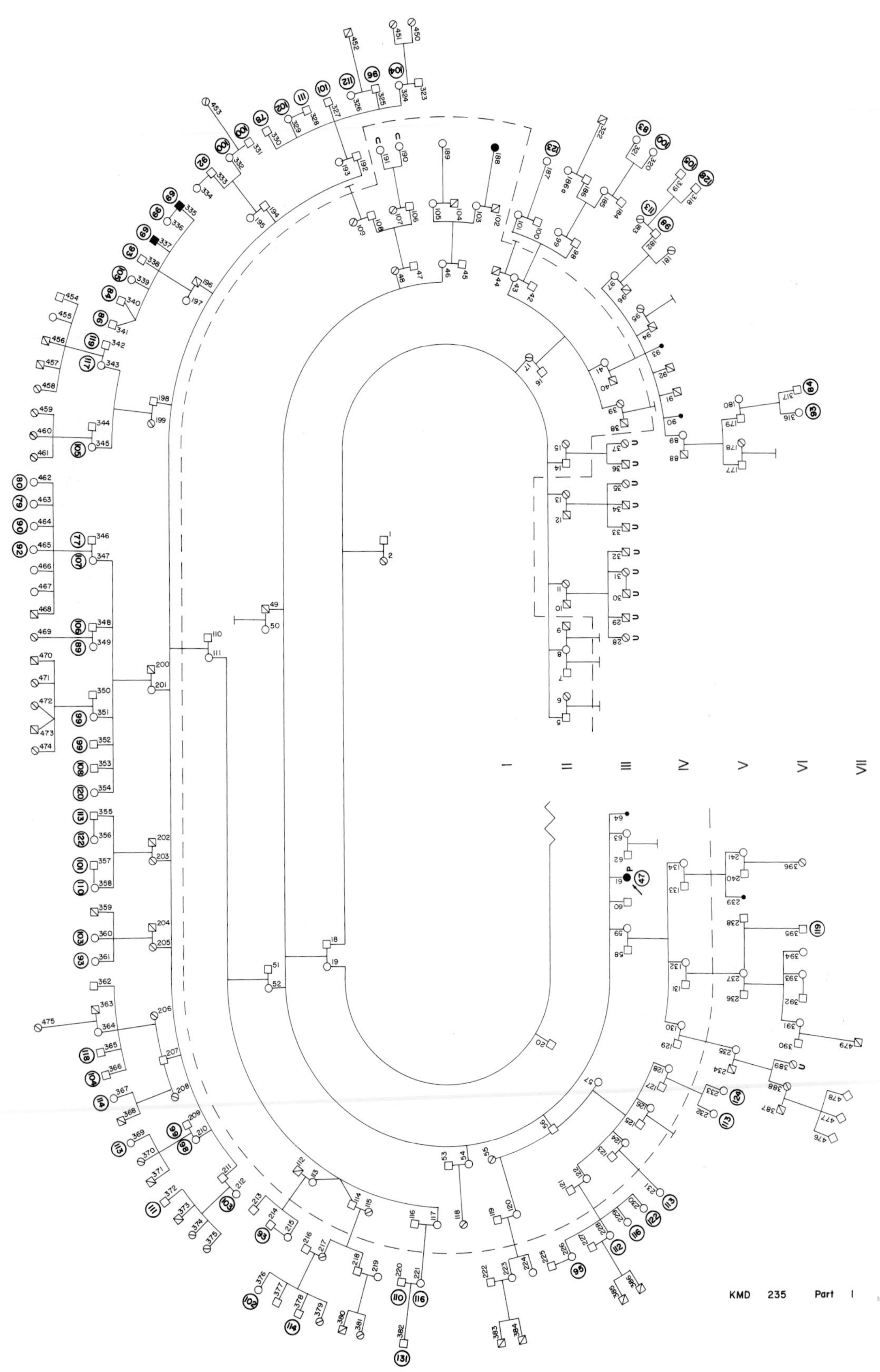
I
II
III
IV
V
VI
VII
KMD 235 Part I

KMD 235

The Proband

The proband (61) was born in 1873 and institutionalized at age 11 years. She was transferred in 1920 to a mental hospital and died of pneumonia there in 1943. She was very slow to walk and talk and had cataracts of the eyes which were removed. She developed epilepsy at age 39 years and in 1920 was adjudged mentally ill by two physicians and hospitalized. There was no history of birth injury or perinatal infection. IQ 47. *Diagnosis:* mental retardation with subsequent psychosis and epilepsy.

Grandparents

Not of interest.

Parents

Father (18) was a prosperous carriage maker but in later life became fanatically religious and traveled about preaching. He was subject to "terrible boils all his life" as was his father.

Mother (19) had normal intelligence.

Aunts and Uncles

Not of interest.

Siblings

Sisters (46), (52), (54), (59) and (63) have normal intelligence, as do their children.

Sister (48) had unknown intelligence.

Brothers (56) and (60) had normal intelligence but (56) committed suicide.

Brother (49) married, but childless, died in a mental hospital.

Sister (64) died of convulsions apparently following an attack of spinal meningitis at 9 months.

Nieces and Nephews

Not of interest.

First Cousins

Not of interest.

More Distant Relatives

Niece (103) had a child (188) who was a low- or middle-grade retardate.

(292) is an institutionalized retardate with Down's syndrome, IQ 10.

(304) is being considered for possible commitment, IQ 36, no diagnosis.

(335) and (337), siblings, both have IQ's of 69.

Family Summary

The proband, IQ 47, had cataracts of the eyes very early in life (not known if they were congenital). She was the only retardate in her immediate family although there are six others among the relatives. Some years after her institutionalization she developed epilepsy and eight years later became mentally ill and was hospitalized. The proband's parents had normal intelligence, but the father and two of the proband's siblings were somewhat unbalanced mentally. There is some evidence for a possible syphilitic infection of the father, but the proband had a negative Wassermann and no signs of congenital syphilis. The proband's parents had 11 children and 17 grandchildren.

Retardation of proband of unknown origin.

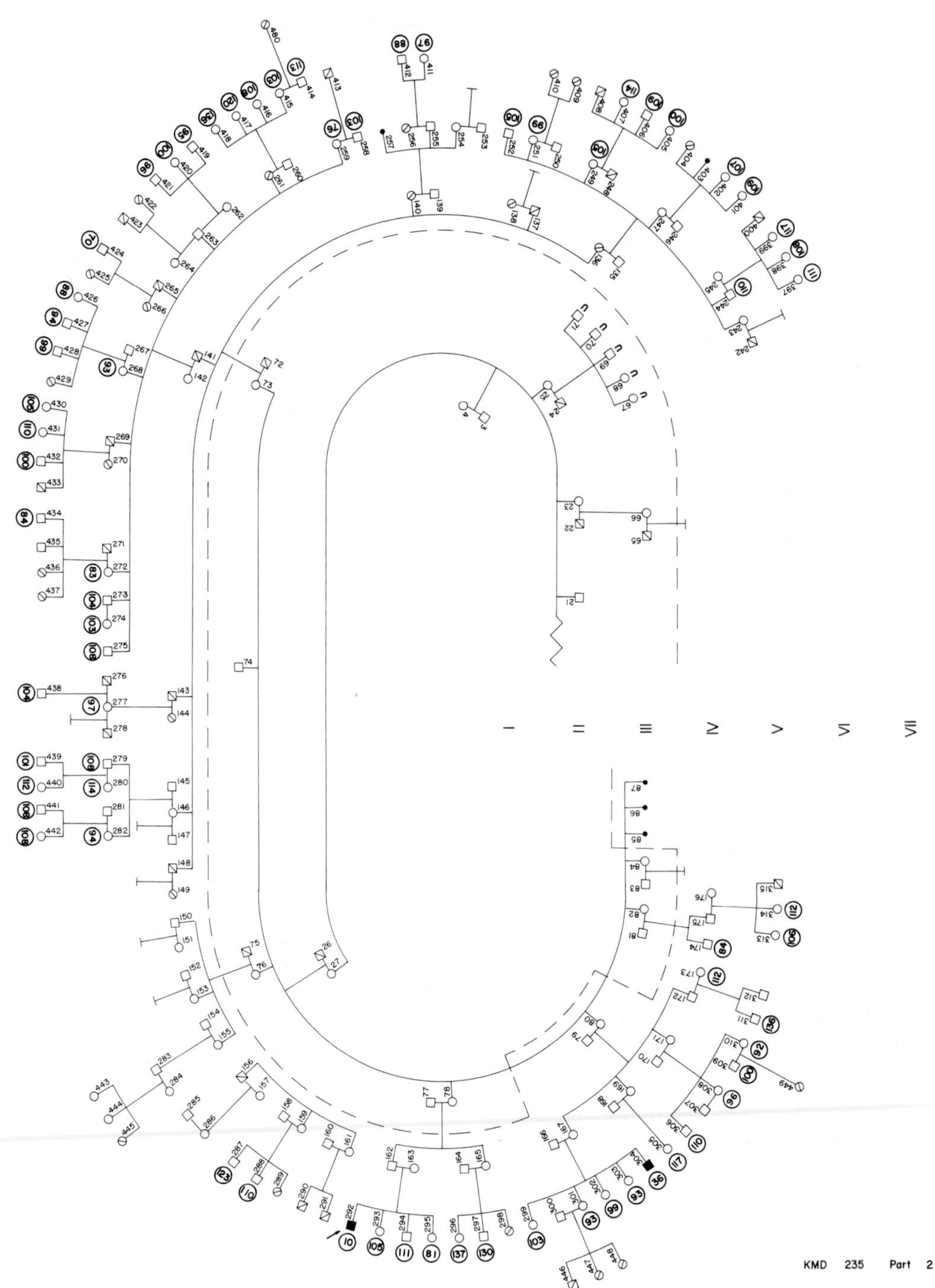

KMD 235 Part 2

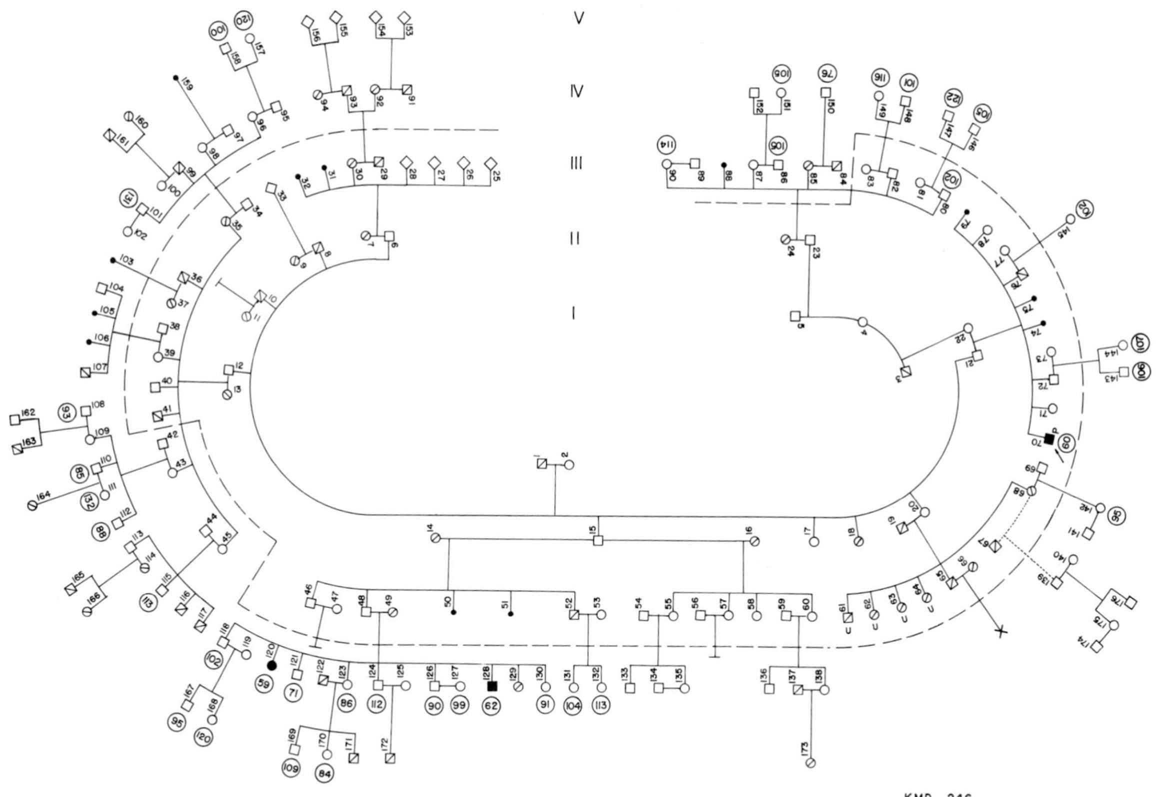

KMD 246

The Proband

The proband (70) was born in 1895, institutionalized at age 15 years, was discharged to his parents four years later and was living with his sister in 1961. He is a painter and is unmarried and childless. He had "brain fever" at age 6 months. His skull was slow to calcify and his second teeth were late in erupting. He has eye and nose malformations and athetoid movements. His home environment was good. IQ 60. *Diagnosis:* undifferentiated mental retardation.

Grandparents

Not of interest.

Parents

Father (21) was a school janitor and farm laborer with normal intelligence.

Mother (22) was "mentally slow" and very obese.

Aunts and Uncles

Not of interest.

Siblings

Sister (71) is a stenographer.

Brother (72) is comanager of an auditorium.

Brothers (74), (75) and (79) died at birth.

Brother (76) is a stationary engineer employed by (72). His intelligence is unknown.

Sister (78) is an invalid as the result of an infection, but has normal intelligence.

Nieces and Nephews

Only three, with IQ's of 106, 107 and 102, respectively.

First Cousins

Not of interest.

More Distant Relatives

First cousin (48) has two retarded children, (120) with an IQ of 59 and (128) with an IQ of 62. In this sibship of nine children, only one completed school at the proper age. All the others left school when they passed the compulsory age limit. The IQ range in this family included the two retardates, (121) with IQ 71, (123) with IQ 86 and four with IQ's in the normal range. One, (129), has never been tested. The father is an electrician, the mother had unknown intelligence.

Family Summary

The proband, IQ 60, and two children of a first cousin were the only retarded persons in this kindred. The proband had "brain fever" at age 6 months and was slow in physical development. The alleged cause (as given in institution records) was "acute sickness." However, the proband had stigmata of malformed eyes and nose, and showed athetoid movements. The proband's parents had eight children and three grandchildren.

Retardation of proband of unknown origin.

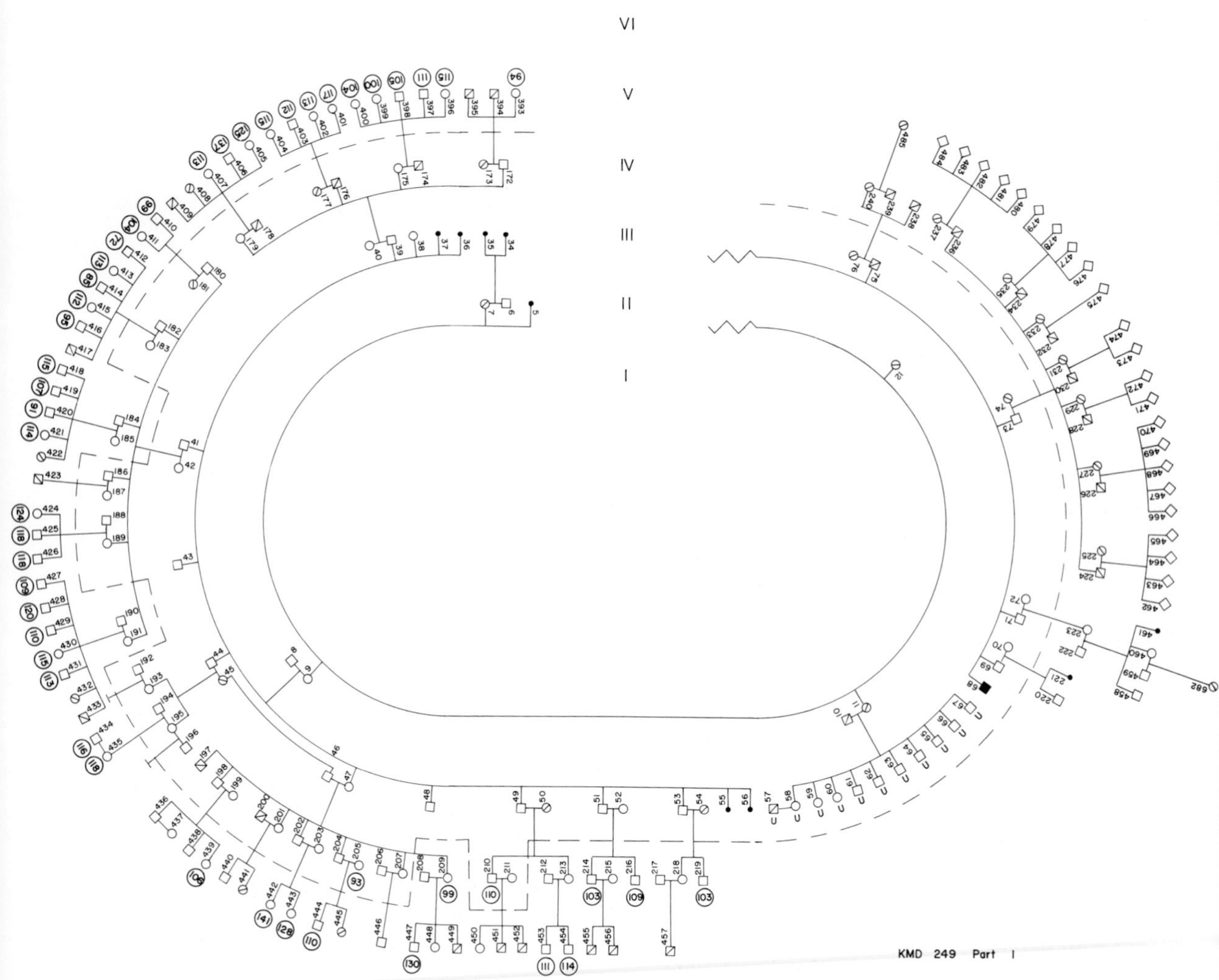

KMD 249 Part I

KMD 249

The Proband

The proband (116) was born in 1889, institutionalized at age 20 years, transferred to a mental hospital in 1924 and to a second one in 1929 where he was in 1961. He was a delicate, frail child who frequently wandered away from home. He attended school for seven years but reached only the fourth grade. He was originally placed in a mental hospital but was found "not to be a fit subject." The old record (1916) states he is "undoubtedly insane," but the most recent diagnosis from the mental hospital where he was in 1961 states "moderate mental deficiency (idiopathic)" without qualifying phrase. IQ 47. *Diagnosis:* undifferentiated mental retardation.

Grandparents

Paternal grandfather was mentally ill. He was a Greek and Latin scholar before his illness.

Parents

Father (20) had unknown intelligence. There were conflicting records as to whether or not he was mentally ill.

Mother (21) was similar to the father in mental make-up. Some persons thought she should have been hospitalized for mental illness. She also had epileptoid attacks.

Aunts and Uncles

Five paternal aunts (7), (9), (12), (14) and (19) were mentally ill. (9), (12) and (19) died in mental hospitals.

Paternal uncles (16) and (17) were mentally ill. (17) died in a mental hospital.

Maternal uncle (28) had normal intelligence but was epileptic and mentally ill.

Siblings

Sister (106) was "nervous and peculiar" but had normal intelligence. She was a teacher, with a normal husband and children.

Sister (108) graduated from a teacher training course but was hospitalized twice for manic depressive psychosis. Her husband is normal but she has a retarded child.

Sister (110) was a teacher, twice married, with apparently normal children.

Sister (113) graduated from high school, husband and surviving child normal.

Sister (115) was a teacher. She died of epilepsy. Her children are apparently normal.

Brother (117) was mentally ill. He wandered away from home in 1916 at age 25 years and has never been heard from since that time.

Brother (118) died in a mental hospital, diagnosis dementia praecox.

Sister (120) had unknown intelligence but was "nervous and peculiar," her husband and children are normal.

Nieces and Nephews

Niece (324) is hospitalized for "schizophrenic reaction, hebephrenic type."

Nephew (325) is hospitalized for "psychosis with mental deficiency."

First Cousins

(43) is hospitalized for "chronic brain syndrome associated with senile brain disease."

(44) was hospitalized for mental illness.

(68) is unmarried, childless and retarded.

(90) was hospitalized for nine years for manic depressive psychosis. The old records classified her as retarded and obese. Her parents were first cousins. (Her mother was the proband's paternal aunt who was hospitalized for mental illness.) They had (90), also (94), a "peculiar" woman who lived with her cousin as his common-law wife, and they also had (104) who was an institutionalized low-grade retardate, and five miscarriages. Only three of their 13 children reproduced.

More Distant Relatives

Proband's niece (353) has a retarded child (647) with IQ 60.

Family Summary

The proband, IQ 47, a nephew and a great-nephew were retarded, as were three first cousins. This family has an extensive history of mental illness with diagnoses of both schizophrenia and manic depressive psychoses. There was one case of psychosis with mental retardation and one of low-grade retardation. Conflicting diagnoses were given for the proband, but the most recent was "mental deficiency without psychosis." Of nine paternal aunts and uncles who lived to adulthood, seven were known to have been mentally ill and four of these died in mental hospitals.

Retardation of proband of unknown origin.

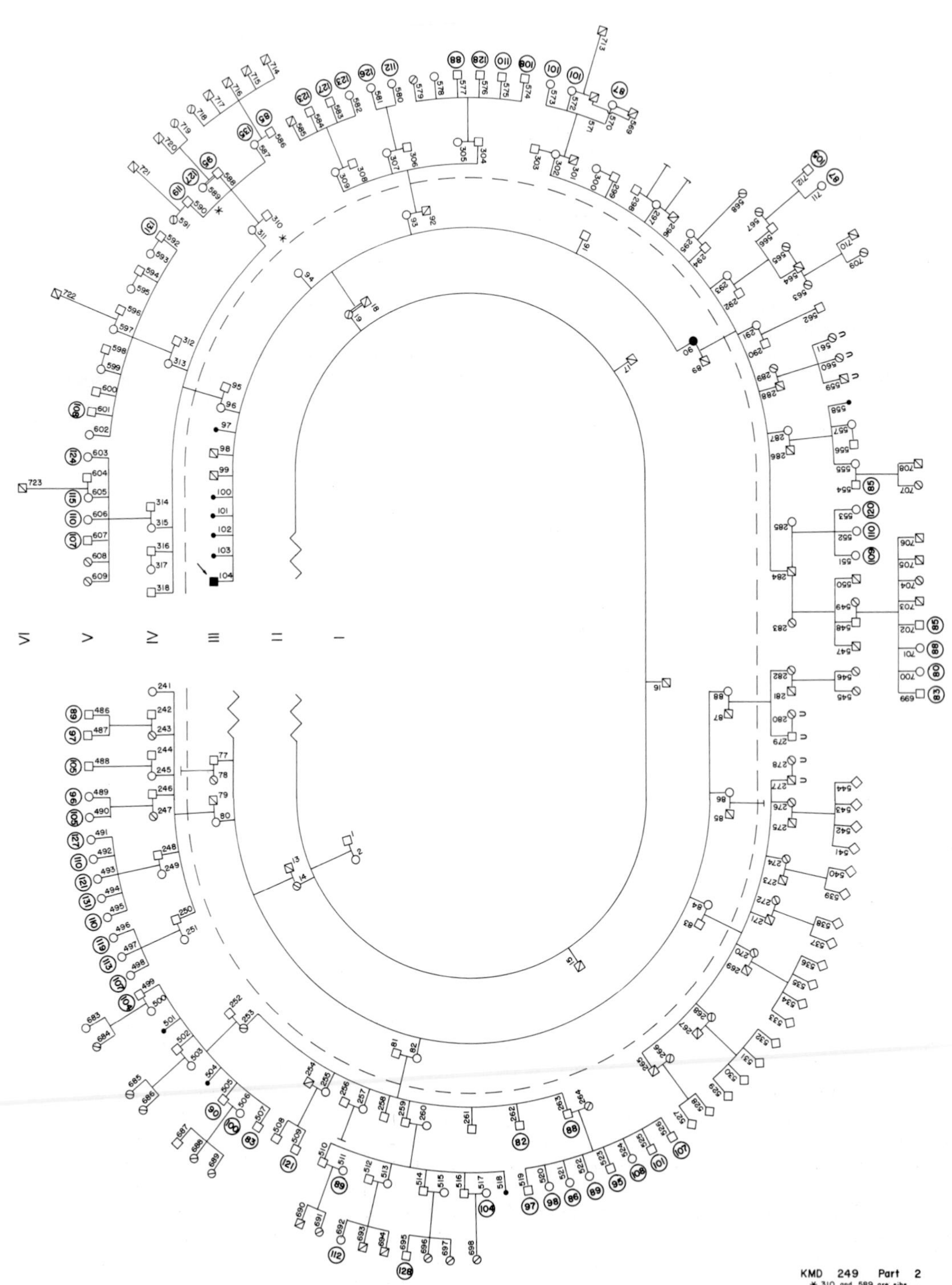
KMD 249 Part 2
* 310 and 589 are sibs

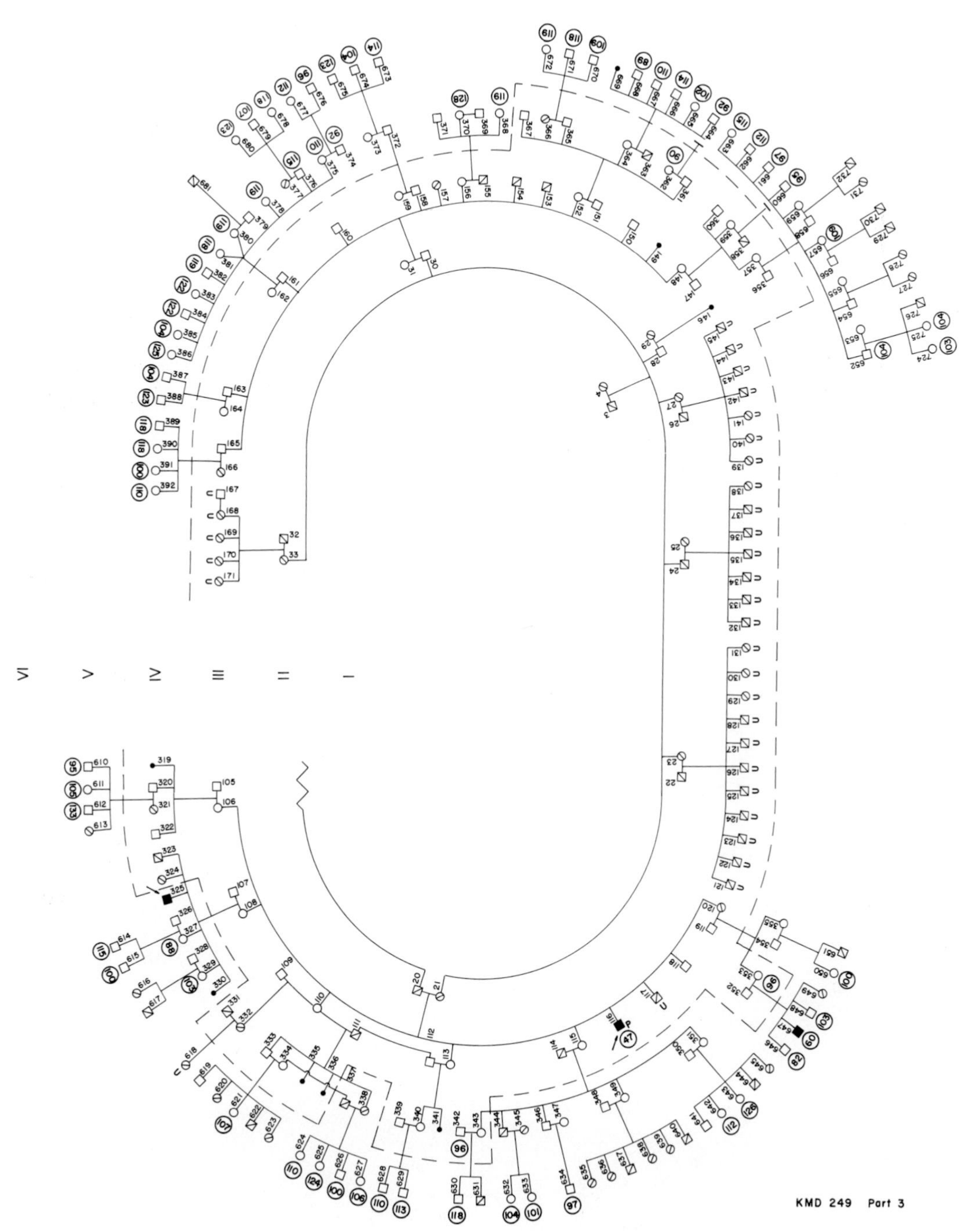

KMD 249 Part 3

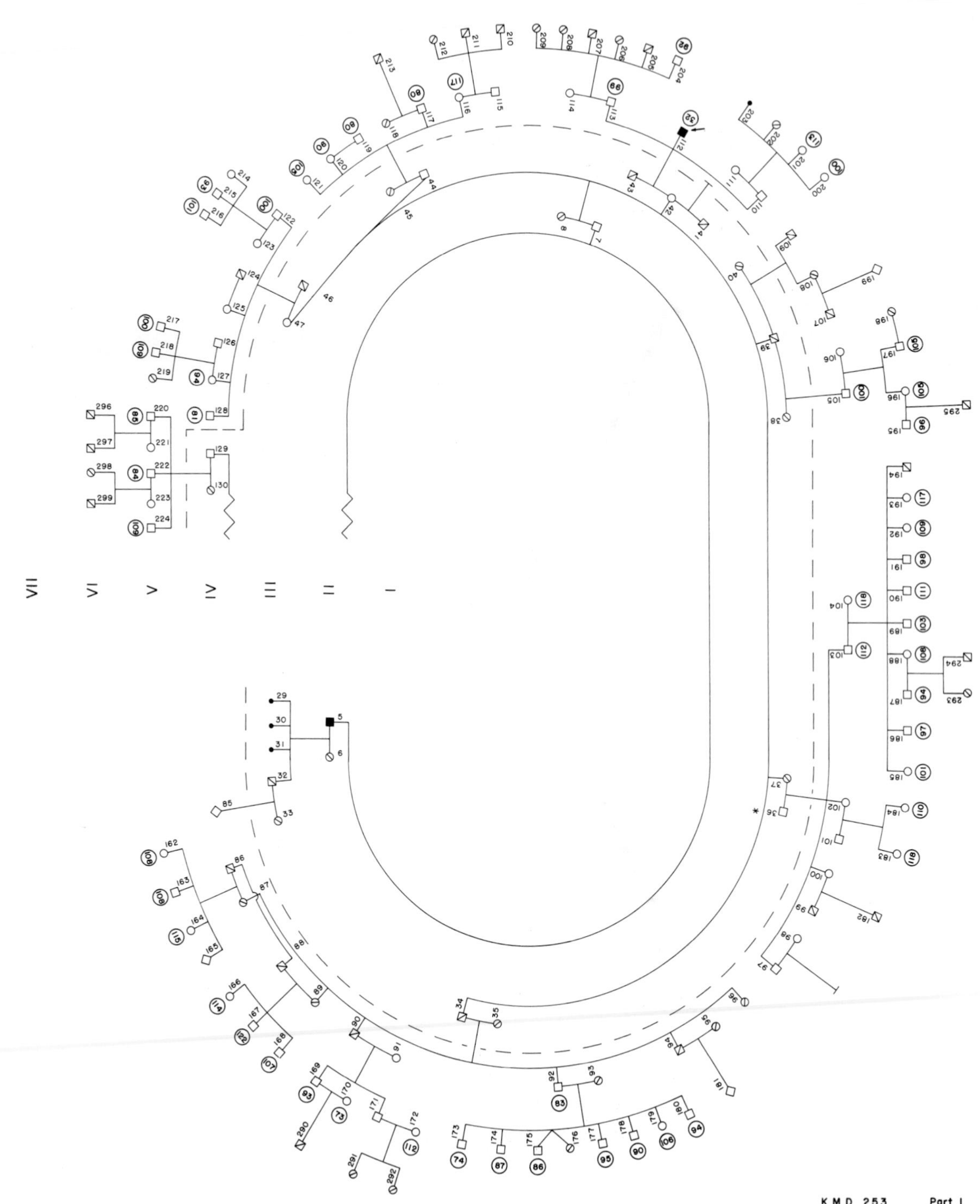

KMD 253 Part I

* 36 half brother of 151 in Part 2

KMD 253

The Proband

The proband (76) was born in 1889, institutionalized at age 6 years and died of pneumonia and measles in the institution in 1913. Labor was prolonged and the infant was deficient in respiration after birth. She never walked or talked and had no stigmata or history of perinatal infection. Her home environment was excellent. There was one report she had had nonepileptic convulsions but this was not verified by the medical records. IQ 13. *Diagnosis:* undifferentiated mental retardation.

Grandparents

Not of interest.

Parents

Father (17) was captain of a fire station.

Mother (18) was hospitalized twice for mental illness. She could not keep house or manage her home, but it is not known whether her mental illness influenced her performance or whether she was retarded.

Aunts and Uncles

Paternal uncle (5) was retarded.

Paternal uncle (10) had normal intelligence but married a retarded woman who was promiscuous and incorrigible.

Paternal uncle (12) was a married, but childless, retardate.

Siblings

Brother (75) died at 3 months, cause unknown.

Brother (77) was a Christian Brother but later left the Brotherhood, graduated from college and became an advertising consultant.

Brother (79) had unknown intelligence.

Brother (81) is a credit manager.

Brother (83) graduated from high school and is a truck driver.

Nieces and Nephews

Only two, (160) of unknown intelligence and (161), a high school student.

First Cousins

(48) served a prison term for stealing. He was classified as retarded in the old records but operates heavy machinery so he probably has an IQ above 70. His wife (49) came from a welfare family and has been blind for many years. She had an illegitimate child. They have a retarded grandchild.

(60) was institutionalized in 1906 at age 13 years and discharged ten years later. Her present status is unknown. Apparently she was single when last heard from by relatives in 1944. She was premature, had "abscesses" on neck and around ears at age 6 months (syphilis?) and a high arched palate. Her mother had both gonorrhea and syphilis. Of her 13 siblings, eight were stillborn or died in infancy. The IQ of (60) was 67.

(69), brother to (60), was in a reformatory for stealing, worked as an elevator boy and died in Oregon. It is not known whether he had a family or not.

(71) had "abscesses" around his ears, Hutchinson's teeth and was retarded.

(72) was a juvenile delinquent.

The maternal first cousins of the proband are unknown.

More Distant Relatives

(112) is institutionalized with Down's syndrome, IQ 32.

(231) has an IQ of 69.

(232) died of cellulitis, septicemia and mental deficiency at age 5 years. He was diagnosed as spastic.

(236) is of interest because she had six husbands, but only four children, all by her first husband. She had a spastic grandchild (330) who died in infancy.

(242) died of Little's disease at age 7 years.

(243) died at age 6 years. He was "spastic."

(248), brother to (232), (242) and (243), died of pulmonary edema at age 23 years. He was "spastic" and the family reported he had Little's disease. Four of the eight siblings in this family apparently had Little's disease.

(269) has an IQ of 69 and his father and five of his six tested siblings have IQ's in the low-normal range, 82-88; mother's IQ unknown.

(330) died in infancy. He was "spastic," apparently Little's disease according to the doctor who warned the parents it was hereditary in their family. [See (248), a great-uncle.]

Family Summary

The proband, IQ 13, two paternal uncles, two first cousins (one the other proband for this combined history) and five more distant relatives were retarded. Among these last was one with Down's syndrome and two brothers with Little's disease. All the other retardates, with the exception of the proband, were high-grade. The proband's mother was hospitalized twice for mental illness. The proband was born after prolonged labor and was deficient in animation for some time. The proband's parents had six children and only two grandchildren.

Retardation of proband of unknown origin.

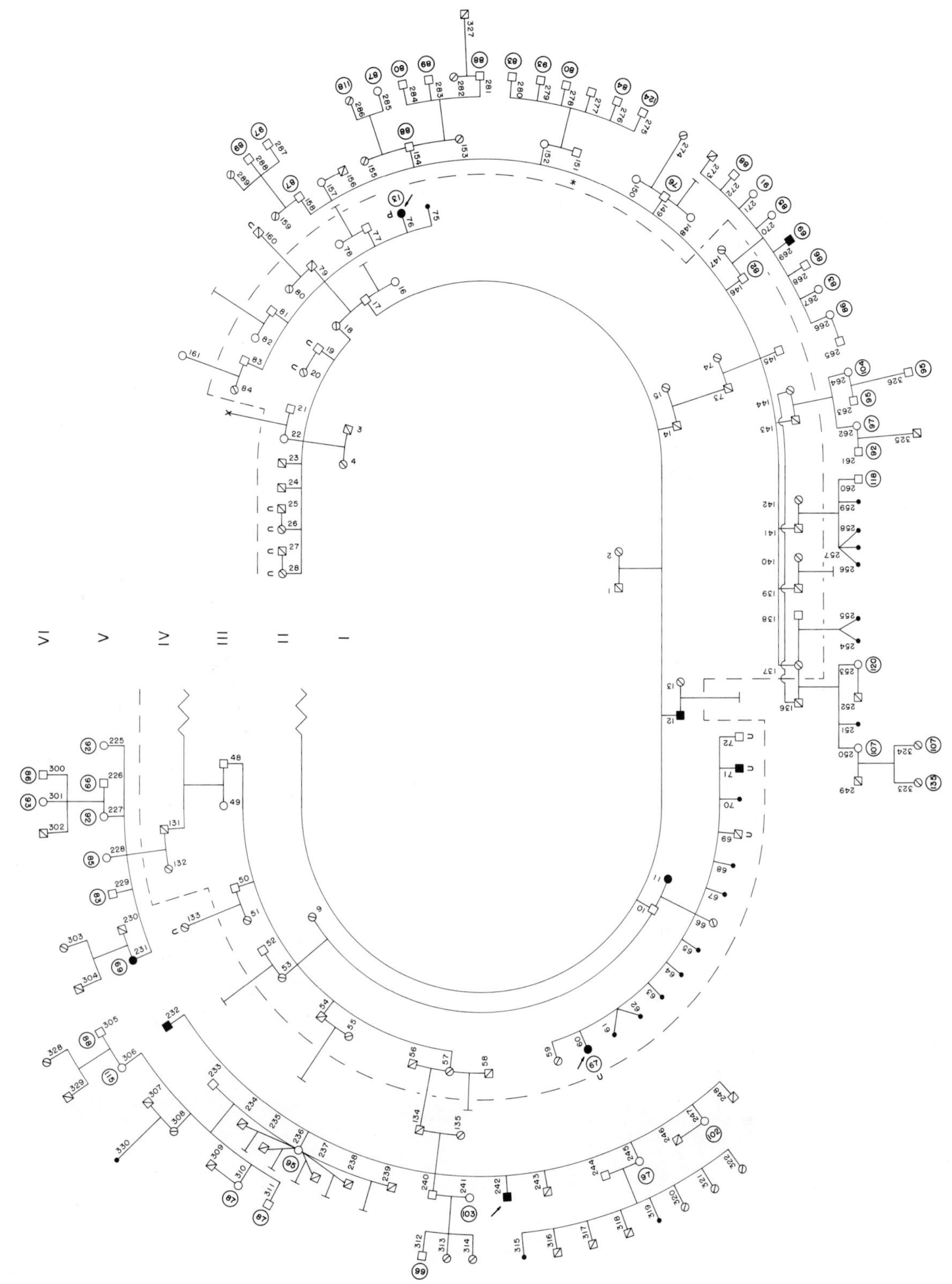

KMD 253 Part 2

* 151 half brother of 36 in Part I

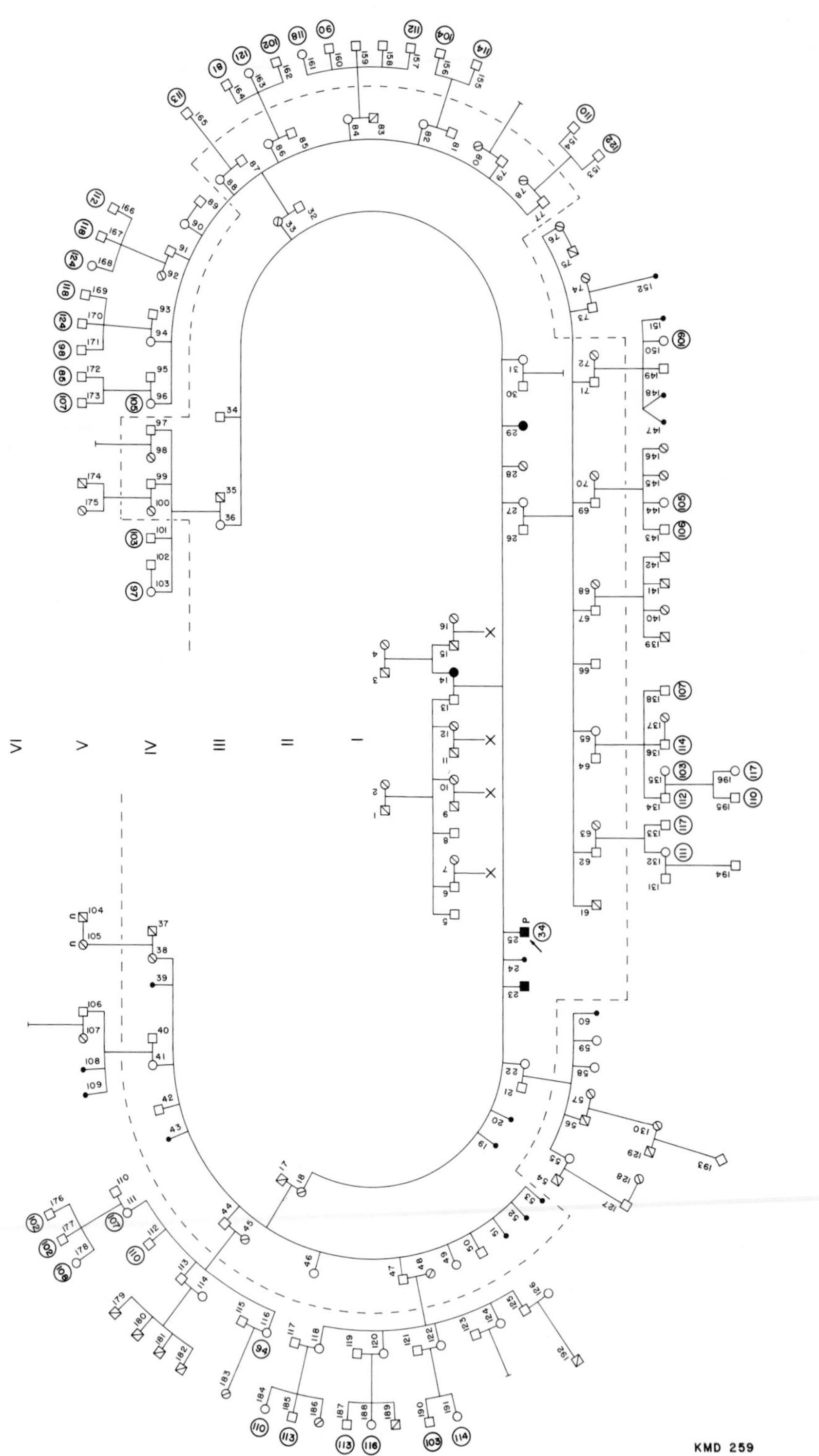

KMD 259

KMD 259

The Proband

The proband (25) was born in 1868 and was first admitted to a mental hospital in 1900 for six months, and was then transferred to the institution for the retarded. He had no history of birth injury or perinatal infection but had stigmata of kyphosis of lower lumbar region, left shoulder lower than right and nose turned to the left. He ran away ten years later and was found dead of exposure. His mother reported he began to act strangely after the age of 15 years. The mental hospital reported he was only retarded, not mentally ill, and was not a "fit subject" for hospitalization. IQ 34. *Diagnosis:* undifferentiated mental retardation.

Grandparents

Maternal grandfather died of alcoholism.

Parents

Father (13) had normal intelligence.

Mother (14) was "queer." She stayed in bed for 26 years. The early workers reported her as retarded.

Aunts and Uncles

Paternal uncle (8) was found shot to death.

Paternal aunts (10) and (12) were mentally ill. (12) drowned herself.

Siblings

Sister (18) was hospitalized for mental illness. Her husband had unknown intelligence. Her children were all normal although five of the 13 died in infancy.

Sisters (19), (20) and (24) died in infancy.

Sister (22) was "slow and dull," husband and children normal.

Brother (23) was a high-grade retardate and died unmarried and childless.

Sisters (27), (31) and (36) had normal intelligence. (27) and (31) had normal husbands. (36) had a husband of unknown intelligence. No retardation has appeared among their descendants.

Sister (28) died of diphtheria at 13 years.

Sister (29) died at age 2 years and was retarded.

Sister (33) has unknown intelligence, husband and children normal.

Brother (34) died of appendicitis at age 18 years. He was "slow and dull."

Nieces and Nephews

Not of interest except that of the 13 children of the proband's sister (18), only four married and had children.

First Cousins

Unknown.

More Distant Relatives

Not of interest.

Family Summary

The proband, IQ 34, his mother and two of his siblings were retarded. There were also several cases of mental illness in the family. The proband's parents had 14 children and 41 grandchildren. No retardation has appeared in the last two generations.

Retardation of proband of unknown origin.

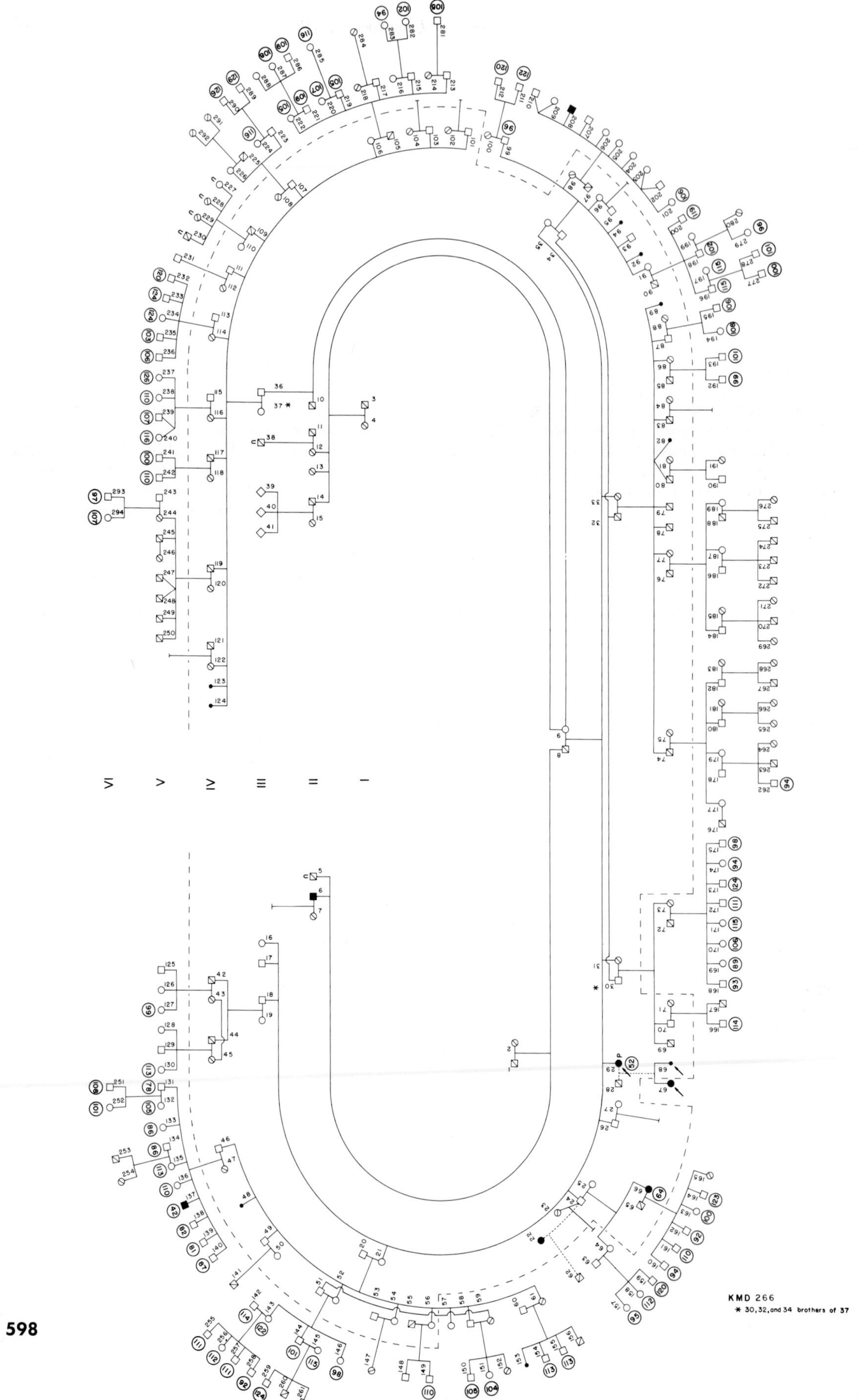

KMD 266
* 30, 32, and 34 brothers of 37

KMD 266

The Proband

The proband (29) was born in 1878, institutionalized at age 33 years and discharged to relatives a year later. She is now deceased. She had two illegitimate children, one born in the institution and one born three years after her discharge. She attended school for eight years with poor results. As a child she was troubled with "sores on her head," but there is no record of syphilis in the family, and no records of early trauma or of the presence of any stigmata. She was "a quiet, inoffensive girl." IQ 52. *Diagnosis:* undifferentiated mental retardation.

Grandparents

Not of interest.

Parents

Father (8) was a farmer of unknown intelligence.

Mother (9) had normal intelligence.

Aunts and Uncles

Paternal uncle (6) was retarded.

Maternal relatives remained in Germany and are unknown.

Siblings

Sister (16) is a nun.

Sister (21) has normal intelligence and her husband and children are also normal.

Brothers (17), (18), (24) and (26) have normal intelligence and all were prosperous farmers with normal wives. (24) fathered an illegitimate child, (62), and his second and third children were committed as dependent and neglected.

Sisters (31) and (33) have unknown intelligence. (35) developed a paranoid type senile psychosis but had normal intelligence.

Half Siblings

Half brother (36) has normal intelligence.

Children

Daughter (67) was institutionalized at age 3 years and died of influenza in the institution in 1939 at age 20 years. She was a low-grade retardate with a mental age of less than 3 years.

Son (68) was born in the institution and died of bronchopneumonia at age 6 days. He was a seven months' baby.

Nieces and Nephews

Niece (64) was committed as dependent and neglected at age 14 years. She completed the ninth grade, married a man with normal intelligence and had three children with IQ's of 95, 112 and 120, respectively.

Niece (66), sister to (64), was also committed as dependent and neglected at age 17 years. She was declared retarded three years later but never institutionalized. She married a truck driver and has six children, five with IQ's of 94, 110, 92, 100 and 123, respectively, the sixth is untested as yet.

First Cousins

Unknown.

More Distant Relatives

Proband's nephew (46) has a retarded child (137) with IQ 42. Five of the eight children of (46) have low-normal or borderline IQ's of 78, 86, 82, 81 and 87. Two have IQ's of 113 and 110.

Proband's niece (98) has a child, (208), with Down's syndrome.

Family Summary

The proband, IQ 52, her maternal uncle, her daughter, one niece and two more distant relatives were retarded. The proband was reared in a good home and had no history of early trauma. She had two illegitimate children, one of whom was a low-grade retardate. The proband's parents had ten children and 36 grandchildren.

Retardation of proband of unknown origin.

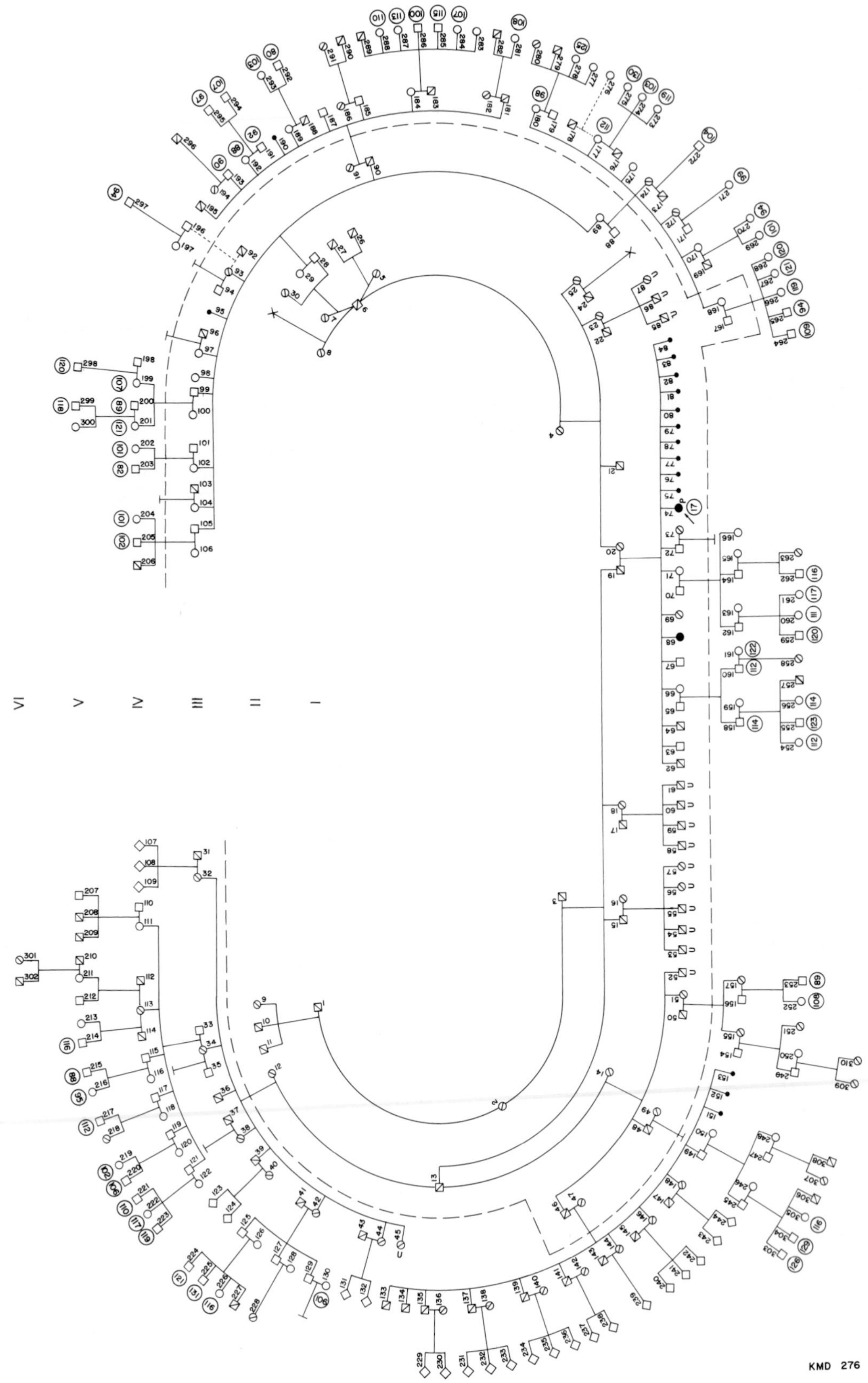

KMD 276

KMD 276

The Proband

The proband (74) was born in 1901, institutionalized at age 6 years and died of influenza in the institution in 1929. He made only inarticulate sounds and would pound his head against the wall. His only stigmata were a high narrow palate and flat feet. His birth was uneventful and there was no history of perinatal infection. IQ 17. *Diagnosis:* undifferentiated mental retardation.

Grandparents

Not of interest.

Parents

Father (19) had unknown intelligence. He was peculiar, erratic and ignorant.

Mother (20) was unknown.

Aunts and Uncles

All paternal and maternal relatives, except two cousins, remained in Germany.

Siblings

Brother (62) was killed by lightning at age 31 years. His intelligence was unknown.

Brother (63) had normal intelligence. He died unmarried and childless.

Brother (64) is thought to have died shortly after he left home at age 17 years. His intelligence was unknown.

Sister (66) has normal intelligence, as do her husband and children. She refused to cooperate.

Brother (67) is an unmarried real estate man.

Sister (68) is an unmarried, childless, high-grade retardate.

Sister (69) died of tuberculosis at age 30. Her intelligence was unknown.

Sister (71) has normal intelligence, as do her husband and children.

Brother (72) is a married but childless welder with normal intelligence. He would not cooperate.

(75) through (84) died in infancy.

Nieces and Nephews

Only five, all with normal intelligence.

First Cousins

Not of interest.

More Distant Relatives

Not of interest.

Family Summary

The proband, IQ 17, and her high-grade retardate sister were the only retarded persons known in this family. The proband's parents had 20 children, only two of whom reproduced, so there were only five grandchildren.

Retardation of proband of unknown origin.

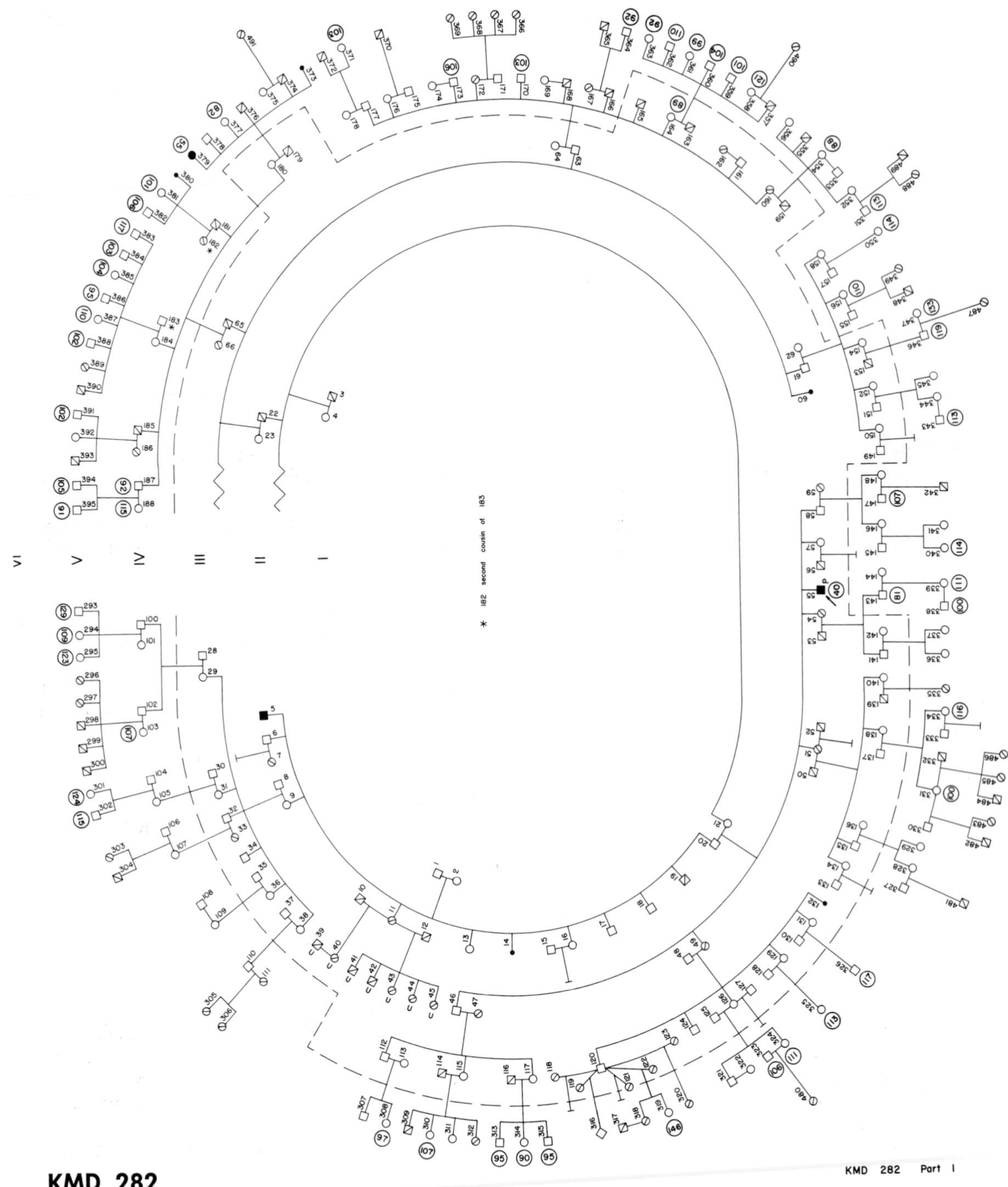

KMD 282

The Proband

The proband (55) was born in 1894, institutionalized at age 13 years and died of coronary thrombosis in 1956. He walked at the usual time but never talked so that he could be understood. He had no history of birth injuries or perinatal infection. Medical history says "never sick." IQ 40. *Diagnosis:* undifferentiated mental retardation.

Grandparents

Not of interest.

Parents

Father (20) and mother (21) both had normal intelligence, although the mother was described as "erratic and peculiar." The father was a janitor.

Aunts and Uncles

Paternal uncle (5) died unmarried and childless. He was retarded.

Siblings

Brother (46) was an engineer in a mill.

Sisters (49), (51) and (54) had unknown intelligence.

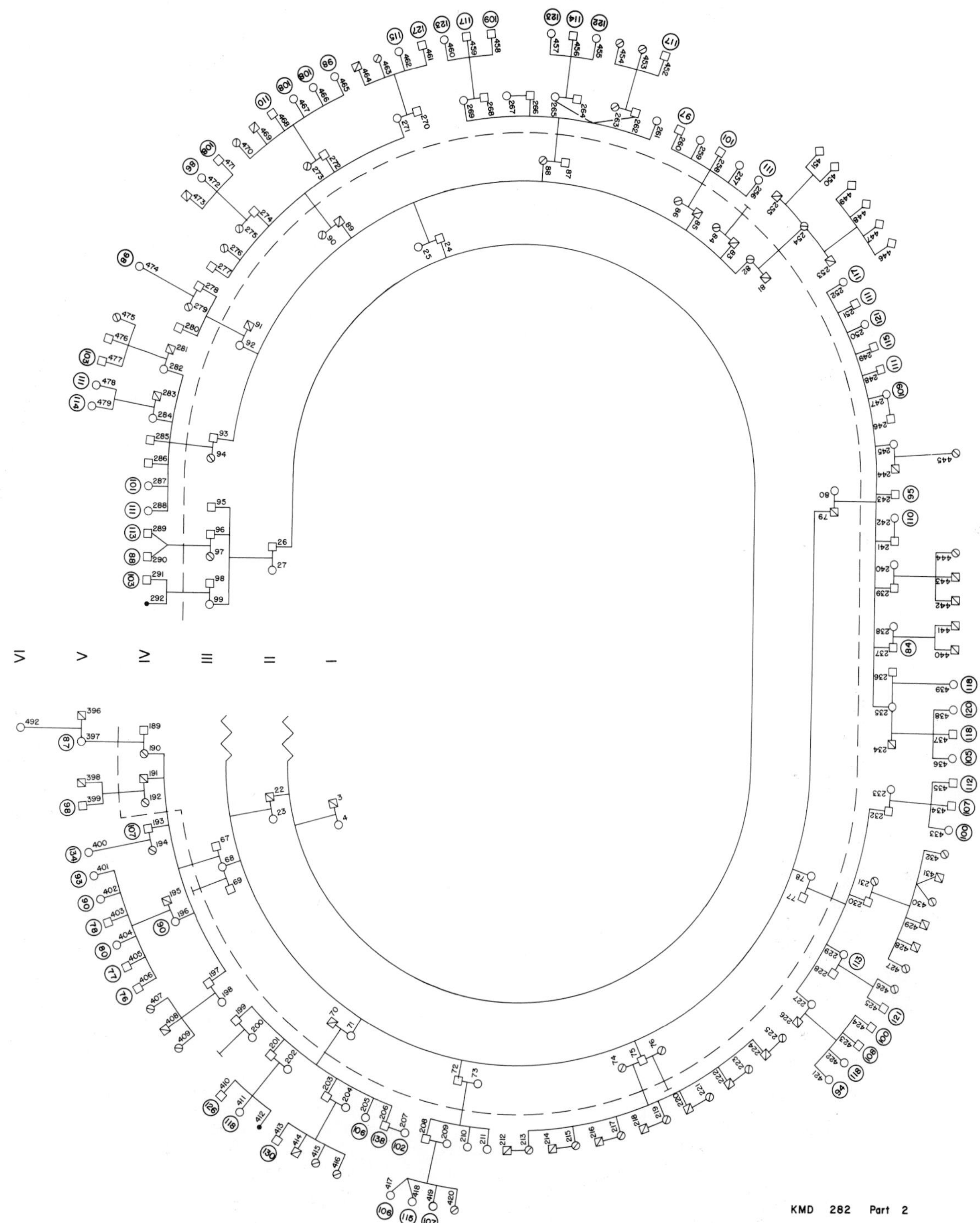

Sister (57) completed the eleventh grade.

Brother (58) probably had normal intelligence. He was described as "mentally slow."

All the siblings were married to spouses of unknown intelligence except (49) whose husband had normal intelligence. No retardation has appeared among their descendants.

Nieces and Nephews

All have normal intelligence.

First Cousins

Not of interest.

More Distant Relatives

Not of interest.

Family Summary

The proband, IQ 40, was the only known retardate in this family. He had a normal birth and a good environment. His parents had seven children and 17 grandchildren.

Retardation of proband of unknown origin.

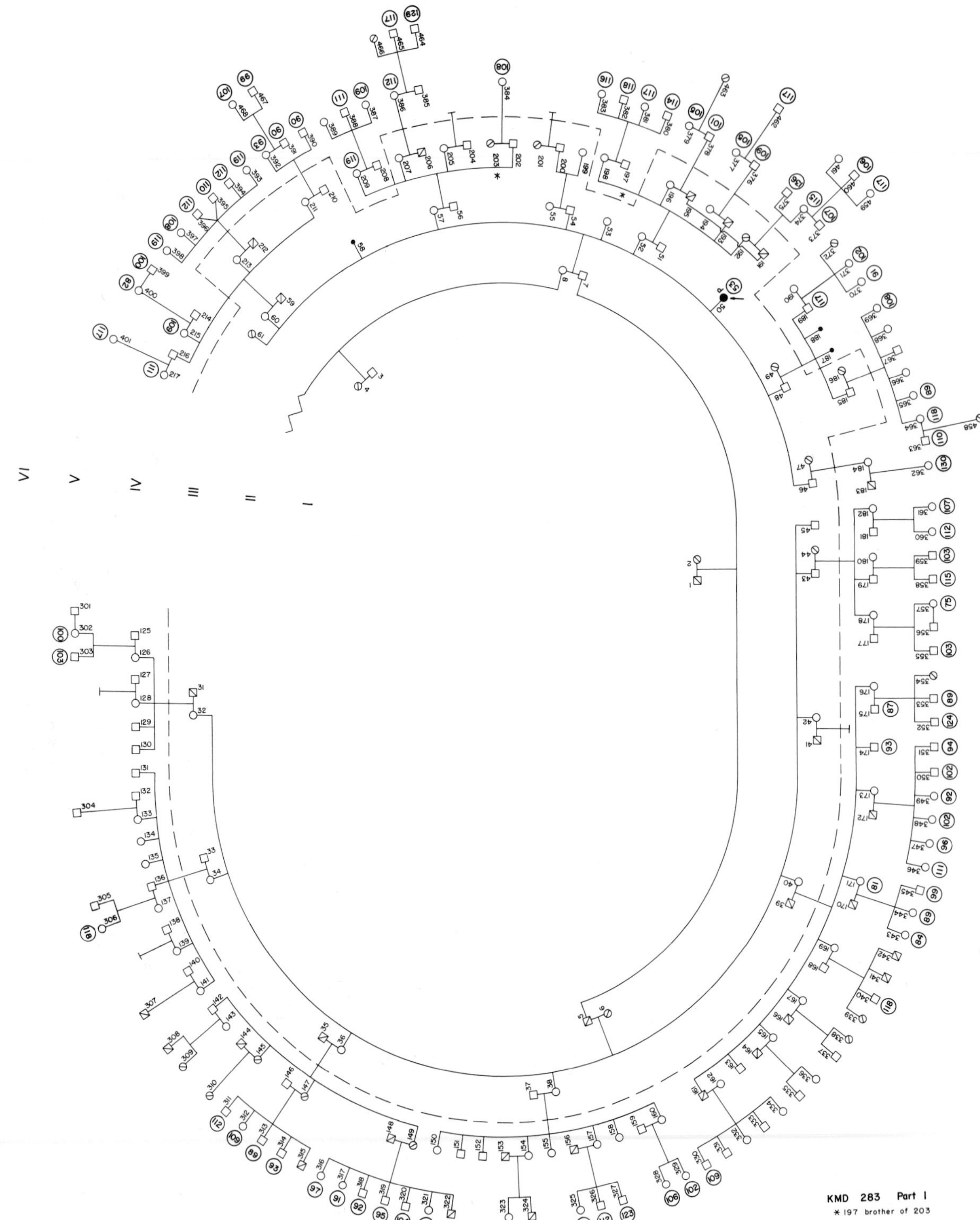

KMD 283

The Proband

The proband (50) was born in 1878 and institutionalized at age 16 years. She was discharged to her parents in 1912 and died of acute peritonitis in 1937. She never married or had children. There was no history of birth injury or perinatal infection and she had no stigmata. IQ 53. *Diagnosis:* undifferentiated mental retardation.

Grandparents

Not of interest.

Parents

Father (7) and mother (8) both had normal intelligence.

Aunts and Uncles

Not of interest.

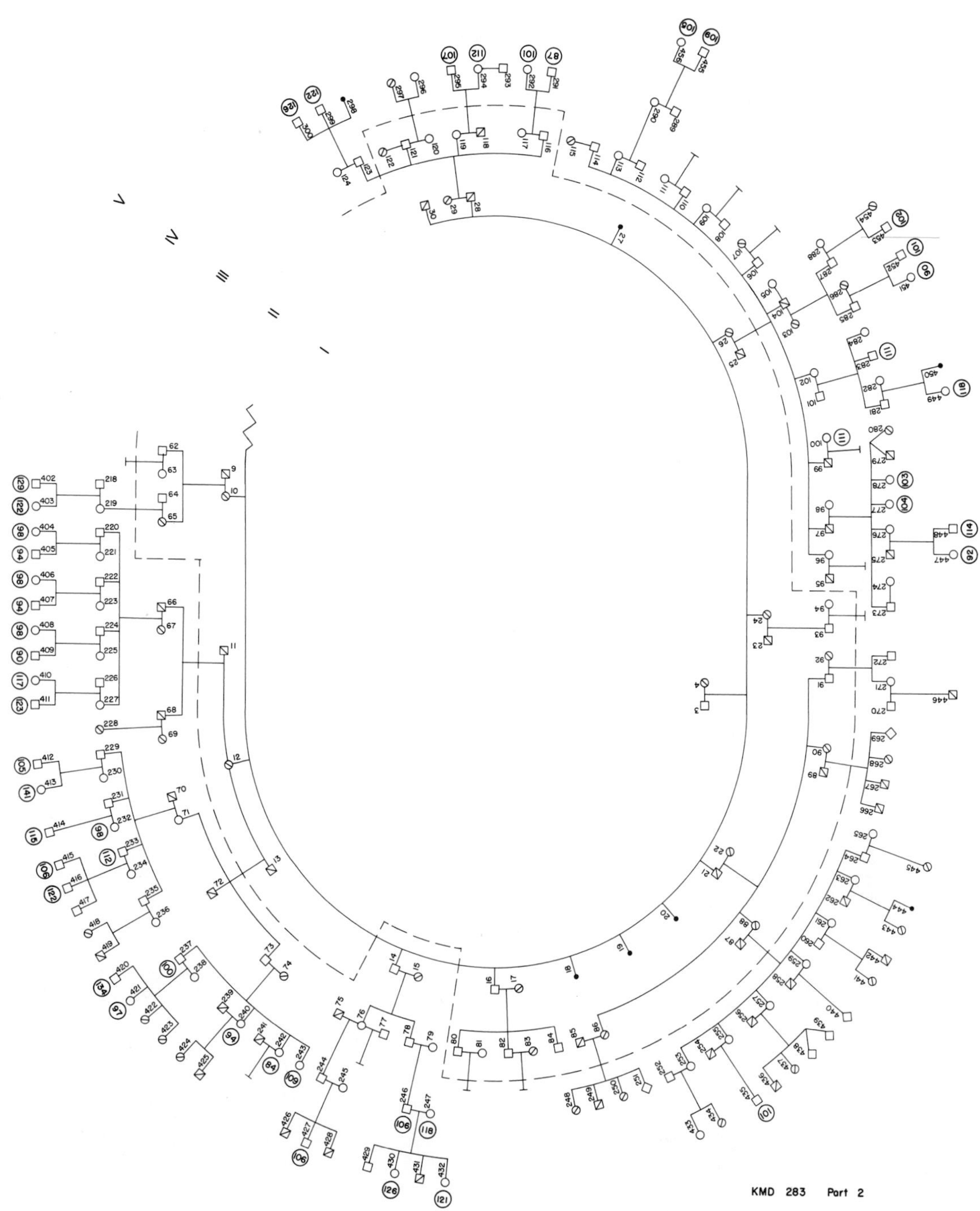

KMD 283 Part 2

Siblings

All the adult married ones had normal intelligence. Three married normal spouses, three had unknown spouses, all had normal children. (58) died of measles and spasms at 7 months. (53) and (61) died single and childless.

Nieces and Nephews

Not of interest.

First Cousins

Not of interest.

More Distant Relatives

Not of interest.

Family Summary

The proband, IQ 53, was the only retarded person found in this family. Her birth and early history were uneventful. Her parents had ten children and 19 grandchildren.

Retardation of proband of unknown origin.

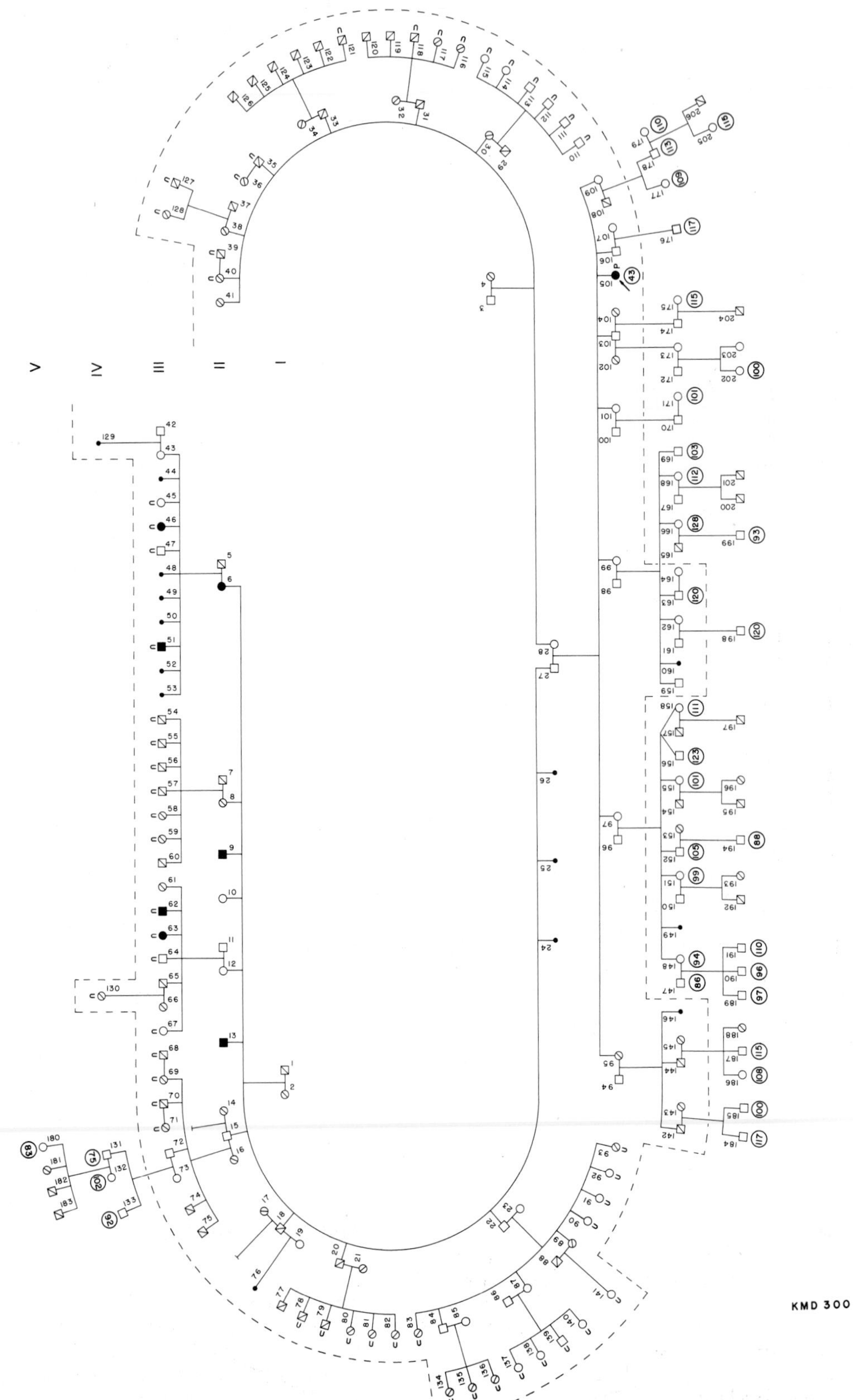

KMD 300

KMD 300

The Proband

The proband (105) was born in 1895, institutionalized at age 16 years and died of pulmonary tuberculosis in the institution in 1921. She had rickets and "spinal trouble" and was not able to sit up until the age of 3 years. She went to school for a short time but learned little. Her home environment was good and she had no history of difficult birth or perinatal infection and no stigmata. IQ 43. *Diagnosis:* undifferentiated mental retardation.

Grandparents

Not of interest.

Parents

Father (27) had normal intelligence. He was a day laborer with a good income.

Mother (28) had normal intelligence. She was a "hard working woman."

Aunts and Uncles

Paternal aunt (6) and paternal uncles (9) and (13) were retarded. Neither of the uncles ever married nor had children.

Maternal aunt (30) was hospitalized for mental illness.

Siblings

Sister (95) had unknown intelligence, husband normal.

Sisters (97), (99), (101) and (109) have normal intelligence. All have normal husbands except (109) whose husband is unknown.

Brothers (103) and (106) have normal intelligence. The wives of (103) have unknown intelligence. The wife of (106) is normal.

Nieces and Nephews

Not of interest. No retardation has appeared among them.

First Cousins

(46) and (51), siblings, are retarded.

(62) and (63), siblings, are deaf and retarded.

More Distant Relatives

Not of interest.

Family Summary

The proband, IQ 41, a paternal aunt and two paternal uncles, together with four first cousins, were retarded. The proband's parents had eight children and 23 grandchildren.

Retardation of proband of unknown origin.

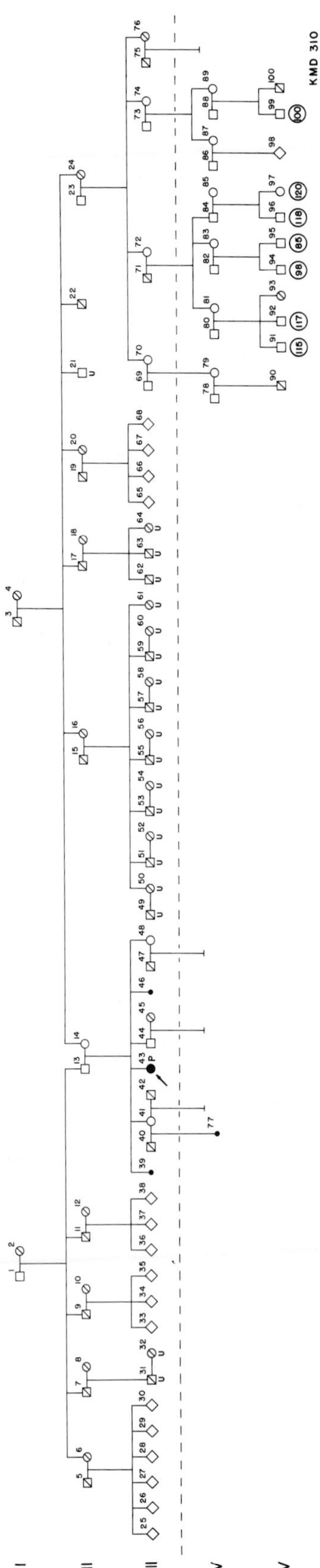

KMD 310

The Proband

The proband (43) was born in 1887, institutionalized at age 10 years, discharged in 1915 and was living with her brother in 1961. Her birth was uneventful, but her mother was knocked unconscious in a buggy accident in the fifth month of pregnancy. She cried incessantly, walked at age 2 years and does not talk. She has no stigmata. Her home environment was good. She was not tested but was classified as "very low grade." *Diagnosis:* undifferentiated mental retardation.

Grandparents

Not of interest.

Parents

Father (13) had normal intelligence.

Mother (14) was very nervous and erratic, and fanatically religious. She had a large, well cared for house and probably had normal intelligence.

Aunts and Uncles

Maternal uncle (22) died of "convulsions" at age 15 years.

Siblings

Brother (39) died of a respiratory ailment at age 2 weeks.

Sister (41) was a teacher.

Brother (44) went to college.

(46) was a miscarriage.

Sister (48) graduated from high school and is a secretary.

Nieces and Nephews

Only one, (77), who died at birth or shortly after.

First Cousins

Not of interest.

More Distant Relatives

Not of interest.

Family Summary

The proband, a low-grade retardate, was the only affected person in her family. The proband's parents had six children and one grandchild who died in infancy. All of the proband's normal adult siblings married, but only one pregnancy resulted.

Retardation of proband of unknown origin.

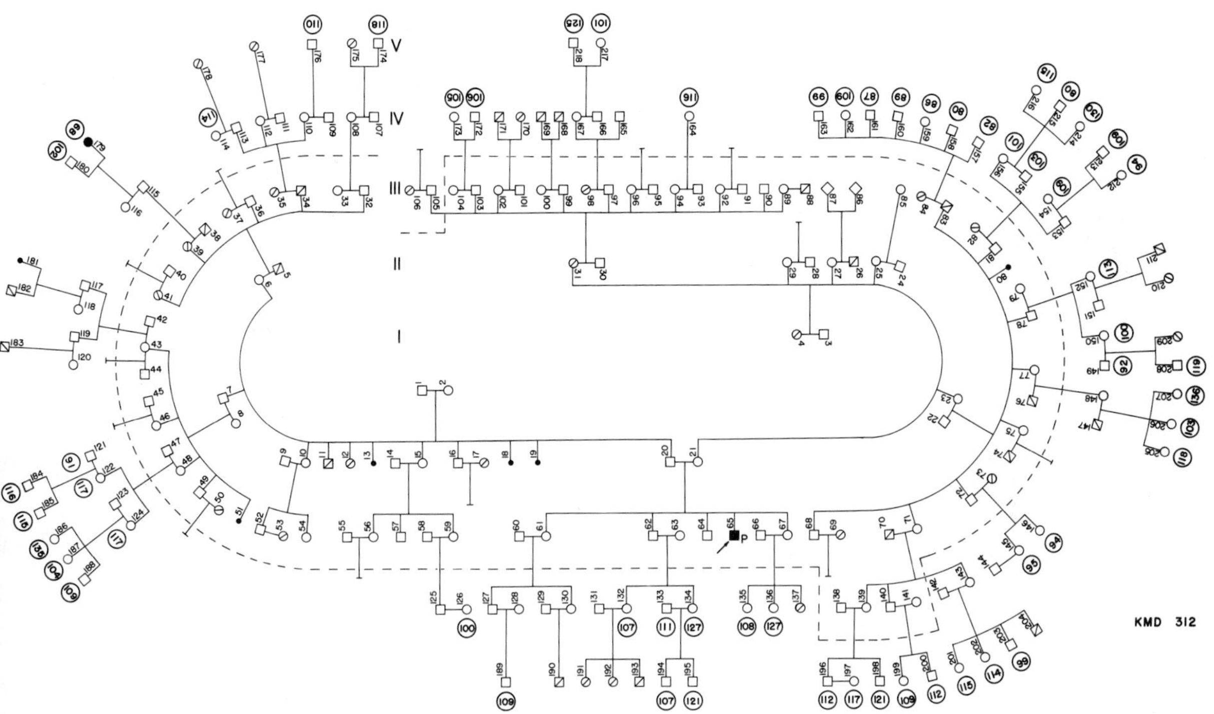

KMD 312

KMD 312

The Proband

The proband (65) was born in 1902 and institutionalized at age 10 years. He was discharged in 1913 to his mother and readmitted in 1943 after three months in a mental hospital and died the same year of heart trouble. He was delivered by instruments. The mother refused to have him institutionalized despite the efforts of relatives and neighbors, so he was removed to the institution by the Humane Society. The mother became so upset that the child was returned to her after six months and was not institutionalized again until after her death in 1943. He was a very low-grade retardate, most destructive and with no bowel or bladder control. *Diagnosis:* undifferentiated mental retardation.

Grandparents

Not of interest.

Parents

Both parents (20) and (21) had normal intelligence, but the mother was fanatically devoted to the proband and sacrificed herself and her family for him. He was so destructive that they could have very little furniture in the house.

Aunts and Uncles

Not of interest.

Siblings

All have normal intelligence.

Nieces and Nephews

All except one (too young to test) are known to have normal intelligence.

First Cousins

Not of interest.

More Distant Relatives

Proband's cousin (39) has a grandchild (179) with an IQ of 68.

Family Summary

The proband, a low-grade, destructive retardate with no speech and no bowel or bladder control, was the only retarded person in this kindred with the exception of a first cousin's grandchild who had IQ 68. The proband's parents had five children and seven grandchildren.

Retardation of proband of unknown origin.

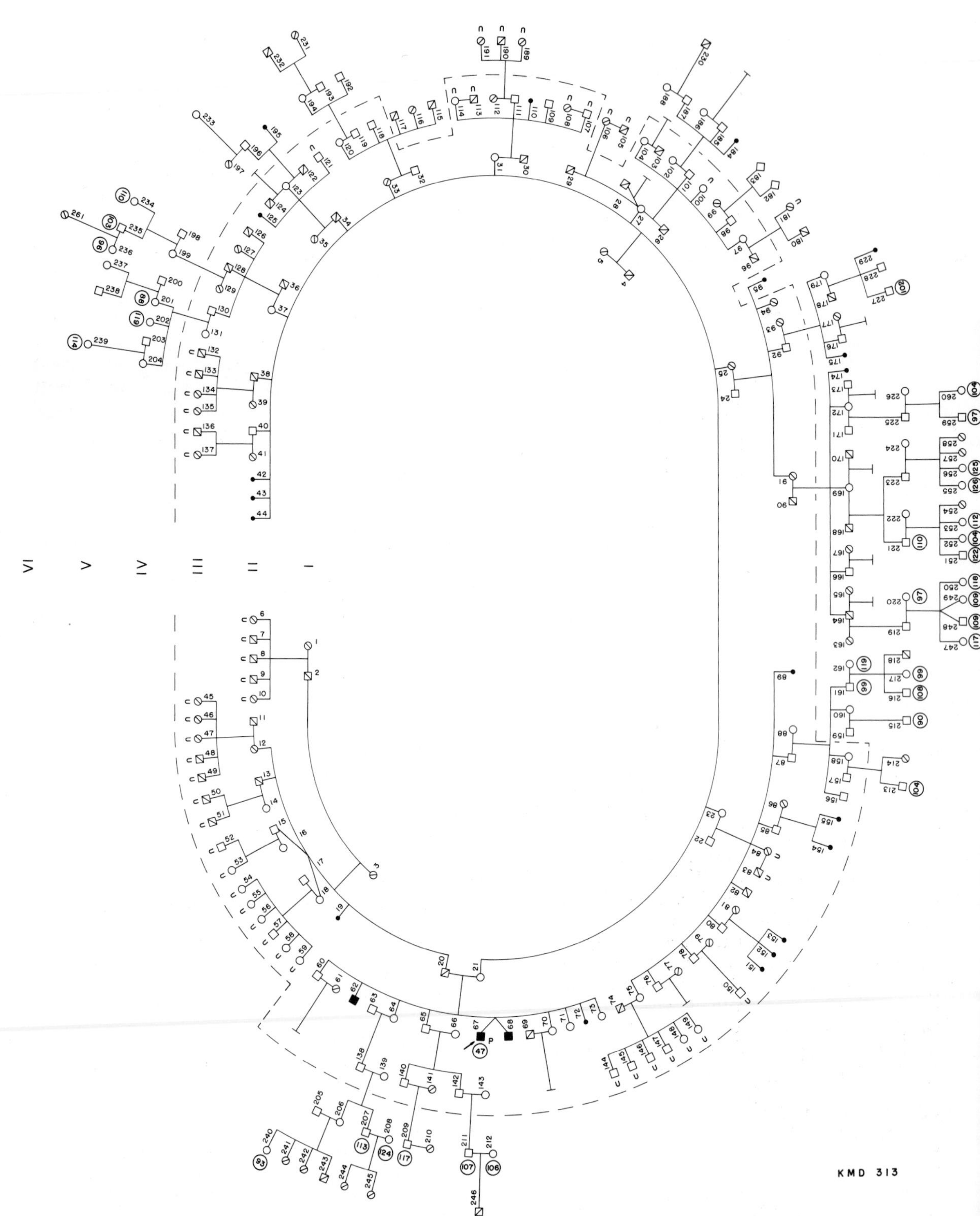

KMD 313

KMD 313

The Proband

The proband (67) was born in 1878, institutionalized at age 32 years and died of carcinoma of the stomach in the institution in 1939. He had no history of birth injury or perinatal infection and had no stigmata. His home environment was good. The proband had considerable musical talent and could play second violin in an orchestra although he could not read music. IQ 47. *Diagnosis:* undifferentiated mental retardation.

Grandparents

Not of interest.

Parents

Father (20) was a cornetist with a band. He was always supported by his family since he was an alcoholic and did not work. His intelligence is unknown, although he was interviewed by the early workers.

Mother (21) had normal intelligence.

Aunts and Uncles

Not of interest.

Siblings

Brother (60) was a talented violinist but could not advance in his career because he was an alcoholic.

Brother (62) was a retarded alcoholic but could play second violin by ear.

Sister (64) operated her husband's business after his death.

Brother (65) was a good flutist despite the fact that he was an alcoholic and choreic. He died of Parkinson's disease. He had normal intelligence.

Brother (68), twin to the proband, was retarded and mentally ill. He died in a mental hospital. He had regressed to the point where he did not talk. He was a violinist and drummer.

Sister (70) was an excellent pianist who traveled with a musical comedy company. She was an alcoholic and "peculiar," but had normal intelligence.

Sister (71) could play the piano by ear, elaborating on melodies and was also a good singer, but had a baritone voice. She died in a mental hospital but had worked as a bookkeeper.

Brother (72) died of meningitis at age 1 year.

Sister (73) was a singer in a cafe. She was "peculiar" but had normal intelligence.

Nieces and Nephews

Only three, all with normal intelligence and no particular musical talent.

First Cousins

Paternal cousins are unknown.

Maternal cousins not of interest.

More Distant Relatives

Not of interest.

Family Summary

The proband, IQ 47, his twin brother and one other brother were retarded. The proband's family presents an interesting picture of unusual musical ability which was possessed by all but one of the proband's siblings without regard to their mental status. The proband's father was also a talented musician but an alcoholic as were four of his children, including one daughter. Two of the proband's siblings died in mental hospitals and all were described as peculiar and erratic. The proband's parents had ten children but only three grandchildren.

Retardation of proband of unknown origin.

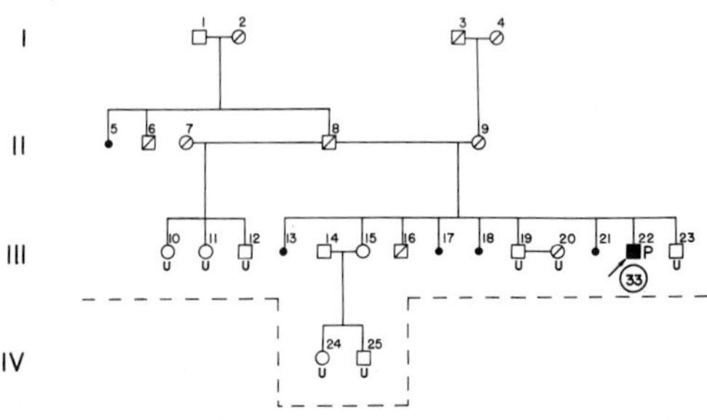

KMD 315

The Proband

The proband (22) was born in 1886, institutionalized at age 25 years and died of cerebral hemorrhage and disease of the coronary artery in the institution in 1945. He walked and talked at age 3 years. There was no history of difficult birth or perinatal infection and no record of stigmata. IQ 33. *Diagnosis:* undifferentiated mental retardation.

Grandparents

Not of interest.

Parents

Father (8) and mother (9) had unknown intelligence.

Aunts and Uncles

Both paternal relatives died young.

No maternal relatives. Proband's mother was an only child.

Siblings

Sister (13) died at age 3 days, cause unknown.

Sister (15) and brothers (19) and (23) had normal intelligence. (15) had a normal husband and children. The wife of (19) had unknown intelligence.

Brother (16) died of pneumonia at age 7 years.

Sister (17) died at age 3 weeks.

Brother (21) was born without an anus. He was operated on successfully but died at age 6 weeks.

Nieces and Nephews

Only two known, both with normal intelligence.

First Cousins

None.

More Distant Relatives

Unknown.

Family Summary

The proband, IQ 33, was the only retarded person in his immediate family. No new information could be obtained about relatives since the family had a frequently occurring Scandinavian name which made them impossible to trace. The proband's parents had nine children and an unknown number of grandchildren—at least two.

Retardation of proband of unknown origin.

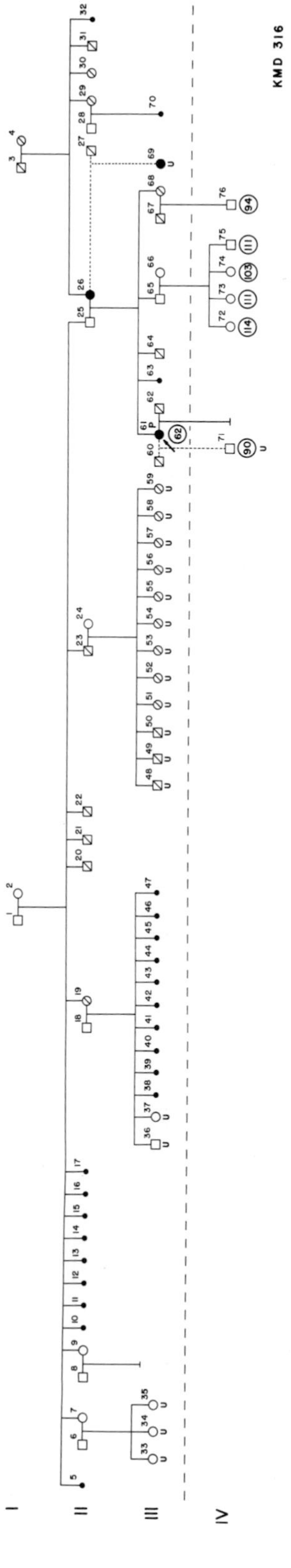

KMD 316

The Proband

The proband (61) was born in 1903. She was institutionalized at age 10 years and escaped and was returned twice (the second time she was returned from the county jail). Her illegitimate child was born three months before her jail sentence. A sterilization operation was performed in 1926 and she was paroled. She was discharged from guardianship in 1948 and her present whereabouts are unknown. She was married for a short time but the marriage was annulled. She was syphilitic. She was a healthy child but was neglected by her family. IQ 62. *Diagnosis:* undifferentiated mental retardation.

Grandparents

Paternal grandmother was epileptic.

Parents

Father (25) was ignorant and "of poor mentality," but was not classified as retarded.

Mother (26) was retarded.

Aunts and Uncles

Not of interest except for a large number of infant deaths (5), (10 to 17) and (32).

Child

Son (71) was sent to the State School when his mother was institutionalized. He was placed in several boarding homes and when he became 18 years old he was discharged from guardianship. His present status is unknown. IQ 90.

Siblings

Sister (63) died of "summer complaint" at age 6 months.

Brother (64) died of pulmonary tuberculosis at age 6 years.

Brother (65) works in a foundry and has normal intelligence, as do his wife and children.

Sister (68) has unknown intelligence. Her husband's intelligence is also unknown, but they have a daughter of normal intelligence.

Half Sibling

Half sister (69) was an illegitimate, retarded girl who remained in Europe.

Nieces and Nephews

All have normal intelligence.

First Cousins

Not of interest except for the large number of infant deaths (38 to 47) who were all so large they were instrument deliveries and were stillborn.

More Distant Relatives

Unknown.

Family Summary

The proband, IQ 62, her mother and her half sister were retarded. The proband's child and her nieces and nephews all have normal intelligence. The proband's parents had five children and six grandchildren.

Retardation of proband of unknown origin.

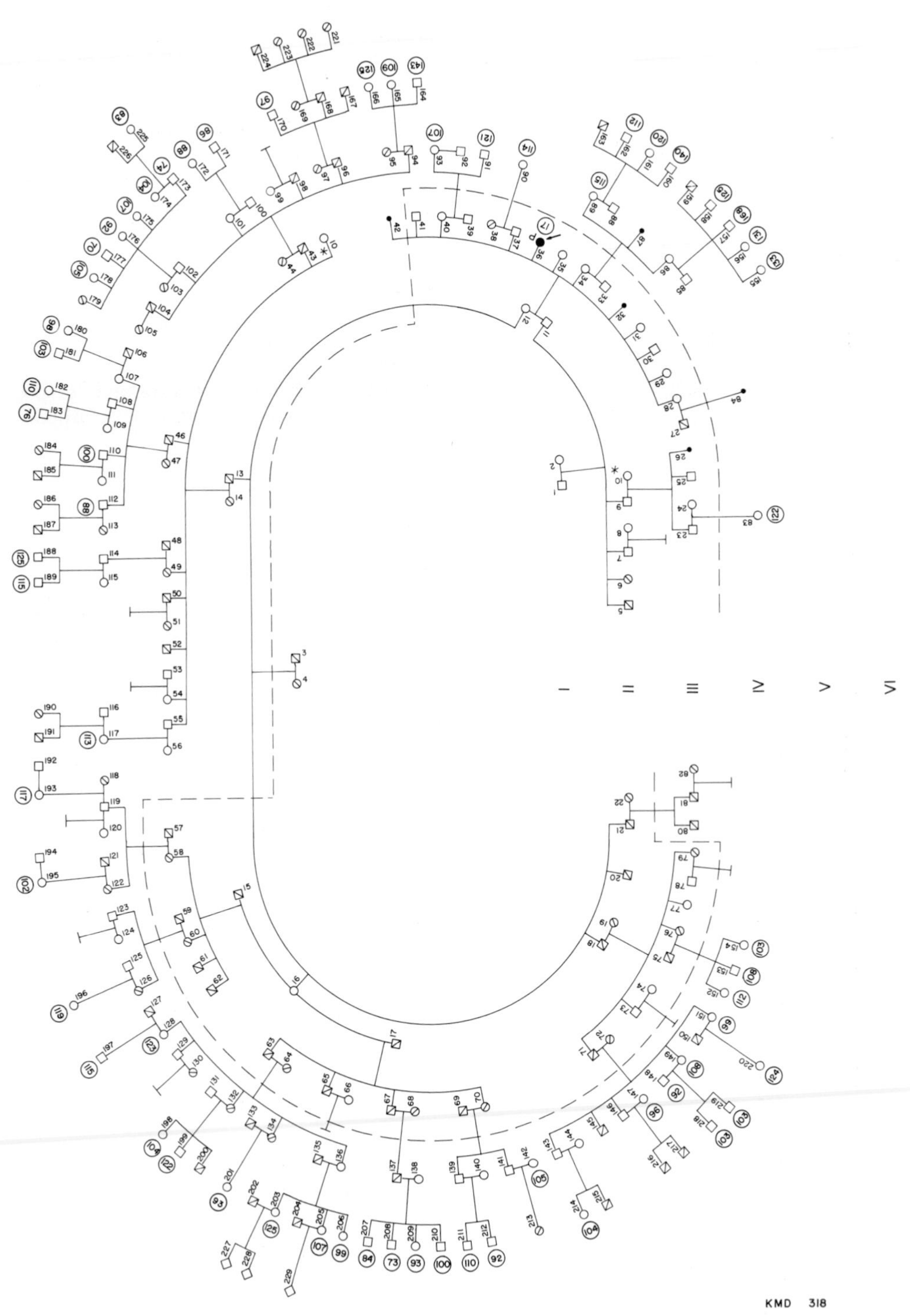

KMD 318

* 10 appears twice

KMD 318

The Proband

The proband (36) was born in 1894 and institutionalized at age 10 years. She was discharged to her parents in 1912 and died of bronchial pneumonia in 1949. She had bronchitis at age 2 years, was weak and sickly and very slow in developing. There was no history of birth injury. She lived in a good home. She had spastic diplegia. IQ 17. *Diagnosis:* mental retardation with spastic diplegia.

Grandparents

Not of interest.

Parents

Father (11) and mother (12) both had normal intelligence.

Aunts and Uncles

Maternal uncle (21) died of a "nervous breakdown" in a mental hospital.

Siblings

Sisters (28), (29), (31) and (40) are all teachers.

Brother (30) died of typhoid pneumonia at age 5 years. He had normal intelligence.

Sister (32) died at age 2 weeks.

Sister (34) completed the ninth grade; husband and children normal.

Sister (35) died of appendicitis at age 29. She was an unmarried music teacher.

Brother (37) went to high school and operates a paint shop. The wife's intelligence is unknown and their daughter is normal.

Sister (40) had normal intelligence, as do her husband and children.

Sister (42) died in infancy.

Nieces and Nephews

All have normal intelligence.

First Cousins

Not of interest.

More Distant Relatives

First cousin (43) has a grandchild (177) with IQ 70 who is blind and who has been recommended for commitment as retarded. He has been given several kinds of tests. His IQ scores range from 85 at age 6 years, 77 at age 7 years, 58, 69 and 78 at age 9 years, 70 at age 12 years (all Stanford-Binet), and 79 at age 17 years on the Hayes-Binet. He was also given a Minnesota Multiphasic. The psychologist reported that he functioned at the moron level, but his good rote memory gave him spuriously high scores. He was anxious, withdrawn, depressed and appeared severely emotionally disturbed tending toward psychosis.

Family Summary

The proband, IQ 17, with spastic diplegia was the only retarded person known in this kindred except for an emotionally disturbed, high-grade retardate among the distant relatives. The proband had no history of injury or poor home environment. The proband's parents had 12 children and seven grandchildren (all seven the offspring of three children), two of whom died in infancy. The high IQ scores in two sibships [(155 to 159) and (160 to 163)] of the proband's great-nieces and nephews are of interest. In the sibship of (155 to 159) the IQ's are 133, 131, 168 and 125, respectively; in the sibship of (160-163) they are 140, 120 and 112.

Retardation of proband of unknown origin.

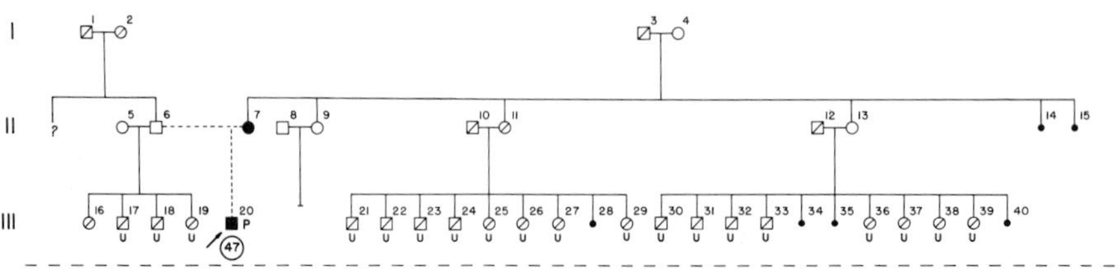

KMD 321

KMD 321

The Proband

The proband (20) was born in 1890, institutionalized at age 14 years and died of lobar pneumonia in the institution in 1941. He was illegitimate and lived with his mother and maternal grandparents. He had no history of difficult birth or childhood illness, and had no stigmata. IQ 47. *Diagnosis:* undifferentiated mental retardation.

Grandparents

Not of interest.

Parents

Father (6) was an alcoholic and promiscuous, but had normal intelligence.

Mother (7) was a retarded domestic worker.

Aunts and Uncles

Paternal relatives unknown.

Maternal relatives not of interest.

Siblings

None.

Half Siblings

Four, three of whom (17), (18) and (19) are unknown and (20) who died of tuberculosis.

Nieces and Nephews

No full nieces and nephews.

Children of half siblings unknown.

First Cousins

Unknown.

More Distant Relatives

Unknown.

Family Summary

The proband, IQ 47, was an illegitimate child. His mother was retarded. The relatives could not be found for the follow-up since they had a frequently occurring Scandinavian name. The proband's parents had one child, no grandchildren.

Retardation of proband of unknown origin.

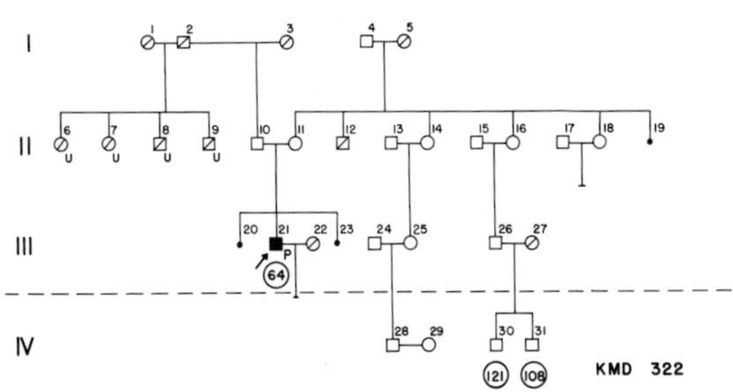

KMD 322

The Proband

The proband (21) was born in 1895 and institutionalized at age 13 years. He was discharged one year later and was an odd job man in 1961. He had been married and divorced, but was childless. He was a healthy child, reared in a good home. He reached the second grade by age 14 years and became so incorrigible that he was sent to the State Training School twice. He has had no prison record since his discharge from the institution, however. IQ 64. *Diagnosis:* undifferentiated mental retardation.

Grandparents

Not of interest.

Parents

Father (10) grew up in a very poor environment and ran away from home at age 9 years because of cruel treatment by his uncles. He operated a barber shop with several assistants.

Mother (11) had normal intelligence.

Aunts and Uncles

Paternal relatives unknown.

Maternal relatives not of interest.

Siblings

(20) was a miscarriage.

Sister (23) died of pneumonia at 3 months.

Nieces and Nephews

None.

First Cousins

Not of interest.

More Distant Relatives

Not of interest.

Family Summary

The proband, IQ 64, was the only retarded person known in this family. He was a healthy child, reared in a good home. The proband's parents had three children, no grandchildren.

Retardation of proband of unknown origin.

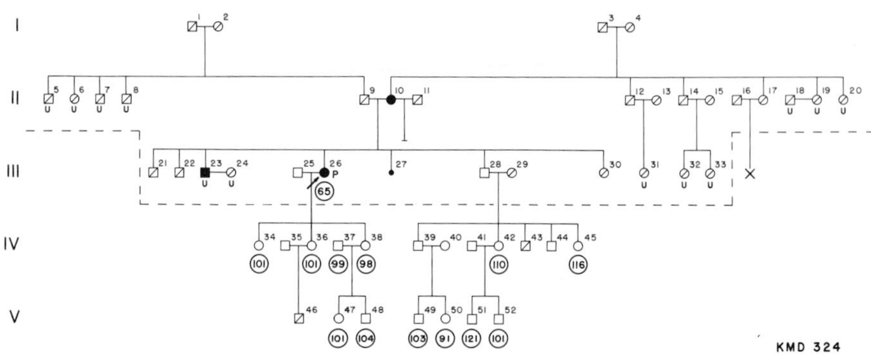

KMD 324

The Proband

The proband (26) was born in 1899 and institutionalized at age 13 years. She was discharged to her mother in 1918 after a court hearing in 1917 found her not retarded. After her discharge she married, but later separated from her husband and died of an abdominal hemorrhage in 1936. She was slow in developing, attended school for seven years and reached the fourth grade. She had no history of difficult birth or perinatal infection and had no stigmata. Her home environment was poor. Her IQ scores over a period of five years were 76, 65, 65 and 63. *Diagnosis:* undifferentiated mental retardation.

Grandparents

Not of interest.

Parents

Father (9) was an alcoholic laborer of unknown intelligence.

Mother (10) was promiscuous, an alcoholic and retarded. She could not keep house.

Aunts and Uncles

Paternal relatives all remained in Europe.

Maternal relatives lived in other states and could not be found.

Siblings

Brother (21) died of measles at age 3½ years.

Brother (22) died of pneumonia at age 16 years. He had been in the reformatory for burglary and incorrigibility. He reached the seventh grade in school. His intelligence is unknown.

Brother (23) was a retarded laborer who was accused of incest with the proband. He is unknown to relatives. He had meningitis at age 3 years.

Sister (27) died of "brain fever and measles" at age 10 months.

Brother (28) is a foreman in a factory. His wife's intelligence is unknown and the children are normal.

Sister (30) died of typhoid fever at age 6½ years.

Spouse

(25) owned a tavern and probably had normal intelligence.

Children

Daughter (34) graduated from high school, IQ 101.

Daughter (36) graduated from high school, IQ 101. She married a truck driver who had a D average in the ninth grade.

Daughter (38) graduated from high school, IQ 98. Her husband also graduated from high school, IQ 99.

Grandchildren

Three (46), (47) and (48), two with IQ's of 101 and 104, one (46) too young to test.

Nieces and Nephews

Not of interest.

First Cousins

Unknown.

More Distant Relatives

Unknown.

Family Summary

The proband, IQ 65, her mother and one sibling (who had spinal meningitis at age 3 years) were all high-grade retardates. The proband had three children, all with normal intelligence. The proband's parents had seven children and eight grandchildren.

Retardation of proband of unknown origin.

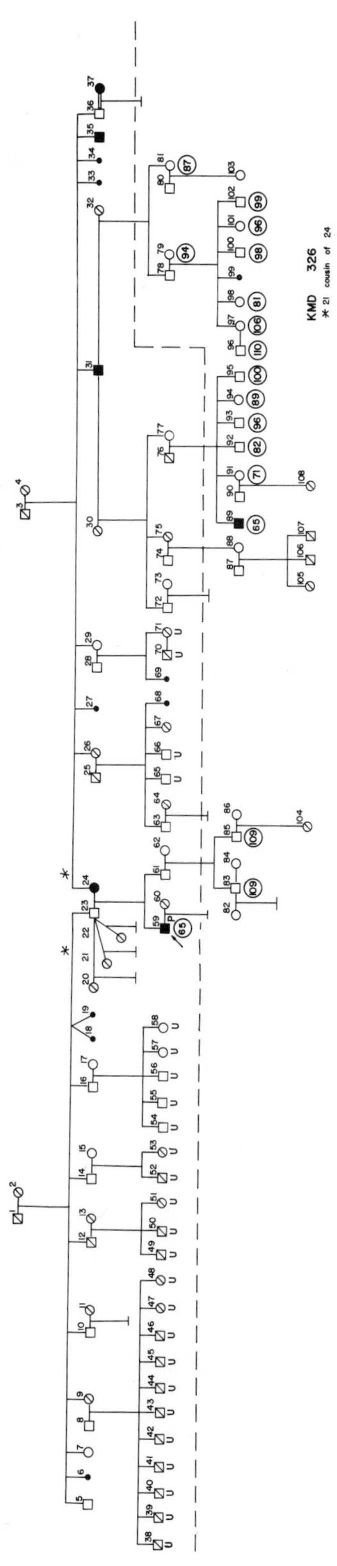

KMD 326

The Proband

The proband (59) was born in 1897 and sent to the School for the Blind at age 9 years. He was transferred to the institution in 1912 and remained there until his discharge to relatives in 1948. He was an instrument delivery, but was not injured and had no history of perinatal infection. He had poor eyesight from birth. He grew up in a good home and after his discharge married a blind woman. He has no children. IQ 65. *Diagnosis:* undifferentiated mental retardation.

Grandparents

Paternal grandmother's relatives had poor eyesight.

Maternal grandmother deserted her family and was murdered in a brothel.

Parents

Father (23) had poor eyesight. He was married four times, but had only two children. He had normal intelligence.

Mother (24) was retarded.

Aunts and Uncles

Paternal aunt (9) died in an epileptic seizure.

Paternal uncle (12) had poor eyesight and was a religious fanatic.

Maternal uncle (31) is said by his son to have been an electrician and engineer, but old records state he was retarded. He became partially deaf and blind as he grew older.

Maternal uncle (35) was a hunter and fisherman. He was retarded and promiscuous. He lived with his maternal aunt as her husband.

Maternal uncle (36) had normal intelligence. He lived with his maternal aunt for many years before marrying her. She was retarded and was a sister to the woman who lived with (35).

Siblings

Brother (61) went to business school and is a foreman for a power company. His wife and children have normal intelligence.

Nieces and Nephews

Not of interest.

First Cousins

Not of interest except (39) and (50) had poor eyesight.

More Distant Relatives

First cousin (77) has a partially blind son (89) with an IQ of 65. He has a sibling (91) with an IQ of 71.

Family Summary

The proband, IQ 65 and partially blind, his mother, two maternal uncles and one first cousin's child were retarded. There was a history of poor eyesight on both sides of the family for four generations. In addition, the maternal side had a bad social history of vagrancy, promiscuity and alcoholism, although the proband's own home environment was good. The proband's parents had two children and two grandchildren.

Retardation of proband of unknown origin.

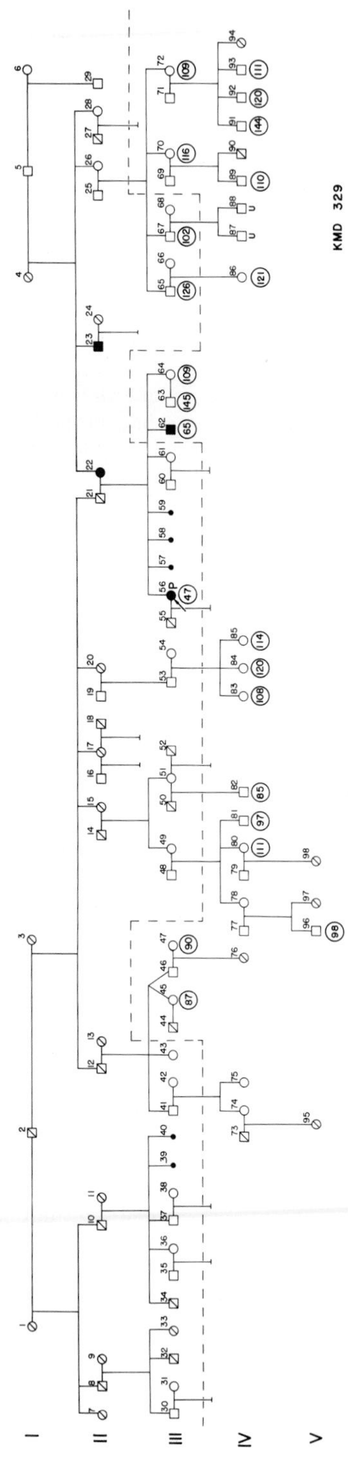
KMD 329

KMD 329

The Proband

The proband (56) was born in 1905 and institutionalized at age 7 years. She was discharged a year later to her parents, readmitted in 1920 and placed under outside supervision the same year. She was a healthy child with no history of birth injury or illness. In 1943 she married a man forty years older than herself. She made a good adjustment and was discharged from guardianship in 1948. She has never been pregnant. Her birth and early development were uneventful; she walked and talked at age 3 years. IQ 47. *Diagnosis:* undifferentiated mental retardation.

Grandparents

Paternal grandmother was mentally ill, as were two of her siblings.

Parents

Father (21) was an ignorant alcoholic of unknown intelligence.

Mother (22) was a retarded woman "not fit to be a mother."

Aunts and Uncles

Maternal uncle (23) left school at age 18 years when in the eighth grade.

Siblings

Sister (57) died of "spasms" at 3 weeks.

Sister (58) died of "spasms" at 5 months.

(59) was a miscarriage.

Sister (61) completed two years of college and married a banker.

Brother (62) is an unmarried, childless laborer with an IQ of 65.

Sister (64) graduated from high school, IQ 109. Her husband is a high school graduate and mechanic with an IQ of 145.

Nieces and Nephews

None. Only proband's sister (64) is still young enough to reproduce.

First Cousins

Not of interest.

More Distant Relatives

Not of interest.

Family Summary

The proband, IQ 47, her mother, a maternal uncle and one sibling were retarded. The proband's birth and early development were uneventful. The proband's parents had seven children, no grandchildren. This kindred showed a very low reproductive rate.

Retardation of proband of unknown origin.

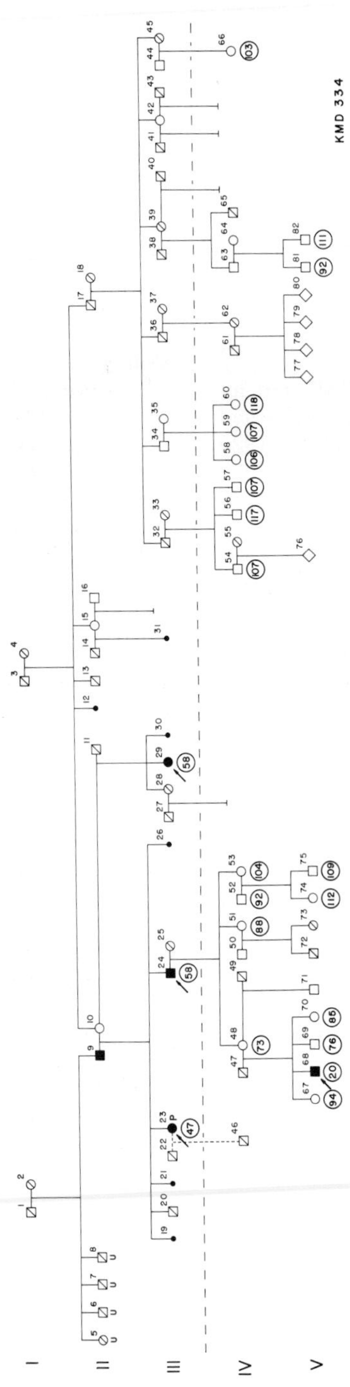
KMD 334
I
II
III
IV
V

KMD 334

The Proband

The proband (23) was born in 1890 and institutionalized at age 17 years after she had an illegitimate child. She was discharged from the institution in 1909, readmitted in 1912, discharged in 1919, readmitted in 1926 and was still in the institution in 1961. Her birth and early development were uneventful. She attended school until the age of 12 years with poor results. She was given a physical and neurological examination in 1950 by J. A. Böök, M.D., and John Schut, M.D. They found no stigmata and gave a diagnosis of imbecility. IQ 47. *Diagnosis:* undifferentiated mental retardation.

Grandparents

Not of interest.

Parents

Father (9) was a retarded farmer. He was a good worker, but his wife managed the farm.

Mother (10) had normal intelligence.

Aunts and Uncles

Paternal relatives remained in Europe.

Maternal relatives not of interest.

Siblings

Sister (19) died of cholera infantum at age 2 years.

Brother (20) died at age 3 years.

Brother (21) died before the age of 2 years.

Brother (24) was institutionalized in 1927 at age 33 years, after a jail sentence. He was sterilized and then placed under outside supervision. He was a laborer in a flour mill and was found murdered in 1931. He had been forced to marry (25) in 1918.

Brother (26) died in infancy.

Half Siblings

Half sister (28) was sent to the state orphanage as a child. She refused to cooperate. Her intelligence is unknown.

Half sister (29) was in reform school, then institutionalized in 1934 at age 31 for several months before she was transferred to a church home where she has remained ever since. IQ 58. She had congenital syphilis.

Half brother (30) died one day after birth.

The father (11) of these half siblings (proband's stepfather) became mentally unbalanced before his death.

Child

Son (46) died as a child. His intelligence was unknown.

Nieces and Nephews

All are the children of the proband's retarded brother (24). They have IQ's of 73, 88 and 104, respectively. (48) with IQ 73 was sent to the reformatory as an unmarried mother. She later married the child's father but divorced him and married a man 17 years older than herself who works in a meat packing plant. She has five children: (67) with IQ 94; (68) with IQ 20 and congenital cerebral spastic infantile quadriplegia and scoliosis who is institutionalized; (69) with IQ 76 and a behavior problem who is in special classes; (70) has been in a girls' reformatory, IQ 85 and (71) who is apparently normal at age 6 years.

First Cousins

Not of interest.

More Distant Relatives

(68) with IQ 20 and partially paralyzed with a diagnosis of imbecile—congenital cerebral spastic infantile quadriplegia scoliosis, cause unknown.

Family Summary

The proband, IQ 47, her father, one brother and one half sister were all of about the same level of retardation and one great-nephew had an IQ of 20. All, except the proband's father, were institutionalized. The proband's retarded brother had three children with an IQ range of 73, 88 and 102. The proband had an illegitimate child of unknown intelligence who died young. The proband's parents had six children and four grandchildren.

Retardation of proband of unknown origin.

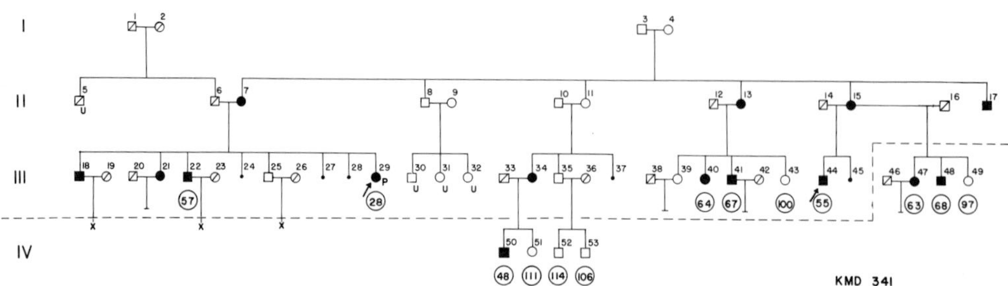

KMD 341

The Proband

The proband (29) was born in 1906, institutionalized at age 8 years and was discharged to relatives in 1918. She was readmitted a year later and was still in the institution in 1961. She was operated on for club feet and did not walk until age 6 years. She never talked plainly. There was no history of difficult birth or perinatal infection. Her home environment was poor. She was given a physical and neurological examination in 1950 by J. A. Böök, M.D., and John Schut, M.D. No stigmata were found and their diagnosis was idiocy. IQ 28. *Diagnosis:* undifferentiated mental retardation.

Grandparents

Maternal grandmother had a retarded father and brother.

Parents

Father (6) was an alcoholic and suicidal. After several attempts at suicide by poisoning and drowning, he hanged himself. His intelligence was unknown. He was recorded as "could not look ahead and plan."

Mother (7) was retarded.

Aunts and Uncles

Maternal aunt (11) had normal intelligence, but was hospitalized for mental illness and, after several attempts, committed suicide by drowning.

Maternal aunt (13) is retarded.

Maternal aunt (15) is retarded. She was abandoned by her husband.

Maternal uncle (17) was hospitalized for schizophrenia in 1919 and has been in the hospital ever since. He was also retarded.

Siblings

Brother (18) left school at age 15 years when in the fourth grade.

Sister (21) left school at age 15 years when in the fourth grade. She has been married and divorced.

Brother (22) had an IQ of 57.

(24) was a miscarriage.

Brother (25) has normal intelligence.

Brothers (27) and (28) both died of whooping cough at age 6 months.

Nieces and Nephews

Unknown. All the proband's siblings moved to California and could not be found since our only contact, an aunt, refused to cooperate.

First Cousins

(34) is a high-grade retardate with one retarded and one normal child.

(40) died single and childless, IQ 64.

(41) is married but childless, IQ 67.

(44) was institutionalized at age 9 years, transferred to a mental hospital in 1946 and died there of tuberculosis in 1950. He developed a manic depressive psychosis, manic type. IQ 55.

(47) is retarded, married twice but childless, IQ 63.

(48) is an unmarried, childless man, IQ 68.

More Distant Relatives

First cousin (34) has a retarded child (50) with IQ 48.

Family Summary

The proband, IQ 28, her mother, two maternal aunts and a maternal uncle, three siblings, six first cousins and one more distant relative were retarded. The father and a maternal aunt committed suicide, a maternal uncle was hospitalized for mental illness. The proband's nephews and nieces could not be found. The informant, an aunt, said they had moved away and she didn't know any addresses, but the interviewer felt she was concealing information. The proband's parents had eight children, grandchildren unknown.

Retardation of proband of unknown origin.

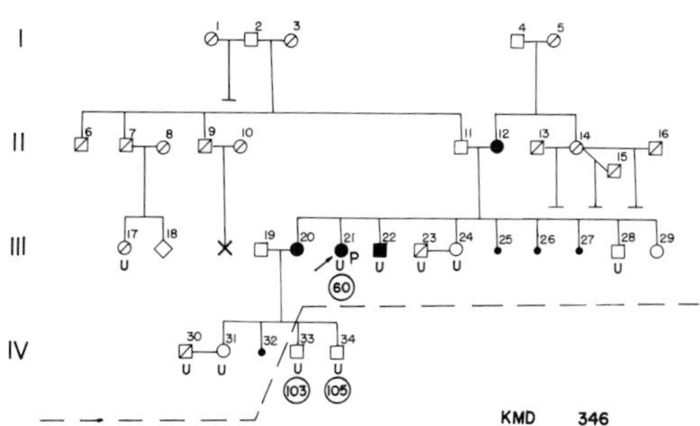

KMD 346

The Proband

The proband (21) was born in 1896, institutionalized at age 16 years and failed to return after a vacation in 1916. Her present status is unknown. She developed normally, attended school for nine years but attained only the fifth grade. Her home environment was very poor. IQ 60. *Diagnosis:* undifferentiated mental retardation.

Grandparents

Not of interest.

Parents

Father (11) was an alcoholic of normal intelligence. He was a baker.

Mother (12) was an alcoholic, retarded and a prostitute. She spent some time in the workhouse. Both parents neglected the children, who were removed to the state orphanage.

Aunts and Uncles

Maternal aunt (14) was epileptic.

Siblings

Sister (20) was a high-grade retardate with normal husband and children.

Brother (22) was a high-grade retardate.

Sister (24) took typing and shorthand in high school, which indicates she was not retarded as the old record stated.

(25) and (27) were miscarriages.

Sister (26) died of "brain fever" at age 1 year.

Brother (28) had normal intelligence.

Sister (29) was adopted from the state orphanage. She is unmarried at age 46 and has normal intelligence.

Nieces and Nephews

Only four are known, but there may be more.

First Cousins

Only paternal ones, all unknown.

More Distant Relatives

Unknown.

Family Summary

The proband, IQ 60, two siblings and the mother were retarded. Unfortunately, the proband's immediate family were unknown to the only correspondent who could be found, a niece to the proband's sister's divorced husband. The proband's parents had nine children and four known grandchildren.

Retardation of proband of unknown origin.

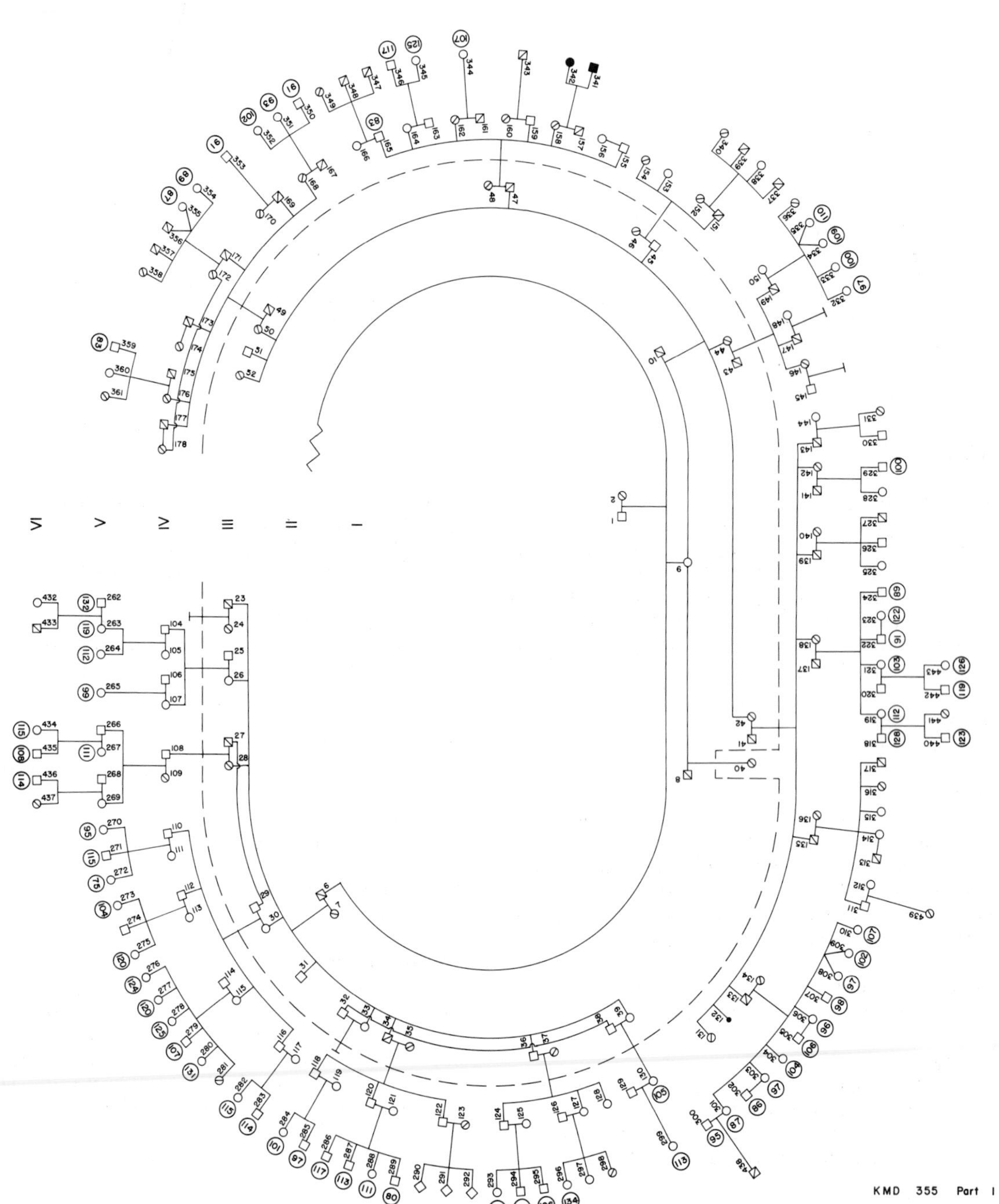

KMD 355 Part I

KMD 355

The Proband

The proband (69) was born in 1895 and institutionalized at age 17 years. She was discharged to her parents in 1913, readmitted in 1916 and discharged to her parents in 1920. In 1939 a petition for commitment was withdrawn and she was living in a county home in 1961. She had a severe attack of bronchitis as a baby. She attended school for several years but learned little. Her home environment was poor. She had no stigmata. IQ 40. *Diagnosis:* undifferentiated mental retardation.

Grandparents

Not of interest.

Parents

Father (14) was a stone mason with normal intelligence.

Mother (15) had normal intelligence.

Aunts and Uncles

Not of interest.

Siblings

Brother (65) was a high-grade retardate. He left the fifth grade at age 15 years.

Sister (68) was classified as retarded in the old records, but was a helpful correspondent. She left school in the seventh grade at age 15 years. Her children and grandchildren have normal intelligence.

Sister (71) was classified as retarded in the old records but was a helpful correspondent. Both she and (68) have unknown intelligence.

Sister (76) completed the eighth grade and works in a factory. She has normal intelligence as do her children.

Sister (79) was an unmarried mother who later married her child's father (78). (79) has normal intelligence. Her child (235) has a borderline IQ of 78.

Sister (82) has unknown intelligence, children normal.

Sister (83) and brother (84) died at age 3 months.

Nieces and Nephews

Niece (205) was epileptic from the age of 2 years and had a borderline IQ of 77 at age 21 years.

Nephew (227) is a spray cleaner, IQ 70. He has a sister with a borderline IQ of 74.

First Cousins

Not of interest.

More Distant Relatives

Proband's cousin (47) has two retarded grandchildren: (341) who repeated the first grade three times, the third and fourth grades twice each and left school after failing the fifth grade at 14 years; and (342) who repeated the first and second grade twice and third grade three times, and left school at the age of 13 years when in the fourth grade. No IQ's or diagnoses were available for these children. The father is a farmer and the mother works in a rest home. Both have unknown intelligence.

Family Summary

The proband, IQ 40, a brother, and two more distant relatives were retarded. The home environment was poor, although the proband's parents had normal intelligence. The proband's parents had ten children and 21 grandchildren.

Retardation of proband of unknown origin.

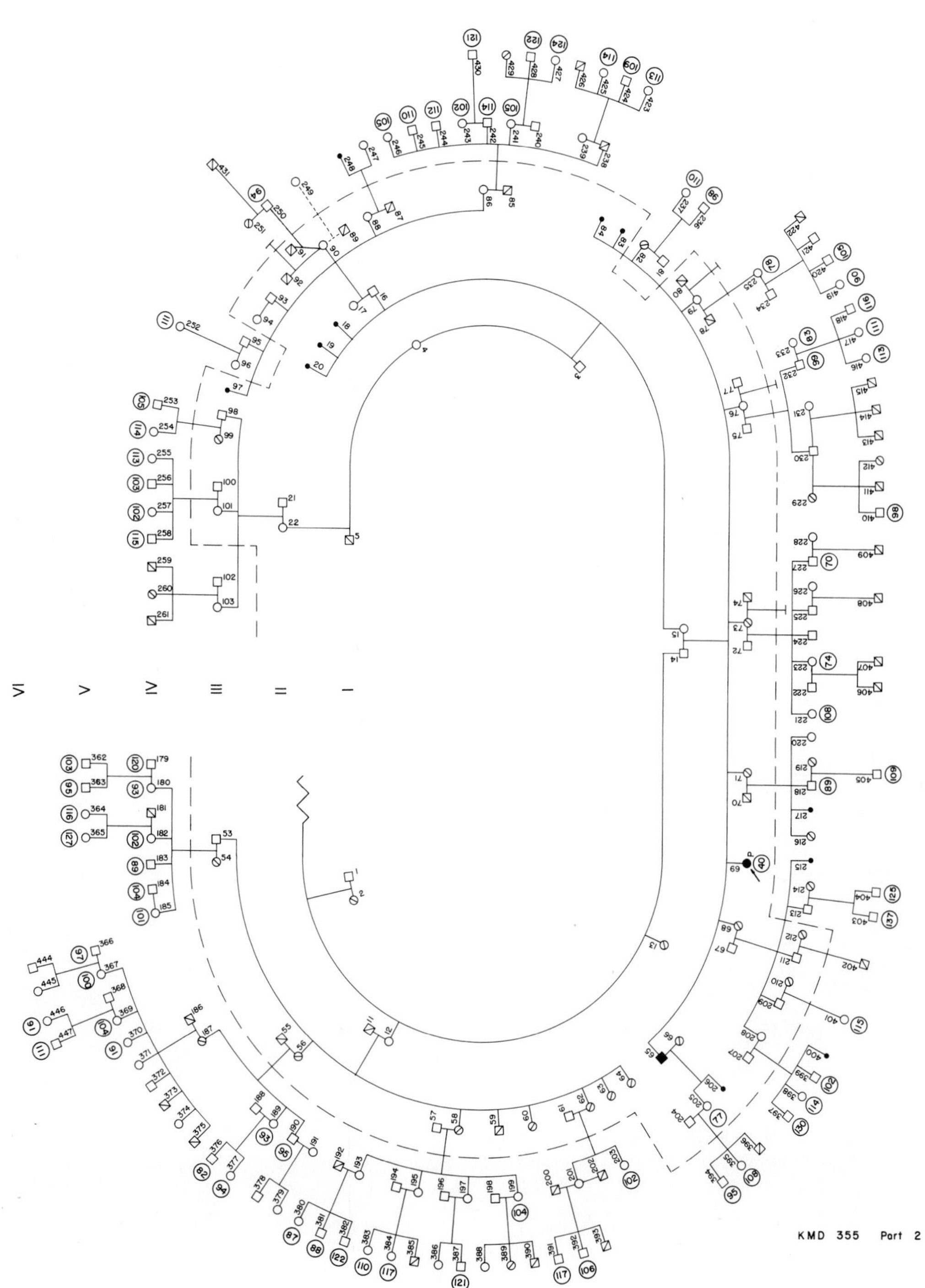

KMD 355 Part 2

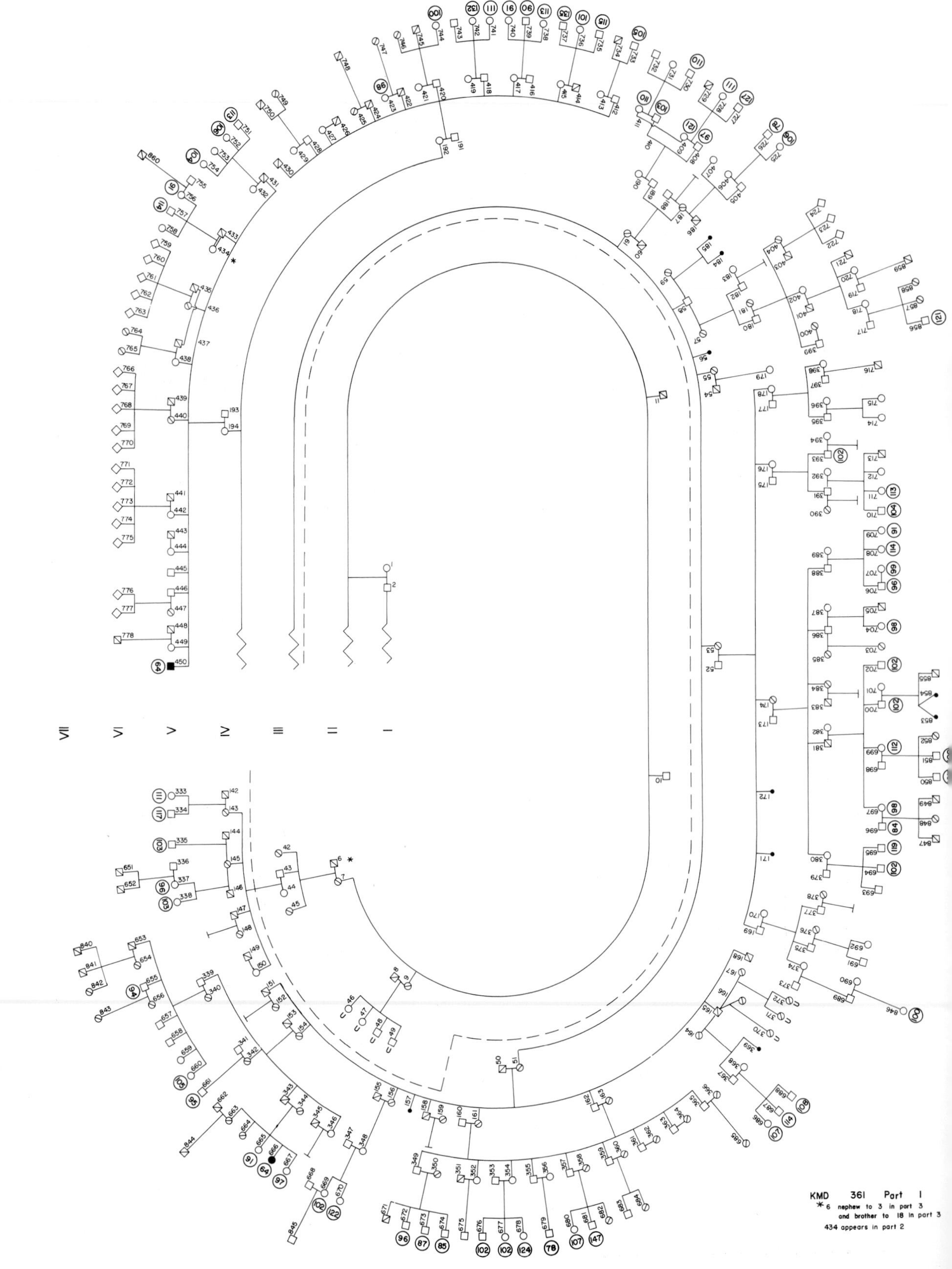
VII
VI
V
IV
III
II
I
KMD 361 Part I
* 6 nephew to 3 in part 3
and brother to 18 in part 3
434 appears in part 2

KMD 361

The Proband

The proband (110) was born in 1899, institutionalized at age 14 years, sterilized in 1928 and placed under outside supervision. She married in 1935 and was discharged from guardianship in 1948. She had poor eyesight and chorea as a child, but no chorea in adulthood. There was no record of difficult birth or perinatal infection. Her home environment was poor. IQ 62. *Diagnosis:* undifferentiated mental retardation.

Grandparents

Not of interest.

Parents

Father (27) could not manage any business, was constantly changing his occupation and was classified as retarded.

Mother (28) was obese, had a "terrible temper," was uneducated and retarded. She and (27) lived "like gypsies" for a number of years.

Aunts and Uncles

Paternal aunt (22) died of convulsions at age 5 months.

Paternal uncle (23) died at age 11 months. He "never grew mentally or physically."

The consanguineous marriage of (19), proband's paternal aunt with normal intelligence, to her normal first cousin (18) resulted in the birth of a normal male (86), a blind male (88) with IQ 90, a girl (89) who was born blind and died in convulsions in infancy, three normal persons (90), (92), (93) and (94) who died of measles at age 1 year.

Siblings

Brother (104) was a retarded laborer, wife's intelligence unknown. None of his children is known to be retarded.

Brother (106) could not tell time. He completed the third grade and was a laborer. His wife and two children have unknown intelligence.

Sister (108) was institutionalized at age 17 years and was discharged to a relative in 1956 with a diagnosis of imbecile–familial. She was neurotic and difficult to manage. Old records state she had convulsions and was partially paralyzed. She was given a physical and neurological examination in 1950 by J. A. Böök, M.D., and John Schut, M.D. They found no paralysis. Their diagnosis was imbecility. IQ 43. *Diagnosis:* undifferentiated mental retardation.

Nieces and Nephews

Both retarded brothers (104) and (106) had children, none of whom is known to have been retarded. Four died in infancy, two have normal intelligence, three went to grade school and have not been tested.

First Cousins

Not of interest except for offspring of consanguineous marriage of (18) and (19). (See under *Aunts and Uncles.*)

More Distant Relatives

(450) completed the seventh grade and is a laborer. IQ 64.

(666) has an IQ of 64.

Family Summary

The proband, IQ 62, her parents, all three of her siblings and two more distant relatives were middle- or high-grade retardates. One paternal uncle was a low-grade retardate. The proband's parents were itinerants who provided a poor environment for their children. The proband's two retarded brothers had nine children, none of whom is known to be retarded. A consanguineous marriage of a paternal aunt to her first cousin resulted in the birth of seven children, two of whom were blind (one of the blind ones dying of convulsions in infancy), but none of the survivors was retarded. The proband's parents had four children and nine grandchildren.

Retardation of proband of unknown origin.

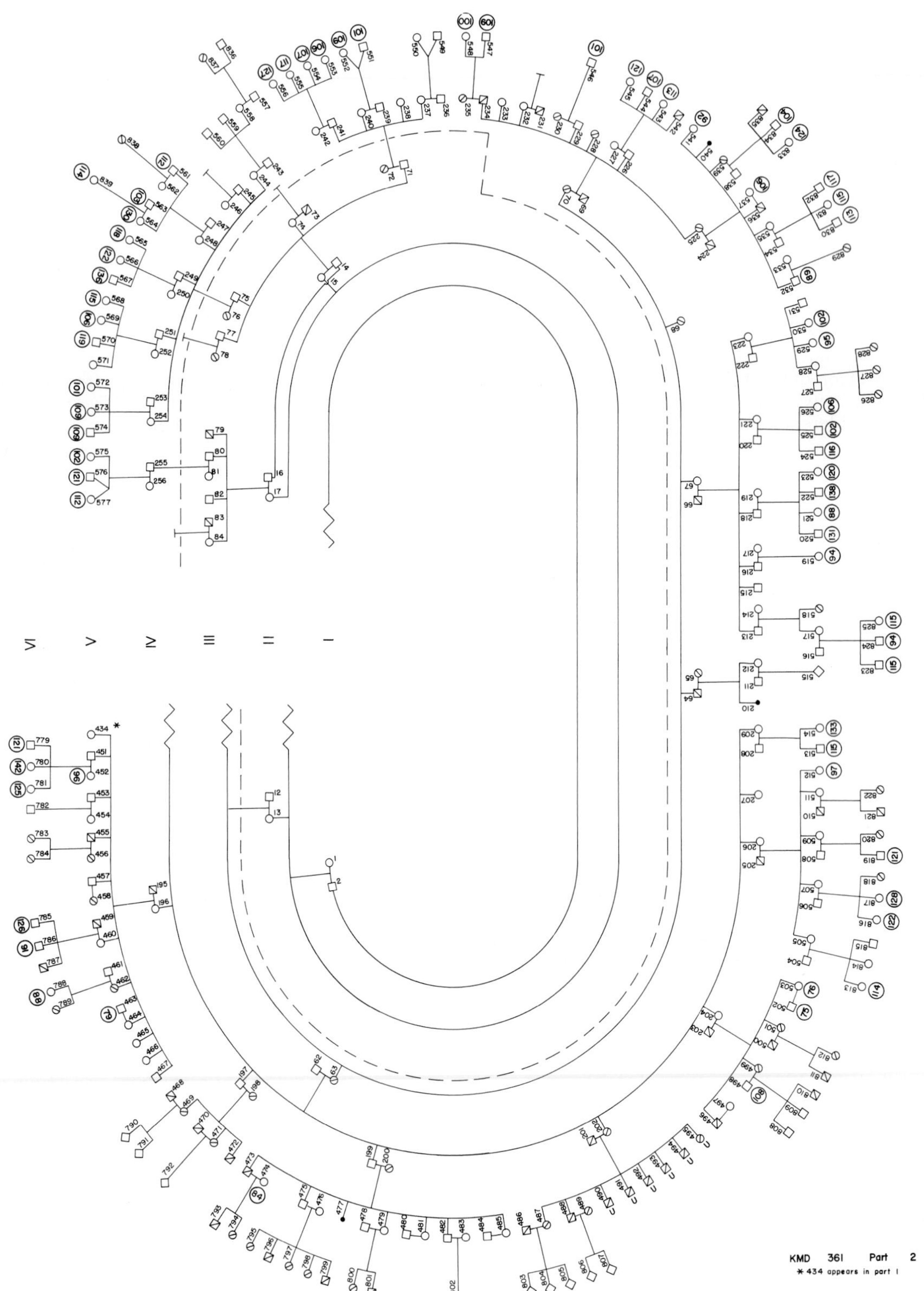

KMD 361 Part 2
* 434 appears in part I

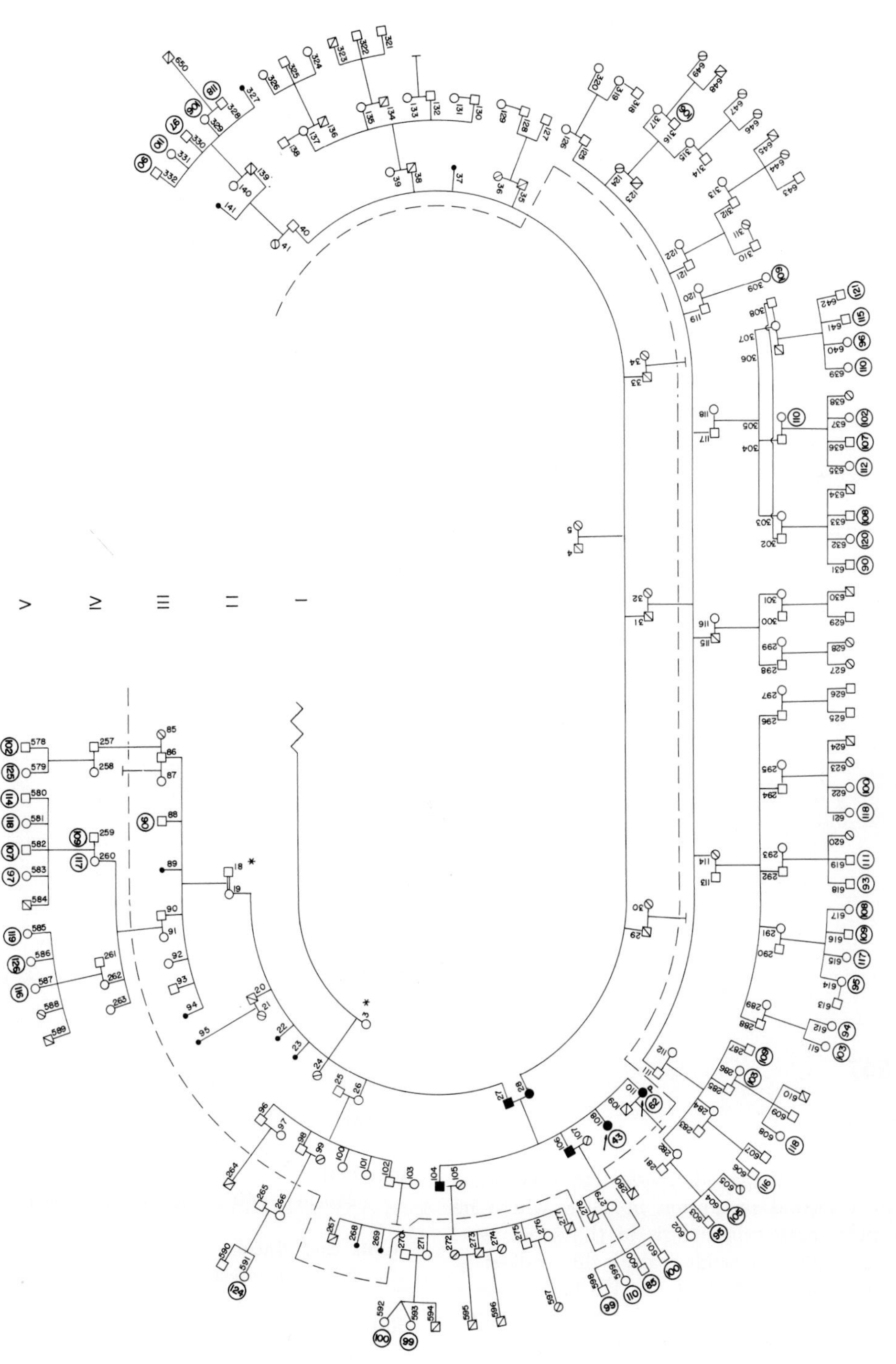

KMD 361 Part 3

* 3 aunt to 18 and to 6 in part 1

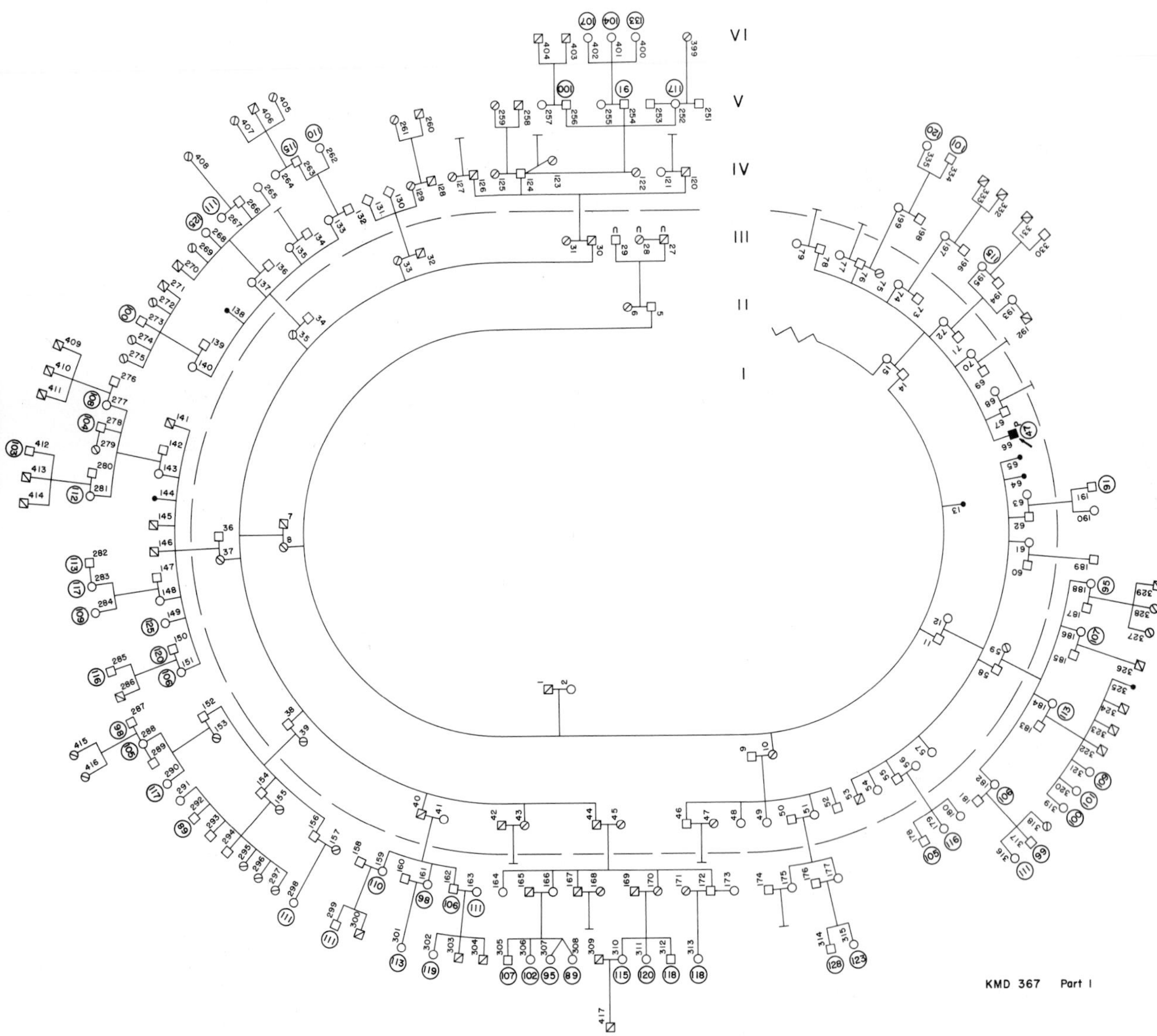

KMD 367

The Proband

The proband (66) was born in 1879 and institutionalized at age 14 years. He was transferred to a second institution in 1938 where he died of pulmonary tuberculosis in the same year. He was a weak and sickly baby who walked at age 4 years and talked at age 5. He had a severe attack of "lung fever" at age 2 years, according to the mother. He had a very bad temper. The home environment was good. IQ 47. *Diagnosis:* undifferentiated mental retardation.

Grandparents

Not of interest.

Parents

Father (14) was a blacksmith and town marshall.

Mother (15) had normal intelligence.

Aunts and Uncles

Not of interest.

Siblings

Brother (67) is a married but childless physician.

Sister (70) completed one year of college. She is married but childless.

Sister (72) graduated from high school, husband and children normal.

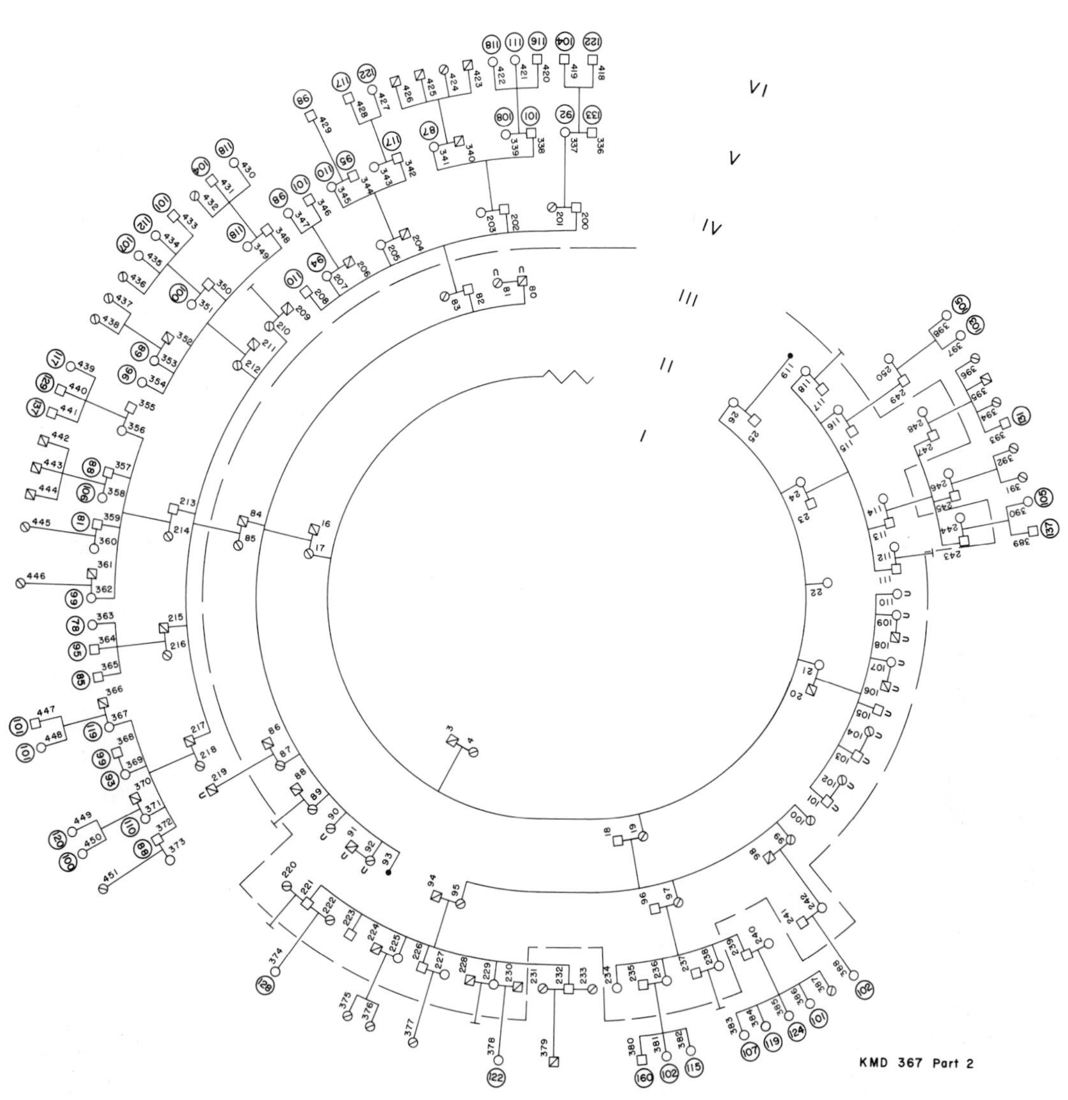

Sister (74) graduated from college, husband and child normal.

Brother (76) graduated from high school and is a mechanic with a normal child.

Brother (78) completed the tenth grade and is a married, but childless, foreman.

Nieces and Nephews

Only four, all with normal intelligence.

First Cousins

Not of interest.

More Distant Relatives

Not of interest.

Family Summary

The proband, IQ 47, was the only retarded person known in this kindred of 451 persons. He was a weak baby who was very slow in developing. His home care and environment were good. The proband's parents had seven children and four grandchildren.

Retardation of proband of unknown origin.

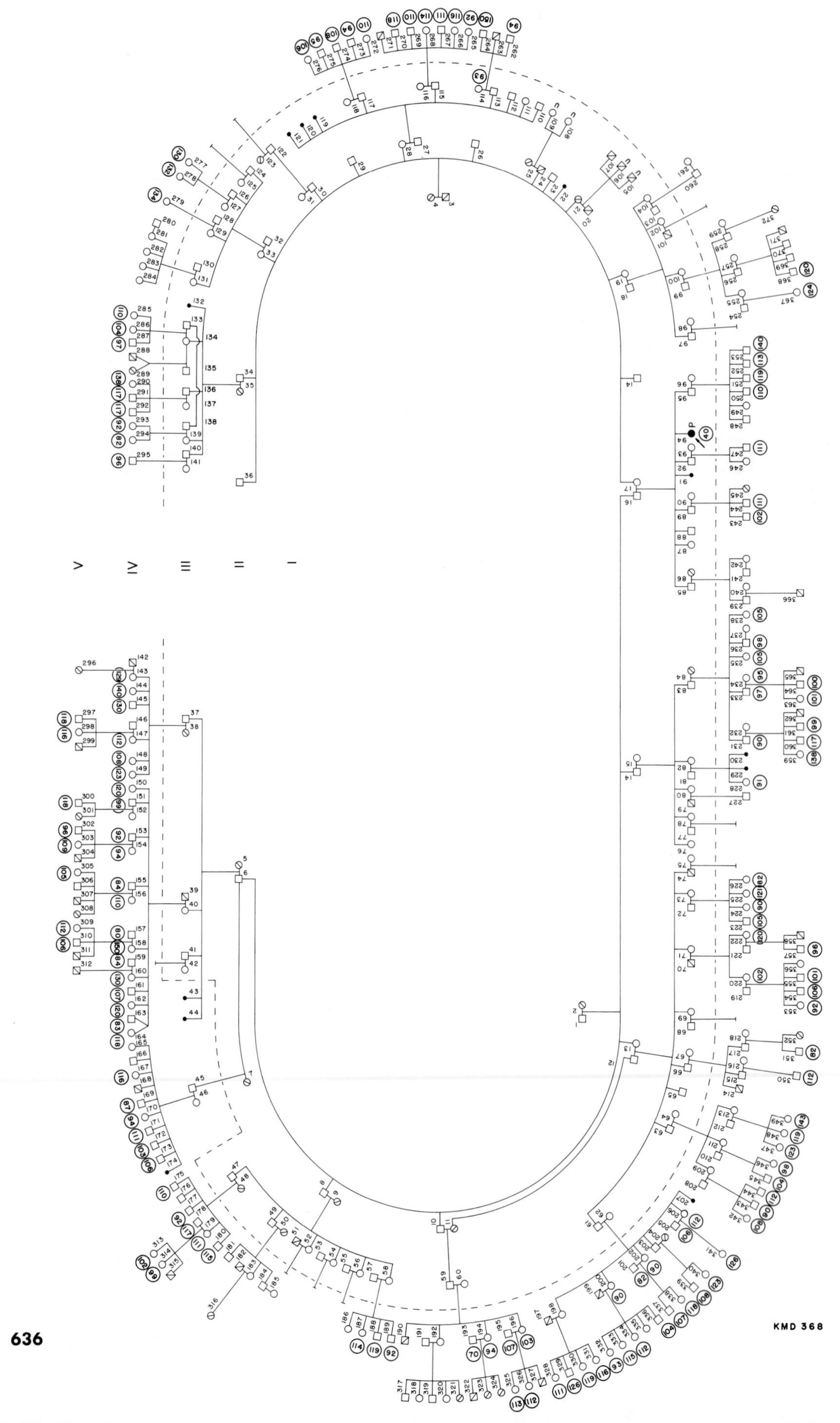
I
II
III
IV
V
KMD 368

KMD 368

The Proband

The proband (94) was born in 1903, institutionalized at age 8 years and died of cancer in the institution in 1955. She was a small, sickly baby who developed very slowly. There was no history of birth injury or perinatal infection. IQ 40. *Diagnosis:* undifferentiated mental retardation.

Grandparents

Not of interest.

Parents

Father (16) was a wealthy farmer.
Mother (17) had normal intelligence.

Aunts and Uncles

Not of interest.

Siblings

Seven siblings, all known to have normal intelligence except for one unknown sister who died in infancy. Three spouses have normal intelligence, one is unknown, and all their children have normal intelligence.

Nieces and Nephews

Not of interest.

First Cousins

Not of interest.

More Distant Relatives

Not of interest.

Family Summary

The proband, IQ 40, was the only retarded person known in this family. The proband was a sickly, undersized infant with no history of birth injury or of infectious disease. The proband's parents had eight children and 13 grandchildren.

Retardation of proband of unknown origin.

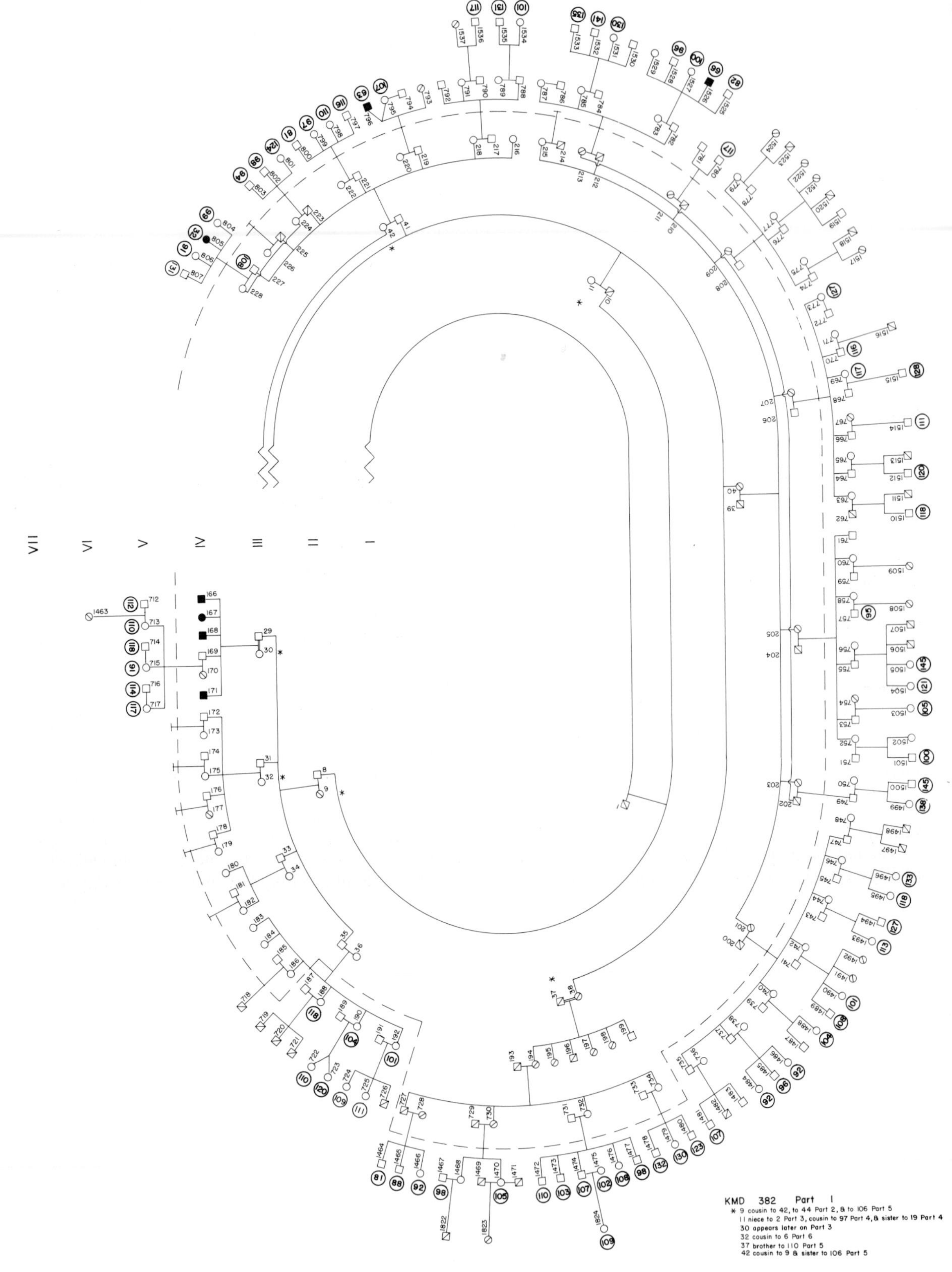
KMD 382 Part I
* 9 cousin to 42, to 44 Part 2, & to 106 Part 5
11 niece to 2 Part 3, cousin to 97 Part 4, & sister to 19 Part 4
30 appears later on Part 3
32 cousin to 6 Part 6
37 brother to 110 Part 5
42 cousin to 9 & sister to 106 Part 5

KMD 382

The Proband

The proband (119) was born in 1886, institutionalized at age 20 years and died of typhoid fever in the institution in 1915. He attended school for seven years at the end of which time he was in the third grade. There was no history of difficult delivery or perinatal infection and he had no stigmata. IQ 40. *Diagnosis:* undifferentiated mental retardation.

Grandparents

Not of interest.

Parents

Father (20) was a farmer and minister.

Mother (21) had unknown intelligence. One relative mentioned the possibility that the parents may have been related, but if so, it was "distant."

Aunts and Uncles

Maternal uncle (22) died in a mental hospital.

Siblings

Brother (104) had normal intelligence. He was "distantly" related to his wife. One of his nine surviving children is retarded.

Sister (107) was retarded, husband and children normal.

Sister (108) died at age 15 years.

Brothers (109), (111) and (115), and sisters (113), (118) and (121) had normal intelligence and normal children.

Brother (114) died in infancy.

Sister (122) died of diphtheria at age 9 years.

Twin brothers (123) and (125) were both retarded. (123) married his first cousin once removed (124). His children have IQ's of 102, 74, 88 and 113, respectively. (125) is single. Both were high-grade retardates.

Nieces and Nephews

Niece (491) is an unmarried, childless retardate.

First Cousins

Not of interest.

Children of Proband's Parent's Half Siblings

Not of interest except for (43) who married a retarded woman and the consanguineous marriages of (29), (70), (80) and (83). (29), (70) and (80) married their "half cousins," (83) married a full cousin. (29) had five children, four of them idiots (described below). (70), (80) and (83) had normal children although (70) had three children who died in infancy, causes unknown.

More Distant Relatives

(166) was helpless, "dreadfully deformed, no shape, . . . joints all drawn out of place," could not talk, and died at age 14 years of malnutrition, "stopped eating."

(167) was a helpless idiot with a keel-shaped palate and protruding, irregular teeth. She talked a little at age 7 years and could walk, but after an attack of measles at this age her condition deteriorated. She died in her twenties.

(168) was like (166) and (167) and died of measles at age 3 years.

(171) was deaf, crippled and retarded, and died in his teens. [All these persons were siblings, the offspring of the consanguineous marriage of (29) and (30).]

(249), a teacher, married a man who is now hospitalized for paranoid schizophrenia and has an IQ of 54 (taken after he developed the disease).

(315), IQ 135, married a man who completed the fourth grade and has an IQ of 67.

(352) married a retarded woman.

(455) completed the fifth grade and is a part time janitor.

(796) is emotionally disturbed and school reports his IQ of 63 may be too low.

(805) has an IQ of 32 with no diagnosis.

(867) has an IQ of 60.

(1061) has an IQ of 70.

(1207), IQ 89, married a man who had "social promotions" from the sixth grade to the ninth grade when he left school after he became 16 years of age.

(1526) has an IQ of 66.

(1652) is a bedridden spastic and microcephalic with an IQ of "about 30."

Family Summary

The proband, IQ 40, three siblings, one niece and 11 more distant relatives were retarded. One retarded sibling of the proband married his first cousin once removed, a woman with normal intelligence. His children have IQ's of 102, 74, 88 and 113. Of the 11 more distant relatives, four were low-grade retardates, the children of a single consanguineous marriage, a fifth was microcephalic and a sixth was mentally disturbed with an IQ which may have been spuriously low, according to the examiner. This family was one of our largest. The relatives were intermarried in a complicated way with an unusual number of consanguineous unions. Only one consanguineous marriage resulted in retarded offspring. The descendants of the proband's grandparents were remarkably free not only of retardation, but also of mental illness. There was only one known divorce, no prison record, and no history of welfare or social problems. The great majority of these persons were well educated, prosperous and intelligent individuals. (They were all originally Mennonites from one large farming community.)

Retardation of proband of unknown origin.

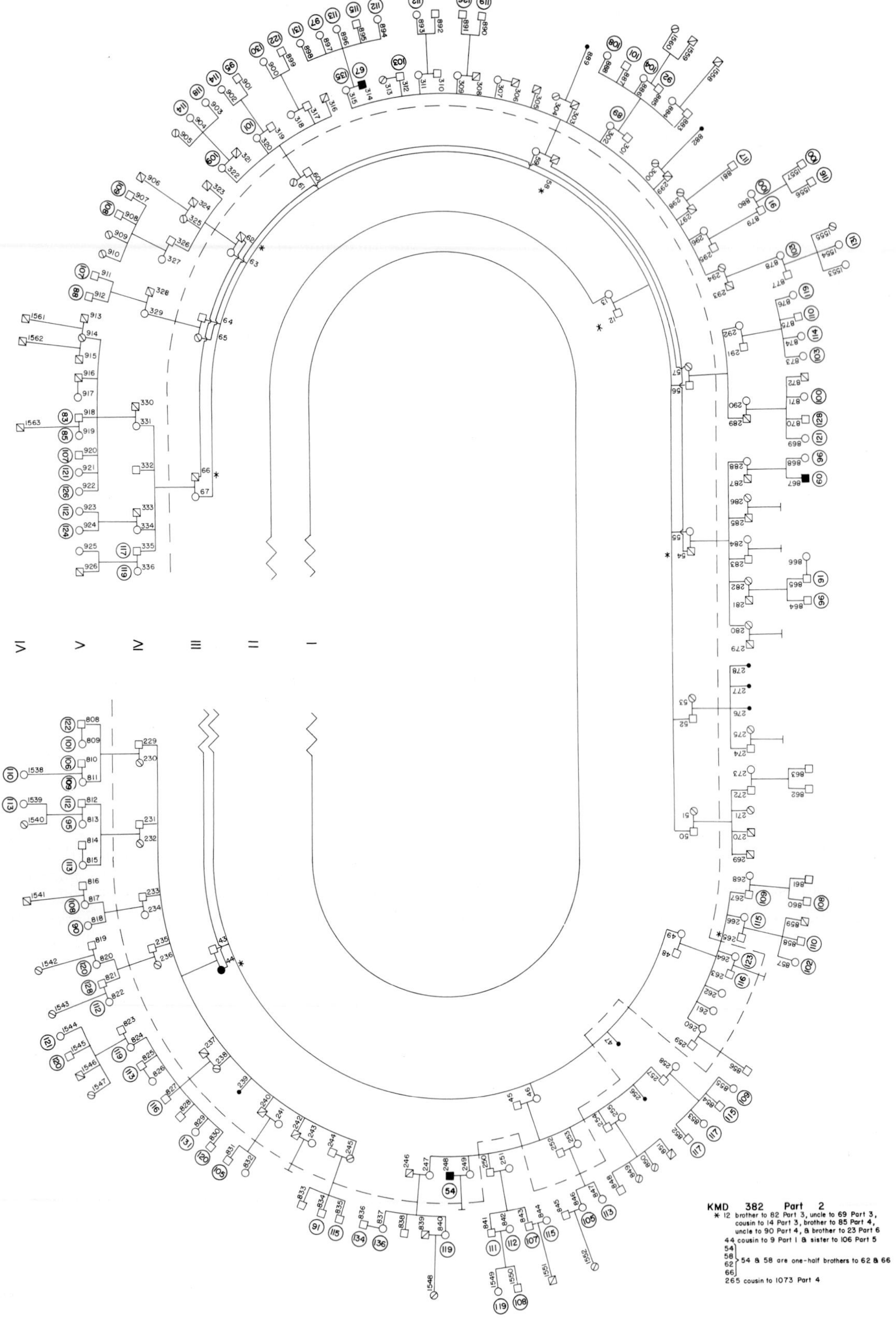
I
II
III
IV
V
VI
KMD 382 Part 2
* 12 brother to 82 Part 3, uncle to 69 Part 3, cousin to 14 Part 3, brother to 85 Part 4, uncle to 90 Part 4, & brother to 23 Part 6
44 cousin to 9 Part 1 & sister to 106 Part 5
54, 58, 62, 66 — 54 & 58 are one-half brothers to 62 & 66
265 cousin to 1073 Part 4

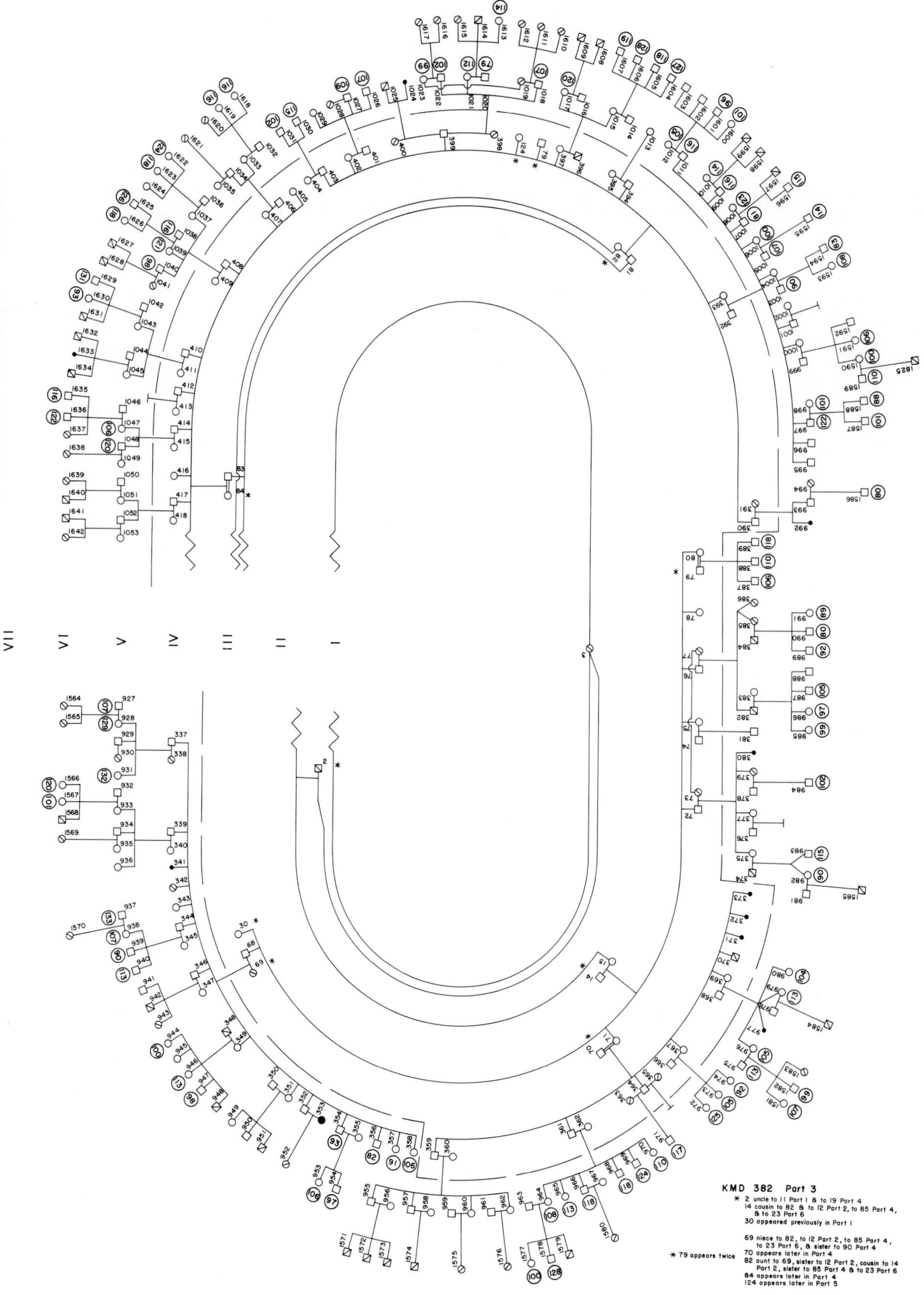
KMD 382 Part 3
* 2 uncle to 11 Part 1 & to 19 Part 4
14 cousin to 82 & to 12 Part 2, to 85 Part 4, & to 23 Part 6
30 appeared previously in Part 1
69 niece to 82, to 12 Part 2, to 85 Part 4, to 23 Part 6, & sister to 90 Part 4
70 appears later in Part 4
82 aunt to 69, sister to 12 Part 2, cousin to 14 Part 2, sister to 85 Part 4 & to 23 Part 6
84 appears later in Part 4
124 appears later in Part 5
* 79 appears twice
I
II
III
IV
V
VI
VII

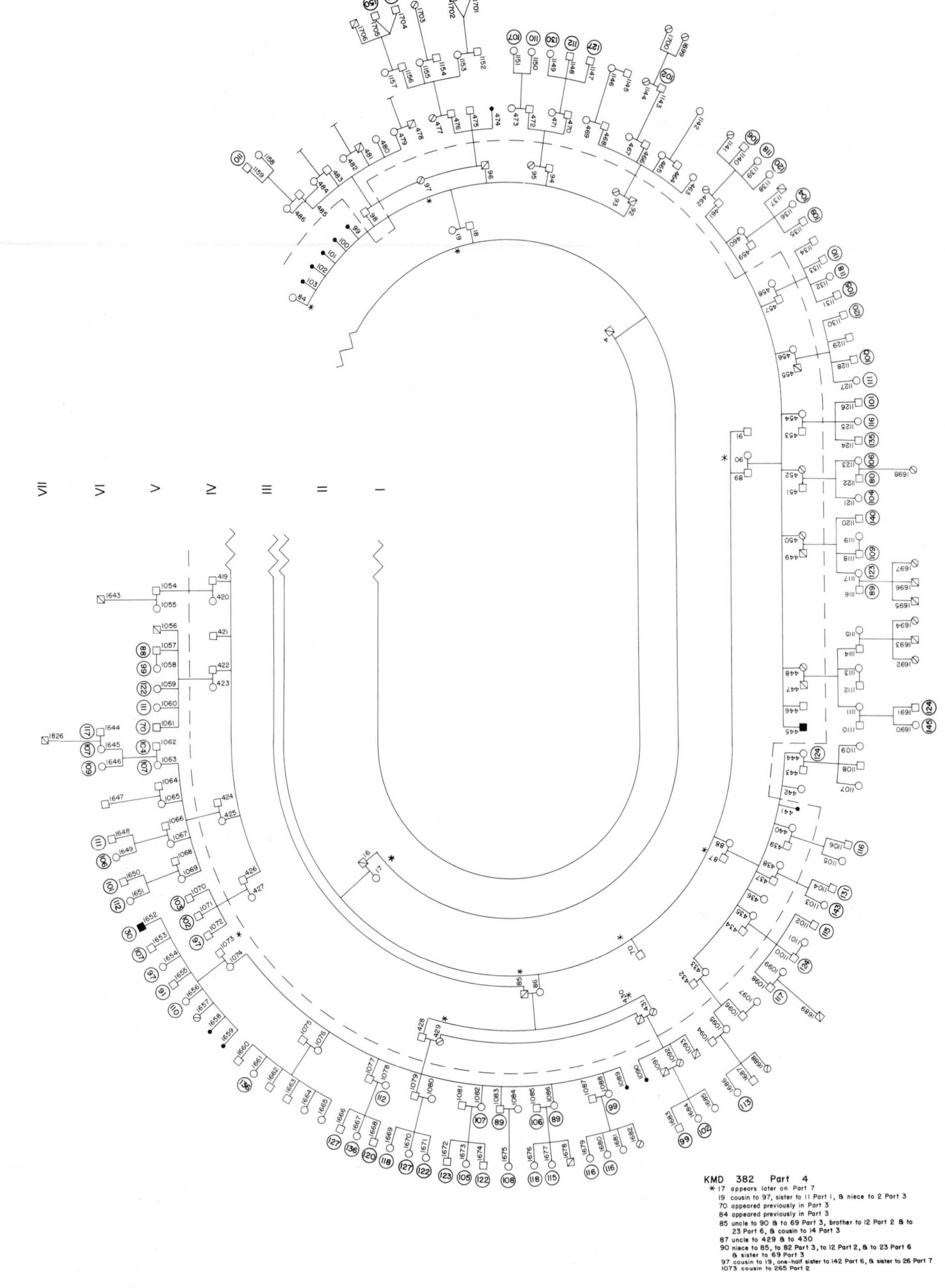

KMD 382 Part 4

* 17 appears later on Part 7
19 cousin to 97, sister to 11 Part 1, & niece to 2 Part 3
70 appeared previously in Part 3
84 appeared previously in Part 3
85 uncle to 90 & to 69 Part 3, brother to 12 Part 2 & to 23 Part 6, & cousin to 14 Part 3
87 uncle to 429 & to 430
90 niece to 85, to 82 Part 3, to 12 Part 2, & to 23 Part 6 & sister to 69 Part 3
97 cousin to 19, one-half sister to 142 Part 6, & sister to 26 Part 7
1073 cousin to 265 Part 2

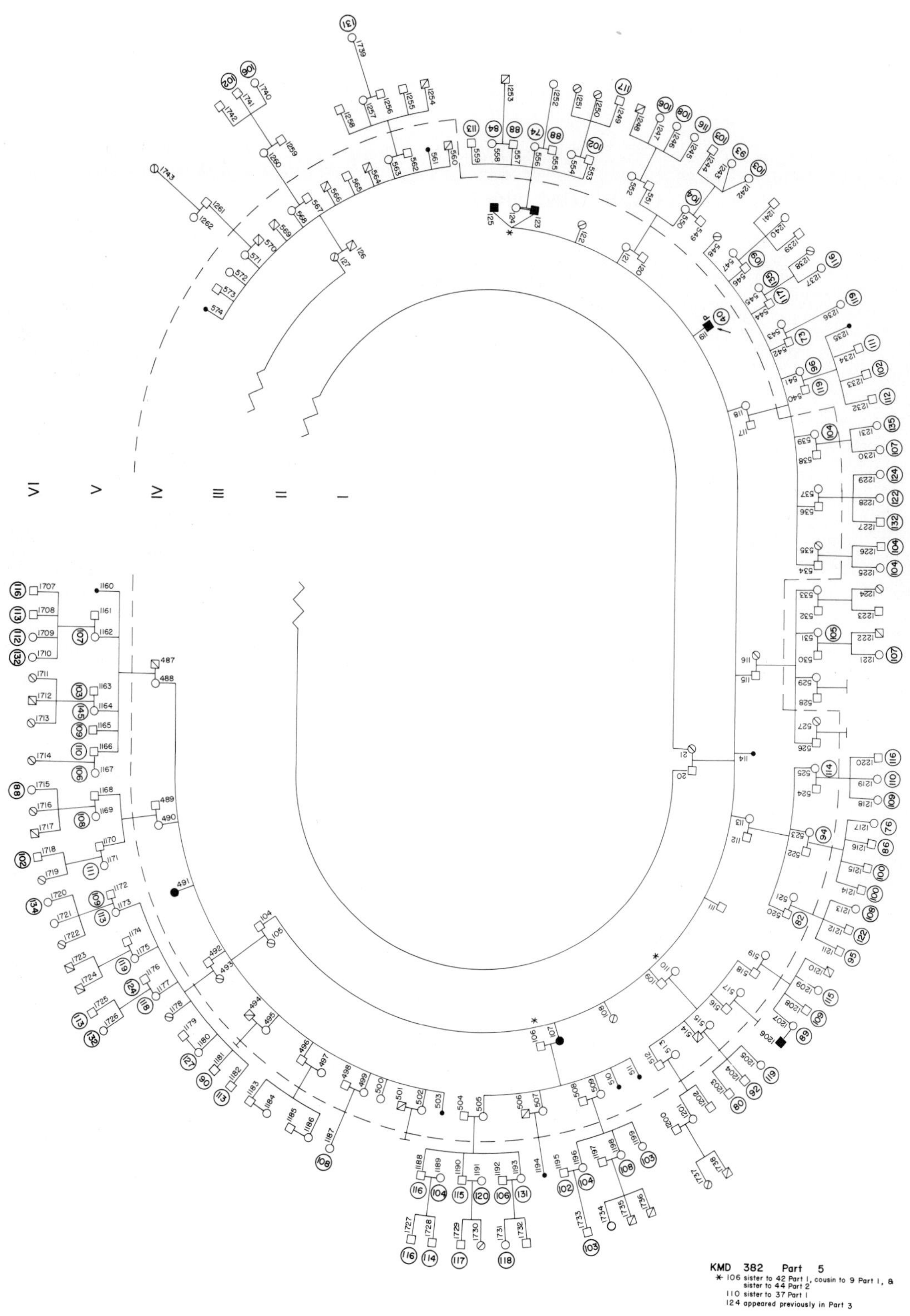
I
II
III
IV
V
VI
KMD 382 Part 5
* 106 sister to 42 Part 1, cousin to 9 Part 1, & sister to 44 Part 2
110 sister to 37 Part 1
124 appeared previously in Part 3

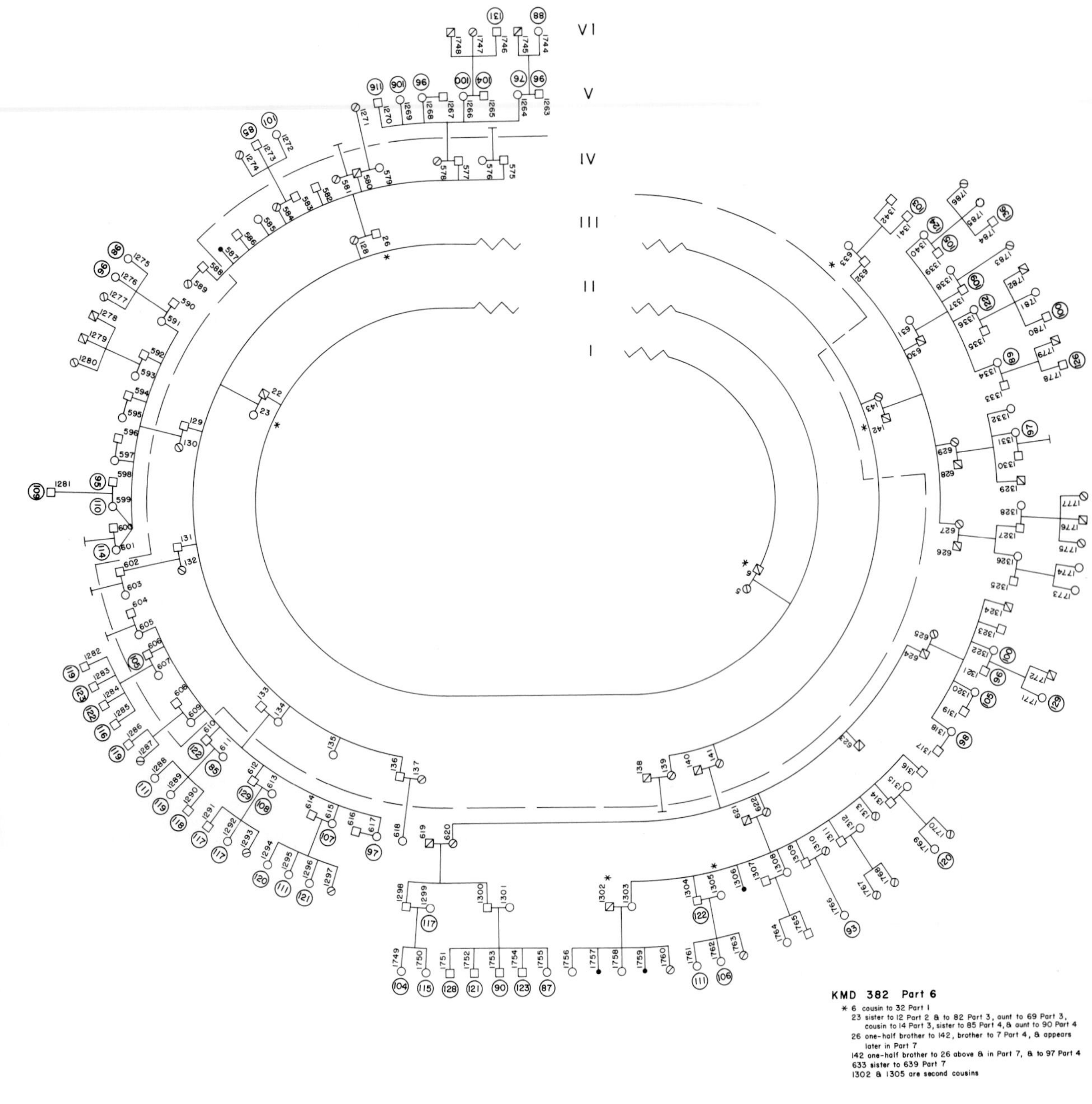
KMD 382 Part 6
* 6 cousin to 32 Part I
23 sister to 12 Part 2 & to 82 Part 3, aunt to 69 Part 3, cousin to 14 Part 3, sister to 85 Part 4, & aunt to 90 Part 4
26 one-half brother to 142, brother to 7 Part 4, & appears later in Part 7
142 one-half brother to 26 above & in Part 7, & to 97 Part 4
633 sister to 639 Part 7
1302 & 1305 are second cousins

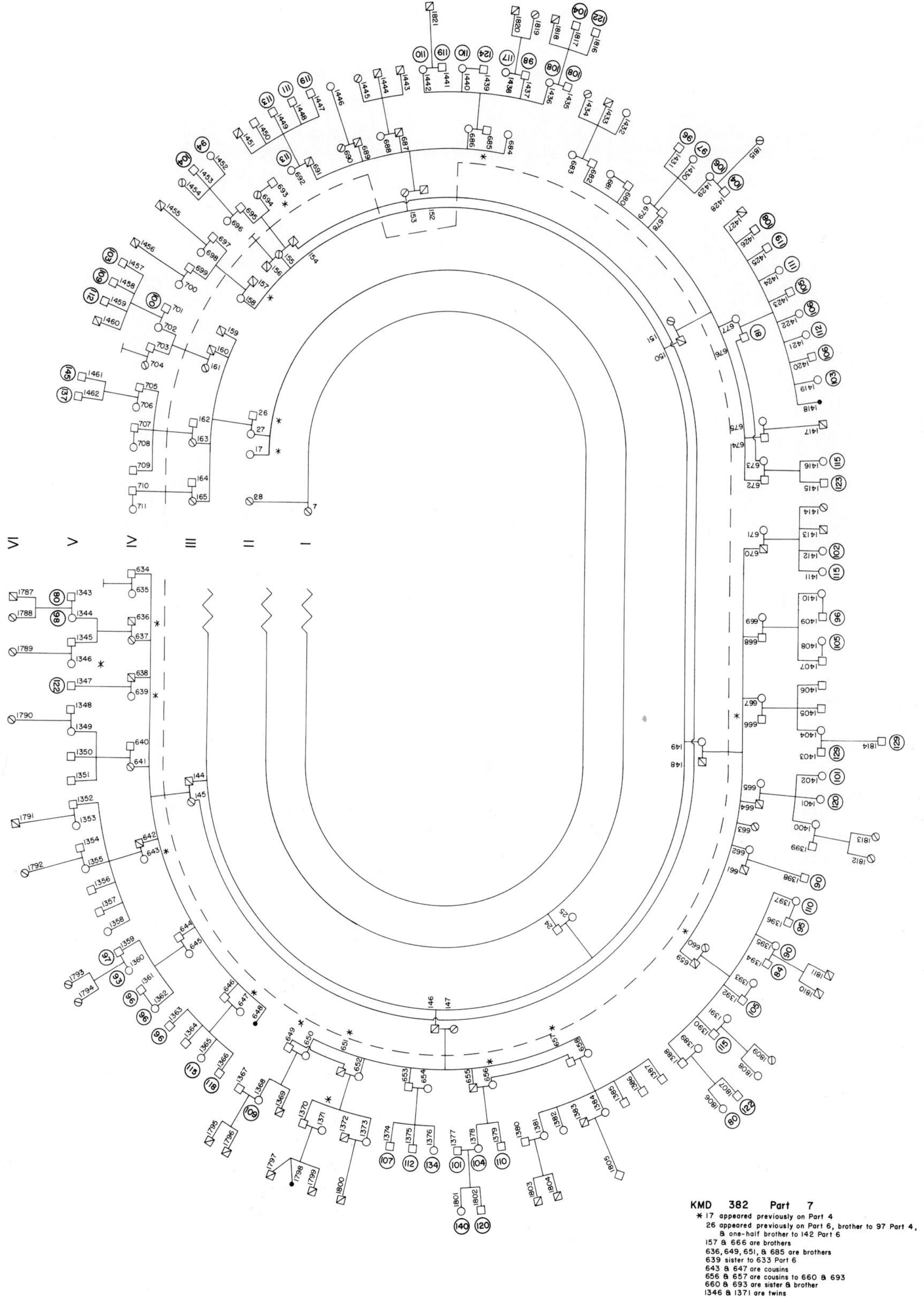
KMD 382 Part 7
* 17 appeared previously on Part 4
26 appeared previously on Part 6, brother to 97 Part 4, & one-half brother to 142 Part 6
157 & 666 are brothers
636, 649, 651, & 685 are brothers
639 sister to 633 Part 6
643 & 647 are cousins
656 & 657 are cousins to 660 & 693
660 & 693 are sister & brother
1346 & 1371 are twins

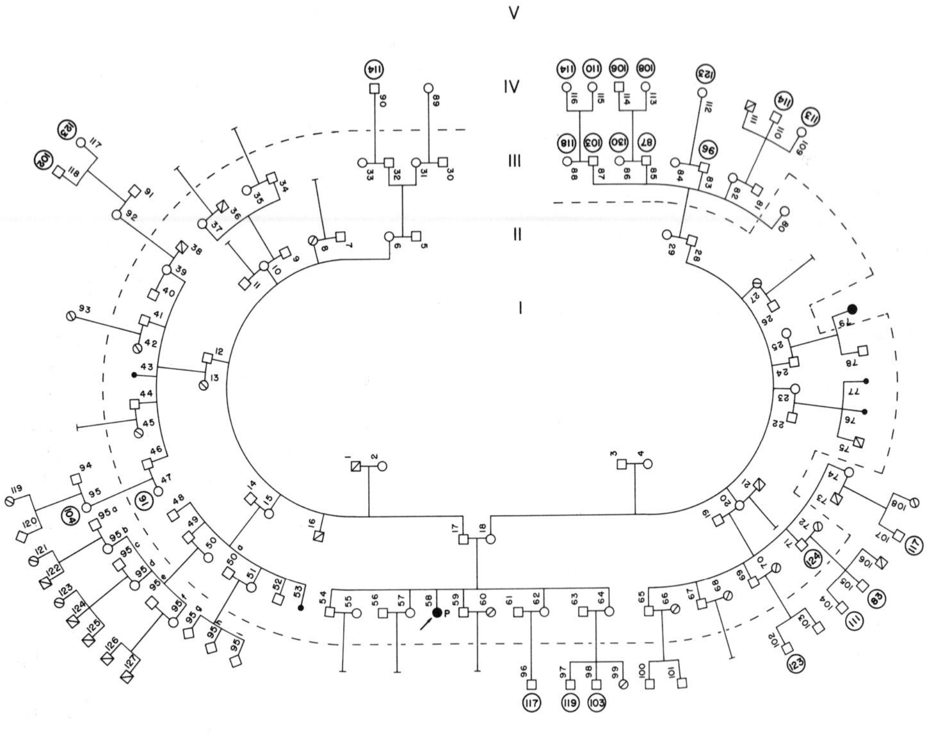

KMD 396

KMD 396

The Proband

The proband (58) was born in 1902, institutionalized at age 7 years and died of marasmus in the institution in 1911. Her birth and infancy were uneventful. She did not sit alone until age 13 months and never talked. She was reared in a good home. She was classified as an "idio-imbecile." *Diagnosis:* undifferentiated mental retardation.

Grandparents

Not of interest.

Parents

Father (17) and mother (18) both had normal intelligence.

Aunts and Uncles

Not of interest.

Siblings

Five, all with normal intelligence. All were married to normal spouses, but only two had children.

Nieces and Nephews

Not of interest.

First Cousins

(79) repeated the fourth, sixth and eighth grades and left school without completing the eighth grade. She lives with her parents.

More Distant Relatives

Not of interest.

Family Summary

The proband, a low-grade retardate, and one first cousin, a high-grade retardate, were the only retarded persons known in this family. The proband's birth and infancy were uneventful and she was reared in a good home with normal parents and siblings. The proband's parents had six children and four grandchildren.

Retardation of proband of unknown origin.

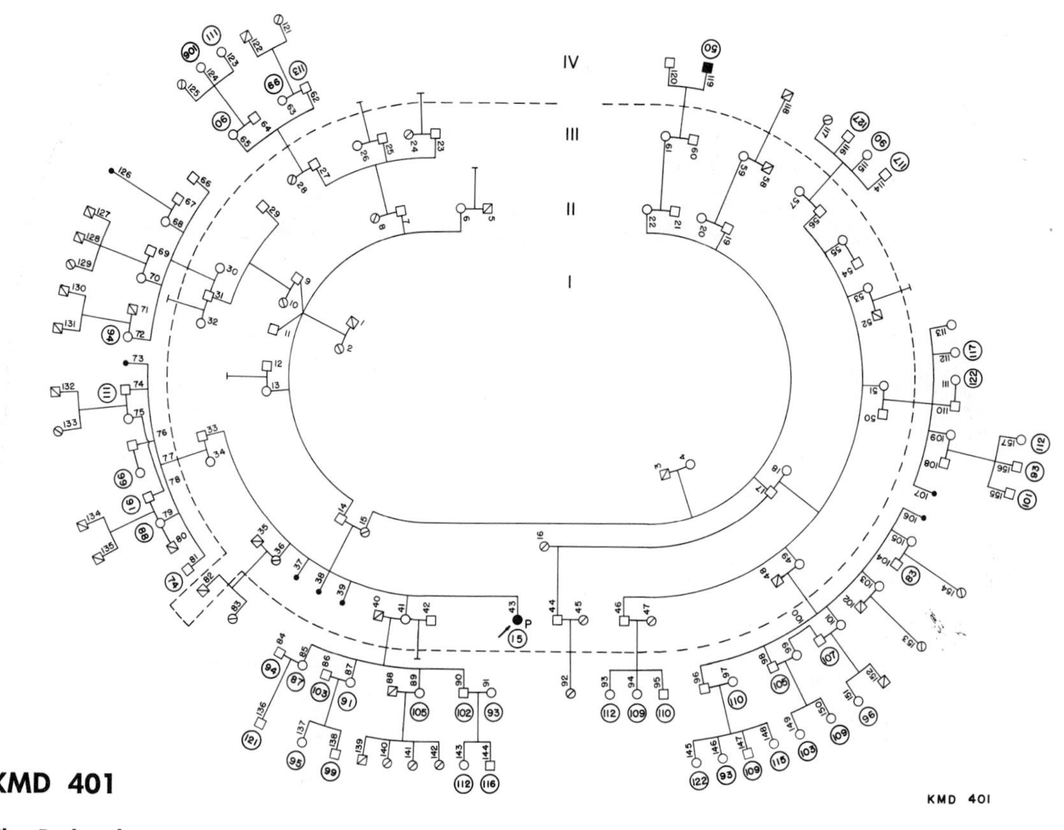

KMD 401

The Proband

The proband (43) was born in 1906 and institutionalized at age 9 years. She was discharged to her parents in 1916, readmitted in 1921, and died of pulmonary tuberculosis in the institution in 1929. Her birth and infancy were uneventful and she was reared in a good home. She walked but never talked, and developed epilepsy at age 16 years. IQ 15. *Diagnosis:* undifferentiated mental retardation.

Grandparents

Not of interest.

Parents

Father (14) was a carpenter and had normal intelligence.

Mother (15) had unknown intelligence.

Aunts and Uncles

All had normal intelligence.

Siblings

Brother (33) completed the eighth grade and a business course and is an inventory clerk. His wife and children have normal intelligence.

Sister (36) has unknown intelligence.

(37) and (38) were miscarriages.

Brother (39) was premature and died three hours after birth.

Sister (41) graduated from high school and is a clerk with normal children.

Nieces and Nephews

(73) died in convulsions at age 2 weeks.

Nephew (76) was discharged from the army because of epilepsy.

Nephew (81) is an epileptic with a borderline IQ of 74.

First Cousins

Not of interest.

More Distant Relatives

First cousin (61) has a retarded child (119) who has been committed to state guardianship, but is not institutionalized. He has been variously diagnosed as mongoloid or brain damaged from birth injuries. He was born when the mother was 44 years old and was described as "typically mongolian."

Family Summary

The proband, IQ 15, was the only retarded person known in this kindred with the exception of a first cousin's child who has Down's syndrome. The birth and infancy of the proband were uneventful. The proband's parents had seven children and 11 grandchildren.

Retardation of proband of unknown origin.

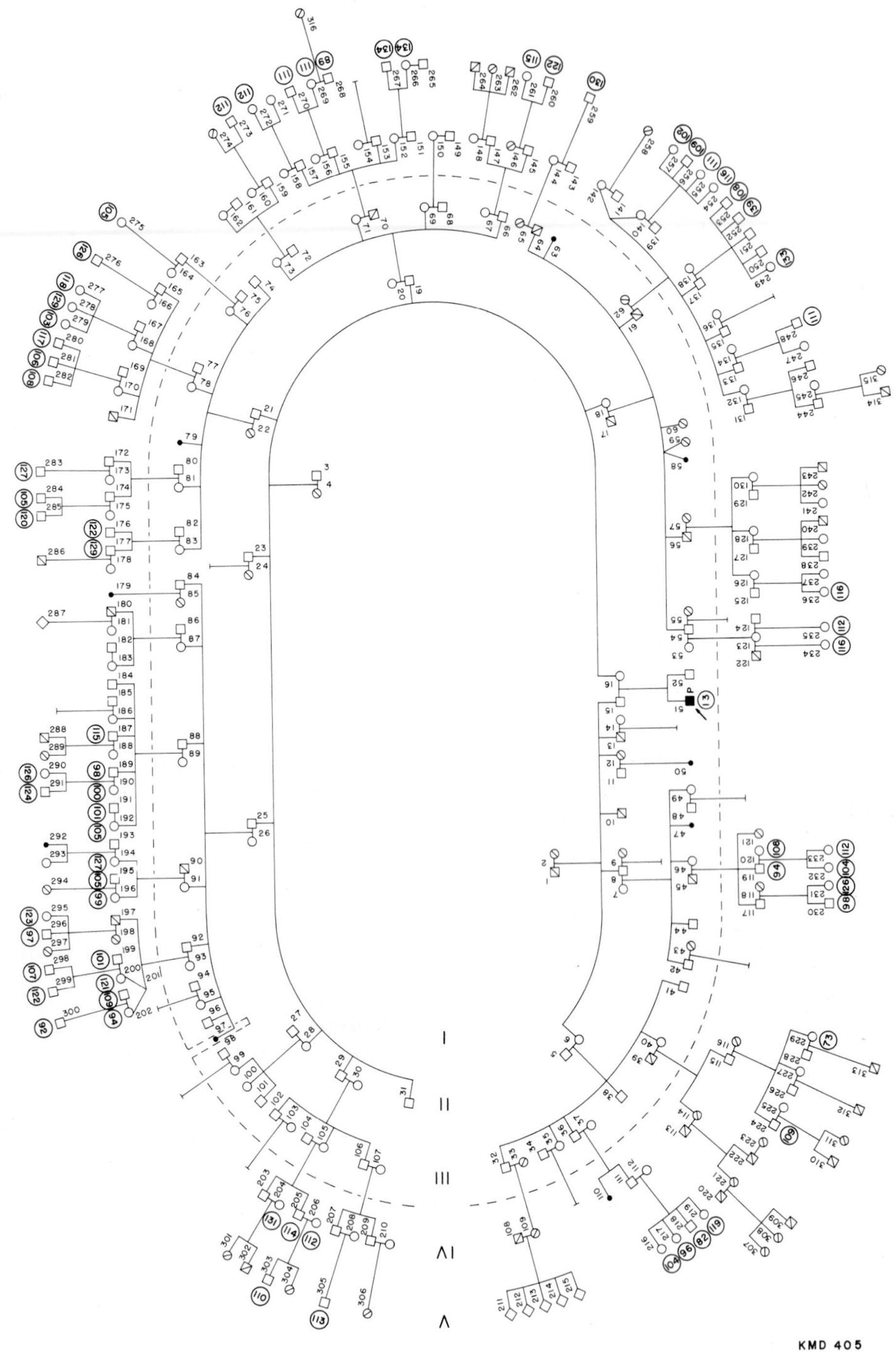

I
II
III
IV
V
VI
KMD 405
P

KMD 405

The Proband

The proband (51) was born in 1893, institutionalized at age 11 years and died of pulmonary tuberculosis in the institution in 1912. He was born after a difficult labor, was very slow to walk and never talked. There was no history of perinatal infection. IQ 13. *Diagnosis:* undifferentiated mental retardation.

Grandparents

Not of interest.

Parents

Father (15) and mother (16) both had normal intelligence.

Aunts and Uncles

Not of interest.

Siblings

Brother (52) had normal intelligence but was confined to a wheelchair most of his life because of osteogenesis imperfecta. He had brittle bones and was deaf.

Nieces and Nephews

None.

First Cousins

Not of interest.

More Distant Relatives

Not of interest.

Family Summary

The proband, IQ 13, was the only retarded person known in this family. (Of the IQ scores known for this family, 56 were above 100, 11 were below.) The proband's only sibling, a brother, had osteogenesis imperfecta. There is no mention of this disease in the parents or grandparents. The proband's parents had two children, no grandchildren.

Retardation of proband of unknown origin.

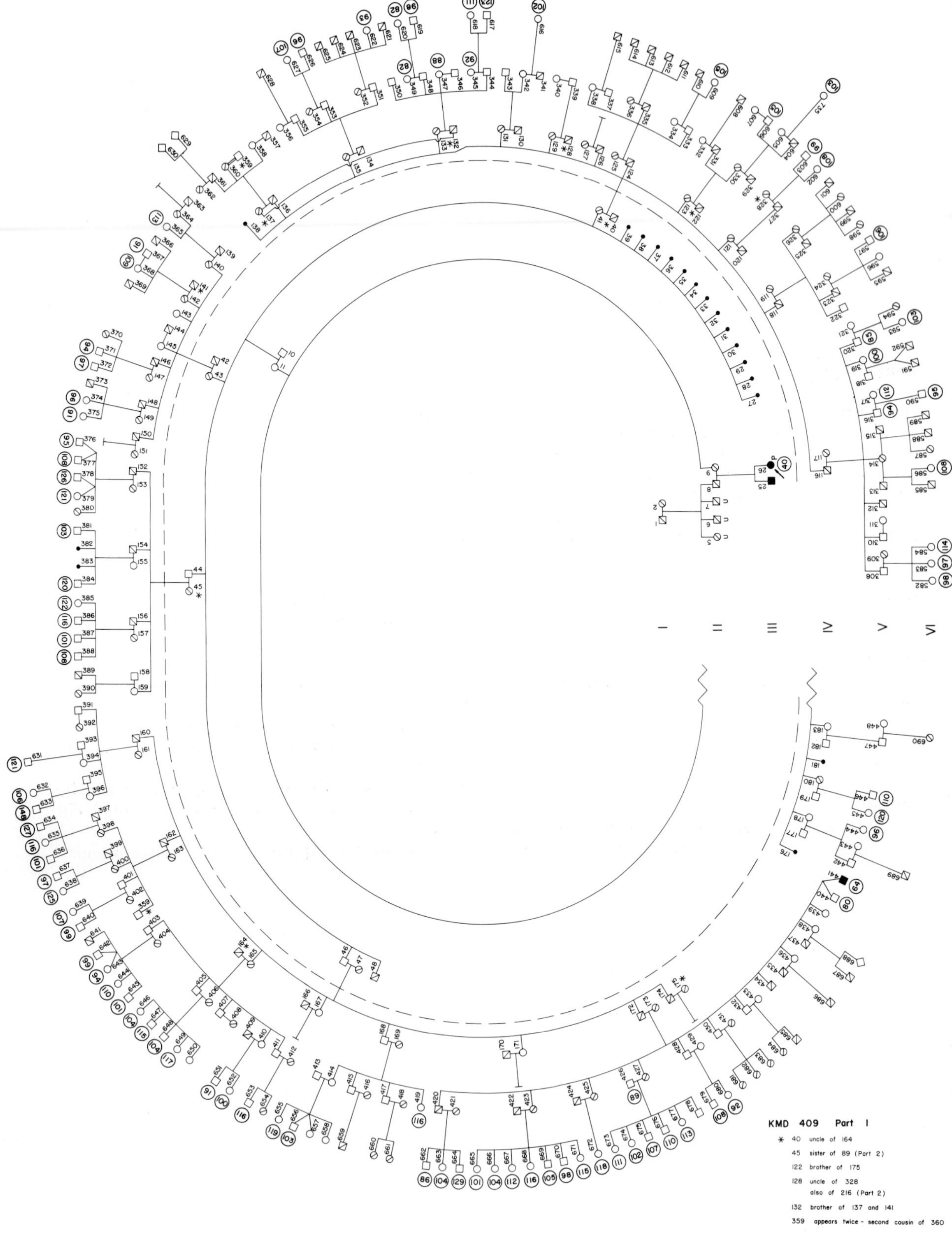

KMD 409 Part I
* 40 uncle of 164
45 sister of 89 (Part 2)
122 brother of 175
128 uncle of 328
also of 216 (Part 2)
132 brother of 137 and 141
359 appears twice - second cousin of 360
I
II
III
IV
V
VI

KMD 409

The Proband

The proband (26) was born in 1871 and institutionalized at age 35 years. She was discharged in 1919 to a guardian and died of heart failure in a home for the aged in 1934. She had senile dementia. She attended school until age 17 years but made poor progress. She was always retarded, but as she became older her condition deteriorated. There was no record of birth injuries or early illness. After the death of both parents, reports were circulated that there was incest between the proband and her retarded brother. The authorities placed (26) in her uncle's home and later removed her to the institution. She never had any children. IQ 40. *Diagnosis:* undifferentiated mental retardation.

Grandparents

Not of interest.

Parents

Father (8) was "kind of stupid" and a "very poor manager," but owned and operated a small farm.

Mother (9) had unknown intelligence.

Aunts and Uncles

Paternal relatives remained in Germany.

Maternal uncle (16) married a retarded woman (17).

Siblings

Brother (25) was retarded. After he and his sister were separated, he returned to Germany and died, unmarried and childless.

Nieces and Nephews

None.

First Cousins

(27) through (39) all died in infancy, causes unknown.

(81) is a high-grade retardate, husband and children normal.

More Distant Relatives

(190) attended a school for the deaf and has an IQ of 50.

(441) has an IQ of 64.

(561), a man with normal intelligence, married a woman with an IQ of 67.

Family Summary

The proband, IQ 40, her brother, one first cousin and two more distant relatives were the only retarded persons known in this family. There was no history of difficult delivery or childhood illness. The proband's parents had two children and no grandchildren.

Retardation of proband of unknown origin.

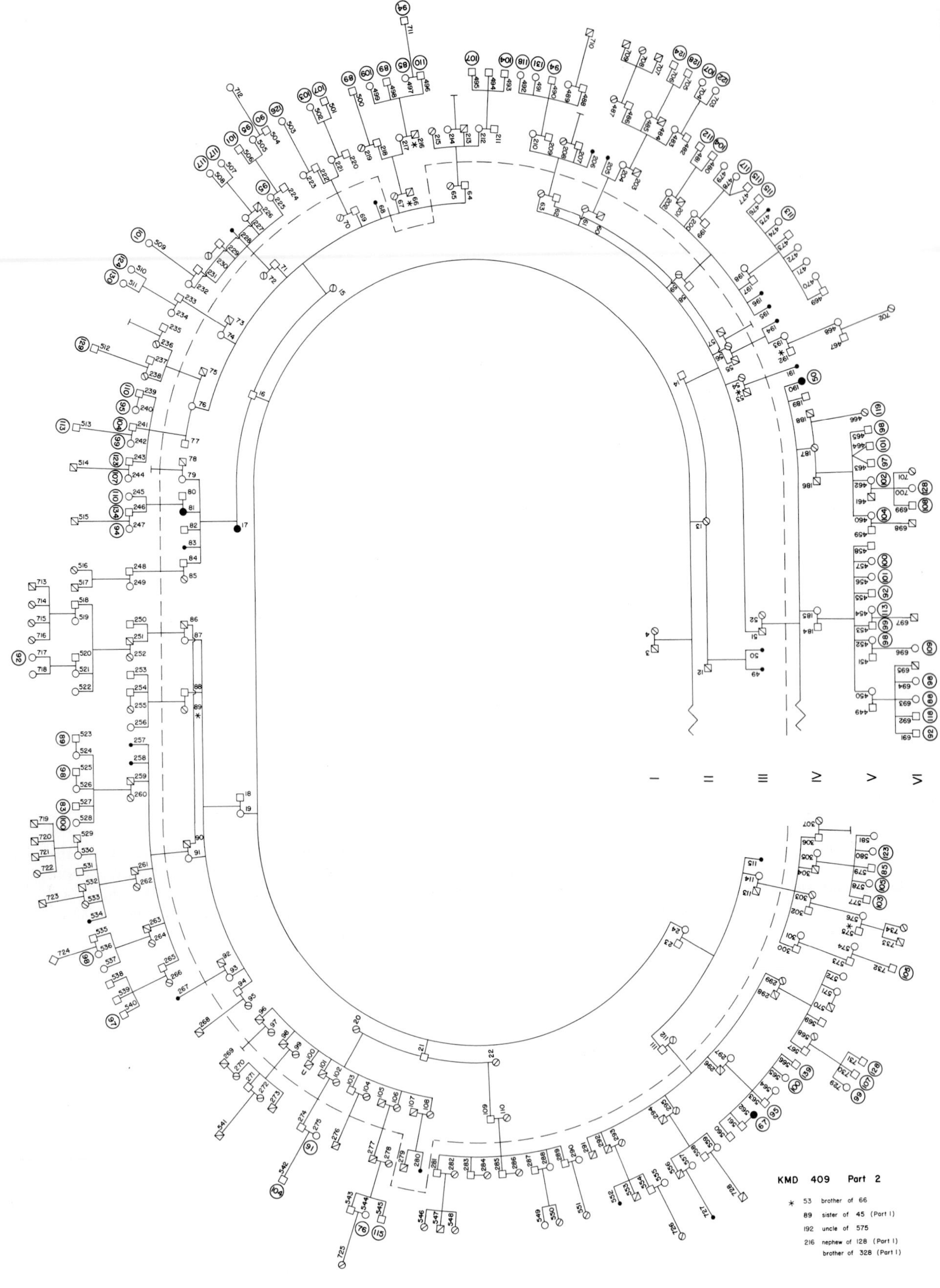
KMD 409 Part 2
* 53 brother of 66
89 sister of 45 (Part I)
192 uncle of 575
216 nephew of 128 (Part I)
brother of 328 (Part I)
I
II
III
IV
V
VI

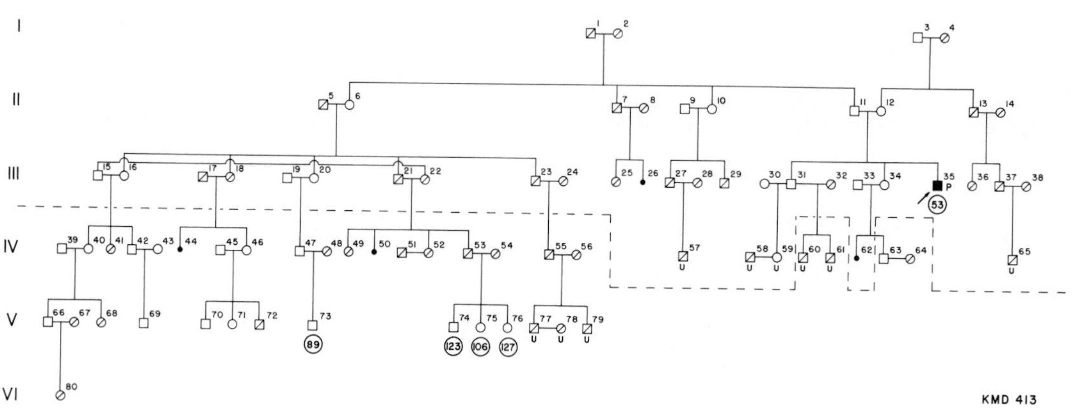

KMD 413

The Proband

The proband (35) was born in 1884, institutionalized at age 28 years and died of coronary disease in the institution in 1952. He attended school for nine years with poor results and spent four years in the armed forces. IQ 53. *Diagnosis:* undifferentiated mental retardation.

Grandparents

Not of interest.

Parents

Father (11) was a manufacturer and merchant.

Mother (12) was separated from (11). She had normal intelligence.

Aunts and Uncles

Not of interest.

Siblings

Brother (31) was an inspector and manager of gas and electric plants. He had one normal child, two of unknown intelligence.

Sister (34) had normal intelligence as did her husband and child.

Nieces and Nephews

Not of interest.

First Cousins

Not of interest.

More Distant Relatives

Not of interest.

Family Summary

The proband, IQ 53, was the only known retardate in this small family. The addresses of the proband's nephews and niece were known, but the correspondents would not cooperate, so little could be learned about them since they all lived in other states. No details concerning the birth and early years of the proband are known. The proband's parents had three children and five grandchildren.

Retardation of proband of unknown origin.

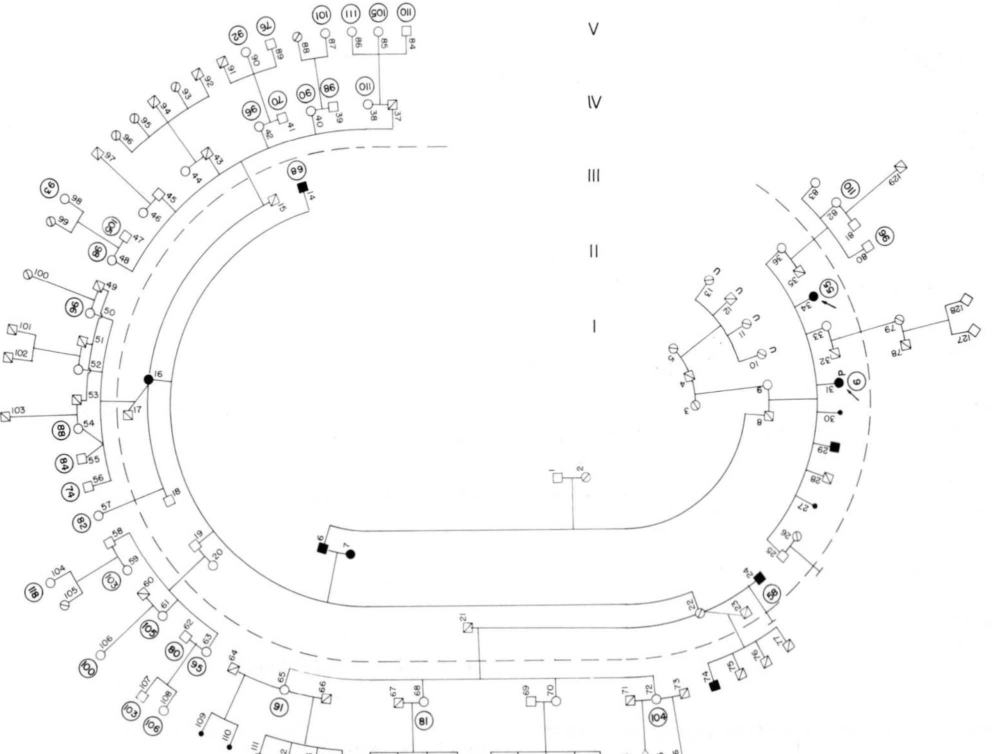

I
II
III
IV
V
KMD 418

KMD 418

The Proband

The proband (31) was born in 1908, institutionalized at age 8 years and died of acute ileocolitis in the institution in 1919. She was very weak at birth, did not walk until after age 2 years and never walked well. At 5 years she "had a stroke of paralysis. It came on gradually." Institution records state she had poliomyelitis at that time. She began to drag her feet and after about two weeks she never walked or talked again and became paralyzed and helpless. IQ 6. *Diagnosis:* undifferentiated mental retardation with subsequent poliomyelitis.

Grandparents

Not of interest.

Parents

Father (8) was a stone mason of unknown intelligence (records conflict as to whether he was retarded or normal) who died in an epileptic seizure at age 38 years.

Mother (9) had normal intelligence.

Aunts and Uncles

Paternal uncle (6) was an alcoholic, promiscuous, high-grade retardate, as was his wife. Two of his four children were retarded.

Proband's mother had no full siblings, only four half siblings who remained in Norway and are unknown.

Siblings

Brother (25) has normal intelligence.

Brother (27) died of "summer complaint" at age 8 months.

Brother (28) was in the fourth grade at age 13 years. He is childless.

Brother (29) was slightly lame from poliomyelitis and was retarded. He died childless.

Brother (30) died of "spasms and measles" at 7 weeks of age. He "never grew a bit."

Sister (33) refused to cooperate, but is known to have normal intelligence. As a child she was badly scarred from burning gasoline. Her husband and child have unknown intelligence.

Sister (34) was institutionalized at age 7 years in 1918 and discharged in 1921. She was readmitted in 1926 and has remained in the institution ever since. IQ 55. The institution diagnosis was postinfectional poliomyelitis.

Sister (36) has normal intelligence, husband unknown, children normal.

Nieces and Nephews

Not of interest.

First Cousins

(14) served a prison term for sexual offenses. He died unmarried and childless. IQ 68.

(16) "never got out of the special school." She is retarded. None of her 12 children by three marriages is retarded although one is borderline, and three are low-normal.

(22), with unknown intelligence, married a retarded laborer, IQ 58, for her third husband. She has one known retarded child in her family of four.

More Distant Relatives

(74) was in the first grade at age 9 years.

Family Summary

The proband, a paralyzed retardate with IQ 6, a paternal uncle, two siblings, two first cousins and one more distant relative were retarded. All except the proband were high-grade retardates. The proband's paralysis developed after an attack of poliomyelitis at age 5 years. The retardation of her sister was attributed to postinfectional poliomyelitis. The sister had poliomyelitis at age 2 years, the proband at age 5 years. The proband's parents had nine children and four grandchildren.

Retardation of proband of unknown origin.

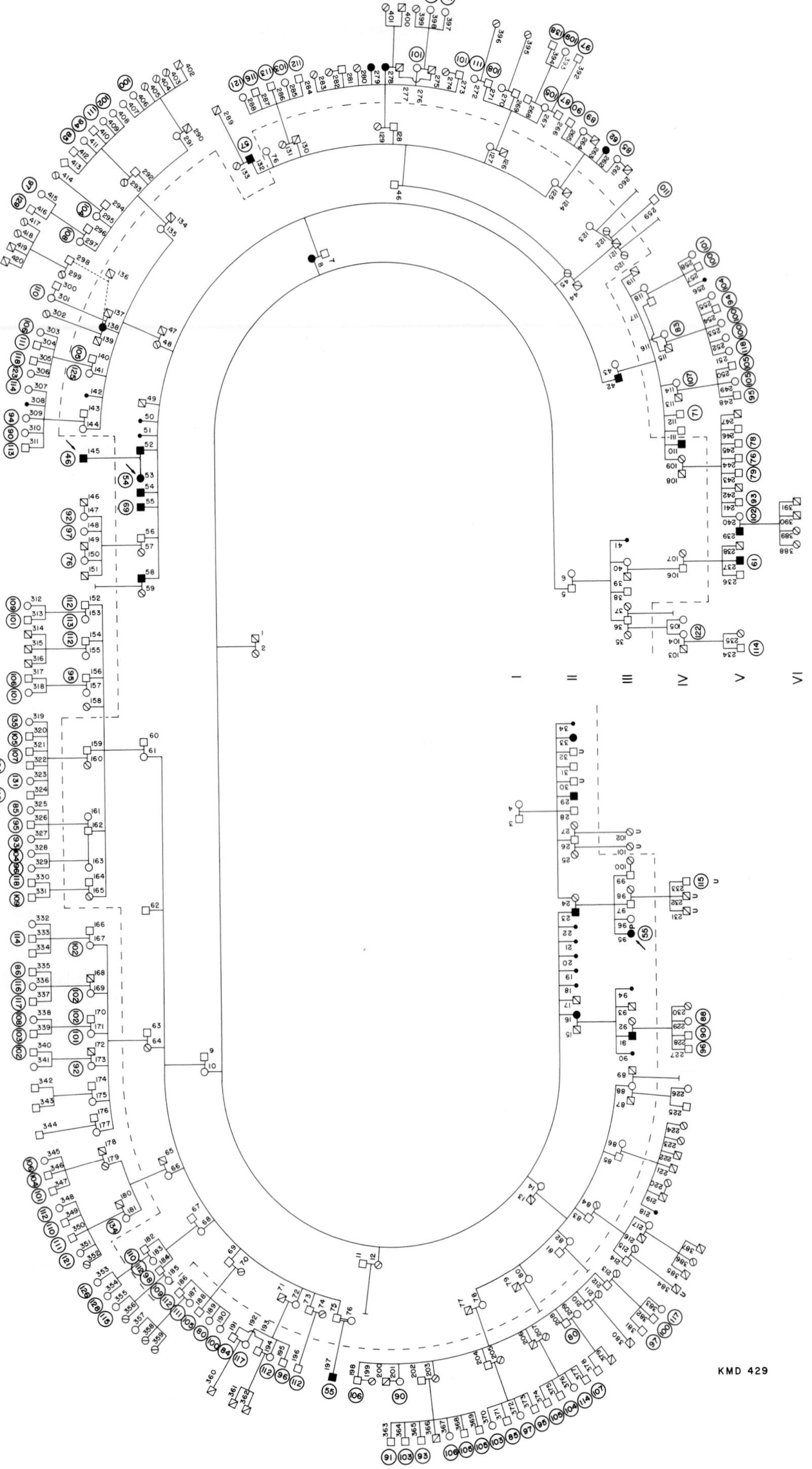

I

II

III

IV

V

VI

KMD 429

KMD 429

The Proband

The proband (95) was born in 1898, institutionalized at age 16 years and left the institution in 1920 to live with relatives. She was unmarried and childless and was still living in 1961. Her birth and early childhood were uneventful. IQ 55. *Diagnosis:* undifferentiated mental retardation.

Grandparents

Not of interest.

Parents

Father (23) was a farm laborer who could not support his family and was retarded.

Mother (24) had unknown intelligence.

Siblings

Sister (96) died of tuberculosis at age 16 years. She had normal intelligence.

Brother (97) has normal intelligence, one child normal, two children and wife unknown.

Brother (99) is a saw filer with normal intelligence. He is married but childless.

Nieces and Nephews

Not of interest as far as known. School records were found only for one of the three, a boy (97) with IQ 115. The father could not be located. (99) will probably not have any children since his wife was childless at age 38 years; he was 52 years of age.

First Cousins

(42) is retarded and his wife (43) was hospitalized for mental illness. One of their eight children is retarded and one has an IQ of 71.

(52) is retarded, as is his wife (53) who was first hospitalized in 1916 at age 19 years as manic depressive, but was institutionalized in 1936 as retarded with IQ 54 and was sterilized. She has been under outside supervision since 1940. This couple has one child, an institutionalized boy (145) with undifferentiated retardation and an IQ of 46.

(54) was an unmarried and childless retarded laborer.

(55) has an IQ of 69 and is hospitalized for manic depressive psychosis.

(58) is a retarded laborer, married but childless.

(75), a normal man, married his first cousin once removed (76), a normal woman. They have one child, a boy with undifferentiated retardation and an IQ of 55.

(91) is retarded.

More Distant Relatives

(110) is a retarded, unmarried laborer. His brother (112) has an IQ of 71.

(132) has an IQ of 57 and is a chauffer.

(138) is retarded. She had an illegitimate child and two other children by two marriages.

(145) was institutionalized in 1933 at age 17 years. IQ 46.

(197), the child of a consanguineous marriage, has an IQ of 55.

(198) is serving a prison term of 10 to 80 years for first degree robbery and prior conviction. He has an IQ of 106.

(237) has an IQ of 61.

(240) has an IQ of 102 but married (241) who was in the fourth grade at age 14 years and does "general work." (240) has three brothers with borderline IQ's of 79, 76 and 78, respectively.

(262) has an IQ of 62.

(278) repeated the second grade twice, the fourth grade four times, the fifth grade four times, the seventh and eighth grades twice.

(279) repeated the second, third and fifth grades and failed the eighth.

Family Summary

The proband, IQ 55, her father, two paternal aunts, a maternal aunt and uncle, six first cousins and nine more distant relatives were all high-grade retardates. Two of the retardates have also been hospitalized for manic depressive psychosis. One retardate was the child of a consanguineous marriage of persons of normal intelligence. The family of (8) shows a probably genetic type of retardation. The proband's parents had four children and three grandchildren.

Retardation of proband of unknown origin.

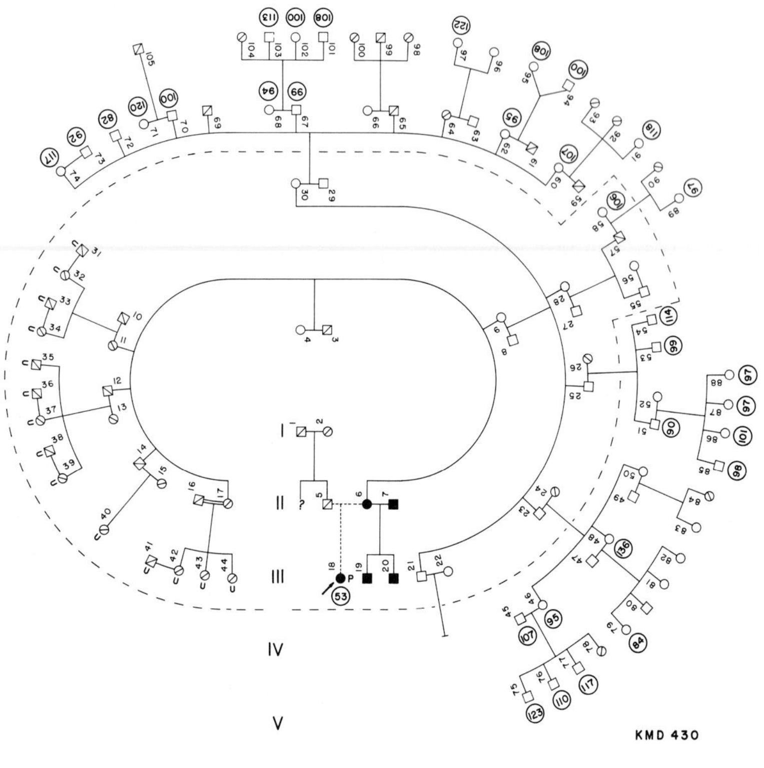

KMD 430

The Proband

The proband (18) was born in 1893, institutionalized at age 18 years and died of heart failure in the institution in 1933. She was an illegitimate child who was greatly abused in a squalid home and was adopted as a small girl when her mother and stepfather refused to keep her. She had no history of difficult birth or perinatal infection and had no stigmata. IQ 53. *Diagnosis:* undifferentiated mental retardation.

Grandparents

Paternal grandparents unknown.

Maternal grandparents not of interest.

Parents

Father (5) is unknown because the proband was illegitimate.

Mother (6) was retarded. She could not keep house and died in a mental hospital at age 75 years. (6) married a retarded "wood chopper" (7). County Welfare records classify (6) and (7) as "insane."

Aunts and Uncles

Paternal relatives are unknown.

Maternal relatives not of interest.

Siblings

No full siblings.

Half Siblings

Half brothers (19) and (20) are unmarried and childless retarded farm laborers.

First Cousins

Not of interest.

More Distant Relatives

Not of interest.

Family Summary

The proband, IQ 53, her mother and her two half siblings were all retardates of about the same grade. The proband was an illegitimate child who was adopted in her childhood from a very squalid and cruel environment into a kind home. The proband's parents had one child, no grandchildren.

Retardation of proband of unknown origin.

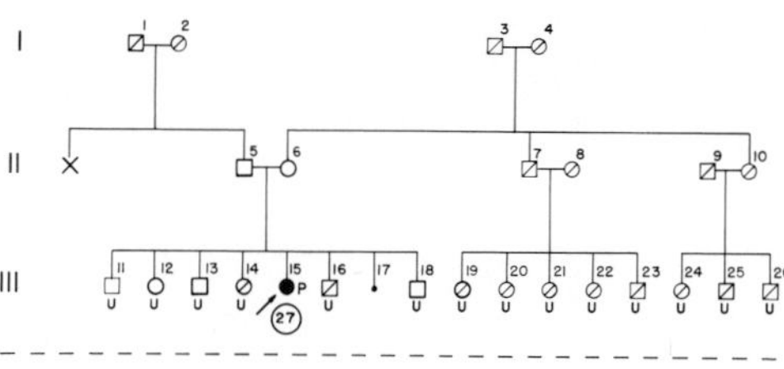

KMD 433

KMD 433

The Proband

The proband (15) was born in 1890, institutionalized at age 13 years and died of adenocarcinoma of the breast in the institution in 1953. She had typhoid fever at age 1½ years, according to her parents. IQ 27. *Diagnosis:* undifferentiated mental retardation.

Grandparents

Not of interest.

Parents

Father (5) and mother (6) had normal intelligence.

Aunts and Uncles

Paternal and maternal relatives all unknown. They remained in Europe.

Siblings

Brothers (11), (13) and (18) and sister (12) have normal intelligence.

Sister (14) and brother (16) have unknown intelligence.

Brother (17) died from a "cold" at age 1 week.

Nieces and Nephews

Unknown. Despite the fact that the proband was still in the institution, all trace of this family has been lost. The proband's father and her siblings had all moved from their old homes leaving no forwarding addresses.

First Cousins

Unknown.

More Distant Relatives

Unknown.

Family Summary

The proband, IQ 27, was the only retarded person known in her immediate family. She had typhoid fever at age 1½ years. Unfortunately, no relative could be found for the follow-up since everyone had moved away leaving no forwarding addresses. The proband's parents had eight children, grandchildren unknown.

Retardation of proband of unknown origin.

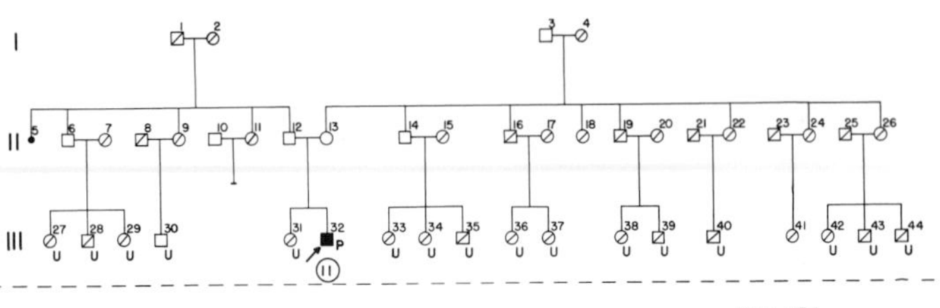

KMD 434

The Proband

The proband (32) was born in 1904, institutionalized at age 9 years and discharged the same year to his parents. His parents applied for his readmission in 1917, but he died at home in 1918. There was no history of difficult birth or perinatal infection. The parents attributed the proband's condition to a fall from his high chair. He had no stigmata. IQ 11. *Diagnosis:* undifferentiated mental retardation.

Grandparents

Not of interest.

Parents

Father (12) and mother (13) both had normal intelligence. They owned and operated a prosperous farm.

Aunts and Uncles

Not of interest.

Siblings

Only one, a sister (31) of unknown intelligence. The early workers classified her as a high-grade retardate, but she completed at least the eighth grade and was talented musically. She could not be found for the follow-up.

Nieces and Nephews

It is not known whether or not the proband's sister had any children.

First Cousins

Mostly unknown since they lived out of the state.

More Distant Relatives

Unknown.

Family Summary

The proband, IQ 11, was the only retarded person known in this family. No relatives could be found for the follow-up. Apparently, the proband's family moved away shortly after his death in 1918. The proband's parents had two children, grandchildren unknown.

Retardation of proband of unknown origin.

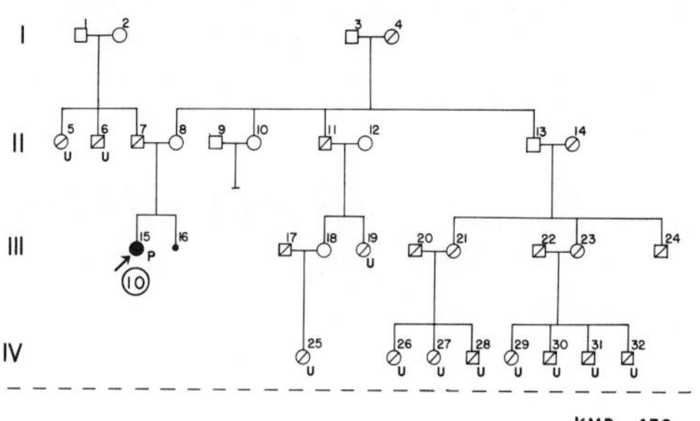

KMD 436

The Proband

The proband (15) was born in 1885, institutionalized at age 18 years and died of uterine tumor in the institution in 1936. She talked at age 3 years but stopped talking by age 12. She attended school for five years and could read, write and play the piano. She is supposed to have "failed mentally" after the age of 10 years, and continued to deteriorate mentally and physically after her institutionalization until she could do very little. IQ 10 (but must have been higher before admission). *Diagnosis:* unknown.

Grandparents

Not of interest.

Parents

Father (7) deserted his family. His intelligence was unknown.

Mother (8) had normal intelligence.

Aunts and Uncles

Paternal relatives unknown.

Maternal relatives not of interest, except that one record states there was mental illness on the maternal side.

Siblings

Brother (16) suffocated in a slough at age 2 years.

Nieces and Nephews

None.

First Cousins

(19) was hospitalized for mental illness at one time.

More Distant Relatives

Unknown.

Family Summary

The proband, IQ 10, was the only retarded person known in this family. The proband's developmental history—from a child who could read and write to one who was so deteriorated she could do very little—indicates possible schizophrenia. No relative could be found for the follow-up, so the more recent generations are unknown. The proband's parents had two children, no grandchildren.

Retardation of proband of unknown origin.

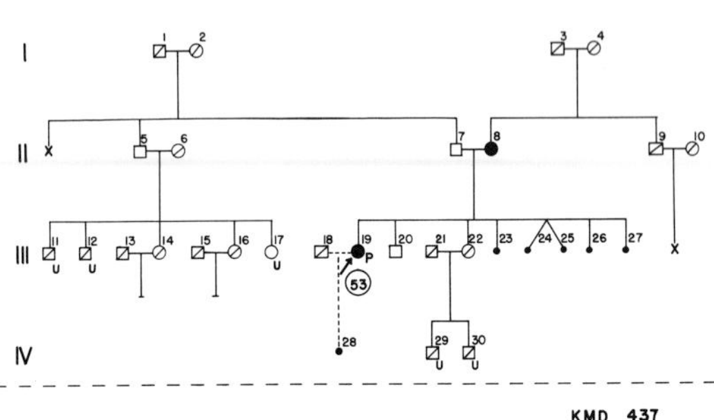

KMD 437

The Proband

The proband (19) was born in 1872, institutionalized at age 30 years and died of lobar pneumonia in the institution in 1927. She talked at age 3 years and went to school until age 16 years with poor results. She was neglected and abused at home, but there was no history of difficult birth or perinatal infection. She had no stigmata. When she became pregnant by the hired man, an abortion was induced with the aid of the proband's father (7) who also insisted on his wife having five abortions. IQ 53. *Diagnosis:* undifferentiated mental retardation.

Grandparents

Not of interest.

Parents

Father (7) was a good farmer with normal intelligence, but was very disagreeable and abusive.

Mother (8) tried to poison (7) then deserted him and engaged in petty crimes with her daughter (22) and son-in-law (21). When (8) was arrested for theft she pleaded insanity and was sent to a mental hospital. She was considered to have been retarded also.

Aunts and Uncles

Paternal and maternal relatives nearly all unknown, except that the proband's father's brother (5) tried to steal the property of (7).

Siblings

Brother (20) drowned at age 26 years. He had normal intelligence.

Sister (22), of unknown intelligence, married (21) a vagrant with a prison record, and they, together with the proband's mother engaged in petty crime in various towns. They were evicted from several towns, and could not be traced for the follow-up.

(23), (24), (25), (26) and (27) were criminal abortions.

Nieces and Nephews

Only two are known, of unknown intelligence, but referred to as "thieves" in the old records.

First Cousins

Unknown.

More Distant Relatives

Unknown.

Family Summary

The proband, IQ 53, and her mother were retarded. This family presented a very sordid picture of social degeneracy, mental illness and crime. Unfortunately, their frequent changes of address made it impossible to trace them for the follow-up. The proband's parents had three children (and five abortions) and at least two grandchildren.

Retardation of proband of unknown origin.

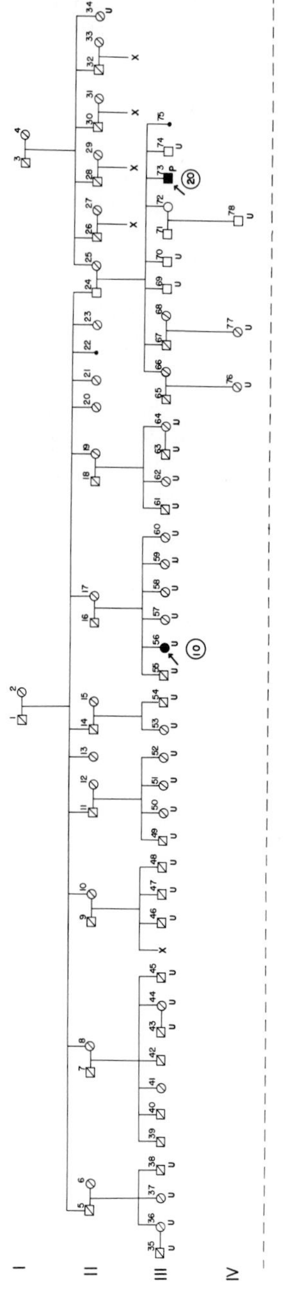

KMD 438

The Proband

The proband (73) was born in 1887, institutionalized at age 18 years and died of enteritis in the institution in 1918. He walked at age 2½ years and talked at age 7 years. The father said he had measles and scarlet fever at the same time in infancy. He had no stigmata. IQ 20. *Diagnosis:* undifferentiated mental retardation.

Grandparents

Not of interest.

Parents

Father (24) was a prosperous farmer.

Mother (25) died of acute mania in a mental hospital.

Aunts and Uncles

Paternal side not of interest.

Maternal relatives all remained in Sweden.

Siblings

Sister (66) and brother (67) had unknown intelligence.

Brothers (69), (70) and (74), and sister (72) had normal intelligence.

Sister (75) was an eight months' baby who died at age 3 days.

Nieces and Nephews

Only three are known, one with normal intelligence, two of unknown intelligence.

First Cousins

(56) was institutionalized in 1894 at age 11 years, and died of epileptic exhaustion in the institution in 1915. She had a large head and did not walk. IQ 10.

More Distant Relatives

Unknown.

Family Summary

The proband, IQ 20, and her first cousin, IQ 10 and probably hydrocephalic, were the only known retardates in this family. The father attributed the proband's retardation to simultaneous attacks of measles and scarlet fever in infancy. The proband's parents had eight children and at least three grandchildren. This family could not be found for the follow-up because they had a frequently occurring Scandinavian name.

Retardation of proband of unknown origin.

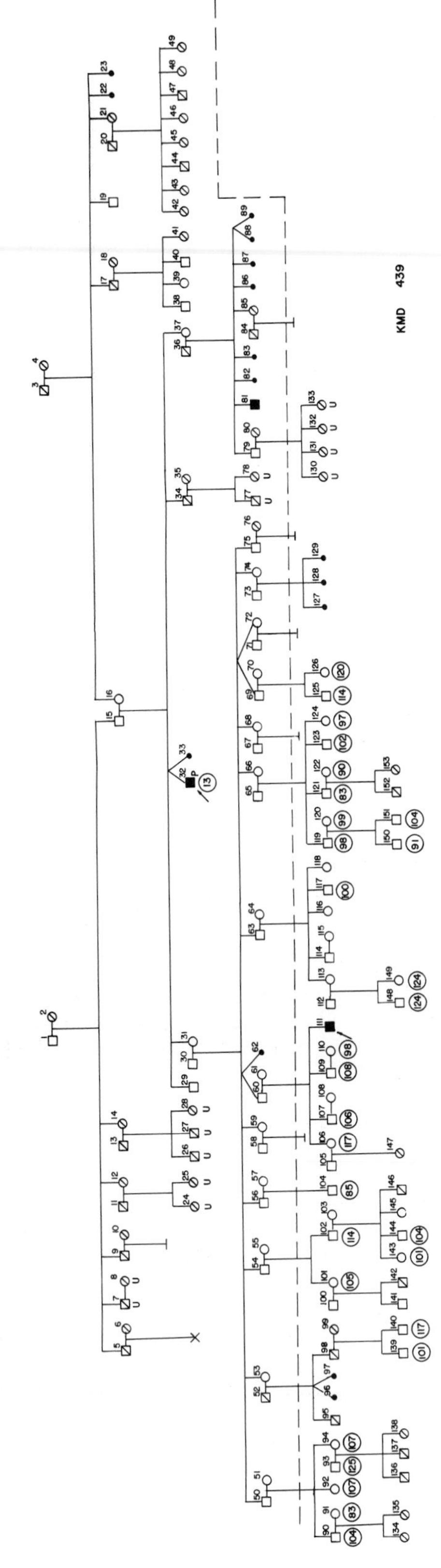

KMD 439

The Proband

The proband (32) was born in 1871, institutionalized at age 14 years and died there of auricular fibrillation in 1937. He was a twin and was "defective from birth." There was no history of difficult birth or perinatal infection. The family reported he had fallen downstairs at age 2 years and was unconscious for "some time." IQ 13. *Diagnosis:* undifferentiated mental retardation.

Grandparents

Not of interest.

Parents

Father (15) was a prosperous farmer.
Mother (16) had normal intelligence.

Aunts and Uncles

Paternal relatives all lived in Canada or New York State and are unknown.

Maternal relatives not of interest.

Siblings

Brother (29) had normal intelligence. He was unmarried and died of tuberculosis at age 36.

Sisters (31) and (37) had normal intelligence. The children of (31) had normal intelligence but (37) had a retarded child.

Sister (33), twin to proband, died at age 9 months of "inflammation of the bowels."

Brother (34) had unknown intelligence, as did his wife and children.

Nieces and Nephews

Nephew (81) left school when in the fifth grade at age 15 years. He died childless at age 56.

First Cousins

All cousins (38) through (49), with the exception of (46), died of pulmonary tuberculosis in their early years (teens through twenties).

More Distant Relatives

(111) was institutionalized at age 6 years in 1947. He is epileptic, has a spastic right side and is unable to walk or stand, but can creep. The mother attributes his condition to birth injury. Institution diagnosis is imbecile with congenital cerebrospastic infantile hemiplegia.

Family Summary

The proband, IQ 13, a first cousin who is a high-grade retardate and a great-nephew who is an epileptic and spastic imbecile, are the only retarded persons known in this family. The proband's parents had six children and 25 grandchildren, of whom seven died in infancy. The maternal side of this family, with the exception of the proband's mother, had no descendants. All the proband's 12 maternal cousins died of pulmonary tuberculosis with the exception of one unmarried, childless woman.

Retardation of proband of unknown origin.

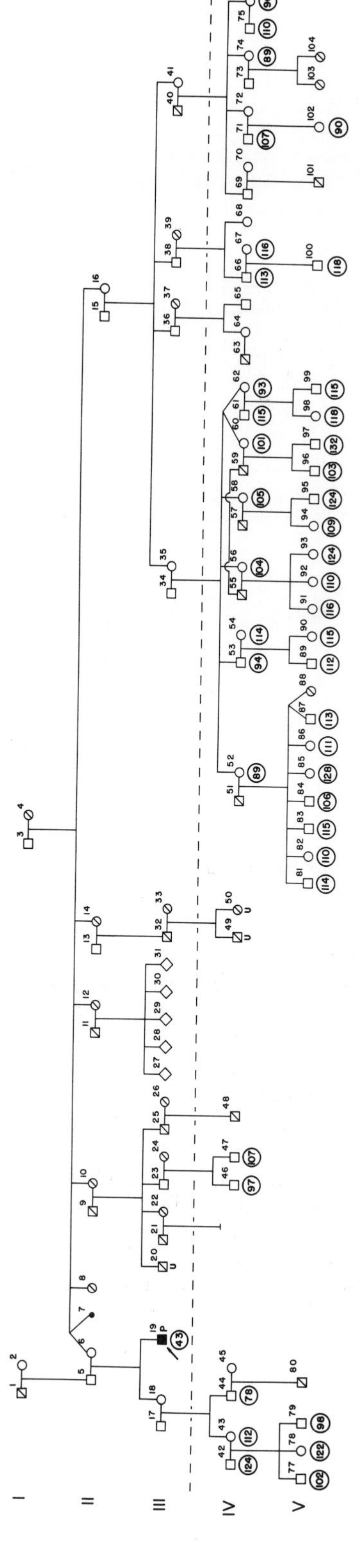

KMD 441

The Proband

The proband (19) was born in 1901, institutionalized at age 12 years and died of pleurisy and bronchopneumonia in the institution in 1919. He was a "blue baby" and had "brain fever when small." He was blind. His teeth were very late in coming in and soon decayed and fell out. He was reared in a good home. IQ 43. *Diagnosis:* mental retardation with blindness.

Grandparents

Not of interest.

Parents

Father (5) and mother (6) both had normal intelligence. There was some evidence that (6) was syphilitic, but the doctor was not certain about this. (6) became totally blind before her death at age 37 years.

Aunts and Uncles

No paternal relatives since (5) was an only child.

Maternal relatives not of interest.

Siblings

Only a sister (18) who has normal intelligence, as do her husband and children.

Nieces and Nephews

Only two, IQ's of 112 and 78, respectively.

First Cousins

Not of interest.

More Distant Relatives

Not of interest.

Family Summary

The proband, IQ 43 and blind, was the only retarded person known in this family. He had a history of "brain fever" and heart trouble ("blue baby"). The proband's mother was suspected of being syphilitic because of blindness and invalidism which developed before her death at age 37 years of brain tumor. The proband's parents had two children and two grandchildren.

Retardation of proband of unknown origin.

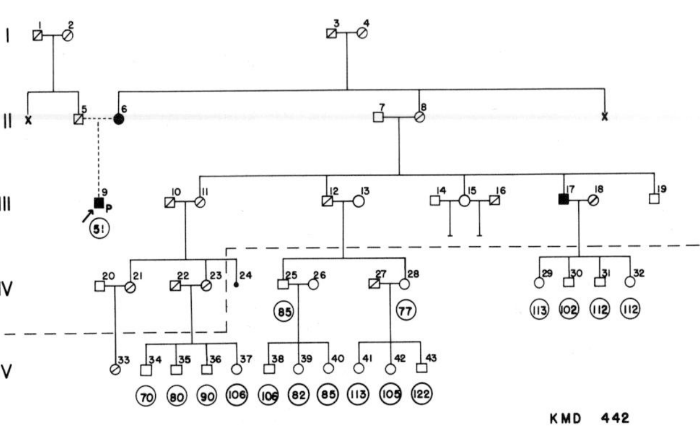

KMD 442

The Proband

The proband (9) was born in 1898, institutionalized at age 14 years, discharged to his relatives in 1913 and died in 1918. He was an illegitimate child who lived with his mother. The mother had no home but stayed with various people for whom she did housework, and the proband moved about with her. He had no history of difficult birth or perinatal infection and had no stigmata. IQ 51. *Diagnosis:* undifferentiated mental retardation.

Grandparents

Nothing is known about them.

Parents

Father (5) was an alcoholic of unknown intelligence.

Mother (6) was a high-grade retardate.

Aunts and Uncles

All the paternal relatives and nearly all the maternal relatives are unknown.

Siblings

None.

Nieces and Nephews

None.

First Cousins

(17) was in the third grade at age 14 years and was considered retarded. He has four children all with normal intelligence.

Family Summary

The proband, IQ 51, his mother and a first cousin were high-grade retardates. The retarded cousin had four normal children. The proband was an illegitimate child who moved about the community with his mother, a domestic. The proband's parents had one child, no grandchildren.

Retardation of proband of unknown origin.

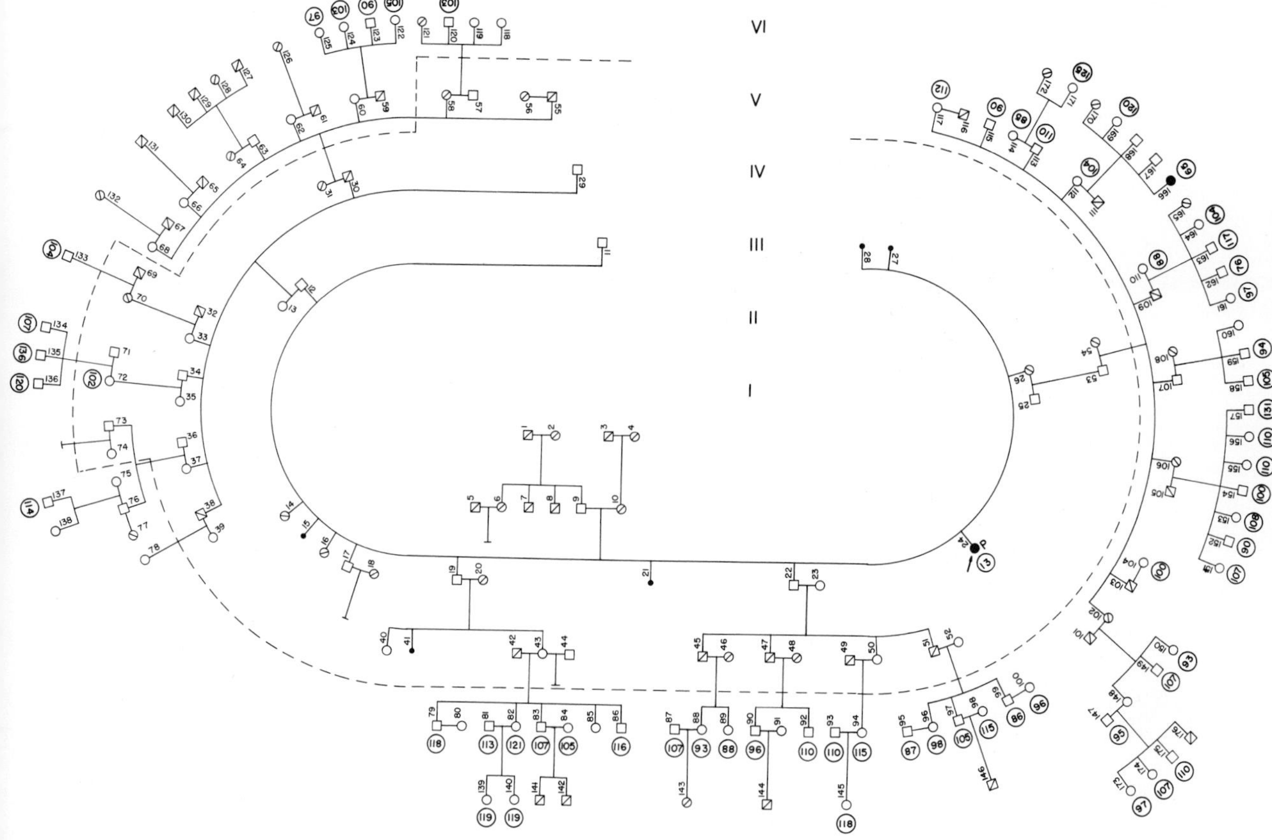

KMD 443

KMD 443

The Proband

The proband (24) was born in 1875, institutionalized at age 37 years and died of influenza in the institution in 1918. Nothing is known of her early years except that the parents attributed the proband's condition to an attack of "brain fever." She had excellent health and no stigmata. IQ 13. *Diagnosis:* undifferentiated mental retardation.

Grandparents

Nothing is known about them.

Parents

Father (9) had normal intelligence.
Mother (10) had unknown intelligence.

Aunts and Uncles

Not of interest.

Siblings

Brother (11) was an unmarried, childless laborer who was "barely up to par."

Brother (12) was a real estate dealer and grain inspector, wife and four children normal, two children of unknown intelligence.

Sister (14) died young.

(15) was a stillbirth.

Sister (16) died of rheumatism at age 19 years.

Brother (17) completed one year of college and operated a hotel. He was married but childless.

Brother(19) was in the hardware business, wife unknown, children normal.

(21) was a stillbirth.

Brother (22) completed two years of college and was a farmer with normal wife and children.

Sister (26) "never could learn in school" but was not classified as retarded, husband and son normal.

(27) and (28) were stillbirths.

Nieces and Nephews

Not of interest.

First Cousins

None, so far as is known.

More Distant Relatives

(166) has an IQ of 65.

Family Summary

The proband, IQ 13, and a more distant relative with IQ 65 were the only retarded persons found in the proband's family. The parents attributed the proband's retardation to "brain fever," but there was no medical confirmation of this. The proband's parents had 13 children, including four stillbirths, and 14 grandchildren.

Retardation of proband of unknown origin.

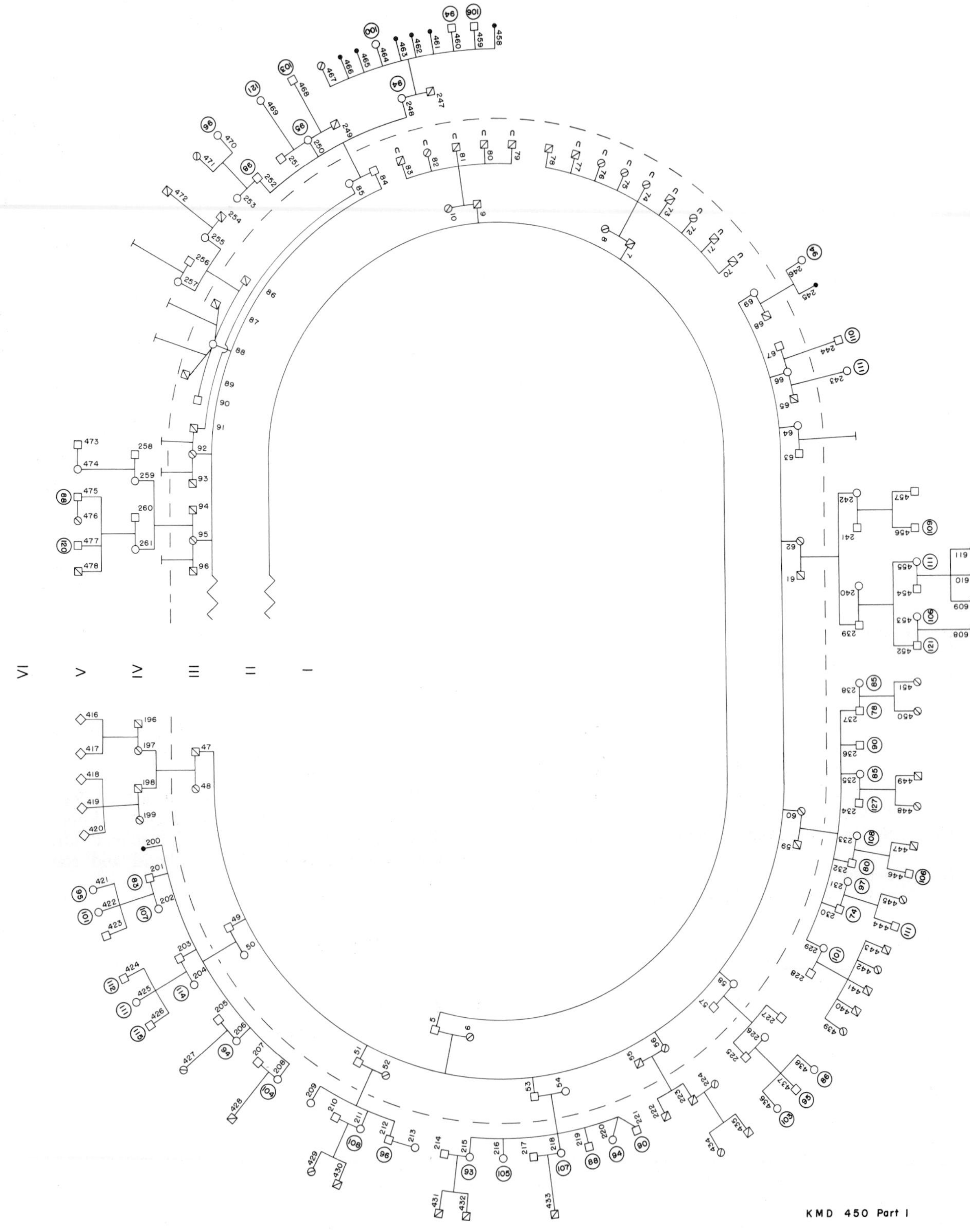
VI
V
IV
III
II
I
KMD 450 Part I

KMD 450

The Proband

The proband (159) was born in 1906, institutionalized at age 9 years, transferred to four other institutions for varying reasons and was still institutionalized in 1961. His birth and early life were uneventful and he had no stigmata. His home treatment was fairly good. His IQ report of 57 in 1917 was accompanied by a note from the psychologist that he had "aphasia—understands perfectly but does not talk." Diagnosis from the institution is moron, cause undiagnosed. *Diagnosis:* undifferentiated mental retardation.

Grandparents

Both grandmothers had normal intelligence, but the maternal grandmother was "very peculiar and erratic" and her husband, the proband's maternal grandfather, was mentally ill. He remained in bed for about 14 years. He had normal intelligence, however.

Parents

Father (29) was an alcoholic, retarded laborer who deserted his family several times.

Mother (30) was retarded.

Aunts and Uncles

Maternal uncle (35) was an unmarried, childless retardate.

Maternal uncle (36) was retarded and had epileptiform attacks. Two of his children were retarded, his wife and one child had normal intelligence.

Maternal uncle (42) had normal intelligence, but died of alcoholism.

Maternal uncles (44) and (45) were unmarried, childless retardates. (45) died in a mental hospital where he was sent after he attacked his brother.

Siblings

(158) was a miscarriage.

(161) is unknown to relatives.

(162) is unmarried, mental status unknown.

(163), of unknown intelligence, died childless.

(164), (165) and (166) are unknown even as to sex or date of birth.

(167) has unknown intelligence.

(168) is an institutionalized retardate.

(169) left school at age 16 years after completing the sixth grade and is probably retarded. The information about this family is very scanty because the proband's mother moved to Canada where the last six siblings were born.

Nieces and Nephews

Nothing is known about any possible children of siblings.

First Cousins

(88) is of interest because, although she was married four times, she had only two children (255) and (257) and one grandchild (472).

(102) was a prostitute who had an illegitimate child.

(108) has an IQ of 67, husband and children unknown.

(129) has normal intelligence, but his wife and one of his two adult children are retarded.

(137) is retarded, eight children, all normal, wife's intelligence unknown.

(140), brother to (137), is retarded, four children all normal, wife's intelligence unknown.

(180) was epileptic.

(186) and (187), siblings, are high-grade retardates.

More Distant Relatives

(287) has an IQ of 58.

(346) was institutionalized for mental retardation and epilepsy. IQ 56.

Family Summary

The proband, IQ 57, two siblings, his parents, four maternal uncles, five first cousins and two more distant relatives were all high-grade retardates. In addition, the proband's maternal grandfather and one maternal uncle were mentally ill. Nothing could be learned about the fourth generation in the proband's immediate family because his mother and her younger children moved to Canada. The proband's parents had 11 children, number of grandchildren unknown.

Retardation of proband of unknown origin.

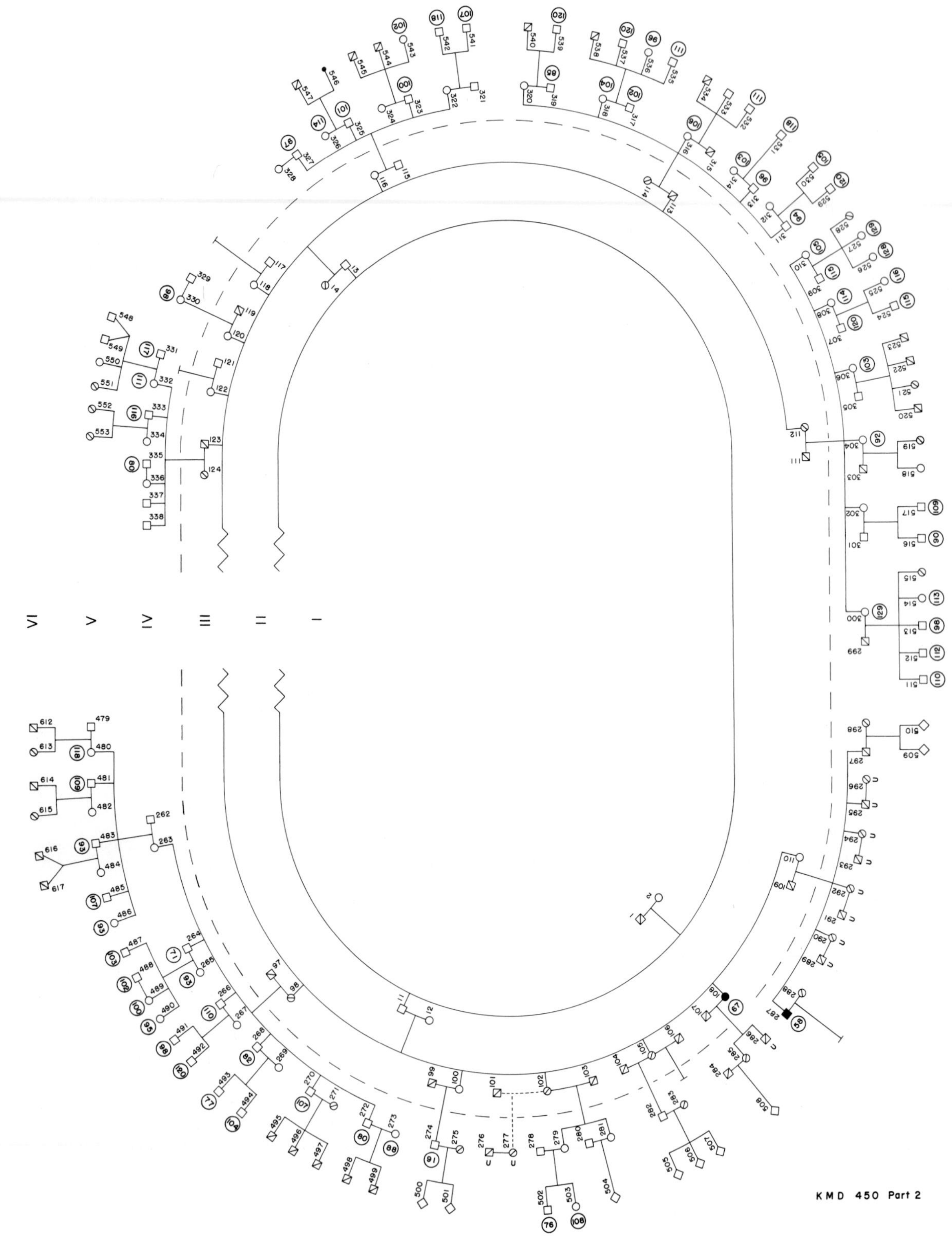

I
II
III
IV
V
VI
KMD 450 Part 2

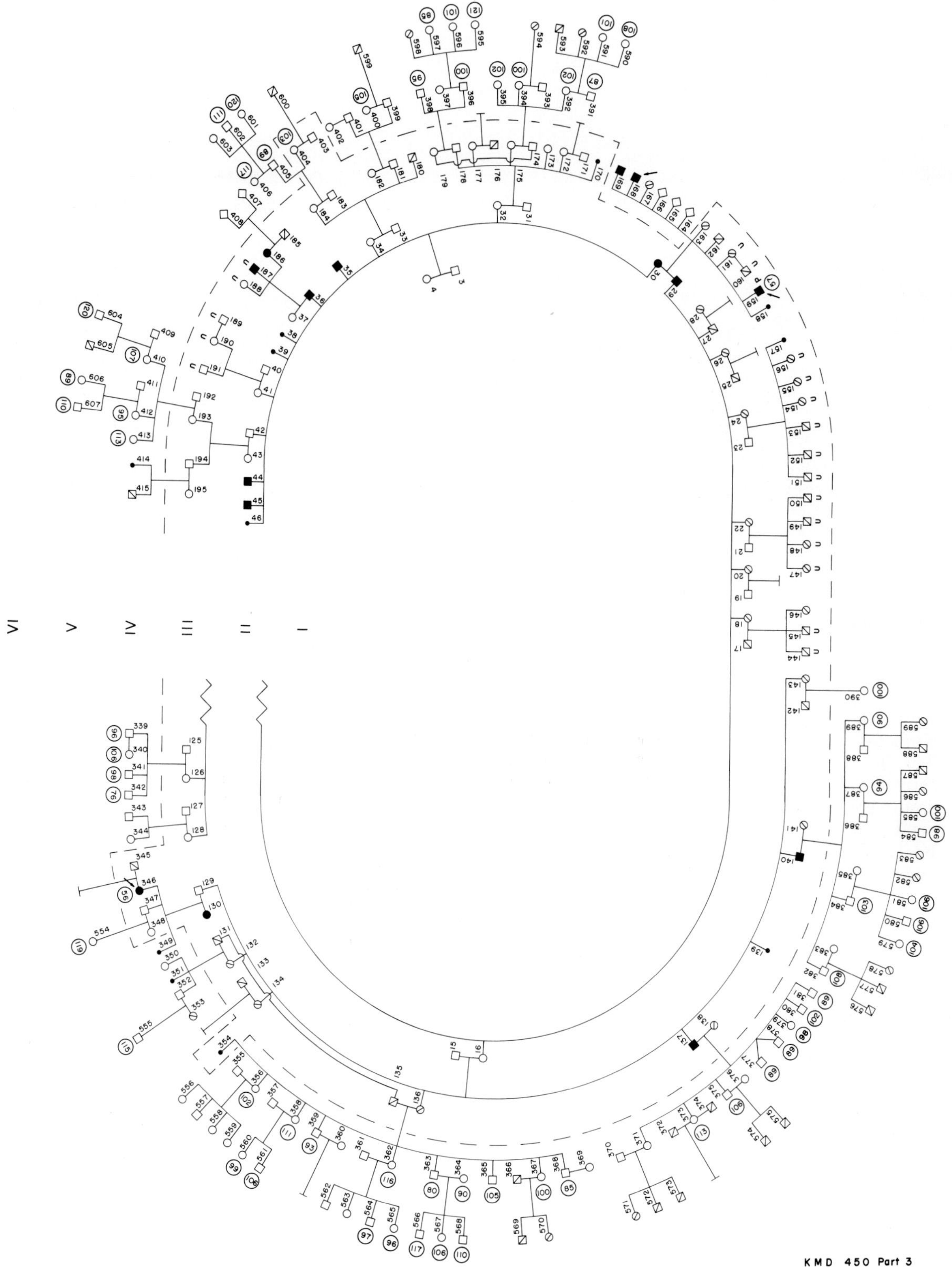

KMD 450 Part 3

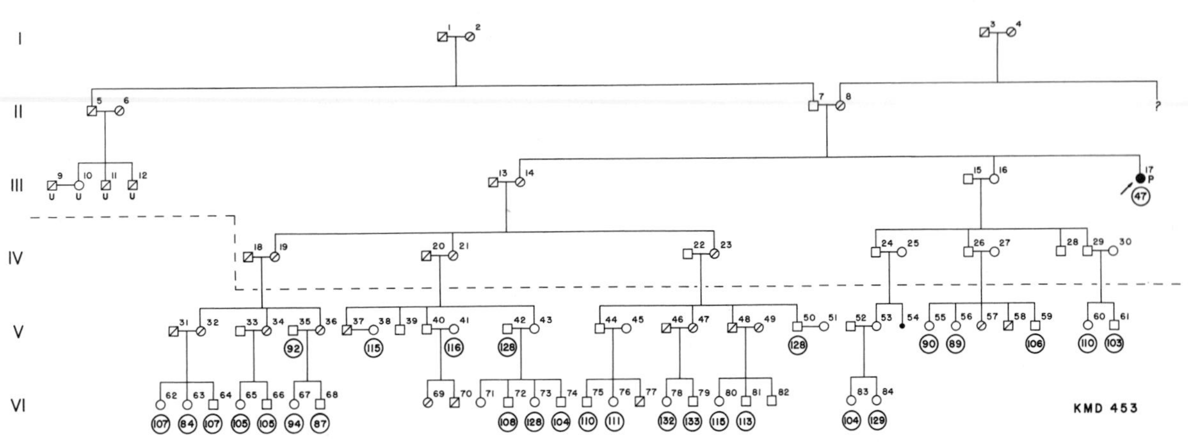

KMD 453

The Proband

The proband (17) was born in 1874, institutionalized at age 16 years and died of auricular fibrillation and hypostatic pneumonia in the institution in 1921. No details are known about her early life since both parents died when the children were young. She had no stigmata. The proband and her siblings grew up in foster homes. IQ 47. *Diagnosis:* undifferentiated mental retardation.

Grandparents

Nothing is known about them.

Parents

Father (7) was a farmer with normal intelligence.

Mother (8) had unknown intelligence.

Aunts and Uncles

Paternal relatives could not be found for the follow-up.

Maternal relatives unknown. They all remained in Europe.

Siblings

Sister (14) had unknown intelligence. No retardation has appeared among her descendants.

Sister (16) had normal intelligence and normal children.

Nieces and Nephews

Not of interest.

First Cousins

Unknown.

More Distant Relatives

Unknown.

Family Summary

The proband, IQ 47, was the only retarded person known in this family. No details of her early life were known. The proband's parents had three children and seven grandchildren.

Retardation of proband of unknown origin.

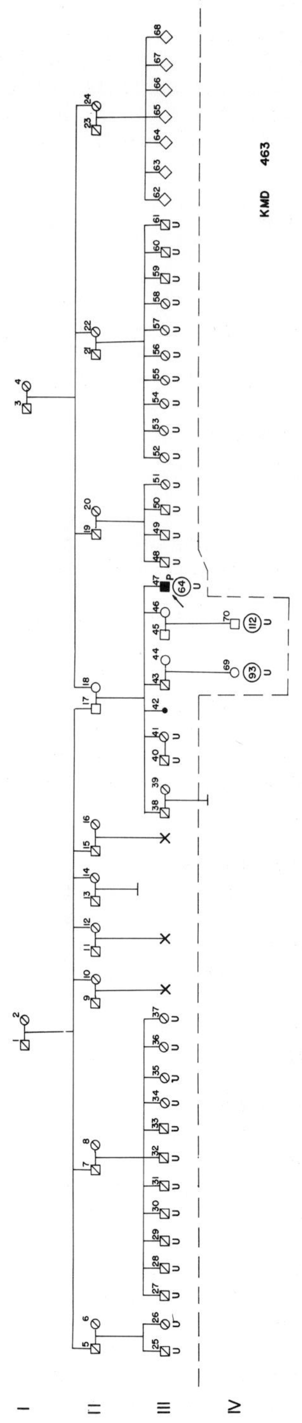

KMD 463

The Proband

The proband (47) was born in 1903, institutionalized at age 12 years and discharged in 1917. He was last heard of when he was on parole from a reformatory in 1922. He walked at age 14 months. He attended school in special classes but learned little. He became incorrigible, began stealing, and became such a behavior problem that he was suspended from school. His mother could not control him and his father punished him severely for his behavior. He grew up in a comfortable, prosperous home. There was no record of difficult birth or perinatal infection and he had no stigmata. IQ 64. *Diagnosis:* undifferentiated mental retardation.

Grandparents

Not of interest.

Parents

Father (17) was an alcoholic, but a prosperous carpenter.

Mother (18) had normal intelligence.

Aunts and Uncles

Nearly all these relatives remained in Germany. (5), (7) and (19) came to this country, but were unknown to the original investigators.

Siblings

Brother (38) could barely read and write. He was last heard of in 1934 when he was released from prison after serving five terms, all for theft. He was childless at age 49 years.

Sister (41) was an alcoholic and a prostitute. Her present status is unknown.

(42) was a miscarriage.

Brother (43) was an alcoholic carpenter who could not earn a living.

Sister (46) was promiscuous, but had normal intelligence. She refused to cooperate in any way.

Nieces and Nephews

Apparently only two, since a search of school records revealed no mention of siblings for either (69) or (70).

First Cousins

Unknown.

More Distant Relatives

Unknown.

Family Summary

The proband, IQ 64, was a behavior problem. He served time in a reformatory. His brother, of unknown intelligence, served five terms for stealing and his two sisters were alcoholic and promiscuous. As far as is known, only the proband was retarded. The proband's parents had six children and probably only two grandchildren.

Retardation of proband of unknown origin.

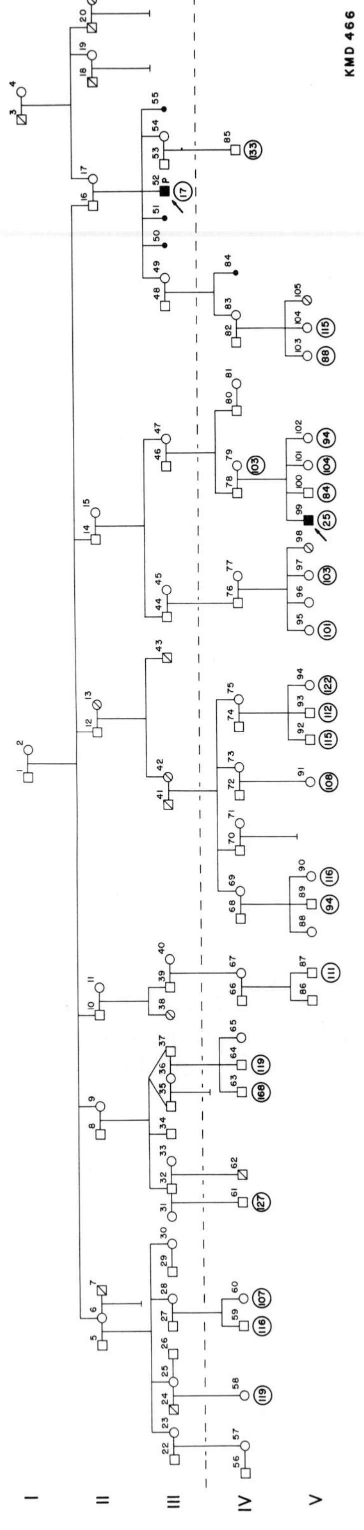

KMD 466

The Proband

The proband (52) was born in 1906, institutionalized at age 9 years and died of pneumonia in the institution in 1916. At birth one of his eyes was bulging and at 4 months he developed a hernia and had "spinal trouble." IQ 17. *Diagnosis:* unknown.

Grandparents

Not of interest.

Parents

Father (16) was secretary of a finance company.

Mother (17) had normal intelligence.

Aunts and Uncles

Not of interest.

Siblings

Sister (49) graduated from college and operates a resort, husband and child normal.

Brother (50) died at 24 hours, cause unknown, "seemed healthy, but just gradually sank away."

Brother (51) died at 36 hours, cause unknown, "just like" (50).

Sister (54) went to graduate school and is a teacher, husband and child normal.

Brother (55) died at 13 months, "gradually wasted away."

Nieces and Nephews

Not of interest.

First Cousins

Not of interest.

More Distant Relatives

(99) is a mongoloid with IQ 25.

Family Summary

The proband, IQ 17, was a deformed, rather low-grade retardate with a bulging eye, hernia and spinal abnormality. He and a distant relative, a mongoloid, were the only known retardates in this family. Three of the proband's brothers died in infancy of malnutrition and general "decline," cause unknown. The proband's parents, a prosperous, intelligent couple, had six children and three grandchildren. One of the grandchildren died in infancy, cause unknown.

Retardation of proband of unknown origin.

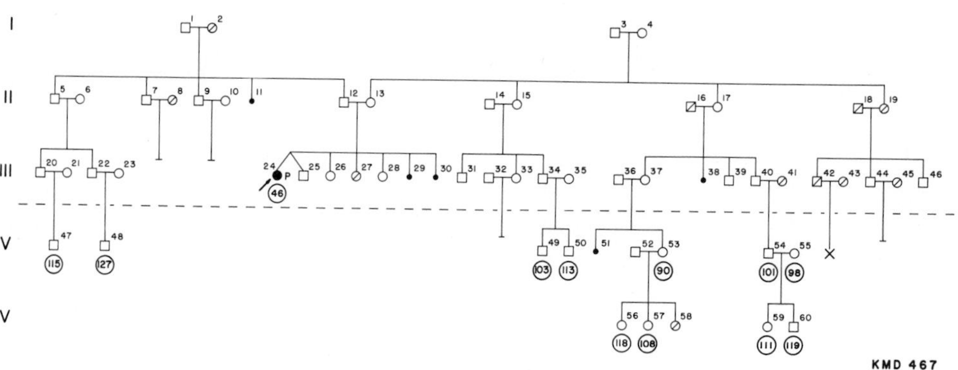

KMD 467

The Proband

The proband (24) was born in 1897, institutionalized at age 18 years and was still in the institution in 1961. She was a healthy child with no history of early trauma. After the death of her mother when the proband was 9 years old, she went to live with several relatives until she was adopted. Her adoptive mother found her to be quite unreliable, unable to progress in school and promiscuous. IQ 46. *Diagnosis:* undifferentiated mental retardation.

Grandparents

Not of interest.

Parents

Father (12) had normal intelligence but was an alcoholic and immoral. He gave his children away after his wife died.

Mother (13) was a teacher.

Aunts and Uncles

Not of interest.

Siblings

Brother (25), twin to the proband, has normal intelligence and is single.

Sister (26) had normal intelligence. She died of measles at age 9 years.

Sister (27) died from pneumonia at age 3 years.

Sister (28) was adopted by her aunt. She has normal intelligence and is single.

Sister (29) died from "cold" at age 8 months.

Sister (30) died of cholera infantum at age 11 months.

Nieces and Nephews

None.

First Cousins

Not of interest.

More Distant Relatives

Not of interest.

Family Summary

The proband, IQ 46, was the only retarded person in this enterprising and well educated family. The maternal grandmother was a pioneer worker for women's rights and several other relatives were interested in politics and writing. The reproductive rate was very low. The proband's parents had seven children, no grandchildren, and the seven maternal and paternal aunts and uncles had 12 children and apparently only seven grandchildren (one family is not accounted for).

Retardation of proband of unknown origin.

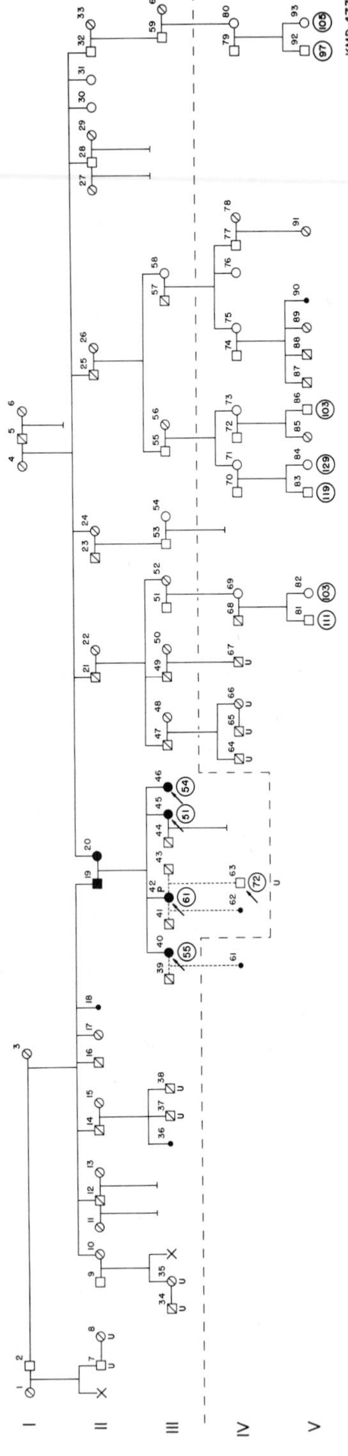
KMD 473

KMD 473

The Proband

The proband (42) was born in 1892. She was institutionalized at age 21 years, sterilized and discharged in 1928, readmitted in 1929 and died of cancer in the institution in 1942. Her birth and early years were uneventful and she had no stigmata. She was in the fifth grade when she left school at age 15 years. At age 16 years she was sent to a reformatory for immorality. Two years later she was released and in 1912 had a syphilitic, illegitimate child who died in infancy. During her second illegitimate pregnancy she was institutionalized for the first time. Her home environment was very poor. IQ 61. *Diagnosis:* undifferentiated mental retardation.

Grandparents

Not of interest.

Parents

Father (19) was an ignorant laborer with a mental age of approximately 10 years.

Mother (20) was epileptic and retarded.

Aunts and Uncles

Not of interest.

Siblings

Sister (40) was institutionalized in 1904 at age 18 years and is still in an institution in another state. She had an illegitimate, syphilitic child who died at birth. IQ 55.

Sister (45) was institutionalized in 1920 at age 30 years, sterilized eight years later and was still in the institution in 1961. She had been a prostitute and was married at one time. She had a negative Wassermann upon admission in 1920. In 1950 she was given a physical and neurological examination by J. A. Böök, M.D., and John Schut, M.D. Their diagnosis was imbecility with parkinsonism. IQ 51.

Sister (46) was institutionalized in 1920 at age 21 years, sterilized in 1928 and was still in the institution in 1961. In 1950 she was given a physical and neurological examination by Dr. Böök and Dr. Schut. Their diagnosis was dementia, idiocy and parkinsonism. IQ 54.

Children

Son (62) died of syphilis at age 2 months.

Son (63) was born in the institution. He was placed in a foster home, later joined the army and is unknown at the present time. IQ 72 at age 11 years, and also 72 at age 29 years. The fathers of these boys were unknown.

Nieces and Nephews

Only (61) who died at birth.

First Cousins

Paternal cousins unknown.

Maternal cousins not of interest.

More Distant Relatives

Not of interest.

Family Summary

The proband, IQ 61, her parents and her three siblings were all retardates of about the same grade. The proband's mother was also epileptic. The home environment was so poor that the institutionalized girls could not go home to live after their sterilization operations. The proband and her sisters were promiscuous, but there was no evidence that they had acquired syphilitic infections as children. The proband's surviving illegitimate child had an IQ of 72 and was reared in a foster home. The proband's parents had four children and three grandchildren, two of whom died in infancy.

Retardation of proband of unknown origin.

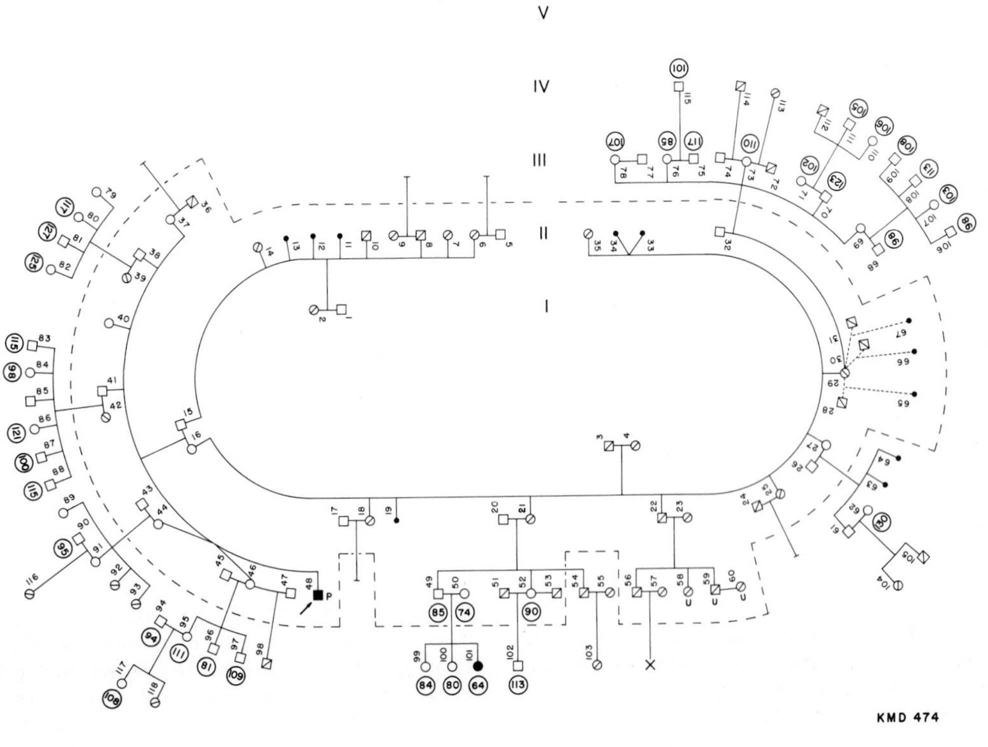
V
IV
III
II
I
P
KMD 474

KMD 474

The Proband

The proband (48) was born in 1901, institutionalized at age 7 years and died of pulmonary tuberculosis in 1914 while at home on vacation from the institution. The mother's pregnancy was abnormal with hydramnios and a duration of ten months. The mother reported that at birth the child's head was "open from the crown to the bridge of the nose" and grew out of proportion to the body. The institution records report a large head with "enormous" mouth but there was no diagnosis of hydrocephalus. He walked at age 5 years. The old record reports his IQ as middle grade, 56, but institution records classify him as low grade. *Diagnosis:* unknown.

Grandparents

Not of interest.

Parents

Father (15) and mother (16) both had normal intelligence.

Aunts and Uncles

Paternal side is of interest in that five of the six surviving children of the proband's paternal grandfather are known to have died of tuberculosis.

Maternal aunt (29) was incorrigible. She had two illegitimate children (65) and (66) and a miscarriage (67) before her marriage to (32). She was epileptic. Her child (66) died of starvation.

Siblings

Sister (37) graduated from high school and is a clerk, married but childless.

Brother (38) graduated from high school and is a salesman. Wife has unknown intelligence, children normal.

Sister (40) graduated from high school and was a nun.

Brother (41) had normal intelligence as do his children.

Sisters (44) and (46) completed the tenth grade. Both married normal men and have normal children.

Nieces and Nephews

Not of interest.

First Cousins

Not of interest.

More Distant Relatives

(101) has an IQ of 64. The parents' IQ's are 85 and 74, the siblings' IQ's are 84 and 80.

Family Summary

The proband, a congenitally malformed child with a frontal fissure from the crown to the bridge of the nose and an abnormally large head, was born after an abnormal and unusually long pregnancy. He was a middle- to low-grade retardate. The only other retarded person known in this kindred is one first cousin's child with IQ 64. The proband's parents had seven children and 18 grandchildren.

Retardation of proband of unknown origin.

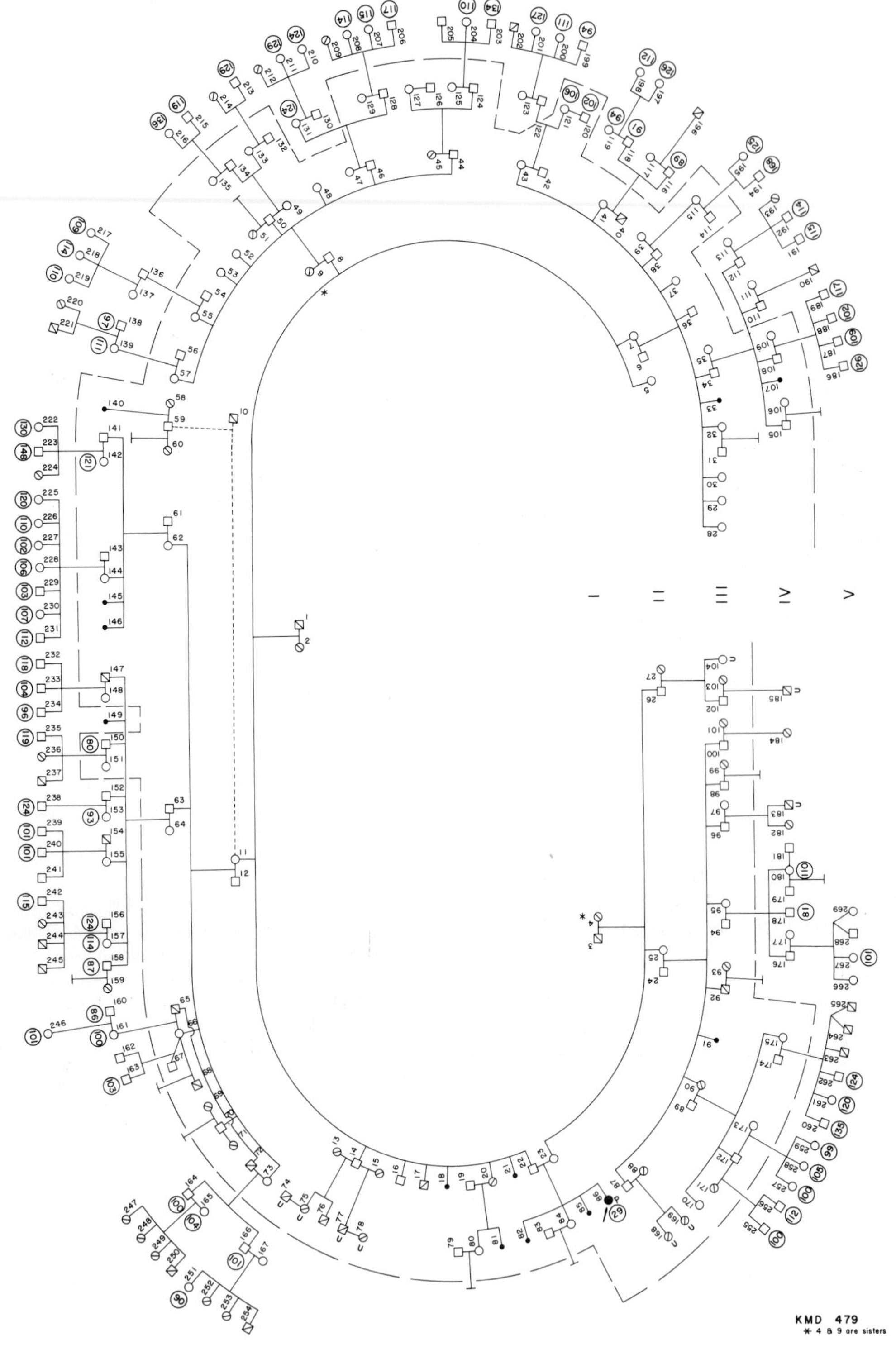
I
II
III
IV
V
KMD 479
* 4 & 9 are sisters

KMD 479

The Proband

The proband (86) was born in 1904, institutionalized at age 7 years and died of lobar pneumonia in the institution in 1925. She was weak at birth and developed very slowly, but her birth and early development were uneventful and she had no stigmata. She walked at age 4½ years and never learned to talk very much. She was reared in a good home. IQ 29. *Diagnosis:* undifferentiated mental retardation.

Grandparents

Not of interest.

Parents

Father (22) was a successful merchant.

Mother (23) had normal intelligence.

Aunts and Uncles

Not of interest.

Siblings

Brother (82) died of bronchitis and convulsions at 8 months. He was considered "very bright."

Sister (84) went to high school. She is married but childless.

Brother (85) died of hydrocephalus at age 1 year. He was born with facial paralysis on one side.

Nieces and Nephews

None.

First Cousins

Not of interest.

More Distant Relatives

First cousin (34) had a child (107) who died of spina bifida at age 5 months.

First cousin (59) had a child (140) who died of "congestion of the brain" at 13 months.

Family Summary

The proband, IQ 29, was the only known retarded person in this family, although a brother died of "water on the brain" at age 1 year and two children of first cousins died of causes indicative of hydrocephalus. There was no suggestion of the proband's having had hydrocephalus, however. The proband's parents had four children, no grandchildren.

Retardation of proband of unknown origin.

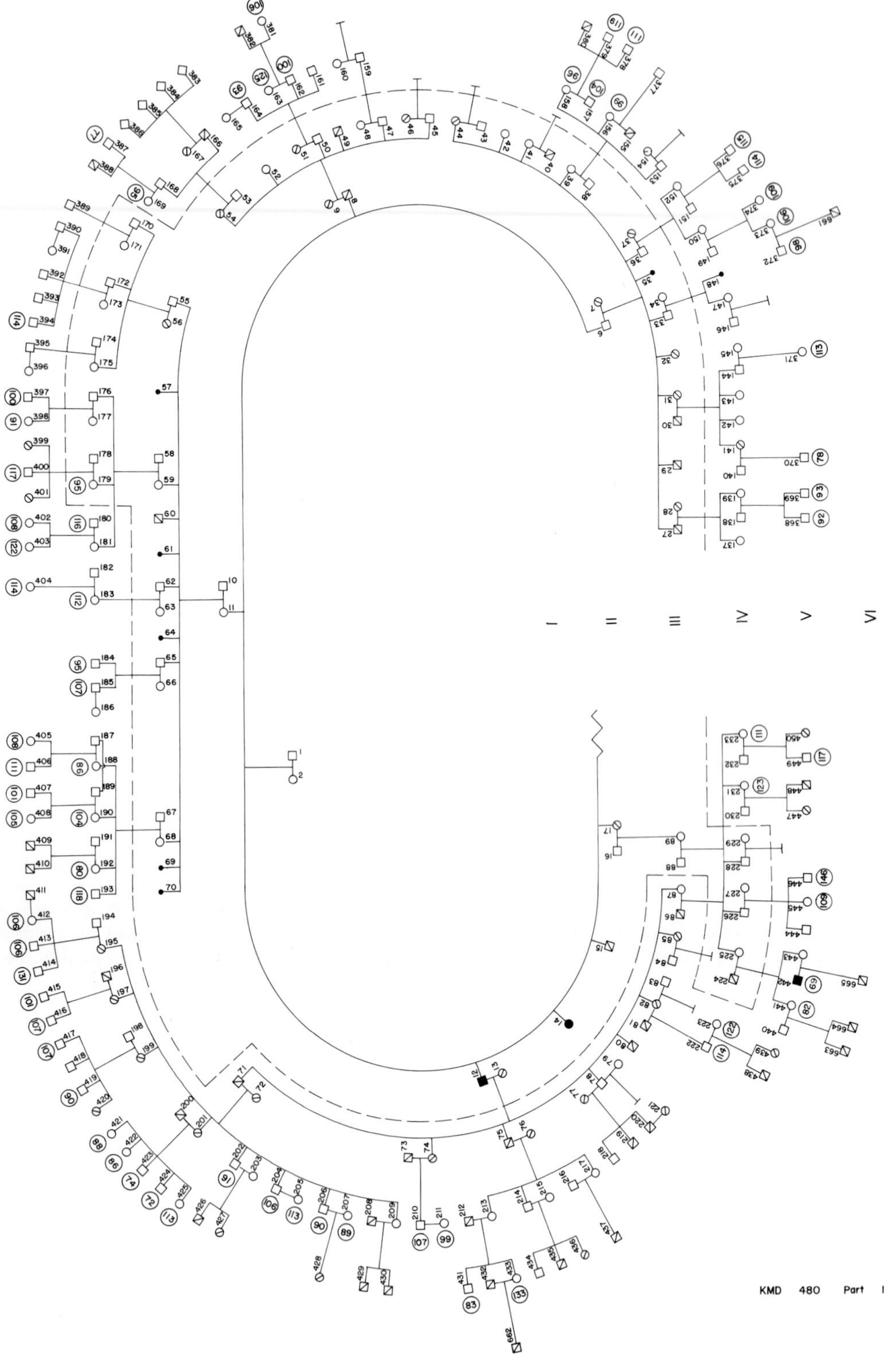
I
II
III
IV
V
VI
KMD 480 Part I

KMD 480

The Proband

The proband (106) was born in 1903, institutionalized at age 12 years and was still in the institution in 1961. His birth and childhood were uneventful and he grew up in a good home. He had lateral curvature of the spine and a deformed palate; the latter was corrected by an operation. He talked at age 6 years and attended school for one year but learned little. IQ 41. *Diagnosis:* undifferentiated mental retardation.

Grandparents

Not of interest.

Parents

Father (18) was a clerk and a good salesman but subject to "spells" during which he seemed unbalanced.

Mother (19) had normal intelligence.

Aunts and Uncles

Paternal uncle (12) and paternal aunt (14) were retarded.

Siblings

Brothers (90), (96), (98) and (100) and sisters (93) and (95) all have normal intelligence. (98) was classified as retarded originally, but later took a business course and works in a creamery. (100) was also classified as retarded, but he is president of a trucking company now.

All the children of the proband's siblings have normal intelligence.

Sister (103) was a waitress and is retarded, children normal.

Brother (104) was in a reformatory at one time. He is a truck driver and was classified as retarded. He is married but childless.

Nieces and Nephews

Not of interest.

First Cousins

Not of interest.

More Distant Relatives

(443), a high school graduate in the 52nd percentile, married a laborer with IQ 69.

Family Summary

The proband, IQ 41, a paternal uncle and aunt and two siblings were retarded, all of high grade except the proband and possibly his aunt. The proband's home was good and, with the exception of a reformatory term for one brother and some kind of undiagnosed attacks of the father, there is no record of social or mental problems among the relatives. The proband's parents had nine children and ten grandchildren. All the grandchildren are known to have normal intelligence except one for whom no school records are available.

Retardation of proband of unknown origin.

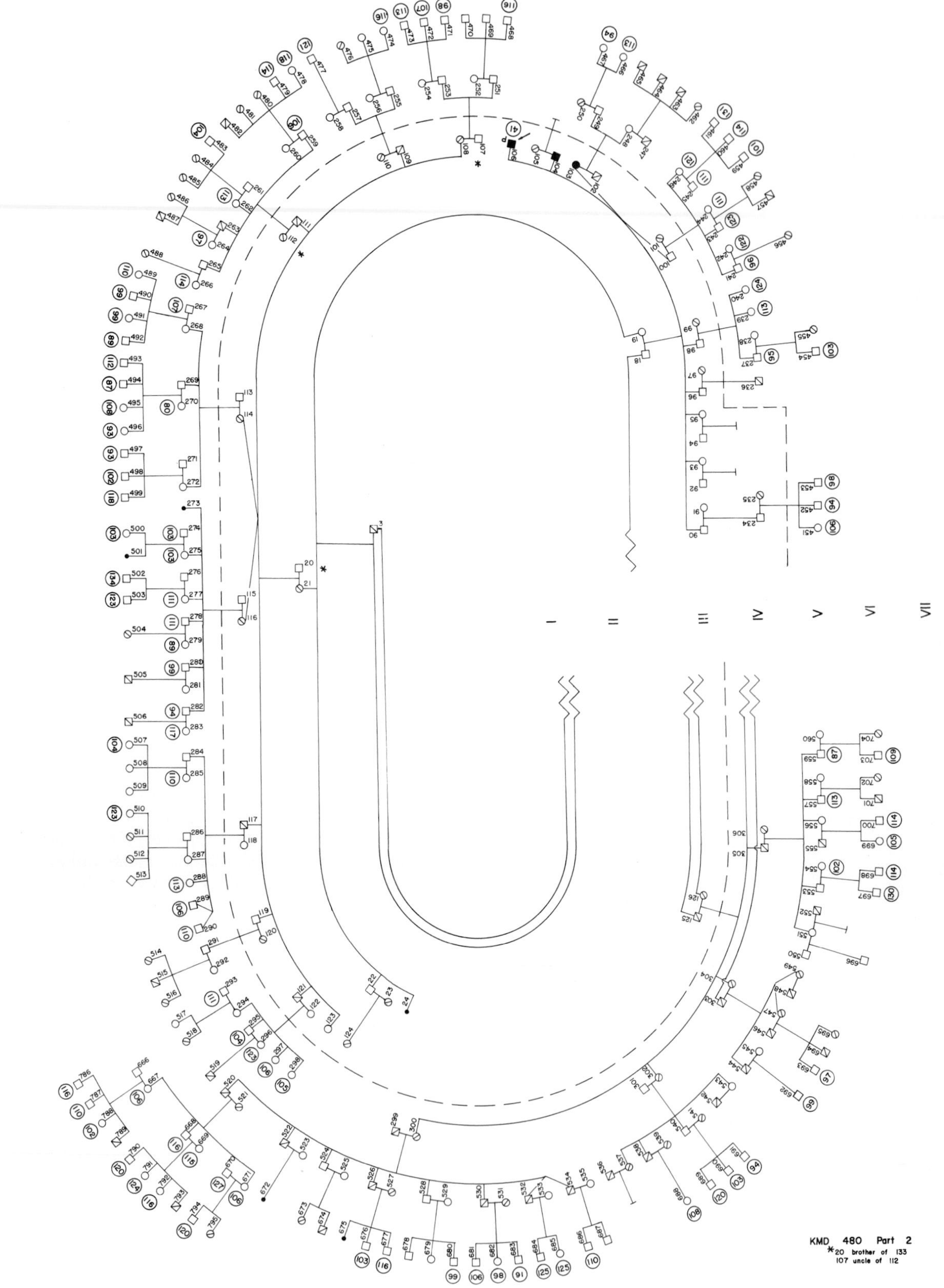
I
II
III
IV
V
VI
VII
KMD 480 Part 2
*20 brother of 133
107 uncle of 112

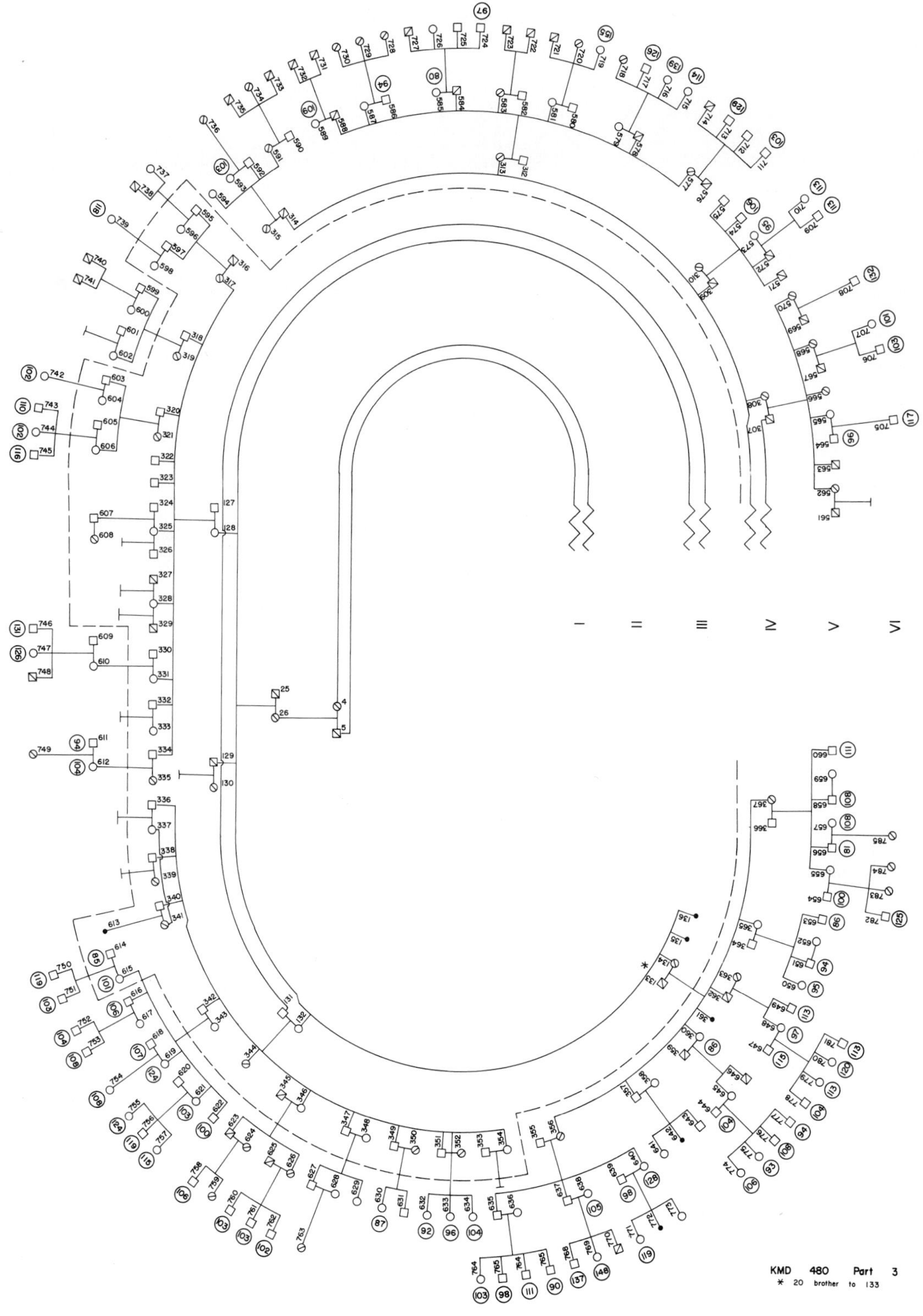
I
II
III
IV
V
VI
KMD 480 Part 3
* 20 brother to 133

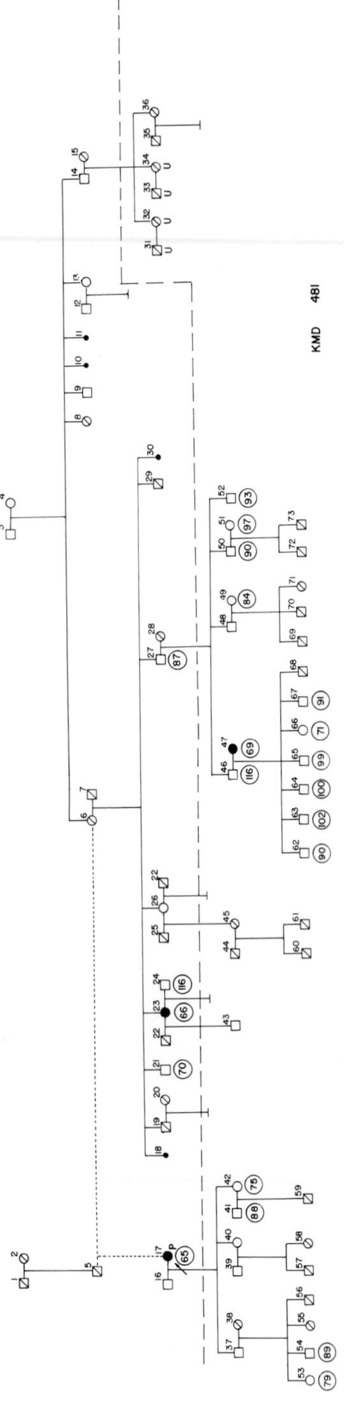

KMD 481
I
II
III
IV
V

KMD 481

The Proband

The proband (17) was born in 1898, institutionalized at age 17 years and discharged to relatives in 1918. She married a cabinet maker with normal intelligence (16) and had three children, (37), (40) and (42), two normal and one with a borderline IQ of 75. She was incorrigible and while working as a nursemaid set her employer's house on fire three times. She was sent to a girls' reformatory for arson at age 21 years and had also been in court several times for petty thievery. Her home environment was kind and prosperous despite the fact she was an illegitimate child. Her birth and early development were uneventful. She attended school until the age of 14 years when she was still in the third grade. IQ 65. *Diagnosis:* undifferentiated mental retardation.

Grandparents

Not of interest.

Parents

Father (5) was an alcoholic, promiscuous and a thief. His intelligence was unknown.

Mother (6) was incorrigible. She had two illegitimate pregnancies, but married the father of the second child shortly before its birth. Her intelligence was unknown.

Aunts and Uncles

No paternal relatives known.

Maternal relatives not of interest.

Siblings

No full siblings.

Half Siblings

Half sister (18) died at age 3 months.

Half brother (19) was incorrigible and slow in school. He is a married, but childless, millworker who finished the fourth grade at age 14 years.

Half brother (21) is an unmarried, childless laborer with IQ 70.

Half sister (23) divorced her first husband (22) who then became the second husband of her sister (26). (23) then married a laborer with IQ 116 who had been in prison for burglary. IQ of (23) is 66. Her only child has normal intelligence.

Half sister (26) was sent to an orphanage from her aunt's home because she was so hard to manage. The orphanage reported she had normal intelligence.

Half brother (27) is a laborer with IQ 87.

Half brother (29) died of diphtheria at age 5 years.

(30) self-induced abortion which caused the mother's death. The father of the above children was an alcoholic, abusive laborer of unknown intelligence.

Children

Son (37) completed the tenth grade at age 18 years. He is an IBM operator. His wife (38) seemed very dull in telephone conversations. She could not remember or calculate the birthdates of her four children.

Daughter (40) graduated from high school and married a bookkeeper.

Daughter (42) has had three intelligence tests with scores of 75 at age 15 years, 69 at age 16 years and 72 at age 19 years. Her husband (41) completed the eleventh grade and is a laborer, IQ 88, who was imprisoned for forgery.

Grandchildren

Most are too young to test, (53) has a borderline IQ of 79.

Nieces and Nephews

None.

Children of Half Siblings

(46), with IQ 116, married (47) who went to a special school and has an IQ of 69. One of their seven children (66) now attends the same special school. She has an IQ of 71.

First Cousins

Unknown.

More Distant Relatives

Not of interest.

Family Summary

The proband, IQ 65, was an illegitimate child who was convicted of arson and theft. After she left the institution she married a man of normal intelligence and had two normal children and a third with a borderline IQ of 75. One grandchild has an IQ of 79. The proband had one retarded half sibling with IQ 66. One nephew, with IQ 116, married a woman with IQ 69 and one of their children, IQ 71, is in special classes. The proband's paternal grandparents, parents and three half siblings were behavior problems in school and in society. The proband's parents had one child and three grandchildren. The total reproduction in this family was low. The proband had six half siblings who survived to adulthood, but these six persons had only six children. The IQ's of the last two generations show definite regression toward the mean. However, the total family picture does not fit either the genetic or environmental categories classification.

Retardation of proband of unknown origin.

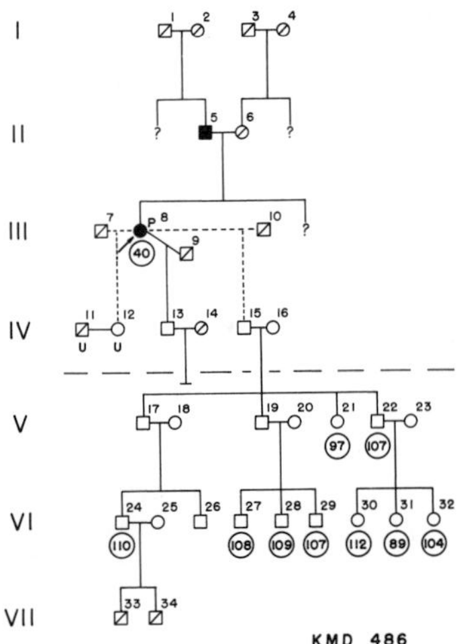

KMD 486

KMD 486

The Proband

The proband (8) was born in 1858, institutionalized at age 31 years and died of acute dilation of the heart in the institution in 1916. Nothing is known of her early life except that she was reared in a foster home. She had two illegitimate children and one legitimate child. After her husband deserted her she became quite promiscuous and was institutionalized. IQ 40. *Diagnosis:* undifferentiated mental retardation.

Grandparents

Unknown.

Parents

Father (5) was a retarded cobbler.

Mother (6) had unknown intelligence.

Aunts and Uncles

Nothing is known about possible siblings of (5) and (6).

Siblings

Nothing is known about possible siblings of the proband.

Children

Daughter (12), illegitimate, was reared by the proband's foster father and could not be found for the follow-up. She had normal intelligence.

Son (13) was reared in the state orphanage. He is an engineer on the railroad and is married but childless.

Son (15), illegitimate, was adopted. He was a steam shovel operator who died of pulmonary edema secondary to alcoholism. His wife, children and grandchildren all have normal intelligence.

Grandchildren

Four are known, all with normal intelligence, as have their spouses and children.

Nieces and Nephews

None is known.

First Cousins

None is known.

More Distant Relatives

All known great-grandchildren have normal intelligence.

Family Summary

The proband, IQ 40, and her father were retarded. The proband had three children and four known grandchildren, all with normal intelligence. It is not known whether or not the proband's parents had any other children or grandchildren.

Retardation of proband of unknown origin.

KMD 489

The Proband

The proband (59) was born in 1905, institutionalized at age 11 years, sterilized and placed under outside supervision in 1934 at age 29 years. She was discharged from guardianship in 1953. There was no history of birth injury or perinatal infection and no stigmata. Her home environment was very poor. The proband and three siblings were taken from the parents and placed in the state orphanage. IQ 67. *Diagnosis:* undifferentiated mental retardation.

Grandparents

Maternal grandmother deserted her family, but had normal intelligence.

Parents

Father (17) and mother (18) were both retarded. The father was forced to marry the mother who was 18 years younger than he.

Aunts and Uncles

Maternal aunt (20) was retarded, as was her husband and four of their five surviving children (67), (69), (71) and (72). She also had an illegitimate child (77) who had normal intelligence.

Maternal uncle (24) was retarded, as was his wife and five of their six surviving children (81), (82), (84), (86) and (88).

Maternal uncle (30) was an alcoholic and retarded.

The half sister (35) of proband's mother was a middle-grade retardate. The mother (8) of (35) was also retarded.

Siblings

Sister (52) and her husband are of unknown intelligence. Two of their ten children are retarded.

Sister (54) has an IQ of 60, husband also retarded. She is childless.

Sister (56) was a high-grade retardate, husband unknown, children normal.

Brother (57) is a retarded truck driver, wife unknown, children normal.

Brother (60) was institutionalized in 1915 at age 11 years, escaped three times and died of peritonitis in 1919. IQ 65.

Brother (61) was institutionalized in 1917 at age 10 years, escaped several times, was sterilized in 1933 and discharged. He married a widow with four children and has made a good adjustment. IQ 67.

Sister (64) went to high school and has normal intelligence. One of her seven children is retarded.

Brother (65) completed the eighth grade and is a laborer of unknown intelligence, wife unknown, one normal child, one of borderline intelligence.

Nieces and Nephews

Nephew (150) has an IQ of 48 and is deaf, wife's IQ 107, four children, three normal, one died young. (150) was institutionalized in 1926 at age 13 years and discharged in 1932.

Niece (153) with IQ 75 married a retarded man 17 years her senior with IQ 59. Their children's IQ's range from 69 to 94.

Nephew (154), brother to (150) and (153), was committed as retarded at age 16 years but was never institutionalized. He has a record of thievery. His wife has IQ 94. Their children's IQ's range from 74 to 117.

Three siblings to the above, (158), (161) and (162), have borderline IQ's of 78, 78 and 74, respectively.

Niece (195) has an IQ of 55.

First Cousins

(67) was institutionalized in 1906 at age 20 years, withdrawn two years later and died of tuberculosis in a second institution in 1923. His intelligence was never tested.

(69) is a retarded farm laborer who was married twice but had only a stillborn child by a retarded woman.

(71) was retarded.

(72), a brother to (67), (69) and (71), was institutionalized in 1906 at age 10 years and withdrawn two years later. He died single and childless.

(77) had normal intelligence, but was married several times and gave her children away to strangers.

(81) was sent to a girls' reformatory at age 12 years, institutionalized in 1927 at age 20 years, sterilized and placed under outside supervision in 1936. She married a man with IQ 81 who is a janitor and has a bad speech defect. Her IQ is 68.

(82) was an idiot who died of a brain tumor at age 3 years.

(84) was sent to a girls' reformatory for sex offenses in 1921 at age 9 years, institutionalized at age 17 years, sterilized and placed under outside supervision at age 24 years. She married a psychotic man with IQ 128.

(86) was institutionalized in 1940 at age 22 years and was placed under outside supervision seven years later. She has IQ scores of 70, 64 and 59.

(88), sister to (81), (82), (84) and (86), was institutionalized at age 18 years, sterilized and placed under outside supervision for several years but was later returned to the institution. She was married twice and has a son (206) with IQ 61 who was born in the institution. The father's IQ was 76. All the retarded cousins are the children of a retarded maternal aunt (20) and uncle (24). Institutionalization and sterilization stopped the

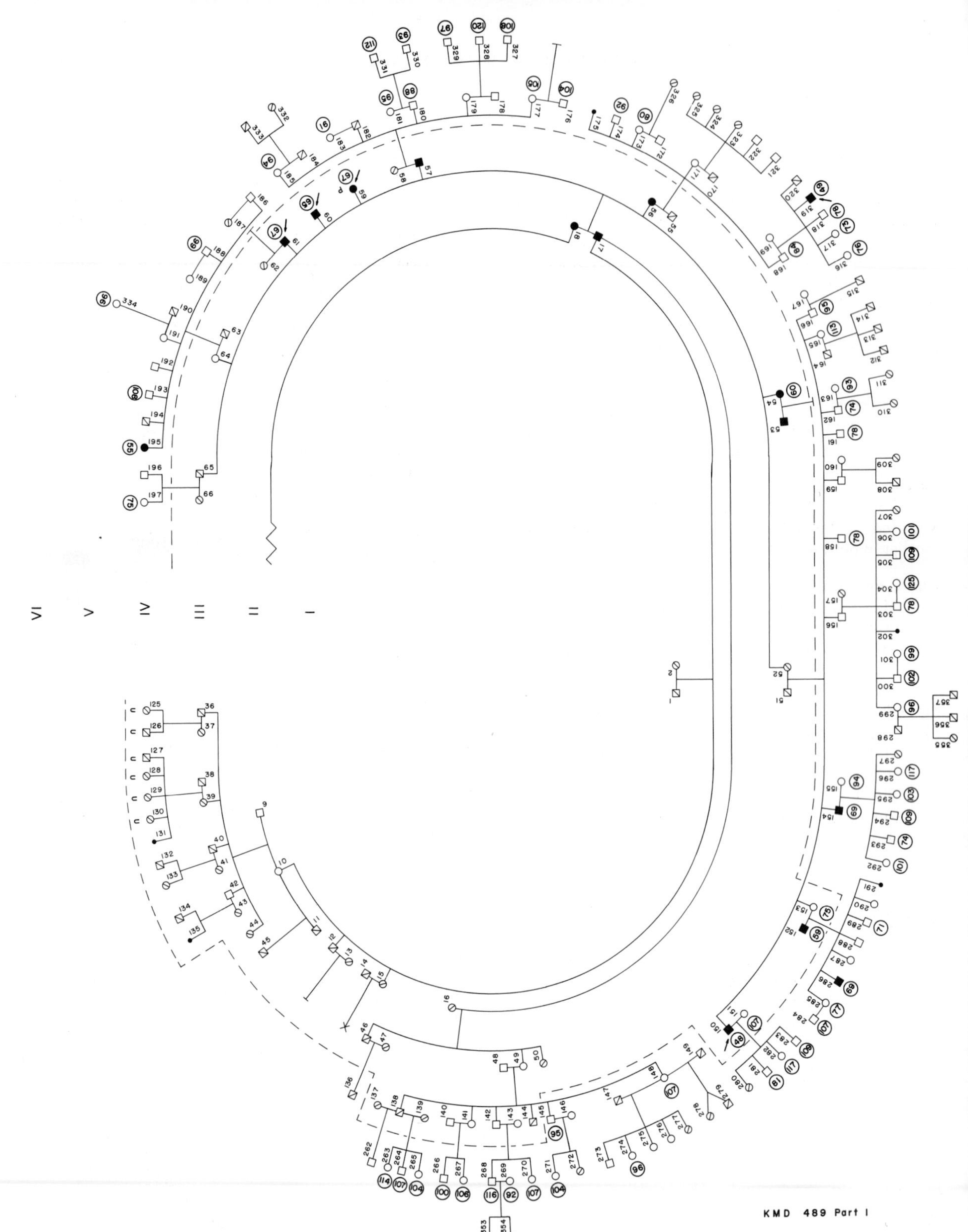

KMD 489 Part I

reproduction of the retardates in three families. (20) had seven children by two husbands and has seven surviving grandchildren, all belonging to her two normal children. (24) had seven children and only one grandchild, an institutionalized retardate.

More Distant Relatives

(206) was born in the institution and is now under outside supervision. IQ 61.

(286) has an IQ of 69. One sibling (285) has an IQ of 74 and one, (289), has an IQ of 71.

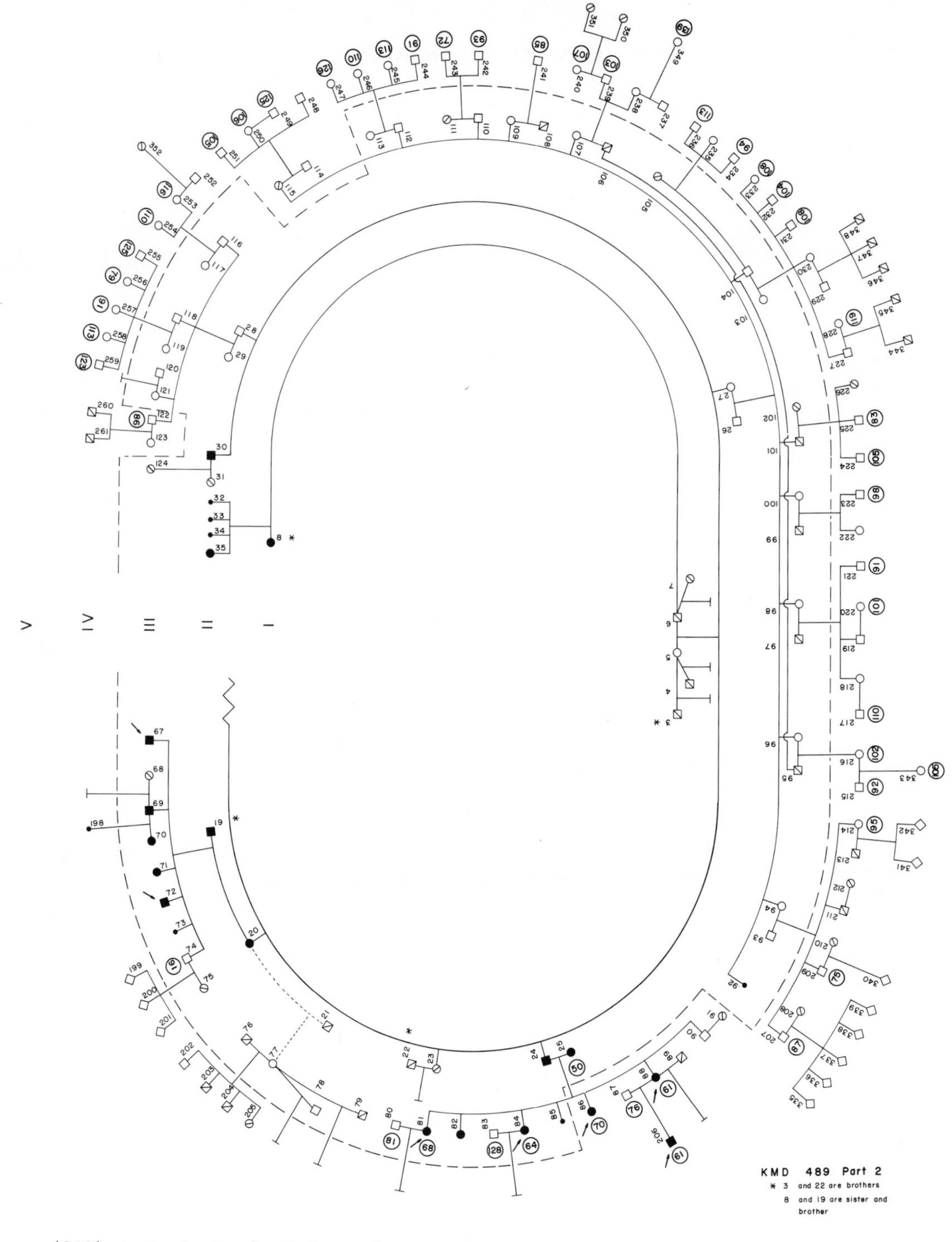

(319) is institutionalized for epilepsy and retardation, IQ 49. Three siblings (316), (317) and (318) have IQ's of 76, 73 and 78, respectively.

(330) has muscular dystrophy but an IQ of 93.

Family Summary

The proband, IQ 67, her parents, five siblings, three nephews and one niece, one maternal uncle, three maternal aunts and one maternal half aunt, nine first cousins and three more distant relatives were retarded. All but two of these were high-grade retardates. The two exceptions, one half aunt and one great-nephew, were middle-grade retardates. Twelve of these retardates were institutionalized and all are with one exception, the offspring of three matings. Institutionalization and sterilization reduced the reproductive rate in these problem families drastically.

The proband's parents had nine children, six of whom were retarded (two of the retarded reproduced) and 29 grandchildren, four of whom were retarded. While the proband's own family does not fall into either genetic category, that of (24) and (25) has three generations of retardates which puts it in the probably genetic group.

Retardation of proband of unknown origin.

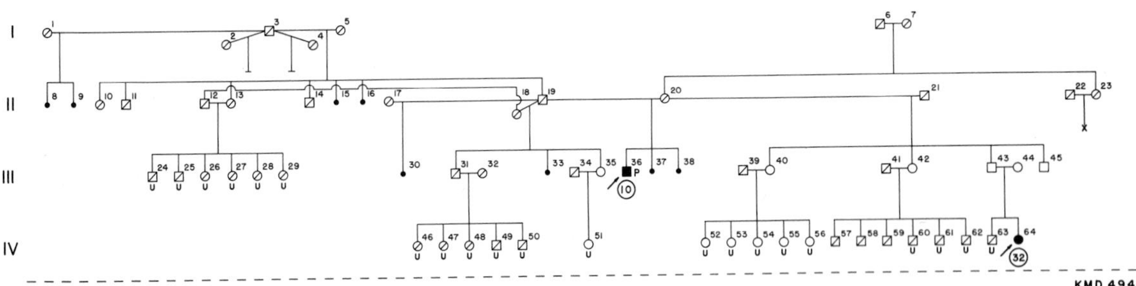
I
II
III
IV
P
10
32
KMD 494

KMD 494

The Proband

The proband (36) was born in 1890, institutionalized at age 22 years and died of pulmonary tuberculosis in the institution in 1912. He had no history of difficult birth or perinatal infection. He was blind from birth, his feet were deformed and his IQ was 10. *Diagnosis:* mental retardation with blindness.

Grandparents

Not of interest.

Parents

Father (19) was illiterate and "mentally weak." He was 80 years old when interviewed.

Mother (20) had unknown intelligence.

Aunts and Uncles

Not of interest.

Siblings

Sister (37) died of prematurity.

Brother (38) died at age 6 months. He was weak from birth.

Half Siblings

Half brother (30) died in infancy.

Half brother (31) could not be found for the follow-up.

Half sister (33) died at 4 days. She was weak from birth.

Half sister (35) had normal intelligence.

Half sisters (40) and (42) and half brothers (43) and (45) had normal intelligence, but (43) had an institutionalized retarded child who was also epileptic.

Nieces and Nephews

None.

Children of Half Siblings

(64) was institutionalized in 1911 at age 6 years and discharged in 1917. She was epileptic with IQ 32. Her epilepsy was ascribed by the mother to whooping cough at age 22 months.

First Cousins

Unknown.

More Distant Relatives

Unknown. The family could not be found for the follow-up.

Family Summary

The proband, IQ 10 and blind, and one "half niece," epileptic with IQ 32, were the only retardates known in this family. There were several infant deaths caused by prematurity or "weakness," including the proband's two siblings. The proband's parents had three children, no grandchildren. The more recent generations could not be found for the follow-up since all the known relatives have left the state, leaving no forwarding addresses.

Retardation of proband of unknown origin.

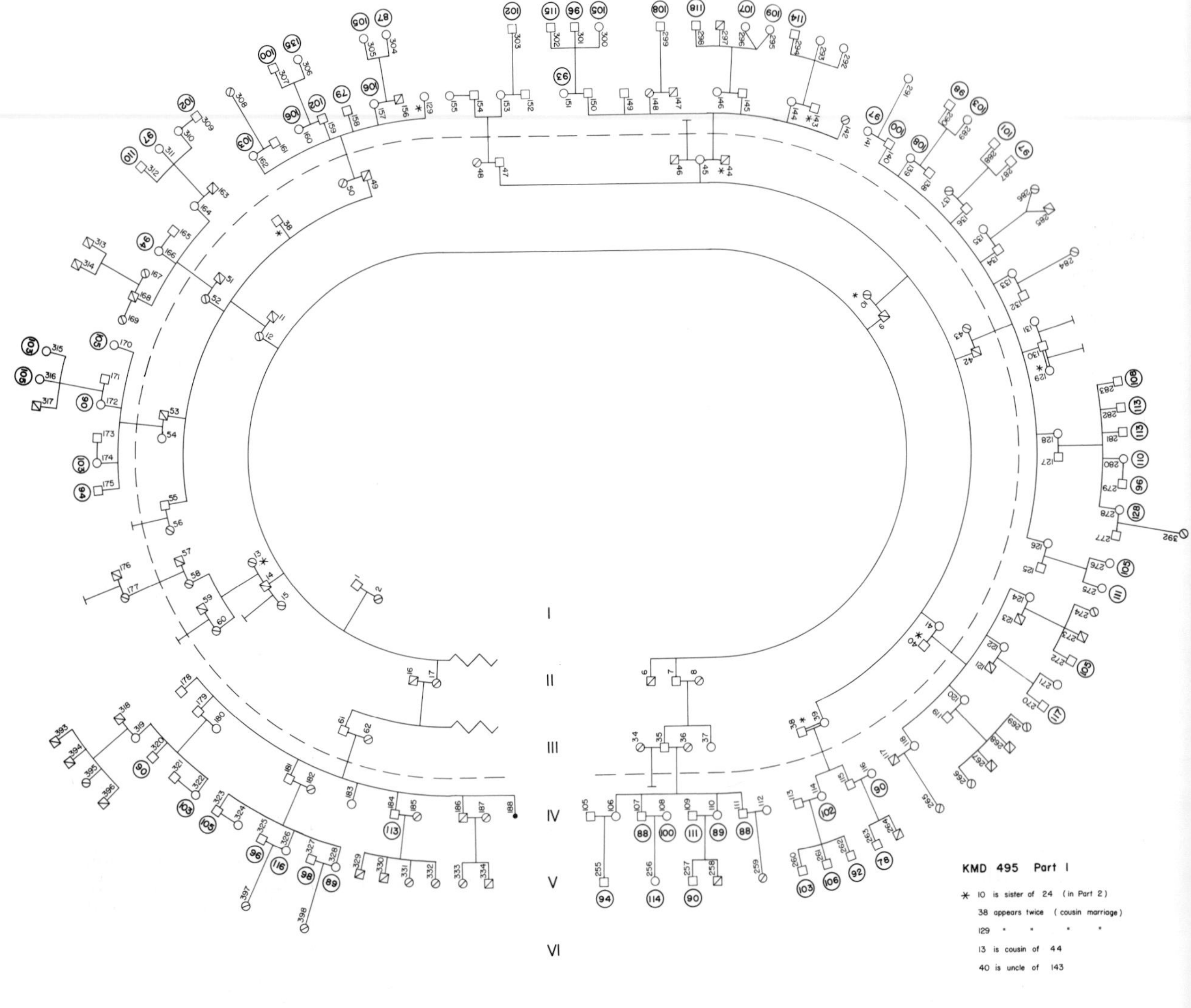

KMD 495

The Proband

The proband (104) was born in 1898, institutionalized at age 15 years, sterilized in 1929 and placed in boarding homes until her marriage in 1949. She married a man 18 years older than herself. She had been placed in an orphanage for five years before the institutionalization. She learned to read but was difficult to care for because of her violent temper and a tendency to steal. No details are known about her birth or early development except that her home environment was very poor and neglectful. She had no stigmata. IQ 57. *Diagnosis:* undifferentiated mental retardation.

Grandparents

Not of interest.

Parents

Father (27) was an alcoholic laborer with a mental age of 9 or 10 years. His second wife (26), stepmother of the proband, was a retarded woman, IQ 57, with three retarded children.

Mother (28) had unknown intelligence.

Aunts and Uncles

Paternal side not of interest. Maternal side is unknown.

Siblings

Brother (100) was imprisoned in 1937 at age 44 years for uttering and publishing. He was discharged from parole in 1941 and could not be found after that. IQ 50.

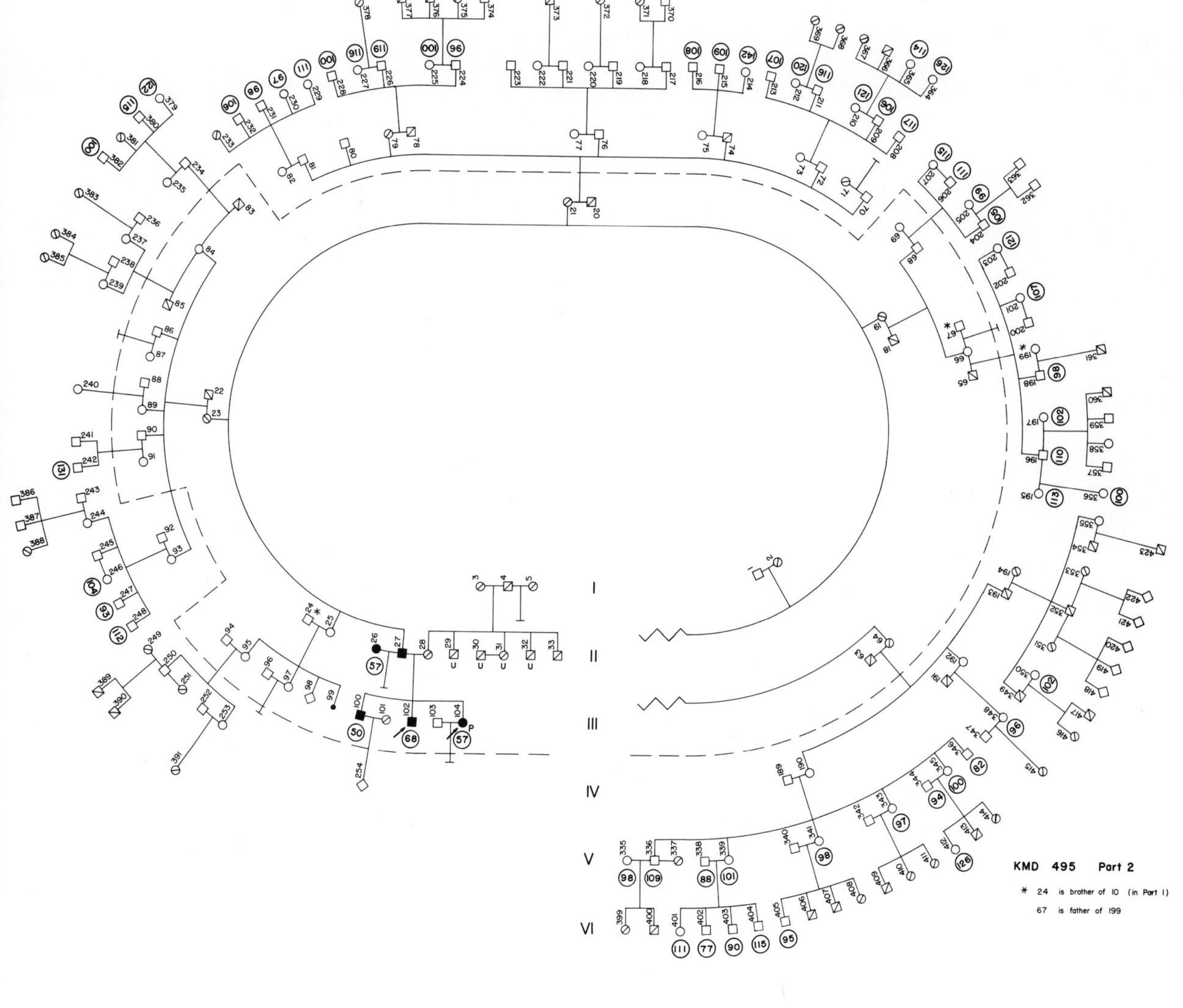

Brother (102) was institutionalized in 1910 at age 12 years. He had a violent temper and a tendency to steal. He was transferred to the institution from a mental hospital and remained until 1954 when he was discharged. He is now back in the institution. He is crippled from anterior poliomyelitis which he had in childhood. There is a possibility this infection may have caused his mental condition also. IQ 68.

Nieces and Nephews

Only one (254) known to exist. The prison records indicated that (100) had a child, but its present status is unknown.

First Cousins

Not of interest except for the first cousin marriage of (38) and (39) which resulted in the birth of two normal children.

More Distant Relatives

Not of interest.

Family Summary

The proband, IQ 57, his father and his two siblings were the only retarded persons known in this family. One sibling had a prison record and the other was difficult to control because of his violent temper and thievery. This latter person exhibited some symptoms of postpoliomyelitis disabilities. There was no evidence of syphilitic infections in this family. The proband herself had a violent temper and a propensity for theft. The home environment was very poor. The proband's parents had three children and probably one grandchild.

Retardation of proband of unknown origin.

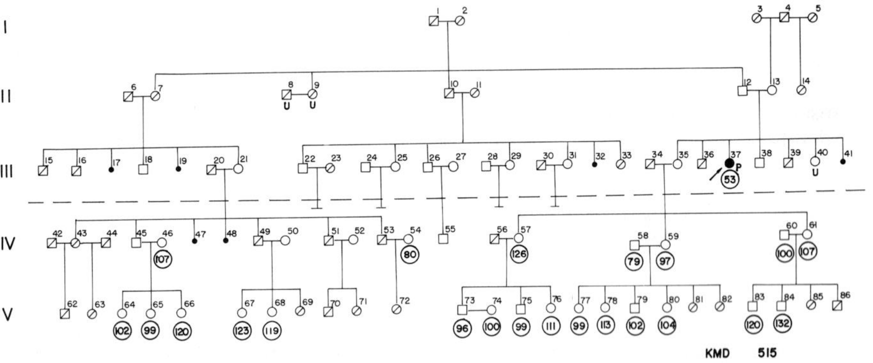
I
II
III
IV
V
P
KMD 515

KMD 515

The Proband

The proband (37) was born in 1891, institutionalized at age 19 years, transferred to a second institution in 1930 and died there of coronary occlusion, pneumonia and mental deficiency in 1957. She was fretful and ailing as a child but walked and talked at the usual time, had no history of birth injury or perinatal infection and had no stigmata. The family stated she had "brain fever" at the age of 10 years. This was not confirmed by a physician. She was slow in school from age 6 years. Institution records state "tendency to insanity." IQ 53. *Diagnosis:* undifferentiated mental retardation.

Grandparents

Unknown. They remained in Europe.

Parents

Father (12) died in a mental hospital. He was accidentaly shot in the face with resultant injury to his eyes and brain. He had normal intelligence.

Mother (13) had normal intelligence.

Aunts and Uncles

Not of interest.

Siblings

Sister (35) has normal intelligence, husband unknown, child normal.

Brother (36) died single and childless. He was a miner of unknown intelligence.

Brother (38) is a retired, unmarried and childless shipyard foreman.

Brother (39) died of pulmonary tuberculosis at age 21 years. He was a messenger boy.

Sister (40), of normal intelligence, was adopted and could not be found for the follow-up.

(41) was a miscarriage that caused the mother's death.

Nieces and Nephews

Not of interest.

First Cousins

Not of interest except that of the nine paternal cousins who survived to adulthood, only six married and only two had children, giving a total of six descendants in the next generation (excluding two who died in infancy).

More Distant Relatives

Not of interest.

Family Summary

The proband, IQ 53, was the only retarded person known in this family. She had a history of "brain fever" at age 10 years, but was slow in school from the time she started at age 6 years. The whole family is characterized by a low reproductive rate (see above). Twenty births in generation III resulted in 11 births in generation IV. The proband's parents had seven children and at least three grandchildren. One of the proband's sisters could not be found for the follow-up, so nothing is known about her reproductive history.

Retardation of proband of unknown origin.

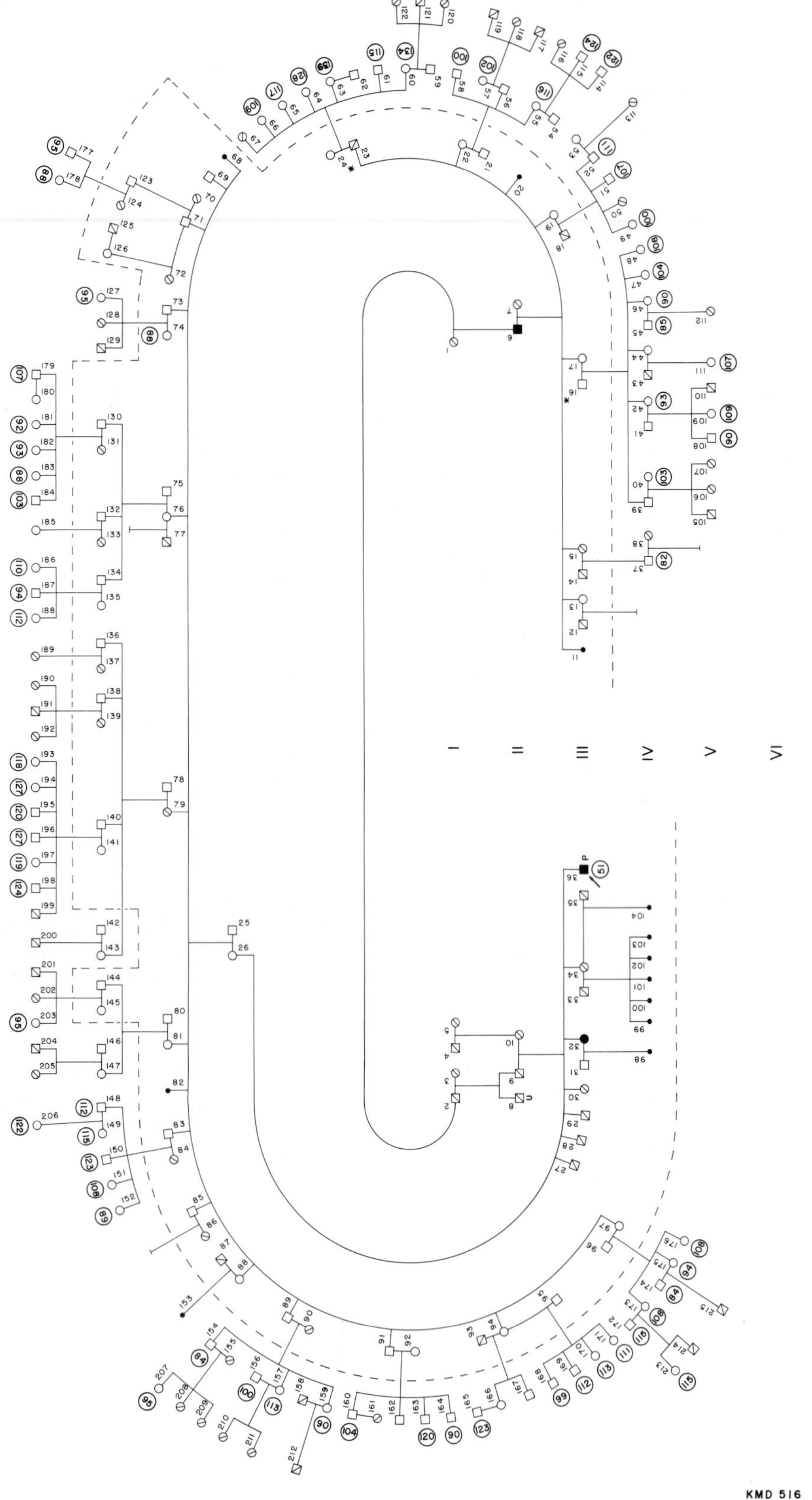

KMD 516
✱ 16 uncle to 24

KMD 516

The Proband

The proband (36) was born in 1885, institutionalized at age 30 years and died of influenzal pneumonia in the institution in 1920. He was a delicate child, learned little in school and was found living alone in a shack on a river bank. He was illiterate and wholly unable to support himself. There was no history of injury or illness in his early life and he had no stigmata. IQ 51. *Diagnosis:* undifferentiated mental retardation.

Grandparents

Unknown because they remained in Europe.

Parents

Father (9) was an alcoholic and was "sick for 20 years—couldn't work." His intelligence and that of the mother (10) was unknown.

Aunts and Uncles

No maternal relatives since the proband's mother was an only child.

Proband's father's full brother (8) is unknown. He remained in Europe. The proband's father's half brother (6) was an alcoholic, retarded painter whose wife (7) was an epileptic with unknown intelligence. He served many terms in the workhouse for non-support, cruelty and drunkenness. As far as is known, however, his children and grandchildren all have normal intelligence.

Siblings

Sister (26) had normal intelligence, as did her husband and all her known descendants.

Brothers (27), (28) and (29) and sister (30) all had unknown intelligence. They all died young.

Sister (32) was promiscuous, retarded and a drug addict. She lived in one room of a three room house that was filled with rubbish. Her husband (31), of normal intelligence, died of locomotor ataxia. Their only child (98) died at age 9 months, cause unknown.

Sister (34) was thought to have been institutionalized somewhere. She was a drug addict and wandered from town to town selling pencils. All her six children died in infancy. No estimate could be made of her intelligence.

Nieces and Nephews

Twenty-two, nine of whom died in infancy [one (68) died of convulsions, the other eight of unknown causes], the rest are known to have normal intelligence, and these are all the children of the normal sister.

First Cousins

Unknown.

More Distant Relatives

Not of interest.

Family Summary

The proband, IQ 51, one sister, and his father's half brother were retarded. The retarded sister and one of unknown intelligence were drug addicts. The father's half brother was imprisoned for non-support and drunkenness. His family had a long history of welfare help, but his children and grandchildren are all apparently normal and self-supporting. The proband's parents had eight children and 22 grandchildren. Only three of their children reproduced and of these, only the known normal sister had children who survived to adulthood, all with normal intelligence, giving the proband's parents 13 grandchildren who lived to grow up. No children of the retarded sister or the drug addict survived infancy.

Retardation of proband of unknown origin.

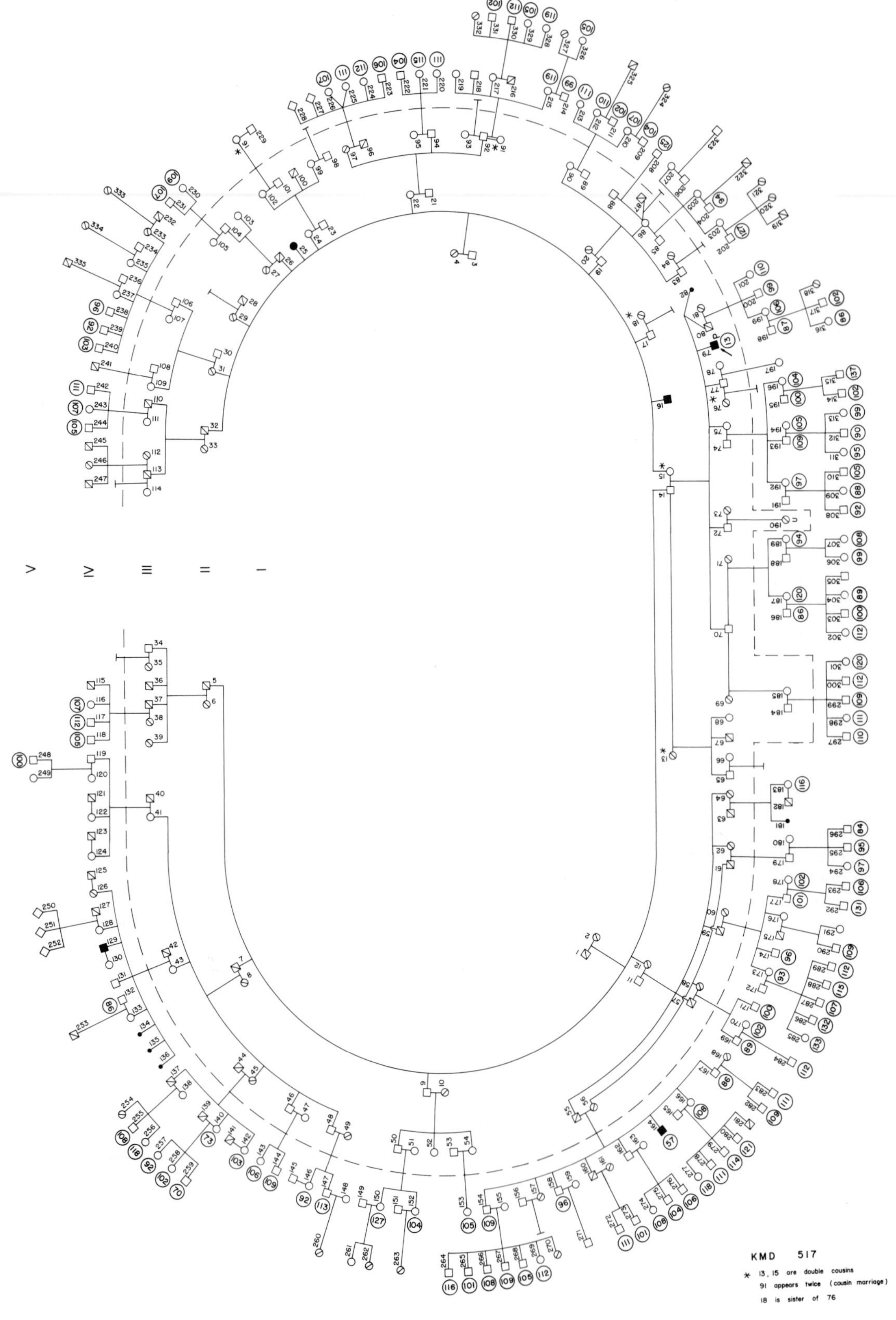
I
II
III
IV
V
KMD 517
* 13, 15 are double cousins
91 appears twice (cousin marriage)
18 is sister of 76

KMD 517

The Proband

The proband (79) was born in 1888, institutionalized at age 9 years and died of influenza in the institution in 1918. He was always a delicate child, but had no history of birth injury or perinatal infection. He had a peculiar gait. IQ 13. *Diagnosis:* undifferentiated mental retardation.

Grandparents

Not of interest.

Parents

Father (14) and mother (15) both had normal intelligence. The father was a prosperous merchant.

Aunts and Uncles

Maternal uncle (16) could support himself as a farmer but was considered retarded. He died unmarried and childless.

Maternal aunt (25) was a high-grade retardate who died unmarried and childless.

Siblings

Brother (70) was a salesman with normal intelligence and normal children.

Brother (72) was last heard of when he escaped from a reformatory in 1912 while under sentence for forgery. He had normal intelligence, wife and child unknown.

Sister (75) graduated from high school, husband and children normal.

Brother (77) was a bookkeeper and later a rancher. His only child is normal.

Brother (80) is a farmer of unknown intelligence. His children have normal intelligence.

(82) was the stillborn twin of (80).

Half Siblings

Half brother (65) graduated from high school and is a merchant.

Half brother (67) committed suicide.

Half sister (68) graduated from high school and is a clerk.

Nieces and Nephews

All have normal intelligence.

The proband's half siblings had no children.

First Cousins

Not of interest, except for the consanguineous marriage of first cousins (91) and (92) that resulted in the birth of four normal children.

More Distant Relatives

First cousin's (43) child (129) was in an ungraded class and is a pressman's helper. His wife has normal intelligence.

First cousin's (55) child (164) is an unmarried and childless laborer with IQ 57.

Family Summary

The proband, IQ 13, was the only low-grade retardate known in this family. A maternal uncle and aunt and two children of first cousins were high-grade retardates. The proband had no history of difficult delivery or childhood illness. The proband's parents had seven children and 11 grandchildren.

Retardation of proband of unknown origin.

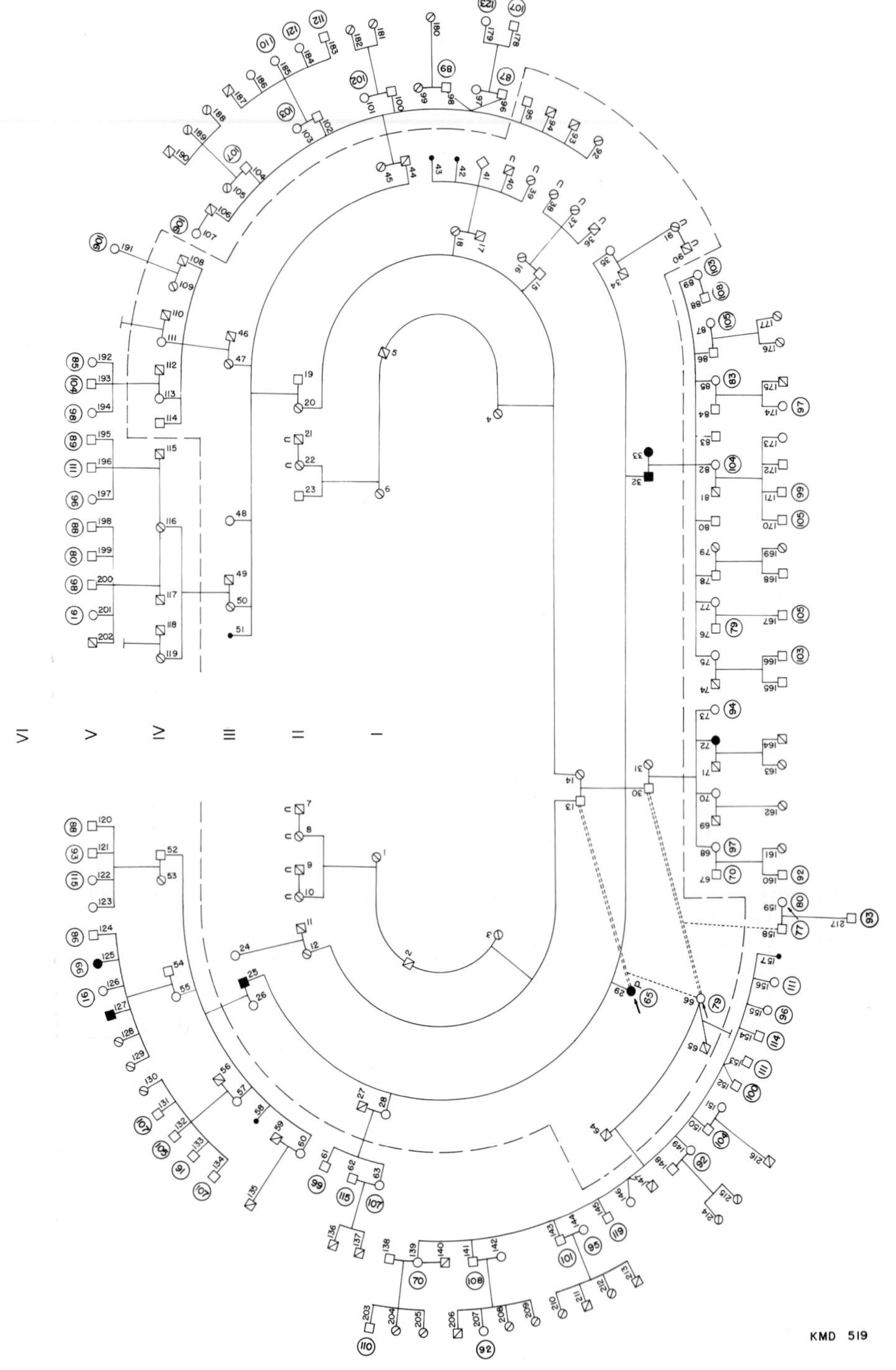
I
II
III
IV
V
VI
KMD 519

KMD 519

The Proband

The proband (29) was born in 1887 and institutionalized at age 15 years when illegitimately pregnant by her father. She was discharged in 1910, but readmitted in 1913 and died of exophthalmic goiter in the institution in 1933. She attended school until age 15 years, but "never picked up much," and remained in the first grade all the time. Her birth was uneventful, she had no history of perinatal infection and had no stigmata. She grew up in a very poor environment. IQ 65. *Diagnosis:* undifferentiated mental retardation.

Grandparents

Not of interest.

Aunts and Uncles

Not of interest.

Parents

Father (13) was a cooper and "below par" mentally.

Mother (14) had "no judgment" and did not take care of her family, but was not classified as retarded.

Siblings

Brother (25) left school at age 15 years when in the sixth grade. He is a retarded laborer and his wife is a teacher. There are three normal children, but two retarded grandchildren.

Sister (28) left school at age 15 years when in the sixth grade. She was promiscuous and "mentally slow," husband unknown, children normal.

Brother (30) completed the sixth grade and is a farmer of normal intelligence, wife unknown, one child retarded, three normal.

Brother (32) completed the fifth grade and is a retarded farmer, wife also retarded, but all nine of their children have normal intelligence.

Sister (35) died at age 23 years. She had normal intelligence.

Child

Daughter (66) lived with her aunt in a very poor environment and became promiscuous herself. She was sent to a girls' reformatory in 1917 at age 14 years, was paroled to another relative but was returned to the reformatory when she had an illegitimate child in 1921. The paternity of this child was not legally established, but was ascribed to her uncle (30). She left the reformatory when she married in 1924. She is now a practical nurse and is married a second time. IQ 79.

Nieces and Nephews

Niece (72), sister to (68), repeated the first, fourth, fifth, and seventh grades, finally leaving school at age 16 years in the seventh grade.

Grandchildren

Granddaughter (139) has an IQ of 70. Her first husband, a contractor, divorced her.

Grandson (147) died of accidental carbon monoxide poisoning at age 26 years. He was up for trial at age 25 years for indecent exposure.

Grandson (158) was given a medical discharge by the army in 1944 and hospitalized in 1947 because he was "emotionally disturbed and rather violent." In 1948 he was sentenced to the state reformatory for carnal knowledge. He is now out of prison. His IQ is 77. His wife (159) was institutionalized as retarded at age 15 years in 1941 and discharged in 1944. She divorced (158) in 1948, married again in 1950 and has moved out of the state. Her IQ is 80. Their child has an IQ of 93.

First Cousins

Not of interest.

More Distant Relatives

(125) has an IQ of 66.

(127), brother to (125), is a high-grade retardate. Both are children of niece (55).

Family Summary

The proband, IQ 65, two brothers, a niece and two more distant relatives were retarded. The home environment was a very poor one of promiscuity and incest. The proband had a child by her father and this child had a son by her uncle. This son is psychotic with IQ 77. One normal niece married a retarded man. The proband's daughter had an IQ of 79 and her grandchildren have an IQ range from 70 to 119. The proband's parents had six children and 22 grandchildren. The proband herself had one child and 15 grandchildren, one with IQ 70, one borderline and psychotic, one a delinquent.

Retardation of proband of unknown origin.

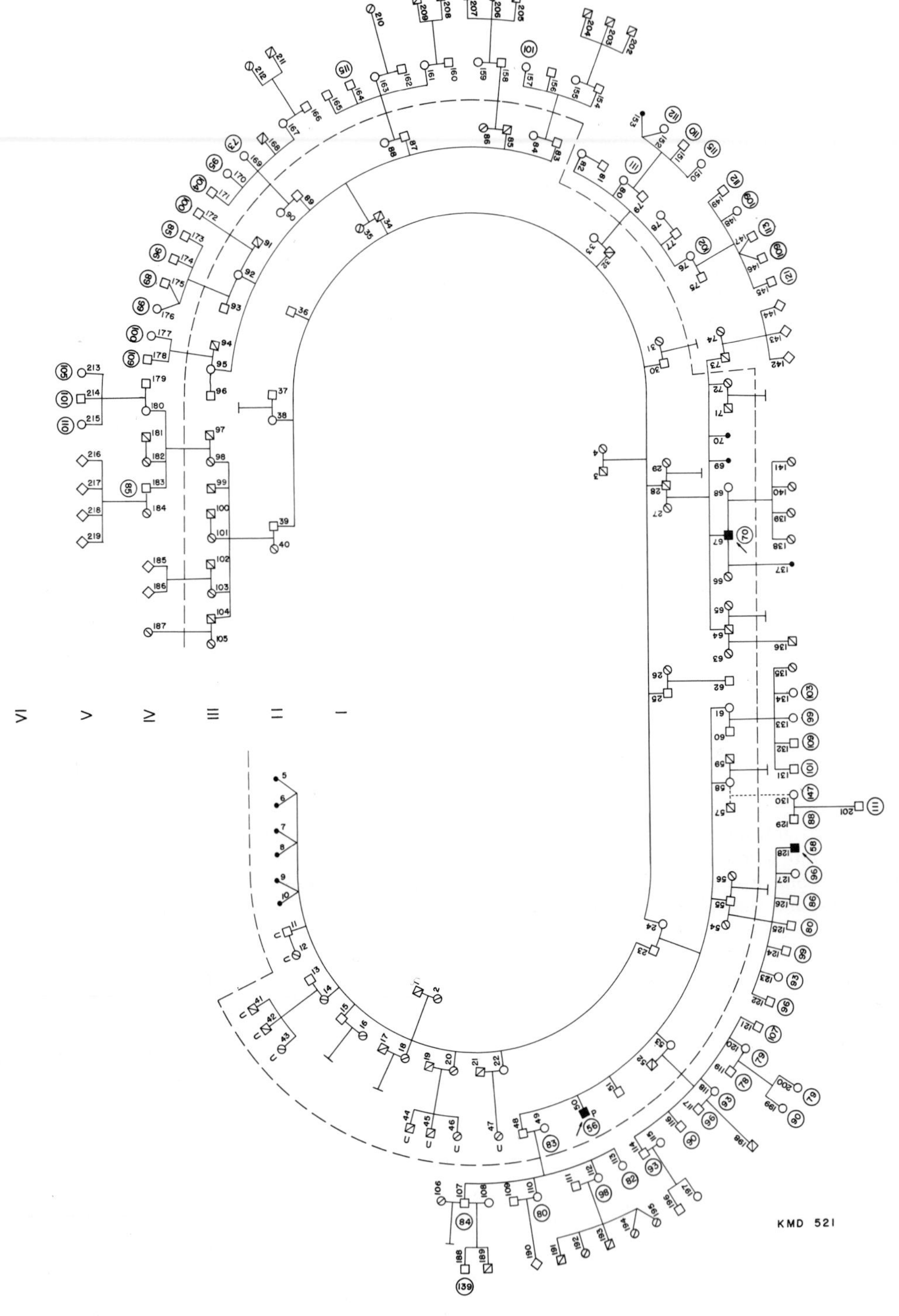
I
II
III
IV
V
VI
KMD 521

KMD 521

The Proband

The proband (50) was born in 1900, institutionalized at age 14 years and was killed by a truck while at home on vacation in 1916. The mother reported he was apparently bright until he had measles at the age of 3 years. After this he became deaf and stopped talking. He lived in a good home and attended school for two years but learned little. IQ 56. *Diagnosis:* mental retardation with deafness.

Grandparents

Not of interest.

Parents

Father (23) was a brakeman on the railroad. He was an irresponsible alcoholic who abandoned his family and was never heard of again.

Mother (24) had normal intelligence.

Aunts and Uncles

Not of interest.

Siblings

Brothers (48) and (51) and sisters (53) and (61) all had normal intelligence, children also normal.

Brother (55) has normal intelligence, but has been hospitalized for paranoia. He had a retarded child.

Sister (58) had normal intelligence. She had an illegitimate child (130) with IQ 147.

Sister (61) has normal intelligence, as do her husband and children.

Nieces and Nephews

Niece (113) was hospitalized in 1934 at age 11 years for a "conduct disorder" and has remained in the hospital ever since. Her IQ is 82.

Nephew (124) has defective speech but an IQ of 99.

Nephew (125) is partly deaf and has an IQ of 80.

Nephew (128) is in the state school for educable retarded with IQ 58. (124), (125) and (128) are all brothers.

First Cousins

(67) has been a social problem for a long time. His stepmother refused to keep him so he was placed in boarding homes. He was a troublemaker at school, was arrested for shoplifting and was committed as retarded in 1942 at age 17 years. He married an illegitimately pregnant woman but soon deserted her, then married a second illegitimately pregnant woman who claimed he abused her. He has a violent temper, is considered to be psychotic and is now in the annex for defective delinquents in a reformatory. His IQ is 70. The father of (67), the proband's maternal uncle (28), kept trying to trick welfare agencies into supporting him while he had a job in a defense plant.

More Distant Relatives

Not of interest.

Family Summary

The proband, IQ 56 and deaf from measles, his nephew and one first cousin were retarded, all of high grade. The proband's father abandoned his family. One maternal uncle, one niece and a first cousin are psychotic. The proband's parents and siblings had normal intelligence, but the IQ level of the family in general was low. Of 21 tested nieces and nephews, only four had IQ's of 100 or above; one illegitimate child had an IQ of 147, the other three had IQ's of 107, 101 and 109, respectively. The proband's mother attributed her son's retardation to an attack of measles at age 3 years. After this illness he became deaf. One nephew is partly deaf, cause unknown. The proband's parents had seven children and 22 grandchildren.

Retardation of proband of unknown origin.

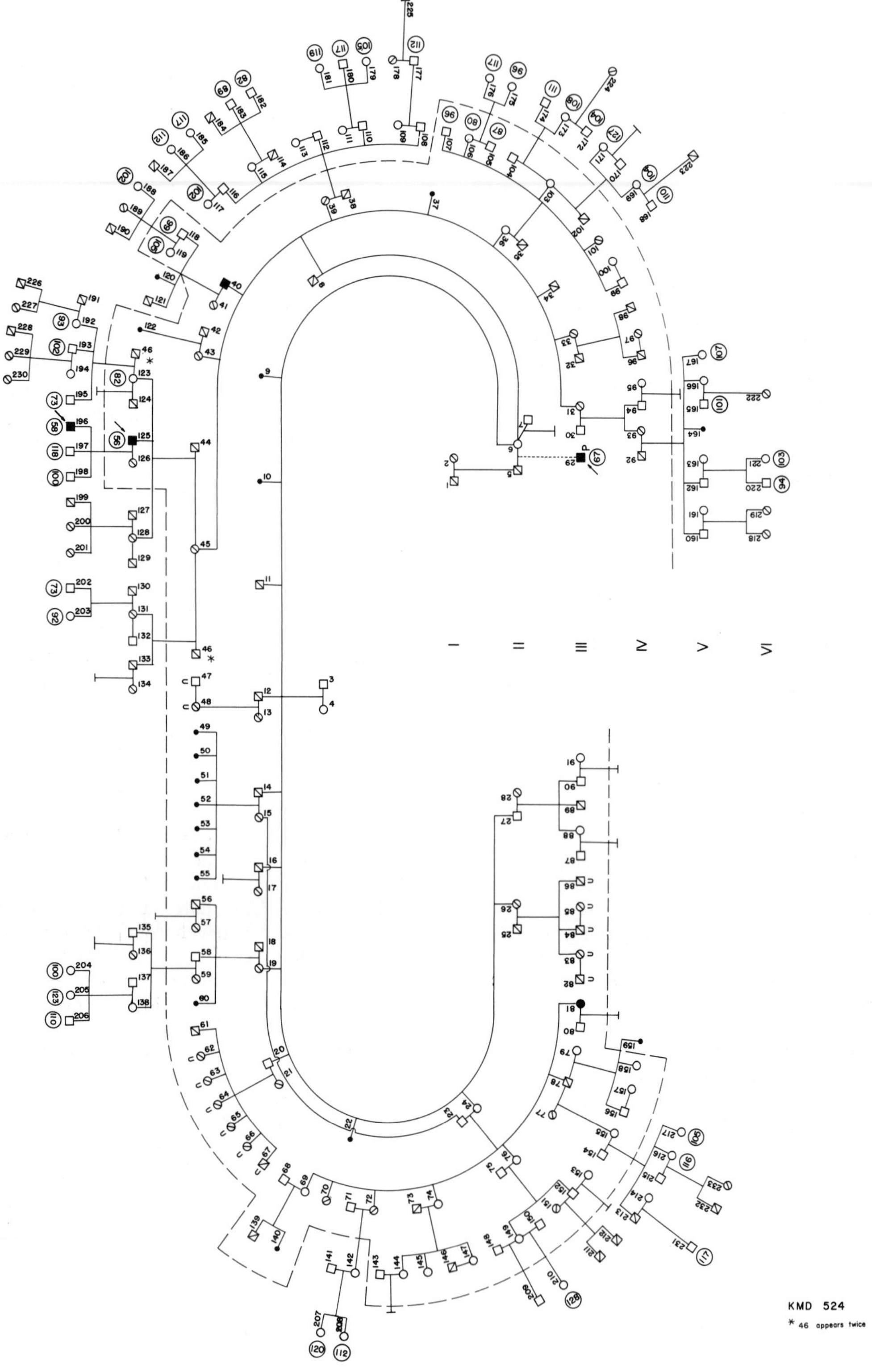
I
II
III
IV
V
VI
KMD 524
* 46 appears twice

KMD 524

The Proband

The proband (29) was born in 1871, institutionalized at age 11 years, escaped in 1918, readmitted in 1919 and discharged in the same year. Later he was admitted to a sanatarium in another state where he died in 1934. He was an illegitimate child who was badly treated by his stepfather. There was no history of difficult birth or perinatal infection. There was gossip that the proband's father was his mother's brother but there was no confirmation of this. IQ 67. *Diagnosis:* undifferentiated mental retardation.

Grandparents

Not of interest.

Parents

Father (5) was unknown.

Mother (6) had normal intelligence.

Aunts and Uncles

Paternal side of the family is unknown since the proband was illegitimate.

Maternal uncle (14) died of alcoholism. He had seven children, all of whom died in infancy.

Siblings

None.

Half Siblings

Half brother (40) was retarded. Of his three children, one (118) has IQ 99, one (120) died at birth and one (121) died at age 6 years, intelligence unknown. The proband's half siblings were described as "all the girls are immoral and the boys are alcoholic and good for nothing." Their father was an alcoholic and a poor provider.

Nieces and Nephews

Only the children of the half siblings. (125) was institutionalized as a child and has an IQ of 56. He married a woman of unknown intelligence who came from a family well known to welfare agencies. Their three children (196), (197) and (198) have IQ's of 58, 118 and 100, respectively.

First Cousins

(81) is retarded. She married a normal man, but has no children.

More Distant Relatives

(196) is institutionalized with IQ 58.

Family Summary

The proband, IQ 67, was an illegitimate child. Four other persons in this family were known to be retarded, a half brother, a first cousin, a child of a half sister and one more distant relative. The proband's parents had one child, no grandchildren.

Retardation of proband of unknown origin.

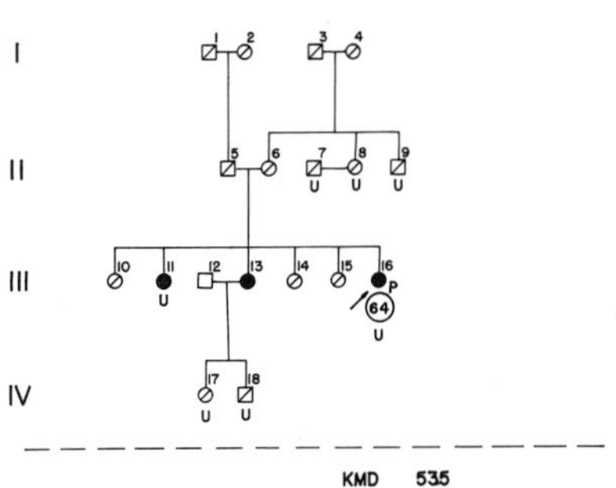

KMD 535

The Proband

The proband (16) was born in 1900 and institutionalized at age 13 years after a stay in the state orphanage. She was discharged in 1922 and has not been heard from since that time. She could not adjust in boarding homes because she was promiscuous and incorrigible. No record of her birth or early life was available. IQ 64. *Diagnosis:* undifferentiated mental retardation.

Grandparents

Unknown.

Parents

Father (5) and mother (6) had unknown intelligence.

Aunts and Uncles

Unknown.

Siblings

Sister (10) died at age 20 years.

Sister (11) was promiscuous and had a mental age of about 9 years.

Sister (13) was retarded. She deserted her family several times.

Sister (14) died as a young girl.

Sister (15) died in childhood.

Nieces and Nephews

Only two are known to exist. They have unknown intelligence.

First Cousins

Unknown.

More Distant Relatives

Unknown.

Family Summary

The proband, IQ 64, and two of her siblings were retarded. No member of this family could be found for the follow-up. The proband's parents had six children, grandchildren unknown.

Retardation of proband of unknown origin.

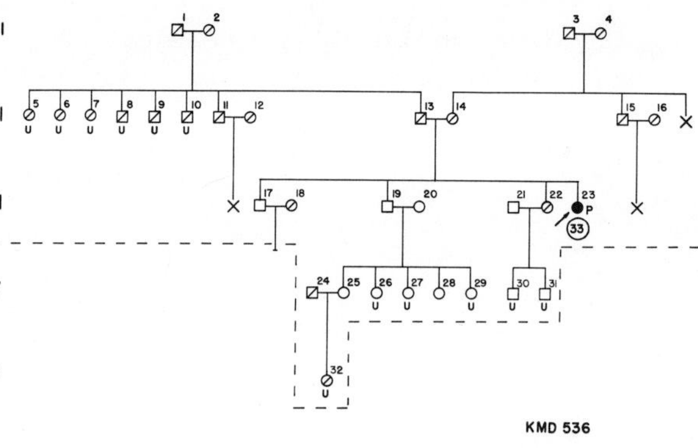

KMD 536

The Proband

The proband (23) was born in 1884, institutionalized at age 28 years and was still in the institution in 1961. Her birth and infancy were uneventful and she grew up in a good home. She was very slow to develop and did not walk and talk until about the age of 5 years. She attended school for four years but learned little. IQ 33. *Diagnosis:* undifferentiated mental retardation.

Grandparents

Unknown.

Parents

Father (13) and mother (14) had unknown intelligence. They died before the old history was written. The proband lived with her brother (17).

Aunts and Uncles

Unknown. All of the proband's paternal relatives remained in Europe, except (11) who lived in Chicago and lost contact with his family. The same is true for (15) on the maternal side.

Siblings

Brother (17) had normal intelligence. His wife (18) was hospitalized for mental illness. They had no children.

Brother (19) had normal intelligence, as did his wife and children.

Sister (22) had unknown intelligence. Her husband (21) was a druggist who had been hospitalized for mental illness. Their children had normal intelligence.

Nieces and Nephews

Seven, all with normal intelligence.

First Cousins

Unknown.

More Distant Relatives

Unknown.

Family Summary

The proband, IQ 33, was the only retarded person in her immediate family. The collateral relatives were unknown, and the more recent generations in the proband's family could not be found. There was no history of difficult delivery or childhood accident or illness for the proband. The proband's parents had four children and seven grandchildren.

Retardation of proband of unknown origin.

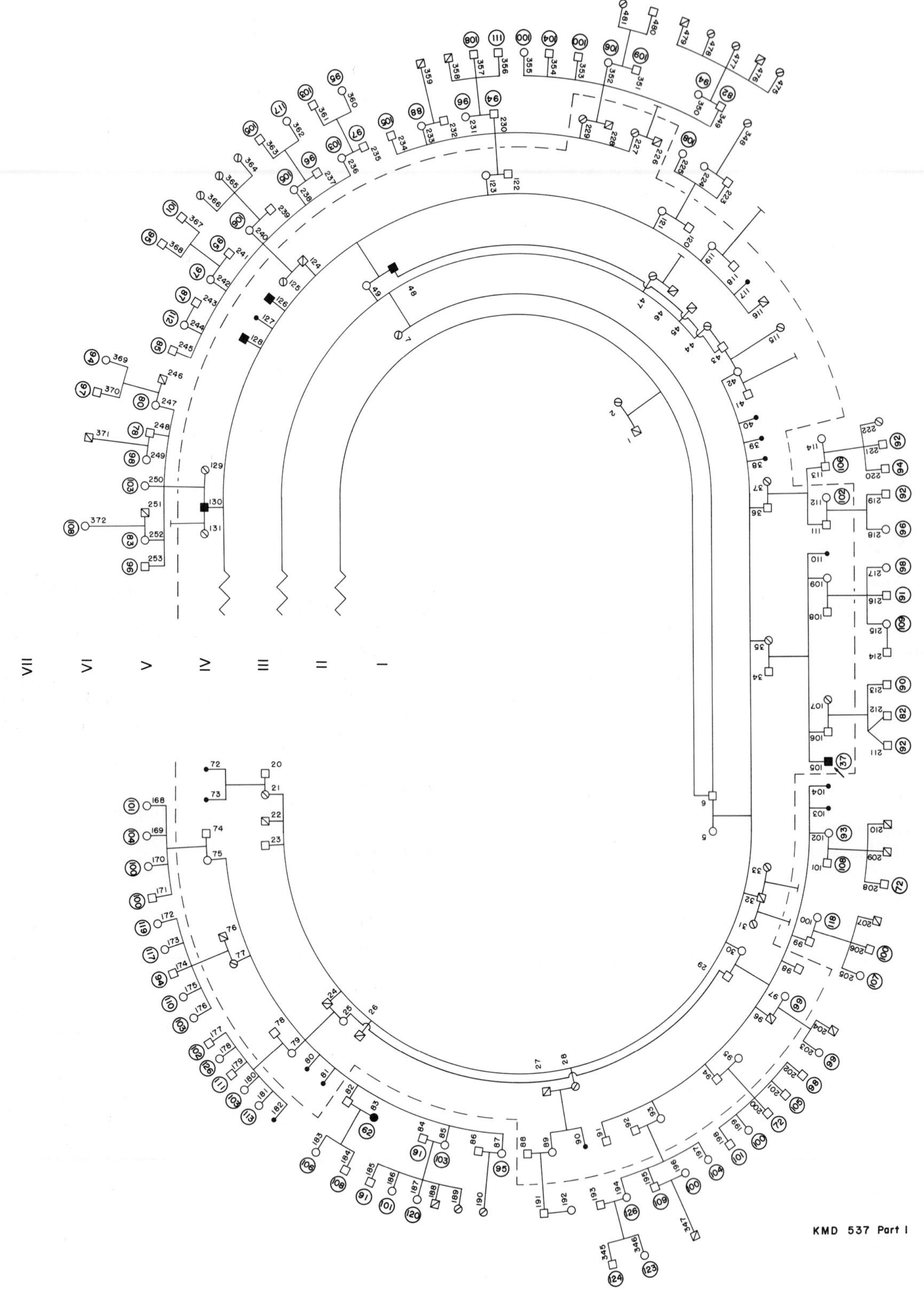
KMD 537 Part I

KMD 537

The Proband

The proband (55) was born in 1882, institutionalized at age 29 years and left the institution three years later to live with her mother. She later married and moved to the state of Washington. She had two illegitimate children, one by a brother-in-law and one by a cook in a hotel. The first child died at age 2 weeks, the second was a normal boy (described below). The proband had no known history of difficult birth or perinatal infection and no stigmata. She and her siblings were neglected by their parents. IQ 53. *Diagnosis:* undifferentiated mental retardation.

Grandparents

Not of interest.

Parents

Father (10) was a storekeeper.

Mother (11) was illiterate, a poor housekeeper and had once been hospitalized for mental illness.

Aunts and Uncles

Not of interest.

Siblings

All the surviving siblings, sisters (59), (63), (69) and (71), had left home and moved out of the state by the time the proband was institutionalized, so they were not seen by the original workers. (64), (65) and (66) died in infancy and (67) died at age 8 years. The intelligence of none of these persons was known. This is true also for their children.

Nieces and Nephews

See above.

Children

(159) died at age 2 weeks.

(160), a son with normal intelligence, was adopted by cousins. His wife has an IQ of 85 and four of his eight tested children (338), (339), (340) and (341) have IQ's of 87, 104, 108 and 88, respectively.

The fathers of both these children were unknown as to intelligence.

First Cousins

(49) had normal intelligence, but married a retarded spouse (48).

Maternal ones are unknown.

Grandchildren

(338), (339), (340) and (341) have IQ's of 87, 104, 108 and 88, respectively.

More Distant Relatives

(82), with normal intelligence, has a wife (83) with IQ 62. Their two children have IQ's of 106 and 108, respectively.

(105) is institutionalized for mental retardation with epilepsy. His sibling, (110), died at age 1 day and was "deformed."

(126) and (128) were unmarried, childless retardate brothers.

(130), brother to (126) and (128), was retarded. His five children range in IQ from 78 to 103, mother's intelligence unknown.

(132), brother to (130), (126) and (128), was a married, but childless, retardate.

(412) is in special classes with IQ 48.

Family Summary

The proband, IQ 53, and her mother were the only retardates in the immediate family. Six more distant relatives were also retarded. The proband had two illegitimate children, one of whom died in infancy and a normal son who had eight children of whom the four tested ones all showed normal intelligence. The proband's siblings and their children could not be found for the follow-up. The proband had two children and eight grandchildren. The proband's parents had ten children, number of grandchildren unknown.

Retardation of proband of unknown origin.

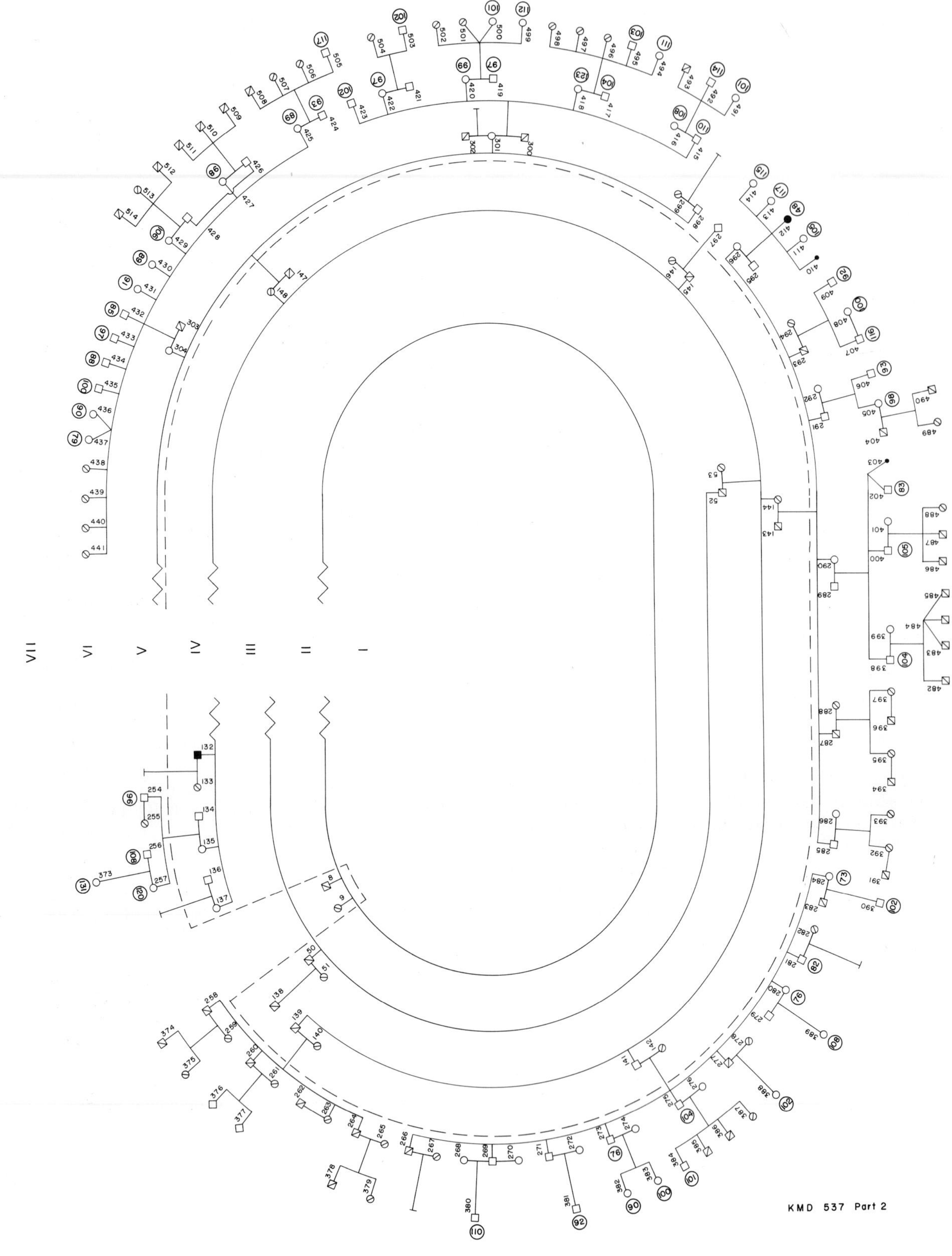
I
II
III
IV
V
VI
VII
KMD 537 Part 2

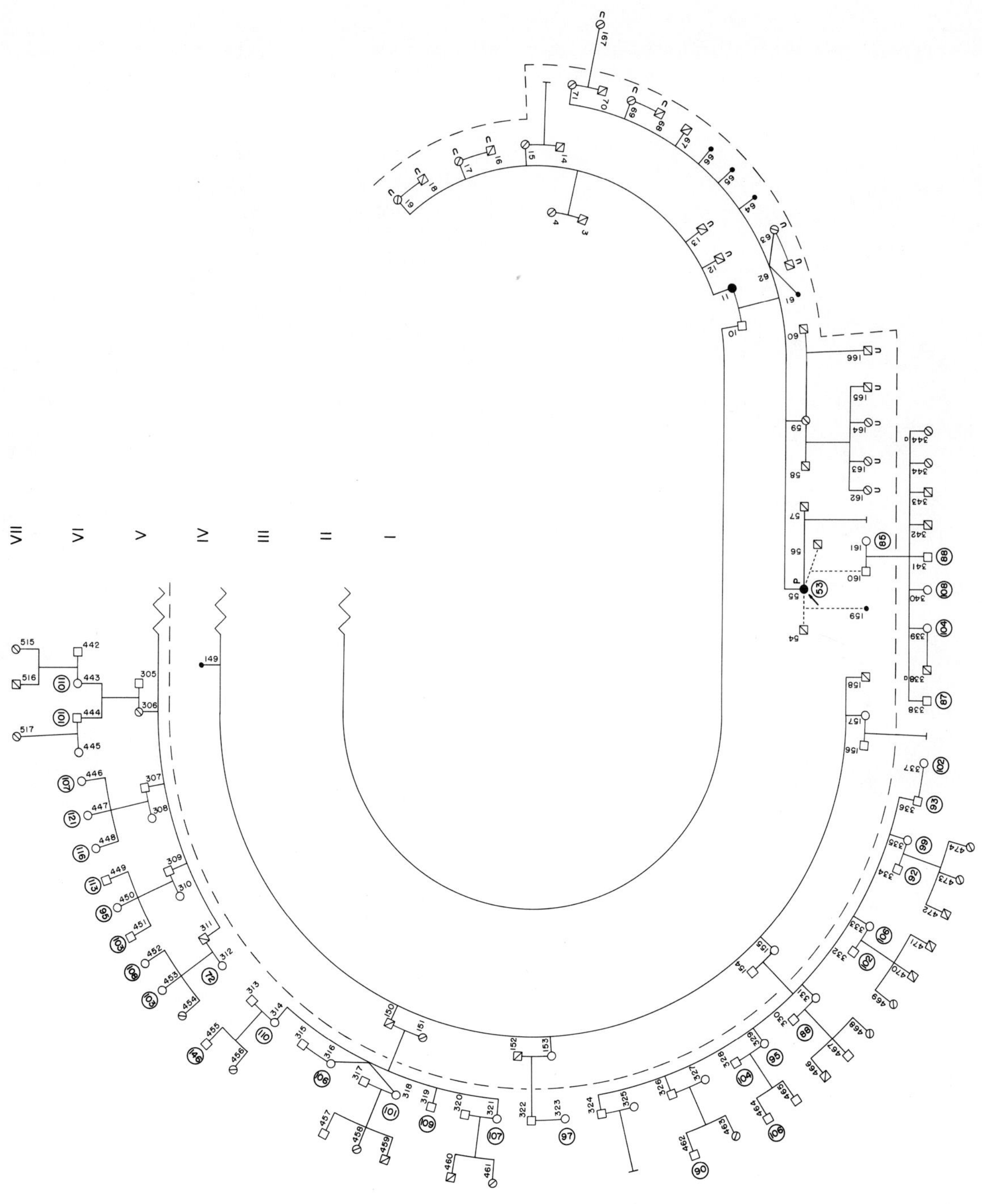

KMD 537 Part 3

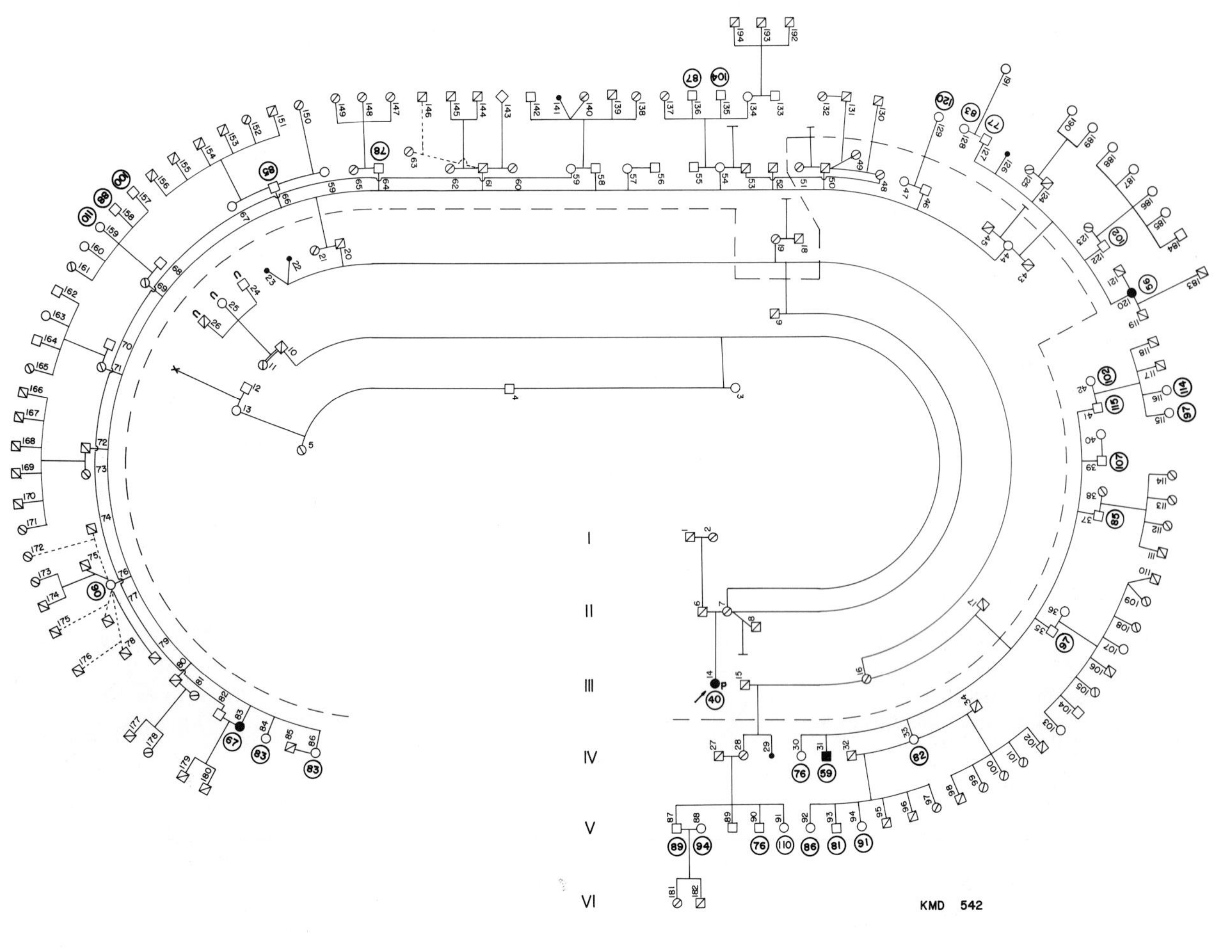
I
II
III
IV
V
VI
KMD 542

KMD 542

The Proband

The proband (14) was born in 1877, institutionalized at age 13 years and died of myocardial insufficiency, heat exhaustion and manic depressive psychosis in the institution in 1932. Her birth was uneventful and there was no history of perinatal infection. She walked at 2 years, talked at 3. She had an IQ of 40 upon admission at age 12 years. *Diagnosis:* mental retardation with subsequent psychosis.

Grandparents

Not of interest, except that the maternal grandmother stayed in bed the last 20 years of her life because she imagined she was ill. She was a "great reader."

Parents

Father (6) was an alcoholic, shiftless man of unknown intelligence.

Mother (7) separated from (6). Her first husband deserted her. She was "not very bright."

Aunts and Uncles

No paternal relatives since the proband's father was an only child.

The only maternal relatives were half siblings of the proband's mother. Her half brother (10) was an alcoholic and had a prison record for theft. He was a junkman. He married his first cousin and after her death gave his children away. Of the three children of this consanguineous marriage, two are known to have had normal intelligence. The other was adopted very young and was unknown to the early workers.

Siblings

No full siblings.

Half Siblings

Half sister (16) had unknown intelligence. Her first husband (15) deserted her. She had one retarded child (31) and one borderline (30), two low normal (33) and (37), three with normal intelligence (35), (39) and (41) and one unknown (28).

Half sister (19) had unknown intelligence.

Half brother (20) has a large family that has been a social welfare problem for years. He had 18 children: one retarded, one who had an illegitimate child and one who had three illegitimate children and has served time for forgery. All the children had poor school records and the ones tested (64), (66), (76), (83), (84) and (86) have IQ's of 78, 85, 90, 67, 83 and 83, respectively. Six of these children have had more than one spouse. These six have had 17 spouses (or parents of illegitimate children) among them.

Nieces and Nephews

No full nephews and nieces. Of the children of half siblings, (83) has an IQ of 67.

(31) has an IQ of 59 and has been arrested for grand larceny.

(35) lived in a boarding home where he was abused. After (35) left he returned and assaulted the man who abused him. For this, (35) served five days in jail. (35) has an IQ of 97.

(37) ran away from his foster home three times and is an itinerant farm laborer with IQ 85.

(39) was in both a reformatory and a prison for a time. His IQ is 107.

First Cousins

None.

More Distant Relatives

(120) has an IQ of 56.

Family Summary

The proband, IQ 40, two children of half-siblings and one more distant relative were the only known retardates in a family with a poor social history and extensive welfare records. The proband developed a manic depressive psychosis in later life. Proportionately very few of the more recent generations have had intelligence tests. They had very poor school records and it may be that some retardates have not been found. Of the 31 IQ scores known, nine were 100 or above and 22 were below 100. The proband's parents had one child, no grandchildren.

Retardation of proband of unknown origin.

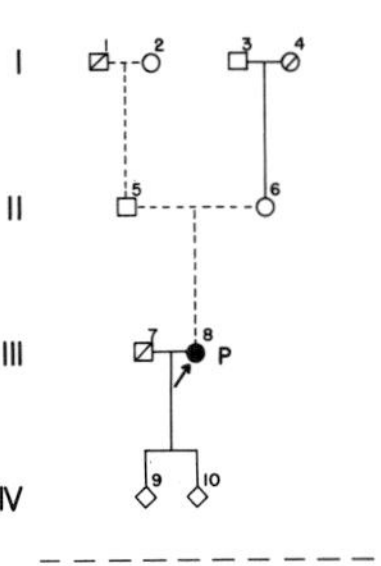

KMD 545

The Proband

The proband (8) was born in 1895, institutionalized at age 14 years and was discharged in 1915 to a foster home. She ran away from there and married a laborer in a flour mill. She had two children and later moved out of the state so she could not be found for the follow-up. The proband was an illegitimate child who was abandoned by her parents. She was a high-grade retardate of unknown IQ. *Diagnosis:* undifferentiated mental retardation.

Grandparents

Not of interest.

Parents

Father (5) was himself an illegitimate child. He had normal intelligence, but was "very immoral."

Mother (6) was "bright" but was very immoral and unstable. She abandoned the proband and traveled about the country with a peddler.

Aunts and Uncles

It is not known whether the proband's parents had any siblings.

Siblings

None.

Children

Two, both unknown.

Nieces and Nephews

None.

First Cousins

Unknown.

More Distant Relatives

Unknown.

Family Summary

The proband, a high-grade retardate, was the illegitimate child of parents of normal intelligence but with somewhat maladjusted personalities. She left the institution at age 20, married and left the state in 1918 so her present status is unknown. The proband's parents had one child and at least two grandchildren.

Retardation of proband of unknown origin.

INDEX

Folios followed by T refer to tables